PRENTICE HALL

Algebra 1

Solution Key

Boston, Massachusetts
Upper Saddle River, New Jersey
Glenview, Illinois

To the Teacher

This *Solution Key* provides complete step-by-step solutions for all the exercises in Prentice Hall *Algebra 1,* including the Try This exercises.

Answers are also given in the Teacher's Edition, either in the margins of the pages where the exercises occur or in the Additional Answers section located in the back of the Teacher's Edition.

Selected answers are provided in the back of the Student Edition.

Contents

1.	Introduction to Algebra	1
2.	Integers and Rational Numbers	10
3.	Equations	21
4.	Inequalities	51
5.	Exponents and Polynomials	68
6.	Polynomials and Factoring	84
7.	Graphs and Linear Equations	98
8.	Systems of Equations	123
9.	Inequalities and Absolute Value	143
10.	Rational Expressions and Equations	157
11.	Radical Expressions and Equations	187
12.	Relations and Functions	209
13.	Quadratic Equations	220
	Mixed Practice	251

ISBN 0-13-044403-0
11 12 06 05

CHAPTER 1

SKILLS & CONCEPTS p. 2

1. $\frac{3}{7} + \frac{2}{7} = \frac{3+2}{7} = \frac{5}{7}$ **2.** $\frac{3}{8} + \frac{1}{6} = \frac{9}{24} + \frac{4}{24} = \frac{9+4}{24} = \frac{13}{24}$

3. $6\frac{3}{4} + 9\frac{5}{8} = 6\frac{6}{8} + 9\frac{5}{8} = 15\frac{11}{8} = 16\frac{3}{8}$

4. $3\frac{1}{2} + 4\frac{2}{3} + 7\frac{1}{4} = 3\frac{6}{12} + 4\frac{8}{12} + 7\frac{3}{12} = 14\frac{17}{12} = 15\frac{5}{12}$

5. $\frac{5}{9} - \frac{2}{9} = \frac{3}{9} = \frac{1}{3}$ **6.** $\frac{5}{6} - \frac{2}{5} = \frac{25}{30} - \frac{12}{30} = \frac{13}{30}$

7. $1\frac{7}{8} - \frac{3}{4} = 1\frac{7}{8} - \frac{6}{8} = 1\frac{1}{8}$ **8.** $7 - \frac{5}{8} = 6\frac{8}{8} - \frac{5}{8} = 6\frac{3}{8}$

9. $\frac{3}{4} \times \frac{3}{4} = \frac{3 \times 3}{4 \times 4} = \frac{9}{16}$

10. $\frac{5}{8} \times 18 = \frac{5}{8} \times \frac{18}{1} = \frac{5}{4} \times \frac{9}{1} = \frac{45}{4}$ or $11\frac{1}{4}$

11. $4\frac{1}{5} \times 3\frac{5}{7} = \frac{21}{5} \times \frac{26}{7} = \frac{3}{5} \times \frac{26}{1} = \frac{78}{5}$ or $15\frac{3}{5}$

12. $2\frac{3}{10} \times 3\frac{1}{3} = \frac{23}{10} \times \frac{10}{3} = \frac{23}{1} \times \frac{1}{3} = \frac{23}{3}$ or $7\frac{2}{3}$

13. $\frac{7}{12} \div \frac{7}{12} = \frac{7}{12} \times \frac{12}{7} = 1$ **14.** $\frac{3}{4} \div 2 = \frac{3}{4} \times \frac{1}{2} = \frac{3 \times 1}{4 \times 2} = \frac{3}{8}$

15. $3\frac{1}{3} \div 1\frac{1}{4} = \frac{10}{3} \div \frac{5}{4} = \frac{10}{3} \times \frac{4}{5} = \frac{2}{3} \times \frac{4}{1} = \frac{8}{3}$ or $2\frac{2}{3}$

16. $3 \div \frac{1}{3} = \frac{3}{1} \times \frac{3}{1} = 9$

17. $\begin{array}{r} 0.50 \\ 0.35 \\ +\ 1.50 \\ \hline 2.35 \end{array}$ **18.** $\begin{array}{r} 14.00 \\ 3.75 \\ +\ 8.60 \\ \hline 26.35 \end{array}$ **19.** $\begin{array}{r} 1.00 \\ 0.02 \\ +\ 0.20 \\ \hline 1.22 \end{array}$ **20.** $\begin{array}{r} 7.00 \\ -\ 4.38 \\ \hline 2.62 \end{array}$

21. $\begin{array}{r} 11.20 \\ -\ 6.09 \\ \hline 5.11 \end{array}$ **22.** $\begin{array}{r} 8.90 \\ -\ 0.76 \\ \hline 8.14 \end{array}$ **23.** $\begin{array}{r} 8.75 \\ \times\ \ 6 \\ \hline 52.50 \end{array} = 52.5$

24. $\begin{array}{r} 0.75 \\ \times\ 0.003 \\ \hline 0.00225 \end{array}$ **25.** $\begin{array}{r} 7.82 \\ \times\ 7.9 \\ \hline 7038 \\ 5474\ \\ \hline 61.778 \end{array}$ **26.** $\begin{array}{r} 57 \\ \times\ 0.0004 \\ \hline 0.0228 \end{array}$

27. $7\overline{)8.10}$, quotient $1.157 \approx 1.16$
$\begin{array}{r} 7 \\ \hline 11 \\ 7 \\ \hline 40 \\ 35 \\ \hline 50 \\ 49 \\ \hline \end{array}$

28. $0.08\overline{)396.7000}$, quotient 4958.75
$\begin{array}{r} 32 \\ \hline 76 \\ 72 \\ \hline 47 \\ 40 \\ \hline 70 \\ 64 \\ \hline 60 \\ 56 \\ \hline 40 \\ 40 \\ \hline \end{array}$

29. $1.1\overline{)0.44}$, quotient 0.4
$\begin{array}{r} 44 \\ \hline \end{array}$

30. $0.6\overline{)5.82}$, quotient 9.7
$\begin{array}{r} 54 \\ \hline 42 \\ 42 \\ \hline \end{array}$

31. $0.065\overline{)333.000\ 00}$, quotient $5123.076 \approx 5123.08$
$\begin{array}{r} 325 \\ \hline 80 \\ 65 \\ \hline 150 \\ 130 \\ \hline 200 \\ 195 \\ \hline 500 \\ 455 \\ \hline 450 \\ 390 \\ \hline \end{array}$

32. $8\overline{)0.910}$, quotient $0.113 \approx 0.11$
$\begin{array}{r} 8 \\ \hline 11 \\ 8 \\ \hline 30 \\ 24 \\ \hline \end{array}$

LESSON 1-1 TRY THIS pp. 4–6

a. $y + 8 = 9 + 8$ Substituting 9 for the variable y
$= 17$

b. $2 + x = 2 + 6$ Substituting 6 for the variable x
$= 8$

c. $t + 3 + t = 4 + 3 + 4$ Substituting 4 for the variable t
$= 11$

d. $\frac{x}{12} = \frac{36}{12}$ Substituting 36 for the variable x
$= 3$

e. $6m = 6(3)$ Substituting 3 for the variable m
$= 18$

f. $\frac{18}{g} = \frac{18}{2}$ Substituting 2 for the variable g
$= 9$

g. $a + b = 3 + 7$ Substituting 3 for a and 7 for b and adding
$= 10$

h. $mn = 2(6)$ Substituting 2 for m and 6 for n and multiplying
$= 12$

i. $14 - (b + 5) = 14 - (3 + 5)$ Substituting 3 for b
$= 14 - (8)$ Working inside parentheses
$= 6$

j. $\frac{x+5}{2 \cdot 3} = \frac{7+5}{2 \cdot 3}$ Substituting 7 for x
$= \frac{12}{6}$ Adding and multiplying
$= 2$

k. $3 + (6x) = 3 + (6 \cdot 2)$ Substituting 2 for x
$= 3 + (12)$ Working inside parentheses
$= 15$

l. $s(t - 4) = 4(8 - 4)$ Substituting for s and t
$= 4(4)$ Working inside parentheses
$= 16$

m. $36 \div (4 + 5) = 36 \div 9$ Working inside parentheses
$= 4$ Dividing

n. $24 - (12 + 3) \div 5 = 24 - 15 \div 5$ Working inside parentheses
$= 24 - 3$ Dividing first
$= 21$ Subtracting

o. $4 \times 3 + 6 \div 2 = 12 + 3$ Multiplying and dividing first
$= 15$ Adding

p. $3x + y = 3(2) + 5$ Substituting 2 for x and 5 for y
$= 6 + 5$ Multiplying first
$= 11$ Adding

q. $\frac{2a + b}{5} = \frac{2(4) + 2}{5}$ Substituting 4 for a and 2 for b
$= \frac{8 + 2}{5}$ Multiplying
$= \frac{10}{5}$ Adding
$= 2$ Dividing

LESSON 1-1 EXERCISES pp. 7–8

1. $x + 6 = 7 + 6 = 13$ **2.** $3 + y = 3 + 9 = 12$ **3.** $m - 2 = 12 - 2 = 10$

4. $9 - h = 9 - 3 = 6$ **5.** $t + 24 = 11 + 24 = 35$

6. $18 + x = 18 + 30 = 48$ **7.** $12 - x = 12 - 5 = 7$

8. $k - 6 = 15 - 6 = 9$ **9.** $4 - x - x = 4 - 1 - 1 = 2$

10. $k + 8 - k = 10 + 8 - 10 = 8$ **11.** $4h = 4(12) = 48$

12. $8m = 8(3) = 24$ **13.** $3t = 3(9) = 27$ **14.** $6y = 6(12) = 72$

15. $\frac{12}{y} = \frac{12}{2} = 6$ **16.** $\frac{p}{5} = \frac{30}{5} = 6$ **17.** $\frac{h}{7} = \frac{63}{7} = 9$ **18.** $\frac{x}{y} = \frac{16}{4} = 4$

19. $a - b = 12 - 3$
$= 9$

20. $mn = 3(7)$
$= 21$

21. $p + q = 7 + 9$
$= 16$

22. $\frac{m}{n} = \frac{36}{9}$
$= 4$

23. $13 + 54 \div 9 = 13 + 6 = 19$

24. $64 \div 16 + 8 = 4 + 8 = 12$

25. $12 + 3 - 7 \cdot 2 + 8 = 12 + 3 - 14 + 8 = 15 - 14 + 8$
$= 1 + 8$
$= 9$

26. $12 \div 2 \times 3 \div 9 = 6 \times 3 \div 9 = 18 \div 9 = 2$

27. $4 + 12 \times 2 - 8 \div 4 = 4 + 24 - 2 = 26$

28. $15 \div 5 \times 5 \times 0 = 3 \times 5 \times 0 = 0$

29. $32 \div 8 + 4 \times 3 = 4 + 12 = 16$

30. $18 \times 2 \div 9 - 3 = 36 \div 9 - 3 = 4 - 3 = 1$

31. $2x + y = 2(5) + 4 = 10 + 4 = 14$

32. $x + 4y = 2 + 4(3) = 2 + 12 = 14$

33. $3m + 4n = 3(2) + 4(6) = 6 + 24 = 30$

34. $\frac{x + y}{4} = \frac{4 + 8}{4} = \frac{12}{4} = 3$

35. $\frac{a + 3b}{5} = \frac{4 + 3(2)}{5} = \frac{4 + 6}{5} = \frac{10}{5} = 2$

36. $\frac{4p}{3q} = \frac{4(6)}{3(8)} = \frac{24}{24} = 1$

37. $\frac{n}{3m} = \frac{12}{3(4)} = \frac{12}{12} = 1$

38. $\frac{ab}{8} = \frac{5(8)}{8} = 5$

39. $\frac{3x}{2y + 1} = \frac{3(7)}{2(3) + 1} = \frac{21}{6 + 1} = \frac{21}{7} = 3$

40. $\frac{a + b}{2a} = \frac{5 + 15}{2(5)} = \frac{20}{10} = 2$

41. $2x + 3x - 4x = 2(5) + 3(5) - 4(5) = 10 + 15 - 20 = 5$

42. $\frac{24}{2x} + \frac{36}{3x} + \frac{6}{x} = \frac{24}{2(6)} + \frac{36}{3(6)} + \frac{6}{6}$
$= \frac{24}{12} + \frac{36}{18} + 1$
$= 2 + 2 + 1$
$= 5$

43. $\frac{x + y}{4} + \frac{x - y}{4} = \frac{12 + 8}{4} + \frac{12 - 8}{4}$
$= \frac{20}{4} + \frac{4}{4} = 5 + 1 = 6$

44. $\frac{4y}{4y} + (2x + y) - 3z = 1 + (2 \cdot 3 + 2) - 3(1)$
$= 1 + (6 + 2) - 3$
$= 1 + 8 - 3$
$= 6$

45. $\frac{y + x}{2} + \frac{3y}{x} = \frac{4 + 2}{2} + \frac{3(4)}{2}$
$= \frac{6}{2} + \frac{12}{2}$
$= 3 + 6$
$= 9$

46. Possible answers are $\frac{2 + 8 - 4 - 6}{10} = 0$ or
$10(2 + 8 - 4 - 6) = 0.$

47. Rob did not use the order of operations. He added 6 and 3 before dividing. Using the order of operations and dividing first, $72 \div 6 + 3 = 12 + 3 = 18$.

48. Substituting 6 for x in $\frac{4x + 2}{2} - x$ results in $\frac{4(6) + 2}{2} - 6 = \frac{24 + 2}{2} - 6 = \frac{26}{2} - 6 = 13 - 6 = 7$. The correct answer is **C**.

49. $12 \times 5 = 60$ and $12 + 5 = 17$, so 12 and 5

50. $4 - 4 = 0 \quad \frac{4}{4} = 1 \quad \frac{4 + 4}{4} = 2 \quad 4 - \frac{4}{4} = 3$
$4 = 4 \quad 4 + \frac{4}{4} = 5 \quad 4 + \frac{4 + 4}{4} = 6 \quad 4 + 4 - \frac{4}{4} = 7$
$4 + 4 = 8 \quad 4 + 4 + \frac{4}{4} = 9 \quad 4 + 4 + \frac{4 + 4}{4} = 10$
Many other answers are possible.

51. 72 52. 401 53. 57 54. 1.73 55. 14.1

56. 14.896

57. $\frac{3}{4} + \frac{2}{7} = \frac{21}{28} + \frac{8}{28} = \frac{29}{28}$ or $1\frac{1}{28}$

58. $\frac{5}{8} - \frac{1}{3} = \frac{15}{24} - \frac{8}{24} = \frac{7}{24}$

59. $2\frac{5}{6} - \frac{2}{3} = 2\frac{5}{6} - \frac{4}{6} = 2\frac{1}{6}$

60. $4 \div \frac{1}{2} = 4 \times \frac{2}{1} = 8$

61. $1\frac{1}{4} \div 2\frac{1}{3} = \frac{5}{4} \div \frac{7}{3}$
$= \frac{5}{4} \times \frac{3}{7} = \frac{15}{28}$

LESSON 1-2 TRY THIS pp. 10–13

a. $9 + x$; commutative property of addition
b. qp; commutative property of multiplication
c. $yx + t$; commutative property of multiplication
or $t + xy$; commutative property of addition
or $t + yx$; both commutative properties

d. $\frac{7}{5} \cdot \frac{4}{4} = \frac{28}{20}$

e. $\frac{3}{8} \cdot \frac{5}{5} = \frac{15}{40}$

f. $\frac{y}{2x} \cdot \frac{z}{z} = \frac{yz}{2xz}$

g. $\frac{2m}{n} \cdot \frac{p}{p} = \frac{2mp}{np}$

h. $\frac{18}{27} = \frac{2 \cdot 9}{3 \cdot 9} = \frac{2}{3} \cdot \frac{9}{9} = \frac{2}{3}$

i. $\frac{48}{18} = \frac{8 \cdot 6}{3 \cdot 6} = \frac{8}{3} \cdot \frac{6}{6} = \frac{8}{3}$

j. $\frac{56}{49} = \frac{8 \cdot 7}{7 \cdot 7} = \frac{8}{7} \cdot \frac{7}{7} = \frac{8}{7}$

k. $\frac{27}{54} = \frac{1 \cdot 27}{2 \cdot 27} = \frac{1}{2} \cdot \frac{27}{27} = \frac{1}{2}$

l. $\frac{48}{12} = \frac{4 \cdot 12}{1 \cdot 12} = \frac{4}{1} \cdot \frac{12}{12} = \frac{4}{1} = 4$

m. $\frac{5xy}{3x} = \frac{5y}{3} \cdot \frac{x}{x} = \frac{5y}{3}$

n. $\frac{m}{8mn} = \frac{1}{8n} \cdot \frac{m}{m} = \frac{1}{8n}$

o. $\frac{14ab}{7b} = \frac{2a}{1} \cdot \frac{7b}{7b} = 2a$

LESSON 1-2 EXERCISES p. 14

1. $y + 8 = 8 + y$

2. $x + 3 = 3 + x$

3. $mn = nm$

4. $ab = ba$

5. $9 + xy = 9 + yx$
$= yx + 9$
$= xy + 9$

6. $11 + ab = ab + 11$
$= ba + 11$
$= 11 + ba$

7. $ab + c = ba + c$
$= c + ba$
$= c + ab$

8. $rs + t = t + rs$
$= t + sr$
$= sr + t$

9. $\frac{5}{6} \cdot \frac{8}{8} = \frac{40}{48}$

10. $\frac{9}{10} \cdot \frac{11}{11} = \frac{99}{110}$

11. $\frac{6}{7} \cdot \frac{100}{100} = \frac{600}{700}$

12. $\frac{y}{10} \cdot \frac{z}{z} = \frac{yz}{10z}$

13. $\frac{s}{20} \cdot \frac{t}{t} = \frac{st}{20t}$

14. $\frac{m}{3n} \cdot \frac{p}{p} = \frac{mp}{3np}$

15. $\frac{13}{104} = \frac{13 \cdot 1}{13 \cdot 8} = \frac{1}{8}$

16. $\frac{56}{7} = \frac{8 \cdot 7}{1 \cdot 7} = 8$

17. $\frac{132}{11} = \frac{12 \cdot 11}{1 \cdot 11} = 12$

18. $\frac{5y}{5} = \frac{5 \cdot y}{5 \cdot 1} = y$

19. $\frac{ab}{9b} = \frac{a \cdot b}{9 \cdot b} = \frac{a}{9}$

20. $\frac{x}{9xy} = \frac{x \cdot 1}{x \cdot 9y} = \frac{1}{9y}$

21. $\frac{q}{8pq} = \frac{q \cdot 1}{q \cdot 8p} = \frac{1}{8p}$

22. $\frac{8a}{3ab} = \frac{a \cdot 8}{a \cdot 3b} = \frac{8}{3b}$

23. $\frac{9p}{17pq} = \frac{p \cdot 9}{p \cdot 17q} = \frac{9}{17q}$

24. $\frac{3pq}{6q} = \frac{3q \cdot p}{3q \cdot 2} = \frac{p}{2}$

25. $\frac{51d}{17sd} = \frac{17d \cdot 3}{17d \cdot s} = \frac{3}{s}$

26. $\frac{9nz}{19tn} = \frac{n \cdot 9z}{n \cdot 19t} = \frac{9z}{19t}$

27. $\frac{13rv}{3vh} = \frac{v \cdot 13r}{v \cdot 3h} = \frac{13r}{3h}$

28. $\frac{9abc}{3ab} = \frac{3ab \cdot 3c}{3ab \cdot 1} = 3c$

29. $\frac{32prq}{4qrp} = \frac{4prq \cdot 8}{4prq \cdot 1} = 8$

30. No 31. No 32. Yes 33. No 34. No 35. Yes

36. $\frac{33sba}{2 \cdot (11a)} = \frac{(3 \cdot 11)sba}{2(11a)} = \frac{3sb(11a)}{2(11a)} = \frac{3sb}{2}$

37. $\frac{36 \cdot 2rh}{3 \cdot (9hg)} = \frac{(4 \cdot 9) \cdot 2rh}{3 \cdot 9 \cdot hg} = \frac{4 \cdot 2r \cdot 9h}{3g \cdot 9h} = \frac{8r}{3g}$

38. $\frac{3 \cdot (4xy) \cdot (5)}{2 \cdot (3x) \cdot (4y)} = \frac{5 \cdot 3 \cdot 4xy}{2 \cdot 3 \cdot 4xy} = \frac{5}{2}$

39. Answers may vary. $\frac{8ab}{2c}, \frac{4abd}{cd}$ **40.** No; $12 \div 4 \neq 4 \div 12$

41. $12 + 8 \div 2 = 12 + 4 = 16$ **42.** $16 \div 8 \cdot 2 \div 4 = \frac{2 \cdot 2}{4} = 1$

43. $(3 + 4)6 = 7 \cdot 6 = 42$ **44.** $\frac{2}{5} + \frac{3}{8} = \frac{16}{40} + \frac{15}{40} = \frac{31}{40}$

45. $\frac{5}{8} \div \frac{2}{3} = \frac{5}{8} \times \frac{3}{2} = \frac{15}{16}$ **46.** 0.062 **47.** 0.48

LESSON 1-3 TRY THIS pp. 15–17

a. $5 \cdot 5 \cdot 5 \cdot 5$ **b.** $b \cdot b \cdot b$ **c.** $2 \cdot x \cdot x \cdot x$ **d.** $12 \cdot y \cdot y \cdot y \cdot y$
e. 9^3 **f.** y^5 **g.** $4n^5$ **h.** $15x^4$ **i.** $10b^3$
j. $a^2 = 10^2$ Substituting
$= 10 \cdot 10$
$= 100$
k. $y^5 = 2^5$ Substituting
$= 2 \cdot 2 \cdot 2 \cdot 2 \cdot 2$
$= 32$
l. $x^4 = 0^4$ Substituting
$= 0 \cdot 0 \cdot 0 \cdot 0$
$= 0$
m. $x^3 + 2 = 3^3 + 2$
$= (3 \cdot 3 \cdot 3) + 2$
$= 27 + 2$
$= 29$
n. $n^5 + 8 = 2^5 + 8$
$= (2 \cdot 2 \cdot 2 \cdot 2 \cdot 2) + 8$
$= 32 + 8$
$= 40$
o. $(2x)^2 = (2x)(2x)$
$= (2 \cdot 4)(2 \cdot 4)$ Substituting
$= 8 \cdot 8$
$= 64$
p. $(5y)^3 = (5y)(5y)(5y)$
$= (5 \cdot 2)(5 \cdot 2)(5 \cdot 2)$ Substituting
$= 10 \cdot 10 \cdot 10$
$= 1000$
q. $3x^2 = 3 \cdot x \cdot x$
$= 3 \cdot 3 \cdot 3$ Substituting
$= 27$

LESSON 1-3 EXERCISES pp. 17–18

1. $2 \cdot 2 \cdot 2 \cdot 2$ **2.** $5 \cdot 5 \cdot 5$ **3.** 3 **4.** $1 \cdot 1 \cdot 1$ **5.** $a \cdot a \cdot a$

6. $5 \cdot y \cdot y \cdot y \cdot y$ **7.** 10^6 **8.** 6^4 **9.** x^5 **10.** $4y^3$

11. $5m^4$ **12.** $2n^6$ **13.** $m^3 = 3^3 = 3 \cdot 3 \cdot 3 = 27$

14. $x^6 = 2^6 = 2 \cdot 2 \cdot 2 \cdot 2 \cdot 2 \cdot 2 = 64$ **15.** $p^1 = 19^1 = 19$

16. $x^{19} = 0^{19} = 0$

17. $x^4 - 8 = 4^4 - 8 = 4 \cdot 4 \cdot 4 \cdot 4 - 8 = 256 - 8 = 248$

18. $y^{15} + 4 = 1^{15} + 4 = 1 + 4 = 5$

19. $x^3 + 2 = 4^3 + 2 = 4 \cdot 4 \cdot 4 + 2 = 64 + 2 = 66$

20. $y^2 - 3 = 5^2 - 3 = 25 - 3 = 22$

21. $3m^3 = 3 \cdot 1^3 = 3 \cdot 1 \cdot 1 \cdot 1 = 3$ **22.** $4x^2 = 4 \cdot 3^2 = 4 \cdot 9 = 36$

23. $2n^4 = 2 \cdot 2^4 = 2 \cdot 2 \cdot 2 \cdot 2 \cdot 2 = 32$

24. $(4x)^3 = (4 \cdot 2)^3 = 8^3 = 8 \cdot 8 \cdot 8 = 512$

25. $(2a)^4 = (2 \cdot 3)^4 = 6^4 = 6 \cdot 6 \cdot 6 \cdot 6 = 1296$

26. $(5n)^2 = (5 \cdot 6)^2 = 30^2 = 30 \cdot 30 = 900$

27. $(6y)^4 = (6 \cdot 2)^4 = 12^4 = 12 \cdot 12 \cdot 12 \cdot 12 = 20{,}736$

28. $(2ab)^3 = (2ab)(2ab)(2ab)$
$= (2 \cdot 2 \cdot 4)(2 \cdot 2 \cdot 4)(2 \cdot 2 \cdot 4)$
$= 16 \cdot 16 \cdot 16$
$= 4096$

29. $(3mn)^3 = (3mn)(3mn)(3mn)$
$= (3 \cdot 2 \cdot 0)(3 \cdot 2 \cdot 0)(3 \cdot 2 \cdot 0)$
$= 0 \cdot 0 \cdot 0$
$= 0$

30. $\frac{10^5}{10^3} = \frac{10 \cdot 10 \cdot 10 \cdot 10 \cdot 10}{10 \cdot 10 \cdot 10} = 10 \cdot 10 = 10^2$

31. $\frac{10^7}{10^2} = \frac{10 \cdot 10 \cdot 10 \cdot 10 \cdot 10 \cdot 10 \cdot 10}{10 \cdot 10} = 10 \cdot 10 \cdot 10 \cdot 10 \cdot 10 = 10^5$

32. $\frac{5^4}{5^2} = \frac{5 \cdot 5 \cdot 5 \cdot 5}{5 \cdot 5} = 5 \cdot 5 = 5^2$

33. $\frac{8^6}{8^2} = \frac{8 \cdot 8 \cdot 8 \cdot 8 \cdot 8 \cdot 8}{8 \cdot 8} = 8 \cdot 8 \cdot 8 \cdot 8 = 8^4$

34. $x^3y^2 + zx = 2^3 \cdot 1^2 + 3 \cdot 2$
$= 2 \cdot 2 \cdot 2 \cdot 1 \cdot 1 + 3 \cdot 2$
$= 8 + 6$
$= 14$

35. No. Let $x = 1$ and $y = 2$; $1^2 \neq 2^1$.

36. Never; Let x equal the number. If you square the number, then double the result, you get $2x^2$. If you double the number then square the result, you get $(2x)^2$, which equals $4x^2$; $2x^2 \leq 4x^2$ for all x.

37. Answers may vary. Sample: 1; $1^2 = 1$.

38. $yx^{149} = 0 \cdot 13^{149}$
$= 0$
39. $x^{410}y^2 = 1^{410} \cdot 3^2$
$= 1 \cdot 3 \cdot 3$
$= 9$

40. 10^1 is 1 followed by 1 zero, 10^2 is 1 followed by 2 zeros, so 10^{127} is 1 followed by 127 zeros.

41. $(x^2)^2 = (3^2)^2 = 9^2 = 9 \cdot 9 = 81$

42. $8\frac{1}{3} + 2\frac{2}{3} = \frac{25}{3} + \frac{8}{3} = \frac{33}{3} = 11$

43. $1\frac{5}{8} - \frac{3}{4} = \frac{13}{8} - \frac{6}{8} = \frac{7}{8}$ **44.** $\frac{3}{8} \div 3 = \frac{3}{8} \div \frac{3}{1} = \frac{3}{8} \times \frac{1}{3} = \frac{1}{8}$

45. $5 \times 2\frac{1}{2} = \frac{5}{1} \times \frac{5}{2} = \frac{25}{2} = 12\frac{1}{2}$

46. $2(m + n) = 2(7 + 1) = 2 \cdot 8 = 16$

47. $(3 + n)n = (3 + 2)2 = 5 \cdot 2 = 10$

48. $\frac{7}{56} = \frac{1 \cdot 7}{8 \cdot 7} = \frac{1}{8} \cdot \frac{7}{7} = \frac{1}{8}$ **49.** $\frac{96}{12} = \frac{8 \cdot 12}{1 \cdot 12} = \frac{8}{1} \cdot \frac{12}{12} = 8$

50. $\frac{r}{8rs} = \frac{1}{8s} \cdot \frac{r}{r} = \frac{1}{8s}$ **51.** $\frac{18x}{2xy} = \frac{9 \cdot 2 \cdot x}{y \cdot 2 \cdot x} = \frac{9}{y} \cdot \frac{2x}{2x} = \frac{9}{y}$

52. $\frac{3ab}{12b} = \frac{3 \cdot a \cdot b}{3 \cdot 4 \cdot b} = \frac{a}{4} \cdot \frac{3b}{3b} = \frac{a}{4}$

LESSON 1-4 TRY THIS pp. 19–22

a. $(3 \cdot 5)^2 = (15)^2 = 15 \cdot 15 = 225$
b. $3 \cdot 5^2 = 3 \cdot 5 \cdot 5 = 75$ **c.** $4 \cdot 2^3 = 4 \cdot 2 \cdot 2 \cdot 2 = 32$
d. $(4 \cdot 2)^3 = (8)^3 = 8 \cdot 8 \cdot 8 = 512$
e. $4 + 2^2 = 4 + 4 = 8$ **f.** $(4 + 2)^2 = (6)^2 = 6 \cdot 6 = 36$
g. $(5 - 1)^2 = (4)^2 = 4 \cdot 4 = 16$
h. $5 - 1^2 = 5 - 1 \cdot 1 = 5 - 1 = 4$
i. $(4y)^2 - 5 = (4 \cdot 3)^2 - 5 = 12^2 - 5 = 144 - 5 = 139$
j. $6(x + 12) = 6(8 + 12) = 6(20) = 120$
k. $t + \frac{6}{5t^2} = 2 + \frac{6}{5 \cdot 2^2} = 2 + \frac{6}{5 \cdot 4} = 2 + \frac{6}{20} = 2\frac{3}{10}$
l. $(x - 4)^3 = (6 - 4)^3 = 2^3 = 2 \cdot 2 \cdot 2 = 8$
m. $(4 + y) \cdot (x - 3) = (4 + 3) \cdot (12 - 3) = 7 \cdot 9 = 63$
n. $(a + b) + 2$ by the associative property of addition
o. $(3 \cdot v) \cdot w$ by the associative property of multiplication
p. $(4 \cdot u) \cdot t$ or $u \cdot (4 \cdot t)$ or $t \cdot (4 \cdot u)$, etc.
q. $r + (5 + 2)$ or $(2 + 5) + r$ or $(r + 5) + 2$, etc.

LESSON 1-4 EXERCISES pp. 22–23

1. $(5 \cdot 4)^2 = 20^2 = 400$ **2.** $(6 \cdot 3)^2 = 18^2 = 324$

3. $5 \cdot 4^2 = 5 \cdot 16 = 80$ **4.** $6 \cdot 3^2 = 6 \cdot 9 = 54$

5. $7 + 2^2 = 7 + 4 = 11$ **6.** $5 + 3^2 = 5 + 9 = 14$

7. $(7 + 2)^2 = 9^2 = 81$ 8. $(5 + 3)^2 = 8^2 = 64$

9. $(5 - 2)^2 = 3^2 = 9$ 10. $(3 - 2)^2 = 1^2 = 1$

11. $10 - 3^2 = 10 - 9 = 1$ 12. $16 - 4^2 = 16 - 16 = 0$

13. $12 - 2^3 = 12 - 8 = 4$ 14. $30 - 3^3 = 30 - 27 = 3$

15. $(2 + 3)^3 = 5^3 = 5 \cdot 5 \cdot 5 = 125$ 16. $3 \cdot 2^3 = 3 \cdot 8 = 24$

17. $5x^2 - 4 = 5 \cdot 4^2 - 4 = 5 \cdot 16 - 4 = 80 - 4 = 76$

18. $3a^3 + 2 = 3 \cdot 1^3 + 2 = 3 \cdot 1 + 2 = 3 + 2 = 5$

19. $(5y)^3 - 75 = (5 \cdot 2)^3 - 75 = 10^3 - 75 = 1000 - 75 = 925$

20. $(7x)^2 + 59 = (7 \cdot 3)^2 + 59 = 21^2 + 59 = 441 + 59 = 500$

21. $3(a + 10) = 3(12 + 10) = 3 \cdot 22 = 66$

22. $b(7 + b) = 5(7 + 5) = 5 \cdot 12 = 60$

23. $(t + 3)^3 = (4 + 3)^3 = 7^3 = 343$

24. $(12 - w)^3 = (12 - 7)^3 = 5^3 = 125$

25. $(x + 5)(12 - x) = (7 + 5)(12 - 7) = 12 \cdot 5 = 60$

26. $(y - 4)(y + 6) = (10 - 4)(10 + 6) = 6 \cdot 16 = 96$

27. $\frac{y + 3}{2y} = \frac{5 + 3}{2 \cdot 5} = \frac{8}{10} = \frac{4}{5}$

28. $\frac{(4x) + 2}{2x} = \frac{(4 \cdot 5) + 2}{2 \cdot 5} = \frac{20 + 2}{10} = \frac{22}{10} = \frac{11}{5}$

29. $\frac{w^2 + 4}{5w} = \frac{4^2 + 4}{5 \cdot 4} = \frac{16 + 4}{20} = \frac{20}{20} = 1$

30. $\frac{b^2 + b}{2b} = \frac{5^2 + 5}{2 \cdot 5} = \frac{25 + 5}{10} = \frac{30}{10} = 3$

31. $a + (b + 3)$ 32. $5 + (x + y)$

33. $(3 \cdot a) \cdot b$ 34. $6 \cdot (x \cdot y)$

35. $(2 + b) + a$ or $(2 + a) + b$ or $b + (a + 2)$

36. $(y + 3) + x$ or $3 + (y + x)$ or $x + (3 + y)$

37. $v + (w + 5)$ or $(5 + w) + v$ or $w + (5 + v)$

38. $x + (y + 6)$ or $y + (6 + x)$ or $(x + 6) + y$

39. $(y \cdot 3) \cdot x$ or $x \cdot (3 \cdot y)$ or $y \cdot (x \cdot 3)$

40. $(5 \cdot a) \cdot b$ or $b \cdot (a \cdot 5)$ or $a \cdot (5 \cdot b)$

41. $a \cdot (b \cdot 7)$ or $(a \cdot 7) \cdot b$ or $b \cdot (7 \cdot a)$

42. $(x \cdot 5) \cdot y$ or $(5 \cdot y) \cdot x$ or $y \cdot (5 \cdot x)$

43. $c \cdot (2 \cdot d)$ or $d \cdot (c \cdot 2)$ or $2 \cdot (d \cdot c)$

44. $(a \cdot 4 + b) + 2$ or $(b + 4a) + 2$

45. $7 \cdot (n \cdot m) + 3$ or $3 + m \cdot (7 \cdot n)$

46. $(2 + 6) + 5x^3$ or $2 + (5x^3 + 6)$

47. $6(mp)n$ or $m(6n)p$ 48. $(x + 3)2y$ or $(x + 3)y \cdot 2$

49. $(3 + 5) + 7y + 4$ or $5 + 3 + (4 + 7y)$

50. Any number except 0 51. Any number except 0 or -2

52. Any number except 2

53. Any number except 1. 0 is not acceptable.

54. $A + (C + B) = (A + C) + B = 85$;
$(A + B) + C = A + (B + C) = A + (C + B) = (A + C) + B = 85$; $(A + B) + C = 85$ and $A + B = 25$, so by substitution, $25 + C = 85$, and $C = 60$

55. $a - (b - c) = 12 - (7 - 4) = 12 - 3 = 9$
$(a - b) - c = (12 - 7) - 4 = 5 - 4 = 1$
$9 \neq 1$ so there is no associative property for subtraction.

56. $a \div (b \div c) = 32 \div (8 \div 4) = 32 \div 2 = 16$
$(a \div b) \div c = (32 \div 8) \div 4 = 4 \div 4 = 1$
$16 \neq 1$ so there is no associative property for division.

57. a. No; 2 @ 3 = $2 \cdot 2 + 3 = 7$ and 3 @ 2 = $2 \cdot 3 + 2 = 8$
b. No; (1 @ 2) @ 3 = 4 @ 3 = 11
and 1 @ (2 @ 3) = 1 @ 7 = 9

58. $12\frac{1}{4} + 7\frac{3}{8} = \frac{49}{4} + \frac{59}{8} = \frac{98}{8} + \frac{59}{8} = \frac{157}{8} = 19\frac{5}{8}$

59. $3\frac{3}{5} + 5\frac{1}{2} = \frac{18}{5} + \frac{11}{2} = \frac{36}{10} + \frac{55}{10} = \frac{91}{10} = 9\frac{1}{10}$

60. $8\frac{1}{3} + 3\frac{3}{5} = \frac{25}{3} + \frac{18}{5} = \frac{125}{15} + \frac{54}{15} = \frac{179}{15} = 11\frac{14}{15}$

61. $3\frac{3}{4} - 2\frac{1}{3} = \frac{15}{4} - \frac{7}{3} = \frac{45}{12} - \frac{28}{12} = \frac{17}{12} = 1\frac{5}{12}$

62. $\frac{7}{8} \times \frac{2}{3} = \frac{14}{24} = \frac{7 \cdot 2}{12 \cdot 2} = \frac{7}{12}$

63. $1\frac{1}{5} \times 1\frac{1}{3} = \frac{6}{5} \times \frac{4}{3} = \frac{24}{15} = \frac{8 \cdot 3}{5 \cdot 3} = \frac{8}{5} = 1\frac{3}{5}$

64. $3.75 \times 0.3 = 1.125$ 65. $\frac{6x}{7xy} = \frac{6 \cdot x}{7 \cdot y \cdot x} = \frac{6}{7y}$

66. $\frac{12t}{24t} = \frac{1 \cdot 12 \cdot t}{2 \cdot 12 \cdot t} = \frac{1}{2}$ 67. $\frac{6mn}{11mt} = \frac{6 \cdot n \cdot m}{11 \cdot t \cdot m} = \frac{6n}{11t}$

68. $\frac{14n}{28ny} = \frac{14 \cdot n}{2 \cdot 14 \cdot n \cdot y} = \frac{1 \cdot 14 \cdot n}{2 \cdot y \cdot 14 \cdot n} = \frac{1}{2y}$

69. $(3a^3) = (3)(5^3) = (3)(125) = 375$

70. $4y^2 = 4 \cdot y \cdot y = 4 \cdot 7 \cdot 7 = 196$

71. $2w^3 - 9 = 2 \cdot (2)^3 - 9 = 2 \cdot 8 - 9 = 16 - 9 = 7$

72. $4r + \frac{3t}{6} = 4 \cdot 4 + \frac{3 \cdot 8}{6} = 16 + \frac{24}{6} = 16 + 4 = 20$

73. $3(m + 2n) = 3(4 + 2 \cdot 3) = 3(4 + 6) = 3(10) = 30$

74. $2a + 5b = 2 \cdot 2 + 5 \cdot 6 = 4 + 30 = 34$

75. $\frac{3s + 7}{t} = \frac{3 \cdot 1 + 7}{5} = \frac{3 + 7}{5} = \frac{10}{5} = 2$

76. $\frac{x + x}{7} = \frac{7 + 7}{7} = \frac{14}{7} = 2$

77. $\frac{w + 2z}{z} = \frac{6 + 2 \cdot 3}{3} = \frac{6 + 6}{3} = \frac{12}{3} = 4$

78. $\frac{6 + 3x}{6y} = \frac{6 + 3 \cdot 4}{6 \cdot 1} = \frac{6 + 12}{6} = \frac{18}{6} = 3$

LESSON 1-5 TRY THIS pp. 24–26

a. $4(x + y + z) = 4x + 4y + 4z$
b. $(y + 3)5 = 5y + 15$ c. $(8a + 3)2 = 16a + 6$
d. $6(x + 2y + 5) = 6x + 12y + 30$
e. $5x + 10 = 5 \cdot x + 5 \cdot 2 = 5(x + 2)$
f. $12 + 3x = 3 \cdot 4 + 3 \cdot x = 3(4 + x)$
g. $6x + 12 + 9y = 3 \cdot 2x + 3 \cdot 4 + 3 \cdot 3y = 3(2x + 4 + 3y)$
h. $5x + 10y + 5 = 5 \cdot x + 5 \cdot 2y + 5 \cdot 1 = 5(x + 2y + 1)$
i. $9x + 3y = 3(3x + y)$ Check: $3(3x + y) = 3 \cdot 3x + 3 \cdot y = 9x + 3y$

j. $5 + 10x + 15y = 5(1 + 2x + 3y)$
Check: $5(1 + 2x + 3y) = 5 \cdot 1 + 5 \cdot 2x + 5 \cdot 3y = 5 + 10x + 15y$

k. $6y + 2y = (6 + 2)y = 8y$
l. $7x + 3y + 5y + 4x = 7x + 4x + 3y + 5y = (7 + 4)x + (3 + 5)y = 11x + 8y$
m. $10p + 8q + 4p + 5q = 10p + 4p + 8q + 5q = (10 + 4)p + (8 + 5)q = 14p + 13q$
n. $7x^2 + x^2 = (7 + 1)x^2 = 8x^2$

LESSON 1-5 EXERCISES pp. 27–28

1. $2(b + 5) = 2 \cdot b + 2 \cdot 5 = 2b + 10$

2. $4(x + 3) = 4 \cdot x + 4 \cdot 3 = 4x + 12$

3. $(1 + t)7 = 7 \cdot 1 + 7 \cdot t = 7 + 7t$

4. $6(v + 4) = 6 \cdot v + 6 \cdot 4 = 6v + 24$

5. $3(x + 1) = 3 \cdot x + 3 \cdot 1 = 3x + 3$

6. $(x + 8)7 = 7 \cdot x + 7 \cdot 8 = 7x + 56$

7. $4(1 + y) = 4 \cdot 1 + 4 \cdot y = 4 + 4y$

8. $9(s + 1) = 9 \cdot s + 9 \cdot 1 = 9s + 9$

9. $6(5x + 2) = 6 \cdot 5x + 6 \cdot 2 = 30x + 12$

10. $9(6m + 7) = 9 \cdot 6m + 9 \cdot 7 = 54m + 63$

11. $7(x + 4 + 6y) = 7\cdot x + 7\cdot 4 + 7\cdot 6y = 7x + 28 + 42y$

12. $(5x + 8 + 3p)4 = 4\cdot 5x + 4\cdot 8 + 4\cdot 3p = 20x + 32 + 12p$

13. $2x + 4 = 2\cdot x + 2\cdot 2 = 2(x + 2)$

14. $5y + 20 = 5\cdot y + 5\cdot 4 = 5(y + 4)$

15. $30 + 5y = 5\cdot 6 + 5\cdot y = 5(6 + y)$

16. $7x + 28 = 7\cdot x + 7\cdot 4 = 7(x + 4)$

17. $14x + 21y = 7\cdot 2x + 7\cdot 3y = 7(2x + 3y)$

18. $18a + 24b = 6\cdot 3a + 6\cdot 4b = 6(3a + 4b)$

19. $5x + 10 + 15y = 5\cdot x + 5\cdot 2 + 5\cdot 3y = 5(x + 2 + 3y)$

20. $9a + 27b + 81 = 9\cdot a + 9\cdot 3b + 9\cdot 9 = 9(a + 3b + 9)$

21. $14c + 63d + 7 = 7\cdot 2c + 7\cdot 9d + 7\cdot 1 = 7(2c + 9d + 1)$

22. $4y + 10 + 8x = 2\cdot 2y + 2\cdot 5 + 2\cdot 4x = 2(2y + 5 + 4x)$

23. $9r + 27s + 18 = 9\cdot r + 9\cdot 3s + 9\cdot 2 = 9(r + 3s + 2)$

24. $24x + 72y + 8 = 8\cdot 3x + 8\cdot 9y + 8\cdot 1 = 8(3x + 9y + 1)$

25. $9x + 27 = 9\cdot x + 9\cdot 3 = 9(x + 3)$
Check: $9(x + 3) = 9\cdot x + 9\cdot 3 = 9x + 27$

26. $6x + 24 = 6\cdot x + 6\cdot 4 = 6(x + 4)$
Check: $6(x + 4) = 6\cdot x + 6\cdot 4 = 6x + 24$

27. $9x + 3y = 3\cdot 3x + 3\cdot y = 3(3x + y)$
Check: $3(3x + y) = 3\cdot 3x + 3\cdot y = 9x + 3y$

28. $15x + 5y = 5\cdot 3x + 5\cdot y = 5(3x + y)$
Check: $5(3x + y) = 5\cdot 3x + 5\cdot y = 15x + 5y$

29. $8a + 16b + 64 = 8\cdot a + 8\cdot 2b + 8\cdot 8 = 8(a + 2b + 8)$
Check: $8(a + 2b + 8) = 8\cdot a + 8\cdot 2b + 8\cdot 8 = 8a + 16b + 64$

30. $5 + 20x + 35y = 5\cdot 1 + 5\cdot 4x + 5\cdot 7y = 5(1 + 4x + 7y)$
Check: $5(1 + 4x + 7y) = 5\cdot 1 + 5\cdot 4x + 5\cdot 7y = 5 + 20x + 35y$

31. $11x + 44y + 121 = 11\cdot x + 11\cdot 4y + 11\cdot 11$
$= 11(x + 4y + 11)$
Check: $11(x + 4y + 11) = 11\cdot x + 11\cdot 4y + 11\cdot 11$
$= 11x + 44y + 121$

32. $7 + 14b + 56w = 7\cdot 1 + 7\cdot 2b + 7\cdot 8w = 7(1 + 2b + 8w)$
Check: $7(1 + 2b + 8w) = 7\cdot 1 + 7\cdot 2b + 7\cdot 8w = 7 + 14b + 56w$

33. $5x + 10y + 45z = 5\cdot x + 5\cdot 2y + 5\cdot 9z = 5(x + 2y + 9z)$
Check: $5(x + 2y + 9z) = 5\cdot x + 5\cdot 2y + 5\cdot 9z = 5x + 10y + 45z$

34. $9p + 3q + 27r = 3\cdot 3p + 3\cdot q + 3\cdot 9r = 3(3p + q + 9r)$
Check: $3(3p + q + 9r) = 3\cdot 3p + 3\cdot q + 3\cdot 9r = 9p + 3q + 27r$

35. $9a + 10a = (9 + 10)a = 19a$

36. $12x + 2x = (12 + 2)x = 14x$

37. $10a + a = 10a + 1a = (10 + 1)a = 11a$

38. $16x + x = 16x + 1x = (16 + 1)x = 17x$

39. $2x + 9z + 6x = (2 + 6)x + 9z = 8x + 9z$

40. $3a + 5b + 7a = (3 + 7)a + 5b = 10a + 5b$

41. $7x + 6y^2 + 9y^2 = 7x + (6 + 9)y^2 = 7x + 15y^2$

42. $12m^2 + 6q + 9m^2 = (12 + 9)m^2 + 6q = 21m^2 + 6q$

43. $41a + 90 + 60a + 2 = (41 + 60)a + 90 + 2 = 101a + 92$

44. $42x + 6 + 4x + 2 = (42 + 4)x + 6 + 2 = 46x + 8$

45. $8a + 8b + 3a + 3b = (8 + 3)a + (8 + 3)b = 11a + 11b$

46. $100y + 200z + 190y + 400z = (100 + 190)y + (200 + 400)z$
$= 290y + 600z$

47. $8u^2 + 3t + 10t + 6u^2 + 2 = (8 + 6)u^2 + (3 + 10)t + 2$
$= 14u^2 + 13t + 2$

48. $5 + 6h + t + 8 + 9h = 5 + 8 + (6 + 9)h + t$
$= 13 + 15h + t$

49. $23 + 5t + 7y + t + y + 27 = 23 + 27 + (5 + 1)t + (7 + 1)y$
$= 50 + 6t + 8y$

50. $45 + 90d + 87 + 9d + 3 + 7d = 45 + 87 + 3 + (90 + 9 + 7)d$
$= 135 + 106d$

51. $\frac{1}{2}b + \frac{1}{2}b = \left(\frac{1}{2} + \frac{1}{2}\right)b = 1b = b$

52. $\frac{2}{3}x + \frac{1}{3}x = \left(\frac{2}{3} + \frac{1}{3}\right)x = 1x = x$

53. $2y + \frac{1}{4}y + y = \left(2 + \frac{1}{4} + 1\right)y = 3\frac{1}{4}y$ or $\frac{13}{4}y$

54. $\frac{1}{2}a + a + 5a = \left(\frac{1}{2} + 1 + 5\right)a = 6\frac{1}{2}a$ or $\frac{13}{2}a$

55. $4x + 5y + 6x = (4 + 6)x + 5y = 10x + 5y$

56. $6z + 3k + 9z = (6 + 9)z + 3k = 15z + 3k$

57. $4p^2 + 2p + 4p + 8p^2 = (4 + 8)p^2 + (2 + 4)p$
$= 12p^2 + 6p$

58. $2m + 3mn + 2m + mn = (2 + 2)m + (3 + 1)mn$
$= 4m + 4mn$

59. $7xy + 3y + 6x + 2xy = (7 + 2)xy + 3y + 6x$
$= 9xy + 3y + 6x$

60. $6tp + 3t^2 + 9t^2 + 2tp = (6 + 2)tp + (3 + 9)t^2$
$= 8tp + 12t^2$

61. $4(x + 3) + 5(x + 3) = 4x + 12 + 5x + 15 = 9x + 27$

62. $7(m^2 + 2) + 7(m^2 + 2) = 7m^2 + 14 + 7m^2 + 14$
$= 14m^2 + 28$

63. $8(a + b) + 4(a + 2b) = 8a + 8b + 4a + 8b$
$= 12a + 16b$

64. $4(5x + 6y + 3) + 2(x + 2y) = 20x + 24y + 12 + 2x + 4y$
$= (20 + 2)x + (24 + 4)y + 12$
$= 22x + 28y + 12$

65. **a.** $P + Prt = P\cdot 1 + P\cdot rt = P(1 + rt)$
b. Substituting $P = 400$, $r = 0.03$, and $t = 1$, $P + Prt = 400 + 400(0.03)(1) = 400 + 12 = 412$. The new principal at the end of one year is \$412.

66. **a.** $17x + 34 = 17(x + 2) = 17(10 + 2) = 17(12) = 204$
$17\cdot 10 + 34 = 170 + 34 = 204$
b. Yes; distributive property

67. No $[(2 + 3)^2 = 5^2 = 25$ is not equal to $2^2 + 3^2 = 4 + 9 = 13$, for example]; they are equal only when $x = 0$ or $y = 0$.

68. $(b + c)a = a(b + c)$ by the commutative property of multiplication; $a(b + c) = ab + ac$ by the distributive property; $ab + ac = ba + ca$ by the commutative property of multiplication. Thus, $(b + c)a = ba + ca$.

69. Both answers are correct. $ax + ay + bx + by = a(x + y) + b(x + y)$ and $ax + ay + bx + by = ax + bx + ay + by = xa + xb + ya + yb = x(a + b) + y(a + b)$

70. $\frac{3a + 6}{2a + 4} = \frac{3(a + 2)}{2(a + 2)} = \frac{3}{2}$

71. $\frac{4x + 12y}{3x + 9y} = \frac{4(x + 3y)}{3(x + 3y)} = \frac{4}{3}$

72. $x + 2x^2 + 3x^3 + 4x^2 + 5x = 1x + 5x + 2x^2 + 4x^2 + 3x^3$
$= (1 + 5)x + (2 + 4)x^2 + 3x^3$
$= 6x + 6x^2 + 3x^3$
$= (3x\cdot 2) + (3x\cdot 2x) + (3x\cdot x^2)$
$= 3x(2 + 2x + x^2)$

73. $q + qr + qrs + qrst = q(1 + r + rs + rst)$

74. $21x + 44xy + 15y - 16x - 8y - 38xy + 2x + xy$
$= 21x - 16x + 2x + 44xy - 38xy + xy + 15y - 8y$
$= (21 - 16 + 2)x + (44 - 38 + 1)xy + (15 - 8)y$
$= 7x + 7xy + 7y = 7(x + xy + y)$

75. $a\{1 + b[1 + c(1 + d)]\} = a\{1 + b[1 + c + cd]\}$
$= a\{1 + b + bc + bcd\}$
$= a + ab + abc + abcd$

76. $(4\cdot 3)^2 = 12^2 = 12\cdot 12 = 144$

77. $6\cdot 2^3 = 6\cdot 8 = 48$

78. $(3 - 2)^3 = 1^3 = 1$

79. $8 - 2^3 = 8 - 8 = 0$

80. $\frac{8xy}{2x} = \frac{4\cdot 2\cdot x\cdot y}{2\cdot x} = \frac{4y\cdot 2x}{2x} = 4y$

81. $\frac{6b}{18ab} = \frac{6b}{3\cdot 6\cdot a\cdot b} = \frac{6b}{3a\cdot 6b} = \frac{1}{3a}$

82. $\frac{15c}{30c} = \frac{15c}{2\cdot 15c} = \frac{1}{2}$

83. $\frac{24xy}{3y} = \frac{8\cdot 3\cdot x\cdot y}{3y} = \frac{8\cdot x\cdot 3y}{3y} = 8x$

84. $6(t + 4) = 6(2 + 4) = 6(6) = 36$

85. $w(5 + w) = 3(5 + 3) = 3(8) = 24$ **86.** $k^1 = 5^1 = 5$

87. $(x + 3)\cdot(5 - x) = (2 + 3)\cdot(5 - 2) = 5\cdot 3 = 15$

LESSON 1-6 TRY THIS pp. 29–30

a. $n + 7$ **b.** $4n$ **c.** $y - 4$ **d.** $x - 6$
e. $m - n$ **f.** $2y$ **g.** $b - a$ **h.** $7n$

i. "Divides her money among 7 people" suggests division. $\frac{a}{7}$

j. "24 fewer stamps than coins" suggests subtraction. $c - 24$

LESSON 1-6 EXERCISES pp. 30–32

1. $b + 6$ **2.** $t + 8$ **3.** $c - 9$ **4.** $d - 4$ **5.** $q + 6$

6. $z + 11$ **7.** $a + b$ **8.** $d + c$ **9.** $y - x$ **10.** $h - c$

11. $w + x$ **12.** $t + s$ **13.** $n - m$ **14.** $q - p$

15. $r + s$ **16.** $d + f$ **17.** $2x$ **18.** $3p$ **19.** $5t$

20. $9d$ **21.** $3b$ **22.** $\frac{x}{5}$ **23.** $2h$ **24.** $\frac{x}{2}$ **25.** $x - y$

26. $n + 6$ **27.** $m - 5$ **28.** $p - q$ **29.** $a + 5$ **30.** $2p$

31. $m - \$4.50$ **32.** $\frac{t}{5}$ **33.** $a + \$45$ **34.** $\frac{n}{2}$

35. $w - 2$ **36.** $a + \$8$ **37.** $3K$ **38.** $32w$

39. $\frac{1}{4}t$ or $\frac{t}{4}$ **40.** $\frac{1}{3}d$ or $\frac{d}{3}$ **41.** $R - 3$ **42.** $x + 3y$

43. $y + 2x$ **44.** $a + (b + 2)$ **45.** $2x - 3$

46. $x + x$ or $2x$ **47.** lw **48.** $4s$

49. $\frac{256y}{32x} = \frac{256\cdot 1}{32\cdot 4} = \frac{256}{128} = 2$

50. $\frac{y + x}{2} + \frac{3y}{x} = \frac{4 + 2}{2} + \frac{3\cdot 4}{2} = \frac{6}{2} + \frac{12}{2} = 3 + 6 = 9$

51. $\frac{a + b}{4} + \frac{a\cdot b}{2} = \frac{3 + 4}{4} + \frac{3\cdot 4}{2} = \frac{7}{4} + \frac{12}{2} = \frac{7}{4} + \frac{24}{4} = \frac{31}{4}$

52. $\frac{x + y}{4} = \frac{14 + 2}{4} = \frac{16}{4} = 4$ **53.** $\frac{x + y}{4} = \frac{9 + 27}{4} = \frac{36}{4} = 9$

54. $\frac{x + y}{4} = \frac{16 + 8}{4} = \frac{24}{4} = 6$

55. $\frac{x + y}{4} = \frac{64 + 32}{4} = \frac{96}{4} = 24$

56. Answers may vary; the number of cents in a quarters and b dimes

57. a. $x - 6$ **b.** $\frac{x - 6}{3}$ **c.** $\frac{x - 6}{3} + 4$

d. $\frac{x - 6}{3} + 4 - \frac{x}{9}$

e. Substituting $x = 27$, $\frac{x - 6}{3} + 4 - \frac{x}{9} = \frac{27 - 6}{3} + 4 - \frac{27}{9} = \frac{21}{3} + 4 - 3 = 8$. There were 8 students in Ed's group at lunchtime.

58. a. No; let $n = 9$; $2(9 + 1) = 20$
b. Yes; $2n$ is always even because it has a factor of 2, so $2n + 1$ is always odd.
c. Yes; $10n$ is always even because it has a factor of 2, so $10n - 1$ is always odd.
d. No; let $n = 10$; $11(10) = 110$.

59. "The next whole number" suggests adding 1.
$(w + 3) + 1 = w + 4$

60. "The preceding odd number" suggests subtracting 2.
$(d + 2) - 2 = d + 2 - 2 = d$

61. "The difference is 3" suggests either adding or subtracting 3.
$t + 3$ or $t - 3$

62. "Sum" suggests adding.
$(v + 2) + (v - 2) = v + 2 + v - 2$
$= v + v + 2 - 2$
$= 2v$

63. "Sum" suggests adding.
$(2 + w) + (2 - w) = 2 + w + 2 - w$
$= 2 + 2 + w - w$
$= 4$

64. $4c^2 = 4(6)^2 = 4(36) = 144$ **65.** $3t^4 = 3(2)^4 = 3(16) = 48$

66. $(4x)^2 = (4\cdot 3)^2 = (12)^2 = 144$

67. $3x + 6 = 3\cdot x + 3\cdot 2 = 3(x + 2)$

68. $20a + 30b = 2\cdot 10\cdot a + 3\cdot 10\cdot b = 10(2a + 3b)$

69. $8 + 16y + 40y = 8\cdot 1 + 8\cdot 2\cdot y + 8\cdot 5\cdot y$
$= 8(1 + 2x + 5y)$

70. $14c + 8c = (14 + 8)c = 22c$

71. $4a + 7b + 8a = 4a + 8a + 7b$
$= (4 + 8)a + 7b = 12a + 7b$

72. $\frac{1}{3}c + \frac{2}{3}c = \left(\frac{1}{3} + \frac{2}{3}\right)c = 1c$ or c

73. $3y + 7y + y = (3 + 7 + 1)y = 11y$

74. $\frac{1}{4}d + \frac{3}{4}d = \left(\frac{1}{4} + \frac{3}{4}\right)d = 1d$ or d

75. $5 + 7c + 4 = 5 + 4 + 7c = 9 + 7c$

LESSON 1-7 TRY THIS pp. 33–36

a. $3\cdot 5 + 2 = 15 + 2 = 17$; False
b. $4\cdot 2 - 3 = 8 - 3 = 5$; True **c.** Open
d.

$(0)^2 + 3 = 12$	$(3)^2 + 3 = 12$	$(9)^2 + 3 = 12$
$0 + 3 = 12$	$9 + 3 = 12$	$81 + 3 = 12$
$3 = 12$	$12 = 12$	$84 = 12$
False	True	False

The solution set is {3}.

e.

$\frac{12}{(2)} = 3(2)$	$\frac{12}{(4)} = 3(4)$	$\frac{12}{(12)} = 3(12)$
$6 = 6$	$3 = 12$	$1 = 36$
True	False	False

The solution set is {2}.

f. $x = 6$ **g.** $y = 24$ **h.** $y = 5$ **i.** $x = 17$
j. 4 was added to both sides of the equation.
k. 5 was subtracted from both sides of the equation.
l. Both sides of the equation were divided by 2.

LESSON 1-7 EXERCISES pp. 36–37

1. $2 + 3\cdot 5 = 2 + 15 = 17$; False **2.** Open

3. $2^3 + 8 = 8 + 8 = 16$; True

4.

$3(5) + 2 = 23$	$3(7) + 2 = 23$	$3(9) + 2 = 23$
$15 + 2 = 23$	$21 + 2 = 23$	$27 + 2 = 23$
$17 = 23$	$23 = 23$	$29 = 23$
False	True	False

The solution set is {7}.

5.

$6(5) - 2 = 46$	$6(6) - 2 = 46$	$6(8) - 2 = 46$
$30 - 2 = 46$	$36 - 2 = 46$	$48 - 2 = 46$
$28 = 46$	$34 = 46$	$46 = 46$
False	False	True

The solution set is {8}.

6.

$2(1)^2 - 1 = 7$	$2\left(\frac{3}{2}\right)^2 - 1 = 7$	$2(2)^2 - 1 = 7$
$2(1) - 1 = 7$	$2\left(\frac{9}{4}\right) - 1 = 7$	$2(4) - 1 = 7$
$2 - 1 = 7$	$\frac{9}{2} - 1 = 7$	$8 - 1 = 7$
$1 = 7$	$\frac{7}{2} = 7$	$7 = 7$
False	False	True

The solution set is {2}.

7. $(0)^2 + (0) = 0$ $\quad$ $(100)^2 + (100) = 0$
$0 + 0 = 0$ $\quad$ $10{,}000 + 100 = 0$
$0 = 0$ $\quad$ $10{,}100 = 0$
True $\quad$ False
$(1000)^2 + (1000) = 0$
$1{,}000{,}000 + 1{,}000 = 0$
$1{,}001{,}000 = 0$
False
The solution set is $\{0\}$.

8. $8 - (1) = 2(1)$ $\quad$ $8 - (2) = 2(2)$ $\quad$ $8 - (4) = 2(4)$
$7 = 2$ $\quad$ $6 = 4$ $\quad$ $4 = 8$
False $\quad$ False $\quad$ False
No solution

9. $(8) - 8 = 4(8) - 44$ $\quad$ $(12) - 8 = 4(12) - 44$
$0 = 32 - 44$ $\quad$ $4 = 48 - 44$
False $\quad$ $4 = 4$
True
$(18) - 8 = 4(18) - 44$
$10 = 72 - 44$
$10 = 28$
False
The solution set is $\{12\}$.

10. $x = 10$ **11.** $m = 23$ **12.** $x = 19$ **13.** $y = 27$

14. $a = 9$ **15.** $y = 9$ **16.** $x = 30$ **17.** $c = 48$

18. $d = 2$ **19.** 5 was added to both sides.

20. 3 was subtracted from both sides.

21. 10 was subtracted from both sides.

22. Both sides were divided by 3.

23. Both sides were multiplied by 4.

24. Both sides were multiplied by 5.

25. Both sides were multiplied by 8.

26. Both sides were multiplied by 3.

27. Both sides were multiplied by 4.

28. $5x + 3x = 24$
$8x = 24$
$x = 3$

29. $9y + 4y = 26$
$13y = 26$
$y = 2$

30. $6t + 3t = 0$
$9t = 0$
$t = 0$

31. $\frac{y}{2} + \frac{y}{2} = 31$
$y = 31$

32. $\frac{2}{3}y + \frac{1}{3}y = 2$
$y = 2$

33. $20x - 6x = 7$
$14x = 7$
$x = \frac{1}{2}$

34. $\frac{10d}{5} = 10$
$2d = 10$
$d = 5$

35. $\frac{20k}{4} = 10$
$5k = 10$
$k = 2$

36. $4t^2 = 0$
$t^2 = 0$
$t = 0$

37. Add 12 to both sides.

38. Subtract 34 from both sides.

39. Divide both sides by 3.

40. Divide both sides by 5.

41. Multiply both sides by 8.

42. Multiply both sides by 5.

43. The equations are not equivalent because 5 was added to the left side of the second equation, but was subtracted from the right side.

44. The equations are not equivalent because the left side of the second equation was multiplied by 12, but the right side was multiplied by 6.

45. $n = 125$ is a solution of $25 = \frac{n}{5}$ because $25 = \frac{125}{5}$.
The correct answer is **D** because it is the only set that contains 125.

46. Answers may vary. $x + 2 = 8$

47. Answers may vary. $3x = 2$

48. Answers may vary. $x - x = 0$

49. Answers may vary. $12x = 0$

50. m^3 **51.** $5n^5$ **52.** $(3 \cdot 2)^2 = 6^2 = 36$

53. $(4 + 4)^2 = 8^2 = 64$ **54.** $9 + 3^2 = 9 + 9 = 18$

55. $(9 - 6)^3 = 3^3 = 3 \cdot 3 \cdot 3 = 27$

56. $4x + 12 = 4 \cdot x + 4 \cdot 3$
$= 4(x + 3)$

57. $13t + 52 = 13 \cdot t + 13 \cdot 4$
$= 13(t + 4)$

58. $10t + 25m = 5 \cdot 2t + 5 \cdot 5m$
$= 5(2t + 5m)$

59. $16 + 8y = 8 \cdot 2 + 8 \cdot y$
$= 8(2 + y)$

60. $8a + 16b = 8 \cdot a + 8 \cdot 2b$
$= 8(a + 2b)$

61. $9x + 3 = 3 \cdot 3x + 3 \cdot 1$
$= 3(3x + 1)$

62. $8 + 24c = 8 \cdot 1 + 8 \cdot 3c$
$= 8(1 + 3c)$

LESSON 1-8 PROBLEMS p. 39

1. Strategy: Draw a diagram
The ocean is 14,250 feet deep. From the top of the mountain to the surface is 8700 feet.

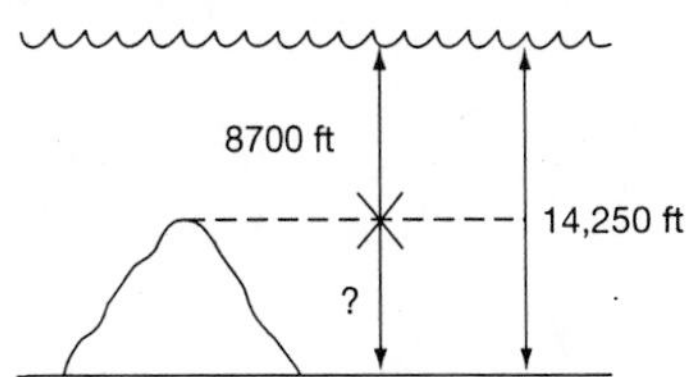

$14{,}250 - 8700 = 5550$
The underwater mountain is 5550 ft high.

2. Strategy: Draw a diagram
Thirteen posts will be needed for each of the two sides that are 300 ft long. The other sides (250 ft) need only 9 posts each, because the corners already have posts.

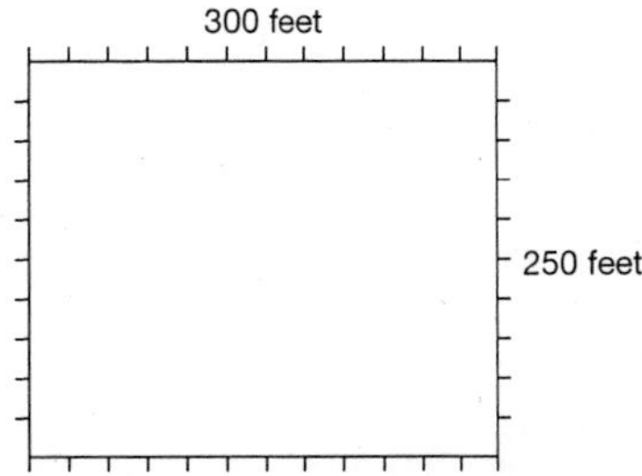

$13 + 13 + 9 + 9 = 44$
Forty-four posts are needed.

3. Strategy: Draw a diagram
The rocket is 180 ft long. The booster is $\frac{1}{2}$ the total length $\left(\frac{1}{2} \times 180 = 90 \text{ ft}\right)$. The cargo and navigation section is $\frac{1}{6}$ the booster $\left(\frac{1}{6} \times 15 \text{ ft}\right)$. The fuel tank is the only section left $(180 - [90 + 15] = 75 \text{ ft})$.

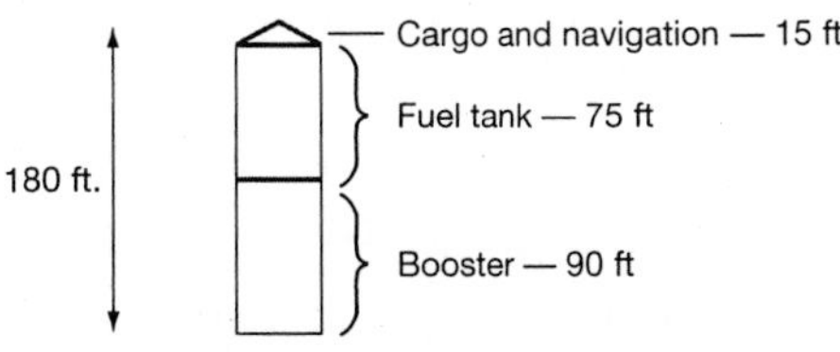

The booster is 90 ft long, the fuel tank is 75 ft long, and the cargo and navigation section is 15 ft long.

4. Strategy: Draw a diagram
Start with person number 1 and mark out every second person. On the first round 2, 4, 6, 8, 10, 12, 14, 16, 18, and 20 sit down. Second round begins with number 1 and numbers 3, 7, 11, 15, and 19 sit down. Next round begins with number 1 and 5, 13, and 1 sit down. Next round begins with 9 and number 17 sits down. Number 9 is the last student standing.
A student should stand in position 9 to attend the conference.

LESSON 1-9 TRY THIS pp. 40–41

a. $a = Ms$
$a = 1.5(1130)$
$a = 1695$ km/h

b. $a = Ms$
$a = 2(685)$
$a = 1370$ mi/h

c. $P = 3s$
$P = 3(13)$
$P = 39$ cm

d. $A = s^2$
$A = 7^2$
$A = 49 \text{ in.}^2$

e. $r = \frac{d}{t}$
$r = \frac{63}{7}$
$r = 9$ ft/sec

f. $V = lwh$
$V = 4 \cdot 2 \cdot 2\frac{1}{2}$
$V = 20 \text{ ft}^3$

LESSON 1-9 EXERCISES pp. 42–43

1. $d = rt$
$d = 55(8)$
$d = 440$ mi

2. $A = 3.14\,r^2$
$A = 3.14(4)^2$
$A = 3.14(16)$
$A = 50.24 \text{ m}^2$

3. $T = 0.04p$
$T = 0.04(170)$
$T = \$6.80$

4. $\text{km} = \frac{\text{m}}{1000}$
$\text{km} = \frac{2500}{1000}$
$\text{km} = 2.5$ km

5. $a = Ms$
$a = 1.4(1025)$
$a = 1435$ ft/s

6. $a = Ms$
$a = 2.3(714)$
$a = 1642.2$ mi/h

7. $A = lw$
$A = 26(14)$
$A = 364 \text{ m}^2$

8. $A = \frac{1}{2}bh$
$A = \frac{1}{2}(12)(9)$ or $\frac{1}{2}(1)\left(\frac{3}{4}\right)$
$A = 54 \text{ in.}^2$ or $\frac{3}{8} \text{ ft}^2$

9. $P = 2(l + w)$
$P = 2(66 + 33)$ or $2(198 + 99)$
$P = 2(99)$ or $2(297)$
$P = 198$ yd or 594 ft

10. $C = \frac{5}{9}(F - 32)$
$C = \frac{5}{9}(75 - 32)$
$C = \frac{5}{9}(43)$
$C \approx 24°\text{C}$

11. $I = prt$
$I = 2000(0.15)(3)$
$I = \$900$

12. $U = \frac{P}{n}$
$U = \frac{2.50}{40}$
$U = \$0.0625$ per oz

13. $d = \frac{a}{a + 12} \cdot D = \frac{5}{5 + 12} \cdot 2.5 \approx 0.7$ mL

14. $d = \frac{a}{a + 12} \cdot D = \frac{10}{10 + 12} \cdot 8 \approx 3.6$ mL

15. $d = \frac{a}{a + 12} \cdot D = \frac{2}{2 + 12} \cdot 4 \approx 0.6$ mL

16. $d = \frac{a}{a + 12} \cdot D = \frac{1}{1 + 12} \cdot (1.5) \approx 0.1$ mL

17. $d = x + \frac{x^2}{20} = 25 + \frac{(25)^2}{20} = 56.25$ ft

18. $d = x + \frac{x^2}{20} = 10 + \frac{(10)^2}{20} = 15$ ft

19. $d = x + \frac{x^2}{20} = 55 + \frac{(55)^2}{20} = 206.25$ ft

20. $d = x + \frac{x^2}{20} = 50 + \frac{(50)^2}{20} = 175$ ft

21. $A = \frac{1}{2}h(b + c)$
$= \frac{1}{2}(2)(5 + 12)$
$= 1(17)$
$A = 17 \text{ ft}^2$

22. $A = \frac{1}{2}h(b + c)$
$= \frac{1}{2}(10)(8 + 14)$
$= 5(22)$
$A = 110 \text{ in.}^2$

23. $A = \frac{1}{2}h(b + c)$
$= \frac{1}{2}(4)\left(\frac{1}{2} + \frac{3}{4}\right)$
$= 2\left(\frac{5}{4}\right)$
$A = 2\frac{1}{2} \text{ m}^2$

24. $P = 2l + 2w$
$14 = 2(l + w)$ so $l + w = 7$
Since l and w are whole numbers, the dimensions could be 1 cm × 6 cm, 2 cm × 5 cm, or 3 cm × 4 cm. The corresponding areas are thus 6 cm^2, 10 cm^2, or 12 cm^2.

25. a. Andrew did not convert 0.5 km to meters. Marie did not convert 150 m to kilometers.
b. Using meters and substituting $l = 500$ and $w = 150$, $A = lw = 500(150) = 75{,}000$. The area is 75,000 m^2. Using kilometers and substituting $l = 0.5$ and $w = 0.15$, $A = lw = 0.5(0.15) = 0.075$. The area is 0.075 km^2.

26. $A = lw$
$64 = l(16)$
$\frac{64}{16} = l$
$4 = l$
The length is 4 cm.

27. $a^2 - b^2$

28. $x^2 + y^2 - y^2 = x^2$

29. $t + 5$ **30.** $x + y$ **31.** $3k$ **32.** $m - 3$

33. $15c + c = 15 \cdot c + 1 \cdot c$
$= (15 + 1)c$
$= 16c$

34. $3x + 4 + 5x = 3x + 5x + 4$
$= (3 + 5)x + 4$
$= 8x + 4$

35. $x = 9$ **36.** $m = 7$

LESSON 1-10 PROBLEMS pp. 45–46

1. 7 **2.** 3 **3.** 7 **4.** 8 **5.** 8 **6.** 4 **7.** 9
8. 5 **9.** 5 **10.** 2 **11.** 12 and 48 **12.** 23, 24, and 25
13. 24 in., 12 in. **14.** $l = 22$, $w = 14$ **15.** 45°, 45°, 90°
16. 30°, 60°, 90° **17.** 22 and 11 **18.** 32 and 25
19. 59 **20.** 6, 11, and 30

21. Strategy: Try, test, revise

Try	Test	Revised Try
First Try	Overtime: $\frac{1}{2} \times 20 = 10$h	30 is less than 33
Regular hours: 20	$20 + 10 = 30$h	Revise try up Revised try: 22h
Second Try	Overtime: $\frac{1}{2} \times 22 = 11$h	This is correct.
Regular hours: 22	$22 + 11 = 33$h	

Eunpyo worked 11 hours of overtime.

22. Strategy: Draw a diagram
Try, test, revise

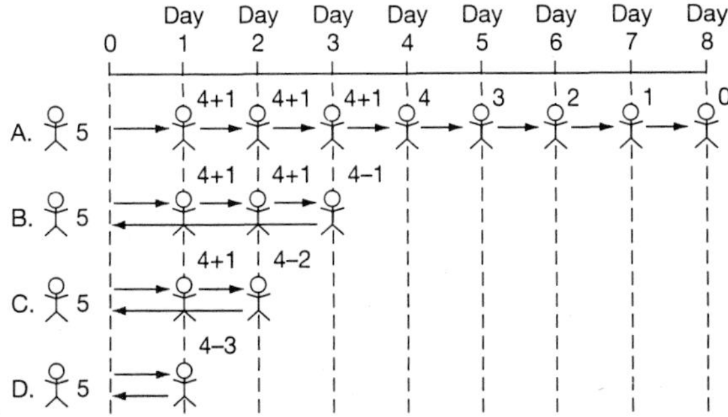

The expedition starts with 4 people each carrying water for 5 days. Person D travels one day and gives persons A, B, and C each one day's water supply, and returns to the starting point. A, B, and C travel another day. At this point person C gives persons A and B each one day's water supply, and returns to the starting point. A and B travel another day. Person B gives A one day's water supply and returns to the starting point. Person A now has enough water to finish the expedition.

Four people are needed to start the journey.

23. Strategy: Try, test, revise

Try	Test	Revised Try
First Try 1st week: \$10	2nd week: 3 × 10 = \$30	\$30 is less than \$45.75 Revise try up Revised try: 1st week \$15
Second Try 1st week: \$15	2nd week: 3 × 15 = \$45	\$45 is less than \$45.75 Revise try up Revised try: 1st week \$15.25
Third Try 1st week: \$15.25	2nd week: 3 × 15.25 = \$45.75	This is correct

Peter earned \$15.25 the first week.

24. Strategy: Try, test, revise

Try	Test	Revised Try
First Try: Number of 4 wheelers: 20	20 × 4 = 80 wheels 98 − 80 = 18	18 wheels—not divisible by 5 Revised try: 17
Second Try: Number of 4 wheelers: 17	17 × 4 = 68 wheels 98 − 68 = 30 30 ÷ 5 = 6 (5 wheelers)	This is correct.

Juanita could have built 17 four-wheel lawnmowers and 6 lawnmowers with five wheels. Total of 23 lawnmowers.
Other answers: 12 four-wheelers & 10 five-wheelers. Total 22
7 four-wheelers & 14 five-wheelers. Total 21
2 four-wheelers & 18 five-wheelers. Total 20
22 four-wheelers & 2 five-wheelers. Total 24
24 × \$6 = \$144, 23 × \$6 = \$138, 22 × \$6 = \$132,
21 × \$6 = \$126, 20 × \$6 = \$120
Juanita could have earned \$120, \$126, \$132, \$138, or \$144 for her workday.

CHAPTER 1 WRAP UP pp. 47–49

1. $y + 7 = 4 + 7 = 11$ **2.** $n - 6 = 15 - 6 = 9$

3. $\frac{30}{x} = \frac{30}{6} = 5$ **4.** $4t = 4(8) = 32$

5. $ab = 8(9) = 72$ **6.** $x - y = 19 - 11 = 8$

7. $\frac{a}{3b} = \frac{18}{3(3)} = \frac{18}{9} = 2$ **8.** $p(6 + q) = 3(6 + 5) = 3(11) = 33$

9. $15 \div 3 + 6 \cdot 8 = 5 + 48 = 53$

10. $2 \cdot 10 \div 5 + 6 = 20 \div 5 + 6 = 4 + 6 = 10$

11. $\frac{4a}{2b + 3} = \frac{4(7)}{2(2) + 3} = \frac{28}{4 + 3} = \frac{28}{7} = 4$

12. $6x + \frac{3y}{2} = 6(8) + \frac{3(4)}{2} = 48 + \frac{12}{2} = 48 + 6 = 54$

13. $8 + x$ **14.** $ab + 11, ba + 11$, or $11 + ba$

15. $\frac{4}{5} \cdot \frac{9}{9} = \frac{36}{45}$ **16.** $\frac{2x}{y} \cdot \frac{z}{z} = \frac{2xz}{yz}$

17. $\frac{6}{18} = \frac{6 \cdot 1}{6 \cdot 3} = \frac{1}{3}$ **18.** $\frac{56}{16} = \frac{8 \cdot 7}{8 \cdot 2} = \frac{7}{2}$

19. $\frac{35ab}{105bc} = \frac{35b \cdot a}{35b \cdot 3c} = \frac{a}{3c}$ **20.** $\frac{96z}{24xyz} = \frac{24z \cdot 4}{24z \cdot xy} = \frac{4}{xy}$

21. $\frac{mn}{6m} = \frac{m \cdot n}{m \cdot 6} = \frac{n}{6}$ **22.** $\frac{9pq}{72p} = \frac{9p \cdot q}{9p \cdot 8} = \frac{q}{8}$

23. 6^5 **24.** $3y^4$ **25.** $y^3 = 4^3 = 4 \cdot 4 \cdot 4 = 64$

26. $2x^2 = 2(6)^2 = 2 \cdot 36 = 72$

27. $a^2 - 2 = 8^2 - 2 = 64 - 2 = 62$

28. $b^4 + 3 = 2^4 + 3 = 2 \cdot 2 \cdot 2 \cdot 2 + 3 = 19$

29. $(2a)^3 = (2 \cdot 3)^3 = 6^3 = 6 \cdot 6 \cdot 6 = 216$

30. $(5t)^5 = (5 \cdot 2)^5 = 10^5 = 10 \cdot 10 \cdot 10 \cdot 10 \cdot 10 = 100{,}000$

31. $(4 \cdot 5)^2 = 20^2 = 400$ **32.** $6 + 7^2 = 6 + 49 = 55$

33. $6 + (4y)^2 = 6 + (4 \cdot 2)^2 = 6 + 8^2 = 6 + 64 = 70$

34. $(6 + a) \cdot (b - 4) = (6 + 8) \cdot (6 - 4) = 14 \cdot 2 = 28$

35. $a + (b + 6)$

36. $7 \cdot (y \cdot x)$

37. Answers may vary. $1 + (n + m), n + (m + 1), m + (1 + n)$

38. Answers may vary. $4 \cdot (y \cdot x), y \cdot (x \cdot 4), x \cdot (y \cdot 4)$

39. $7(y + 5) = 7 \cdot y + 7 \cdot 5 = 7y + 35$

40. $(6m + 4n + 5)3 = 18m + 12n + 15$

41. $18x + 6y = 6 \cdot 3x + 6 \cdot y = 6(3x + y)$

42. $4 + 12b + 36a = 4 \cdot 1 + 4 \cdot 3b + 4 \cdot 9a = 4(1 + 3b + 9a)$

43. $3a + 2b + 5a + 7b = (3 + 5)a + (2 + 7)b = 8a + 9b$

44. $15m^2 + 12m + 4m^2 = (15 + 4)m^2 + 12m = 19m^2 + 12m$

45. $5n$ **46.** $n - 7$ **47.** $n + 4$

48. $2n$ **49.** $x + 2x$ or $3x$ **50.** $a + 12$

51.

$3(1) + 7 = 16$	$3(3) + 7 = 16$	$3(5) + 7 = 16$
$3 + 7 = 16$	$9 + 7 = 16$	$15 + 7 = 16$
$10 = 16$	$16 = 16$	$22 = 16$
False	True	False

The solution set is {3}.

52.

$(0)^2 - (0) = 0$	$(1)^2 - (1) = 0$	$(10)^2 - (10) = 0$
$0 - 0 = 0$	$1 - 1 = 0$	$100 - 10 = 0$
$0 = 0$	$0 = 0$	$90 = 0$
True	True	False

The solution set is {0, 1}.

53. $a = 7$ **54.** $c = 24$

55. 5 was subtracted from both sides.

56. Both sides were multiplied by 10.

57. $A = bh$
$A = 12.5(7.5)$
$A = 93.75 \text{ cm}^2$

58. $A = 3.14r^2$
$A = 3.14(3)^2$
$A = 3.14(9)$
$A = 28.26 \text{ ft}^2$

CHAPTER 1 ASSESSMENT pp. 50–51

1. $p - 11 = 25 - 11 = 14$ **2.** $\frac{40}{x} = \frac{40}{8} = 5$

3. $\frac{3x}{y} = \frac{3(10)}{5} = \frac{30}{5} = 6$ **4.** $a - 2b = 16 - 2(3) = 16 - 6 = 10$

5. $16 \div 8 + 8 = 2 + 8 = 10$ 6. $3 \cdot 4 + 2 \cdot 8 = 12 + 16 = 28$

7. $3(2a + b) = 3(2 \cdot 2 + 4) = 3(4 + 4) = 3(8) = 24$

8. $\frac{2x + y}{4} = \frac{2 \cdot 3 + 6}{4} = \frac{6 + 6}{4} = \frac{12}{4} = 3$

9. $3 + xy, 3 + yx$, or $yx + 3$ 10. $6 + a$

11. $\frac{3}{7} \cdot \frac{4}{4} = \frac{12}{28}$ 12. $\frac{6}{3y} \cdot \frac{x}{x} = \frac{6x}{3yx}$

13. $\frac{16}{24} = \frac{8 \cdot 2}{8 \cdot 3} = \frac{2}{3}$ 14. $\frac{81}{45} = \frac{9 \cdot 9}{9 \cdot 5} = \frac{9}{5}$

15. $\frac{xy}{12x} = \frac{x \cdot y}{x \cdot 12} = \frac{y}{12}$ 16. $\frac{9xy}{15yz} = \frac{3y \cdot 3x}{3y \cdot 5z} = \frac{3x}{5z}$

17. $2 \cdot 2 \cdot 2 \cdot 2$ 18. $5 \cdot x \cdot x \cdot x$ 19. 7^4 20. $8x^5$

21. $(5x)^2 = (5 \cdot 4)^2 = 20^2 = 20 \cdot 20 = 400$

22. $(3y)^4 = (3 \cdot 0)^4 = 0^4 = 0$

23. $x^3 = 3^3 = 3 \cdot 3 \cdot 3 = 27$

24. $3y^2 = 3 \cdot 4^2 = 3 \cdot 16 = 48$

25. $b^2 - 5 = 7^2 - 5 = 49 - 5 = 44$

26. $(4t)^3 = (4 \cdot 2)^3 = 8^3 = 8 \cdot 8 \cdot 8 = 512$

27. $(3 \cdot 6)^2 = 18^2 = 324$ 28. $6 + 3^3 = 6 + 27 = 33$

29. $(3x)^3 + 4 = (3 \cdot 2)^3 + 4 = 6^3 + 4 = 216 + 4 = 220$

30. $(r + 5)(s - 4) = (5 + 5)(10 - 4) = 10 \cdot 6 = 60$

31. $x + (y + 5)$ 32. $(3 \cdot b) \cdot a, b \cdot (a \cdot 3), a(b \cdot 3)$

33. $6(4y + 3) = 6 \cdot 4y + 6 \cdot 3 = 24y + 18$

34. $8a + 12b = 4 \cdot 2a + 4 \cdot 3b = 4(2a + 3b)$

35. $18x + 6y + 12 = 6 \cdot 3x + 6 \cdot y + 6 \cdot 2 = 6(3x + y + 2)$

36. $3 + 12b + 36a = 3 \cdot 1 + 3 \cdot 4b + 3 \cdot 12a = 3(1 + 4b + 12a)$

37. $8a + 4 + 12c = 4 \cdot 2a + 4 \cdot 1 + 4 \cdot 3c = 4(2a + 1 + 3c)$

38. $7a + 3b + 8a + 4b = (7 + 8)a + (3 + 4)b = 15a + 7b$

39. $6m + 9m^2 + 3m + 7m^2 = (6 + 3)m + (9 + 7)m^2 = 9m + 16m^2$

40. $x - 11$ 41. $\frac{n}{2}$ 42. $2n$

43. $6 + n$ 44. $w - 7$ 45. $\frac{t}{3}$

46.

$5(2) - 4 = 11$	$5(3) - 4 = 11$	$5(4) - 4 = 11$
$10 - 4 = 11$	$15 - 4 = 11$	$20 - 4 = 11$
$6 = 11$	$11 = 11$	$16 = 11$
False	True	False

The solution set is {3}.

47.

$(0)^2 - (0) = 2$	$(2)^2 - (2) = 2$	$(4)^2 - (4) = 2$
$0 - 0 = 2$	$4 - 2 = 2$	$16 - 4 = 2$
$0 = 2$	$2 = 2$	$12 = 2$
False	True	False

The solution set is {2}.

48.

$7.2(5) = 36$	$7.2(50) = 36$	$7.2(500) = 36$
$36 = 36$	$360 = 36$	$3600 = 36$
True	False	False

The solution set is {5}.

49. Both sides were multiplied by 2.

50. 4 was added to both sides.

51. $d = rt$
$d = 50(3)$
$d = 150$ mi

52. $C = \frac{5}{9}(F - 32)$
$C = \frac{5}{9}(77 - 32)$
$C = \frac{5}{9}(45)$
$C = 25°C$

CHAPTER 2

SKILLS & CONCEPTS p. 52

1. $\frac{12}{27} = \frac{3 \cdot 4}{3 \cdot 9} = \frac{4}{9}$ 2. $\frac{a}{4ab} = \frac{a \cdot 1}{a \cdot 4b} = \frac{1}{4b}$

3. $\frac{13xy}{xy} = \frac{xy \cdot 13}{xy \cdot 1} = 13$ 4. $\frac{18cd}{15d} = \frac{3d \cdot 6c}{3d \cdot 5} = \frac{6c}{5}$

5. $(4n)^2 = (4 \cdot 2)^2 = 8^2 = 8 \cdot 8 = 64$

6. $p^1 = 24^1 = 24$

7. $3x^3 = 3 \cdot 2^3 = 3 \cdot 2 \cdot 2 \cdot 2 = 24$

8. $5(a + b + d) = 5a + 5b + 5d$

9. $11(w + 4) = 11w + 11 \cdot 4 = 11w + 44$

10. $7(3z + y + 2) = 7 \cdot 3z + 7 \cdot y + 7 \cdot 2 = 21z + 7y + 14$

11. $45 + 9y = 9 \cdot 5 + 9 \cdot y = 9(5 + y)$

12. $3a + 12b = 3 \cdot a + 3 \cdot 4b = 3(a + 4b)$

13. $4x + 10 + 8y = 2 \cdot 2x + 2 \cdot 5 + 2 \cdot 4y = 2(2x + 5 + 4y)$

14. $5x + 3y + 2x = (5 + 2)x + 3y = 7x + 3y$

15. $b^2 + 3a + 4b^2 = (1 + 4)b^2 + 3a = 5b^2 + 3a$

16. $5t + 2 + 3t + 7 = (5 + 3)t + (2 + 7) = 8t + 9$

17.

$4(3) + 2 = 30$	$4(5) + 2 = 30$	$4(7) + 2 = 30$
$12 + 2 = 30$	$20 + 2 = 30$	$28 + 2 = 30$
$14 = 30$	$22 = 30$	$30 = 30$
False	False	True

The solution set is {7}.

18.

$8(0.5) = 4$	$8(5) = 4$	$8(50) = 4$
$4 = 4$	$40 = 4$	$400 = 4$
True	False	False

The solution set is {0.5}.

LESSON 2-1 TRY THIS pp. 55–56

a. Debt suggests a negative integer; -12.
b. Gain suggests a positive integer; 8.
c. A loss suggests a negative integer; -5.
d. Before liftoff suggests a negative integer; -3.
e. Since 14 is to the right of 7, $14 > 7$.
f. Since 11 is to the right of -2, $11 > -2$.
g. Since -15 is to the left of -5, $-15 < -5$.
h. 17 is 17 units from 0, so $|17| = 17$.
i. -8 is 8 units from 0, so $|-8| = 8$.
j. -14 is 14 units from 0, so $|-14| = 14$.
k. 21 is 21 units from 0, so $|21| = 21$.
l. 0 is 0 units from 0, so $|0| = 0$.
m. -21 is 21 units from 0, so $|-21| = 21$.

LESSON 2-1 EXERCISES pp. 57–58

1. A loss suggests a negative integer; -12.
2. A win suggests a positive integer; 5.
3. Above zero suggests a positive integer; 18.
4. Debt suggests a negative integer; -17.
5. Profit suggests a positive integer; 2500.
6. Below sea level suggests a negative integer; -1299.
7. Withdrew suggests a negative integer; -125.
8. A win suggests a positive integer; 34.
9. Excess suggests a positive integer; 3,000,000.

10. $5 > 0$ 11. $9 > 0$ 12. $-9 < 5$ 13. $8 > -8$

14. $-6 < 6$ 15. $0 > -7$ 16. $-8 < -5$ 17. $-4 < -3$

18. $-5 > -11$ 19. $-3 > -4$ 20. $-6 < -5$

21. $-10 > -14$ 22. 3 23. 7 24. 10 25. 11

26. 0 **27.** 4 **28.** 24 **29.** 325 **30.** 125 **31.** 5.5

32. 4.2 **33.** 120.2 **34.** 755 **35.** 340 **36.** 5.8

37. 0.3 **38.** 12.75 **39.** 0.07 **40.** 80 **41.** 3.75

42. $|-5| + |-6| = 5 + 6 = 11$

43. $|17| + |-17| = 17 + 17 = 34$ **44.** $|12| \cdot |-3| = 12 \cdot 3 = 36$

45. $|-5| \cdot |-6| \cdot |0| = 5 \cdot 6 \cdot 0 = 0$

46. $|-3| \cdot |-7| + |-4| = 3 \cdot 7 + 4 = 21 + 4 = 25$

47. $|8| \cdot |-2| - |5| = 8 \cdot 2 - 5 = 16 - 5 = 11$

48. $-17, -12, 5, 13$ **49.** $-23, -17, 0, 4$

50. $-32, -26, -24, -18, -16, -5$

51. $-24, -16, -14, -13, -5, 12, 15$

52. $|x| + 24 = |-7| + 24 = 7 + 24 = 31$

53. $|t| - 15 = |-36| - 15 = 36 - 15 = 21$

54. $|a| + |b| = |-5| + |-12| = 5 + 12 = 17$

55. $2|x| + |y| = 2|8| + |15| = 2 \cdot 8 + 15 = 16 + 15 = 31$

56. $3a - |b| + |c| = 3 \cdot 5 - |-4| + |-12| = 15 - 4 + 12 = 23$

57. **a.** Move 4 to the left: $-3, -7, -11$
b. Move to the left, first 1, then 2, then 3, and so on: $-4, -9, -15$
c. Move to the left, first 2, then 3, then 4, and so on: $-17, -23, -30$
d. Sample answer: Add the previous 2 numbers: $-11, -18, -29$

58. $|5.3| = 5.3$; C

59. $|-3.1| = 3.1$ and $-3.1 < 3.1$; B

60. $|0| = 0$; C

61. $-|2.7| = -2.7$ and $2.7 > -2.7$; A

62. If $x < 0, x < |x|$; if $x > 0, x = |x|$; D

63. If $x = 0, |x| = -|x|$; if $x \neq 0, |x| > -|x|$; D

64. $|-3| = 3$. Since $3 < 5, |-3| < 5$.

65. $|-4| = 4$. Since $2 < 4, 2 < |-4|$.

66. $|-1| = 1$. Since $-2 < 1, -2 < |-1|$.

67. $|0| = 0$. Since $0 = 0, 0 = |0|$.

68. $|-5| = 5$ and $|-2| = 2$. Since $5 > 2, |-5| > |-2|$.

69. $|4| = 4$ and $|-7| = 7$. Since $4 < 7, |4| < |-7|$.

70. Since $|x| \geq 0$ for all $x, |x| > -1$.

71. $|-8| = 8$ and $|8| = 8$. Since $8 = 8, |-8| = |8|$.

72. $-100, -5, 0, 1, |3|, \frac{14}{4}, 4, |-6|, 7^1$

73. $6m + 11m + 4m = (6 + 11 + 4)m = 21m$

74. $\frac{1}{2}a + \frac{1}{2}a = \left(\frac{1}{2} + \frac{1}{2}\right)a = 1a$ or a

75. $8x^2 + 3x^2 + 7x = (8 + 3)x^2 + 7x = 11x^2 + 7x$

76. $4c^2 + 7c + 2c^2 = 4c^2 + 2c^2 + 7c$
$= (4 + 2)c^2 + 7c = 6c^2 + 7c$

77. $4m + 24c = 4 \cdot m + 4 \cdot 6 \cdot c = 4(m + 6c)$

78. $7b + 14 = 7 \cdot b + 7 \cdot 2 = 7(b + 2)$

79. $14x + 28y + 7 = 7 \cdot 2x + 7 \cdot 4y + 7 \cdot 1 = 7(2x + 4y + 1)$

80. $(14) + 3 = 42$ / $17 = 42$ / False; $(39) + 3 = 42$ / $42 = 42$ / True; $(45) + 3 = 42$ / $48 = 42$ / False
The solution set is {39}.

81. $(361) + 3911 = 4272$ / $4272 = 4272$ / True; $(7183) + 3911 = 4272$ / $11{,}094 = 4272$ / False
$(8183) + 3911 = 4272$ / $12{,}094 = 4272$ / False
The solution set is {361}.

82. $14(2) = 42$ / $28 = 42$ / False; $14(3) = 42$ / $42 = 42$ / True; $14(28) = 42$ / $392 = 42$ / False
The solution set is {3}.

83. $(2.7) + 9.7 = 12.4$ / $12.4 = 12.4$ / True; $(3.3) + 9.7 = 12.4$ / $13 = 12.4$ / False
$(22.1) + 9.7 = 12.4$ / $31.8 = 12.4$ / False
The solution set is {2.7}.

84. $2.6(3) = 7.8$ / $7.8 = 7.8$ / True; $2.6(5.2) = 7.8$ / $13.52 = 7.8$ / False; $2.6(10.4) = 7.8$ / $27.04 = 7.8$ / False
The solution set is {3}.

85. $x = 22$ **86.** $c = 55$ **87.** $y = 90$ **88.** $a = 80$

89. $x = 24$ **90.** $d = 140$

LESSON 2-2 TRY THIS pp. 59–61

a. $\frac{45}{10}$ or $\frac{9}{2}$ **b.** $-\frac{10}{1}$ **c.** $-\frac{143}{10}$ **d.** $-\frac{1}{100}$

e.
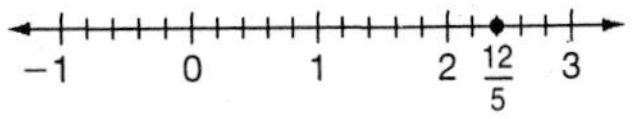

f.
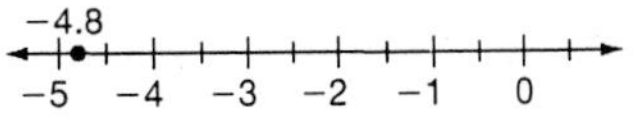

g.
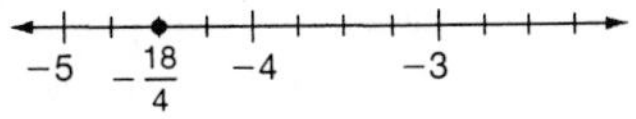

h.
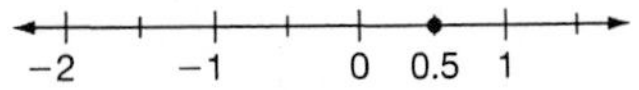

i. 62 hundredths is greater than 26 hundredths, so $4.62 > 4.26$.
j. -3.11 is farther to the right on the number line than -3.22 so $-3.11 > -3.22$.

k. Find a common denominator. $\frac{5}{6} = \frac{20}{24}, \frac{7}{8} = \frac{21}{24}$;
$\frac{20}{24}$ is farther to the left on the number line than $\frac{21}{24}$;
$\frac{20}{21} < \frac{21}{24}$, so $\frac{5}{6} < \frac{7}{8}$.

l. Find a common denominator. $-\frac{2}{3} = -\frac{10}{15}, -\frac{4}{5} = -\frac{12}{15}$;
$-\frac{10}{15}$ is farther to the right on the number line than $-\frac{12}{15}$;
$-\frac{10}{15} > -\frac{12}{15}$, so $-\frac{2}{3} > -\frac{4}{5}$.

LESSON 2-2 EXERCISES pp. 61–62

1. $\frac{14}{1}$ **2.** $-\frac{7}{1}$ **3.** $\frac{42}{10}$ or $\frac{21}{5}$ **4.** $\frac{15}{10}$ or $\frac{3}{2}$

5. $-\frac{5}{10}$ or $-\frac{1}{2}$ **6.** $-\frac{3}{100}$ **7.** $\frac{3444}{1000}$ or $\frac{861}{250}$

8. $-\frac{5333}{1000}$ **9.** $-\frac{68}{100}$ or $-\frac{17}{25}$

10. $-\frac{4}{1}$ **11.** $\frac{15}{2}$ **12.** $\frac{5}{3}$

13.
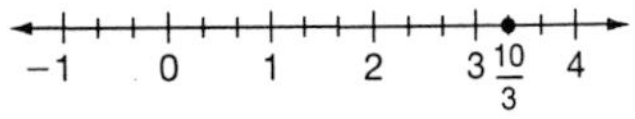

14.
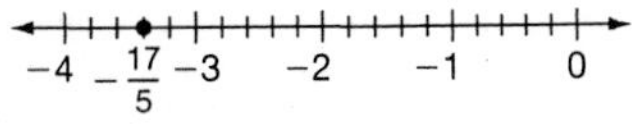

15.
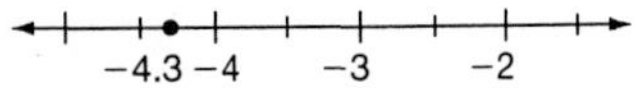

16. 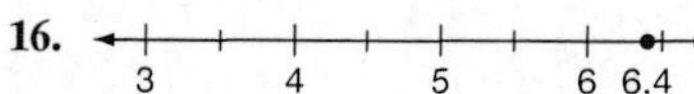

17. The number is expressed as a ratio of integers, so it is rational. It can also be expressed as the integer -5. **c**

18. $2.14 > 1.24$ **19.** $-3.3 < -2.2$ **20.** $7.075 < 7.750$

21. $-14.5 < 0.011$ **22.** $17.2 > -1.67$ **23.** $-345 > -354$

24. $-12.88 > -13$ **25.** $-14.34 > -17.88$

26. $-0.606 > -0.660$

27. $\frac{4}{10} > 0$ and $-\frac{1}{2} < 0$, so $\frac{4}{10} > -\frac{1}{2}$

28. $-\frac{5}{12} = -\frac{10}{24}$ and $-\frac{3}{8} = -\frac{9}{24}$, so $-\frac{5}{12} < -\frac{3}{8}$

29. $-\frac{5}{3} = -\frac{25}{15}$ and $-\frac{7}{5} = -\frac{21}{15}$, so $-\frac{5}{3} < -\frac{7}{5}$

30. $\frac{1}{3} = 0.333\ldots > 0.33;$

$-\frac{1}{3} = -0.333\ldots < 0.33$

31–34. Answers may vary. Examples are given.

31. $\frac{3}{8}$ **32.** $\frac{3}{10}$ **33.** 0.455 **34.** 0.0125

35. $-\frac{8}{8}, -\frac{4}{8}, \frac{1}{8}, \frac{3}{8}, \frac{5}{8}, \frac{7}{8}$ **36.** $-\frac{7}{5}, -\frac{4}{5}, -\frac{2}{5}, -\frac{1}{5}, \frac{4}{5}, \frac{6}{5}$

37. If two positive fractions have the same numerator, the fraction with the smaller denominator is the larger. $\frac{4}{9}, \frac{4}{8}, \frac{4}{6}, \frac{4}{5}, \frac{4}{3}, \frac{4}{2}$

38. Common denominator is 24.

$-\frac{2}{3} = -\frac{16}{24}, \frac{1}{2} = \frac{12}{24}, -\frac{3}{4} = -\frac{18}{24}, -\frac{5}{6} = -\frac{20}{24}, \frac{3}{8} = \frac{9}{24}, \frac{1}{6} = \frac{4}{24}$

Order: $-\frac{5}{6}, -\frac{3}{4}, -\frac{2}{3}, \frac{1}{6}, \frac{3}{8}, \frac{1}{2}$

39. Answers may vary. $\frac{2}{3} > \frac{4}{7}, \frac{3}{2} > \frac{5}{7}, \frac{3}{2} > \frac{4}{5}, \frac{4}{5} > \frac{2}{7}, \frac{7}{2} > \frac{5}{4}$

40. $\frac{a}{b} < \frac{c}{d}$ Common denominator is bd.

$\frac{ad}{bd} < \frac{cb}{bd}$ Rewriting with common denominator

$\therefore ad < cb$ Numerators are unequal.

41. $\frac{2}{2} = \frac{2+1}{2+1}$ and $\frac{2}{3} \neq \frac{2+1}{3+1}\left(\text{or } \frac{3}{4}\right)$ so sometimes true.

42. $m - 11$ **43.** $\frac{y}{x}$ **44.** $9 + t$ **45.** $4w$ **46.** 0.06

47. 2.3 **48.** 41

49. $y + \frac{3}{5} = \frac{4}{5}$

$y = \frac{1}{5}$

50. $a - \frac{1}{7} = \frac{6}{7}$

$a = \frac{7}{7}$ or 1

51. $x + \frac{2}{3} = \frac{5}{6}$

$x + \frac{4}{6} = \frac{5}{6}$

$x = \frac{1}{6}$

52. $\frac{a}{7} = 8$

$a = 56$

53. $\frac{c}{6} = 12$

$c = 72$

54. $\frac{y}{4} = 32$

$y = 128$

55. $\frac{y}{3} = 7 + \frac{1}{3}$

$y = 21 + 1$

$y = 22$

56. $D = r \cdot k$

$= 45(3)$

$D = 135$

57. $A = bh$

$= 10.2(5)$

$A = 51$

58. $P = 2w + 2l$

$= 2 \cdot 17 + 2(2.5)$

$= 34 + 5$

$P = 39$

LESSON 2-3 TRY THIS pp. 64–68

a. 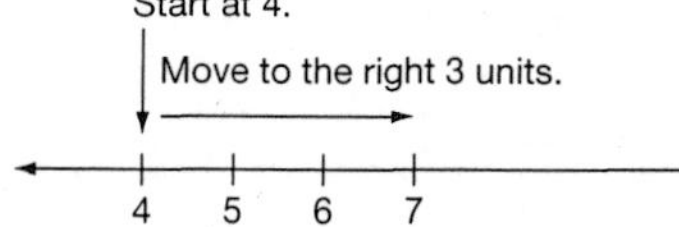

$4 + 3 = 7$

b. 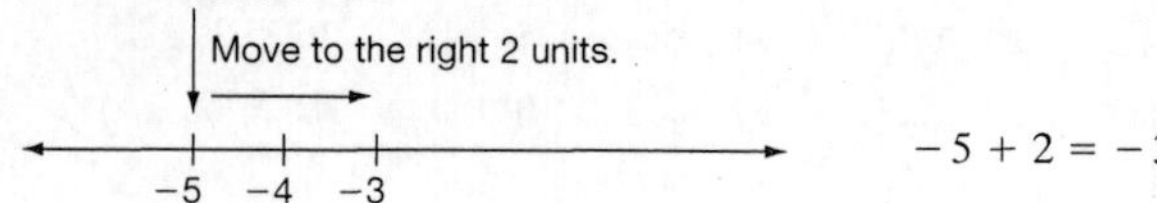

$-5 + 2 = -3$

c. 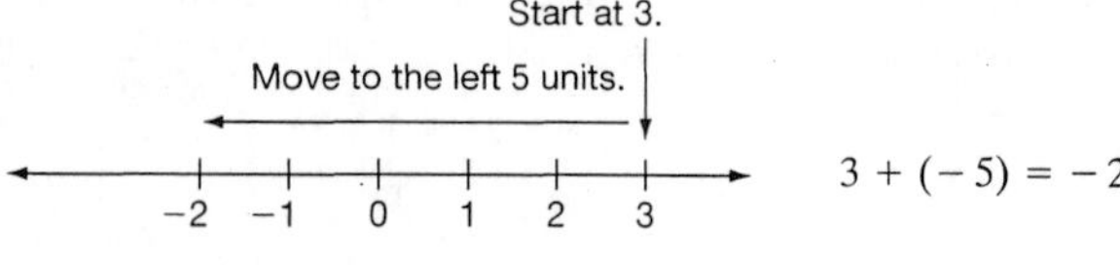

$3 + (-5) = -2$

d. 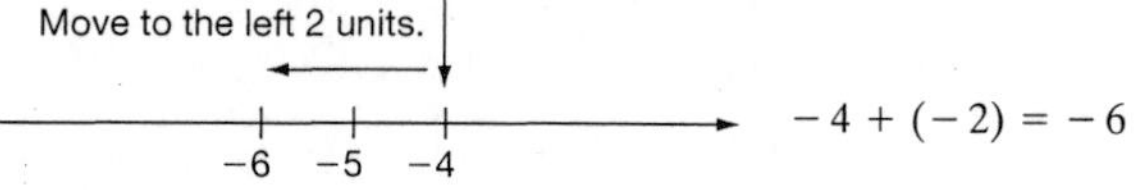

$-4 + (-2) = -6$

e. 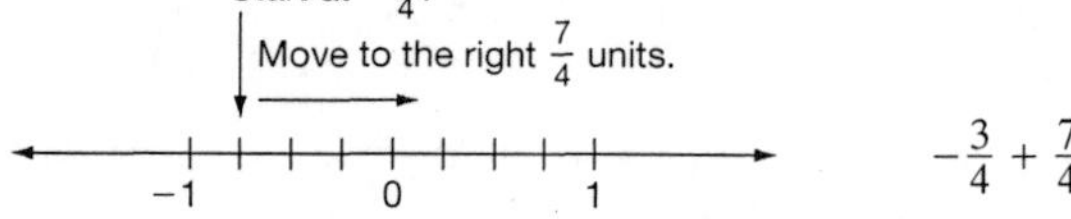

$-\frac{3}{4} + \frac{7}{4} = 1$

f. $-17 + 17 = 0$ The difference of the absolute values is 0. Neither addend is greater.

g. $-13 + (-7) = -20$ Since both addends are negative, the sum is negative.

h. $-15 + (-10) = -25$ Since both addends are negative, the sum is negative.

i. $-0.17 + 0.7 = 0.53$ The difference of the absolute values is 0.53. The positive addend has the greater absolute value, so the sum is positive.

j. $-12 + 25 = 13$ The difference of the absolute values is 13. The positive addend has the greater absolute value, so the sum is positive.

k. $14 + (-21) = -7$ The difference of the absolute values is 7. The negative addend has the greater absolute value, so the sum is negative.

l. $\frac{3}{4} + \left(-\frac{5}{4}\right) = -\frac{2}{4}$ or $-\frac{1}{2}$ The difference of the absolute values is $\frac{1}{2}$. The negative addend has the greater absolute value, so the sum is negative.

m. $-\frac{5}{8} + \left(-\frac{1}{4}\right) = -\frac{5}{8} + \left(-\frac{2}{8}\right)$

$= -\frac{7}{8}$ Since both addends are negative, the sum is negative.

n. $-\frac{4}{5} + \frac{5}{7} = -\frac{28}{35} + \frac{25}{35}$

$= -\frac{3}{35}$ The difference of the absolute values is $\frac{3}{35}$.

The negative addend has the greater absolute value, so the sum is negative.

o. $(-15) + (-37) + 25 + 42 + (-59) + (-14)$

$= (25 + 42)$
$+ [(-15) + (-37) + (-59) + (-14)]$ Grouping positives and negatives

$= 67 + (-125)$ Adding the results

$= -58$

p. $42 + (-81) + (-28) + 24 + 18 + (-31)$

$= (42 + 24 + 18)$
$+ [(-18) + (-28) + (-31)]$ Grouping positives and negatives

$= 84 + (-140)$ Adding the results

$= -56$

q. The additive inverse is 19. $-19 + 19 = 0$

r. The additive inverse is -54. $54 + (-54) = 0$

s. The additive inverse is 0. $0 + 0 = 0$

t. The additive inverse is 7.4. $-7.4 + 7.4 = 0$

u. The additive inverse is $\frac{8}{3}$. $-\frac{8}{3} + \frac{8}{3} = 0$

v. If $x = 14$, then $-x = -(14)$ Replacing x with 14
$= -14$
$-(-x) = -(-14)$ Replacing x with 14
$= 14$

w. If $x = 1$, then $-x = -(1)$ Replacing x with 1
$= -1$
$-(-x) = -(-1)$ Replacing x with 1
$= 1$

x. If $x = -19$, then $-x = -(-19)$ Replacing x with -19
$= 19$
$-(-x) = -(-(-19))$ Replacing x with -19
$= -19$

y. $11 + (-4) + (-6) + 5 + 8 + (-2)$ Represent gains with positive numbers, losses with negative numbers.
$= 11 + 5 + 8 + [(-4) + (-6) + (-2)]$
$= 24 + (-12)$
$= 12$
He gained 12 yards.

LESSON 2-3 EXERCISES pp. 68–70

1. Start at −9. Move to the right 2 units.
−9 −8 −7 −6 −5 −4 −3
$-9 + 2 = -7$

2. Start at 2. Move to the left 5 units.
−4 −3 −2 −1 0 1 2
$2 + (-5) = -3$

3. Start at −10. Move to the right 6 units.
−10 −9 −8 −7 −6 −5 −4
$-10 + 6 = -4$

4. Start at 8. Move to the left 3 units.
1 2 3 4 5 6 7 8
$8 + (-3) = 5$

5. Start at −8. Move to the right 8 units.
−8 −7 −6 −5 −4 −3 −2 −1 0
$-8 + 8 = 0$

6. Start at 6. Move to the left 6 units.
0 1 2 3 4 5 6 7
$6 + (-6) = 0$

7. Start at −3. Move to the left 5 units.
−8 −7 −6 −5 −4 −3 −2
$-3 + (-5) = -8$

8. Start at −4. Move to the left 6 units.
−10 −9 −8 −7 −6 −5 −4
$-4 + (-6) = -10$

9. -7 **10.** -13 **11.** -27 **12.** -35 **13.** 0 **14.** 0

15. -42 **16.** -41 **17.** -43 **18.** $-\frac{3}{8}$ **19.** $-\frac{1}{6}$

20. $-\frac{29}{35}$ **21.** $-\frac{23}{24}$ **22.** $-\frac{11}{15}$ **23.** $-\frac{11}{18}$

24. 50 **25.** $\frac{3}{4}$ **26.** 37.9 **27.** -5 **28.** 7

29. -1093 **30.** -1021

31. $-35 > -36$, so $14 + (-35)$ is greater.

32. $-8 > -9$, so $-32 + (-8)$ is greater.

33. $\frac{3}{5} > \frac{2}{5}$, so $-\frac{3}{5} + \frac{3}{5}$ is greater.

34. $9 > -9$ so $-16 + 9$ is greater.

35. -24 **36.** 64 **37.** 9 **38.** $-\frac{7}{2}$ **39.** 26.9

40. -48.2 **41.** -9 **42.** 26 **43.** $\frac{14}{3}$

44. $-\frac{1}{328}$ **45.** -0.101 **46.** 0

47. $x = -65$
$-x = 65$
$-(-x) = -65$

48. $x = 29$
$-x = -29$
$-(-x) = 29$

49. $x = \frac{5}{3}$
$-x = -\frac{5}{3}$
$-(-x) = \frac{5}{3}$

50. $x = -9.1$
$-x = 9.1$
$-(-x) = -9.1$

51. $-4 + (-6) = -10$ and $-1 + (-11) = -12$; never

52. $2 + 4 = 6$ and $1 + 6 = 7$; always

53. $9 + (-5) = 4$ and $3 + (-5) = -2$; sometimes

54. The additive inverse of 2 is -2 and the additive inverse of -4 is 4; sometimes

55. $5 + 6 = 11$ and $5 + (-6) = -1$; sometimes

56. $2 + 3 = 5$ and $-2 + (-6) = -8$; sometimes

57. Total $= 1012 + (-6) + 3 + (-14) + 4 = +999$
The pressure was 999 mb.

58. Total $= +13 + 0 + (-12) + 21 + (-14) = +8$
The total was an 8-yd gain.

59. Total $= +357 + (-144) + (-250) + 347 + 420 + (-188)$
$= +542$
The total was 542 above last year's attendance.

60. Total $= -120 + (-150) + 350 + (-100) + 180 = +160$
The market had gained 160 points.

61. Total $= +1475 + (-1700) + 1640 + (-900) + 1200$
$= +1715$
Alice had \$1715.

62. Total $= +32{,}056 + (-2{,}925) + 81{,}429 + (-19{,}365) + (-13{,}875) + 384$
$= +77{,}704$
The profit is \$77,704.

63. Total $= 5.00 + (-0.59) + (-1.75) + 10.50 + (-6.75) = 6.41$
She had \$6.41.

64. When x is positive **65.** When x is negative

66. n is positive and $-m$ is positive, so their sum is positive.

67. $-n$ is negative and m is negative, so their sum is negative.

68. $-n$ is positive and $-m$ is positive, so their sum is positive.

69. $-m$ is the additive inverse of n, so their sum is zero.

70. -1

71. Answers may vary but should include the idea that since $-n + n = 0$, the additive inverse of $-n$ is n.

72. $x + x = 0$
$2x = 0$
$x = \frac{0}{2} = 0$

73. We must start at x, move 5 units to the left, and end where we started. Since this is impossible, no value of x will satisfy this equation.

74. $3y + (-2) = 7$
$3y = 7-(-2)$
$3y = 7 + 2$ $\quad -(-2)$ is the same as $+2$.
$3y = 9$
$y = \frac{9}{3} = 3$

75. $x + (-5) = 16$
$x = 16 - (-5)$
$x = 16 + 5$ $\quad -(-5)$ is the same as $+5$.
$x = 21$

76. Yes **77.** $2.6n = 6.24$
$n = \frac{6.24}{2.6} = 2.4$

78. $w - 1.07 = 3.24$
$w = 3.24 + 1.07$
$w = 4.31$

79. $7r = 84$
$r = \frac{84}{7}$
$r = 12$

80. $-9 < 2$ **81.** $-4 > -6$ **82.** $-1 < 0$

83. $3.62 > 3.26$ **84.** $0 < 0.001$

85. 2 **86.** 4 **87.** 2.03 **88.** 0

89. Let x = number of members
$8x = 104$
$x = \frac{104}{8} = 13$
There are 13 class members.

LESSON 2-4 TRY THIS pp. 71–74

a.
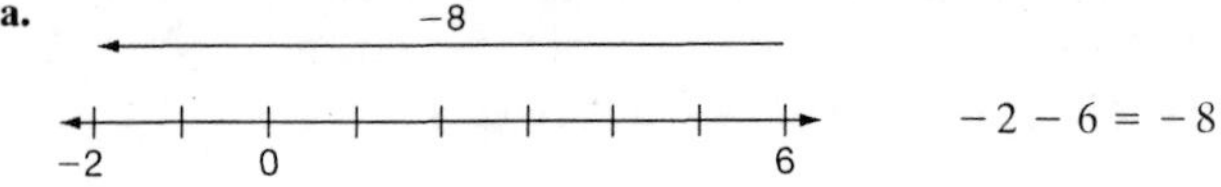

$-2 - 6 = -8$

b.
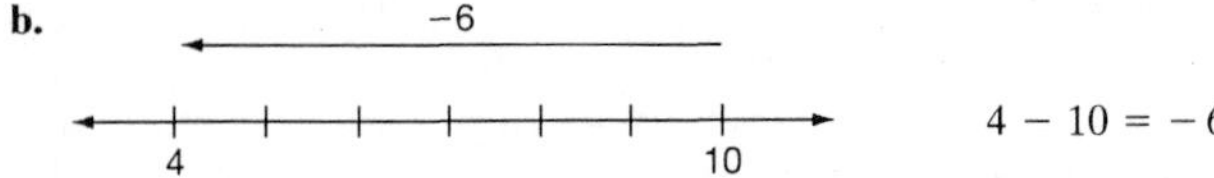

$4 - 10 = -6$

c.
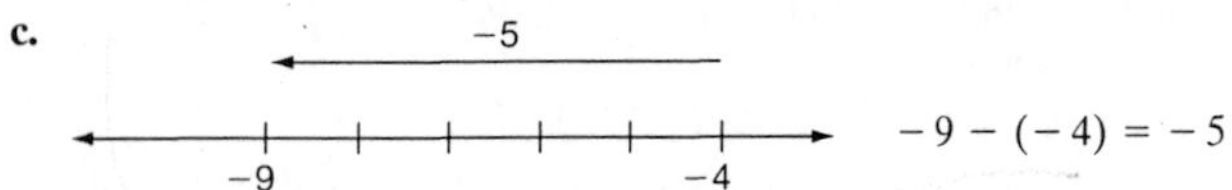

$-9 - (-4) = -5$

d. $4 - 9 = 4 + (-9) = -5$ **e.** $6 - (-4) = 6 + 4 = 10$
f. $-4 - 17 = -4 + (-17) = -21$
g. $-3 - (-12) = -3 + 12 = 9$
h. $\frac{3}{8} - \left(-\frac{1}{4}\right) = \frac{3}{8} + \frac{1}{4} = \frac{3}{8} + \frac{2}{8} = \frac{5}{8}$
i. $-6 - (-2) - (-4) - 12 + 3 = -6 + 2 + 4 - 12 + 3$
$= -9$
j. $3 - (-7.1) + 6.3 - (-5.2) = 3 + 7.1 + 6.3 + 5.2 = 21.6$
k. $-8 - (-3x) + 2x - (-13) = -8 + 3x + 2x + 13 = 5x + 5$
l. Let m = how much more he needs.
$m = 125 - 35$
$m = 90$
He needs $90 more.

LESSON 2-4 EXERCISES pp. 74–76

1., **2.**
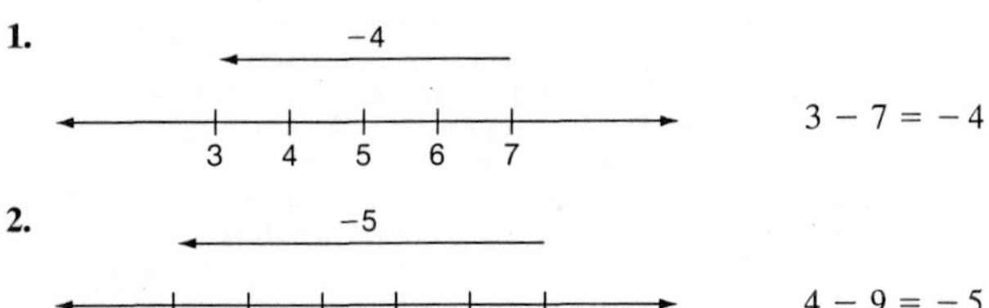

1. $3 - 7 = -4$
2. $4 - 9 = -5$

3.
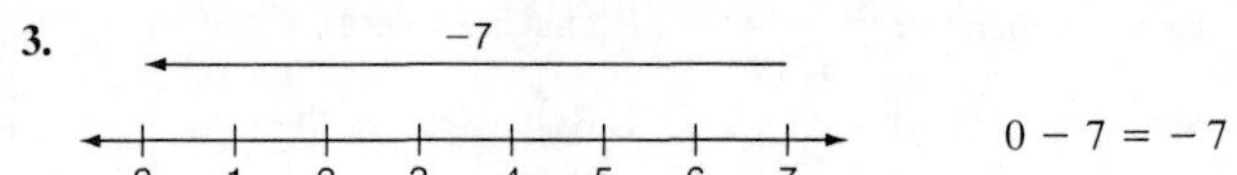

$0 - 7 = -7$

4.
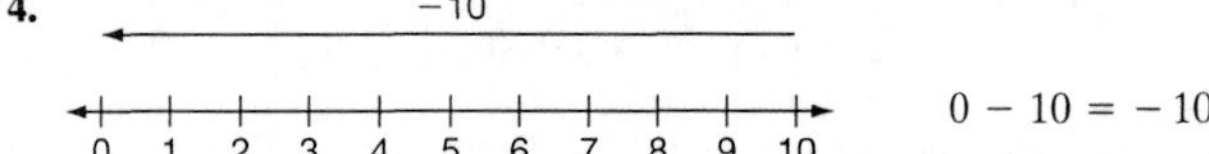

$0 - 10 = -10$

5. +7; −2 −1 0 1 2 3 4 5 $\quad 5 - (-2) = +7$

6. +2; −8 −7 −6 $\quad -6 - (-8) = +2$

7. −10 $\quad -10 - (-10) = 0$

8. −8 $\quad -8 - (-8) = 0$

9. 0 **10.** 0 **11.** 14 **12.** 8 **13.** 11 **14.** -11
15. -14 **16.** 16 **17.** 5 **18.** 21 **19.** -5
20. -0.6 **21.** -49 **22.** 2 **23.** -193 **24.** -413
25. 500 **26.** 1500 **27.** -2.8 **28.** 4.94 **29.** -3.53
30. 17.3 **31.** $-\frac{1}{2}$ **32.** $\frac{1}{8}$ **33.** 0 **34.** $\frac{6}{7}$
35. $-\frac{41}{30}$ **36.** 0 **37.** $-\frac{1}{156}$ **38.** $\frac{1}{42}$ **39.** 37
40. -22 **41.** -62 **42.** 22 **43.** -139 **44.** 5
45. 4 **46.** $10x + 7$ **47.** $-3x + 46$
48. $15x + 66$ **49.** $15x + 39$

50. Sample answers: If you owe $12 and a $3 debt is taken away, then the remaining debt is $9.
$-12 - (-3) = -12 + -(-3) =$
$-12 + (+3) = -9$

51. $619.46 − $950.00 = − $330.54
She was overdrawn by $330.54.

52. $137.40 − $225.20 = − $87.80
He was overdrawn by $87.80.

53. $-5 - (-12) = 7$ The temperature dropped 7°.

54. $5 - (-5) = 10$ The temperature fell 10°.

55. $163 - 47 = 116$ There are 116 males in the band.

56. $45 − $12 = $33 She has $33.

57. $-40 - (-156) = 116$ It is 116 m lower.

58. $-8{,}648 - (-10{,}415) = 1{,}767$ It is 1767 m lower.

59. The smaller the number that is subtracted, the greater the difference. A

60. The greater the number that is subtracted, the smaller the difference. B

61. The smaller the number that is subtracted, the greater the difference. A

62. The greater the number that is subtracted, the smaller the difference. B

63. The smaller the number that is subtracted, the greater the difference. A

64. The greater the number that is subtracted, the smaller the difference. B

65. a. $(a + x) - b = (5 + [-2.3]) - (-8)$
$= 2.7 + 8$
$= 10.7$

b. $z - (b - x) = 0 - (-8 - [-2.3])$
$= 0 - (-5.7)$
$= 5.7$

c. $(x - y) + (a - b) = (-2.3 - [4.1]) + (5 - [-8])$
$= -6.4 + 13$
$= 6.6$

d. $(y - x) - (b - a) = (4.1 - [-2.3]) - (-8 - [5])$
$= 6.4 - (-13)$
$= 19.4$

e. $b - |x - a| = -8 - |-2.3 - (5)|$
$= -8 - |-7.3|$
$= -8 - (7.3)$
$= -15.3$

f. $|x| - a - (|b| + y) = |-2.3| - 5 - (|-8| + 4.1)$
$= 2.3 - 5 - (8 + 4.1)$
$= -2.7 - 12.1$
$= -14.8$

66. a. Add 2 pyramids to right side.
b. Add 3 pyramids to right side.

67. False; $3 - 0 \neq 0 - 3$ **68.** False; $0 - 3 \neq 3$ **69.** True

70. True **71.** True **72.** False. If $3 - 3 = 0, 3 \neq -3$.

73. Neither holds. Commutative: $7 - 5 \neq 5 - 7$
Associative: $7 - (5 - 2) \neq (7 - 5) - 2$

74. $-[-(-5)] = -5; -\{-[-(-5)]\} = 5$
A term with an even number of negative signs is positive. A term with an odd number of negative signs is negative.

75. $a - 1$ is always 1 unit to the left of a. Thus, it is less than a for all rational numbers a.

76. Yes **77.** $(n + 3)^2 = (4 + 3)^2 = 7^2 = 49$

78. $(3n)^3 - 100 = (3 \cdot 2)^3 - 100 = 6^3 - 100 = 216 - 100 = 116$

79. $t^4 = 3^4 = 81$ **80.** $n^5 = 2^5 = 32$

81. $9y^3 = 9(3^3) = 9(27) = 243$ **82.** $m^3 = O^3 = 0$

83. $3t^2 + 6 = 3(2)^2 + 6 = 3 \cdot 4 + 6 = 18$

84. $2|m| = 2|-3| = 2 \cdot 3 = 6$ **85.** $y = 1$

86. $a = 8$ **87.** $y = \frac{1}{4}$

88. $3x + 5x^2 + 5x + 2x^2 = (3 + 5)x + (5 + 2)x^2$
$= 8x + 7x^2$

89. $2a + 3b + 4c + 5b = 2a + (3 + 5)b + 4c$
$= 2a + 8b + 4c$

90. $3c^2 + 5c = c \cdot 3c + c \cdot 5 = c(3c + 5)$

91. $6x + 24y - 18z = 6 \cdot x + 6 \cdot 4y - 6 \cdot 3z$
$= 6(x + 4y - 3z)$

92. $6m + 9p = 3 \cdot 2m + 3 \cdot 3p = 3(2m + 3p)$

LESSON 2-5 TRY THIS pp. 77–78

a. -18 **b.** -100 **c.** -90 **d.** $-\frac{18}{12} = -\frac{3}{2}$

e. 20 **f.** 0 **g.** 12.6 **h.** $\frac{3}{56}$

i. $-5(-6)(-3) = 30(-3)$ Multiplying the first two numbers
$= -90$ Multiplying the results

j. $-4(5)(-3)(2) = 12(5)(2)$ Multiplying the negative numbers
$= 120$ Multiplying the results

k. $(-7)\left(-\frac{2}{3}\right)\left(-\frac{1}{7}\right)(9) = 1\left(-\frac{2}{3}\right)(9)$ Multiplying first and third numbers
$= -6$ Multiplying the results

LESSON 2-5 EXERCISES pp. 79–80

1. -16 **2.** -10 **3.** -42 **4.** -18 **5.** -24

6. -45 **7.** -72 **8.** -30 **9.** 16 **10.** 10 **11.** 42

12. 18 **13.** -120 **14.** 120 **15.** -238 **16.** 195

17. 1200 **18.** -1677 **19.** 98 **20.** 203.7 **21.** $\frac{-2}{45}$

22. $\frac{6}{35}$ **23.** 1911 **24.** -5712 **25.** 50.4 **26.** -52

27. $\frac{10}{189}$ **28.** -1 **29.** -960 **30.** 120 **31.** 17.64

32. -518.4 **33.** $-\frac{5}{784}$ **34.** $\frac{4}{7}$ **35.** 0 **36.** 0

37. -0.104 **38.** 0.1683 **39.** $-6(-12) = 72$

40. $7(-7) = -49$ **41.** $\frac{-3(-14)}{-7} = \frac{42}{-7} = -6$

42. $\frac{8(20)}{-4} = \frac{160}{-4} = -40$ **43.** $-(243) \cdot (-8) = 1944$

44. $4(16)(-27)6 = -10{,}368$

45. $(-2)^5 = -2 \cdot -2 \cdot -2 \cdot -2 \cdot -2 = -32$

46. -1. There are an odd number of negatives, so the answer is negative.

47. $xy + z = -2(-4) + 5 = 8 + 5 = 13$

48. $-4y + 3x + z = -4(-4) + 3(-2) + 5 = 16 + -6 + 5 = 15$

49. $-6(3x - 5y) + z = -6(3(-2) - 5(-4)) + 5$
$= -6(-6 - (-20)) + 5$
$= -6(14) + 5 = -79$

50. $(-9z)(-5x)(-7y) = (-9(5))(-5(-2))(-7(-4))$
$= (-45)(10)(28) = -12{,}600$

51. $y(x^4) - z = -4([-2]^4) - 5 = -4(16) - 5 = -64 - 5 = -69$

52. $3z^2 - xy = 3(5^2) - (-2)(-4) = 3(25) - (8) = 75 - 8 = 67$

53. 12 and -7 (use try, test, and revise)

54. A and C are positive, B and D are negative. Since $\frac{4}{3} > \frac{2}{3}$, the product in B is least.

55. Either m or n is negative and the other is positive.

56. Both m and n are positive or both are negative.

57. For all values of a and b, $|ab|$ is not negative and $|ab| = |a||b|$. For all values of a and b, $|-a|$ is not negative and $|-b|$ is not negative. So, $|-a||-b| = |a||b|$. It is always true that $|ab| = |-a||-b|$.

58. Either (1) $x < 0$ and $x - 2 > 0 \rightarrow x < 0$ and $x > 2$ (impossible) or (2) $x > 0$ and $x - 2 < 0 \rightarrow x > 0$ and $x < 2$; so $0 < x < 2$.

59. Since $|z|$ is never less than 0, z must be less than 0.

60. $4 - 9 = 4 + (-9) = -5$ **61.** $3 - (-1) = 3 + 1 = 4$

62. $0 + (-4) = -4$ **63.** $-8 + 8 = 0$

64. $6 - (-2) = 6 + 2 = 8$ **65.** $-37 + 52 = 15$

66. $67 + (-8) = 59$ **67.** $-1.01 < -1$ **68.** $2.5 > -2.4$

69. $\frac{7}{2} < \frac{8}{2}$; so $\frac{7}{2} < 4$.

70. $|-3| = |3|$ since $3 = 3$ **71.** $4x + 10 + 8y = 2(2x + 5 + 4y)$

72. $10a + 15b + 5 = 5(2a + 3b + 1)$

73. $3x^3 = 3(2)^3 = 3(8) = 24$ **74.** $5x^3 = 5(1)^3 = 5(1) = 5$

SUBSETS OF THE RATIONAL NUMBERS p. 80

1. Answers may vary. Samples: Let E = the set of real numbers. $N \subset I, N \subset R, N \subset E, W \subset R, W \subset E, R \subset E$.

2. $\varnothing$ is a subset of R. ($\varnothing$ is a subset of every set.)

LESSON 2-6 TRY THIS pp. 81–84

a. $15 \div (-3) = -5$ Check: $(-5)(-3) = 15$

b. $-21 \div (-7) = 3$ Check: $3(-7) = -21$

c. $\frac{-44}{-11} = 4$ Check: $4(-11) = -44$

d. $\frac{35}{-5} = -7$ Check: $-7(-5) = 35$

e. $\frac{-8}{-4} = 2$ Check: $2(-4) = -8$

f. $\frac{45}{-9} = -5$ Check: $(-5)(-9) = 45$

g. $-24 \div -8 = 3$ Check: $3(-8) = -24$

h. $\frac{105}{-5} = -21$ Check: $(-21)(-5) = 105$

i. $\frac{6}{3}$ or 2 **j.** $-\frac{1}{4}$ **k.** $\frac{1}{-0.5} = -2$

l. $1\frac{1}{3} = \frac{4}{3}$ so reciprocal is $\frac{3}{4}$. **m.** $\frac{y}{x}$ **n.** $-6(5)$

o. $-5\left(\frac{1}{7}\right)$ **p.** $(x^2 - 2)\frac{1}{3}$ **q.** $x\left(\frac{1}{y}\right)$ **r.** $-15x$

s. $-\frac{4}{7}\left(-\frac{5}{3}\right)$ **t.** $13\left(\frac{3}{2}\right)$ **u.** ab

v. $-\frac{3}{5} \div \left(-\frac{12}{11}\right) = -\frac{3}{5}\left(-\frac{11}{12}\right) = \frac{3 \cdot 11}{5 \cdot 3 \cdot 4} = \frac{11}{20}$

w. $-\frac{8}{5} \div \frac{2}{3} = -\frac{8}{5}\left(\frac{3}{2}\right) = -\frac{2 \cdot 4 \cdot 3}{5 \cdot 2} = -\frac{12}{5}$

x. $-64.8 \div 4 = -16.2$ **y.** $78.6 \div (-3) = -26.2$

LESSON 2-6 EXERCISES pp. 84–86

1. $36 \div (-6) = -6$ Check: $(-6)(-6) = 36$
2. $\frac{28}{-7} = -4$ Check: $(-4)(-7) = 28$
3. $\frac{-16}{8} = -2$ Check: $(-2)(8) = -16$
4. $-22 \div (-2) = 11$ Check: $(11)(-2) = -22$
5. $\frac{-48}{-12} = 4$ Check: $4(-12) = -48$
6. $-63 \div (-9) = 7$ Check: $7(-9) = -63$
7. $\frac{-50}{25} = -2$ Check: $(-2)(25) = -50$
8. $-100 \div (-50) = 2$ Check: $2(-50) = -100$
9. $\frac{-200}{8} = -25$ Check: $-25(8) = -200$
10. $-108 \div 9 = -12$ Check: $(-12)(9) = -108$
11. $\frac{-63}{-7} = 9$ Check: $9(-7) = -63$
12. $\frac{200}{-25} = -8$ Check: $(-8)(-25) = 200$
13. $(-300) \div (0)$ None
14. $\frac{75}{5} = 15$ Check: $15(5) = 75$
15. $\frac{0}{-5} = 0$ Check: $0(-5) = 0$

16. $\frac{7}{15}$ **17.** $\frac{8}{3}$ **18.** $\frac{13}{47}$ **19.** $-\frac{12}{31}$

20. $13 = \frac{13}{1}$, so reciprocal is $\frac{1}{13}$.

21. $-10 = -\frac{10}{1}$, so reciprocal is $-\frac{1}{10}$.

22. $0.3 = \frac{3}{10}$, so reciprocal is $\frac{10}{3}$.

23. $-0.4 = -\frac{4}{10}$, so reciprocal is $-\frac{10}{4} = -\frac{5}{2}$.

24. $1\frac{1}{2} = \frac{3}{2}$, so reciprocal is $\frac{2}{3}$. **25.** $2\frac{2}{3} = \frac{8}{3}$, so reciprocal is $\frac{3}{8}$.

26. $\frac{q}{p}$ **27.** $\frac{t}{s}$ **28.** $4y$ **29.** $-8a$ **30.** $\frac{3b}{2a}$ **31.** $-\frac{3x}{4y}$

32. $3\left(\frac{1}{19}\right)$ **33.** $4\left(\frac{-1}{9}\right)$ **34.** $6\left(-\frac{1}{13}\right)$ **35.** $-12\left(\frac{1}{41}\right)$

36. $13.9\left(-\frac{1}{1.5}\right)$ **37.** $x \cdot y$ **38.** $\frac{1}{5}(3x + 4)$

39. $(5a - b)\left(\frac{1}{5a + b}\right)$ **40.** $\frac{3}{4} \div \left(-\frac{2}{3}\right) = \frac{3}{4} \cdot \left(-\frac{3}{2}\right) = -\frac{9}{8}$

41. $\frac{7}{8} \div \left(-\frac{1}{2}\right) = \frac{7}{8} \cdot \left(-\frac{2}{1}\right) = -\frac{14}{8} = -\frac{7}{4}$

42. $-\frac{5}{4} \div \left(-\frac{3}{4}\right) = -\frac{5}{4} \cdot \left(-\frac{4}{3}\right) = \frac{5}{3}$

43. $-\frac{5}{9} \div \left(-\frac{5}{6}\right) = -\frac{5}{9} \cdot \left(-\frac{6}{5}\right) = \frac{6}{9} = \frac{2}{3}$

44. $-\frac{2}{7} \div \left(-\frac{4}{9}\right) = -\frac{2}{7} \cdot \left(-\frac{9}{4}\right) = \frac{18}{28} = \frac{9}{14}$

45. $-\frac{3}{5} \div \left(-\frac{5}{8}\right) = -\frac{3}{5} \cdot \left(-\frac{8}{5}\right) = \frac{24}{25}$ **46.** 7

47. None **48.** 0 **49.** $-\frac{1}{3} \div \frac{1}{3} = -\frac{1}{3} \cdot \frac{3}{1} = -\frac{3}{3} = -1$

50. $-\frac{1}{4} \div \frac{1}{2} = -\frac{1}{4} \cdot \frac{2}{1} = -\frac{2}{4} = -\frac{1}{2}$

51. $-\frac{5}{6} \div \frac{3}{4} = -\frac{5}{6} \cdot \frac{4}{3} = -\frac{20}{18} = -\frac{10}{9}$

52. $\frac{20}{10} = 2, \frac{20}{5} = 4$, and $2 < 4$; B

53. $\frac{-20}{10} = -2, \frac{-20}{5} = -4$, and $-2 > -4$; A

54. $\frac{20}{-10} = -2; \frac{20}{-5} = -4$, and $-2 > -4$; A

55. $\frac{-20}{-10} = 2; -\frac{-20}{-5} = 4$, and $2 < 4$; B

56. If $x > 0, \frac{x}{10} < \frac{x}{5}$.

If $x = 0, \frac{x}{10} = \frac{x}{5}$.

If $x < 0, \frac{x}{10} > \frac{x}{5}$. D

57. If $x > 0, \frac{x}{10} > \frac{x}{5}$.

If $x = 0, \frac{x}{10} = \frac{x}{5}$.

If $x < 0, \frac{x}{10} < \frac{x}{5}$. D

58. $\frac{72 - 3}{25} = \frac{69}{25}$ **59.** $\frac{27 + 7}{-4} = \frac{34}{-4} = -\frac{17}{2}$

60. $\frac{-128}{16} = -8$ **61.** $\frac{81}{-9} = -9$

62. $5\frac{3}{7} \div 4\frac{2}{5} = \frac{38}{7} \div \frac{22}{5} = \frac{38}{7} \cdot \frac{5}{22} = \frac{190}{154} = \frac{95}{77}$

63. $\frac{10}{7} \div 1\frac{3}{4} = \frac{10}{7} \div \frac{7}{4} = \frac{10}{7} \cdot \frac{4}{7} = \frac{40}{49}$

64. $2\frac{2}{3} \div \frac{40}{15} = \frac{8}{3} \cdot \frac{15}{40} = \frac{120}{120} = 1$ **65.** $\frac{(-4)^3}{(-8)^3} \div \frac{-64}{-512} = \frac{1}{8}$

66. $-0.095238095238\ldots$ **67.** 0.238095238

68. You would get the original number. The reciprocal of a reciprocal is the original number.

69. Yes, it is true for both 1 and -1. **70.** No, $\frac{4}{2} \neq \frac{2}{4}$.

71. No; $(12 \div 6) \div 2 = 2 \div 2 = 1$, but $12 \div (6 \div 2) = 12 \div 3 = 4$.

72. No. A reciprocal has the same sign as the number, but the additive inverse has a different sign. Zero has no reciprocal.

73. $\frac{1}{\left(\frac{a}{b}\right)} \cdot \frac{\left(\frac{b}{a}\right)}{\left(\frac{b}{a}\right)} = \frac{\left(\frac{b}{a}\right)}{1} = \frac{b}{a}$

74. $6 + (-3) - 5 - (-9) = 3 - 5 + 9 = 7$

75. $12 - 7 - (-4) + (-2) = 5 + 4 + (-2) = 7$

76. $9 + 11 + (-8) - 4 = 20 + (-8) - 4 = 12 - 4 = 8$

77. $8 + (-15) - 4 - (-18) = -7 - 4 + 18 = -11 + 18 = 7$

78. $t + 5$ **79.** $2m$ **80.** $\frac{36}{y}$ **81.** $25 - x$ **82.** mn

83. $12 = 24p$ **84.** $20n = 5$

$\frac{12}{24} = p$ $n = \frac{5}{20}$

$p = \frac{1}{2}$ $n = \frac{1}{4}$

85. $42x = 14$
$x = \frac{14}{42}$
$x = \frac{1}{3}$

86. $3 = 6y$
$\frac{3}{6} = y$
$y = \frac{1}{2}$

TERMINATING AND REPEATING DECIMALS p. 86

1. $0.\overline{36}$ **2.** 0.35 **3.** $2.\overline{5}$ **4.** $0.2\overline{7}$

5. $0.\overline{4}$ **6.** $0.\overline{153846}$

7.

```
   0.142857
7)1.000000
  0
  10
   7
   30
   28
    20
    14
     60
     56
      40
      35
       50
       49
        1
```

The repeating pattern of remainders is 1, 3, 2, 6, 4, 5. There are 6 digits in this pattern.

8. $\frac{1}{7} = 0.\overline{142857}$; 6 digits repeat.

9. For the divisor 17, the 16 possible remainders are 1, 2, . . . , 16. As soon as any remainder repeats, the digits in the quotient repeat. So there can be no more than 16 digits in the quotient that repeat.

APPLICATION p. 88

1. Answers may vary. The moment should equal 15,000 ft-lb. Some examples are 15 ft, 1000 lb and 30 ft, 500 lb.

2. $125(?) = 15{,}000$
Divide 15,000 by 125.
$\frac{15{,}000}{125} = 120$
The boom must be 120 ft long.

3. Bale's moment $= (1500)(8) = 12{,}000$
Farmer's moment $= (?)(20)$
To balance, the moments must be equal.
$(?)(20) = 12{,}000$
Divide 12,000 by 20.
$\frac{12{,}000}{20} = 600$
A 600-lb force is required.

4. $(3)(420) = (?)(7)$
$1260 = (?)(7)$
Divide 1260 by 7.
$\frac{1260}{7} = 180$
A 180-lb force must be exerted.

5. Use try, test, and revise to equalize the moments. The fulcrum would have to be 60 cm from the 10 kg weight and 40 cm from the 15 kg weight.

LESSON 2-7 TRY THIS pp. 89–91

a. $8(y - 7) = 8y - 8(7)$
$= 8y - 56$

b. $\frac{5}{6}(x - y + 7z) = \frac{5}{6}x - \frac{5}{6}y + \frac{5}{6}(7z)$
$= \frac{5}{6}x - \frac{5}{6}y + \frac{35}{6}z$

c. $-5(x - 3y + 8z) = -5x + (-5)(-3y) + (-5)(8z)$
$= -5x + 15y - 40z$

d. $4 \cdot x - 4 \cdot 2 = 4(x - 2)$

e. $3 \cdot x - 3 \cdot 2y - 3 \cdot 5 = 3(x - 2y - 5)$

f. $b \cdot x - b \cdot y + b \cdot z = b(x - y + z)$

g. $-2 \cdot y - (-2)(4z) + (-2)(1) = -2(y - 4z + 1)$
or $2(-y + 4z - 1)$

h. $4 \cdot 3z - 4 \cdot 4x - 4 = 4(3z - 4x - 1)$

i. $5a, -4b, 3$

j. $-5y, -3x, 5z$

k. $6x - 3x = (6 - 3)x = 3x$

l. $7y - y = (7 - 1)y = 6y$

m. $m - 0.44m = (1 - 0.44)m = 0.56m$

n. $5x + 4y - 2x - y = 5x - 2x + 4y - y$
$= (5 - 2)x + (4 - 1)y = 3x + 3y$

o. $3x - 7x - 11 + 8y - 4 - 13y$
$= (3 - 7)x - 11 - 4 + (8 - 13y)y$
$= -4x - 5y - 15$

LESSON 2-7 EXERCISES pp. 91–92

1. $7(x - 2) = 7 \cdot x + 7(-2) = 7x - 14$

2. $5(x - 8) = 5 \cdot x + 5(-8) = 5x - 40$

3. $-7(y - 2) = -7 \cdot y - 7(-2) = -7y + 14$

4. $-9(y - 7) = -9 \cdot y - 9(-7) = -9y + 63$

5. $-9(-5x - 6y + 8) = -9(-5x) - 9(-6y) - 9(8)$
$= 45x + 54y - 72$

6. $-7(-2x - 5y + 9) = -7(-2x) - 7(-5y) - 7(9)$
$= 14x + 35y - 63$

7. $-4(x - 3y - 2z) = -4(x) - 4(-3y) - 4(-2z)$
$= -4x + 12y + 8z$

8. $8(2x - 5y - 8z) = 8(2x) + 8(-5y) + 8(-8z)$
$= 16x - 40y - 64z$

9. $3.1(-1.2x + 3.2y - 1.1)$
$= 3.1(-1.2x) + 3.1(3.2y) + 3.1(-1.1)$
$= -3.72x + 9.92y - 3.41$

10. $-2.1(-4.2x - 4.3y - 2.2)$
$= -2.1(-4.2x) - 2.1(-4.3y) - 2.1(-2.2)$
$= 8.82x + 9.03y + 4.62$

11. $\frac{2}{3}(3a - 6b + 9) = \frac{2}{3}(3a) + \frac{2}{3}(-6b) + \frac{2}{3}(9)$
$= 2a - 4b + 6$

12. $\frac{1}{2}(4c + 5d - 6) = \frac{1}{2}(4c) + \frac{1}{2}(5d) + \frac{1}{2}(-6)$
$= 2c + \frac{5}{2}d - 3$

13. $-\frac{4}{5}\left(-\frac{1}{2}x + \frac{2}{3}y - 1\right) = -\frac{4}{5}\left(-\frac{1}{2}x\right) - \frac{4}{5}\left(\frac{2}{3}y\right) - \frac{4}{5}(-1)$
$= \frac{2}{5}x - \frac{8}{15}y + \frac{4}{5}$

14. $-\frac{7}{8}\left(\frac{2}{3}x - \frac{1}{2}y - 8\right) = -\frac{7}{8}\left(\frac{2}{3}x\right) - \frac{7}{8}\left(-\frac{1}{2}y\right) - \frac{7}{8}(-8)$
$= -\frac{7}{12}x + \frac{7}{16}y + 7$

15. $8x - 24 = 8 \cdot x - 8 \cdot 3 = 8(x - 3)$

16. $-10x - 50 = -10 \cdot x - 10 \cdot 5 = -10(x + 5)$
or $-10x - 50 = 10(-x) + 10(-5) = 10(-x - 5)$

17. $32 - 4y = 4 \cdot 8 - 4 \cdot y = 4(8 - y)$

18. $24 - 6m = 6 \cdot 4 - 6 \cdot m = 6(4 - m)$

19. $8x + 10y - 22 = 2 \cdot 4x + 2 \cdot 5y - 2 \cdot 11 = 2(4x + 5y - 11)$

20. $-9a + 6b - 15 = 3(-3a) + 3(2b) + 3(-5)$
$= 3(-3a + 2b - 5)$
or $-9a + 6b - 15 = -3(3a) - 3(-2b) - 3(5)$
$= -3(3a - 2b + 5)$

21. $ax - 7a = a \cdot x - a \cdot 7 = a(x - 7)$

22. $by - 9b = b \cdot y - b \cdot 9 = b(y - 9)$

23. $ax - ay - az = a \cdot x - a \cdot y - a \cdot z = a(x - y - z)$

24. $cx + cy - cz = c \cdot x + c \cdot y - c \cdot z = c(x + y - z)$

25. $\frac{3}{4}x - \frac{1}{4}y - \frac{1}{4} = \frac{1}{4}(3x) + \frac{1}{4}(-y) + \frac{1}{4}(-1)$
$= \frac{1}{4}(3x - y - 1)$

26. $\frac{2}{3}x - \frac{1}{3}y + \frac{1}{3} = \frac{1}{3}(2x) + \frac{1}{3}(-y) + \frac{1}{3}(1)$
$= \frac{1}{3}(2x - y + 1)$

27. $4x, 3z$ **28.** $8x, -1.4y$ **29.** $7x, 8y, -9z$

30. $8a, 10b, -18c$ **31.** $12x, -13.2y, \frac{5}{8}z, -4.5$

32. $3ab, -4cd$ **33.** $x - 3x = 1x - 3x = (1 - 3)x = -2x$

34. $9t - 17t = (9 - 17)t = -8t$

35. $6n - n = 6n - 1n = (6 - 1)n = 5n$

36. $y - 17y = 1y - 17y = (1 - 17)y = -16y$

37. $9x + 2y - 5x = (9 - 5)x + 2y = 4x + 2y$

38. $8y - 3z + 4y = (8 + 4)y - 3z = 12y - 3z$

39. $11x + 2y - 4x - y = (11 - 4)x + (2 - 1)y = 7x + y$

40. $13a + 9b - 2a - 4b = (13 - 2)a + (9 - 4)b = 11a + 5b$

41. $2.7x + 2.3y - 1.9x - 1.8y = (2.7 - 1.9)x + (2.3 - 1.8)y$
$= 0.8x + 0.5y$

42. $6.7a + 4.3b - 4.1a - 2.9b = (6.7 - 4.1)a + (4.3 - 2.9)b$
$= 2.6a + 1.4b$

43. $5y - 3x - 7y = (5 - 7)y - 3x = -2y - 3x$

44. $13m + 5m - 3n - 18m = (13 + 5 - 18)m - 3n$
$= 0 \cdot m - 3n = -3n$

45. $-8t + p + 4p - t = (-8 - 1)t + (1 + 4)p$
$= -9t + 5p$

46. $q + q + q + 5p = (1 + 1 + 1)q + 5p = 3q + 5p$

47. $17a - 17b - 17c + 15a = (17 + 15)a - 17b - 17c$
$= 32a - 17b - 17c$

48. $6m - 3.5n - 2.5m - 7n = (6 + 2.5)m + (-3.5 - 7)n$
$= 8.5m - 10.5n$

49. $5.5d - 1.2a + 3d + 4.2a = (5.5 + 3)d + (-1.2 + 4.2)a$
$= 8.5d + 3a$

50. $17z + 3x - 2y + y - 5z - 3x$
$= (17 - 5)z + (3 - 3)x + (-2 + 1)y$
$= 12z + 0 \cdot x - 1 \cdot y = 12z - y$

51. $\frac{1}{5}x + \frac{4}{5}y + \frac{2}{5}x - \frac{1}{5}y = \left(\frac{1}{5} + \frac{2}{5}\right)x + \left(\frac{4}{5} - \frac{1}{5}\right)y$
$= \frac{3}{5}x + \frac{3}{5}y$

52. $\frac{7}{8}x + \frac{5}{8}y + \frac{1}{8}x - \frac{3}{8}y = \left(\frac{7}{8} + \frac{1}{8}\right)x + \left(\frac{5}{8} - \frac{3}{8}\right)y$
$= 1 \cdot x + \frac{2}{8}y$
$= x + \frac{1}{4}y$

53. $8(x - y)$ or $8x - 8y$ **54.** $9(y - z) + 3z$ or $9y - 6z$

55. $3(a + b) - 7a$ or $3b - 4a$

56. $2.95(x + y)$ or $2.95x + 2.95y$

57. No; $1 \cdot (3 - 2) = 1$ but $1 - (3 \cdot 2) = 1 - 6 = -5$

58. $\frac{9}{5}(C - 5) + 32$ or $\frac{9}{5}C + 23$

59. $5420\left(41\frac{1}{8} - 37\frac{3}{4}\right)$ or $5420\left(41\frac{1}{8}\right) - 5420\left(37\frac{3}{4}\right)$

Her loss is $18,292.50.

60. $\frac{15}{2}$ **61.** $-\frac{11}{6}$ **62.** $\frac{1}{4}$ **63.** $3c$

64. $11 - |-3| + (-9) - 16 = 11 - 3 + (-9) - 16 = -17$

65. $4x - (-9x) - x = 4x + 9x - x = 12x$ **66.** $\frac{4}{5}\left(\frac{2}{3}\right) = \frac{8}{15}$

67. $-\frac{3}{8}\left(\frac{1}{2}\right) = -\frac{3}{16}$ **68.** $\frac{2}{3} \div \left(-\frac{1}{2}\right) = \frac{2}{3}\left(-\frac{2}{1}\right) = -\frac{4}{3}$

69. $\frac{4}{5} \div \frac{2}{5} = \frac{4}{5} \cdot \frac{5}{2} = \frac{20}{10} = 2$

LESSON 2-8 TRY THIS pp. 93–96

a. $-(x + 2) = -1(x + 2) = -1(x) + (-1)(2) = -x - 2$

b. $-(5x + 2y + 8) = -1(5x + 2y + 8)$
$= -1(5x) + (-1)(2y) + (-1)(8)$
$= -5x - 2y - 8$

c. $-(a - 7) = -1(a - 7) = -1(a) - (-1)(7) = -a + 7$

d. $-(3c - 4d + 1) = -1(3c - 4d + 1)$
$= -1(3c) - (-1)(4d) + (-1)(1)$
$= -3c + 4d - 1$

e. $-(6 - t) = -6 + t$

f. $-(-4a + 3t - 10) = 4a - 3t + 10$

g. $-(18 - m - 2n + 4t) = -18 + m + 2n - 4t$

h. $5x - (3x + 9) = 5x - 3x - 9 = 2x - 9$

i. $5x - 2y - (2y - 3x - 4) = 5x - 2y - 2y + 3x + 4$
$= 8x - 4y + 4$

j. $y - 9(x + y) = y + (-9(x + y))$
$= y + (-9x - 9y)$
$= y - 9x - 9y$
$= -9x - 8y$

k. $5a - 3(7a - 6) = 5a + (-3(7a - 6))$
$= 5a + (-21a + 18)$
$= 5a - 21a + 18$
$= -16a + 18$

l. $[9 - (6 + 4)] = 9 - (10) = -1$

m. $3(4 + 2) - \{7 - [4 - (6 + 5)]\}$
$= 12 + 6 - \{7 - [4 - 11]\}$
$= 12 + 6 - \{7 - [-7]\}$
$= 12 + 6 - \{7 + 7\}$
$= 12 + 6 - 14 = 4$

n. $[3(4 + 2) + 2x] - [4(y + 2) - 3(y - 2)]$
$= [12 + 6 + 2x] - [4y + 8 - 3y + 6]$
$= [18 + 2x] - [y + 14]$
$= 18 + 2x - y - 14$
$= 2x - y + 4$

LESSON 2-8 EXERCISES pp. 96–97

1. $-(2x + 7) = -1(2x + 7) = -1(2x) + (-1)(7) = -2x - 7$

2. $-(3x + 5) = -1(3x + 5) = -1(3x) + (-1)(5) = -3x - 5$

3. $-(5x - 8) = -1(5x - 8)$
$= -1(5x) + (-1)(-8)$
$= -5x + 8$

4. $-(6x - 7) = -1(6x - 7)$
$= -1(6x) + (-1)(-7)$
$= -6x + 7$

5. $-(4a - 3b + 7c) = -1(4a - 3b + 7c)$
$= -1(4a) + (-1)(-3b) + (-1)(7c)$
$= -4a + 3b - 7c$

6. $-(5x - 2y - 3z) = -1(5x - 2y - 3z)$
$= -1(5x) + (-1)(-2y) + (-1)(-3z)$
$= -5x + 2y + 3z$

7. $-(6x - 8y + 5) = -1(6x - 8y + 5)$
$= -1(6x) + (-1)(-8y) + (-1)(5)$
$= -6x + 8y - 5$

8. $-(8x + 3y + 9) = -1(8x + 3y + 9)$
$= -1(8x) + (-1)(3y) + (-1)(9)$
$= -8x - 3y - 9$

9. $-(3x - 5y - 6) = -1(3x - 5y - 6)$
$= -1(3x) + (-1)(-5y) + (-1)(-6)$
$= -3x + 5y + 6$

10. $-(6a - 4b - 7) = -1(6a - 4b - 7)$
$= -1(6a) + (-1)(-4b) + (-1)(-7)$
$= -6a + 4b + 7$

11. $-(-8x - 6y - 43) = -1(-8x - 6y - 43)$
$= -1(-8x) + (-1)(-6y) + (-1)(-43)$
$= 8x + 6y + 43$

12. $-(-2a + 9b - 5c) = -1(-2a + 9b - 5c)$
$= -1(-2a) + (-1)(9b) + (-1)(-5c)$
$= 2a - 9b + 5c$

13. $9x - (4x + 3) = 9x - 4x - 3 = 5x - 3$

14. $7y - (2y + 9) = 7y - 2y - 9 = 5y - 9$

15. $2a - (5a - 9) = 2a - 5a + 9 = -3a + 9$

16. $11n - (3n - 7) = 11n - 3n + 7 = 8n + 7$

17. $2x + 7x - (4x + 6) = 9x - 4x - 6 = 5x - 6$

18. $3a + 2a - (4a + 7) = 5a - 4a - 7 = a - 7$

19. $2x - 4y - 3(7x - 2y) = 2x - 4y - 21x + 6y$
$= -19x + 2y$

20. $3a - 7b - 1(4a - 3b) = 3a - 7b - 4a + 3b$
$= -a - 4b$

21. $15x - y - 5(3x - 2y + 5z)$
$= 15x - y - 15x + 10y - 25z$
$= 9y - 25z$

22. $4a - b - 4(5a - 7b + 8c)$
$= 4a - b - 20a + 28b - 32c$
$= -16a + 27b - 32c$

23. $(3x + 2y) - (5x - 4y) = 3x + 2y - 5x + 4y$
$= -2x + 6y$

24. $(-6a - b) - (4b + a) = -6a - b - 4b - a$
$= -7a - 5b$

25. $6m - n - 4m - (5n - m) = 6m - n - 4m - 5n + m$
$= 3m - 6n$

26. $7p - (q + 8p) - 5p + 3q = 7p - q - 8p - 5p + 3q$
$= -6p + 2q$

27. $-(7u - 8v) - (8v - 7u) = -7u + 8v - 8v + 7u$
$= 0$

28. $7m + 8n - (4n - 5m) + n = 7m + 8n - 4n + 5m + n$
$= 12m + 5n$

29. $5a - 3b - (-6b + 4a) - (-b)$
$= 5a - 3b + 6b - 4a + b$
$= a + 4b$

30. $-(-4x - 3y) - 6y + 3x - x - y$
$= 4x + 3y - 6y + 3x - x - y$
$= 6x - 4y$

31. $[9 - 2(5 - 4)] = [9 - 2(1)] = 9 - 2 = 7$

32. $[6 - 5(8 - 4)] = [6 - 5(4)] = 6 - 20 = -14$

33. $8[7 - 6(4 - 2)] = 8[7 - 6(2)] = 8(7 - 12) = 8(-5) = -40$

34. $10[7 - 4(7 - 5)] = 10[7 - 4(2)] = 10(7 - 8)$
$= 10(-1) = -10$

35. $[4(9 - 6) + 11] - [14 - (6 + 4)]$
$= [4(3) + 11] - [14 - 10]$
$= (12 + 11) - 4 = 23 - 4 = 19$

36. $[7(8 - 4) + 16] - [15 - (7 + 3)]$
$= [7(4) + 16] - [15 - 10]$
$= (28 + 16) - 5 = 44 - 5 = 39$

37. $[10(x + 3) - 4] + [2(x - 1) + 6]$
$= [10x + 30 - 4] + [2x - 2 + 6]$
$= (10x + 26) + (2x + 4) = 12x + 30$

38. $[9(x + 5) - 7] + [4(x - 12) + 9]$
$= [9x + 45 - 7] + [4x - 48 + 9]$
$= (9x + 38) + (4x - 39)$
$= 13x - 1$

39. $[7(x + 5) - 19] - [4(x - 6) + 10]$
$= [7x + 35 - 19] - [4x - 24 + 10]$
$= (7x + 16) - (4x - 14)$
$= 7x + 16 - 4x + 14$
$= 3x + 30$

40. $[6(x + 4) - 12] - [5(x - 8) + 11]$
$= [6x + 24 - 12] - [5x - 40 + 11]$
$= (6x + 12) - (5x - 29)$
$= 6x + 12 - 5x + 29$
$= x + 41$

41. $x - (y + a + b)$ 42. $6y - (-2x + 3a - c)$

43. $6m - (-3n + 5m - 4b)$

44. $3q - (2p - 4q + 5)$

45. $3a + 4 - \{-2 - [-3 - (a - 1)]\}$
$= 3a + 4 - \{-2 - [-3 - a + 1]\}$
$= 3a + 4 - \{-2 - [-2 - a]\}$
$= 3a + 4 - \{-2 + 2 + a\}$
$= 3a + 4 - \{a\}$
$= 3a + 4 - a$
$= 2a + 4$

46. $2s + 2 - \{-3 - [2 - (3 - s)]\}$
$= 2s + 2 - \{-3 - [2 - 3 + s]\}$
$= 2s + 2 - \{-3 - [-1 + s]\}$
$= 2s + 2 - \{-3 + 1 - s\}$
$= 2s + 2 - \{-2 - s\}$
$= 2s + 2 + 2 + s$
$= 3s + 4$

47. $0; a + b + (-a) + (-b) = a + (-a) + b + (-b) = 0$

48. $z - \{2z - [3z - (4z - 5z) - 6z] - 7z\} - 8z$
$= z - \{2z - [3z - (-z) - 6z] - 7z\} - 8z$
$= z - \{2z - [3z + z - 6z] - 7z\} - 8z$
$= z - \{2z - (-2z) - 7z\} - 8z$
$= z - \{2z + 2z - 7z\} - 8z$
$= z - \{-3z\} - 8z$
$= z + 3z - 8z$
$= -4z$

49. $\{x - [f - (f - x)] + [x - f]\} - 3x$
$= \{x - [f - f + x] + x - f\} - 3x$
$= \{x - [x] + x - f\} - 3x$
$= \{x - x + x - f\} - 3x$
$= x - f - 3x$
$= -2x - f$

50. $x - \{x - 1 - [x - 2 - (x - 3 - \{x - 4 - [x - 5 - (x - 6)]\})]\}$
$= x - \{x - 1 - [x - 2 - (x - 3 - \{x - 4 - [x - 5 - x + 6]\})]\}$
$= x - \{x - 1 - [x - 2 - (x - 3 - \{x - 4 - [1]\})]\}$
$= x - \{x - 1 - [x - 2 - (x - 3 - \{x - 5\})]\}$
$= x - \{x - 1 - [x - 2 - (x - 3 - x + 5)]\}$
$= x - \{x - 1 - [x - 2 - 2]\} = x - \{x - 1 - [x - 4]\}$
$= x - \{x - 1 - x + 4\} = x - \{3\} = x - 3$

51. $\{y - [y + (3 - y)] - \overline{y + 1}\} + 5y$
$= \{y - [y + 3 - y] - y - 1\} + 5y$
$= \{y - 3 - y - 1\} + 5y$
$= \{-4\} + 5y$
$= 5y - 4$

52. $3x + 12y = 3 \cdot x + 3 \cdot 4y = 3(x + 4y)$

53. $2a - 6b + 12 = 2 \cdot a - 2 \cdot 3b + 2 \cdot 6 = 2(a - 3b + 6)$

54. $an + 2a = a \cdot n + a \cdot 2 = a(n + 2)$

55. $2x^3 = 2(3)^3 = 2 \cdot 27 = 54$

56. $-3z^2 = -3(5)^2 = -3(25) = -75$

57. $6x + 2y^4 = 6(3) + 2(2)^4 = 18 + 2 \cdot 16$
$= 18 + 32 = 50$

58. $2x^2 + 3z = 2(3)^2 + 3(5) = 2 \cdot 9 + 15$
$= 18 + 15 = 33$

59. $x + 2y - 3z = 3 + 2 \cdot 2 - 3 \cdot 5$
$= 3 + 4 - 15 = -8$

60. $\frac{2}{3} + \frac{1}{4} - \left(-\frac{3}{8}\right) = \frac{16}{24} + \frac{6}{24} + \frac{9}{24} = \frac{31}{24}$

61. $\frac{1}{2}\left(\frac{4}{5}\right) + \left(\frac{5}{6}\right)\left(-\frac{2}{3}\right) = \frac{2}{5} - \frac{5}{9} = \frac{18}{45} - \frac{25}{45} = -\frac{7}{45}$

62. $16b$ 63. $2x^2 + x$ 64. $x^2 + 3$ 65. $3x - 5$

LESSON 2-9 PROBLEMS pp. 100–101

1. (B) or (C) **2.** (A) **3.** (A) or (B)
4. (B) **5.** (B) or (C) **6.** (A) or (C)

7–24. Answers may vary.

7. Let h = height of the Statue of Liberty.
$h + 203 = 295$

8. Let d = number of tickets sold first day.
$127 + d = 318$

9. Let a = amount of money Alberto has.
$a = 115 - 48$

10. Let c = cost of a single bagel.
$12c = 3.12$

11. Let p = price of a ticket.
$117p = 438.75$

12. Let c = number of hours the consultant worked.
$80c = 53{,}400$

13. Let a = area of Lake Ontario.
$4a = 78{,}114$

14. Let t = time it takes 150-watt bulb to use 1-kWh.
$2.5t = 16.6$

15. Let a = area of Rhode Island.
$483a = 1{,}519{,}202$

16. Let b = boiling point of methyl alcohol.
$b + 13.5 = 78.3$

17. Let d = distance from Earth to moon.
$391d = 150{,}000{,}000$

18. Let m = middle wattage of a 3-way bulb.
$m + 30 = 150$

19. Let t = time.
$325 = 50t$

20. Let c = cost of each print.
$36c = 13.53$

21. Let q = number of quarters required.
$7q = 45$

22. Let x = number of inches in a meter.
$x = 2.54 \cdot 100$

23. Let t = time for sound to reach you.
$1087t = 10{,}000$

24. Let b = batting average.
$125b = 36$

25–28. Answers will vary.

LESSON 2-10 TRY THIS pp. 103–105

a. Associative property of addition
b. Inverse property of multiplication
c. Inverse property of addition
d. Since $1 + 1 = 2$ and 2 is not in the set, the set is not closed for addition.
Since -1, 0, and 1 are the only possible products of -1, 0, and 1, the set is closed for multiplication.
e. Reflexive property
f. Transitive property
g. Symmetric property
h. Distributive property; distributive property
i. Distributive property; multiplicative identity; additive inverses

LESSON 2-10 EXERCISES pp. 105–106

1. Commutative property of addition

2. Commutative property of addition

3. Distributive property of multiplication over addition

4. Distributive property of multiplication over addition

5. Additive inverses

6. Distributive property of multiplication over addition

7. Additive inverses

8. Distributive property of multiplication over subtraction

9. Associative property of multiplication

10. Multiplicative identity

11. Distributive property of multiplication over addition

12. Commutative property of addition

13. Multiplicative inverse

14. Additive inverse

15. Reflexive property of equality

16. Symmetric property of equality

17. Reflexive property of equality

18. Commutative property of multiplication

19. The set of whole numbers is closed for addition and multiplication. It is not closed for subtraction; example, $1 - 2$ is not a whole number. It is not closed for division; example, $1 \div 2$ is not a whole number.

20. The set of rational numbers is closed for the four operations.

21. The set of integers is closed for addition, subtraction, and multiplication. It is not closed for division; example, $-2 \div 3$ is not an integer.

22. 1. Additive identity; 3. Associative property of addition; 5. Distributive property; 7. Multiplication property of zero; 8. Additive identity

23. Yes. Any two even numbers are of the form $2a$ and $2b$ where a and b are whole numbers. $2a + 2b = 2(a + b)$ by the distributive property. $a + b$ is a whole number because the set of whole numbers is closed for addition. So $2(a + b)$ is even by definition.

24. No. $1 + 3 = 4$; 4 is not in the set of odd whole numbers.

25. Yes. Any two numbers in the set are of the form $3a$ and $3b$. $(3a)(3b) = 3(3ab)$ by the commutative and associative properties. $3ab$ is a whole number because the set of whole numbers is closed for multiplication, so $3(3ab)$ is in the set by definition.

26.

Statement	Reason
1. $(-a)b = (-1 \cdot a)b$	Property of -1
2. $\quad = -1(ab)$	Associative property of multiplication
3. $\quad = -ab$	Property of -1
4. $(-a)b = -ab$	Transitive property of equality

27.

Statement	Reason
1. $-(a + b) = -1(a + b)$	Property of -1
2. $\quad = (-1)a + (-1)b$	Distributive property
3. $\quad = -\alpha + (-b)$	Property of -1
4. $-(a + b) = -a + (-b)$	Transitive property of equality

28. Let c = cost of 1 print. $36c = 4.80 + 8.35$ or $c = \frac{4.80 + 8.35}{36}$

29. $16(a - 3)$ **30.** $2(4y - 5 + 6x)$

31. $15(3 - n)$ **32.** $9c - 2a$ **33.** $9 - 17c$

CHAPTER 2 WRAP UP pp. 107–109

1. Owes suggests a negative integer, -25.

2. Deposited suggests a positive integer, $+50$.

3. 38 **4.** 91 **5.** 0.02

8. 6. 7.
−4 −3 −2 −1 0 1 2

9. $>$ **10.** $<$ **11.** $<$ **12.** $-\frac{42}{10}$ **13.** $\frac{8}{5}$ **14.** $-\frac{8}{1}$

15. -19 **16.** $-\frac{6}{4}$ or $-\frac{3}{2}$ **17.** 3.5

18. $13 - 17 = -4$

19. $-3.8 + 5.1 + (-12) + 4.3 = -15.8 + 9.4 = -6.4$

20. -27 **21.** 7.45 **22.** $\frac{7}{3}$ **23.** 34

24.
$$\begin{aligned} x &= 5 \\ -x &= -5 \\ -(-x) &= -(-5) = 5 \end{aligned}$$

25. $+5 + (-12) + 15 = 8$
The total is an 8-yd gain.

26. -2 **27.** $-7 - (-3) = -7 + 3 = -4$

28. $-\frac{9}{10} - \frac{1}{2} = -\frac{9}{10} - \frac{5}{10} = -\frac{14}{10} = -\frac{7}{5}$

29. $13 - 4 + 8 - (-2) = 21 - 4 + 2 = 19$

30. $4y - 19 - (-7y) + 3 = 4y - 16 + 7y = 11y - 16$

31. $2500 - (-1500) = 2500 + 1500 = 4000$
It is 4000 ft above the floor of the canyon.

32. $89.00 - 105.95 = -16.95$
He is overdrawn by \$16.95.

33. -24 **34.** $-\frac{6}{21} = -\frac{2}{7}$ **35.** 210 **36.** -3 **37.** 5

38. $-\frac{7}{8} \div \frac{5}{4} = -\frac{7}{8} \cdot \frac{4}{5} = -\frac{28}{40} = -\frac{7}{10}$

39. $2(6x - 1) = 2 \cdot 6x + 2(-1) = 12x - 2$

40. $-7(1 + 4x) = -7(1) + (-7)(4x) = -7 - 28x$

41.
$$\begin{aligned} -3(2a - 3b + c) &= -3(2a) + (-3)(-3b) + (-3)(c) \\ &= -6a + 9b - 3c \end{aligned}$$

42. $9a - 9 = 9 \cdot a - 9 \cdot 1 = 9(a - 1)$

43. $8x - 32y - 8 = 8 \cdot x - 8 \cdot 4y - 8 \cdot 1 = 8(x - 4y - 1)$

44. $42z - 21x + 7 = 7 \cdot 6z - 7 \cdot 3x + 7 \cdot 1 = 7(6z - 3x + 1)$

45. $7x$ **46.** $2a$ **47.** $2m + 6$

48. $-(x + 7) = -1(x + 7) = -1(x) + (-1)(7) = -x - 7$

49.
$$\begin{aligned} -(7a + 12b + c) &= -1(7a + 12b + c) \\ &= -1(7a) + (-1)(12b) + (-1)(c) \\ &= -7a - 12b - c \end{aligned}$$

50.
$$\begin{aligned} -(6 - z) &= -1(6 - z) \\ &= -1(6) + (-1)(-z) \\ &= -6 + z \end{aligned}$$

51. $3a - (8a + 3) = 3a - 8a - 3 = -5a - 3$

52.
$$\begin{aligned} 7x - 5 - (10x - 4) &= 7x - 5 - 10x + 4 \\ &= -3x - 1 \end{aligned}$$

53. $a - 5(a + b) = a - 5a - 5b = -4a - 5b$

54.
$$\begin{aligned} 3p - 4(8p - 3) &= 3p - 32p + 12 \\ &= -29p + 12 \end{aligned}$$

55. $[12 - (8 + 3)] = [12 - 11] = 1$

56.
$$\begin{aligned} 15 - [9 - (11 + 4)] &= 15 - [9 - 15] \\ &= 15 - (-6) \\ &= 15 + 6 = 21 \end{aligned}$$

57. (A) or (C)

58. Let a = amount made each game.
$162a = 1{,}289{,}170$

CHAPTER 2 ASSESSMENT pp. 110–111

1. Lost suggests a negative integer, -16.

2. Above sea level suggests a positive integer, $+9000$.

3. 6.5 **4.** 105.5

6. 5.
−3 −2 −1 0 1 2 3 4 5

7. $<$ **8.** $<$ **9.** $-\frac{35}{10}$ **10.** $\frac{7}{3}$ **11.** -1.6

12. $-\frac{7}{5}$ **13.** $-8 + 4 + (-7) + 3 = -15 + 7 = -8$

14. $-\frac{2}{3}$ **15.** 1.4 **16.** $43 - 25 + 30 = 48$
She has \$48 now.

17. $-\frac{1}{3}$ **18.** $2 - (-8) = 2 + 8 = 10$ **19.** -2.5

20. $6 + 7 - 4 + 3 = 12$ **21.** $3y + 16 + 4y + 7 = 7y + 23$

22. $5 - (-7) = 5 + 7 = 12$
It dropped 12°.

23. $170 - 300 = -130$
Your net worth is $-$\$130.

24. -48 **25.** $\frac{3}{16}$ **26.** 240 **27.** -5 **28.** 6

29. -5 **30.** $-\frac{7}{8}$ **31.** $-\frac{7}{24}$ **32.** $\frac{1}{3y}$

33. $\frac{4}{9} \div \left(\frac{-7}{3}\right) = \frac{4}{9} \cdot \frac{3}{-7} = -\frac{12}{63} = -\frac{4}{21}$

34. $\frac{-15}{\frac{1}{x}} = -15 \cdot x = -15x$

35. $\frac{-3}{5} \div \left(-\frac{5}{6}\right) = \frac{-3}{5} \cdot \left(-\frac{6}{5}\right) = \frac{18}{25}$

36. $-7(x + 3) = -7 \cdot x + (-7)(3) = -7x - 21$

37.
$$\begin{aligned} \left(\frac{5}{3}\right)(x - 2y + z) &= \frac{5}{3}(x) + \frac{5}{3}(-2y) + \frac{5}{3}(z) \\ &= \frac{5}{3}x - \frac{10}{3}y + \frac{5}{3}z \end{aligned}$$

38.
$$\begin{aligned} -7(-3a - 2b - 8) &= -7(-3a) + (-7)(-2b) + (-7)(-8) \\ &= 21a + 14b + 56 \end{aligned}$$

39. $4x - 12 = 4 \cdot x - 4 \cdot 3 = 4(x - 3)$

40.
$$\begin{aligned} 4a + 12b - 16 &= 4 \cdot a + 4 \cdot 3b - 4 \cdot 4 \\ &= 4(a + 3b - 4) \end{aligned}$$

41. $\frac{2x}{3} - \frac{y}{3} = \frac{1}{3} \cdot 2x - \frac{1}{3} \cdot y = \frac{1}{3}(2x - y)$

42. $-11x + 4x = -7x$ **43.** $2q - t$ **44.** $3m + 3$

45. $(-1)(-21) = 21$ **46.** $-1 \cdot 17 = -17$

47.
$$\begin{aligned} -(y - 8) &= -1(y - 8) = -1(y) + (-1)(-8) \\ &= -y + 8 \end{aligned}$$

48.
$$\begin{aligned} -(2a + 5b - c) &= -1(2a + 5b - c) \\ &= -1(2a) + (-1)(5b) + (-1)(-c) \\ &= -2a - 5b + c \end{aligned}$$

49. $5n - (2n + m) = 5n - 2n - m = 3n - m$

50. $4x - 3(y + 2x) = 4x - 3y - 6x = -2x - 3y$

51.
$$\begin{aligned} 50 - [12 - (16 + 5)] &= 50 - [12 - 21] \\ &= 50 - [-9] \\ &= 50 + 9 \\ &= 59 \end{aligned}$$

52.
$$\begin{aligned} 6(9 - 4) - [10 - (6 + 8)] &= 6(5) - [10 - 14] \\ &= 30 - (-4) \\ &= 30 + 4 \\ &= 34 \end{aligned}$$

53. (C)

54. Let p = price of admission.

$576p = 3456$ or $p = \frac{3456}{576}$

55. Let d = distance she rode.
$d + 31 = 57$ or $d = 57 - 31$

CHAPTER 3

SKILLS & CONCEPTS p. 112

1. $-3 + (-8) = -11$

2.
$$\begin{aligned} 8 + (-3) + (-11) &= 5 + (-11) \\ &= -6 \end{aligned}$$

3. $-3.1 + 6.8 = 3.7$ **4.** $9 - (-13) = 9 + 13 = 22$

5. $-7.2 - (-10.1) = -7.2 + 10.1 = 2.9$

6. $\frac{2}{3} - \frac{9}{10} = \frac{20}{30} - \frac{27}{30} = -\frac{7}{30}$ 7. $9 \cdot (-4) = -36$

8. $\frac{3}{2} \cdot \frac{-4}{7} = \frac{-12}{14} = -\frac{6}{7}$ 9. $-\frac{2}{3} \cdot \frac{5}{8} = -\frac{10}{24} = -\frac{5}{12}$

10. $-6 \cdot 8 = -48$ 11. $-11(-3) = 33$

12. $-7(-5) = 35$ 13. $\frac{3}{4} \div \left(-\frac{1}{8}\right) = \frac{3}{4} \cdot \left(-\frac{8}{1}\right) = -\frac{24}{4} = -6$

14. $-\frac{7}{9} \div \left(-\frac{2}{3}\right) = -\frac{7}{9}\left(-\frac{3}{2}\right) = \frac{21}{18} = \frac{7}{6}$

15. $-9.37 \div (-0.1) = -9.37 \div \left(-\frac{1}{10}\right)$
$= -9.37\left(-\frac{10}{1}\right)$
$= 93.7$

16. $9y - 45 = 9 \cdot y - 9 \cdot 5 = 9(y - 5)$

17. $bw + bx - by = b(w + x - y)$

18. $3y + 15 - 21x = 3 \cdot y + 3 \cdot 5 - 3 \cdot 7x = 3(y + 5 - 7x)$

19. $6w - 12x + 10 = 2 \cdot 3w - 2 \cdot 6x + 2 \cdot 5 = 2(3w - 6x + 5)$

20. $3(x - 5) = 3 \cdot x - 3 \cdot 5 = 3x - 15$

21. $8(4 + w) = 8 \cdot 4 + 8 \cdot w = 32 + 8w$

22. $5x - (6 + 3x) = 5x - 6 - 3x = 2x - 6$

23. $7w - 3 - (4w - 8) = 7w - 3 - 4w + 8$
$= 3w + 5$

24. $[3(5 - 2) + 18] - [12 - (3 + 4)]$
$= [3(3) + 18] - [12 - 7] = (9 + 18) - 5$
$= 27 - 5 = 22$

25. $[2(4x + 7) - 3] + [5(3 + x) + 2x]$
$= [8x + 14 - 3] + [15 + 5x + 2x]$
$= 8x + 11 + 15 + 7x$
$= 15x + 26$

LESSON 3-1 TRY THIS pp. 115–116

a. $x + 7 = 2$
$x + 7 + (-7) = 2 + (-7)$
$x = -5$

b. $y - 8 = -3$
$y - 8 + 8 = -3 + 8$
$y = 5$

c. $5 = -4 + a$
$5 + 4 = -4 + 4 + a$
$9 = a$

d. Let x = previous rent.
$x + 82 = 675$
$x + 82 + (-82) = 675 + (-82)$
$x = 593$
The previous rent was $593.

LESSON 3-1 EXERCISES pp. 116–118

1. $x + 2 = 6$
$x + 2 + (-2) = 6 + (-2)$
$x = 4$

2. $x + 5 = 8$
$x + 5 - 5 = 8 - 5$
$x = 3$

3. $x + 15 = 26$
$x + 15 + (-15) = 26 + (-15)$
$x = 11$

4. $y + 9 = 43$
$y + 9 + (-9) = 43 + (-9)$
$y = 34$

5. $x + 6 = -8$
$x + 6 + (-6) = -8 + (-6)$
$x = -14$

6. $t + 9 = -12$
$t + 9 + (-9) = -12 + (-9)$
$t = -21$

7. $x + 16 = -2$
$x + 16 + (-16) = -2 + (-16)$
$x = -18$

8. $y + 25 = -6$
$y + 25 + (-25) = -6 + (-25)$
$y = -31$

9. $x - 9 = 6$
$x - 9 + 9 = 6 + 9$
$x = 15$

10. $x - 8 = 5$
$x - 8 + 8 = 5 + 8$
$x = 13$

11. $x - 7 = -21$
$x - 7 + 7 = -21 + 7$
$x = -14$

12. $x - 3 = -14$
$x - 3 + 3 = -14 + 3$
$x = -11$

13. $5 + t = 7$
$5 + (-5) + t = 7 + (-5)$
$t = 2$

14. $8 + y = 12$
$8 + (-8) + y = 12 + (-8)$
$y = 4$

15. $-7 + y = 13$
$-7 + 7 + y = 13 + 7$
$y = 20$

16. $-9 + z = 15$
$-9 + 9 + z = 15 + 9$
$z = 24$

17. $-3 + t = -9$
$-3 + 3 + t = -9 + 3$
$t = -6$

18. $-6 + y = -21$
$-6 + 6 + y = -21 + 6$
$y = -15$

19. $b - 31 = 12$
$b - 31 + 31 = 12 + 31$
$b = 43$

20. $-18 = y - 4$
$-18 + 4 = y - 4 + 4$
$-14 = y$

21. $-14 = p + 6$
$-14 + (-6) = p + 6 + (-6)$
$-20 = p$

22. $a + 1.5 = 3$
$a + 1.5 + (-1.5) = 3 + (-1.5)$
$a = 1.5$

23. $n - 0.6 = 4$
$n - 0.6 + 0.6 = 4 + 0.6$
$n = 4.6$

24. $x + 3.2 = 7$
$x + 3.2 + (-3.2) = 7 + (-3.2)$
$x = 3.8$

25. $c + 4 = -2.5$
$c + 4 + (-4) = -2.5 + (-4)$
$c = -6.5$

26. $x + 5.7 = 15$
$x + 5.7 + (-5.7) = 15 + (-5.7)$
$x = 9.3$

27. $s - 10 = -3.1$
$s - 10 + 10 = -3.1 + 10$
$s = 6.9$

28. $r + \frac{1}{3} = \frac{8}{3}$
$r + \frac{1}{3} + \left(-\frac{1}{3}\right) = \frac{8}{3} + \left(-\frac{1}{3}\right)$
$r = \frac{7}{3}$

29. $t + \frac{3}{8} = \frac{5}{8}$
$t + \frac{3}{8} + \left(-\frac{3}{8}\right) = \frac{5}{8} + \left(-\frac{3}{8}\right)$
$t = \frac{2}{8} = \frac{1}{4}$

30. $m + \frac{5}{6} = -\frac{11}{12}$
$m + \frac{5}{6} + \left(-\frac{5}{6}\right) = -\frac{11}{12} + \left(-\frac{5}{6}\right)$
$m = -\frac{11}{12} + \left(-\frac{10}{12}\right) = -\frac{21}{12} = -\frac{7}{4}$

31. $x + \frac{2}{3} = -\frac{5}{6}$
$x + \frac{2}{3} + \left(-\frac{2}{3}\right) = -\frac{5}{6} + \left(-\frac{2}{3}\right)$
$x = -\frac{5}{6} + \left(-\frac{4}{6}\right) = -\frac{9}{6} = -\frac{3}{2}$

32. $x - \frac{5}{6} = \frac{7}{8}$

$x - \frac{5}{6} + \frac{5}{6} = \frac{7}{8} + \frac{5}{6}$

$x = \frac{21}{24} + \frac{20}{24} = \frac{41}{24}$

33. $y - \frac{3}{4} = \frac{5}{6}$

$y - \frac{3}{4} + \frac{3}{4} = \frac{5}{6} + \frac{3}{4}$

$y = \frac{10}{12} + \frac{9}{12} = \frac{19}{12}$

34. $x - \frac{3}{8} = \frac{1}{4}$

$x - \frac{3}{8} + \frac{3}{8} = \frac{1}{4} + \frac{3}{8}$

$x = \frac{2}{8} + \frac{3}{8} = \frac{5}{8}$

35. $a + \frac{4}{5} = \frac{1}{10}$

$a + \frac{4}{5} + \left(-\frac{4}{5}\right) = \frac{1}{10} + \left(-\frac{4}{5}\right)$

$a = \frac{1}{10} + \left(-\frac{8}{10}\right) = -\frac{7}{10}$

36. $m + \frac{2}{9} = \frac{2}{3}$

$m + \frac{2}{9} + \left(-\frac{2}{9}\right) = \frac{2}{3} + \left(-\frac{2}{9}\right)$

$m = \frac{6}{9} + \left(-\frac{2}{9}\right) = \frac{4}{9}$

37. $x + 6 = 57$
$x + 6 + (-6) = 57 + (-6)$
$x = 51$

38. $x - 18 = -53$
$x - 18 + 18 = -53 + 18$
$x = -35$

39. $x - 4 = 11$
$x - 4 + 4 = 11 + 4$
$x = 15$

40. $x + 42 = -100$
$x + 42 + (-42) = -100 + (-42)$
$x = -142$

41. $x + 4 = -4$
$x + 4 - 4 = -4 - 4$
$x = -8$
$x - 4 = -8 - 4$
$x - 4 = -12$
The answer is A.

42. You can subtract a number from both sides of an equation by adding its opposite, or inverse, to both sides.

43. **a.** $t - 55$
b. $-35°$
c. The average daily low temperature in Key West in January
d. $t - 55 = -35$
e. $t - 55 + 55 = -35 + 55$
$t = 20°$

44. **a.** $h + 565$
b. 1017 ft
c. the height of City Hall
d. $h + 565 = 1017$
e. 565 must be added to h to equal the height of Library Tower.
f. $h = 452$ ft

45. **a.** $c + 15{,}918{,}215$
b. 18,870,730
c. The newspaper's circulation
d. $c + 15{,}918{,}215 = 18{,}870{,}730$
e. Less
f. $c + 15{,}918{,}215 + (-15{,}918{,}215)$
$= 18{,}870{,}730 + (-15{,}918{,}215)$
$c = 2{,}952{,}515$

46. $8 - 25 = 8 + x - 21$
$-17 = -13 + x$
$-17 + 13 = -13 + 13 + x$
$-4 = x$

47. $16 + x - 22 = -16$
$x - 6 = -16$
$x - 6 + 6 = -16 + 6$
$x = -10$

48. $x + 5 = x - (3 + x)$
$x + 5 = x - 3 - x$
$x + 5 = -3$
$x + 5 - 5 = -3 - 5$
$x = -8$

49. $x + 3 = 3 + a - b$
$x + 3 - 3 = 3 - 3 + a - b$
$x = a - b$

50. $x + 7 = b + 10$
$x + 7 + (-7) = b + 10 + (-7)$
$x = b + 3$

51. $1 - c = a + x$
$1 - c + (-a) = a + (-a) + x$
$1 - c - a = x$

52. Let x = number in stock at beginning.
$x - 142 + 75 = 319$
$x - 67 = 319$
$x - 67 + 67 = 319 + 67$
$x = 386$
386 videocassettes

53. Let x = amount at beginning.
$x - 12.24 - 15.05 - 22.00 + 55.12 = 124.23$
$x + 5.83 = 124.23$
$x + 5.83 + (-5.83) = 124.23 + (-5.83)$
$x = 118.40$
$118.40 in account

54. Answers may vary. Sample: $x - \frac{1}{4} = -\frac{5}{6}$

55. Sometimes; if k and $-k$ are each a solution of $x + a = b$, or $x = b - a$, then $k = b - a$ and $-k = b - a$. Thus, $k = -k$, and k must be 0 since 0 is the only number that is equal to its opposite. Hence, $-k$ is a solution only for $k = 0$ (in which case $a = b$, also).
Always; If $k + a = b$, then $a - b = -k$. Using $-k$ for x, $x - a = -k - a = a - b - a = -b$ and $-k$ is a solution of $x - a = -b$.

56. $x - 1 + 2x - 2 + 3x - 3 = 30 + 4x$
$6x - 6 = 30 + 4x$
$6x - 6 + 6 = 30 + 6 + 4x$
$6x = 36 + 4x$
$6x + (-4x) = 36 + 4x + (-4x)$
$2x = 36$
$2x = 2(18)$
Since twice x is twice 18, $x = 18$.

57. $x - 4720 = 1634$
$x - 4720 + 4720 = 1634 + 4720$
$x = 6354$
$x + 4720 = 6354 + 4720$
$x + 4720 = 11{,}074$

58. $x + x = x$
$x + x + (-x) = x + (-x)$
$x = 0$

59. **a.** $x + 3 = 3 + x$
$x + (-x) + 3 = 3 + x + (-x)$
$3 = 3$
True for any value of x
b. $x - 3 = 3 + x$
$x - x - 3 = 3 + x - x$
$-3 = 3$
True for no value of x. The equation has no solution.

60. $6 - x = 10$
$6 + (-6) - x = 10 + (-6)$
$-x = 4$
The student solved for $-x$.
$x = -4$

61. $9y - (2y + 4) = 9y - 2y - 4 = 7y - 4$

62. $7c - (8c + 2) = 7c - 8c - 2 = -c - 2$

63. $8w - 3(5w - 8) = 8w - 15w + 24 = -7w + 24$

64. $6a + 2c - 3(2a + 3c) = 6a + 2c - 6a - 9c = -7c$

65. $3[5 + 4(3 - y)] = 3[5 + 12 - 4y]$
$= 3[17 - 4y]$
$= 51 - 12y$

66. $5t - (3 + 9t) = 5t - 3 - 9t$
$= -3 - 4t$

67. $(5a)^2 = (5 \cdot 2)^2 = (10)^2 = 100$

68. $5a^2 = 5 \cdot (2)^2 = 5 \cdot 4 = 20$ **69.** $s^1 = 32^1 = 32$

70. $3(-5) = -15$ **71.** $\left(-\frac{1}{3}\right)\left(-\frac{3}{5}\right) = \frac{3}{15} = \frac{1}{5}$

72. $4(-2)(-1)(-3) = (-8)(3) = -24$ **73.** $-4 \div 2 = -2$

74. $\frac{2}{7} \div \left(-\frac{3}{8}\right) = \frac{2}{7} \cdot \left(-\frac{8}{3}\right) = -\frac{16}{21}$

75. $-\frac{14}{15} \div \frac{5}{7} = -\frac{14}{15} \cdot \frac{7}{5} = -\frac{98}{75}$

76. $\frac{1}{2}a = 5.75$ or $2(5.75) = a$

LESSON 3-2 TRY THIS pp. 120–122

a. $5x = 25$
$\frac{1}{5} \cdot 5x = 25 \cdot \frac{1}{5}$
$x = 5$

b. $4a = -7$
$\frac{1}{4} \cdot 4a = -7 \cdot \frac{1}{4}$
$a = -\frac{7}{4}$

c. $-3y = -42$
$-\frac{1}{3}(-3y) = (-42)\left(-\frac{1}{3}\right)$
$y = 14$

d. $-\frac{1}{3}y = 4$
$-3\left(-\frac{1}{3}y\right) = -3(4)$
$y = -12$

e. $\frac{5}{6} = -\frac{2}{3}x$
$-\frac{3}{2} \cdot \frac{5}{6} = -\frac{3}{2}\left(-\frac{2}{3}x\right)$
$-\frac{15}{12} = x$
$x = -\frac{5}{4}$

f. $-x = 6$
$-1(-x) = -1(6)$
$x = -6$

g. $\frac{x}{5} = 10$
$5 \cdot \frac{x}{5} = 10 \cdot 5$
$x = 50$

h. $\frac{m}{-3} = -12$
$-3\left(\frac{m}{-3}\right) = -3(-12)$
$m = 36$

i. $\frac{-t}{4} = 6$
$-4\left(\frac{-t}{4}\right) = -4(6)$
$t = -24$

j. Let $x =$ the price of each bottle.
$12x = 6.72$
$\frac{1}{12} \cdot 12x = \frac{1}{12}(6.72)$
$x = 56$
The price was \$0.56.

LESSON 3-2 EXERCISES pp. 122–124

1. $6x = 36$
$\frac{1}{6} \cdot 6x = \frac{1}{6} \cdot 36$
$x = 6$

2. $3x = 39$
$\frac{1}{3} \cdot 3x = \frac{1}{3} \cdot 39$
$x = 13$

3. $5x = 45$
$\frac{1}{5} \cdot 5x = \frac{1}{5} \cdot 45$
$x = 9$

4. $9x = 72$
$\frac{1}{9} \cdot 9x = \frac{1}{9} \cdot 72$
$x = 8$

5. $84 = 7x$
$\frac{1}{7} \cdot 84 = \frac{1}{7} \cdot 7x$
$12 = x$

6. $56 = 8x$
$\frac{1}{8} \cdot 56 = \frac{1}{8} \cdot 8x$
$7 = x$

7. $-x = 40$
$(-1)(-x) = (-1)40$
$x = -40$

8. $100 = -x$
$(-1)100 = (-1)(-x)$
$-100 = x$

9. $-x = -1$
$(-1)(-x) = (-1)(-1)$
$x = 1$

10. $-68 = -r$
$(-1)(-68) = (-1)(-r)$
$68 = r$

11. $7x = -49$
$\frac{1}{7} \cdot 7x = \frac{1}{7}(-49)$
$x = -7$

12. $9x = -36$
$\frac{1}{9} \cdot 9x = \frac{1}{9} \cdot (-36)$
$x = -4$

13. $-12x = 72$
$\left(-\frac{1}{12}\right)(-12x) = \left(-\frac{1}{12}\right)72$
$x = -6$

14. $-15x = 105$
$\left(-\frac{1}{15}\right)(-15x) = \left(-\frac{1}{15}\right)105$
$x = -7$

15. $-21x = -126$
$\left(-\frac{1}{21}\right)(-21x) = \left(-\frac{1}{21}\right)(-126)$
$x = 6$

16. $-13x = -104$
$\left(-\frac{1}{13}\right)(-13x) = \left(-\frac{1}{13}\right)(-104)$
$x = 8$

17. $\frac{t}{7} = -9$
$7\left(\frac{t}{7}\right) = 7(-9)$
$t = -63$

18. $\frac{y}{-8} = 11$
$(-8)\left(\frac{y}{-8}\right) = (-8)(11)$
$y = -88$

19. $\frac{3}{4}x = 27$
$\frac{4}{3}\left(\frac{3}{4}x\right) = \frac{4}{3}(27)$
$x = \frac{108}{3} = 36$

20. $\frac{4}{5}x = 16$
$\frac{5}{4}\left(\frac{4}{5}x\right) = \frac{5}{4}(16)$
$x = \frac{80}{4} = 20$

21. $\frac{-t}{3} = 7$
$-3\left(\frac{-t}{3}\right) = -3(7)$
$t = -21$

22. $\frac{-x}{6} = 9$
$-6\left(\frac{-x}{6}\right) = -6(9)$
$x = -54$

23. $-\frac{m}{3} = \frac{1}{5}$
$-3\left(-\frac{m}{3}\right) = -3\left(\frac{1}{5}\right)$
$m = -\frac{3}{5}$

24. $\frac{1}{9} = -\frac{z}{7}$
$-7\left(\frac{1}{9}\right) = -7\left(-\frac{z}{7}\right)$
$-\frac{7}{9} = z$

25. $-\frac{3}{5}r = -\frac{9}{10}$
$-\frac{5}{3}\left(-\frac{3}{5}r\right) = -\frac{5}{3}\left(-\frac{9}{10}\right)$
$r = \frac{45}{30} = \frac{3}{2}$

26. $-\frac{2}{5}y = -\frac{4}{15}$
$-\frac{5}{2}\left(-\frac{2}{5}y\right) = -\frac{5}{2}\left(-\frac{4}{15}\right)$
$y = \frac{20}{30} = \frac{2}{3}$

27. $-\frac{3}{2}r = -\frac{27}{4}$
$-\frac{2}{3}\left(-\frac{3}{2}r\right) = -\frac{2}{3}\left(-\frac{27}{4}\right)$
$r = \frac{54}{12} = \frac{9}{2}$

28. $\frac{5}{7}x = -\frac{10}{14}$
$\frac{7}{5}\left(\frac{5}{7}x\right) = \frac{7}{5}\left(-\frac{10}{14}\right)$
$x = -\frac{70}{70} = -1$

29. $6.3x = 44.1$
$\frac{1}{6.3}(6.3x) = \frac{1}{6.3}(44.1)$
$x = 7$

30. $2.7y = 54$
$\frac{1}{2.7}(2.7y) = \frac{1}{2.7}(54)$
$y = 20$

31. $-3.1y = 21.7$
$\frac{1}{-3.1}(-3.1y) = \frac{1}{-3.1}(21.7)$
$y = -7$

32. $-3.3y = 6.6$
$\frac{1}{-3.3}(-3.3y) = \frac{1}{-3.3}(6.6)$
$y = -2$

33. $38.7m = 309.6$
$\frac{1}{38.7}(38.7m) = \frac{1}{38.7}(309.6)$
$m = 8$

34. $18x = -1008$
$\frac{1}{18}(18x) = \frac{1}{18}(-1008)$
$x = -56$

35. $-8x = 744$
$-\frac{1}{8}(-8x) = -\frac{1}{8}(744)$
$x = -93$

36. Yes.
$a = b$ and $c = 0$
$ac = a(0) = 0$
$bc = b(0) = 0$
Therefore, $ac = bc$.

37. a. $8p$ **b.** \$170
c. The price of one ticket
d. $8p = 170$
e. Less; 8 tickets at \$30 would cost \$240.
f. $8p = 170$
$\frac{1}{8}(8p) = \frac{1}{8}(170)$
$p = \$21.25$

38. a. $5.8s$
b. 16,700 mi/h
c. the speed of *Columbia* 2 min into the flight
d. $5.8s = 16{,}700$
e. Round the numbers in the equation $5.8s = 16{,}700$ to get the equation
$6s \approx 18{,}000$
$\frac{1}{6}(6s) \approx \frac{1}{6}(18{,}000)$
$s \approx 3000$
At 2 min, the speed was about 3000 mi/h.
f. $5.8s = 16{,}700$
$\frac{1}{5.8}(5.8s) = \frac{1}{5.8}(16{,}700)$
$s \approx 2879.3$
At 2 min, the speed was about 2879.3 mi/h.

39. a. $42w$
b. 258,295
c. the population of Winnemucca
d. $42w = 258{,}295$
e. Round the numbers in the equation $42w = 258{,}295$ to get the equation
$40w \approx 240{,}000$
$\frac{1}{40}(40w) \approx \frac{1}{40}(240{,}000)$
$w \approx 6000$
The population of Winnemucca was about 6000.
f. $42w = 258{,}295$
$\frac{1}{42}(42w) = \frac{1}{42}(258{,}295)$
$w \approx 6150$
The population of Winnemucca was about 6150.

40. $12t = 23.40$
$\frac{1}{12}(12t) = \frac{1}{12}(23.40)$
$t = \$1.95$

41. $1131 \approx \frac{1}{3}f$
$3(1131) \approx 3\left(\frac{1}{3}f\right)$
$3393 \approx f$

42. You can divide both sides of an equation by a nonzero number by multiplying both sides by the reciprocal of the number.

43. $\frac{3}{7}C \approx 1{,}170{,}000$
$\frac{7}{3}\left(\frac{3}{7}C\right) \approx \frac{7}{3}(1{,}170{,}000)$
$C \approx 2{,}730{,}000$

44. $\frac{7}{11}M \approx 3409$
$\frac{11}{7}\left(\frac{7}{11}M\right) \approx \frac{11}{7}(3409)$
$M \approx 5357$
Montana threw about 5357 passes.
$\frac{3}{4}C \approx 3409$
$\frac{4}{3}\left(\frac{3}{4}C\right) \approx \frac{4}{3}(3409)$
$C \approx 4545$
Elway completed about 4545 passes.
$\frac{4}{7}E \approx 4545$
$\frac{7}{4}\left(\frac{4}{7}E\right) \approx \frac{7}{4}(4545)$
$E \approx 7954$
Elway threw about 7954 passes.
Since $7954 > 5357$, Elway threw more passes.
He threw $E - M \approx 7954 - 5357 = 2597$ more passes than Montana.

45. $6a + 6b = 72$
$\frac{1}{6}(6a + 6b) = \frac{1}{6}(72)$
$a + b = 12$

46. $\frac{x}{3} + 2 = 12$
$3\left(\frac{x}{3} + 2\right) = 3(12)$
$x + 6 = 36$

47. $\frac{2m}{5} - 2 = 12$
$5\left(\frac{2m}{5} - 2\right) = 5(12)$
$2m - 10 = 60$

48. $\frac{2a^2}{3} + 1 = 8$
$3\left(\frac{2a^2}{3} + 1\right) = 3(8)$
$2a^2 + 3 = 24$

49. $ax = 5a, ax \cdot \frac{1}{a} = 5a \cdot \frac{1}{a}, x = \frac{5a}{a} = 5$

50. $3x = \frac{b}{a}, 3x \cdot \frac{1}{3} = \frac{b}{a} \cdot \frac{1}{3}$
$x = \frac{b}{3a}$

51. $cx = a^2 + 1, cx \cdot \frac{1}{c} = (a^2 + 1) \cdot \frac{1}{c}$
$x = \frac{a^2 + 1}{c}$

52. $abx = 1, abx \cdot \frac{1}{ab} = 1 \cdot \frac{1}{ab}$
$x = \frac{1}{ab}$

53. Answers may vary.

54. a. $0 \cdot x = 0$
Zero times any number is zero, so the equation is true for all values of x.
b. $0 \cdot x = 9$
Zero times any number is zero, so the equation is true for no value of x. The equation has no solution.

55. a. Yes; If $a = b$, then $a^2 = ab$. Also, $ab = b^2$. Therefore, $a^2 = b^2$.
b. No; for example, $3^2 = (-3)^2$, but $3 \neq -3$.

56. $8x + 4y - (4x - 5y) = 8x + 4y - 4x + 5y = 4x + 9y$

57. $3 - (4a + 7) = 3 - 4a - 7 = -4a - 4$

58. $7r - (s + 2r) - 4s = 7r - s - 2r - 4s = 5r - 5s$

59. $(2a + 4b) - (2a + 4b) = 2a + 4b - 2a - 4b = 0$

60. $-5 \cdot 8 \cdot 2 = -40 \cdot 2 = -80$ **61.** $(-7)(-24) \cdot 0 = 0$

62. $(-2.1)(-1.2) = 2.52$ **63.** $(-3)(-7)(-2) = 21(-2) = -42$

64. $(-4)(-2.2)(-5) = 8.8(-5) = -44$

65. $(-2)(-3.1)(3) = 6.2(3) = 18.6$

66. $t^4 + 1 = 2^4 + 1 = 16 + 1 = 17$

67. $8y^3 = 8(3^3) = 8 \cdot 27 = 216$ **68.** $3|x| = 3|-8| = 3 \cdot 8 = 24$

69. $y^2 + 2y = (-3)^2 + 2(-3) = 9 - 6 = 3$

70. $4z + |z| = 4(-1) + |-1| = -4 + 1 = -3$

71. $4x + 8y - 12z = 4 \cdot x + 4 \cdot 2y - 4.3z = 4(x + 2y - 3z)$

72. $6a - 12b - 9c = 3 \cdot 2a - 3 \cdot 4b - 3 \cdot 3c = 3(2a - 4b - 3c)$

LESSON 3-3 TRY THIS pp. 126–127

a. $9x + 6 = 51$
$9x + 6 + (-6) = 51 + (-6)$
$9x = 45$
$\frac{1}{9} \cdot 9x = \frac{1}{9} \cdot 45$
$x = 5$

b. $-8y - 4 = 28$
$-8y - 4 + 4 = 28 + 4$
$-8y = 32$
$-\frac{1}{8} \cdot -8y = -\frac{1}{8} \cdot 32$
$y = -4$

c.
$$\begin{aligned} -18 - 3x &= -57 \\ -18 + 18 - 3x &= -57 + 18 \\ -3x &= -39 \\ -\tfrac{1}{3}\cdot(-3x) &= -\tfrac{1}{3}(-39) \\ x &= 13 \end{aligned}$$

d.
$$\begin{aligned} 4 - 8x &= 12 \\ 4 + (-4) - 8x &= 12 + (-4) \\ -8x &= 8 \\ -\tfrac{1}{8}\cdot 8x &= -\tfrac{1}{8}\cdot 8 \\ x &= -1 \end{aligned}$$

e.
$$\begin{aligned} 4c + 3c &= 21 \\ 7c &= 21 \\ \tfrac{1}{7}\cdot 7c &= 21\cdot\tfrac{1}{7} \\ c &= 3 \end{aligned}$$

f.
$$\begin{aligned} 9x - 4x &= 20 \\ 5x &= 20 \\ \tfrac{1}{5}\cdot 5x &= \tfrac{1}{5}\cdot 20 \\ x &= 4 \end{aligned}$$

g.
$$\begin{aligned} 9 &= 3(x + 6) \\ 9 &= 3x + 18 \\ 9 + (-18) &= 3x + 18 + (-18) \\ -9 &= 3x \\ \tfrac{1}{3}\cdot(-9) &= \tfrac{1}{3}\cdot 3x \\ x &= -3 \end{aligned}$$

h.
$$\begin{aligned} 24 - 2(2m + 1) &= -6 \\ 24 - 4m - 2 &= -6 \\ 22 - 4m &= -6 \\ 22 + (-22) - 4m &= -6 + (-22) \\ -4m &= -28 \\ -\tfrac{1}{4}\cdot(-4m) &= -28\cdot\left(-\tfrac{1}{4}\right) \\ m &= 7 \end{aligned}$$

i.
$$\begin{aligned} 3a + 5(a - 2) &= 6 \\ 3a + 5a - 10 &= 6 \\ 8a - 10 &= 6 \\ 8a - 10 + 10 &= 6 + 10 \\ 8a &= 16 \\ \tfrac{1}{8}\cdot 8a &= \tfrac{1}{8}\cdot 16 \\ a &= 2 \end{aligned}$$

LESSON 3-3 EXERCISES pp. 127–129

1.
$$\begin{aligned} 5x + 6 &= 31 \\ 5x + 6 + (-6) &= 31 + (-6) \\ 5x &= 25 \\ \tfrac{1}{5}(5x) &= \tfrac{1}{5}(25) \\ x &= 5 \end{aligned}$$

2.
$$\begin{aligned} 3x + 6 &= 30 \\ 3x + 6 + (-6) &= 30 + (-6) \\ 3x &= 24 \\ \tfrac{1}{3}(3x) &= \tfrac{1}{3}(24) \\ x &= 8 \end{aligned}$$

3.
$$\begin{aligned} 8x + 4 &= 68 \\ 8x + 4 + (-4) &= 68 + (-4) \\ 8x &= 64 \\ \tfrac{1}{8}(8x) &= \tfrac{1}{8}(64) \\ x &= 8 \end{aligned}$$

4.
$$\begin{aligned} 7z + 9 &= 72 \\ 7z + 9 + (-9) &= 72 + (-9) \\ 7z &= 63 \\ \tfrac{1}{7}(7z) &= \tfrac{1}{7}(63) \\ z &= 9 \end{aligned}$$

5.
$$\begin{aligned} 4x - 6 &= 34 \\ 4x - 6 + 6 &= 34 + 6 \\ 4x &= 40 \\ \tfrac{1}{4}(4x) &= \tfrac{1}{4}(40) \\ x &= 10 \end{aligned}$$

6.
$$\begin{aligned} 6x - 3 &= 15 \\ 6x - 3 + 3 &= 15 + 3 \\ 6x &= 18 \\ \tfrac{1}{6}(6x) &= \tfrac{1}{6}(18) \\ x &= 3 \end{aligned}$$

7.
$$\begin{aligned} 3x - 9 &= 33 \\ 3x - 9 + 9 &= 33 + 9 \\ 3x &= 42 \\ \tfrac{1}{3}(3x) &= \tfrac{1}{3}(42) \\ x &= 14 \end{aligned}$$

8.
$$\begin{aligned} 5x - 7 &= 48 \\ 5x - 7 + 7 &= 48 + 7 \\ 5x &= 55 \\ \tfrac{1}{5}(5x) &= \tfrac{1}{5}(55) \\ x &= 11 \end{aligned}$$

9.
$$\begin{aligned} 7x + 2 &= -54 \\ 7x + 2 + (-2) &= -54 + (-2) \\ 7x &= -56 \\ \tfrac{1}{7}(7x) &= \tfrac{1}{7}(-56) \\ x &= -8 \end{aligned}$$

10.
$$\begin{aligned} 5x + 4 &= -41 \\ 5x + 4 + (-4) &= -41 + (-4) \\ 5x &= -45 \\ \tfrac{1}{5}(5x) &= \tfrac{1}{5}(-45) \\ x &= -9 \end{aligned}$$

11.
$$\begin{aligned} -4x + 7 &= 35 \\ -4x + 7 - 7 &= 35 - 7 \\ -4x &= 28 \\ \tfrac{1}{-4}(-4x) &= \tfrac{1}{-4}(28) \\ x &= -7 \end{aligned}$$

12.
$$\begin{aligned} -5x - 7 &= 108 \\ -5x - 7 + 7 &= 108 + 7 \\ -5x &= 115 \\ \tfrac{1}{-5}(-5x) &= \tfrac{1}{-5}(115) \\ x &= -23 \end{aligned}$$

13.
$$\begin{aligned} -7x - 24 &= -129 \\ -7x - 24 + 24 &= -129 + 24 \\ -7x &= -105 \\ \tfrac{1}{-7}(-7x) &= \tfrac{1}{-7}(-105) \\ x &= 15 \end{aligned}$$

14.
$$\begin{aligned} -6z - 18 &= -132 \\ -6z - 18 + 18 &= -132 + 18 \\ -6z &= -114 \\ \tfrac{1}{-6}(-6z) &= \tfrac{1}{-6}(-114) \\ z &= 19 \end{aligned}$$

15.
$$\begin{aligned} 5x + 7x &= 72 \\ 12x &= 72 \\ \tfrac{1}{12}(12x) &= \tfrac{1}{12}(72) \\ x &= 6 \end{aligned}$$

16.
$$\begin{aligned} 4x + 5x &= 45 \\ 9x &= 45 \\ \tfrac{1}{9}(9x) &= \tfrac{1}{9}(45) \\ x &= 5 \end{aligned}$$

17.
$$\begin{aligned} 4x + 3x &= 42 \\ 7x &= 42 \\ \tfrac{1}{7}(7x) &= \tfrac{1}{7}(42) \\ x &= 6 \end{aligned}$$

18.
$$\begin{aligned} 6x + 19x &= 100 \\ 25x &= 100 \\ \tfrac{1}{25}(25x) &= \tfrac{1}{25}(100) \\ x &= 4 \end{aligned}$$

19.
$$\begin{aligned} 4y - 2y &= 10 \\ 2y &= 10 \\ \tfrac{1}{2}(2y) &= \tfrac{1}{2}(10) \\ y &= 5 \end{aligned}$$

20.
$$\begin{aligned} 8y - 5y &= 48 \\ 3y &= 48 \\ \tfrac{1}{3}(3y) &= \tfrac{1}{3}(48) \\ y &= 16 \end{aligned}$$

21.
$$\begin{aligned} -6y - 3y &= 27 \\ -9y &= 27 \\ \tfrac{1}{-9}(-9y) &= \tfrac{1}{-9}(27) \\ y &= -3 \end{aligned}$$

22.
$$\begin{aligned} -4y - 8y &= 48 \\ -12y &= 48 \\ \tfrac{1}{-12}(-12y) &= \tfrac{1}{-12}(48) \\ y &= -4 \end{aligned}$$

23.
$$\begin{aligned} -7y - 8y &= -15 \\ -15y &= -15 \\ \tfrac{1}{-15}(-15y) &= \tfrac{1}{-15}(-15) \\ y &= 1 \end{aligned}$$

24.
$$\begin{aligned} -10y - 3y &= -39 \\ -13y &= -39 \\ \tfrac{1}{-13}(-13y) &= \tfrac{1}{-13}(-39) \\ y &= 3 \end{aligned}$$

25.
$$\begin{aligned} 10.2y - 7.3y &= -58 \\ 2.9y &= -58 \\ \tfrac{1}{2.9}(2.9y) &= \tfrac{1}{2.9}(-58) \\ y &= -20 \end{aligned}$$

26.
$$\begin{aligned} 6.8y - 2.4y &= -88 \\ 4.4y &= -88 \\ \tfrac{1}{4.4}(4.4y) &= \tfrac{1}{4.4}(-88) \\ y &= -20 \end{aligned}$$

27.
$$4x - 8 = 32$$
$$\frac{1}{4}(4x - 8) = \frac{1}{4} \cdot 32$$
$$x - 2 = 8$$
$$x - 2 + 2 = 8 + 2$$
$$x = 10$$

$$4x - 8 = 32$$
$$4x - 8 + 8 = 32 + 8$$
$$4x = 40$$
$$\frac{1}{4} \cdot 4x = \frac{1}{4} \cdot 40$$
$$x = 10$$

Results are the same.

28.
$$5(3x - 2) = 35$$
$$15x - 10 = 35$$
$$15x - 10 + 10 = 35 + 10$$
$$15x = 45$$
$$\frac{1}{15}(15x) = \frac{1}{15}(45)$$
$$x = 3$$

29.
$$3(2y - 3) = 27$$
$$6y - 9 = 27$$
$$6y - 9 + 9 = 27 + 9$$
$$6y = 36$$
$$\frac{1}{6}(6y) = \frac{1}{6}(36)$$
$$y = 6$$

30.
$$-2(4y - 3) = 6$$
$$-8y + 6 = 6$$
$$-8y + 6 + (-6) = 6 + (-6)$$
$$-8y = 0$$
$$\frac{1}{-8}(-8y) = \frac{1}{-8}(0)$$
$$y = 0$$

31.
$$(4 + 3x)(-3) = -9$$
$$-12 - 9x = -9$$
$$-12 + 12 - 9x = -9 + 12$$
$$-9x = 3$$
$$\frac{1}{-9}(-9x) = \frac{1}{-9}(3)$$
$$x = -\frac{3}{9} = -\frac{1}{3}$$

32.
$$2(3 + 4m) - 9 = 45$$
$$6 + 8m - 9 = 45$$
$$8m - 3 = 45$$
$$8m - 3 + 3 = 45 + 3$$
$$8m = 48$$
$$\frac{1}{8}(8m) = \frac{1}{8}(48)$$
$$m = 6$$

33.
$$3(5 + 3m) - 8 = 88$$
$$15 + 9m - 8 = 88$$
$$9m + 7 = 88$$
$$9m + 7 + (-7) = 88 + (-7)$$
$$9m = 81$$
$$\frac{1}{9}(9m) = \frac{1}{9}(81)$$
$$m = 9$$

34.
$$12 - 3(x - 5) = 21$$
$$12 - 3x + 15 = 21$$
$$27 - 3x = 21$$
$$27 + (-27) - 3x = 21 + (-27)$$
$$-3x = -6$$
$$\frac{1}{-3}(-3x) = \frac{1}{-3}(-6)$$
$$x = 2$$

35.
$$5 - 2(y + 1) = 21$$
$$5 - 2y - 2 = 21$$
$$3 - 2y = 21$$
$$3 + (-3) - 2y = 21 + (-3)$$
$$-2y = 18$$
$$\frac{1}{-2}(-2y) = \frac{1}{-2}(18)$$
$$y = -9$$

36.
$$5r - 2(2r + 8) = 16$$
$$5r - 4r - 16 = 16$$
$$r - 16 = 16$$
$$r - 16 + 16 = 16 + 16$$
$$r = 32$$

37.
$$6b - 4(2b + 8) = 16$$
$$6b - 8b - 32 = 16$$
$$-2b - 32 = 16$$
$$-2b - 32 + 32 = 16 + 32$$
$$-2b = 48$$
$$\frac{1}{-2}(-2b) = \frac{1}{-2}(48)$$
$$b = -24$$

38.
$$2(2x - 4) + 3x = -1$$
$$4x - 8 + 3x = -1$$
$$7x - 8 = -1$$
$$7x - 8 + 8 = -1 + 8$$
$$7x = 7$$
$$\frac{1}{7}(7x) = \frac{1}{7}(7)$$
$$x = 1$$

39.
$$-5a + 4(2 + 2a) = -1$$
$$-5a + 8 + 8a = -1$$
$$3a + 8 = -1$$
$$3a + 8 + (-8) = -1 + (-8)$$
$$3a = -9$$
$$\frac{1}{3}(3a) = \frac{1}{3}(-9)$$
$$a = -3$$

40.
$$\frac{1}{3}x + 2\left(\frac{1}{3}x + 5\right) = 12$$
$$\frac{1}{3}x + \frac{2}{3}x + 10 = 12$$
$$x + 10 = 12$$
$$x + 10 + (-10) = 12 + (-10)$$
$$x = 2$$

41.
$$3\left(\frac{1}{8}m - \frac{1}{2}\right) + \frac{3}{4}m = \frac{3}{2}$$
$$\frac{3}{8}m - \frac{3}{2} + \frac{3}{4}m = \frac{3}{2}$$
$$\frac{9}{8}m - \frac{3}{2} = \frac{3}{2}$$
$$\frac{9}{8}m - \frac{3}{2} + \frac{3}{2} = \frac{3}{2} + \frac{3}{2}$$
$$\frac{9}{8}m = 3$$
$$\frac{8}{9}\left(\frac{9}{8}m\right) = \frac{8}{9}(3)$$
$$m = \frac{24}{9} = \frac{8}{3}$$

42. Let g = original intended value of gift.
$$2(g + 15) = 90$$
$$2g + 30 = 90$$
$$2g + 30 + (-30) = 90 + (-30)$$
$$2g = 60$$
$$\frac{1}{2}(2g) = \frac{1}{2}(60)$$
$$g = 30$$

Erica originally intended to give $30.

43.
- **a.** Distributive property
- **b.** Addition property
- **c.** Simplify.
- **d.** Multiplication property
- **e.** Simplify.

44.
- **a.** Multiplication property
- **b.** Simplify.
- **c.** Addition property
- **d.** Simplify.
- **e.** Multiplication property
- **f.** Simplify.

45.
- **a.** Commutative property of addition
- **b.** Associative property of addition
- **c.** Collect like terms
- **d.** Addition property
- **e.** Simplify.
- **f.** Multiplication property
- **g.** Simplify.

46.
- **a.** Distributive property
- **b.** Collect like terms.
- **c.** Addition property
- **d.** Simplify.
- **e.** Multiplication property
- **f.** Simplify.

47.
$$(0.26 + y) + 3y = 0.98$$
$$0.26 + 4y = 0.98$$
$$0.26 + (-0.26) + 4y = 0.98 + (-0.26)$$
$$4y = 0.72$$
$$\frac{1}{4} \cdot 4y = \frac{1}{4} \cdot (0.72)$$
$$y = 0.18$$

48.
$$0 = y - (-14) - (-3y)$$
$$0 = y + 14 + 3y$$
$$0 = 4y + 14$$
$$-14 = 4y + 14 + (-14)$$
$$-14 = 4y$$
$$\frac{1}{4}(-14) = \frac{1}{4} \cdot 4y$$
$$-\frac{14}{4} = y$$
$$y = -\frac{7}{2}$$

49. $12 - (-5m) + 3m + 12 = 0$
$$12 + 5m + 3m + 12 = 0$$
$$8m + 24 = 0$$
$$8m + 24 + (-24) = 0 - 24$$
$$8m = -24$$
$$\frac{1}{8} \cdot 8m = \frac{1}{8}(-24)$$
$$m = -3$$

50. $4a + 5a - 2(2a) + 35 = 0$
$$9a - 4a + 35 = 0$$
$$5a + 35 = 0$$
$$5a + 35 + (-35) = -35$$
$$5a = -35$$
$$\frac{1}{5} \cdot 5a = \frac{1}{5}(-35)$$
$$a = -7$$

51. $4(a - 2) + 3(2a + 1) = 5$
$$4a - 8 + 6a + 3 = 5$$
$$10a - 5 = 5$$
$$10a - 5 + 5 = 5 + 5$$
$$10a = 10$$
$$\frac{1}{10} \cdot 10a = \frac{1}{10} \cdot 10$$
$$a = 1$$

52. $2(3x + 5) + 3(2x + 5) = 1$
$$6x + 10 + 6x + 15 = 1$$
$$12x + 25 = 1$$
$$12x + 25 + (-25) = 1 + (-25)$$
$$12x = -24$$
$$\frac{1}{12} \cdot 12x = \frac{1}{12} \cdot (-24)$$
$$x = -2$$

53. Let x = cost of gas per mile.
$$972 + 114 + 12{,}500x = 2011$$
$$1086 + 12{,}500x = 2011$$
$$1086 + (-1086) + 12{,}500x = 2011 + (-1086)$$
$$12{,}500x = 925$$
$$\frac{1}{12{,}500} \cdot 12{,}500x = \frac{1}{12{,}500} \cdot 925$$
$$x = 0.074$$
\$0.074 per mile or 7.4¢ per mile

54.
$$9x - 5 = 22$$
$$9x - 5 + 5 = 22 + 5$$
$$9x = 27$$
$$\frac{1}{9} \cdot 9x = \frac{1}{9} \cdot 27$$
$$x = 3 \rightarrow 4(3) + 2y = 2$$
$$12 + 2y = 2$$
$$12 + (-12) + 2y = 2 + (-12)$$
$$2y = -10$$
$$\frac{1}{2} \cdot 2y = \frac{1}{2}(-10)$$
$$y = -5$$

55.
$$9x + 2 = -1$$
$$9x + 2 + (-2) = -1 + (-2)$$
$$9x = -3$$
$$\frac{1}{9} \cdot 9x = \frac{1}{9} \cdot (-3)$$
$$x = -\frac{1}{3} \rightarrow 4\left(-\frac{1}{3}\right) - y = \frac{11}{3}$$
$$-\frac{4}{3} - y = \frac{11}{3}$$
$$-\frac{4}{3} + \frac{4}{3} - y = \frac{11}{3} + \frac{4}{3}$$
$$-y = \frac{15}{3} = 5$$
$$y = -5$$

56. In the Check, $-4.8 + 7.7 = 2.9$, not 3.9.

57. $-5.2 < 4$

58. $-2.3 < 2.2$

59. $\frac{2}{3} = \frac{10}{15}, \frac{3}{5} = \frac{9}{15}, \frac{2}{3} > \frac{3}{5}$

60. $\frac{1}{5} > -\frac{3}{5}$

61. $-6.7 < -3.9$

62. $\frac{5}{12} \div \frac{3}{4} = \frac{5}{12} \cdot \frac{4}{3} = \frac{20}{36} = \frac{5}{9}$

63. $-\frac{2}{5} \div -\frac{5}{6} = -\frac{2}{5} \cdot -\frac{6}{5} = \frac{12}{25}$

64. $\frac{2}{9} \div -\frac{1}{2} = \frac{2}{9} \cdot \frac{-2}{1} = -\frac{4}{9}$

65.
$$x + 10 = 25$$
$$x + 10 + (-10) = 25 + (-10)$$
$$x = 15$$

66.
$$t - 84 = 72$$
$$t - 84 + 84 = 72 + 84$$
$$t = 156$$

67.
$$5y = 30$$
$$\frac{1}{5}(5y) = \frac{1}{5}(30)$$
$$y = 6$$

68. $4t + 4n - 12m = 4(t + n - 3m)$

69. $3a - 3c - 3d = 3(a - c - d)$

70. $4c - 12d = 4(c - 3d)$

71. $4(3x - 4y) = 12x - 16y$

72. $3(2q - r - 4) = 6q - 3r - 12$

CONNECTIONS: GEOMETRY p. 129

1. perimeter $= 4(3x - 2) = 64$
$$12x - 8 = 64$$
$$12x - 8 + 8 = 64 + 8$$
$$12x = 72$$
$$\frac{1}{12}(12x) = \frac{1}{12}(72)$$
$$x = 6$$
side $= 3x - 2 = 3(6) - 2 = 18 - 2 = 16$
The side is 16 feet.

2. perimeter $= (x) + (2x + 3) + (x) + (2x + 3) = 36$
$$x + 2x + 3 + x + 2x + 3 = 36$$
$$6x + 6 = 36$$
$$6x + 6 + (-6) = 36 + (-6)$$
$$6x = 30$$
$$\frac{1}{6}(6x) = \frac{1}{6}(30)$$
$$x = 5$$
longer side $= 2x + 3 = 2(5) + 3 = 10 + 3 = 13$
The sides are 5 inches and 13 inches.

LESSON 3-4 TRY THIS pp. 131–133

a. $2n - 3$ **b.** $\frac{1}{2}(n - 1)$ **c.** $4(n + 3)$ **d.** $10n - 2$

e. $2n - 5$ **f.** $\frac{1}{2}t + 2$

g. Let n = the number of buckets Jack sold,
$3n - 2$ = the number of buckets Jill sold.
$$3n - 2 = 19$$
$$3n - 2 + 2 = 19 + 2$$
$$3n = 21$$
$$\frac{1}{3} \cdot 3n = \frac{1}{3} \cdot 21$$
$$n = 7$$
Jack has sold 7 buckets.

h. Let n = the number of miles to be paved each day,
$10n$ = the number of miles to be paved in 10 days.
$$10n + 3 = 18$$
$$10n + 3 - 3 = 18 - 3$$
$$10n = 15$$
$$\frac{1}{10} \cdot 10n = \frac{1}{10} \cdot 15$$
$$n = 1.5$$
1.5 miles should be paved each day.

LESSON 3-4 EXERCISES pp. 133–135

1. $5n - 3$ **2.** $2n + 5$ **3.** $\frac{1}{2}n - 18$ **4.** $\frac{1}{2}n + 12$

5. $\frac{n}{5} - 3$ **6.** $\frac{n}{2} + 3$ **7.** $4(n - 1)$ **8.** $2(n + 4)$

9. $\frac{1}{2}(n + 6)$ **10.** $\frac{3}{4}(n - 3)$ **11.** $\frac{1}{3}n - 4$ **12.** $\frac{1}{2}n + 7$

13. $2y + 2$ **14.** $4B - 3$ **15.** $\frac{1}{2}a + 2$ **16.** $2(r + 3)$

17. a. $s + 15$ **b.** $L - 15$ **18. a.** $\frac{1}{2}C + 25$ **b.** $2(c - 25)$

19. a.

55 mi

20 mi 10*h*

b. $10h + 20$
c. The number of additional hours Elena must ride
d. $10h + 20 = 55$
e.
$$10h + 20 = 55$$
$$10h + 20 + (-20) = 55 + (-20)$$
$$10h = 35$$
$$\frac{1}{10}(10h) = \frac{1}{10}(35)$$
$$h = 3.5$$
She must ride 3.5 h more.

20. a. The number of vans in the railroad cars
b. $8v + 2$
c. $8v + 2 = 122$
d.
$$8v + 2 = 122$$
$$8v + 2 + (-2) = 122 + (-2)$$
$$8v = 120$$
$$\frac{1}{8}(8v) = \frac{1}{8}(120)$$
$$v = 15$$
There are 15 vans in each railroad car.

21. B

22. Let n = total number of boys and girls.
$n - 30$ = number of girls
$$30 = \frac{1}{2}(n - 30) + 10$$
$$30 = \frac{1}{2}n - 15 + 10$$
$$30 = \frac{1}{2}n - 5$$
$$30 + 5 = \frac{1}{2}n - 5 + 5$$
$$35 = \frac{1}{2}n$$
$$2 \cdot 35 = 2 \cdot \frac{1}{2}n$$
$$70 = n$$
There are 70 boys and girls in the club.

23. Let m = number of miles traveled.
$$19.50 + 0.26(m) = 39$$
$$19.50 + (-19.50) + 0.26m = 39 + (-19.50)$$
$$0.26m = 19.50$$
$$\frac{1}{0.26} \cdot 0.26m = \frac{1}{0.26}(19.50)$$
$$m = 75$$
He traveled 75 miles.

24. Let c = cost per game.
$$3c + 2c + 2(0.75) = 9.00$$
$$5c + 1.50 = 9.00$$
$$5c + 1.50 + (-1.50) = 9.00 + (-1.50)$$
$$5c = 7.50$$
$$\frac{1}{5} \cdot 5c = \frac{1}{5} \cdot 7.50$$
$$c = 1.50$$
Each game cost \$1.50.

25. Let p = price of juice.
$$3p + 2p + 2(0.75) = 5.25$$
$$5p + 1.50 = 5.25$$
$$5p + 1.50 + (-1.50) = 5.25 + (-1.50)$$
$$5p = 3.75$$
$$\frac{1}{5} \cdot 5p = \frac{1}{5} \cdot 3.75$$
$$p = 0.75$$
Each can cost \$0.75.

26. Let n = the number.
$$\frac{3(n + 2) - 1}{2} = 10$$
$$2 \cdot \frac{3(n + 2) - 1}{2} = 2 \cdot 10$$
$$3(n + 2) - 1 = 20$$
$$3n + 6 - 1 = 20$$
$$3n + 5 = 20$$
$$3n + 5 + (-5) = 20 + (-5)$$
$$3n = 15$$
$$\frac{1}{3} \cdot 3n = \frac{1}{3} \cdot 15$$
$$n = 5$$
The number is 5.

27. Let n = number of days working together.
$\frac{1}{3}$ = amount Ronald does in one day
$\frac{1}{6}$ = amount assistant does in one day
$$n\left(\frac{1}{3} + \frac{1}{6}\right) = 1$$
$$n\left(\frac{2}{6} + \frac{1}{6}\right) = 1$$
$$n\left(\frac{3}{6}\right) = 1$$
$$n\left(\frac{1}{2}\right) = 1$$
$$2 \cdot \frac{1}{2}n = 2 \cdot 1$$
$$n = 2$$
It would take 2 days.

28. Number served per minute by first cashier $= \frac{1}{3}$
Number served per minute by second cashier $= 2$
Number served by both in one hour $= 60\left(\frac{1}{3} + 2\right)$
$$= 60\left(\frac{1}{3} + \frac{6}{3}\right)$$
$$= 60\left(\frac{7}{3}\right)$$
$$= \frac{420}{3}$$
$$= 140$$
140 customers can be served in an hour.

29. Let d = amount before interest.
$$d + 0.05d = 126$$
$$d(1 + 0.05) = 126$$
$$d(1.05) = 126$$
$$\frac{1}{1.05} \cdot 1.05d = \frac{1}{1.05} \cdot 126$$
$$d = 120$$
\$120 was in the account.

30.
$$3x + 2x = 15$$
$$5x = 15$$
$$\frac{1}{5} \cdot 5x = \frac{1}{5} \cdot 15$$
$$x = 3$$

31. $-\frac{1}{2}x + 3 = 1$

$-\frac{1}{2}x + 3 + (-3) = 1 + (-3)$

$-\frac{1}{2}x = -2$

$-2\left(-\frac{1}{2}x\right) = -2(-2)$

$x = 4$

32. $3(4y - 2) = 18$
$12y - 6 = 18$
$12y - 6 + 6 = 18 + 6$
$12y = 24$
$\frac{1}{12} \cdot 12y = \frac{1}{12} \cdot 24$
$y = 2$

33. $12n^3m^2$

34. y^3x

35. $30t^3$

36. $12r^2$

37. $\frac{w}{-5} = -4$
$-5 \cdot \frac{w}{-5} = -5(-4)$
$w = 20$

38. $\frac{1}{2} = -\frac{1}{8}c$
$-8 \cdot \frac{1}{2} = -8\left(-\frac{1}{8}c\right)$
$-4 = c$

39. $\frac{5}{7} = \frac{2}{3}x$
$\frac{3}{2} \cdot \frac{5}{7} = \frac{3}{2} \cdot \frac{2}{3}x$
$\frac{15}{14} = x$

40. $\frac{4}{9}y = 2$
$\frac{9}{4} \cdot \frac{4}{9}y = \frac{9}{4} \cdot 2$
$y = \frac{18}{4} = \frac{9}{2}$

LESSON 3-5 TRY THIS p. 137

a. $7y + 5 = 2y + 10$
$7y - 2y + 5 = 2y - 2y + 10$
$5y + 5 = 10$
$5y + 5 - 5 = 10 - 5$
$5y = 5$
$\frac{1}{5} \cdot 5y = \frac{1}{5} \cdot 5$
$y = 1$

b. $5 - 2p = 3p - 5$
$5 - 2p + 2p = 3p + 2p - 5$
$5 = 5p - 5$
$5 + 5 = 5p - 5 + 5$
$10 = 5p$
$\frac{1}{5}(10) = \frac{1}{5} \cdot 5p$
$2 = p$

c. $7x - 17 + 2x = 2 - 8x + 15$
$9x - 17 = 17 - 8x$
$9x + 8x - 17 = 17 - 8x + 8x$
$17x - 17 = 17$
$17x - 17 + 17 = 17 + 17$
$17x = 34$
$\frac{1}{17} \cdot 17x = \frac{1}{17} \cdot 34$
$x = 2$

d. $3n - 15 = 5n + 3 - 4n$
$3n - 15 = n + 3$
$3n - n - 15 = n - n + 3$
$2n - 15 = 3$
$2n - 15 + 15 = 3 + 15$
$2n = 18$
$\frac{1}{2} \cdot 2n = \frac{1}{2} \cdot 18$
$n = 9$

e. $3(7 + 2x) = 30 + 7(x - 1)$
$21 + 6x = 30 + 7x - 7$
$21 + 6x = 23 + 7x$
$21 + 6x - 6x = 23 + 7x - 6x$
$21 = 23 + x$
$21 - 23 = 23 - 23 + x$
$-2 = x$

f. $4(3 + 5y) - 4 = 3 + 2(y - 2)$
$12 + 20y - 4 = 3 + 2y - 4$
$8 + 20y = 2y - 1$
$8 + 20y - 2y = 2y - 2y - 1$
$8 + 18y = -1$
$8 - 8 + 18y = -1 - 8$
$18y = -9$
$\frac{1}{18} \cdot 18y = \frac{1}{18} \cdot (-9)$
$y = -\frac{9}{18} = -\frac{1}{2}$

LESSON 3-5 EXERCISES pp. 137–138

1. $4x - 7 = 3x$
$4x - 3x - 7 = 3x - 3x$
$x - 7 = 0$
$x - 7 + 7 = 7$
$x = 7$

2. $9x - 6 = 3x$
$9x - 3x - 6 = 3x - 3x$
$6x - 6 = 0$
$6x - 6 + 6 = 6$
$6x = 6$
$\frac{1}{6}(6x) = \frac{1}{6}(6)$
$x = 1$

3. $8x - 1 = 23 - 4x$
$8x + 4x - 1 = 23 - 4x + 4x$
$12x - 1 = 23$
$12x - 1 + 1 = 23 + 1$
$12x = 24$
$\frac{1}{12}(12x) = \frac{1}{12}(24)$
$x = 2$

4. $5y - 2 = 28 - y$
$5y + y - 2 = 28 - y + y$
$6y - 2 = 28$
$6y - 2 + 2 = 28 + 2$
$6y = 30$
$\frac{1}{6}(6y) = \frac{1}{6}(30)$
$y = 5$

5. $2x - 1 = 4 + x$
$2x - x - 1 = 4 + x - x$
$x - 1 = 4$
$x - 1 + 1 = 4 + 1$
$x = 5$

6. $5x - 2 = 6 + x$
$5x - x - 2 = 6 + x - x$
$4x - 2 = 6$
$4x - 2 + 2 = 6 + 2$
$4x = 8$
$\frac{1}{4}(4x) = \frac{1}{4} \cdot 8$
$x = 2$

7. $6x + 3 = 2x + 11$
$6x - 2x + 3 = 2x - 2x + 11$
$4x + 3 = 11$
$4x + 3 - 3 = 11 - 3$
$4x = 8$
$\frac{1}{4}(4x) = \frac{1}{4} \cdot 8$
$x = 2$

8. $5y + 3 = 2y + 15$
$5y - 2y + 3 = 2y - 2y + 15$
$3y + 3 = 15$
$3y + 3 - 3 = 15 - 3$
$3y = 12$
$\frac{1}{3}(3y) = \frac{1}{3} \cdot 12$
$y = 4$

9. $5 - 2x = 3x - 7x + 25$
$5 - 2x = -4x + 25$
$5 - 2x + 4x = -4x + 4x + 25$
$5 + 2x = 25$
$5 - 5 + 2x = 25 - 5$
$2x = 20$
$\frac{1}{2}(2x) = \frac{1}{2} \cdot 20$
$x = 10$

10.
$$\begin{aligned} 10 - 3x &= 2x - 8x + 40 \\ 10 - 3x &= -6x + 40 \\ 10 - 3x + 6x &= -6x + 6x + 40 \\ 10 + 3x &= 40 \\ 10 - 10 + 3x &= 40 - 10 \\ 3x &= 30 \\ \tfrac{1}{3}(3x) &= \tfrac{1}{3}(30) \\ x &= 10 \end{aligned}$$

11.
$$\begin{aligned} 4 + 3x - 6 &= 3x + 2 - x \\ 3x - 2 &= 2x + 2 \\ 3x - 2x - 2 &= 2x - 2x + 2 \\ x - 2 &= 2 \\ x - 2 + 2 &= 2 + 2 \\ x &= 4 \end{aligned}$$

12.
$$\begin{aligned} 5 + 4x - 7 &= 4x + 3 - x \\ 4x - 2 &= 3x + 3 \\ 4x - 3x - 2 &= 3x - 3x + 3 \\ x - 2 &= 3 \\ x - 2 + 2 &= 3 + 2 \\ x &= 5 \end{aligned}$$

13. Let n = the number.
$$\begin{aligned} 3n - 2 &= 2n + 3 \\ 3n - 2 + 2 &= 2n + 3 + 2 \\ 3n &= 2n + 5 \\ 3n - 2n &= 2n - 2n + 5 \\ n &= 5 \end{aligned}$$
The number is 5.

14. Let n = the number.
$$\begin{aligned} 2n - 3 &= 3n + 2 \\ 2n - 3 - 2 &= 3n + 2 - 2 \\ 2n - 5 &= 3n \\ 2n - 2n - 5 &= 3n - 2n \\ -5 &= n \end{aligned}$$
The number is -5.

15.
$$\begin{aligned} 5r - (2r + 8) &= 16 \\ 5r - 2r - 8 &= 16 \\ 3r - 8 &= 16 \\ 3r - 8 + 8 &= 16 + 8 \\ 3r &= 24 \\ \tfrac{1}{3}(3r) &= \tfrac{1}{3}(24) \\ r &= 8 \end{aligned}$$

16.
$$\begin{aligned} 6b - (3b + 8) &= 16 \\ 6b - 3b - 8 &= 16 \\ 3b - 8 &= 16 \\ 3b - 8 + 8 &= 16 + 8 \\ 3b &= 24 \\ \tfrac{1}{3}(3b) &= \tfrac{1}{3}(24) \\ b &= 8 \end{aligned}$$

17.
$$\begin{aligned} 3g - 3 &= 3(7 - g) \\ 3g - 3 &= 21 - 3g \\ 3g + 3g - 3 &= 21 - 3g + 3g \\ 6g - 3 &= 21 \\ 6g - 3 + 3 &= 21 + 3 \\ 6g &= 24 \\ \tfrac{1}{6}(6g) &= \tfrac{1}{6}(24) \\ g &= 4 \end{aligned}$$

18.
$$\begin{aligned} 3d - 10 &= 5(d - 4) \\ 3d - 10 &= 5d - 20 \\ 3d - 3d - 10 &= 5d - 3d - 20 \\ -10 &= 2d - 20 \\ -10 + 20 &= 2d \\ 10 &= 2d \\ \tfrac{1}{2}(10) &= \tfrac{1}{2}(2d) \\ 5 &= d \end{aligned}$$

19.
$$\begin{aligned} 5(d + 4) &= 7(d - 2) \\ 5d + 20 &= 7d - 14 \\ 5d - 5d + 20 &= 7d - 5d - 14 \\ 20 &= 2d - 14 \\ 20 + 14 &= 2d - 14 + 14 \\ 34 &= 2d \\ \tfrac{1}{2}(34) &= \tfrac{1}{2}(2d) \\ 17 &= d \end{aligned}$$

20.
$$\begin{aligned} 9(t + 2) &= 3(t - 2) \\ 9t + 18 &= 3t - 6 \\ 9t - 3t + 18 &= 3t - 3t - 6 \\ 6t + 18 &= -6 \\ 6t + 18 - 18 &= -6 - 18 \\ 6t &= -24 \\ \tfrac{1}{6}(6t) &= \tfrac{1}{6}(-24) \\ t &= -4 \end{aligned}$$

21.
$$\begin{aligned} 8(3t - 2) &= 4(7t - 1) \\ 24t - 16 &= 28t - 4 \\ 24t - 28t - 16 &= 28t - 28t - 4 \\ -4t - 16 &= -4 \\ -4t - 16 + 16 &= -4 + 16 \\ -4t &= 12 \\ \tfrac{1}{-4}(-4t) &= \tfrac{1}{-4}(12) \\ t &= -3 \end{aligned}$$

22.
$$\begin{aligned} 7(5x - 2) &= 6(6x - 1) \\ 35x - 14 &= 36x - 6 \\ 35x - 35x - 14 &= 36x - 35x - 6 \\ -14 &= x - 6 \\ -14 + 6 &= x - 6 + 6 \\ -8 &= x \end{aligned}$$

23.
$$\begin{aligned} 3(r - 6) + 2 &= 4(r + 2) - 21 \\ 3r - 18 + 2 &= 4r + 8 - 21 \\ 3r - 16 &= 4r - 13 \\ 3r - 3r - 16 &= 4r - 3r - 13 \\ -16 &= r - 13 \\ -16 + 13 &= r - 13 + 13 \\ -3 &= r \end{aligned}$$

24.
$$\begin{aligned} 5(t + 3) + 9 &= 3(t - 2) + 6 \\ 5t + 15 + 9 &= 3t - 6 + 6 \\ 5t + 24 &= 3t \\ 5t - 3t + 24 &= 3t - 3t \\ 2t + 24 &= 0 \\ 2t + 24 - 24 &= -24 \\ 2t &= -24 \\ \tfrac{1}{2}(2t) &= \tfrac{1}{2}(-24) \\ t &= -12 \end{aligned}$$

25.
$$\begin{aligned} 19 - (2x + 3) &= 2(x + 3) + x \\ 19 - 2x - 3 &= 2x + 6 + x \\ -2x + 16 &= 3x + 6 \\ -2x + 2x + 16 &= 3x + 2x + 6 \\ 16 &= 5x + 6 \\ 16 - 6 &= 5x + 6 - 6 \\ 10 &= 5x \\ \tfrac{1}{5}(10) &= \tfrac{1}{5}(5x) \\ 2 &= x \end{aligned}$$

26.
$$\begin{aligned} 13 - (2c + 2) &= 2(c + 2) + 3c \\ 13 - 2c - 2 &= 2c + 4 + 3c \\ 11 - 2c &= 5c + 4 \\ 11 - 2c + 2c &= 5c + 2c + 4 \\ 11 &= 7c + 4 \\ 11 - 4 &= 7c + 4 - 4 \\ 7 &= 7c \\ \tfrac{1}{7}(7) &= \tfrac{1}{7}(7c) \\ 1 &= c \end{aligned}$$

27.
$$\begin{aligned} \tfrac{1}{4}(8y + 4) - 17 &= \tfrac{-1}{2}(4y - 8) \\ 2y + 1 - 17 &= -2y + 4 \\ 2y - 16 &= -2y + 4 \\ 2y + 2y - 16 &= -2y + 2y + 4 \\ 4y - 16 &= 4 \\ 4y - 16 + 16 &= 4 + 16 \\ 4y &= 20 \\ \tfrac{1}{4}(4y) &= \tfrac{1}{4}(20) \\ y &= 5 \end{aligned}$$

28. $\frac{1}{3}(6x + 24) - 20 = \frac{-1}{4}(12x - 72)$

$$\begin{aligned} 2x + 8 - 20 &= -3x + 18 \\ 2x - 12 &= -3x + 18 \\ 2x + 3x - 12 &= -3x + 3x + 18 \\ 5x - 12 &= 18 \\ 5x - 12 + 12 &= 18 + 12 \\ 5x &= 30 \\ \tfrac{1}{5}(5x) &= \tfrac{1}{5}(30) \\ x &= 6 \end{aligned}$$

29. Let p = the length of each plank.

$$\begin{aligned} 3p + 1 &= 4p - 2 \\ 3p + 1 + 2 &= 4p - 2 + 2 \\ 3p + 3 &= 4p \\ 3p - 3p + 3 &= 4p - 3p \\ 3 &= p \end{aligned}$$

Each plank was 3 ft long.

30.

$$\begin{aligned} \frac{2x + 4}{4} &= 3x - 4 \\ 4 \cdot \left(\frac{2x + 4}{4}\right) &= 4(3x - 4) \\ 2x + 4 &= 12x - 16 \\ 2x - 2x + 4 &= 12 - 2x - 16 \\ 4 &= 10x - 16 \\ 4 + 16 &= 10x - 16 + 16 \\ 20 &= 10x \\ \frac{1}{10} \cdot 20 &= \frac{1}{10} \cdot 10x \\ 2 &= x \end{aligned}$$

31.

$$\begin{aligned} \frac{3x - 14}{-2} &= 3x - 2 \\ -2\left(\frac{3x - 14}{-2}\right) &= -2(3x - 2) \\ 3x - 14 &= -6x + 4 \\ 3x + 6x - 14 &= -6x + 6x + 4 \\ 9x - 14 &= 4 \\ 9x - 14 + 14 &= 4 + 14 \\ 9x &= 18 \\ \frac{1}{9} \cdot 9x &= \frac{1}{9} \cdot 18 \\ x &= 2 \end{aligned}$$

32.

$$\begin{aligned} 5(x - 1) &= \frac{2(x + 4)}{-2} \\ -2 \cdot 5(x - 1) &= -2\left(\frac{2(x + 4)}{-2}\right) \\ -10(x - 1) &= 2(x + 4) \\ -10x + 10 &= 2x + 8 \\ -10x + 10x + 10 &= x + 10x + 8 \\ 10 &= 12x + 8 \\ 10 - 8 &= 12x + 8 - 8 \\ 2 &= 12x \\ \frac{1}{12} \cdot 2 &= \frac{1}{12} \cdot 12x \\ \frac{1}{6} &= x \end{aligned}$$

33.

$$\begin{aligned} -4(2x + 2) &= \frac{-4(x + 1)}{4} \\ 4 \cdot (-4)(2x + 2) &= 4\left(\frac{-4(x + 1)}{4}\right) \\ -16(2x + 2) &= -4(x + 1) \\ -32x - 32 &= -4x - 4 \\ -32x + 32x - 32 &= -4x + 32x - 4 \\ -32 &= 28x - 4 \\ -32 + 4 &= 28x - 4 + 4 \\ -28 &= 28x \\ \frac{1}{28} \cdot (-28) &= \frac{1}{28} \cdot 28x \\ -1 &= x \end{aligned}$$

34. Let h = number of additional hours.

$$\begin{aligned} 3 + 4h &= 13 \\ 3 - 3 + 4h &= 13 - 3 \\ 4h &= 10 \\ \frac{1}{4} \cdot 4h &= \frac{1}{4} \cdot 10 \\ h &= \frac{10}{4} = 2\frac{1}{2} \end{aligned}$$

It will take $2\frac{1}{2}$ more hours.

35. **a.** $2x + 4 + x = 4 + 3x$

$3x + 4 = 4 + 3x$

True for all values of x, so the equation is an identity.

b. $2(x - 3) + 5 = 3(x - 2) + 5$

$$\begin{aligned} 2x - 6 + 5 &= 3x - 6 + 5 \\ 2x - 1 &= 3x - 1 \\ 2x - 2x - 1 &= 3x - 2x - 1 \\ -1 &= x - 1 \\ -1 + 1 &= x - 1 + 1 \\ 0 &= x \end{aligned}$$

True only for $x = 0$, so the equation is not an identity.

36.

$$\begin{aligned} a - b(x + c) &= d \\ a - bx - bc &= d \\ a - a - bx - bc + bc &= d - a + bc \\ -bx &= d - a + bc \\ -\frac{1}{b}(-bx) &= -\frac{1}{b}(d - a + bc) \\ x &= \frac{d - a + bc}{-b} \end{aligned}$$

37.

$$\begin{aligned} a(bx - c) &= d - (x + e) \\ abx - ac &= d - x - e \\ abx - ac + ac &= d - x - e + ac \\ abx + x &= d - x + x - e + ac \\ abx + x &= d - e + ac \\ x(ab + 1) &= d - e + ac \\ \frac{1}{ab + 1} \cdot x(ab + 1) &= \frac{1}{ab + 1} \cdot (d - e + ac) \\ x &= \frac{d - e + ac}{ab + 1} \end{aligned}$$

38. There are three terms on each side. There are two ways to group each set of three terms, so four equations are possible:

$(4 - 2x) - 3 = (2 - x) + 1$

$(4 - 2x) - 3 = 2 - (x + 1)$

$4 - (2x - 3) = (2 - x) + 1$

$4 - (2x - 3) = 2 - (x + 1)$

Solving:

$$\begin{aligned} (4 - 2x) - 3 &= (2 - x) + 1 \\ 4 - 2x - 3 &= 2 - x + 1 \\ 1 - 2x &= 3 - x \\ 1 - 2x + 2x &= 3 - x + 2x \\ 1 &= 3 + x \\ 1 - 3 &= 3 - 3 + x \\ -2 &= x \end{aligned}$$

$$\begin{aligned} (4 - 2x) - 3 &= 2 - (x + 1) \\ 4 - 2x - 3 &= 2 - x - 1 \\ 1 - 2x &= 1 - x \\ 1 - 2x + 2x &= 1 - x + 2x \\ 1 &= 1 + x \\ 1 - 1 &= 1 - 1 + x \\ 0 &= x \end{aligned}$$

$$\begin{aligned} 4 - (2x - 3) &= (2 - x) + 1 \\ 4 - 2x + 3 &= 2 - x + 1 \\ 7 - 2x &= 3 - x \\ 7 - 2x + 2x &= 3 - x + 2x \\ 7 &= 3 + x \\ 7 - 3 &= 3 - 3 + x \\ 4 &= x \end{aligned}$$

$$\begin{aligned} 4 - (2x - 3) &= 2 - (x + 1) \\ 4 - 2x + 3 &= 2 - x - 1 \\ 7 - 2x &= 1 - x \\ 7 - 2x + 2x &= 1 - x + 2x \\ 7 &= 1 + x \\ 7 - 1 &= 1 - 1 + x \\ 6 &= x \end{aligned}$$

There are 4 equations with 4 different solutions, $-2, 0, 4, 6$.

39. $\frac{2}{5}x + \frac{1}{7}y - \frac{3}{5}x + \frac{2}{7}y = x\left(\frac{2}{5} - \frac{3}{5}\right) + y\left(\frac{1}{7} + \frac{2}{7}\right)$
$$= -\frac{1}{5}x + \frac{3}{7}y$$

40. $\frac{3}{8}m - \frac{7}{8}n + \frac{1}{8}m + \frac{3}{8}n = m\left(\frac{3}{8} + \frac{1}{8}\right) + n\left(\frac{-7}{8} + \frac{3}{8}\right)$
$$= \frac{4}{8}m - \frac{4}{8}n$$
$$= \frac{1}{2}m - \frac{1}{2}n$$

41. $\frac{2}{3}a - \frac{1}{3}a + \frac{4}{9} - \frac{1}{9} = a\left(\frac{2}{3} - \frac{1}{3}\right) + \frac{3}{9}$
$$= \frac{1}{3}a + \frac{1}{3}$$

42. $3 + 2n$ 43. $5(n - 2)$ 44. $\frac{n}{2} + 4$

LESSON 3-6 TRY THIS p. 140

a.
$$\begin{aligned} \frac{7}{8}x + \frac{3}{4} &= \frac{1}{2}x + \frac{3}{2} \\ 8\left(\frac{7}{8}x + \frac{3}{4}\right) &= 8\left(\frac{1}{2}x + \frac{3}{2}\right) \\ 8 \cdot \frac{7}{8}x + 8 \cdot \frac{3}{4} &= 8 \cdot \frac{1}{2}x + 8 \cdot \frac{3}{2} \\ 7x + 6 &= 4x + 12 \\ 7x - 4x + 6 &= 4x - 4x + 12 \\ 3x + 6 &= 12 \\ 3x + 6 - 6 &= 12 - 6 \\ 3x &= 6 \\ \frac{1}{3} \cdot 3x &= \frac{1}{3} \cdot 6 \\ x &= 2 \end{aligned}$$

b.
$$\begin{aligned} \frac{5}{6}x + \frac{1}{2} &= \frac{2}{3}x + 4 \\ 6\left(\frac{5}{6}x + \frac{1}{2}\right) &= 6\left(\frac{2}{3}x + 4\right) \\ 6 \cdot \frac{5}{6}x + 6 \cdot \frac{1}{2} &= 6 \cdot \frac{2}{3}x + 6 \cdot 4 \\ 5x + 3 &= 4x + 24 \\ 5x - 4x + 3 &= 4x - 4x + 24 \\ x + 3 &= 24 \\ x + 3 - 3 &= 24 - 3 \\ x &= 21 \end{aligned}$$

c.
$$\begin{aligned} 26.45 &= 4.2x + 1.25 \\ 100(26.45) &= 100(4.2x + 1.25) \\ 2645 &= 420x + 125 \\ 2645 - 125 &= 420x + 125 - 125 \\ 2520 &= 420x \\ \frac{1}{420} \cdot 2520 &= \frac{1}{420} \cdot 420x \\ 6 &= x \end{aligned}$$

d.
$$\begin{aligned} 41.68 &= 4.7 - 8.6y \\ 100(41.68) &= 100(4.7 - 8.6y) \\ 4168 &= 470 - 860y \\ 4168 - 470 &= 470 - 470 - 860y \\ 3698 &= -860y \\ \frac{1}{-860} \cdot 3698 &= \frac{1}{-860} \cdot -860y \\ -4.3 &= y \end{aligned}$$

LESSON 3-6 EXERCISES pp. 140–141

1. The only denominator is 4, so multiply both sides of the equation by 4.
2. The only denominator is 3, so multiply both sides of the equation by 3.
3. The least common denominator for $\frac{3}{4}$ and $\frac{3}{8}$ is 8. Multiply both sides of the equation by 8.
4. The least common denominator for $\frac{4}{5}, \frac{7}{15}$, and $\frac{1}{5}$ is 15. Multiply both sides of the equation by 15.
5. The least common denominator for $\frac{1}{3}, \frac{1}{2}$, and $\frac{5}{6}$ is 6. Multiply both sides of the equation by 6.
6. The least common denominator for $\frac{3}{4}, \frac{1}{6}$, and $\frac{2}{3}$ is 12. Multiply both sides of the equation by 12.

7.
$$\begin{aligned} \frac{7}{2}x + \frac{1}{2}x &= 3x + \frac{3}{2} + \frac{5}{2}x \\ 2\left(\frac{7}{2}x + \frac{1}{2}x\right) &= 2\left(3x + \frac{3}{2} + \frac{5}{2}x\right) \\ 7x + x &= 6x + 3 + 5x \\ 8x &= 11x + 3 \\ 8x - 11x &= 11x - 11x + 3 \\ -3x &= 3 \\ -\frac{1}{3}(-3x) &= -\frac{1}{3} \cdot 3 \\ x &= -1 \end{aligned}$$

8.
$$\begin{aligned} \frac{1}{2} + 4m &= 3m - \frac{5}{2} \\ \frac{1}{2} + 4m - 3m &= 3m - 3m - \frac{5}{2} \\ \frac{1}{2} + m &= -\frac{5}{2} \\ \frac{1}{2} - \frac{1}{2} + m &= -\frac{5}{2} - \frac{1}{2} \\ m &= -\frac{6}{2} = -3 \end{aligned}$$

9.
$$\begin{aligned} \frac{5}{3} + \frac{2}{3}x &= \frac{25}{12} + \frac{5}{4}x + \frac{3}{4} \\ 12\left(\frac{5}{3} + \frac{2}{3}x\right) &= 12\left(\frac{25}{12} + \frac{5}{4}x + \frac{3}{4}\right) \\ 20 + 8x &= 25 + 15x + 9 \\ 20 + 8x &= 34 + 15x \\ 20 + 8x - 8x &= 34 + 15x - 8x \\ 20 &= 34 + 7x \\ 20 - 34 &= 34 - 34 + 7x \\ -14 &= 7x \\ \frac{1}{7}(-14) &= \frac{1}{7} \cdot 7x \\ -2 &= x \end{aligned}$$

10.
$$\begin{aligned} 1 - \frac{2}{3}y &= \frac{9}{5} - \frac{y}{5} + \frac{3}{5} \\ 15\left(1 - \frac{2}{3}y\right) &= 15\left(\frac{9}{5} - \frac{y}{5} + \frac{3}{5}\right) \\ 15 - 10y &= 27 - 3y + 9 \\ 15 - 10y &= 36 - 3y \\ 15 - 10y + 10y &= 36 - 3y + 10y \\ 15 &= 36 + 7y \\ 15 - 36 &= 36 - 36 + 7y \\ -21 &= 7y \\ \frac{1}{7}(-3) &= \frac{1}{7} \cdot 7y \\ -3 &= y \end{aligned}$$

11.
$$\begin{aligned} \frac{4}{5}x - \frac{3}{4}x &= \frac{3}{10}x - 1 \\ 20\left(\frac{4}{5}x - \frac{3}{4}x\right) &= 20\left(\frac{3}{10}x - 1\right) \\ 16x - 15x &= 6x - 20 \\ x &= 6x - 20 \\ x - 6x &= 6x - 6x - 20 \\ -5x &= -20 \\ -\frac{1}{5}(-5x) &= -\frac{1}{5}(-20) \\ x &= 4 \end{aligned}$$

12.
$$\begin{aligned}\tfrac{8}{5}y - \tfrac{2}{3}y &= 23 - \tfrac{1}{15}y\\ 15\left(\tfrac{8}{5}y - \tfrac{2}{3}y\right) &= 15\left(23 - \tfrac{1}{15}y\right)\\ 24y - 10y &= 345 - y\\ 14y &= 345 - y\\ 14y + y &= 345 - y + y\\ 15y &= 345\\ \tfrac{1}{15}\cdot 15y &= \tfrac{1}{15}\cdot 345\\ y &= 23\end{aligned}$$

13.
$$\begin{aligned}\tfrac{7}{8}x - \tfrac{1}{4} + \tfrac{3}{4}x &= \tfrac{1}{16} + x\\ 16\left(\tfrac{7}{8}x - \tfrac{1}{4} + \tfrac{3}{4}x\right) &= 16\left(\tfrac{1}{16} + x\right)\\ 14x - 4 + 12x &= 1 + 16x\\ 26x - 4 &= 1 + 16x\\ 26x - 16x - 4 &= 1 + 16x - 16x\\ 10x - 4 &= 1\\ 10x - 4 + 4 &= 1 + 4\\ 10x &= 5\\ \tfrac{1}{10}\cdot 10x &= \tfrac{1}{10}\cdot 5\\ x &= \tfrac{5}{10} = \tfrac{1}{2}\end{aligned}$$

14.
$$\begin{aligned}\tfrac{2}{3} + \tfrac{1}{4}t &= \tfrac{1}{3}\\ 12\left(\tfrac{2}{3} + \tfrac{1}{4}t\right) &= 12\left(\tfrac{1}{3}\right)\\ 8 + 3t &= 4\\ 8 - 8 + 3t &= 4 - 8\\ 3t &= -4\\ \tfrac{1}{3}\cdot 3t &= \tfrac{1}{3}\cdot(-4)\\ t &= -\tfrac{4}{3}\end{aligned}$$

15.
$$\begin{aligned}-\tfrac{3}{2} + x &= -\tfrac{5}{6} - \tfrac{4}{3}\\ 6\left(-\tfrac{3}{2} + x\right) &= 6\left(-\tfrac{5}{6} - \tfrac{4}{3}\right)\\ -9 + 6x &= -5 - 8\\ -9 + 6x &= -13\\ -9 + 9 + 6x &= -13 + 9\\ 6x &= -4\\ \tfrac{1}{6}\cdot 6x &= \tfrac{1}{6}(-4)\\ x &= -\tfrac{4}{6} = -\tfrac{2}{3}\end{aligned}$$

16.
$$\begin{aligned}\tfrac{2}{3} + 3y &= 5y - \tfrac{2}{15}\\ 15\left(\tfrac{2}{3} + 3y\right) &= 15\left(5y - \tfrac{2}{15}\right)\\ 10 + 45y &= 75y - 2\\ 10 + 45y - 45y &= 75y - 45y - 2\\ 10 &= 30y - 2\\ 10 + 2 &= 30y - 2 + 2\\ 12 &= 30y\\ \tfrac{1}{30}\cdot 12 &= \tfrac{1}{30}\cdot 30y\\ y &= \tfrac{12}{30} = \tfrac{2}{5}\end{aligned}$$

17.
$$\begin{aligned}\tfrac{2}{7}x + \tfrac{1}{2}x &= \tfrac{3}{4}x + 1\\ 28\left(\tfrac{2}{7}x + \tfrac{1}{2}x\right) &= 28\left(\tfrac{3}{4}x + 1\right)\\ 8x + 14x &= 21x + 28\\ 22x &= 21x + 28\\ 22x - 21x &= 21x - 21x + 28\\ x &= 28\end{aligned}$$

18.
$$\begin{aligned}\tfrac{5}{16}y + \tfrac{3}{8}y &= 2 + \tfrac{1}{4}y\\ 16\left(\tfrac{5}{16}y + \tfrac{3}{8}y\right) &= 16\left(2 + \tfrac{1}{4}y\right)\\ 5y + 6y &= 32 + 4y\\ 11y &= 32 + 4y\\ 11y - 4y &= 32 + 4y - 4y\\ 7y &= 32\\ \tfrac{1}{7}\cdot 7y &= \tfrac{1}{7}\cdot 32\\ y &= \tfrac{32}{7}\end{aligned}$$

19.
$$\begin{aligned}2.1x + 45.2 &= 3.2 - 8.4x\\ 10(2.1x + 45.2) &= 10(3.2 - 8.4x)\\ 21x + 452 &= 32 - 84x\\ 21x + 84x + 452 &= 32 - 84x + 84x\\ 105x + 452 &= 32\\ 105x + 452 - 452 &= 32 - 452\\ 105x &= -420\\ \tfrac{1}{105}\cdot 105x &= \tfrac{1}{105}(-420)\\ x &= -4\end{aligned}$$

20.
$$\begin{aligned}0.96y - 0.79 &= 0.21y + 0.46\\ 100(0.96y - 0.79) &= 100(0.21y + 0.46)\\ 96y - 79 &= 21y + 46\\ 96y - 21y - 79 &= 21y - 21y + 46\\ 75y - 79 &= 46\\ 75y - 79 + 79 &= 46 + 79\\ 75y &= 125\\ \tfrac{1}{75}\cdot 75y &= \tfrac{1}{75}(125)\\ y &= \tfrac{125}{75} = \tfrac{5}{3} \quad \text{or about} \quad 1.67\end{aligned}$$

21.
$$\begin{aligned}1.03 - 0.62x &= 0.71 - 0.22x\\ 100(1.03 - 0.62x) &= 100(0.71 - 0.22x)\\ 103 - 62x &= 71 - 22x\\ 103 - 62x + 62x &= 71 - 22x + 62x\\ 103 &= 71 + 40x\\ 103 - 71 &= 71 - 71 + 40x\\ 32 &= 40x\\ \tfrac{1}{40}\cdot 32 &= \tfrac{1}{40}\cdot 40x\\ x &= \tfrac{32}{40} = \tfrac{4}{5} \quad \text{or} \quad 0.8\end{aligned}$$

22.
$$\begin{aligned}0.42 - 0.03y &= 3.33 - y\\ 100(0.42 - 0.03y) &= 100(3.33 - y)\\ 42 - 3y &= 333 - 100y\\ 42 - 3y + 100y &= 333 - 100y + 100y\\ 42 + 97y &= 333\\ 42 - 42 + 97y &= 333 - 42\\ 97y &= 291\\ y &= 3\end{aligned}$$

23.
$$\begin{aligned}1.7t + 8 - 1.62t &= 0.4t - 0.32 + 8\\ 100(1.7t + 8 - 1.62t) &= 100(0.4t - 0.32 + 8)\\ 170t + 800 - 162t &= 40t - 32 + 800\\ 8t + 800 &= 40t + 768\\ 8t - 8t + 800 &= 40t - 8t + 768\\ 800 &= 32t + 768\\ 800 - 768 &= 32t + 768 - 768\\ 32 &= 32t\\ \tfrac{1}{32}\cdot 32 &= \tfrac{1}{32}\cdot 32t\\ 1 &= t\end{aligned}$$

24.
$$\begin{aligned}0.7n - 15 + n &= 2n - 8 - 0.4n\\ 10(0.7n - 15 + n) &= 10(2n - 8 - 0.4n)\\ 7n - 150 + 10n &= 20n - 80 - 4n\\ 17n - 150 &= 16n - 80\\ 17n - 16n - 150 &= 16n - 16n - 80\\ n - 150 &= -80\\ n - 150 + 150 &= -80 + 150\\ n &= 70\end{aligned}$$

25.
$$\begin{aligned}7\tfrac{1}{2}x - \tfrac{1}{2}x &= 3\tfrac{3}{4}x + 39\\ 7x &= 3\tfrac{3}{4}x + 39\\ 4\cdot 7x &= 4\left(3\tfrac{3}{4}x + 39\right)\\ 28x &= 15x + 156\\ 28x - 15x &= 15x - 15x + 156\\ 13x &= 156\\ \tfrac{1}{13}\cdot 13x &= \tfrac{1}{13}\cdot 156\\ x &= 12\end{aligned}$$

26. $$\frac{1}{5}t - 0.4 + \frac{2}{5}t = 0.6 - \frac{1}{10}t$$
$$10\left(\frac{1}{5}t - 0.4 + \frac{2}{5}t\right) = 10\left(0.6 - \frac{1}{10}t\right)$$
$$2t - 4 + 4t = 6 - t$$
$$6t - 4 = 6 - t$$
$$6t + t - 4 = 6 - t + t$$
$$7t - 4 = 6$$
$$7t - 4 + 4 = 6 + 4$$
$$7t = 10$$
$$\frac{1}{7}\cdot 7t = \frac{1}{7}\cdot 10$$
$$t = \frac{10}{7}$$

27. $$\frac{1}{4}(8y + 4) - 17 = -\frac{1}{2}(4y - 8)$$
$$4\left(\frac{1}{4}(8y + 4)\right) - 4\cdot 17 = 4\left(-\frac{1}{2}\right)(4y - 8)$$
$$8y + 4 - 68 = -2(4y - 8)$$
$$8y - 64 = -8y + 16$$
$$8y + 8y - 64 = -8y + 8y + 16$$
$$16y - 64 = 16$$
$$16y - 64 + 64 = 16 + 64$$
$$16y = 80$$
$$\frac{1}{16}\cdot 16y = \frac{1}{16}\cdot 80$$
$$y = 5$$

28. $$\frac{1}{3}(6x + 24) - 20 = -\frac{1}{4}(12x - 72)$$
$$12\left(\frac{1}{3}(6x + 24)\right) - 12\cdot 20 = 12\left(-\frac{1}{4}\right)(12x - 72)$$
$$4(6x + 24) - 240 = -3(12x - 72)$$
$$24x + 96 - 240 = -36x + 216$$
$$24x - 144 = -36x + 216$$
$$24x + 36x - 144 = -36x + 36x + 216$$
$$60x - 144 = 216$$
$$60x - 144 + 144 = 216 + 144$$
$$60x = 360$$
$$\frac{1}{60}\cdot 60x = \frac{1}{60}\cdot 360$$
$$x = 6$$

29. $$30{,}000 + 20{,}000x = 55{,}000$$
$$30{,}000 - 30{,}000 + 20{,}000x = 55{,}000 - 30{,}000$$
$$20{,}000x = 25{,}000$$
$$\frac{1}{20{,}000}\cdot 20{,}000x = \frac{1}{20{,}000}\cdot 25{,}000$$
$$x = \frac{25{,}000}{20{,}000} = \frac{5}{4}$$

30. $$25{,}000(4 + 3x) = 125{,}000$$
$$\frac{1}{25{,}000}\cdot 25{,}000(4 + 3x) = \frac{1}{25{,}000}\cdot 125{,}000$$
$$4 + 3x = 5$$
$$4 - 4 + 3x = 5 - 4$$
$$3x = 1$$
$$\frac{1}{3}\cdot 3x = \frac{1}{3}\cdot 1$$
$$x = \frac{1}{3}$$

31. Let n = Diophantus's age at death.
$$\frac{1}{6}n + \frac{1}{12}n + \frac{1}{7}n + 5 + \frac{1}{2}n + 4 = n$$
$$84\left(\frac{1}{6}n + \frac{1}{12}n + \frac{1}{7}n + 5 + \frac{1}{2}n + 4\right) = 84n$$
$$14n + 7n + 12n + 420 + 42n + 336 = 84n$$
$$75n + 756 = 84n$$
$$75n - 75n + 756 = 84n - 75n$$
$$756 = 9n$$
$$\frac{1}{9}\cdot 756 = \frac{1}{9}\cdot 9n$$
$$84 = n$$
Diophantus was 84 years old.

32. Let x = number of apples.
$$\frac{1}{3}x + \frac{1}{4}x + \frac{1}{8}x + \frac{1}{5}x + 10 + 1 = x$$
$$120\left(\frac{1}{3}x + \frac{1}{4}x + \frac{1}{8}x + \frac{1}{5}x + 10 + 1\right) = 120x$$
$$40x + 30x + 15x + 24x + 1200 + 120 = 120x$$
$$109x + 1320 = 120x$$
$$109x - 109x + 1320 = 120x - 109x$$
$$1320 = 11x$$
$$\frac{1}{11}\cdot 1320 = \frac{1}{11}\cdot x$$
$$x = 120$$
There were 120 apples in the basket.

33. Let n = number of sheets to start.
Willy took $\frac{1}{4}n$, leaving $\frac{3}{4}n$ for Sara.
Sara took $\frac{1}{3}$ of this $\left(\frac{1}{3}\cdot\frac{3}{4}n = \frac{1}{4}n\right)$, leaving $\frac{3}{4}n - \frac{1}{4}n = \frac{1}{2}n$ for Marcy.
Marcy took $\frac{1}{6}$ of this $\left(\frac{1}{6}\cdot\frac{1}{2}n = \frac{1}{12}n\right)$, leaving 30 for Carol.
$$\frac{1}{4}n + \frac{1}{4}n + \frac{1}{12}n + 30 = n$$
$$12\left(\frac{1}{4}n + \frac{1}{4}n + \frac{1}{12}n + 30\right) = 12n$$
$$3n + 3n + n + 360 = 12n$$
$$7n + 360 = 12n$$
$$7n - 7n + 360 = 12n - 7n$$
$$360 = 5n$$
$$\frac{1}{5}\cdot 360 = \frac{1}{5}\cdot 5n$$
$$72 = n$$
There were 72 sheets to start.

34. $<$ **35.** $>$ **36.** $<$ **37.** $<$ **38.** $\frac{n}{2} + 7$

39. $2n - 5$ **40.** $2(n + 3)$

41. $$-4(2t + 7) = -4$$
$$-8t - 28 = -4$$
$$-8t - 28 + 28 = -4 + 28$$
$$-8t = 24$$
$$-\frac{1}{8}\cdot -8t = -\frac{1}{8}\cdot 24$$
$$t = -3$$

42. $$3a + 2(2a + 5) = 3$$
$$3a + 4a + 10 = 3$$
$$7a + 10 = 3$$
$$7a + 10 - 10 = 3 - 10$$
$$7a = -7$$
$$\frac{1}{7}\cdot 7a = \frac{1}{7}\cdot(-7)$$
$$a = -1$$

43. $$x + \frac{1}{3}x = 8$$
$$3\left(x + \frac{1}{3}x\right) = 3\cdot 8$$
$$3x + x = 24$$
$$4x = 24$$
$$\frac{1}{4}\cdot 4x = \frac{1}{4}\cdot 24$$
$$x = 6$$

44. $$x + \frac{1}{4}x = 10$$
$$4\left(x + \frac{1}{4}x\right) = 4\cdot 10$$
$$4x + x = 40$$
$$5x = 40$$
$$\frac{1}{5}\cdot 5x = 40\cdot\frac{1}{5}$$
$$x = 8$$

45. $$\frac{3}{8}y + \frac{3}{4}y = 3$$
$$8\left(\frac{3}{8}y + \frac{3}{4}y\right) = 8\cdot 3$$
$$3y + 6y = 24$$
$$9y = 24$$
$$\frac{1}{9}\cdot 9y = \frac{1}{9}\cdot 24$$
$$y = \frac{24}{9} = \frac{8}{3}$$

46. $9x^2 - 4 = 9(-2)^2 - 4 = 9(4) - 4 = 36 - 4 = 32$

47. $\frac{1}{2}x^3 + 32 = \frac{1}{2}(-2)^3 + 32 = \frac{1}{2}(-8) + 32 = -4 + 32 = 28$

LESSON 3-7 TRY THIS pp. 142–143

a. $C = 2\pi r$

$\frac{1}{2\pi} \cdot C = \frac{1}{2\pi} \cdot 2\pi r$

$\frac{C}{2\pi} = r$

b. $P = 2l + 35$

$P - 35 = 2l + 35 - 35$ Addition property

$P - 35 = 2l$ Simplify.

$\frac{1}{2}(P - 35) = \frac{1}{2} \cdot 2l$ Multiplication Property

$\frac{P - 35}{2} = l$ Simplify.

c. $A = \frac{a + b + c + d}{4}$

$4A = 4\left(\frac{a + b + c + d}{4}\right)$

$4A = a + b + c + d$

$4A - a - b - d = a + b + c + d - a - b - d$

$4A - a - b - d = c$

d. $r = \frac{y}{n}$

$n \cdot r = n \cdot \frac{y}{n}$

$nr = y$

$\frac{1}{r} \cdot nr = \frac{1}{r} \cdot y$

$n = \frac{y}{r}$

LESSON 3-7 EXERCISES pp. 143–144

1. $A = bh$

$\frac{1}{h} \cdot A = bh \cdot \frac{1}{h}$

$\frac{A}{h} = b$

2. $A = bh$

$\frac{1}{b} \cdot A = bh \cdot \frac{1}{b}$

$\frac{A}{b} = h$

3. $d = rt$

$\frac{1}{t} \cdot d = rt \cdot \frac{1}{t}$

$\frac{d}{t} = r$

4. $d = rt$

$\frac{1}{r} \cdot d = rt \cdot \frac{1}{r}$

$\frac{d}{r} = t$

5. $I = Prt$

$\frac{1}{rt} \cdot I = Prt \cdot \frac{1}{rt}$

$\frac{I}{rt} = P$

6. $I = Prt$

$\frac{1}{Pr} \cdot I = Prt \cdot \frac{1}{Pr}$

$\frac{I}{Pr} = t$

7. $F = ma$

$\frac{1}{m} \cdot F = ma \cdot \frac{1}{m}$

$\frac{F}{m} = a$

8. $F = ma$

$\frac{1}{a} \cdot F = ma \cdot \frac{1}{a}$

$\frac{F}{a} = m$

9. $P = 2l + 2w$

$P - 2l = 2w$

$\frac{1}{2} \cdot (P - 2l) = 2w \cdot \frac{1}{2}$

$\frac{P - 2l}{2} = w$

10. $P = 2l + 2w$

$P - 2w = 2l$

$\frac{1}{2}(P - 2w) = 2l \cdot \frac{1}{2}$

$\frac{P - 2w}{2} = 1$

11. $A = \pi r^2$

$\frac{1}{\pi} \cdot A = \pi r^2 \cdot \frac{1}{\pi}$

$\frac{A}{\pi} = r^2$

12. $A = \pi r^2$

$\frac{1}{r^2} \cdot A = \pi r^2 \cdot \frac{1}{r^2}$

$\frac{A}{r^2} = \pi$

13. $A = \frac{1}{2}bh$

$\frac{2}{h} \cdot A = \frac{1}{2}bh \cdot \frac{2}{h}$

$\frac{2A}{h} = b$

14. $A = \frac{1}{2}bh$

$\frac{2}{b} \cdot A = \frac{1}{2}bh \cdot \frac{2}{b}$

$\frac{2A}{b} = h$

15. $E = mc^2$

$\frac{1}{c^2} \cdot E = mc^2 \cdot \frac{1}{c^2}$

$\frac{E}{c^2} = m$

16. $E = mc^2$

$\frac{1}{m} \cdot E = mc^2 \cdot \frac{1}{m}$

$\frac{E}{m} = c^2$

17. $A = \frac{a + b + c}{3}$

$3 \cdot A = \frac{a + b + c}{3} \cdot 3$

$3A = a + b + c$

$3A - a - c = b$

18. $A = \frac{a + b + c}{3}$

$3 \cdot A = \frac{a + b + c}{3} \cdot 3$

$3A = a + b + c$

$3A - a - b = c$

19. $v = \frac{3k}{t}$

$vt = \frac{3k}{t} \cdot t$

$vt = 3k$

$\frac{1}{v} \cdot t = 3k \cdot \frac{1}{v}$

$t = \frac{3k}{v}$

20. $P = \frac{ab}{c}$

$cP = \frac{ab}{c} \cdot c$

$cP = ab$

$\frac{1}{P} \cdot cP = ab \cdot \frac{1}{P}$

$c = \frac{ab}{P}$

21. $A = \frac{\pi r^2 S}{360}$

$\frac{360}{\pi r^2} \cdot A = \frac{\pi r^2 S}{360} \cdot \frac{360}{\pi r^2}$

$\frac{360A}{\pi r^2} = S$

22. $A = \frac{\pi r^2 S}{360}$

$\frac{360}{\pi S} \cdot A = \frac{\pi r^2 S}{360} \cdot \frac{360}{\pi S}$

$\frac{360A}{\pi S} = r^2$

23. $H = \frac{D^2 N}{2.5}$

$\frac{2.5}{N} \cdot H = \frac{D^2 N}{2.5} \cdot \frac{2.5}{N}$

$\frac{2.5H}{N} = D^2$

24. $H = \frac{D^2 N}{2.5}$

$\frac{2.5}{D^2} \cdot H = \frac{D^2 N}{2.5} \cdot \frac{2.5}{D^2}$

$\frac{2.5H}{D^2} = N$

25. $A = \frac{1}{R}$

$R \cdot A = \frac{1}{R} \cdot R$ Multiplication property

$\frac{1}{A} \cdot RA = 1 \cdot \frac{1}{A}$ Simplify; multiplication property

$R = \frac{1}{A}$ Simplify.

26. $g = 40n + 20k$

$g - 40n = 20k$ Addition property; simplify.

$\frac{g - 40n}{20} = k$ Multiplication property; simplify.

27. $r = 2h - \frac{1}{4}f$

$-4(r - 2h) = \left(-\frac{1}{4}f\right)(-4)$ Multiplication property

$-4r + 8h = f$ Distributive property; simplify.

28. $\frac{s}{t} = \frac{t}{v}$

$t \cdot \frac{s}{t} = \frac{t}{v} \cdot t$ Multiplication property

$s = \frac{t^2}{v}$ Simplify

29. $a^2 = b^2 + 2xc$

$a^2 - b^2 = b^2 - b^2 + 2xc$ Addition property

$a^2 - b^2 = 2xc$ Simplify.

$\frac{1}{2c}(a^2 - b^2) = \frac{1}{2c} \cdot 2xc$ Multiplication property

$\frac{a^2 - b^2}{2c} = x$ Simplify.

30.
$$m = ax^2 + bx + c$$
$$m - ax^2 - c = bx \quad \text{Addition property; simplify.}$$
$$\left(\frac{1}{x}\right)(m - ax^2 - c) = bx\left(\frac{1}{x}\right) \quad \text{Multiplication property}$$
$$\frac{m - ax^2 - c}{x} = b \quad \text{Simplify.}$$

31. $\frac{a}{b} = \frac{c}{d}$

$b \cdot \frac{a}{b} = \frac{c}{d} \cdot b$ Multiplication property

$a = \frac{cb}{d}$ Simplify.

$\frac{1}{c} \cdot a = \frac{cb}{d} \cdot \frac{1}{c}$ Multiplication property

$\frac{a}{c} = \frac{b}{d}$ Simplify.

32.
$$d = \frac{1}{e + f}$$
$(e + f) \cdot d = \frac{1}{e + f}(e + f)$ Multiplication property

$\left(\frac{1}{d}\right)(e + f)d = 1\left(\frac{1}{d}\right)$ Simplify; multiplication property

$e + f = \frac{1}{d}$ Simplify.

$f = \frac{1}{d} - e$ Addition property; simplify

33.
$l = a + (n - 1)d$

$l = a + nd - d$ Distributive property

$l - a + d = a + nd - d - a + d$ Addition property

$l - a + d = nd$ Simplify.

$(l - a + d) \cdot \frac{1}{d} = nd \cdot \frac{1}{d}$ Multiplication property

$\frac{d - a + l}{d} = n$ Simplify.

34. No, a may be $-b$.

35.
$$R = -0.00625t + 3.85$$
$$R - 3.85 = -0.00625t$$
$$\frac{1}{-0.00625}(R - 3.85) = \left(\frac{1}{-0.00625}\right)(-0.00625t)$$
$$-160R + 616 = t$$

36. by taking the square root of D^2; $D = \sqrt{\frac{2.5H}{N}}$

37.
$$y = a - ab$$
$$y = a(1 - b)$$
$$\left(\frac{1}{1 - b}\right)y = a(1 - b)\left(\frac{1}{1 - b}\right)$$
$$\frac{y}{1 - b} = a$$

38.
$$ax + b = cb$$
$$ax + b - b = cb - b$$
$$ax = b(c - 1)$$
$$\frac{1}{c - 1} \cdot ax = b(c - 1) \cdot \frac{1}{c - 1}$$
$$\frac{ax}{c - 1} = b$$

39.
$$x = a + b - 2ab$$
$$x = b + a(1 - 2b)$$
$$x - b = b - b + a(1 - 2b)$$
$$x - b = a(1 - 2b)$$
$$\frac{1}{1 - 2b} \cdot (x - b) = a(1 - 2b) \cdot \frac{1}{1 - 2b}$$
$$\frac{x - b}{1 - 2b} = a$$

40.
$$x - a = a(y - b)$$
$$x - a = ay - ab$$
$$x - a + a = ay - ab + a$$
$$x = ay - ab + a$$
$$x = a(y - b + 1)$$
$$\frac{1}{y - b + 1}x = a(y - b + 1)\frac{1}{y - b + 1}$$
$$\frac{x}{y - b + 1} = a$$

41.
$$2p - q = 2r - s$$
$$2(2p - q) = 2(2r - s)$$
$$4p - 2q = 4r - 2s$$
$$4p + 2s - 2q = 4r - 2s + 2s$$
$$4p + 2s - 2q = 4r$$
$$4p + 2s - 2q + 2q = 4r + 2q$$
$$4p + 2s = 4r + 2q$$

42.
$$\frac{a}{b - c} = d$$
$$(b - c)\frac{a}{b - c} = (b - c)d$$
$$a = (b - c)d$$
$$a = bd - cd$$
$$a + cd = bd - cd + cd$$
$$a + cd = bd$$
$$\frac{1}{d}(a + cd) = \frac{1}{d}(bd)$$
$$\frac{a + cd}{d} = b$$

The answer is B.

43. $4x + 12 = 4 \cdot x + 4 \cdot 3 = 4(x + 3)$

44. $3c + 12d - 9 = 3 \cdot c + 3 \cdot 4d - 3 \cdot 3$
$= 3(c + 4d - 3)$

45. $2x + 3y - 4x = (2 - 4)x + 3y$
$= -2x + 3y$ or $3y - 2x$

46. $8a - 3c + 4 - 2a = (8 - 2)a - 3c + 4$
$= 6a - 3c + 4$

47.
$$16 - 2c = 4c - 2$$
$$16 - 2c + 2c = 4c + 2c - 2$$
$$16 = 6c - 2$$
$$16 + 2 = 6c - 2 + 2$$
$$18 = 6c$$
$$\frac{1}{6} \cdot 18 = \frac{1}{6} \cdot 6c$$
$$3 = c$$

48.
$$1.7m + 16.8 = 25.8 - 0.55m$$
$$100(1.7m + 16.8) = 100(25.8 - 0.55m)$$
$$170m + 1680 = 2580 - 55m$$
$$170m + 55m + 1680 = 2580 - 55m + 55m$$
$$225m + 1680 = 2580$$
$$225m + 1680 - 1680 = 2580 - 1680$$
$$225m = 900$$
$$\frac{1}{225} \cdot 225m = \frac{1}{225} \cdot 900$$
$$m = 4$$

49. $\frac{1}{2}(8m + 4) + 2 = \frac{1}{3}(18m - 18)$
$$4m + 2 + 2 = 6m - 6$$
$$4m + 4 = 6m - 6$$
$$4m - 4m + 4 = 6m - 4m - 6$$
$$4 = 2m - 6$$
$$4 + 6 = 2m - 6 + 6$$
$$10 = 2m$$
$$\frac{1}{2} \cdot 10 = \frac{1}{2} \cdot 2m$$
$$5 = m$$

50. $$\frac{2}{5} + 3y = 10y - 1$$
$$5\left(\frac{2}{5} + 3y\right) = 5(10y - 1)$$
$$2 + 15y = 50y - 5$$
$$2 + 15y - 15y = 50y - 15y - 5$$
$$2 = 35y - 5$$
$$2 + 5 = 35y - 5 + 5$$
$$7 = 35y$$
$$\frac{1}{35} \cdot 7 = \frac{1}{35} \cdot 35y$$
$$\frac{7}{35} = y$$
$$y = \frac{1}{5}$$

51. $$15.4 - 9.1t = 2.4t - 19.1$$
$$10(15.4 - 9.1t) = 10(2.4t - 19.1)$$
$$154 - 91t = 24t - 191$$
$$154 - 91t + 91t = 24t + 91t - 191$$
$$154 = 115t - 191$$
$$154 + 191 = 115t - 191 + 191$$
$$345 = 115t$$
$$\frac{1}{115} \cdot 345 = \frac{1}{115} \cdot 115t$$
$$\frac{345}{115} = t$$
$$t = 3$$

52. $$27 - 3(t + 4) = 9(t - 2) - 15$$
$$27 - 3t - 12 = 9t - 18 - 15$$
$$15 - 3t = 9t - 33$$
$$15 - 3t + 3t = 9t + 3t - 33$$
$$15 = 12t - 33$$
$$15 + 33 = 12t - 33 + 33$$
$$48 = 12t$$
$$\frac{1}{12} \cdot 48 = \frac{1}{12} \cdot 12t$$
$$\frac{48}{12} = t$$
$$t = 4$$

LESSON 3-8 TRY THIS p. 145

a. $|y| = 17$
$y = 17$ or $y = -17$

b. $$|y| - 5 = 1$$
$$|y| - 5 + 5 = 1 + 5$$
$$|y| = 6$$
$y = 6$ or $y = -6$

c. $$2|x| + 1 = 15$$
$$2|x| + 1 - 1 = 15 - 1$$
$$2|x| = 14$$
$$\frac{1}{2} \cdot 2|x| = \frac{1}{2} \cdot 14$$
$$|x| = 7$$
$x = 7$ or $x = -7$

LESSON 3-8 EXERCISES pp. 146–147

1. $|x| = 19$
$x = 19$ or $x = -19$

2. $|y| = 9$
$y = 9$ or $y = -9$

3. $4 = |m|$
$m = 4$ or $m = -4$

4. $|n| = 7$
$n = 7$ or $n = -7$

5. $|h| = 0$
$h = 0$

6. $3 = |a|$
$a = 3$ or $a = -3$

7. $|b| = 12$
$b = 12$ or $b = -12$

8. $|x| = 15$
$x = 15$ or $x = -15$

9. $|a| = |-2|$
$|a| = 2$
$a = 2$ or $a = -2$

10. $|-20| = |-x|$
$20 = |-x|$
$-x = 20$ or $-x = -20$
$x = -20$ or $x = 20$

11. $|y| = 12 - 5$
$|y| = 7$
$y = 7$ or $y = -7$

12. $$|y| + 5 = 16$$
$$|y| + 5 - 5 = 16 - 5$$
$$|y| = 11$$
$y = 11$ or $y = -11$

13. $$|a| - 7 = 21$$
$$|a| - 7 + 7 = 21 + 7$$
$$|a| = 28$$
$a = 28$ or $a = -28$

14. $$4 + |m| = 9$$
$$4 - 4 + |m| = 9 - 4$$
$$|m| = 5$$
$m = 5$ or $m = -5$

15. $$-2 + |n| = 0$$
$$-2 + 2 + |n| = 0 + 2$$
$$|n| = 2$$
$n = 2$ or $n = -2$

16. $$|x| + 3 + 9 = 15$$
$$|x| + 12 = 15$$
$$|x| + 12 - 12 = 15 - 12$$
$$|x| = 3$$
$x = 3$ or $x = -3$

17. $$5 + |x| - 9 = 2$$
$$-4 + |x| = 2$$
$$-4 + 4 + |x| = 2 + 4$$
$$|x| = 6$$
$x = 6$ or $x = -6$

18. $$|x| - 23 = 34$$
$$|x| - 23 + 23 = 34 + 23$$
$$|x| = 57$$
$x = 57$ or $x = -57$

19. $$|-4| + |-6| + |m| = 10$$
$$4 + 6 + |m| = 10$$
$$10 + |m| = 10$$
$$10 - 10 + |m| = 10 - 10$$
$$|m| = 0$$
$$m = 0$$

20. $$|-8| + |x| = |-8| + |-3|$$
$$8 + |x| = 8 + 3$$
$$8 - 8 + |x| = 8 - 8 + 3$$
$$|x| = 3$$
$x = 3$ or $x = -3$

21. $$5|x| = 35$$
$$\frac{1}{5} \cdot 5|x| = 35 \cdot \frac{1}{5}$$
$$|x| = 7$$
$x = 7$ or $x = -7$

22. $$3|y| = 27$$
$$\frac{1}{3} \cdot 3|y| = 27 \cdot \frac{1}{3}$$
$$|y| = 9$$
$y = 9$ or $y = -9$

23. $$2|x| + 6 = 12$$
$$2|x| + 6 - 6 = 12 - 6$$
$$2|x| = 6$$
$$\frac{1}{2} \cdot 2|x| = 6 \cdot \frac{1}{2}$$
$$|x| = 3$$
$x = 3$ or $x = -3$

24. $$4|r| - 2 = 18$$
$$4|r| - 2 + 2 = 18 + 2$$
$$4|r| = 20$$
$$\frac{1}{4} \cdot 4|r| = 20 \cdot \frac{1}{4}$$
$$|r| = 5$$
$r = 5$ or $r = -5$

25. $$\frac{|m|}{4} = 5$$
$$4\left(\frac{|m|}{4}\right) = 4 \cdot 5$$
$$|m| = 20$$
$m = 20$ or $m = -20$

26. $$\begin{aligned} \frac{|t|}{-2} &= -9 \\ -2\left(\frac{|t|}{-2}\right) &= -2(-9) \\ |t| &= 18 \\ t = 18 \quad &\text{or} \quad t = -18 \end{aligned}$$

27. $$\begin{aligned} -4|x| &= -5 \\ -\tfrac{1}{4} \cdot -4|x| &= -5 \cdot -\tfrac{1}{4} \\ |x| &= \tfrac{5}{4} \\ x = \tfrac{5}{4} \quad &\text{or} \quad x = -\tfrac{5}{4} \end{aligned}$$

28. $$\begin{aligned} 4|x| + |-4| &= |-6| \\ 4|x| + 4 &= 6 \\ 4|x| + 4 - 4 &= 6 - 4 \\ 4|x| &= 2 \\ \tfrac{1}{4} \cdot 4|x| &= 2 \cdot \tfrac{1}{4} \\ |x| &= \tfrac{2}{4} = \tfrac{1}{2} \\ x = \tfrac{1}{2} \quad &\text{or} \quad x = -\tfrac{1}{2} \end{aligned}$$

29. $$\begin{aligned} -3|a| - 5 &= -17 \\ -3|a| - 5 + 5 &= -17 + 5 \\ -3|a| &= -12 \\ -\tfrac{1}{3} \cdot -3|a| &= -12 \cdot -\tfrac{1}{3} \\ |a| &= 4 \\ a = 4 \quad &\text{or} \quad a = -4 \end{aligned}$$

30. $$\begin{aligned} -2|b| + 4 &= 2 \\ -2|b| + 4 - 4 &= 2 - 4 \\ -2|b| &= -2 \\ -\tfrac{1}{2} \cdot -2|b| &= -2 \cdot -\tfrac{1}{2} \\ |b| &= 1 \\ b = 1 \quad &\text{or} \quad b = -1 \end{aligned}$$

31. $$\begin{aligned} \frac{|x|}{5} + 7 &= 42 \\ \frac{|x|}{5} + 7 - 7 &= 42 - 7 \\ \frac{|x|}{5} &= 35 \\ 5\left(\frac{|x|}{5}\right) &= 5 \cdot 35 \\ |x| &= 175 \\ x = 175 \quad &\text{or} \quad x = -175 \end{aligned}$$

32. $$\begin{aligned} \tfrac{1}{4} + \tfrac{1}{2}|x| &= \tfrac{5}{8} \\ \tfrac{1}{4} - \tfrac{1}{4} + \tfrac{1}{2}|x| &= \tfrac{5}{8} - \tfrac{1}{4} \\ \tfrac{1}{2}|x| &= \tfrac{3}{8} \\ 2\left(\tfrac{1}{2}|x|\right) &= 2\left(\tfrac{3}{8}\right) \\ |x| &= \tfrac{3}{4} \\ x = \tfrac{3}{4} \quad &\text{or} \quad x = -\tfrac{3}{4} \end{aligned}$$

33. The absolute value of a number cannot be negative.

34. true for $x = 2$; false for $x = -2$

35. true for $x = -2$; false for $x = 2$

36. true for $x = 2$; false for $x = -2$

37. true for $x = -2$; false for $x = 2$

38. true for $x = 2, y = 3$; false for $x = -2, y = 3$

39. true for $x = -2, y = 3$; false for $x = 2, y = 3$

40. $$\begin{aligned} -|x| &= -4 \\ (-1)(-|x|) &= (-1)(-4) \\ |x| &= 4 \\ x = 4 \quad &\text{or} \quad x = -4 \end{aligned}$$

41. $$\begin{aligned} -12 &= -|y| \\ (-1)(-12) &= (-1)(-|y|) \\ 12 &= |y| \\ y = 12 \quad &\text{or} \quad y = -12 \end{aligned}$$

42. $$\begin{aligned} -2|a| + 5 &= 1 \\ -2|a| + 5 - 5 &= 1 - 5 \\ -2|a| &= -4 \\ \tfrac{1}{-2}(-2|a|) &= \tfrac{1}{-2}(-4) \\ |a| &= 2 \\ a = 2 \quad &\text{or} \quad a = -2 \end{aligned}$$

43. $$\begin{aligned} 2|x| + 3|x| + 4 &= 24 \\ 5|x| + 4 &= 24 \\ 5|x| + 4 - 4 &= 24 - 4 \\ 5|x| &= 20 \\ \tfrac{1}{5} \cdot 5|x| &= \tfrac{1}{5} \cdot 20 \\ |x| &= 4 \\ x = 4 \quad &\text{or} \quad x = -4 \end{aligned}$$

44. $$\begin{aligned} -3|m| + 5|m| - 3 &= 1 \\ 2|m| - 3 &= 1 \\ 2|m| - 3 + 3 &= 1 + 3 \\ 2|m| &= 4 \\ \tfrac{1}{2} \cdot 2|m| &= \tfrac{1}{2} \cdot 4 \\ |m| &= 2 \\ m = 2 \quad &\text{or} \quad m = -2 \end{aligned}$$

45. $$\begin{aligned} |n| - 3 + 5|n| &= 15 \\ 6|n| - 3 &= 15 \\ 6|n| - 3 + 3 &= 15 + 3 \\ 6|n| &= 18 \\ \tfrac{1}{6} \cdot 6|n| &= \tfrac{1}{6} \cdot 18 \\ |n| &= 3 \\ n = 3 \quad &\text{or} \quad n = -3 \end{aligned}$$

46. $$\begin{aligned} |x| + 12 &= 5|x| - 4 \\ |x| - |x| + 12 &= 5|x| - |x| - 4 \\ 12 &= 4|x| - 4 \\ 12 + 4 &= 4|x| - 4 + 4 \\ 16 &= 4|x| \\ \tfrac{1}{4} \cdot 16 &= \tfrac{1}{4} \cdot 4|x| \\ 4 &= |x| \\ x = 4 \quad &\text{or} \quad x = -4 \end{aligned}$$

47. $$\begin{aligned} 6 - 3|a| &= 2|a| + 1 \\ 6 - 3|a| + 3|a| &= 2|a| + 3|a| + 1 \\ 6 &= 5|a| + 1 \\ 6 - 1 &= 5|a| + 1 - 1 \\ 5 &= 5|a| \\ \tfrac{1}{5} \cdot 5 &= \tfrac{1}{5} \cdot 5|a| \\ 1 &= |a| \\ a = 1 \quad &\text{or} \quad a = -1 \end{aligned}$$

48. $$\begin{aligned} -\tfrac{2}{3}|m| - \tfrac{4}{5} &= -4 \\ 15\left(-\tfrac{2}{3}|m| - \tfrac{4}{5}\right) &= 15(-4) \\ -10|m| - 12 &= -60 \\ -10|m| - 12 + 12 &= -60 + 12 \\ -10|m| &= -48 \\ -\tfrac{1}{10}(-10|m|) &= -\tfrac{1}{10}(-48) \\ |m| &= \tfrac{48}{10} = \tfrac{24}{5} \\ m = \tfrac{24}{5} \quad &\text{or} \quad m = -\tfrac{24}{5} \end{aligned}$$

49. $-\frac{1}{3}|y| + \frac{5}{6} = \frac{1}{6}$
$$6\left(-\frac{1}{3}|y| + \frac{5}{6}\right) = 6\left(\frac{1}{6}\right)$$
$$-2|y| + 5 = 1$$
$$-2|y| + 5 - 5 = 1 - 5$$
$$-2|y| = -4$$
$$\frac{1}{-2}(-2|y|) = \frac{1}{-2}(-4)$$
$$|y| = 2$$
$$y = 2 \text{ or } y = -2$$

50. $|3m| = 6$
$3m = 6$ or $3m = -6$
$\frac{1}{3} \cdot 3m = \frac{1}{3} \cdot 6$ or $\frac{1}{3} \cdot 3m = \frac{1}{3} \cdot (-6)$
$m = 2$ or $m = -2$

51. $|2a| = 8$
$2a = 8$ or $2a = -8$
$\frac{1}{2} \cdot 2a = \frac{1}{2} \cdot 8$ or $\frac{1}{2} \cdot 2a = \frac{1}{2} \cdot (-8)$
$a = 4$ or $a = -4$

52. $|-m| = 5$
$-m = 5$ or $-m = -5$
$(-1)(-m) = (-1)(5)$ or $(-1)(-m) = (-1)(-5)$
$m = -5$ or $m = 5$

53. $|-x| = 7$
$-x = 7$ or $-x = -7$
$(-1)(-x) = (-1)(7)$ or $(-1)(-x) = (-1)(-7)$
$x = -7$ or $x = 7$

54. x **55.** $-x$ **56.** 0

57. $|x + 2| = 7$
$x + 2 = 7$ or $x + 2 = -7$
$x + 2 - 2 = 7 - 2$ or $x + 2 - 2 = -7 - 2$
$x = 5$ or $x = -9$

58. $|m - 4| = 1$
$m - 4 = 1$ or $m - 4 = -1$
$m - 4 + 4 = 1 + 4$ or $m - 4 + 4 = -1 + 4$
$m = 5$ or $m = 3$

59. $|2a + 1| = 5$
$2a + 1 = 5$ or $2a + 1 = -5$
$2a + 1 - 1 = 5 - 1$ or $2a + 1 - 1 = -5 - 1$
$2a = 4$ or $2a = -6$
$\frac{1}{2} \cdot 2a = \frac{1}{2} \cdot 4$ or $\frac{1}{2} \cdot 2a = \frac{1}{2}(-6)$
$a = 2$ or $a = -3$

60. Sometimes; true for $x = -2$ (in fact, for $x < 0$); false for $x = 2$ (in fact, for $x \geq 0$)

61. Always; a number and its opposite are the same distance from 0.

62. Always; $x^2 \geq 0$, so $|x^2| = x^2$.

63. Sometimes; false only for $x = y = 0$.

64. Always; the factors on the right are the same as the factors inside the absolute value symbol on the left, except possibly for a factor of -1 inside the absolute value symbol. The absolute value symbol eliminates the factor of -1.

65. Sometimes; true for $x = 3, y = 2$; false for $x = 3, y = -2$.

66. $x \neq y, x \neq 0$

67. $4 - 3x = 5$
$$4 - 4 - 3x = 5 - 4$$
$$-3x = 1$$
$$-\frac{1}{3} \cdot -3x = -\frac{1}{3} \cdot 1$$
$$x = -\frac{1}{3}$$
Error: $3x = 9$; the correct result is $x = -\frac{1}{3}$.

68. $ax - b = c$
$$-b = c - ax$$
$$-1(-b) = -1(c - ax)$$
$$b = -c + ax \text{ or } ax - c$$
Error: solved for wrong variable; the correct result is $b = ax - c$.

69. $4|c| - 3 = 1$
$$4|c| = 1 + 3$$
$$4|c| = 4$$
$$\frac{1}{4} \cdot (4|c|) = \frac{1}{4} \cdot 4$$
$$|c| = 1$$
$$c = 1 \text{ or } c = -1$$
Error: did not isolate the absolute value first; the correct result is $c = 1$ or $c = -1$.

70. $|x| = -3$
Error: absolute value cannot be negative. There is no solution.

71. $-12t - 4 = 32$
$$-12t - 4 + 4 = 32 + 4$$
$$-12t = 36$$
$$\frac{1}{-12}(-12t) = \frac{1}{-12}(36)$$
$$t = -3$$

72. $3m + 2m + 15 = 35$
$$5m + 15 = 35$$
$$5m + 15 - 15 = 35 - 15$$
$$5m = 20$$
$$\frac{1}{5} \cdot 5m = \frac{1}{5} \cdot 20$$
$$m = 4$$

73. $x + 0.75x = 21$
$$1.75x = 21$$
$$\frac{1}{1.75} \cdot 1.75x = \frac{1}{1.75} \cdot 21$$
$$x = 12$$

74. $\frac{1}{2}n + \frac{2}{5}n = -\frac{9}{10}$
$$10\left(\frac{1}{2}n + \frac{2}{5}n\right) = 10\left(-\frac{9}{10}\right)$$
$$5n + 4n = -9$$
$$9n = -9$$
$$\frac{1}{9} \cdot 9n = \frac{1}{9} \cdot (-9)$$
$$n = -1$$

75. $\frac{2}{5}(m - 4) = 4$
$$5\left(\frac{2}{5}(m - 4)\right) = 5 \cdot 4$$
$$2(m - 4) = 20$$
$$2m - 8 = 20$$
$$2m - 8 + 8 = 20 + 8$$
$$2m = 28$$
$$\frac{1}{2} \cdot 2m = \frac{1}{2} \cdot 28$$
$$m = 14$$

76. $2x - \frac{1}{2}x + \frac{3}{4}x - 4x = \left(2 - \frac{1}{2} + \frac{3}{4} - 4\right)x$
$$= \left(\frac{8}{4} - \frac{2}{4} + \frac{3}{4} - \frac{16}{4}\right)x$$
$$= -\frac{7}{4}x$$

77. $3a - \frac{2}{5}b - \frac{1}{2}a - 6b = \left(3 - \frac{1}{2}\right)a + \left(-\frac{2}{5} - 6\right)b$
$$= \left(\frac{6}{2} - \frac{1}{2}\right)a + \left(-\frac{2}{5} - \frac{30}{5}\right)b$$
$$= \frac{5}{2}a - \frac{32}{5}b$$

78. $5x + \frac{2}{3}y - \frac{1}{4}x + y = \left(5 - \frac{1}{4}\right)x + \left(\frac{2}{3} + 1\right)y$
$$= \left(\frac{20}{4} - \frac{1}{4}\right)x + \left(\frac{2}{3} + \frac{3}{3}\right)y$$
$$= \frac{19}{4}x + \frac{5}{3}y$$

79. Let $n =$ the first integer,
$n + 2 =$ the second integer.
$$n + (n + 2) = 94$$
$$n + n + 2 = 94$$
$$2n + 2 = 94$$
$$2n + 2 - 2 = 94 - 2$$
$$2n = 92$$
$$\frac{1}{2} \cdot 2n = \frac{1}{2} \cdot 92$$
$$n = 46$$
The integers are 46 and 48.

80. Let n = the first integer,
$n + 2$ = the second integer,
$n + 4$ = the third integer.

$$n + (n + 2) + (n + 4) = 123$$
$$n + n + 2 + n + 4 = 123$$
$$3n + 6 = 123$$
$$3n + 6 - 6 = 123 - 6$$
$$3n = 117$$
$$\frac{1}{3} \cdot 3n = 117 \cdot \frac{1}{3}$$
$$n = 39$$

The integers are 39, 41, and 43.

81. Let d = measure of second angle,
$3d$ = measure of first angle,
$d + 3d - 60$ = measure of third angle.

$$d + 3d + d + 3d - 60 = 180$$
$$8d - 60 = 180$$
$$8d - 60 + 60 = 180 + 60$$
$$8d = 240$$
$$\frac{1}{8} \cdot 8d = \frac{1}{8} \cdot 240$$
$$d = 30$$

The three angles measure 30°, 90°, and 60°.

82. Let w = width, $2w$ = length.

$$2w + 2 \cdot 2w = 24$$
$$2w + 4w = 24$$
$$6w = 24$$
$$\frac{1}{6} \cdot 6w = \frac{1}{6} \cdot 24$$
$$w = 4$$

The width is 4 m; the length is 8 m.

LESSON 3-9 TRY THIS pp. 148–149

a. $$\frac{3}{5} = \frac{12}{y}$$
$$5y \cdot \frac{3}{5} = 5y \cdot \frac{12}{y}$$
$$3y = 60$$
$$\frac{1}{3} \cdot 3y = \frac{1}{3} \cdot 60$$
$$y = 20$$

b. $$\frac{1}{2} = \frac{x}{5}$$
$$10 \cdot \frac{1}{2} = 10 \cdot \frac{x}{5}$$
$$5 = 2x$$
$$\frac{1}{2} \cdot 5 = \frac{1}{2} \cdot 2x$$
$$\frac{5}{2} = x$$

c. $$\frac{m}{4} = \frac{7}{6}$$
$$24 \cdot \frac{m}{4} = 24 \cdot \frac{7}{6}$$
$$6m = 28$$
$$\frac{1}{6} \cdot 6m = \frac{1}{6} \cdot 28$$
$$m = \frac{28}{6} = \frac{14}{3}$$

d. $$\frac{0.5}{25} = \frac{5}{x}$$
$$25x \cdot \frac{0.5}{25} = 25x \cdot \frac{5}{x}$$
$$0.5x = 125$$
$$\frac{1}{0.5} \cdot 0.5x = \frac{1}{0.5} \cdot 125$$
$$x = 250$$

The distance is 250 km.

e. $$\frac{3}{40} = \frac{10}{x}$$
$$40x \cdot \frac{3}{40} = 40x \cdot \frac{10}{x}$$
$$3x = 400$$
$$\frac{1}{3} \cdot 3x = \frac{1}{3} \cdot 400$$
$$x = \frac{400}{3} = 133\frac{1}{3}$$

They are $133\frac{1}{3}$ miles apart.

LESSON 3-9 EXERCISES pp. 150–151

1. $$\frac{y}{3} = \frac{9}{27}$$
$$27\left(\frac{y}{3}\right) = 27\left(\frac{9}{27}\right)$$
$$9y = 9$$
$$\frac{1}{9} \cdot 9y = 9 \cdot \frac{1}{9}$$
$$y = 1$$

2. $$\frac{7}{8} = \frac{m}{4}$$
$$8\left(\frac{7}{8}\right) = 8\left(\frac{m}{4}\right)$$
$$7 = 2m$$
$$\frac{1}{2} \cdot 7 = 2m \cdot \frac{1}{2}$$
$$\frac{7}{2} = m$$

3. $$\frac{9}{x} = \frac{2}{3}$$
$$3x\left(\frac{9}{x}\right) = 3x\left(\frac{2}{3}\right)$$
$$27 = 2x$$
$$\frac{1}{2} \cdot 27 = 2x \cdot \frac{1}{2}$$
$$\frac{27}{2} = x$$

4. $$\frac{25}{75} = \frac{1}{x}$$
$$75x\left(\frac{25}{75}\right) = 75x\left(\frac{1}{x}\right)$$
$$25x = 75$$
$$\frac{1}{25} \cdot 25x = 75 \cdot \frac{1}{25}$$
$$x = 3$$

5. $$\frac{2}{y} = \frac{5}{9}$$
$$9y\left(\frac{2}{y}\right) = 9y\left(\frac{5}{9}\right)$$
$$18 = 5y$$
$$\frac{1}{5} \cdot 18 = 5y \cdot \frac{1}{5}$$
$$\frac{18}{5} = y$$

6. $$\frac{16}{m} = \frac{1}{4}$$
$$4m\left(\frac{16}{m}\right) = 4m\left(\frac{1}{4}\right)$$
$$64 = m$$

7. $$\frac{8}{5} = \frac{40}{y}$$
$$5y\left(\frac{8}{5}\right) = 5y\left(\frac{40}{y}\right)$$
$$8y = 200$$
$$\frac{1}{8} \cdot 8y = 200 \cdot \frac{1}{8}$$
$$y = 25$$

8. $$\frac{12}{15} = \frac{t}{5}$$
$$15\left(\frac{12}{15}\right) = 15\left(\frac{t}{5}\right)$$
$$12 = 3t$$
$$\frac{1}{3} \cdot 12 = 3t \cdot \frac{1}{3}$$
$$4 = t$$

9. $$\frac{y}{4} = \frac{5}{8}$$
$$8\left(\frac{y}{4}\right) = 8\left(\frac{5}{8}\right)$$
$$2y = 5$$
$$\frac{1}{2} \cdot 2y = 5 \cdot \frac{1}{2}$$
$$y = \frac{5}{2}$$

10. $$\frac{3}{8} = \frac{12}{x}$$
$$8x\left(\frac{3}{8}\right) = 8x\left(\frac{12}{x}\right)$$
$$3x = 96$$
$$\frac{1}{3} \cdot 3x = 96 \cdot \frac{1}{3}$$
$$x = 32$$

11. $$\frac{5}{x} = \frac{9}{11}$$
$$11x\left(\frac{5}{x}\right) = 11x\left(\frac{9}{11}\right)$$
$$55 = 9x$$
$$\frac{1}{9} \cdot 55 = 9x \cdot \frac{1}{9}$$
$$\frac{55}{9} = x$$

12. $$\frac{2}{7} = \frac{5}{y}$$
$$7y\left(\frac{2}{7}\right) = 7y\left(\frac{5}{y}\right)$$
$$2y = 35$$
$$\frac{1}{2} \cdot 2y = 35 \cdot \frac{1}{2}$$
$$y = \frac{35}{2}$$

13. $$\frac{x}{40} = \frac{3}{5}$$
$$40\left(\frac{x}{40}\right) = 40\left(\frac{3}{5}\right)$$
$$x = 24$$

14. $$\frac{n}{20} = \frac{3}{4}$$
$$20\left(\frac{n}{20}\right) = 20\left(\frac{3}{4}\right)$$
$$n = 15$$

15. $$\frac{18}{c} = \frac{2}{7}$$
$$7c\left(\frac{18}{c}\right) = 7c\left(\frac{2}{7}\right)$$
$$126 = 2c$$
$$\frac{1}{2} \cdot 126 = 2c \cdot \frac{1}{2}$$
$$63 = c$$

16. $$\frac{24}{x} = \frac{4}{3}$$
$$3x\left(\frac{24}{x}\right) = 3x\left(\frac{4}{3}\right)$$
$$72 = 4x$$
$$\frac{1}{4} \cdot 72 = 4x \cdot \frac{1}{4}$$
$$18 = x$$

17. $\frac{15}{y} = \frac{10}{8}$

$8y\left(\frac{15}{y}\right) = 8y\left(\frac{10}{8}\right)$

$120 = 10y$

$\frac{1}{10} \cdot 120 = 10y \cdot \frac{1}{10}$

$12 = y$

18. $\frac{63}{144} = \frac{u}{16}$

$144\left(\frac{63}{144}\right) = 144\left(\frac{u}{16}\right)$

$63 = 9u$

$\frac{1}{9} \cdot 63 = 9u \cdot \frac{1}{9}$

$7 = u$

19. $\frac{12}{30} = \frac{10}{k}$

$30k\left(\frac{12}{30}\right) = 30k\left(\frac{10}{k}\right)$

$12k = 300$

$\frac{1}{12} \cdot 12k = 300 \cdot \frac{1}{12}$

$k = 25$

20. $\frac{5}{3} = \frac{y}{42}$

$42\left(\frac{5}{3}\right) = 42\left(\frac{y}{42}\right)$

$70 = y$

21. $\frac{7}{b} = \frac{4}{9}$

$9b\left(\frac{7}{b}\right) = 9b\left(\frac{4}{9}\right)$

$63 = 4b$

$\frac{1}{4} \cdot 63 = 4b \cdot \frac{1}{4}$

$\frac{63}{4} = b$

22. $\frac{100}{a} = \frac{90}{45}$

$\frac{100}{a} = 2$

$a\left(\frac{100}{a}\right) = 2a$

$100 = 2a$

$\frac{1}{2} \cdot 100 = 2a \cdot \frac{1}{2}$

$50 = a$

23. $\frac{4}{5} = \frac{28}{h}$

$5h\left(\frac{4}{5}\right) = 5h\left(\frac{28}{h}\right)$

$4h = 140$

$\frac{1}{4} \cdot 4h = 140 \cdot \frac{1}{4}$

$h = 35$

24. $\frac{y}{18} = \frac{150}{126}$

$126\left(\frac{y}{18}\right) = 126\left(\frac{150}{126}\right)$

$7y = 150$

$\frac{1}{7} \cdot 7y = 150 \cdot \frac{1}{7}$

$y = \frac{150}{7}$

25. $\frac{150}{12} = \frac{500}{x}$

$12x\left(\frac{150}{12}\right) = 12x\left(\frac{500}{x}\right)$

$150x = 6000$

$\frac{1}{150} \cdot 150x = 6000 \cdot \frac{1}{150}$

$x = 40$

40 L of gas are needed.

26. $\frac{3.6}{9} = \frac{x}{315}$

$315\left(\frac{3.6}{9}\right) = 315\left(\frac{x}{315}\right)$

$126 = x$

The pitcher would strike out 126 batters.

27. $\frac{2}{15} = \frac{x}{2}$

$30\left(\frac{2}{15}\right) = 30\left(\frac{x}{2}\right)$

$4 = 15x$

$\frac{1}{15} \cdot 4 = 15x \cdot \frac{1}{15}$

$\frac{4}{15} = x$

It will lose $\frac{4}{15}$ minute.

28. $\frac{2}{15} = \frac{x}{180}$

$180\left(\frac{2}{15}\right) = 180\left(\frac{x}{180}\right)$

$24 = x$

24 adults are needed.

29. $\frac{4}{5} = \frac{64}{x}$

$5x\left(\frac{4}{5}\right) = 5x\left(\frac{64}{x}\right)$

$4x = 320$

$\frac{1}{4} \cdot 4x = 320 \cdot \frac{1}{4}$

$x = 80$

80 shovels are needed.

30. $\frac{2}{35} = \frac{x}{1575}$

$1575\left(\frac{2}{35}\right) = 1575\left(\frac{x}{1575}\right)$

$90 = x$

There are 90 international students.

31. $\frac{8}{20} = \frac{x}{60}$

$60\left(\frac{8}{20}\right) = 60\left(\frac{x}{60}\right)$

$24 = x$

They could load 24 boxes.

32. $\frac{1}{3.27} = \frac{24.5}{x}$

$3.27x\left(\frac{1}{3.27}\right) = 3.27x\left(\frac{24.5}{x}\right)$

$x = 80.115$

The distance is 80.115 km.

33. $\frac{145}{350} = \frac{x}{12{,}250}$

$12{,}250\left(\frac{145}{350}\right) = 12{,}250\left(\frac{x}{12{,}250}\right)$

$5075 = x$

About 5075 people watched.

34. $\frac{52}{250} = \frac{x}{35{,}000}$

$35{,}000\left(\frac{52}{250}\right) = 35{,}000\left(\frac{x}{35{,}000}\right)$

$7280 = x$

About 7280 people favor Channel 5.

35. $\frac{2}{5} = \frac{x}{89{,}841}$

$89{,}841 \cdot \frac{2}{5} = 89{,}841 \cdot \frac{x}{89{,}841}$

$35{,}936 \approx x$

35,936 people are wearing red.

36. $\frac{3000}{60} = \frac{50}{x}$

$60x \cdot \frac{3000}{60} = 60x \cdot \frac{50}{x}$

$3000x = 3000$

$\frac{1}{3000} \cdot 3000x = \frac{1}{3000} \cdot 3000$

$x = 1$

It takes 1 second.

37. $\frac{1}{14} = \frac{x}{168}$ (168 hours in a week)

$168\left(\frac{1}{14}\right) = 168\left(\frac{x}{168}\right)$

$12 = x$

It defrosts during 12 hours of the week.

38. $\frac{5}{2} = \frac{x}{120}$

$120 \cdot \frac{5}{2} = 120 \cdot \frac{x}{120}$

$300 = x$

There are 300 full seats.

The seating capacity is 300 + 120 = 420.

39. $9m = 5n$

$\left(\frac{1}{9n}\right)9m = \left(\frac{1}{9n}\right)5n$

$\frac{m}{n} = \frac{5}{9}$ or $m : n = 5 : 9$

40. a. $\frac{4}{5} = \frac{b}{225}$

$225 \cdot \frac{4}{5} = 225 \cdot \frac{b}{225}$

$180 = b$

There are 180 boys.

The total number of students = 180 + 225 = 405.

b. $$\frac{5}{4} = \frac{g}{225 - g}$$
$$4 \cdot (225 - g) \cdot \frac{5}{4} = 4 \cdot (225 - g) \cdot \frac{g}{225 - g}$$
$$1125 - 5g = 4g$$
$$1125 - 5g + 5g = 4g + 5g$$
$$1125 = 9g$$
$$125 = g$$
There are 125 girls.

41. 1 gallon = 128 oz, so 8 gallons = $8 \cdot 128 = 1024$ oz.
$$\frac{46}{8} = \frac{x}{1024}$$
$$1024 \cdot \frac{46}{8} = 1024 \cdot \frac{x}{1024}$$
$$5888 = x$$
She should guess 5888 marbles.

42. A log cut into 4 pieces has 3 cuts.
A log cut into 8 pieces has 7 cuts.
$$\frac{3}{12} = \frac{7}{x}$$
$$12x\left(\frac{3}{12}\right) = 12x\left(\frac{7}{x}\right)$$
$$3x = 84$$
$$\frac{1}{3} \cdot 3x = \frac{1}{3} \cdot 84$$
$$x = 28$$
It would take 28 minutes.

43. $$\frac{60}{2.5} = \frac{h}{\frac{1}{2}}$$
$$5 \cdot \frac{60}{2.5} = 5 \cdot \frac{h}{\frac{1}{2}}$$
$$120 = 10h$$
$$\frac{1}{10} \cdot 120 = \frac{1}{10} \cdot 10h$$
$$12 = h$$
It must be 12 m tall.

44. $\frac{-32}{-8} = 4$

45. $-\frac{7}{8} \div \frac{1}{4} = -\frac{7}{8} \cdot 4 = -\frac{7}{2}$ or $-3\frac{1}{2}$

46. $\frac{1}{6} \div -\frac{2}{3} = \frac{1}{6} \cdot \left(-\frac{3}{2}\right) = -\frac{1}{4}$

47. $$9a - 6 = 30 - 3a$$
$$9a + 3a - 6 = 30 - 3a + 3a$$
$$12a - 6 = 30$$
$$12a - 6 + 6 = 30 + 6$$
$$12a = 36$$
$$\frac{1}{12} \cdot 12a = \frac{1}{12} \cdot 36$$
$$a = 3$$

48. $$17 - 5c = 2c + 3$$
$$17 - 5c + 5c = 2c + 5c + 3$$
$$17 = 7c + 3$$
$$17 - 3 = 7c + 3 - 3$$
$$14 = 7c$$
$$\frac{1}{7} \cdot 14 = \frac{1}{7} \cdot 7c$$
$$2 = c$$

49. $$-11w = -132$$
$$\frac{1}{-11}(-11w) = \frac{1}{-11}(-132)$$
$$w = 12$$

50. $|x| = 15$
$x = 15$ or $x = -15$

51. $$|c| + 9 = 12$$
$$|c| + 9 - 9 = 12 - 9$$
$$|c| = 3$$
$c = 3$ or $c = -3$

52. $$6|m| = 24$$
$$\frac{1}{6} \cdot 6|m| = \frac{1}{6} \cdot 24$$
$$|m| = 4$$
$m = 4$ or $m = -4$

53. $n = 0$

54. $$4(3x - 12) = 12$$
$$12x - 48 = 12$$
$$12x - 48 + 48 = 12 + 48$$
$$12x = 60$$
$$\frac{1}{12} \cdot 12x = \frac{1}{12} \cdot 60$$
$$x = 5$$

55. $$\frac{x}{3} + 5 = \frac{3x}{5} - \frac{7}{3}$$
$$15\left(\frac{x}{3} + 5\right) = 15\left(\frac{3x}{5} - \frac{7}{3}\right)$$
$$5x + 75 = 9x - 35$$
$$5x - 5x + 75 = 9x - 5x - 35$$
$$75 = 4x - 35$$
$$75 + 35 = 4x - 35 + 35$$
$$110 = 4x$$
$$\frac{1}{4} \cdot 110 = \frac{1}{4} \cdot 4x$$
$$\frac{110}{4} = x = \frac{55}{2}$$

56. $$0.3r - 2.8 = 3.2 - 0.2r$$
$$0.3r + 0.2r - 2.8 = 3.2 - 0.2r + 0.2r$$
$$0.5r - 2.8 = 3.2$$
$$0.5r - 2.8 + 2.8 = 3.2 + 2.8$$
$$0.5r = 6$$
$$\frac{1}{0.5} \cdot 0.5r = \frac{1}{0.5} \cdot 6$$
$$r = 12$$

57. $$y = mx + b$$
$$y - b = mx + b - b$$
$$y - b = mx$$
$$\frac{1}{x}(y - b) = \frac{1}{x} \cdot mx$$
$$\frac{y - b}{x} = m \quad \text{or} \quad \frac{y}{x} - \frac{b}{x} = m$$

58. $$PV = nRT$$
$$\frac{1}{nR} \cdot PV = \frac{1}{nR} \cdot nRT$$
$$\frac{PV}{nR} = T$$

59. $$I = Prt$$
$$\frac{1}{Pt} \cdot I = \frac{1}{Pt} \cdot Prt$$
$$\frac{I}{Pt} = r$$

60. $2w - (3w - 1) = 2w - 3w + 1 = -w + 1$

61. $$2[3x - 2(3x + 4)] = 2[3x - 6x - 8]$$
$$= 6x - 12x - 16$$
$$= -6x - 16$$

LESSON 3-10 TRY THIS pp. 152–155

a. 0.48 **b.** 0.03 **c.** 1.45 **d.** 0.005

e. $\frac{3}{4} = 0.75 = \frac{75}{100} = 75\%$ **f.** $\frac{3}{8} = 0.375 = \frac{37.5}{100} = 37.5\%$

g. $\frac{24.5}{5} = 4.9 = \frac{490}{100} = 490\%$

h. $\frac{12.4}{25} = 0.496 = \frac{49.6}{100} = 49.6\%$

i. $\frac{0.02}{500} = 0.00004 = \frac{0.004}{100} = 0.004\%$

j. $\frac{3}{40} = 0.075 = \frac{7.5}{100} = 7.5\%$

k. $n \cdot 40 = 15$ Translating to an equation
$$n = \frac{15}{40} = .0375 = \frac{37.5}{100}$$
$$n = 37.5\%$$

l. $3 = 0.16 \cdot n$ Translating to an equation
$$\frac{3}{0.16} = n$$
$$n = 18.75$$

m. $0.075 \cdot 80 = n$ Translating to an equation
$$6 = n$$

n. $n = 0.125 \cdot 40$ Translating to an equation
$$n = 5$$

o. Let p = percent of pay that is bonus.
$$p \cdot 2500 = 750$$
$$p = \frac{750}{2500} = 0.30 = \frac{30}{100}$$
$$p = 30\%$$

p. Let p = percent that went toward tuition.
$$p = \frac{1500}{5000} = \frac{30}{100} = 30\%$$

LESSON 3-10 EXERCISES pp. 156–157

1. $41\% = 0.41$
2. $60\% = 0.6$
3. $7\% = 0.07$
4. $1\% = 0.01$
5. $125\% = 1.25$
6. $180\% = 1.8$
7. $0.8\% = 0.008$
8. $0.6\% = 0.006$
9. $1.5\% = 0.015$
10. $2.8\% = 0.028$
11. $\frac{3}{4} = 0.75 = \frac{75}{100} = 75\%$
12. $\frac{1}{25} = 0.04 = \frac{4}{100} = 4\%$
13. $\frac{24}{25} = 0.96 = \frac{96}{100} = 96\%$
14. $\frac{3}{8} = 0.375 = \frac{37.5}{100} = 37.5\%$
15. $\frac{1}{3} \approx 0.333 = \frac{33.3}{100} = 33.3\%$
16. $\frac{3}{25} = 0.12 = \frac{12}{100} = 12\%$
17. $\frac{5}{8} = 0.625 = \frac{62.5}{100} = 62.5\%$
18. $\frac{5}{6} \approx 0.833 = \frac{83.3}{100} = 83.3\%$
19. $\frac{3}{16} \approx 0.188 = \frac{18.8}{100} = 18.8\%$
20. $\frac{1}{20} = 0.05 = \frac{5}{100} = 5\%$

21. $n \cdot 68 = 17$

$n = \frac{17}{68} = 0.25 = \frac{25}{100} = 25\%$

22. $p \cdot 75 = 36$

$p = \frac{36}{75} = 0.48 = \frac{48}{100} = 48\%$

23. $p \cdot 125 = 30$

$p = \frac{30}{125} = 0.24 = \frac{24}{100} = 24\%$

24. $p \cdot 300 = 57; p = \frac{57}{300} - 0.19 = \frac{19}{100} = 19\%$

25. $45 = 0.3x$

$\frac{1}{0.3}(45) = \frac{1}{0.3}(0.3x)$

$150 = x$

26. $20.4 = 0.24x$

$\frac{1}{0.24}(20.4) = \frac{1}{0.24}(0.24x)$

$85 = x$

27. $0.3 = 0.12x$

$\frac{1}{0.12}(0.3) = \frac{1}{0.12}(0.12x)$

$2.5 = x$

28. $7 = 1.75x$

$\frac{1}{1.75}(7) = \frac{1}{1.75}(1.75x)$

$4 = x$

29. $80x = 100$

$x = \frac{100}{80} = 1.25 = 125\%$

30. $10x = 205$

$x = \frac{205}{10} = 20.5 = 2050\%$

31. $x = 0.02(40) = 0.8$

32. $x = 0.4(2) = 0.8$

33. $2 = 40x$

$\frac{1}{40}(2) = \frac{1}{40}(40x)$

$\frac{2}{40} = x$

$x = \frac{1}{20} = 0.05 = 5\%$

34. $40 = 0.02x$

$\frac{1}{0.02}(40) = \frac{1}{0.02}(0.02x)$

$2000 = x$

35. $2 = 0.40x$

$\frac{1}{0.40}(2) = \frac{1}{0.40}(0.40x)$

$5 = x$

36. $40 = 2n; n = \frac{40}{2} = 20 = \frac{2000}{100} = 2000\%$

37. $x = \frac{76}{88} \approx 0.864 = \frac{86.4}{100} = 86.4\%$

38. $x = \frac{13}{25} = 0.52 = \frac{52}{100} = 52\%$

39. $408 = 0.26x$

$\frac{1}{0.26}(408) = \frac{1}{0.26}(0.26x)$

$\$1569.23 = x$

40. $0.0825(\$428.86) \approx \$35.38; \$428.86 + \$35.38 = \$464.24$

41. $0.09(400) = 36\text{ cm}^3; 400 + 36 = 436\text{ cm}^3$

42. $0.05(\$775) = \$38.75$

$\$775 + \$38.75 = \$813.75$

43. $10{,}000 = 7{,}500x$

$\frac{10{,}000}{7{,}500} = x$

$x \approx 1.333 = 133.3\%$

44. **a.** They are equal.

$\frac{50}{100} \cdot 40 = \frac{40}{100} \cdot 50$

b. They are equal.

$\frac{20}{100} \cdot 90 = \frac{90}{100} \cdot 20$

c. They are equal.

$\frac{a}{100} \cdot b = \frac{b}{100} \cdot a$

45. Total = tax + tip + cost of meal

$= (0.06)(16.41) + (0.15)(16.41 + [0.06][16.41]) + 16.41$

$= 0.98 + 2.61 + 16.41$

$= \$20.00$

46. Debby's tax $= (0.07)(12.99) \approx 0.91$

cost $= 12.99 + 0.91$

cost $= \$13.90$

DISCount: discount price $= 14.95 - 2.00 = 12.95$

tax $= (0.07)(14.95) \approx 1.05$

cost $= 12.95 + 1.05$

cost $= \$14.00$

47. Increase $= \$6.24 - \$6 = \$0.24$ an hour

Percent increase $= \frac{0.24}{6} = 0.04 = \frac{4}{100} = 4\%$

48. Decrease $= \$175 - \$150 = \$25$

Percent decrease $= \frac{25}{175} \approx 0.143 = \frac{14.3}{100} = 14.3\%$

49. New dimensions are $37\frac{1}{2}\%$ of original.

width: $7.5 = 0.375x$

$\frac{1}{0.375}(7.5) = \frac{1}{0.375}(0.375x)$

$20 = x$

length: $12.5 = 0.375y$

$\frac{1}{0.375}(12.5) = \frac{1}{0.375}(0.375y)$

$33.3 = y$

The original dimensions were 20 cm by 33.3 cm.

50. New price $= 1.25(8800) = 11{,}000$

Old price is $(11{,}000 - 8800)$ lower than new $= 2200$

$2200 = n \cdot 11{,}000$

$n = \frac{2200}{11{,}000} = 0.20 = \frac{20}{100}$

Old price is 20% lower than new.

51. $x = 1.6y$

$y = \frac{1}{1.6}x = (0.625)x = \frac{62.5}{100}x$

y is 62.5% of x.

52. Discount $= (0.30)(10) = \$3.$

Sale price $= 10 - 3 = \$7$

Tax on \$10 $= (0.05)(10) = \$0.50.$

Tax on \$7 $= (0.05)(7) = \$0.35.$

Tax reduced by $0.50 - 0.35 = \$0.15.$

53. Assume \$100 is invested.

First plan:

First year interest $= (0.05)(100) = \$5.$

Total after 1 year $= 100 + 5 = \$105.$

Second year interest $= (0.10)(105) = \$10.50.$

Total after 2 years $= 105 + 10.50 = \$115.50.$

Second plan:

First year interest $= (0.10)(100) = \$10.$

Total after 1 year $= 100 + 10 = \$110.$

Second year interest $= (0.05)(110) = \$5.50.$

Total after 2 years $= 110 + 5.50 = \$115.50.$

The two plans are equal. Both earn \$15.50 interest on \$100 over two years.

54. If p is the initial price, a discount of 10% results in a sale price of $0.90p$.
Successive discounts of 10%, 10%, 10%, 10% result in a sale price of $(0.9)(0.9)(0.9)(0.9)p = 0.6561p$.
Successive discounts of 10%, 10%, 20% result in a sale price of $(0.8)(0.9)(0.9)p = 0.648p$.
Successive discounts of 20%, 10%, 10% result in a sale price of $(0.9)(0.9)(0.8)p = 0.648p$.
Successive discounts of 10%, then 30% result in a sale price of $(0.7)(0.9)p = 0.63p$.
Successive discounts of 30%, then 10% result in a sale price of $(0.9)(0.7)p = 0.63p$.
Successive discounts of 20%, then 20% result in a sale price of $(0.8)(0.8)p = 0.64p$.
Single discount of 40% results in a sale price of $0.60p$.
Listing from best to worst:

Plan	
40%;	pay 60% of original price.
30%, 10%;	pay 63% of original price.
10%, 30%;	pay 63% of original price.
20%, 20%;	pay 64% of original price.
20%, 10%, 10%;	pay 64.8% of original price.
10%, 10%, 20%;	pay 64.8% of original price.
10%, 10%, 10%, 10%	pay 65.6% of original price.

55. -4.1 **56.** 9 **57.** -16

58. $-4-(-2x)+6x+x+9=-4+2x+6x+x+9$
$= 9x+5$

59. $8c+8-(-2c)=8c+8+2c$
$=10c+8$

60. $-6+5x-(-2x)-4x=-6+5x+2x-4x$
$=3x-6$

61. $2t-(-13)-3t-(-6t)-19=2t+13-3t+6t-19$
$=5t-6$

62. $-6(3.4)(-1)=6(3.4)=20.4$ **63.** $-3.2(0)=0$

64. $-2(-8)(-2)=16(-2)=-32$ **65.** $99\div(-3)=-33$

66. $-72\div 3=-24$ **67.** $45\div(-15)=-3$

LESSON 3-11 TRY THIS pp. 158–160

a. Let g = number of girls,
$\frac{1}{2}g$ = number of boys,
$\frac{1}{2}g + g$ = total number of boys and girls.
Or let b = number of boys,
$2b$ = number of girls,
$b + 2b$ = total number of boys and girls.

b. Let x = the first integer,
$x+2$ = the second integer,
$x+4$ = the third integer.
Sum $= x+x+2+x+4 = 3x+6$

c. Let w = width,
$w+15$ = length.
$2w+2(w+15)=150$
$2w+2w+30=150$
$4w+30=150$
$4w+30-30=150-30$
$4w=20$
$\frac{1}{4}\cdot 4w=\frac{1}{4}\cdot 120$
$w=30$
Width is 30 cm; length is 45 cm.

d. Let x = first integer,
$x+1$ = second integer.
$x+2(x+1)=29$
$x+2x+2=29$
$3x+2=29$
$3x+2-2=29-2$
$3x=27$
$\frac{1}{3}\cdot 3x=\frac{1}{3}\cdot 27$
$x=9$
The integers are 9 and 10.

e. Let n = amount invested.
$n+0.04n=9620$
$1.04n=9620$
$\frac{1}{1.04}\cdot(1.04n)=\frac{1}{1.04}\cdot 9620$
$n=9250$
\$9250 was invested.

LESSON 3-11 EXERCISES pp. 160–162

1. Let c = cost of one CD.
$c+(c-3.50)$ or $2c-3.50$
Let t = cost of one tape.
$t+(t+3.50)$ or $2t+3.50$

2. Let t = points on first test.
$t+\frac{1}{2}t$ or $\frac{3}{2}t$
Let s = points on second test.
$s+2s$ or $3s$

3. Let e = number of English books.
$e+(e-9)$ or $2e-9$
Let m = number of math books.
$m+(m+9)$ or $2m+9$

4. Let s = number of science books.
$s+(s+12)$ or $2s+12$
Let h = number of history books.
$h+(h-12)$ or $2h-12$

5. Let p = cost of paperback.
$p+3(p+7)$ or $4p+21$
Let h = cost of hardback.
$3h+(h-7)=4h-7$

6. Let s = cost of small drink.
$3s+2(s+50)=5s+100$
Let l = cost of large drink.
$2l+3(l-50)=5l-150$

7. $x+(x+2)=2x+2$ **8.** $x+(x+2)=2x+2$

9. $x+2(x+2)=3x+4$ **10.** $x+3(x+1)=4x+3$

11. $x+(x+2)+(x+4)=3x+6$

12. $\frac{1}{4}x+\frac{1}{5}(x+1)+\frac{1}{2}(x+2)=\frac{19}{20}x+\frac{6}{5}$

13. $x+\frac{1}{2}(x+2)+\frac{1}{4}(x+4)=\frac{7}{4}x+2$

14. $x+\frac{3}{4}(x+2)+2(x+4)=\frac{15}{4}x+\frac{19}{2}$

15. Let n = the number.
$n+\frac{2}{5}n=56$
$\frac{7}{5}n=56$
$\frac{5}{7}\left(\frac{7}{5}n\right)=\frac{5}{7}(56)$
$n=40$

16. Let n = the number.
$n+\frac{1}{3}n=48$
$\frac{4}{3}n=48$
$\frac{3}{4}\left(\frac{4}{3}n\right)=\frac{3}{4}(48)$
$n=36$

17. Let n = the first integer.
$n+(n+2)=76$
$2n+2=76$
$2n=74$
$\frac{1}{2}\cdot 2n=74\cdot\frac{1}{2}$
$n=37$
The integers are 37 and 39.

18. Let n = the first integer.
$n+(n+2)=106$
$2n+2=106$
$2n=104$
$\frac{1}{2}\cdot 2n=104\cdot\frac{1}{2}$
$n=52$
The integers are 52 and 54.

19. Let n = the first integer.
$$n + (n + 1) + (n + 2) = 126$$
$$3n + 3 = 126$$
$$3n = 123$$
$$\frac{1}{3} \cdot 3n = 123 \cdot \frac{1}{3}$$
$$n = 41$$
The integers are 41, 42, and 43.

20. Let n = the first integer.
$$n + (n + 2) + (n + 4) = 189$$
$$3n + 6 = 189$$
$$3n = 183$$
$$\frac{1}{3} \cdot 3n = 183 \cdot \frac{1}{3}$$
$$n = 61$$
The integers are 61, 63, and 65.

21. Exercise 19:
Let x = second integer.
$x - 1$ = first integer
$x + 1$ = third integer
$$(x - 1) + x + (x + 1) = 126$$
$$3x = 126$$
$$\frac{1}{3} \cdot 3x = 126 \cdot \frac{1}{3}$$
$$x = 42$$
$$x - 1 = 41$$
$$x + 1 = 43$$
The integers are 41, 42, 43.
Exercise 20:
Let x = second odd integer.
$x - 2$ = first odd integer
$x + 2$ = third odd integer
$$(x - 2) + x + (x + 2) = 189$$
$$3x = 189$$
$$\frac{1}{3} \cdot 3x = 189 \cdot \frac{1}{3}$$
$$x = 63$$
$$x - 1 = 61$$
$$x + 1 = 65$$
The integers are 61, 63, 65.

22. Let w = the width.
$$w + w + (w + 25) + (w + 25) = 310$$
$$4w + 50 = 310$$
$$4w + 50 - 50 = 310 - 50$$
$$4w = 260$$
$$\frac{1}{4} \cdot 4w = 260 \cdot \frac{1}{4}$$
$$w = 65$$
The width is 65 m, the length 90 m.

23. Let n = measure of smallest angle.
$$n + 4n + (4n + n) = 180$$
$$10n = 180$$
$$\frac{1}{10} \cdot 10n = 180 \cdot \frac{1}{10}$$
$$n = 18$$
The smallest angle measures 18°.

24.
$$4s + 7 = 1863 - 1776$$
$$4s + 7 = 87$$
$$4s + 7 - 7 = 87 - 7$$
$$4s = 80$$
$$\frac{1}{4} \cdot 4x = 80 \cdot \frac{1}{4}$$
$$s = 20$$
A score is 20 years.

25. Let A = length of Amazon.
$$A + (A + 234) = 13{,}108$$
$$2A + 234 = 13{,}108$$
$$2A + 234 - 234 = 13{,}108 - 234$$
$$2A = 12{,}874$$
$$\frac{1}{2} \cdot 2A = 12{,}874 \cdot \frac{1}{2}$$
$$A = 6437$$
The length of the Amazon is 6437 km, the Nile 6671 km.

26. Let V = Venus's earnings.
$$V + (V + 289{,}097) = 4{,}921{,}107$$
$$2V + 289{,}097 = 4{,}921{,}107$$
$$2V + 289{,}097 - 289{,}097 = 4{,}921{,}107 - 289{,}097$$
$$2V = 4{,}632{,}010$$
$$V = 2{,}316{,}005$$
$$V + 289{,}097 = 2{,}605{,}102$$
Venus earned \$2,316,005. Serena earned \$2,605,102.

27. Let l = length of first piece.
$$l + 3l + 4(3l) = 48$$
$$16l = 48$$
$$\frac{1}{16} \cdot 16l = 48 \cdot \frac{1}{16}$$
$$l = 3$$
The lengths are 3 ft, 9 ft, and 36 ft.

28. Let a = amount borrowed.
$$a + 0.105a = 8287.50$$
$$1.105a = 8287.50$$
$$\frac{1}{1.105} \cdot 1.105a = 8287.50 \cdot \frac{1}{1.105}$$
$$a = 7500$$
She borrowed \$7500.

29. Let d = amount deposited.
$$d + 0.06d = 6272$$
$$1.06d = 6272$$
$$\frac{1}{1.06} \cdot 106d = 6272 \cdot \frac{1}{1.06}$$
$$d \approx 5916.98$$
The amount deposited was \$5916.98.

30. Let p = original price.
$$p - 0.2p = 9600$$
$$0.8p = 9600$$
$$\frac{1}{0.8} \cdot 0.8p = 9600 \cdot \frac{1}{0.8}$$
$$p = 12{,}000$$
The price was \$12,000.

31. Let p = 1950 population.
$$p + 0.79p = 270{,}000{,}000$$
$$1.79p = 270{,}000{,}000$$
$$\frac{1}{1.79} \cdot 1.79p = 270{,}000{,}000 \cdot \frac{1}{1.79}$$
$$p \approx 151{,}000{,}000$$
To the nearest million, the 1950 population was 151 million.

32. a. Let s = number of students in 1995.
$$s = 45{,}600{,}000 - 0.033(45{,}600{,}000)$$
$$s \approx 45{,}600{,}000 - 1{,}500{,}000$$
$$s \approx 44{,}100{,}000$$
In 1995, 44,100,000 were enrolled.

b. No; you need to know the total number of students in this age group.

33. Let x = smaller number, $x + 12$ = larger number.
$$0.25(x + 12) = x$$
$$0.25x + 3 = x$$
$$3 = x - 0.25x$$
$$3 = 0.75x$$
$$\frac{1}{0.75} \cdot 3 = 0.75x \cdot \frac{1}{0.75}$$
$$4 = x, x + 12 = 16$$
The numbers are 4 and 16.

34. Let x = price per mile.
$$38.90 + 190x = 100$$
$$38.90 - 38.90 + 190x = 100 - 38.90$$
$$190x = 61.10$$
$$\frac{1}{190} \cdot 190x = 61.10 \cdot \frac{1}{190}$$
$x \approx 0.322$, 32¢ per mile

35. Let m = the number of correct multiple choice questions.
The points from multiple choice questions plus the points from fill-ins = 78.
$$3m + 7(4 - 1) = 78$$
$$3m + 21 = 78$$
$$3m + 21 - 21 = 78 - 21$$
$$3m = 57$$
$$\frac{1}{3} \cdot 3m = 57 \cdot \frac{1}{3}$$
$m = 19$; 19 multiple choice questions were correct

36. Let l = length. Perimeter $= 2l + 2\left(\frac{3}{4}l\right)$. After increasing each side 2 cm, $2(l + 2) + 2\left(\frac{3}{4}l + 2\right) = 50$.

$$2l + 4 + \frac{3}{2}l + 4 = 50$$
$$\frac{7}{2}l + 8 = 50$$
$$\frac{7}{2}l + 8 - 8 = 50 - 8$$
$$\frac{7}{2}l = 42$$
$$\frac{2}{7} \cdot \frac{7}{2}l = 42 \cdot \frac{2}{7}$$
$$l = 12 \text{ cm, width} = \frac{3}{4}(12) = 9 \text{ cm}$$

37. $13.72 + 35(0.13) + 172(0.08) = 13.72 + 4.55 + 13.76$
$= \$32.03$

38. g represents the number of games they will have to play.

$$15 + 0.5x = 0.6(20 + x)$$
$$15 + 0.5x = 12 + 0.6x$$
$$15 - 12 + 0.5x - 0.5x = 12 - 12 + 0.6x - 0.5x$$
$$3 = 0.1x$$
$$\frac{1}{0.1} \cdot 3 = 0.1x \cdot \frac{1}{0.1}$$
$$30 = x$$

They will play 30 more games and win 15. Total games will be 50, total wins 30.

39. a. Let p = amount that should show on pump for price to be \$10.

$$p + 0.09p = 10$$
$$1.09p = 10$$
$$\frac{1}{1.09} \cdot 1.09p = 10 \cdot \frac{1}{1.09}$$
$$p = \frac{10}{1.09} = \$9.17$$

The pump should have read \$9.17. (The driver received $9.10(1.09) = \$9.92$ worth of gas.)

b. Let p = amount that shows on the pump.
Cost of gas with tax $= p + (0.09)p = 1.09p$.
Amount of 9% discount $= 0.09(1.09p) = 0.0981p$.
Final cost $= 1.09p - 0.0981p = 0.9919p$.
The amount collected, p, is more than the final cost.
(If the pump registered \$10, the driver owed $10 + (0.09)10 = \$10.90$, less the 9% discount, or $10.90 - (0.09)(10.90) = \$9.92$.)

40. $2150 - 2000 = 150$ interest

$$\frac{150}{2000} = 0.075 = 7.5\%$$

41. Amount in savings $= 1000 + 0.07(1000) - 0.20[.07(1000)]$
$= 1000 + 70 - 14$
$= \$1056$

42. Let $12x$ = no. of nickels (0.05 of a dollar),
$4x$ = no. of dimes (0.10 of a dollar),
$2x$ = no. of quarters (0.25 of a dollar),
x = no. of half dollars (0.50 of a dollar).

$$0.05(12x) + 0.10(4x) + 0.25(2x) + 0.50(x) = 10$$
$$0.6x + 0.4x + 0.50x + 0.50x = 10$$
$$2x = 10$$
$$x = 5$$

5 half dollars, 10 quarters, 20 dimes, 60 nickels

43.
$$7x = 10$$
$$\frac{1}{7} \cdot 7x = \frac{1}{7} \cdot 10$$
$$x = \frac{10}{7}$$

44.
$$7a - 9a = 6$$
$$-2a = 6$$
$$\frac{1}{-2} \cdot (-2a) = \frac{1}{-2} \cdot 6$$
$$a = -3$$

45.
$$-8w + 13w = 45$$
$$5w = 45$$
$$\frac{1}{5} \cdot 5w = \frac{1}{5} \cdot 45$$
$$w = 9$$

46.
$$8c + 6 = 6c + 10$$
$$8c - 6c + 6 = 6c - 6c + 10$$
$$2c + 6 = 10$$
$$2c + 6 - 6 = 10 - 6$$
$$2c = 4$$
$$\frac{1}{2} \cdot 2c = \frac{1}{2} \cdot 4$$
$$c = 2$$

47.
$$15 - (5m - 6) = 1$$
$$15 - 5m + 6 = 1$$
$$21 - 5m = 1$$
$$21 - 21 - 5m = 1 - 21$$
$$-5m = -20$$
$$\frac{1}{-5} \cdot 5m = \frac{1}{-5} + (-20)$$
$$m = 4$$

48.
$$\frac{3}{4}b = 9$$
$$\frac{4}{3} \cdot \frac{3}{4}b = \frac{4}{3} \cdot 9$$
$$b = \frac{36}{3}$$
$$b = 12$$

49.
$$\frac{3}{4}a - 6 = 3 + \frac{1}{2}a$$
$$4\left(\frac{3}{4}a - 6\right) = 4\left(3 + \frac{1}{2}a\right)$$
$$3a - 24 = 12 + 2a$$
$$3a - 2a - 24 = 12 + 2a - 2a$$
$$a - 24 = 12$$
$$a - 24 + 24 = 12 + 24$$
$$a = 36$$

50.
$$\frac{3}{5}y + 2 = \frac{1}{2}y$$
$$10\left(\frac{3}{5}y + 2\right) = 10\left(\frac{1}{2}y\right)$$
$$6y + 20 = 5y$$
$$6y - 5y + 20 = 5y - 5y$$
$$y + 20 = 0$$
$$y + 20 - 20 = -20$$
$$y = -20$$

LESSON 3-12 PROBLEMS p. 164

1. Strategy: Make an organized list.

TEAM

A	B	C	D	E	F	G	H	I
B	C	D	E	F	G	H	I	
C	D	E	F	G	H	I		
D	E	F	G	H	I			
E	F	G	H	I				
F	G	H	I					
G	H	I						
H	I							
I								

$\overline{8} + \overline{7} + \overline{6} + \overline{5} + \overline{4} + \overline{3} + \overline{2} + \overline{1} + \overline{0} = 36$
$36 \times 2 = 72$

There will be 72 games played when each team has played each other team twice.

2. Strategy: Try, test, revise

Try	Test	Revise
First Try: 10 cartons with 2 rackets each	$38 - 10 = 28$ $10 \times 2 = 20$ $28 \times 3 = 84$ $20 + 84 = 104$	104 is more than 100. Revise upward. Now try: 12 cartons w/2 rackets
Second Try: 12 cartons with 2 rackets each	$38 - 12 = 26$ $12 \times 2 = 24$ $26 \times 3 = 78$ $24 + 78 = 102$	102 is more than 100. Revise upward. Now try: 14 cartons w/2 rackets
Third Try: 14 cartons with 2 rackets each	$38 - 14 = 24$ $14 \times 2 = 28$ $24 \times 3 = 72$ $28 + 72 = 100$	All rackets are packed.

Fourteen cartons of 2 rackets each and 24 cartons of 3 rackets each were used to pack 100 rackets.

3. a. 1

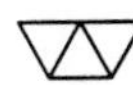

b. 3

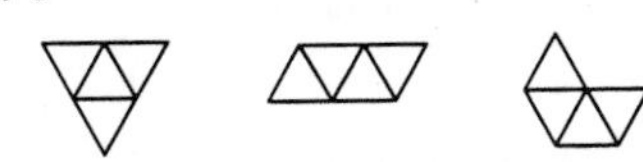

c. 5

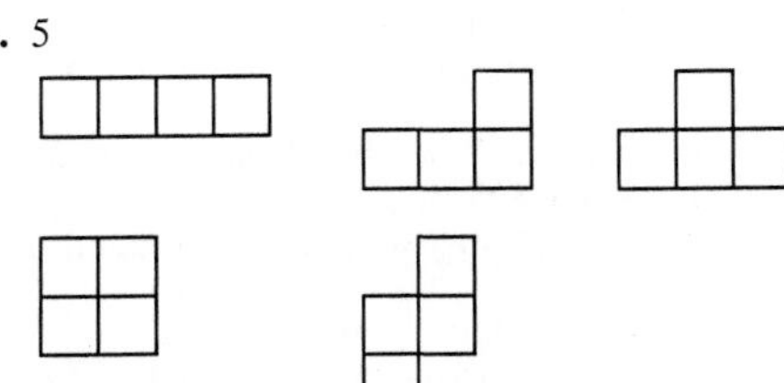

d. 12

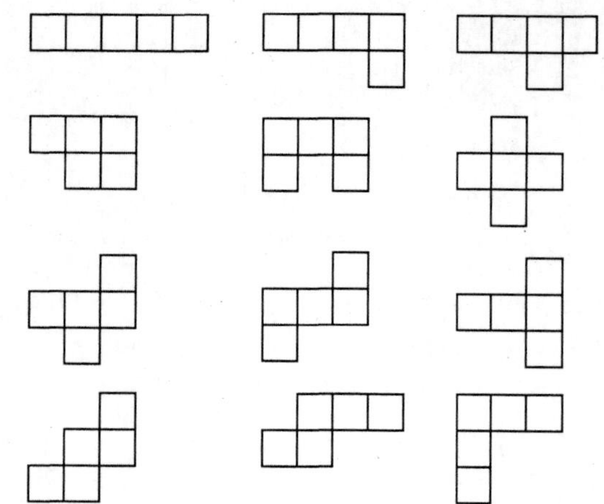

4. Strategy: Make an organized list

Quarters	Dimes	Nickels
1	1	1
1	0	3
0	4	0
0	3	2
0	2	4
0	1	6
0	0	8

There are 7 different combinations possible.

5. Strategy: Try, test, revise

Try	Test	Revise
First Try: Length: 40 m	Width: $120 \div 40 = 3$ Perimeter: $(40 + 3)2 = 86$ m	Revise downward. Now try: length: 20 m
Second Try: Length: 20 m	Width: $120 \div 20 = 6$ Perimeter: $(20 + 6)2 = 52$ m	Revise downward. Now try: length: 10 m
Third Try: Length: 10 m	Width: $120 \div 10 = 12$ Perimeter: $(10 + 12)2 = 44$ m	This is the smallest perimeter.

The garden's measurements are 10 m by 12 m.

6. Strategy: Try, test, revise

Try	Test	Revise
First Try		
soccer shoes—\$25	\$25	
jogging suit—\$35	35	
sweat shirt—\$15	15	
basketball—\$20	20	
softball bat—\$15	+ 15	
	\$110	\$110 is less than \$120 Revise

Some possible solutions:

A. soccer shoes, leg weights, sweat shirt, softball bat, basketball
\$25 + \$45 + \$15 + \$15 + \$20 = \$120

B. tennis outfit, basketball, swimsuit, sweat shirt, soccer shoes
\$50 + \$20 + \$10 + \$15 + \$25 = \$120

C. tennis outfit, basketball, swimsuit, softball bat, soccer shoes
\$50 + \$20 + \$10 + \$15 + \$25 = \$120

D. racketball racket, basketball, jogging suit, swimsuit, softball bat
\$40 + \$20 + \$35 + \$10 + \$15 = \$120

E. racketball racket, basketball, jogging suit, swimsuit, sweat shirt
\$40 + \$20 + \$35 + \$10 + \$15 = \$120

7. Strategy: Draw a diagram

S	M	T	W	T	F	S
(1)	[2]	3	4	5	6	[7]
8	9	(10)	11	[12]	13	14
15	16	[17]	18	(19)	20	21
[22]	23	24	25	26	[27]	(28)
29	30	31	[32]	33	34	35
36	([37])	38	39	40	41	42

○ Charles's night off □ Eva's night off

Charles and Eva will both be off on a Monday five weeks later.

8. Strategy: Try, test, revise

Try	Test	Revise
First Try: large calculators—20	small calculators— $20 \times 3 = 60$; $60 \times \$5 = \$300$; $20 \times \$10 = \$200$; Total cost: \$500	\$500 is less than \$600. Revise upward. Now try: 25 large calculators
Second Try: large calculators—25	small calculators— $25 \times 3 = 75$; $75 \times \$5 = \$375$; $25 \times \$10 = \$250$; Total cost: \$625	\$625 is more than \$600. Revise downward. Now try: 24 large calculators
Third Try: large calculators—24	small calculators— $24 \times 3 = 72$; $72 \times \$5 = \$360$; $24 \times \$10 = \$240$; Total cost: \$600	This is correct.

The club sold 24 large calculators and 72 small ones.

CHAPTER 3 WRAP UP pp. 165–168

1.
$$x + 12 = -8$$
$$x + 12 - 12 = -8 - 12$$
$$x = -20$$

2.
$$-7 = y - 11$$
$$-7 + 11 = y - 11 + 11$$
$$4 = y$$

3.
$$x - 11 = 14$$
$$x - 11 + 11 = 14 + 11$$
$$x = 25$$

4.
$$w + \frac{3}{7} = -\frac{5}{7}$$
$$w + \frac{3}{7} - \frac{3}{7} = -\frac{5}{7} - \frac{3}{7}$$
$$w = -\frac{8}{7}$$

5. Let p = January price.
$$p + 38 = 629$$
$$p + 38 - 38 = 629 - 38$$
$$p = 591$$
The price was \$591.

6. Let t = Ciudad Caliente temperature.
$$t - 150 = -65$$
$$t - 150 + 150 = -65 + 150$$
$$t = 85$$
The Ciudad Caliente temperature is 85°F.

7.
$$6x = 24$$
$$\frac{1}{6}(6x) = \frac{1}{6}(24)$$
$$x = 4$$

8.
$$-\frac{x}{4} = 48$$
$$-4\left(-\frac{x}{4}\right) = -4(48)$$
$$x = -192$$

9.
$$\frac{3}{5} = \frac{-2}{5}x$$
$$\frac{-5}{2}\left(\frac{3}{5}\right) = \frac{-5}{2}\left(\frac{-2}{5}x\right)$$
$$-\frac{3}{2} = x$$

10.
$$-11x = 121$$
$$\frac{1}{-11}(-11x) = \frac{1}{-11}(121)$$
$$x = -11$$

11. Let n = the number of appliances.

$$4n = 108$$
$$\frac{1}{4}(4n) = \frac{1}{4}(108)$$
$$n = 27$$

She sold 27 appliances.

12.
$$\begin{aligned} 2x + 5 &= 13 \\ 2x + 5 - 5 &= 13 - 5 \\ 2x &= 8 \\ \frac{1}{2}(2x) &= \frac{1}{2}(8) \\ x &= 4 \end{aligned}$$

13.
$$\begin{aligned} -8x + 3 &= 27 \\ -8x + 3 - 3 &= 27 - 3 \\ -8x &= 24 \\ \frac{1}{-8}(-8x) &= \frac{1}{-8}(24) \\ x &= -3 \end{aligned}$$

14.
$$\begin{aligned} 50 - 4x &= 14 \\ 50 - 50 - 4x &= 14 - 50 \\ -4x &= -36 \\ \frac{1}{-4}(-4x) &= \frac{1}{-4}(-36) \\ x &= 9 \end{aligned}$$

15.
$$\begin{aligned} 7x + 8x &= 45 \\ 15x &= 45 \\ \frac{1}{15}(15x) &= \frac{1}{15}(45) \\ x &= 3 \end{aligned}$$

16.
$$\begin{aligned} 4(3y + 2) &= 44 \\ 12y + 8 &= 44 \\ 12y + 8 - 8 &= 44 - 8 \\ 12y &= 36 \\ \frac{1}{12}(12y) &= \frac{1}{12}(36) \\ y &= 3 \end{aligned}$$

17.
$$\begin{aligned} 6(3a - 2) + 5a &= 57 \\ 18a - 12 + 5a &= 57 \\ 23a - 12 &= 57 \\ 23a - 12 + 12 &= 57 + 12 \\ 23a &= 69 \\ \frac{1}{23}(23a) &= \frac{1}{23}(69) \\ a &= 3 \end{aligned}$$

18. $2n + 6$ **19.** $5n - 18$ **20.** $\frac{1}{3}n - 6$

21. $\frac{1}{2}(n + 10)$ **22.** $2n - 3$ **23.** $2x + 10$

24. Let b = number of boys.

$$\begin{aligned} 2b - 5 &= 75 \\ 2b - 5 + 5 &= 75 + 5 \\ 2b &= 80 \\ \frac{1}{2}(2b) &= \frac{1}{2}(80) \\ b &= 40 \end{aligned}$$

There are 40 boys.

25. Let h = number of hours Chris must ride.

$$\begin{aligned} 10 + 12h &= 60 \\ 10 - 10 + 12h &= 60 - 10 \\ 12h &= 50 \\ \frac{1}{12}(12h) &= \frac{1}{12}(50) \\ h &= \frac{50}{12} = 4\frac{1}{6} \end{aligned}$$

Chris must ride $4\frac{1}{6}$ hours or 250 more minutes.

26. Let M = number of points Menlo scored.

$$\begin{aligned} M + 4 &= 3(14) \\ M + 4 &= 42 \\ M + 4 - 4 &= 42 - 4 \\ M &= 38 \end{aligned}$$

Menlo scored 38 points.

27.
$$\begin{aligned} 6x - 5 &= -2x + 11 \\ 6x + 2x - 5 &= -2x + 2x + 11 \\ 8x - 5 &= 11 \\ 8x - 5 + 5 &= 11 + 5 \\ 8x &= 16 \\ \frac{1}{8}(8x) &= \frac{1}{8}(16) \\ x &= 2 \end{aligned}$$

28.
$$\begin{aligned} 3y - 6 - 7y &= 12 - 2y + 6 \\ -4y - 6 &= 18 - 2y \\ -4y + 4y - 6 &= 18 - 2y + 4y \\ -6 &= 18 + 2y \\ -6 - 18 &= 18 - 18 + 2y \\ -24 &= 2y \\ \frac{1}{2}(-24) &= \frac{1}{2}(2y) \\ -12 &= y \end{aligned}$$

29.
$$\begin{aligned} 4(x + 3) &= 36 \\ 4x + 12 &= 36 \\ 4x + 12 - 12 &= 36 - 12 \\ 4x &= 24 \\ \frac{1}{4}(4x) &= \frac{1}{4}(24) \\ x &= 6 \end{aligned}$$

30.
$$\begin{aligned} 8(x - 2) &= 5(x + 4) \\ 8x - 16 &= 5x + 20 \\ 8x - 5x - 16 &= 5x - 5x + 20 \\ 3x - 16 &= 20 \\ 3x - 16 + 16 &= 20 + 16 \\ 3x &= 36 \\ \frac{1}{3}(3x) &= \frac{1}{3}(36) \\ x &= 12 \end{aligned}$$

31.
$$\begin{aligned} x + 7 - 2 &= 5 + x \\ x + 5 &= 5 + x \end{aligned}$$

True for all values of x. The equation is an identity.

32.
$$\begin{aligned} 2(x + 3) - 3x &= 5 - x + 1 \\ 2x + 6 - 3x &= 6 - x \\ 6 - x &= 6 - x \end{aligned}$$

True for all values of x. The equation is an identity.

33.
$$\begin{aligned} \frac{3}{4}x + \frac{1}{2}x + \frac{1}{4} &= 1 + 2x \\ 4\left(\frac{3}{4}x + \frac{1}{2}x + \frac{1}{4}\right) &= 4(1 + 2x) \\ 3x + 2x + 1 &= 4 + 8x \\ 5x + 1 &= 4 + 8x \\ 5x - 5x + 1 &= 4 + 8x - 5x \\ 1 &= 4 + 3x \\ 1 - 4 &= 4 - 4 + 3x \\ -3 &= 3x \\ \frac{1}{3}(-3) &= \frac{1}{3}(3x) \\ -1 &= x \end{aligned}$$

34.
$$\begin{aligned} 12.21 - 4.3a &= 24.25 \\ 100(12.21 - 4.3a) &= 100(24.25) \\ 1221 - 430a &= 2425 \\ 1221 - 1221 - 430a &= 2425 - 1221 \\ -430a &= 1204 \\ \frac{1}{-430}(-430a) &= \frac{1}{-430}(1204) \\ a &= -2.8 \end{aligned}$$

35.
$$\begin{aligned} \frac{4}{9}y - \frac{4}{3} &= \frac{1}{6}y + \frac{11}{18} \\ 18\left(\frac{4}{9}y - \frac{4}{3}\right) &= 18\left(\frac{1}{6}y + \frac{11}{18}\right) \\ 8y - 24 &= 3y + 11 \\ 8y - 3y - 24 &= 3y - 3y + 11 \\ 5y - 24 &= 11 \\ 5y - 24 + 24 &= 11 + 24 \\ 5y &= 35 \\ \frac{1}{5}(5y) &= \frac{1}{5}(35) \\ y &= 7 \end{aligned}$$

36.
$$\begin{aligned} 0.83w + 0.29 &= 0.5w - 0.7 \\ 100(0.83w + 0.29) &= 100(0.5w - 0.7) \\ 83w + 29 &= 50w - 70 \\ 83w - 50w + 29 &= 50w - 50w - 70 \\ 33w + 29 &= -70 \\ 33w + 29 - 29 &= -70 - 29 \\ 33w &= -99 \\ \frac{1}{33}(33w) &= \frac{1}{33}(-99) \\ w &= -3 \end{aligned}$$

37.
$$\begin{aligned} V &= Bh \\ \frac{1}{B}(V) &= \frac{1}{B}(Bh) \\ \frac{V}{B} &= h \end{aligned}$$

38.
$$\begin{aligned} b &= \frac{3A}{r} \\ r \cdot b &= r\left(\frac{3A}{r}\right) \\ rb &= 3A \\ \frac{1}{3}(rb) &= \frac{1}{3}(3A) \\ \frac{rb}{3} &= A \end{aligned}$$

39. $P = 2x + 2w$
$P - 2w = 2x + 2w - 2w$
$P - 2w = 2x$
$\frac{1}{2}(P - 2w) = \frac{1}{2}(2x)$
$\frac{P - 2w}{2} = x$

40. $V = \frac{1}{3}Ar$
$3 \cdot V = 3\left(\frac{1}{3}Ar\right)$
$3V = Ar$
$\frac{1}{r}(3V) = \frac{1}{r}(Ar)$
$\frac{3V}{r} = A$

41. $|x| = 5$
$x = 5$ or $x = -5$

42. $|x| - 4 = 6$
$|x| - 4 + 4 = 6 + 4$
$|x| = 10$
$x = 10$ or $x = -10$

43. $-9 + 3|y| = 24$
$-9 + 9 + 3|y| = 24 + 9$
$3|y| = 33$
$\frac{1}{3} \cdot 3|y| = \frac{1}{3}(33)$
$|y| = 11$
$y = 11$ or $y = -11$

44. $\frac{b}{42} = \frac{6}{7}$
$42\left(\frac{b}{42}\right) = 42\left(\frac{6}{7}\right)$
$b = 36$

45. $\frac{45}{15} = \frac{30}{x}$
$15x\left(\frac{45}{15}\right) = 15x\left(\frac{30}{x}\right)$
$45x = 450$
$\frac{1}{45}(45x) = \frac{1}{45}(450)$
$x = 10$

46. $\frac{3}{2} = \frac{324}{x}$
$2x\left(\frac{3}{2}\right) = 2x\left(\frac{324}{x}\right)$
$3x = 648$
$\frac{1}{3}(3x) = \frac{1}{3}(648)$
$x = 216$ votes

47. $\frac{234}{14} = \frac{x}{42}$
$42\left(\frac{234}{14}\right) = 42\left(\frac{x}{42}\right)$
$702 = x$
$x = 702$ km

48. $48\% = 0.48$ 49. $7\% = 0.07$ 50. $150\% = 1.5$

51. $\frac{1}{3} \approx 0.333 = \frac{33.3}{100} = 33.3\%$

52. $\frac{7}{8} = 0.875 = \frac{87.5}{100} = 87.5\%$

53. $0.012 = \frac{1.2}{100} = 1.2\%$

54. $60 = p \cdot 150$
$p = \frac{60}{150} = 0.4 = \frac{40}{100} = 40\%$

55. $0.75x = 187.5$
$\frac{1}{0.75}(0.75x) = \frac{1}{0.75}(187.5)$
$x = 250$

56. $0.065(850) = \$55.25$

57. Increase $= 112 - 80 = \$32$.
Percent increase $= \frac{32}{80} = 0.4 = \frac{40}{100} = 40\%$

58. Let x = cost of child's ticket.
$2x + x = 3x$
Let a = cost of adult ticket.
$a + \frac{1}{2}a = \frac{3}{2}a$

59. $x + (x + 2) = 2x + 2$

60. Let n = the first integer.
$n + (n + 2) = 116$
$2n + 2 = 116$
$2n + 2 - 2 = 116 - 2$
$2n = 114$
$\frac{1}{2} \cdot 2n = 114 \cdot \frac{1}{2}$
$n = 57$
The integers are 57 and 59.

61. Let w = the width.
$w + w + (w + 6) + (w + 6) = 56$
$4w + 12 = 56$
$4w + 12 - 12 = 56 - 12$
$4w = 44$
$\frac{1}{4}(4w) = \frac{1}{4}(44)$
$w = 11$
The width is 11 cm, the length 17 cm.

CHAPTER 3 ASSESSMENT pp. 168–169

1. $x + 7 = 15$
$x + 7 - 7 = 15 - 7$
$x = 8$

2. $t - 9 = 17$
$t - 9 + 9 = 17 + 9$
$t = 26$

3. $3x = -18$
$\frac{1}{3}(3x) = \frac{1}{3}(-18)$
$x = -6$

4. $-7x = -28$
$\frac{1}{-7}(-7x) = \frac{1}{-7}(-28)$
$x = 4$

5. $-\frac{x}{8} = 5$
$-8\left(-\frac{x}{8}\right) = -8(5)$
$x = -40$

6. $-\frac{2}{3}y = -\frac{4}{15}$
$-\frac{3}{2}\left(-\frac{2}{3}y\right) = -\frac{3}{2}\left(-\frac{4}{15}\right)$
$y = \frac{12}{30} = \frac{2}{5}$

7. $8a + 11 = 35$
$8a + 11 - 11 = 35 - 11$
$8a = 24$
$\frac{1}{8}(8a) = \frac{1}{8}(24)$
$a = 3$

8. $-4y + 7 = -21$
$-4y + 7 - 7 = -21 - 7$
$-4y = -28$
$\frac{1}{-4}(-4y) = \frac{1}{-4}(-28)$
$y = 7$

9. $3(x + 2) = 27$
$3x + 6 = 27$
$3x + 6 - 6 = 27 - 6$
$3x = 21$
$\frac{1}{3}(3x) = \frac{1}{3}(21)$
$x = 7$

10. $45 - 3x = 30$
$45 - 45 - 3x = 30 - 45$
$-3x = -15$
$\frac{1}{-3}(-3x) = \frac{1}{-3}(-15)$
$x = 5$

11. $3t + 7 = 2t - 5$
$3t - 2t + 7 = 2t - 2t - 5$
$t + 7 = -5$
$t + 7 - 7 = -5 - 7$
$t = -12$

12. $-3x + 6(x + 4) = 9$
$-3x + 6x + 24 = 9$
$3x + 24 = 9$
$3x + 24 - 24 = 9 - 24$
$3x = -15$
$\frac{1}{3}(3x) = \frac{1}{3}(-15)$
$x = -5$

13. $0.51m + 0.03 = 0.4m - 0.74$
$100(0.51m + 0.03) = 100(0.4m - 0.74)$
$51m + 3 = 40m - 74$
$51m - 40m + 3 = 40m - 40m - 74$
$11m + 3 = -74$
$11m + 3 - 3 = -74 - 3$
$11m = -77$
$\frac{1}{11}(11m) = \frac{1}{11}(-77)$
$m = -7$

14. $\frac{1}{2}x - \frac{3}{5} = \frac{1}{10} + \frac{3}{10}$

$10\left(\frac{1}{2}x - \frac{3}{5}\right) = 10\left(\frac{4}{10}\right)$

$5x - 6 = 4$

$5x - 6 + 6 = 4 + 6$

$5x = 10$

$\frac{1}{5}(5x) = \frac{1}{5}(10)$

$x = 2$

15. $|x| + 3 = 8$

$|x| + 3 - 3 = 8 - 3$

$|x| = 5$

$x = 5$ or $x = -5$

16. $2|y| - 4 = 8$

$2|y| - 4 + 4 = 8 + 4$

$2|y| = 12$

$\frac{1}{2}(2|y|) = \frac{1}{2}(12)$

$|y| = 6$

$y = 6$ or $y = -6$

17. $7x$ **18.** $15 - 4n$ **19.** $x + (x + 1) = 2x + 1$ **20.** $\frac{1}{5}x - 2$

21. $A = 2\pi rh$

$\frac{1}{2\pi h}(A) = \frac{1}{2\pi h}(2\pi rh)$

$\frac{A}{2\pi h} = r$

22. $b = \frac{2A}{h}$

$h \cdot b = h\left(\frac{2A}{h}\right)$

$hb = 2A$

$\frac{1}{2}(hb) = \frac{1}{2}(2A)$

$\frac{hb}{2} = A$

23. $P = 2x + 2w$

$P - 2w = 2x + 2w - 2w$

$P - 2w = 2x$

$\frac{1}{2}(P - 2w) = \frac{1}{2}(2x)$

$\frac{P - 2w}{2} = x$

24. $V = \frac{1}{3}Ar$

$3 \cdot V = 3\left(\frac{1}{3}Ar\right)$

$3V = Ar$

$\frac{1}{A}(3V) = \frac{1}{A}(Ar)$

$\frac{3V}{A} = r$

25. $\frac{16}{3} = \frac{c}{12}$

$12\left(\frac{16}{3}\right) = 12\left(\frac{c}{12}\right)$

$64 = c$

26. $\frac{21}{x} = \frac{105}{5}$

$5x\left(\frac{21}{x}\right) = 5x\left(\frac{105}{5}\right)$

$105 = 105x$

$\frac{1}{105}(105) = \frac{1}{105}(105x)$

$1 = x$

27. $\frac{184}{6} = \frac{1288}{x}$

$6x\left(\frac{184}{6}\right) = 6x\left(\frac{1288}{x}\right)$

$184x = 7728$

$\frac{1}{184}(184x) = \frac{1}{184}(7728)$

$x = 42$ bulbs

28. $\frac{21}{350} = \frac{x}{525}$

$1050\left(\frac{21}{350}\right) = 1050\left(\frac{x}{525}\right)$

$63 = 2x$

$\frac{1}{2}(63) = \frac{1}{2}(2x)$

$31.5 = x$

$x = 31.5$ gallons

29. $89\% = 0.89$ **30.** $3\% = 0.03$ **31.** $200\% = 2$

32. $\frac{2}{5} = 0.4 = \frac{40}{100} = 40\%$

33. $\frac{2}{3} \approx 0.667 = \frac{66.7}{100} = 66.7\%$

34. $96 = n \cdot 150$

$n = \frac{96}{150} = 0.64 = 64\%$

35. $0.9x = 45$

$\frac{1}{0.9}(0.9x) = \frac{1}{0.9}(45)$

$x = 50$

36. $x = 0.875(200) = 175$

37. $660 = 0.3x$

$\frac{1}{0.3}(660) = \frac{1}{0.3}(0.3x)$

$2200 = x$

Their income is \$2200.

38. Let F = number of points Frank scored.

$F + 6 = 22$

$F + 6 - 6 = 22 - 6$

$F = 16$

Frank scored 16 points.

39. Let e = earnings per day.

$5e = 440$

$\frac{1}{5}(5e) = \frac{1}{5}(440)$

$e = 88$

He earned \$88 a day.

40. Let L = Lisa's earnings.

$L + \left(\frac{1}{2}L + 5\right) = 65$

$\frac{3}{2}L + 5 = 65$

$\frac{3}{2}L + 5 - 5 = 65 - 5$

$\frac{3}{2}L = 60$

$\frac{2}{3}\left(\frac{3}{2}L\right) = \frac{2}{3}(60)$

$L = 40$

Lisa earned \$40, Marisa \$25.

41. Let w = width.

$w + w + (w + 4) + (w + 4) = 36$

$4w + 8 = 36$

$4w + 8 - 8 = 36 - 8$

$4w = 28$

$\frac{1}{4}(4w) = \frac{1}{4}(28)$

$w = 7$

The width is 7 cm, the length 11 cm.

42. Let a = amount invested.

$a + 0.12a = 840$

$1.12a = 840$

$\frac{1}{1.12}(1.12a) = \frac{1}{1.12}(840)$

$a = 750$

The amount invested was \$750.

CHAPTER 4

SKILLS & CONCEPTS

p. 170

1. 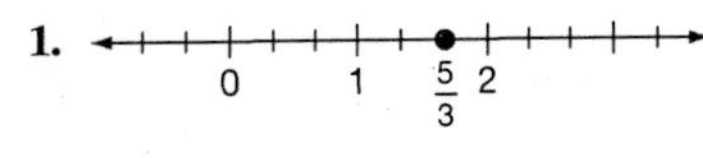

2. 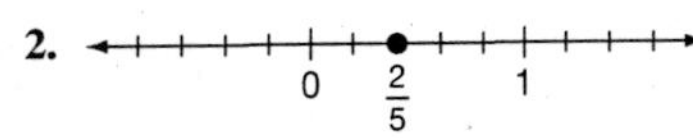

3. $-1\ -\frac{3}{4}\quad 0$

4. $<$ 5. $<$ 6. $>$

7.
$$\begin{aligned} 3x - 2 &= 7 \\ 3x - 2 + 2 &= 7 + 2 \\ 3x &= 9 \\ \frac{1}{3} \cdot 3x &= 9 \cdot \frac{1}{3} \\ x &= 3 \end{aligned}$$

8.
$$\begin{aligned} -6x + 4 &= 28 \\ -6x + 4 - 4 &= 28 - 4 \\ -6x &= 24 \\ \frac{1}{-6} \cdot -6x &= 24 \cdot \frac{1}{-6} \\ x &= -4 \end{aligned}$$

9.
$$\begin{aligned} 40 - 2x &= 26 \\ -2x &= -14 \\ x &= 7 \end{aligned}$$

10.
$$\begin{aligned} 5x + 3x &= 64 \\ 8x &= 64 \\ x &= 8 \end{aligned}$$

11.
$$\begin{aligned} 2(5y + 3) &= 56 \\ 10y + 6 &= 56 \\ 10y + 6 - 6 &= 56 - 6 \\ 10y &= 50 \\ \frac{1}{10} \cdot 10y &= 50 \cdot \frac{1}{10} \\ y &= 5 \end{aligned}$$

12.
$$\begin{aligned} 8(3a + 5) + a &= 65 \\ 24a + 40 + a &= 65 \\ 25a + 40 &= 65 \\ 25a + 40 - 40 &= 65 - 40 \\ 25a &= 25 \\ a &= 1 \end{aligned}$$

13. $n + (n + 2) + (n + 4) = 3n + 6$ 14. $\frac{1}{2}n + 12$

15. $2n - 32$ 16. $3n + 2$

17.
$$\begin{aligned} 2x + 20 + 33x &= 80 + 15x \\ 35x + 20 &= 80 + 15x \\ 35x - 15x + 20 &= 80 + 15x - 15x \\ 20x + 20 &= 80 \\ 20x + 20 - 20 &= 80 - 20 \\ 20x &= 60 \\ \frac{1}{20} \cdot 20x &= 60 \cdot \frac{1}{20} \\ x &= 3 \end{aligned}$$

18.
$$\begin{aligned} 3(2x - 1) + 4 &= x + 25 \\ 6x - 3 + 4 &= x + 25 \\ 6x + 1 &= x + 25 \\ 6x - x + 1 &= x - x + 25 \\ 5x + 1 &= 25 \\ 5x + 1 - 1 &= 25 - 1 \\ 5x &= 24 \\ \frac{1}{5} \cdot 5x &= 24 \cdot \frac{1}{5} \\ x &= \frac{24}{5} \end{aligned}$$

19.
$$\begin{aligned} 14p - 10 &= 8 + 2p \\ 14p - 2p - 10 &= 8 + 2p - 2p \\ 12p - 10 &= 8 \\ 12p - 10 + 10 &= 8 + 10 \\ 12p &= 18 \\ \frac{1}{12} \cdot 12p &= 18 \cdot \frac{1}{12} \\ p &= \frac{18}{12} = \frac{3}{2} \end{aligned}$$

20.
$$\begin{aligned} 4(2x + 1) &= 3(x + 13) \\ 8x + 4 &= 3x + 39 \\ 8x - 3x + 4 &= 3x - 3x + 39 \\ 5x + 4 &= 39 \\ 5x + 4 - 4 &= 39 - 4 \\ \frac{1}{5} \cdot 5x &= 35 \cdot \frac{1}{5} \\ x &= 7 \end{aligned}$$

21.
$$\begin{aligned} \frac{b}{3} - 2 &= 6 \\ \frac{b}{3} - 2 + 2 &= 6 + 2 \\ \frac{b}{3} &= 8 \\ 3\left(\frac{b}{3}\right) &= 3(8) \\ b &= 24 \end{aligned}$$

22.
$$\begin{aligned} \frac{2}{9}b + \frac{1}{3}b &= \frac{4}{9} - \frac{1}{3}b \\ 9\left(\frac{2}{9}b + \frac{1}{3}b\right) &= 9\left(\frac{4}{9} - \frac{1}{3}b\right) \\ 2b + 3b &= 4 - 3b \\ 5b &= 4 - 3b \\ 5b + 3b &= 4 - 3b + 3b \\ 8b &= 4 \\ \frac{1}{8} \cdot 8b &= 4 \cdot \frac{1}{8} \\ b &= \frac{4}{8} = \frac{1}{2} \end{aligned}$$

23.
$$\begin{aligned} 0.9x - 0.5x &= 6 \\ 10(0.9x - 0.5x) &= 10 \cdot 6 \\ 9x - 5x &= 60 \\ 4x &= 60 \\ \frac{1}{4} \cdot 4x &= 60 \cdot \frac{1}{4} \\ x &= 15 \end{aligned}$$

24.
$$\begin{aligned} 0.32y &= 0.3y + 32 \\ 100(0.32y) &= 100(0.3y + 32) \\ 32y &= 30y + 3200 \\ 32y - 30y &= 30y - 30y + 3200 \\ 2y &= 3200 \\ \frac{1}{2} \cdot 2y &= 3200 \cdot \frac{1}{2} \\ y &= 1600 \end{aligned}$$

LESSON 4-1 TRY THIS pp. 172–173

a. (1) Yes (2) Yes (3) Yes (4) No (5) No
b. (1) Yes (2) No (3) No (4) Yes (5) No

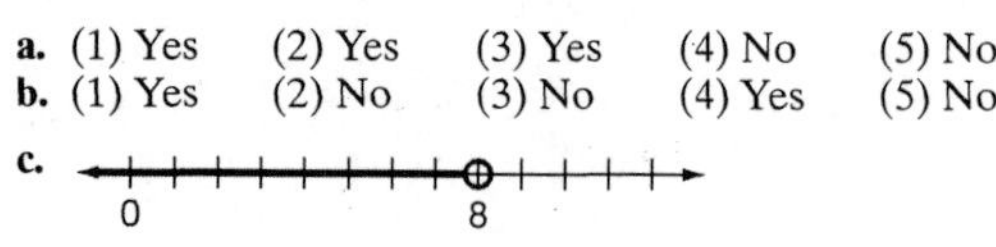

LESSON 4-1 EXERCISES pp. 173–174

	a.	b.	c.	d.
1.	No	No	No	Yes
2.	Yes	No	Yes	Yes
3.	No	No	Yes	Yes
4.	Yes	Yes	Yes	No
5.	No	No	Yes	No
6.	Yes	No	Yes	Yes
7.	Yes	Yes	Yes	No
8.	Yes	Yes	No	Yes

9. 0 5

10. 0

11. −3 0

12. −5 0

13. 0 6

14. 0 4

15. −4 0

16. −2 0

17. 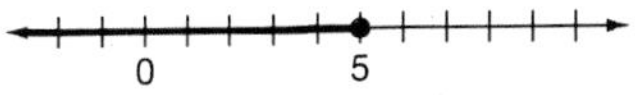

18. 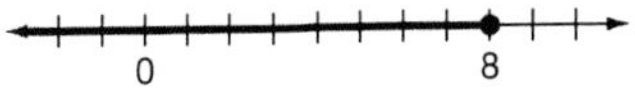

19. 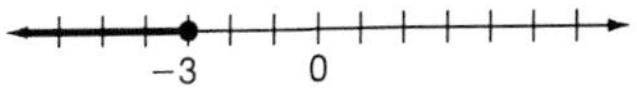

20. 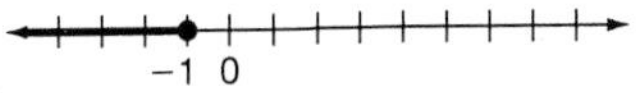

21. True **22.** True **23.** False **24.** True

25. The speed limit is 25 mi/hr, so the possible legal speeds are less than or equal to 25 mi/hr, $s \le 25$.

26. $x \ge 2$ **27.** $x \le -2$ **28.** $x < 4$

29. $x < 0$ **30.** $x \ge 3$ **31.** $x \le 7$

32. They are the same distance from 2.

33. 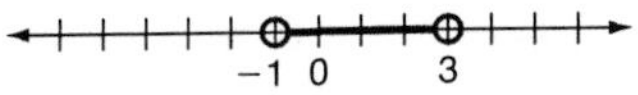

34. No points meet requirements.

35. 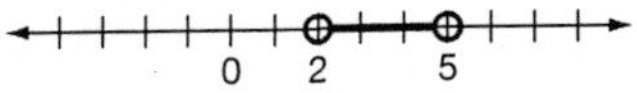

36. 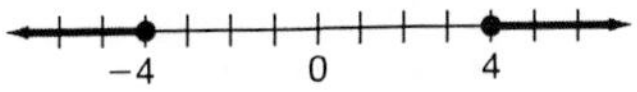

37.
$$\frac{1}{3} + 8m = 3m - \frac{1}{2}$$
$$6\left(\frac{1}{3} + 8m\right) = 6\left(3m - \frac{1}{2}\right)$$
$$2 + 48m = 18m - 3$$
$$2 + 48m - 18m = 18m - 18m - 3$$
$$2 + 30m = -3$$
$$2 - 2 + 30m = -3 - 2$$
$$30m = -5$$
$$\frac{1}{30} \cdot 30m = \frac{1}{30} \cdot (-5)$$
$$m = -\frac{1}{6}$$

38.
$$5x - (2x + 7) = 2$$
$$5x - 2x - 7 = 2$$
$$3x - 7 = 2$$
$$3x - 7 + 7 = 2 + 7$$
$$3x = 9$$
$$\frac{1}{3} \cdot 3x = \frac{1}{3} \cdot 9$$
$$x = 3$$

39.
$$7.5y - 0.5y = 3.75y + 39$$
$$7y = 3.75y + 39$$
$$7y - 3.75y = 3.75y - 3.75y + 39$$
$$3.25y = 39$$
$$\frac{1}{3.25} \cdot 3.25y = \frac{1}{3.25} \cdot 39$$
$$y = 12$$

40.
$$16 - 2w = 10w - 2 - 6w$$
$$16 - 2w = 4w - 2$$
$$16 - 2w + 2w = 4w + 2w - 2$$
$$16 = 6w - 2$$
$$16 + 2 = 6w - 2 + 2$$
$$18 = 6w$$
$$\frac{1}{6} \cdot 18 = \frac{1}{6} \cdot 6w$$
$$3 = w$$

41.
$$|y| + 6 = 21$$
$$|y| + 6 - 6 = 21 - 6$$
$$|y| = 15$$
$$y = 15 \quad \text{or} \quad y = -15$$

42.
$$|a| = |-9|$$
$$|a| = 9$$
$$a = 9 \quad \text{or} \quad a = -9$$

43. $|x| = -6$
No solution

44. Let w = width.
$w + 5$ = length.
$$2w + 2(w + 5) = 30$$
$$2w + 2w + 10 = 30$$
$$4w + 10 = 30$$
$$4w + 10 - 10 = 30 - 10$$
$$4w = 20$$
$$\frac{1}{4} \cdot 4w = \frac{1}{4} \cdot 20$$
$$w = 5$$
The width is 5 in.; the length, 10 in.

45. Let n = number of tickets.
$$12n + 5 = 77$$
$$12n + 5 - 5 = 77 - 5$$
$$12n = 72$$
$$\frac{1}{12} \cdot 12n = \frac{1}{12} \cdot 72$$
$$n = 6$$
He bought 6 tickets.

LESSON 4-2 TRY THIS pp. 176–177

a.
$$x + 3 > 5$$
$$x + 3 + (-3) > 5 + (-3)$$
$$x > 2$$
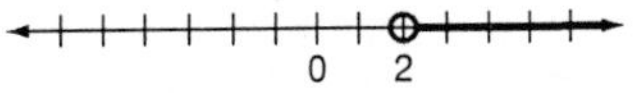

b.
$$x - 5 \le 8$$
$$x - 5 + 5 \le 8 + 5$$
$$x \le 13$$
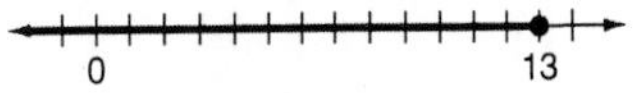

c.
$$x - 2 \ge 7$$
$$x - 2 + 2 \ge 7 + 2$$
$$x \ge 9$$
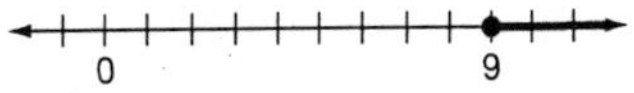

d.
$$x + 1 < 3$$
$$x + 1 - 1 < 3 - 1$$
$$x < 2$$
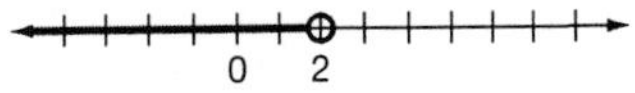

e.
$$y + \frac{1}{8} < -\frac{3}{8}$$
$$y + \frac{1}{8} - \frac{1}{8} < -\frac{3}{8} - \frac{1}{8}$$
$$y < -\frac{4}{8}$$
$$y < -\frac{1}{2}$$
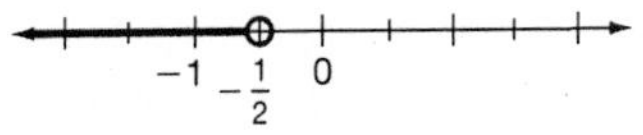

f.
$$\frac{3}{10} \le -\frac{1}{5} + y$$
$$\frac{3}{10} + \frac{1}{5} \le -\frac{1}{5} + \frac{1}{5} + y$$
$$\frac{3}{10} + \frac{2}{10} \le y$$
$$\frac{5}{10} \le y$$
$$y \ge \frac{1}{2}$$
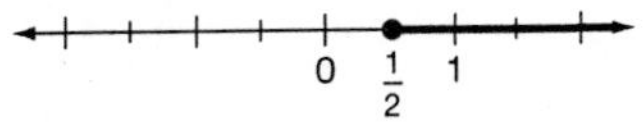

g. $$\begin{aligned} 5y + 2 - 4y &\le -1 \\ y + 2 &\le -1 \\ y + 2 - 2 &\le -1 - 2 \\ y &\le -3 \end{aligned}$$

−3 0

h. $$\begin{aligned} -4x + 5x + 1 &< -2 \\ x + 1 &< -2 \\ x + 1 - 1 &< -2 - 1 \\ x &< -3 \end{aligned}$$

−3 0

LESSON 4-2 EXERCISES pp. 178–179

1. $$\begin{aligned} x + 7 &> 2 \\ x + 7 - 7 &> 2 - 7 \\ x &> -5 \end{aligned}$$

−5 0

2. $$\begin{aligned} x + 6 &> 3 \\ x + 6 - 6 &> 3 - 6 \\ x &> -3 \end{aligned}$$

−3 0

3. $$\begin{aligned} y + 5 &> 8 \\ y + 5 - 5 &> 8 - 5 \\ y &> 3 \end{aligned}$$

0 3

4. $$\begin{aligned} y + 7 &> 9 \\ y + 7 - 7 &> 9 - 7 \\ y &> 2 \end{aligned}$$

0 2

5. $$\begin{aligned} x + 8 &\le -10 \\ x + 8 - 8 &\le -10 - 8 \\ x &\le -18 \end{aligned}$$

−19 −18

6. $$\begin{aligned} x + 9 &\le -12 \\ x + 9 - 9 &\le -12 - 9 \\ x &\le -21 \end{aligned}$$

−22 −21

7. $$\begin{aligned} a + 12 &< 6 \\ a + 12 - 12 &< 6 - 12 \\ a &< -6 \end{aligned}$$

−6 0

8. $$\begin{aligned} a + 20 &< 8 \\ a + 20 - 20 &< 8 - 20 \\ a &< -12 \end{aligned}$$

−13 −12

9. $$\begin{aligned} x - 7 &\le 9 \\ x - 7 + 7 &\le 9 + 7 \\ x &\le 16 \end{aligned}$$

15 16

10. $$\begin{aligned} x - 3 &\le 14 \\ x - 3 + 3 &\le 14 + 3 \\ x &\le 17 \end{aligned}$$

16 17

11. $$\begin{aligned} x - 6 &> 2 \\ x - 6 + 6 &> 2 + 6 \\ x &> 8 \end{aligned}$$

0 8

12. $$\begin{aligned} x - 9 &> 4 \\ x - 9 + 9 &> 4 + 9 \\ x &> 13 \end{aligned}$$

13 14

13. $$\begin{aligned} y - 7 &> -12 \\ y - 7 + 7 &> -12 + 7 \\ y &> -5 \end{aligned}$$

−5 0

14. $$\begin{aligned} y - 10 &> -16 \\ y - 10 + 10 &> -16 + 10 \\ y &> -6 \end{aligned}$$

−6 0

15. $$\begin{aligned} 4m - 3m &< 2 \\ m &< 2 \end{aligned}$$

0 2

16. $$\begin{aligned} 2x + 3 - x &> 5 \\ x + 3 &> 5 \\ x + 3 - 3 &> 5 - 3 \\ x &> 2 \end{aligned}$$

0 2

17. $$\begin{aligned} 3x - 2x + 9 &\le 6 \\ x + 9 &\le 6 \\ x + 9 - 9 &\le 6 - 9 \\ x &\le -3 \end{aligned}$$

18. $$\begin{aligned} -2y + 3y + 10 &\le 8 \\ y + 10 &\le 8 \\ y + 10 - 10 &\le 8 - 10 \\ y &\le -2 \end{aligned}$$

19. $$\begin{aligned} 5n - 6 - 4n &< -2 \\ n - 6 &< -2 \\ n - 6 + 6 &< -2 + 6 \\ n &< 4 \end{aligned}$$

20. $$\begin{aligned} -5x + 6x - 8 &< -9 \\ x - 8 &< -9 \\ x - 8 + 8 &< -9 + 8 \\ x &< -1 \end{aligned}$$

21. $$\begin{aligned} 3y + 4 - 2y &\le -7 \\ y + 4 &\le -7 \\ y + 4 - 4 &\le -7 - 4 \\ y &\le -11 \end{aligned}$$

22. $$\begin{aligned} 4a - 3a + 5 &\ge -8 \\ a + 5 &\ge -8 \\ a + 5 - 5 &\ge -8 - 5 \\ a &\ge -13 \end{aligned}$$

23. $$\begin{aligned} m + \tfrac{1}{4} &\le \tfrac{1}{2} \\ m + \tfrac{1}{4} - \tfrac{1}{4} &\le \tfrac{1}{2} - \tfrac{1}{4} \\ m &\le \tfrac{2}{4} - \tfrac{1}{4} \\ m &\le \tfrac{1}{4} \end{aligned}$$

24. $$\begin{aligned} y + \tfrac{1}{3} &\ge \tfrac{5}{6} \\ y + \tfrac{1}{3} - \tfrac{1}{3} &\ge \tfrac{5}{6} - \tfrac{1}{3} \\ y &\ge \tfrac{5}{6} - \tfrac{2}{6} \\ y &\ge \tfrac{3}{6} \\ y &\ge \tfrac{1}{2} \end{aligned}$$

25. $$\begin{aligned} x - \tfrac{1}{3} &> \tfrac{1}{4} \\ x - \tfrac{1}{3} + \tfrac{1}{3} &> \tfrac{1}{4} + \tfrac{1}{3} \\ x &> \tfrac{3}{12} + \tfrac{4}{12} \\ x &> \tfrac{7}{12} \end{aligned}$$

26. $$\begin{aligned} b - \tfrac{1}{8} &> \tfrac{1}{2} \\ b - \tfrac{1}{8} + \tfrac{1}{8} &> \tfrac{1}{2} + \tfrac{1}{8} \\ b &> \tfrac{4}{8} + \tfrac{1}{8} \\ b &> \tfrac{5}{8} \end{aligned}$$

27. $$\begin{aligned} c + \tfrac{4}{5} &\le \tfrac{3}{10} \\ c + \tfrac{4}{5} - \tfrac{4}{5} &\le \tfrac{3}{10} - \tfrac{4}{5} \\ c &\le \tfrac{3}{10} - \tfrac{8}{10} \\ c &\le -\tfrac{5}{10} \\ c &\le -\tfrac{1}{2} \end{aligned}$$

28. $$\begin{aligned} \tfrac{2}{3} + a &\ge \tfrac{5}{6} \\ \tfrac{2}{3} - \tfrac{2}{3} + a &\ge \tfrac{5}{6} - \tfrac{2}{3} \\ a &\ge \tfrac{5}{6} - \tfrac{4}{6} \\ a &\ge \tfrac{1}{6} \end{aligned}$$

29. $t - 5 \le 1$
$t - 5 + 5 \le 1 + 5$
$t \le 6$
Any number less than or equal to 6 is a solution of the inequality. The only number that is not a solution is 10. The answer is D.

30. $3(r + 2) - 2r < 4$
$3r + 6 - 2r < 4$
$r + 6 < 4$
$r + 6 - 6 < 4 - 6$
$r < -2$

31. $4(r + 5) - 3r \ge 7$
$4r + 20 - 3r \ge 7$
$r + 20 \ge 7$
$r + 20 - 20 \ge 7 - 20$
$r \ge -13$

32. $3a + 6 - 2a \ge -19$
$a + 6 \ge -19$
$a + 6 - 6 \ge -19 - 6$
$a \ge -25$

33. $-5 \le 3m - 10 - 2m$
$-5 \le m - 10$
$-5 + 10 \le m - 10 + 10$
$5 \le m$

34. $4(x + 3) - 3x > 4$
$4x + 12 - 3x > 4$
$x + 12 > 4$
$x + 12 - 12 > 4 - 12$
$x > -8$

35. $5(y - 2) - 4(y - 1) < 0$
$5y - 10 - 4y + 4 < 0$
$y - 6 < 0$
$y - 6 + 6 < 0 + 6$
$y < 6$

36. $-6(a + 2) + 7a \le -12$
$-6a - 12 + 7a \le -12$
$a - 12 \le -12$
$a - 12 + 12 \le -12 + 12$
$a \le 0$

37. $-2(a - 3) + 3(a + 2) < 4$
$-2a + 6 + 3a + 6 < 4$
$a + 12 < 4$
$a + 12 - 12 < 4 - 12$
$a < -8$

38. $y + 2 + 3y > 9$
$y + 2 - 2 + 3y > 9 - 2$
$y + 3y > 7$

39. $a^2 + 4 - b \le -2$
$a^2 + 4 - 4 - b \le -2 - 4$
$a^2 - b \le -6$

40. $m + n - 4 \le n$
$m + n - n - 4 \le n - n$
$m - 4 \le 0$

41. $p + q + z \ge -2$
$p + q - q + z \ge -2 - q$
$p + z \ge -2 - q$

42. $a + b < 2a - 4$
$a - a + b < 2a - a - 4$
$b < a - 4$

43. $x - y > 7 + y$
$x - y + y > 7 + y + y$
$x > 7 + 2y$

44. The student subtracted 6 from the left side, but added 6 to the right side.

45. Answers may vary; $x + 7 \le 2, 2x - 6 \le -16$

46. True. x is to the left of y on the number line, and c is to the left of d. When adding c to x, we add a smaller number than we add to y, so $c + x$ must be to the left of $d + y$.

47. False. (Let $x = 5, y = 4, c = 4, d = 1$.)
$5 - 4 > 4 - 1$
$1 > 3$ is false.

48. The first integer greater than 5 is 6, so $x \ge 6$.

49. The first integer less than 5 is 4, so $y \le 4$.

50. Yes for both. If a is to the right of b on the number line and b is to the right of c, then a is to the right of c.

51. **a.** $x \not> 5$ means $x = 5$ or $x < 5$, so $x \le 5$
b. $x \not< -3$ means $x = -3$ or $x > -3$, so $x \ge -3$
c. $x \ne -\frac{3}{2}$ means $x > -\frac{3}{2}$ or $x < -\frac{3}{2}$
d. $x \not< y$ means $x = y$ or $x > y$, so $x \ge y$
e. $x \not> -y$ means $x = -y$ or $x < -y$, so $x \le -y$
f. $-x \ne y$ means $-x > y$ or $-x < y$

52. $\frac{m}{8} = \frac{3}{4}$
$8 \cdot \frac{m}{8} = 8 \cdot \frac{3}{4}$
$m = 6$

53. $\frac{21}{m} = \frac{7}{3}$
$3m \cdot \frac{21}{m} = 3m \cdot \frac{7}{3}$
$63 = 7m$
$\frac{1}{7} \cdot 63 = \frac{1}{7} \cdot 7m$
$9 = m$

54. $\frac{4}{6} = \frac{m}{9}$
$18 \cdot \frac{4}{6} = 18 \cdot \frac{m}{9}$
$12 = 2m$
$\frac{1}{2} \cdot 12 = \frac{1}{2} \cdot 2m$
$6 = m$

55. $-84x = 4$
$\frac{1}{-84} \cdot (-84x) = \frac{1}{-84} \cdot 4$
$x = -\frac{4}{84}$
$x = -\frac{1}{21}$

56. $-3 = 9c$
$\frac{1}{9} \cdot (-3) = \frac{1}{9} \cdot 9c$
$-\frac{3}{9} = c$
$c = -\frac{1}{3}$

57. $|t| - 4 = 21$
$|t| - 4 + 4 = 21 + 4$
$|t| = 25$
$t = 25$ or $t = -25$

58. $3 - |m| = 1$
$3 - 3 - |m| = 1 - 3$
$-|m| = -2$
$(-1)(-|m|) = (-1)(-2)$
$|m| = 2$
$m = 2$ or $m = -2$

59. $\frac{2}{3} + \frac{1}{8}m = \frac{5}{12}m - \frac{19}{24}$
$24\left(\frac{2}{3} + \frac{1}{8}m\right) = 24\left(\frac{5}{12}m - \frac{19}{24}\right)$
$16 + 3m = 10m - 19$
$16 + 3m - 3m = 10m - 3m - 19$
$16 = 7m - 19$
$16 + 19 = 7m - 19 + 19$
$35 = 7m$
$\frac{1}{7} \cdot 35 = \frac{1}{7} \cdot 7m$
$5 = m$

60. $\frac{2}{3} \cdot |y| = 8$
$\frac{3}{2} \cdot \frac{2}{3} \cdot |y| = \frac{3}{2} \cdot 8$
$|y| = 12$
$y = 12$ or $y = -12$

61. $2x + 3$

62. Let n = number of lifeboats needed.
$\frac{1}{16} = \frac{n}{144}$
$144 \cdot \frac{1}{16} = 144 \cdot \frac{n}{144}$
$9 = n$
9 lifeboats are needed.

63. Let p = number of ounces of peanuts needed.
$\frac{6}{4} = \frac{p}{28}$
$28 \cdot \frac{6}{4} = 28 \cdot \frac{p}{28}$
$42 = p$
42 ounces of peanuts are needed.

CONNECTIONS: GEOMETRY p. 179

$m\angle 1 + m\angle 2 < 90$
$x + (4x + 6) < 90$
$5x + 6 < 90$
$5x + 6 - 6 < 90 - 6$
$5x < 84$

$\frac{1}{5}(5x) < \frac{1}{5}(84)$

$x < \frac{84}{5}$ or $16\frac{4}{5}$

$m\angle 1 < 16\frac{4}{5}^\circ$ $\quad m\angle 2 < 4\left(16\frac{4}{5}\right) + 6$

$m\angle 2 < 73\frac{1}{5}^\circ$

Answers may vary but should satisfy these conditions for $m\angle 1$ and $m\angle 2$.

LESSON 4-3 TRY THIS p. 181

a. $8x < 64$

$\frac{1}{8} \cdot 8x < \frac{1}{8} \cdot 64$

$x < 8$

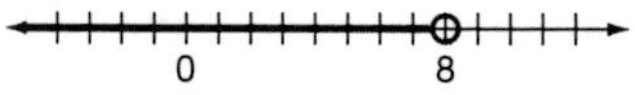

b. $5y \geq 160$

$\frac{1}{5} \cdot 5y \geq \frac{1}{5} \cdot 160$

$y \geq 32$

c. $2t < 56$

$\frac{1}{2} \cdot 2t < 56$

$t < 28$

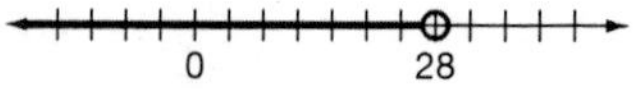

d. $9s > 81$

$\frac{1}{9} \cdot 9s > \frac{1}{9} \cdot 81$

$s > 9$

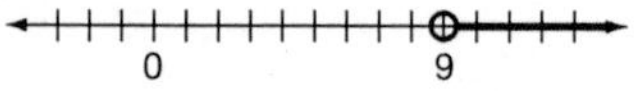

e. $-4x \geq 24$

$\frac{1}{-4}(-4x) \leq \frac{1}{-4} \cdot 24$

$x \leq -6$

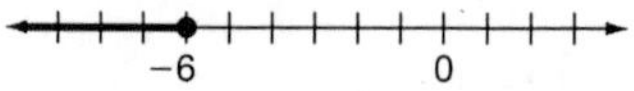

f. $-5y < 13$

$-\frac{1}{5}(-5y) > -\frac{1}{5}(13)$

$y > -\frac{13}{5}$

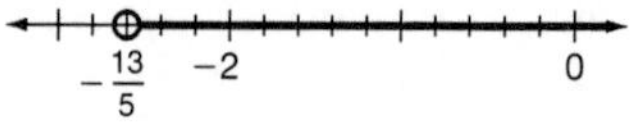

g. $-t < -5$
$(-1)(-t) > (-1)(-5)$
$t > 5$

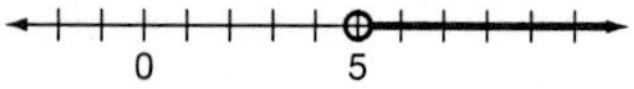

h. $-n > 2$
$(-1)(-n) < (-1)2$
$n < -2$

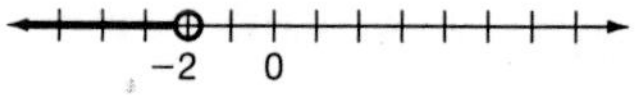

i. $-y \geq \frac{1}{2}$

$(-1)(-y) \leq (-1)\frac{1}{2}$

$y \leq -\frac{1}{2}$

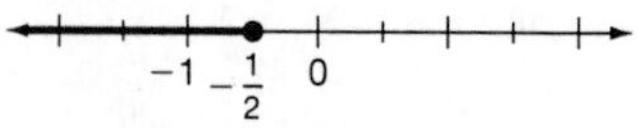

j. $-3x < \frac{1}{6}$

$\frac{1}{-3}(-3x) > \frac{1}{-3}\left(\frac{1}{6}\right)$

$x > -\frac{1}{18}$

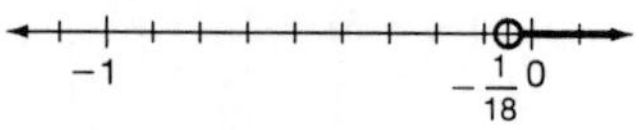

k. $-2x \leq \frac{5}{8}$

$\frac{1}{-2}(-2x) \geq \left(\frac{1}{-2}\right)\left(\frac{5}{8}\right)$

$x \geq -\frac{5}{16}$

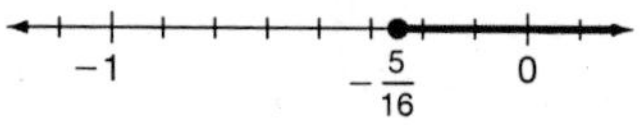

l. $-4y \geq -\frac{3}{7}$

$(-4y)\left(-\frac{1}{4}\right) \leq \left(-\frac{3}{7}\right)\left(-\frac{1}{4}\right)$

$y \leq \frac{3}{28}$

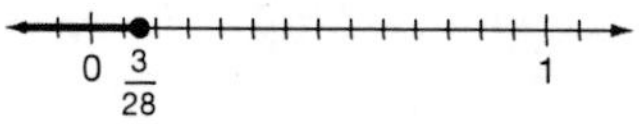

LESSON 4-3 EXERCISES p. 182

1. $5x < 35$

$\frac{1}{5} \cdot 5x < \frac{1}{5} \cdot 35$

$x < 7$

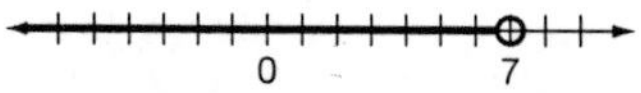

2. $8x \geq 32$

$\frac{1}{8} \cdot 8x \geq \frac{1}{8} \cdot 32$

$x \geq 4$

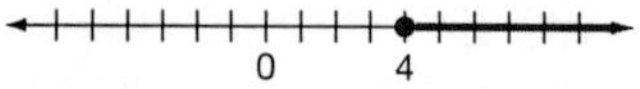

3. $9y \leq 81$

$\frac{1}{9} \cdot 9y \leq \frac{1}{9} \cdot 81$

$y \leq 9$

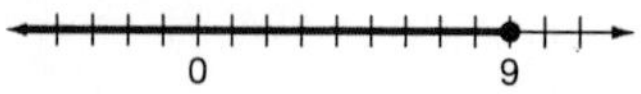

4. $10x > 240$

$\frac{1}{10} \cdot 10x > \frac{1}{10} \cdot 240$

$x > 24$

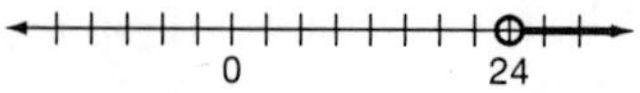

5. $6y > 72$

$\frac{1}{6} \cdot 6y > \frac{1}{6} \cdot 72$

$y > 12$

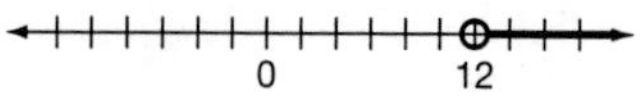

6. $9x \le 63$

$\frac{1}{9} \cdot 9x \le \frac{1}{9} \cdot 63$

$x \le 7$

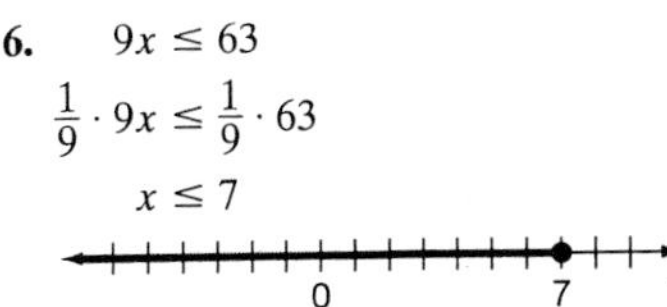

7. $7x < 13$

$\frac{1}{7} \cdot 7x < \frac{1}{7} \cdot 13$

$x < \frac{13}{7}$

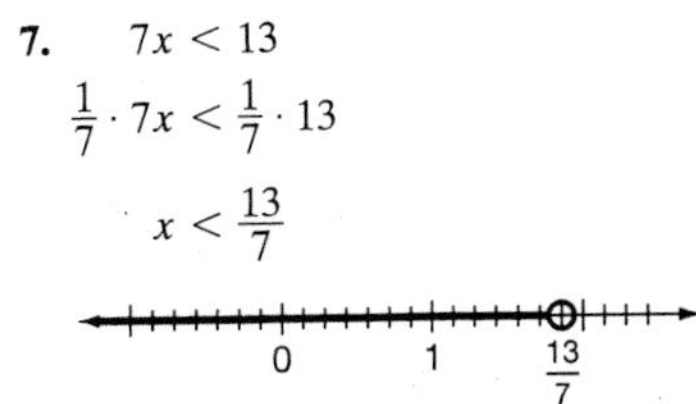

8. $8y < 17$

$\frac{1}{8} \cdot 8y < \frac{1}{8} \cdot 17$

$y < \frac{17}{8}$

9. $4y \ge 15$

$\frac{1}{4} \cdot 4y \ge \frac{1}{4} \cdot 15$

$y \ge \frac{15}{4}$

10. $3y \ge 19$

$\frac{1}{3} \cdot 3y \ge \frac{1}{3} \cdot 19$

$y \ge \frac{19}{3}$

11. $6y \le 3$

$\frac{1}{6} \cdot 6y \le \frac{1}{6} \cdot 3$

$y \le \frac{1}{2}$

12. $14x \le 4$

$\frac{1}{14} \cdot 14x \le \frac{1}{14} \cdot 4$

$x \le \frac{2}{7}$

13. $7y \ge -21$

$\frac{1}{7} \cdot 7y \ge \frac{1}{7} \cdot -21$

$y \ge -3$

14. $6x \ge -18$

$\frac{1}{6} \cdot 6x \ge \frac{1}{6} \cdot -18$

$x \ge -3$

15 $12x < -36$

$\frac{1}{12} \cdot 12x < \frac{1}{12} \cdot -36$

$x < -3$

16. $16y < -64$

$\frac{1}{16} \cdot 16y < \frac{1}{16} \cdot -64$

$y < -4$

17. $5y \ge -2$

$\frac{1}{5} \cdot 5y \ge \frac{1}{5} \cdot -2$

$y \ge -\frac{2}{5}$

18. $7x \ge -4$

$\frac{1}{7} \cdot 7x \ge \frac{1}{7} \cdot -4$

$x \ge -\frac{4}{7}$

19. $-2x \le 12$

$-\frac{1}{2} \cdot -2x \ge -\frac{1}{2} \cdot 12$

$x \ge -6$

20. $-3y \le 15$

$-\frac{1}{3} \cdot -3y \ge -\frac{1}{3} \cdot 15$

$y \ge -5$

21. $-4y \ge 16$

$-\frac{1}{4} \cdot -4y \le -\frac{1}{4} \cdot 16$

$y \le -4$

22. $-7y \le 21$

$-\frac{1}{7} \cdot -7y \ge -\frac{1}{7} \cdot 21$

$y \ge -3$

23. $-6y > 360$

$-\frac{1}{6} \cdot -6y < -\frac{1}{6} \cdot 360$

$y < -60$

24. $-9x > 540$

$-\frac{1}{9} \cdot -9x < -\frac{1}{9} \cdot 540$

$x < -60$

25. $-12x < -24$

$-\frac{1}{12} \cdot -12x > -\frac{1}{12} \cdot -24$

$x > 2$

26. $-14y < -70$

$-\frac{1}{14} \cdot -14y > -\frac{1}{14} \cdot -70$

$y > 5$

27. $-18y \ge -36$

$-\frac{1}{18} \cdot -18y \le -\frac{1}{18} \cdot -36$

$y \le 2$

28. $-20x \ge -400$

$-\frac{1}{20} \cdot -20x \le -\frac{1}{20} \cdot -400$

$x \le 20$

29. $-2x < -17$

$-\frac{1}{2} \cdot -2x > -\frac{1}{2} \cdot -17$

$x > \frac{17}{2}$

30. $-5y < -23$

$-\frac{1}{5} \cdot -5y > -\frac{1}{5} \cdot -23$

$y > \frac{23}{5}$

31. $-8y \ge -31$

$-\frac{1}{8} \cdot -8y \le -\frac{1}{8} \cdot -31$

$y \le \frac{31}{8}$

32. $-7x \ge -43$

$-\frac{1}{7} \cdot -7x \le -\frac{1}{7} \cdot -43$

$x \le \frac{43}{7}$

33. $-3y < \frac{1}{7}$

$-\frac{1}{3} \cdot -3y > -\frac{1}{3} \cdot \frac{1}{7}$

$y > -\frac{1}{21}$

34. The student forgot to reverse the direction of the inequality sign when multiplying both sides of the inequality by a negative number.

35. $-7x \ge -6.3$

$-\frac{1}{7}(-7x) \le -\frac{1}{7}(-6.3)$

$x \le 0.9$

36. $-\frac{5}{6}y \le -\frac{3}{4}$

$-\frac{6}{5}\left(-\frac{5}{6}y\right) \ge -\frac{6}{5}\left(-\frac{3}{4}\right)$

$y \ge \frac{9}{10}$

37. $-8x < 40.5$

$-\frac{1}{8}(-8x) > -\frac{1}{8}(40.5)$

$x > -5.0625$

38. $-\frac{3}{4}x \ge -\frac{1}{8}$

$-\frac{4}{3}\left(-\frac{3}{4}x\right) \le -\frac{4}{3}\left(-\frac{1}{8}\right)$

$x \le \frac{1}{6}$

39. $5x + 6x < -33$

$11x < -33$

$\frac{1}{11} \cdot 11x < \frac{1}{11}(-33)$

$x < -3$

40. $-12 > 2y - 6y$

$-12 > -4y$

$-\frac{1}{4}(-12) < -\frac{1}{4}(4y)$

$3 < y$

41. $0 > -5t + 10t$
$0 > 5t$
$\frac{1}{5} \cdot 0 > \frac{1}{5} \cdot 5t$
$0 > t$

42. $4 \le -9n + n$
$4 \le -8n$
$-\frac{1}{8} \cdot 4 \ge -\frac{1}{8}(-8n)$
$-\frac{1}{2} \ge n$

43. $4m - 9m \ge -12 - 8$
$-5m \ge -20$
$-\frac{1}{5}(-5m) \le -\frac{1}{5}(-20)$
$m \le 4$

44. $3x > 4x$
$3x - 4x > 4x - 4x$
$-x > 0$
$x < 0$

45. False; $-2 > -3$ but $4 < 9$.

46. False; $6 < 10$ but $\frac{6}{-2} > \frac{10}{-2}$.

47. **a.** $-4(10) > 9$
$-40 > 9$
No

b. $-4(6) > 9$
$-24 > 9$
No

c. $-4(-8) > 9$
$32 > 9$
Yes

d. $-4(0) > 9$
$0 > 9$
No

e. $-4(-5) > 9$
$20 > 9$
Yes

48. $4m + 2m - m = (4 + 2 - 1)m = 5m$

49. $7x + 5 + 4x = (7 + 4)x + 5 = 11x + 5$

50. $6(y + 4y) + 3y = 6y + 24y + 3y = 33y$

51. $3(2x - 4) + 2x + 12 = 6x - 12 + 2x + 12 = 8x$

52. $a(b^2 + c)$
$2(3 \cdot 3 + 4)$
$2(9 + 4)$
$2(13)$
26

53. $c(2a - 3b)$
$4(2 \cdot 2 \cdot 3 \cdot 3)$
$4(4 - 9)$
$4(-5)$
-20

LESSON 4-4 TRY THIS p. 183

a. $7 - 4x < -1$
$7 - 7 - 4x < -1 - 7$
$-4x < -8$
$\frac{1}{-4}(-4x) > \frac{1}{-4}(-8)$
$x > 2$

b. $13a + 5 \ge 12a + 4$
$13a - 12a + 5 \ge 12a - 12a + 4$
$a + 5 \ge 4$
$a + 5 - 5 \ge 4 - 5$
$a \ge -1$

c. $4m - 4 > 8 + 2m$
$4m - 2m - 4 > 8 + 2m - 2m$
$2m - 4 > 8$
$2m - 4 + 4 > 8 + 4$
$2m > 12$
$\frac{1}{2}(2m) > \frac{1}{2} \cdot 12$
$m > 6$

LESSON 4-4 EXERCISES pp. 184–186

1. $4 + 3x < 28$
$4 - 4 + 3x < 28 - 4$
$3x < 24$
$\frac{1}{3}(3x) < \frac{1}{3}(24)$
$x < 8$

2. $5 + 4y < 37$
$5 - 5 + 4y < 37 - 5$
$4y < 32$
$\frac{1}{4}(4y) < \frac{1}{4}(32)$
$y < 8$

3. $3x - 5 \le 13$
$3x - 5 + 5 \le 13 + 5$
$3x \le 18$
$\frac{1}{3}(3x) \le \frac{1}{3}(18)$
$x \le 6$

4. $5y - 9 \le 21$
$5y - 9 + 9 \le 21 + 9$
$5y \le 30$
$\frac{1}{5}(5y) \le \frac{1}{5}(30)$
$y \le 6$

5. $13x - 7 < -46$
$13x - 7 + 7 < -46 + 7$
$13x < -39$
$\frac{1}{13}(13x) < \frac{1}{13}(-39)$
$x < -3$

6. $8y - 4 < -52$
$8y - 4 + 4 < -52 + 4$
$8y < -48$
$\frac{1}{8}(8y) < \frac{1}{8}(-48)$
$y < -6$

7. $5x + 3 \ge -7$
$5x + 3 - 3 \ge -7 - 3$
$5x \ge -10$
$\frac{1}{5}(5x) \ge \frac{1}{5}(-10)$
$x \ge -2$

8. $7y + 4 \ge -10$
$7y + 4 - 4 \ge -10 - 4$
$7y \ge -14$
$\frac{1}{7}(7y) \ge \frac{1}{7}(-14)$
$y \ge -2$

9. $4 - 3y > 13$
$4 - 4 - 3y > 13 - 4$
$-3y > 9$
$\frac{1}{-3}(-3y) < \frac{1}{-3}(9)$
$y < -3$

10. $6 - 8x > 22$
$6 - 6 - 8x > 22 - 6$
$-8x > 16$
$\frac{1}{-8}(-8x) < \frac{1}{-8}(16)$
$x < -2$

11. $3 - 9x < 30$
$3 - 3 - 9x < 30 - 3$
$-9x < 27$
$\frac{1}{-9}(-9x) > \frac{1}{-9}(27)$
$x > -3$

12. $5 - 7y < 40$
$5 - 5 - 7y < 40 - 5$
$-7y < 35$
$\frac{1}{-7}(-7y) > \frac{1}{-7}(35)$
$y > -5$

13. $3 - 6y > 23$
$3 - 3 - 6y > 23 - 3$
$-6y > 20$
$\frac{1}{-6}(-6y) < \frac{1}{-6}(20)$
$y < -\frac{20}{6}$ or $-\frac{10}{3}$

14. $8 - 2y > 14$
$8 - 8 - 2y > 14 - 8$
$-2y > 6$
$\frac{1}{-2}(-2y) < \frac{1}{-2}(6)$
$y < -3$

15. $4x + 2 - 3x \le 9$
$x + 2 \le 9$
$x + 2 - 2 \le 9 - 2$
$x \le 7$

16. $15x + 3 - 14x \le 7$
$x + 3 \le 7$
$x + 3 - 3 \le 7 - 3$
$x \le 4$

17. $8x + 7 - 7x > -3$
$x + 7 > -3$
$x + 7 - 7 > -3 - 7$
$x > -10$

18. $9x + 8 - 8x > -5$
$x + 8 > -5$
$x + 8 - 8 > -5 - 8$
$x > -13$

19. $6 - 4y > 4 - 3y$
$6 - 4y + 3y > 4 - 3y + 3y$
$6 - y > 4$
$6 - 6 - y > 4 - 6$
$-y > -2$
$(-1)(-y) < (-1)(-2)$
$y < 2$

20. $7 - 8y > 5 - 7y$
$7 - 8y + 7y > 5 - 7y + 7y$
$7 - y > 5$
$7 - 7 - y > 5 - 7$
$-y > -2$
$(-1)(-y) < (-1)(-2)$
$y < 2$

21. $5 - 9y \le 2 - 8y$
$5 - 9y + 8y \le 2 - 8y + 8y$
$5 - y \le 2$
$5 - 5 - y \le 2 - 5$
$-y \le -3$
$(-1)(-y) \ge (-1)(-3)$
$y \ge 3$

22. $6 - 13y \le 4 - 12y$
$6 - 13y + 12y \le 4 - 12y + 12y$
$6 - y \le 4$
$6 - 6 - y \le 4 - 6$
$-y \le -2$
$(-1)(-y) \ge (-1)(-2)$
$y \ge 2$

23. $19 - 7y - 3y < 39$
$19 - 10y < 39$
$19 - 19 - 10y < 39 - 19$
$-10y < 20$
$\frac{1}{-10}(-10y) > \frac{1}{-10}(20)$
$y > -2$

24. $18 - 6y - 9y < 63$
$18 - 15y < 63$
$18 - 18 - 15y < 63 - 18$
$-15y < 45$
$\frac{1}{-15}(-15y) > \frac{1}{-15}(45)$
$y > -3$

25. $21 - 8y < 6y + 49$
$21 - 8y - 6y < 6y - 6y + 49$
$21 - 14y < 49$
$21 - 21 - 14y < 49 - 21$
$-14y < 28$
$\frac{1}{-14}(-14y) > \frac{1}{-14}(28)$
$y > -2$

26. $33 - 12x < 4x + 97$
$33 - 12x - 4x < 4x - 4x + 97$
$33 - 16x < 97$
$33 - 33 - 16x < 97 - 33$
$-16x < 64$
$\frac{1}{-16}(-16x) > \frac{1}{-16}(64)$
$x > -4$

27. $14 - 5y - 2y \geq -19$
$14 - 7y \geq -19$
$14 - 14 - 7y \geq -19 - 14$
$-7y \geq -33$
$\frac{1}{-7}(-7y) \leq \frac{1}{-7}(-33)$
$y \leq \frac{33}{7}$

28. $17 - 6y - 7y \leq -13$
$17 - 13y \leq -13$
$17 - 17 - 13y \leq -13 - 17$
$-13y \leq -30$
$\frac{1}{-13}(-13y) \geq \frac{1}{-13}(-30)$
$y \geq \frac{30}{13}$

29. $27 - 11x > 14x - 18$
$27 - 11x - 14x > 14x - 14x - 18$
$27 - 25x > -18$
$27 - 27 - 25x > -18 - 27$
$-25x > -45$
$\frac{1}{-25}(-25x) < \frac{1}{-25}(-45)$
$x < \frac{45}{25}$ or $\frac{9}{5}$

30. $42 - 13y > 15y - 19$
$42 - 13y - 15y > 15y - 15y - 19$
$42 - 28y > -19$
$42 - 42 - 28y > -19 - 42$
$-28y > -61$
$\frac{1}{-28}(-28y) < \frac{1}{-28}(-61)$
$y < \frac{61}{28}$

31. $3x - 1 > -7$
$3x - 1 + 1 > -7 + 1$
$3x > -6$
$\frac{1}{3} \cdot 3x > \frac{1}{3}(-6)$
$x > -2$
The solutions of the given inequality are $x > -2$.
$-2x + 4 > 8$
$-2x + 4 - 4 > 8 - 4$
$-2x > 4$
$-\frac{1}{2}(-2x) < -\frac{1}{2}(4)$
$x < -2$
The solutions of the inequality in A are $x < -2$.
$x + 3 - 2x > 5$
$-x + 3 > 5$
$-x + 3 - 3 > 5 - 3$
$-x > 2$
$-1(-x) < -1(2)$
$x < -2$
The solutions of the inequality in B are $x < -2$.
$4x < 6x + 4$
$4x - 6x < 6x - 6x + 4$
$-2x < 4$
$-\frac{1}{2}(-2x) > -\frac{1}{2}(4)$
$x > -2$
The solutions of the inequality in C are $x > -2$.
$9 + 4x \geq 1$
$9 - 9 + 4x \geq 1 - 9$
$4x \geq -8$
$\frac{1}{4} \cdot 4x \geq \frac{1}{4}(-8)$
$x \geq -2$
The solutions of the inequality in D are $x \geq -2$.
The solutions of C are the same as the solutions of the given inequality. The answer is C.

32. $5(12 - 3t) \geq 15(t + 4)$
$60 - 15t \geq 15t + 60$
$60 - 60 - 15t - 15t \geq 15t - 15t + 60 - 60$
$-30t \geq 0$
$-\frac{1}{30}(-30t) \leq -\frac{1}{30} \cdot 0$
$t \leq 0$

33. $6(z - 5) < (7 - 2z)$
$6z - 30 < 35 - 10z$
$6z + 10z - 30 + 30 < 35 + 30 - 10z + 10z$
$16z < 65$
$\frac{1}{16} \cdot 16z < \frac{1}{16} \cdot 65$
$z < \frac{65}{16}$

34. $4(0.5 - y) + y > 4y - 0.2$
$2 - 4y + y > 4y - 0.2$
$2 + 0.2 - 4y + 4y > 4y + 4y - 0.2 + 0.2$
$2.2 > 7y$
$\frac{1}{7} \cdot 2.2 > \frac{1}{7} \cdot 7y$
$\frac{2.2}{7} > y$

35. $3 + 3(0.6 + y) > 2y + 6.6$
$3 + 1.8 + 3y > 2y + 6.6$
$4.8 + 3y > 2y + 6.6$
$4.8 - 4.8 + 3y - 2y > 2y - 2y + 6.6 - 4.8$
$y > 1.8$

36. $\frac{x}{3} - 2 \leq 1$
$6\left(\frac{x}{3} - 2\right) \leq (1)6$
$2x - 12 \leq 6$
$2x - 12 + 12 \leq 6 + 12$
$2x \leq 18$
$\frac{1}{2}(2x) \leq \frac{1}{2}(18)$
$x \leq 9$

37. $\frac{a}{3} - \frac{x}{5} < \frac{4}{15}$
$15\left(\frac{2}{3} - \frac{x}{5}\right) < \left(\frac{4}{15}\right)15$
$10 - 3x < 4$
$10 - 10 - 3x < 4 - 10$
$-3x < -6$
$-\frac{1}{3}(-3x) > -\frac{1}{3}(2)$
$x > 2$

38. $\frac{y}{5} + 1 \le \frac{2}{5}$

$5\left(\frac{y}{5} + 1\right) \le \left(\frac{2}{5}\right)5$

$y + 5 \le 2$

$y + 5 - 5 \le 2 - 5$

$y \le -3$

39. $\frac{3x}{5} \ge -15$

$5\left(\frac{3x}{5}\right) \ge 5(-15)$

$3x \ge -75$

$\frac{1}{3}(3x) \ge \frac{1}{3}(-25)$

$x \ge -25$

40. $-\frac{x}{4} - \frac{3x}{8} + 2 > 3 - x$

$8\left(-\frac{x}{4} - \frac{3x}{8} + 2\right) > (3 - x)8$

$-2x - 3x + 16 > 24 - 8x$

$-5x + 16 > 24 - 8x$

$-5x + 8x + 16 - 16 > 24 - 16 - 8x + 8x$

$3x > 8$

$\frac{1}{3}(3x) > \frac{1}{3}(8)$

$x > \frac{8}{3}$

41. $11 - x > 5 + \frac{2x}{5}$

$5(11 - x) > \left(5 + \frac{2x}{5}\right)5$

$55 - 5x > 25 + 2x$

$55 - 55 - 5x > 25 - 55 + 2x$

$-5x > -30 + 2x$

$-5x - 2x > -30 + 2x - 2x$

$-7x > -30$

$-\frac{1}{7}(-7x) < -\frac{1}{7}(-30)$

$x < \frac{30}{7}$

42. $0.2y + 2.1 \ge 1.2y + 0.3$

$10(0.2y + 2.1) \ge 10(1.2y + 0.3)$

$2y + 21 \ge 12y + 3$

$2y - 2y + 21 \ge 12y - 2y + 3$

$21 \ge 10y + 3$

$21 - 3 \ge 10y + 3 - 3$

$18 \ge 10y$

$\frac{1}{10} \cdot 18 \ge \frac{1}{10} \cdot 10y$

$1.8 \ge y$

43. $0.3b + 5.4 \ge -b + 0.2$

$10(0.3b + 5.4) \ge 10(-b + 0.2)$

$3b + 54 \ge -10b + 2$

$3b + 10b + 54 \ge -10b + 10b + 2$

$13b + 54 \ge 2$

$13b + 54 - 54 \ge 2 - 54$

$13b \ge -52$

$\frac{1}{13} \cdot 13b \ge \frac{1}{13} \cdot (-52)$

$b \ge -4$

44. $0.2(30 + a) < 5$

$6 + 0.2a < 5$

$6 - 6 + 0.2a < 5 - 6$

$0.2a < -1$

$\frac{1}{0.2} \cdot 0.2a < \frac{1}{0.2}(-1)$

$a < -5$

45. $0.3(10 + 2y) \le 9$

$3 + 0.6y \le 9$

$3 - 3 + 0.6y \le 9 - 3$

$0.6y \le 6$

$\frac{1}{0.6} \cdot 0.6y \le \frac{1}{0.6}(6)$

$y \le 10$

46. $\frac{1}{5}(z + 6) \le 0.4(2 + z)$

$10\left(\frac{1}{5}(z + 6)\right) \le 10(0.4(2 + z))$

$2(z + 6) \le 4(2 + z)$

$2z + 12 \le 8 + 4z$

$2z - 2z + 12 \le 8 + 4z - 2z$

$12 \le 8 + 2z$

$12 - 8 \le 8 - 8 + 2z$

$4 \le 2z$

$\frac{1}{2} \cdot 4 \le \frac{1}{2} \cdot 2z$

$2 \le z$

47. $\frac{1}{2}(t + 5) \le 0.2(3 + t)$

$10\left[\frac{1}{2}(t + 5)\right] \le 10[0.2(3 + t)]$

$5(t + 5) \le 2(3 + t)$

$5t + 25 \le 6 + 2t$

$5t - 2t + 25 \le 6 + 2t - 2t$

$3t + 25 \le 6$

$3t + 25 - 25 \le 6 - 25$

$3t \le -19$

$\frac{1}{3} \cdot 3t \le \frac{1}{3}(-19)$

$t \le -\frac{19}{3}$

48. $\frac{1}{2}(c + 3) - \frac{1}{3}(c - 2) > 0$

$6\left[\frac{1}{2}(c + 3) - \frac{1}{3}(c - 2)\right] > 0$

$3(c + 3) - 2(c - 2) > 0$

$3c + 9 - 2c + 4 > 0$

$c + 13 > 0$

$c + 13 - 13 > -13$

$c > -13$

49. $\frac{3}{4}(2d + 1) + \frac{1}{3}(d - 3) < 0$

$12\left[\frac{3}{4}(2d + 1) + \frac{1}{3}(d - 3)\right] < 0$

$9(2d + 1) + 4(d - 3) < 0$

$18d + 9 + 4d - 12 < 0$

$22d - 3 < 0$

$22d - 3 + 3 < 0 + 3$

$22d < 3$

$\frac{1}{22} \cdot 22d < \frac{1}{22} \cdot 3$

$d < \frac{3}{22}$

50. $0.3[4(x - 2) + x] < 0.3x$

$0.3[4x - 8 + x] < 0.3x$

$0.3[5x - 8] < 0.3x$

$\frac{1}{0.3}(0.3[5x - 8]) < \frac{1}{0.3} \cdot 0.3x$

$5x - 8 < x$

$5x - x - 8 < x - x$

$4x - 8 < 0$

$4x - 8 + 8 < 0 + 8$

$4x < 8$

$\frac{1}{4} \cdot 4x < \frac{1}{4} \cdot 8$

$x < 2$

51. $0.4[2(w+3)-5w] < 0.6$
$0.4[2w+6-5w] < 0.6$
$0.4[-3w+6] < 0.6$
$10(0.4[-3w+6]) < 10(0.6)$
$4[-3w+6] < 6$
$-12w+24 < 6$
$-12w+24-24 < 6-24$
$-12w < -18$
$-\frac{1}{12}(-12w) > -\frac{1}{12}(-18)$
$w > \frac{18}{12}$ or 1.5

52. **a.** Simplifying **b.** Using the addition property
c. Simplifying **d.** Using the multiplication property
e. Simplifying

53. **a.** Using the addition property **b.** Simplifying
c. Using the addition property **d.** Simplifying
e. Using the multiplication property **f.** Simplifying

54. **a.** Using the distributive property
b. Using the addition property **c.** Simplifying
d. Using the addition property **e.** Simplifying
f. Using the multiplication property **g.** Simplifying

55. **a.** Using the multiplication property
b. Using the distributive property **c.** Simplifying
d. Using the addition property **e.** Simplifying
f. Using the multiplication property **g.** Simplifying

56. $w+3 \le w-4$
$w-w+3 \le w-w-4$
$3 \le -4$
The inequality is never true.

57. $2t < 5t$
$2t-2t < 5t-2t$
$0 < 3t$
The inequality is true when $t > 0$, and false when $t \le 0$, so the inequality is sometimes true.

58. For the inequality $x^2 > x$, try different values of x. When $x = 1$, the inequality is $1^2 > 1$, which is false. When $x = 2$, the inequality is $2^2 > 2$, which is true. The inequality is sometimes true.

59. In the second line the student added 1 to the right side, but subtracted 1 from the left side.

60. $\frac{1}{2}(5x+5) < \frac{1}{3}(5x-30)$
$6\left[\frac{1}{2}(5x+5)\right] < 6\left[\frac{1}{3}(5x-30)\right]$
$3(5x+5) < 2(5x-30)$
$15x+15 < 10x-60$
$15x-10x+15 < 10x-10x-60$
$5x+15 < -60$
$5x+15-15 < -60-15$
$5x < -75$
$\frac{1}{5}(5x) < \frac{1}{5}(-75)$
$x < -15$
There are no positive solutions.

61. $-(x+5) \ge 4a-5$
$-x-5 \ge 4a-5$
$-x \ge 4a$
$x \le -4a$

62. $\frac{1}{2}(2x+2b) > \frac{1}{3}(21+3b)$
$x+b > 7+b$
$x > 7$

63. $-6(x+3) \le -9(y+2)$
$-6x-18 \le -9y-18$
$-6x \le -9y$
$x \ge \frac{9y}{6}$ or $\frac{3y}{2}$

64. $y < ax+b$
$y-b < ax$
$\frac{y-b}{a} < x$ if $a > 0$
$\frac{y-b}{a} > x$ if $a < 0$

65. $6x+3 > 7x-c$
$6x-6x+3 > 7x-6x-c$
$3 > x-c$
$3+c > x-c+c$
$3+c > x$

66. $8-0.5x < w+6.7$
$8-8-0.5x < w+6.7-8$
$-0.5x < w-1.3$
$\frac{-1}{0.5}(-0.5x) > \frac{-1}{0.5}(w-1.3)$
$x > -2w+2.6$

67. $x \ge y$ and $-x \ge -y$
$x \ge y$ and $x \le y$
Since $x \ge y$ and $x \le y$, $x = y$.

68. $x^2 < x$

69. Chose a value of x between -1 and 0, such as $x = -0.5$.
$x^2 = (-0.5)^2 = 0.25$
$|x| = |-0.5| = 0.5$
$0.25 < 0.5$, so $x^2 < |x|$ for $-1 < x < 0$.

70. $m(m+2) = 6(6+2) = 6 \cdot 8 = 48$

71. $0.5m = 0.5(6) = 3$

72. $(m+3)(m-4) = (6+3)(6-4) = 9 \cdot 2 = 18$

73. $m^2 - m - 12 = 6^2 - 6 - 12 = 36 - 6 - 12 = 30 - 12 = 18$

74. $9y = 3y - 45$
$9y-3y = 3y-3y-45$
$6y = -45$
$\frac{1}{6} \cdot 6y = \frac{1}{6}(-45)$
$y = -\frac{45}{6} = -\frac{15}{2} = -7.5$

75. $3z+45 < 36$
$3z+45-45 < 36-45$
$3z < -9$
$\frac{1}{3} \cdot 3z < \frac{1}{3}(-9)$
$z < -3$

76. $-2.05n = -9.02$
$\frac{1}{-2.05}(-2.05n) = \frac{1}{-2.05}(-9.02)$
$n = 4.4$

77. $2x = 3x-4$
$2x-3x = 3x-3x-4$
$-x = -4$
$-1(-x) = -1(-4)$
$x = 4$

78. $\frac{6}{8} = 0.75 = 75\%$

79. $\frac{27}{15} = 1.8 = 180\%$ **80.** $\frac{60}{12} = 5 = 500\%$

81. $\frac{45}{75} = 0.6 = 60\%$ **82.** $\frac{18}{4} = 4.5 = 450\%$

83. $M - 2$ **84.** $\frac{1}{4}s$ or $\frac{s}{4}$ **85.** $3L$

LESSON 4-5 TRY THIS pp. 187–189

a. $x \ge 8$ **b.** $t < 12$ **c.** $x \le 4\frac{1}{2}$

d. $n \ge 0$ **e.** $n - 3 > 4$

f. Let n = number of packages needed to be sold.
$22 + 18 + n \ge 50$
$40 + n \ge 50$
$40 - 40 + n \ge 50 - 40$
$n \ge 10$
At least 10 packages must be sold.

g. Let s = score on last test.
$s + 85 + 89 + 92 \ge 360$
$s + 266 \ge 360$
$s + 266 - 266 \ge 360 - 266$
$s \ge 94$
You must get 94 or more points.

h. Let n = the first integer.

$$n + n + 2 < 35$$
$$2n + 2 < 35$$
$$2n + 2 - 2 < 35 - 2$$
$$2n < 33$$
$$\frac{1}{2} \cdot 2n < \frac{1}{2} \cdot 33$$
$$n < 16\frac{1}{2}$$

One number is 16; the other 17.

LESSON 4-5 EXERCISES pp. 190–191

1. $y > 3$ **2.** $k < 5\frac{1}{2}$ **3.** $h \geq 4\frac{5}{6}$ **4.** $j \leq 2$ **5.** $x \geq 0$

6. $x - 7 < 5$ **7.** $x + 2 > 9$ **8.** $2x > 12$ **9.** $\frac{x}{2} \leq 6$

10. $\frac{x}{3} + 3 < 9$ **11.** $2x - 4 \leq 18$ **12.** $2x + 4 < -x$

13. $3x + 2 \leq 11$ **14.** $\frac{x}{3} - 5 \leq 15$

15. Let s = score on last quiz.

$$\frac{73 + 75 + 89 + 91 + s}{5} \geq 85$$
$$5\left(\frac{73 + 75 + 89 + 91 + s}{5}\right) \geq 5 \cdot 85$$
$$73 + 75 + 89 + 91 + s \geq 425$$
$$328 + s \geq 425$$
$$328 - 328 + s \geq 425 - 328$$
$$s \geq 97$$

The lowest possible score is 97.

16. Let n = first integer.

$$n + (n + 2) + (n + 4) < 100$$
$$3n + 6 < 100$$
$$3n + 6 - 6 < 100 - 6$$
$$3n < 94$$
$$\frac{1}{3}(3n) < \frac{1}{3}(94)$$
$$n < 31\frac{1}{3}$$

The integers are 31, 33, and 35.

17. Let n = smallest integer.

$$n + 2n < 30$$
$$3n < 30$$
$$\frac{1}{3}(3n) < \frac{1}{3}(30)$$
$$n < 10$$

The integers are 9 and 18.

18. Let n = one integer.

$$n + (2n - 10) > 12$$
$$3n - 10 > 12$$
$$3n - 10 + 10 > 12 + 10$$
$$3n > 22$$
$$\frac{1}{3}(3n) > \frac{1}{3}(22)$$
$$n > 7\frac{1}{3}$$

The least values are 8 and 6.

19. Let n = first even whole number.

$$n + (n + 2) + (n + 4) + (n + 6) < 35$$
$$4n + 12 < 35$$
$$4n + 12 - 12 < 35 - 12$$
$$4n < 23$$
$$\frac{1}{4}(4n) < \frac{1}{4}(23)$$
$$n < 5\frac{3}{4}$$

The sets are {4, 6, 8, 10}, {2, 4, 6, 8}, and {0, 2, 4, 6}.

20. Let b = length of base.

$$b + (b - 2) + (b + 3) > 19$$
$$3b + 1 > 19$$
$$3b + 1 - 1 > 19 - 1$$
$$3b > 18$$
$$\frac{1}{3}(3b) > \frac{1}{3}(18)$$
$$b > 6$$

The base is longer than 6 cm.

21. Let A = number of hours Armando worked.

$$A + (A + 3) > 27$$
$$2A + 3 > 27$$
$$2A + 3 - 3 > 27 - 3$$
$$2A > 24$$
$$\frac{1}{2}(2A) > \frac{1}{2}(24)$$
$$A > 12$$

Armando worked more than 12 hours, Drew more than 15.

22. Let a = amount saved by the younger.

$$a + 2a > 25$$
$$3a > 25$$
$$\frac{1}{3}(3a) > \frac{1}{3}(25)$$
$$a > 8.333$$

The younger must save more than \$8.34, the older more than \$16.68.

23. Let width = w.

$$2w + 2 \cdot 26 > 80$$
$$2w + 52 > 80$$
$$2w + 52 - 52 > 80 - 52$$
$$2w > 28$$
$$\frac{1}{2} \cdot 2w > \frac{1}{2} \cdot 28$$
$$w > 14$$

The width must be greater than 14 cm.

24. Let l = length.

$$8l \geq 150$$
$$\frac{1}{8} \cdot 8l \geq \frac{1}{8} \cdot 150$$
$$l \geq 18.75$$

The length must be greater than or equal to 18.75 cm.

25. Let b = base.

$$\frac{1}{2}b(20) > 40 \quad \left(\text{Area} = \frac{1}{2}bh\right)$$
$$10b > 40$$
$$\frac{1}{10} \cdot 10b > \frac{1}{10} \cdot 40$$
$$b > 4$$

The base must be greater than 4 cm.

26. Half of a number is at least −8.

↓ ↓ ↓ ↓

$\frac{1}{2}$ x $\geq$ -8

$$\frac{1}{2}x \geq -8$$
$$2\left(\frac{1}{2}x\right) \geq 2(-8)$$
$$x \geq -16$$

27. 7 less than a third of a number is less than 12.

↓ ↓ ↓ ↓ ↓

$-7 +$ $\frac{1}{3}$ x $<$ 12

$$-7 + \frac{1}{3}x < 12$$
$$-7 + 7 + \frac{1}{3}x < 12 + 7$$
$$\frac{1}{3}x < 19$$
$$3\left(\frac{1}{3}x\right) < 3(19)$$
$$x < 57$$

28. Plan A earnings: $500 + 19n$
Plan B earnings: $24n$

$$500 + 19n > 24n$$
$$500 + 19n - 19n > 24n - 19n$$
$$500 > 5n$$
$$\frac{1}{5}(500) > \frac{1}{5}(5n)$$
$$100 > n$$

29. Cut all three links of one section (30¢). Use each link to join the remaining 4 sections, requiring 3 welds (60¢). The total cost will be 90¢.

30. Let p = the percent.

$$151 + 179.75 + 191 + p(151 + 179.75 + 191) < 1000$$
$$521.75 + p(521.75) < 1000$$
$$521.75 - 521.75 + p(521.75) < 1000 - 521.25$$
$$p(561.75) < 478.25$$
$$\frac{1}{521.75}[p(521.75)] < \frac{1}{521.75} \cdot 478.25$$
$$p < 0.91662$$

The greatest they can pay is ≈ 91.66%.

31. $n - \frac{3}{2} = \frac{2}{3} - \frac{3}{2} = \frac{4}{6} - \frac{9}{6} = -\frac{5}{6}$

32. $\frac{4}{5}n = \frac{4}{5}\left(\frac{2}{3}\right) = \frac{8}{15}$

33. $\frac{3}{5} - n = \frac{3}{5} - \frac{2}{3} = \frac{9}{15} - \frac{10}{15} = -\frac{1}{15}$

34.
$$4(c + 3) = 14c - 3$$
$$4c + 12 = 14c - 3$$
$$4c - 4c + 12 = 14c - 4c - 3$$
$$12 = 10c - 3$$
$$12 + 3 = 10c - 3 + 3$$
$$15 = 10c$$
$$\frac{1}{10} \cdot 15 = \frac{1}{10} \cdot 10c$$
$$\frac{3}{2} = c$$

35.
$$9y + 16 = 3 - 4y$$
$$9y + 4y + 16 = 3 - 4y + 4y$$
$$13y + 16 = 3$$
$$13y + 16 - 16 = 3 - 16$$
$$13y = -13$$
$$\frac{1}{13} \cdot 13y = \frac{1}{13} \cdot (-13)$$
$$y = -1$$

36.
$$9 - 2x < -11$$
$$9 - 9 - 2x < -11 - 9$$
$$-2x < -20$$
$$\frac{1}{-2} \cdot (-2x) > \frac{1}{-2} \cdot (-20)$$
$$x > 10$$

37.
$$14a + 3 \le 15a + 7$$
$$14a - 14a + 3 \le 15a - 14a + 7$$
$$3 \le a + 7$$
$$3 - 7 \le a + 7 - 7$$
$$-4 \le a$$

38.
$$3x - 2 \,\square\, 3x + 7$$
$$3x - 3x - 2 \,\square\, 3x - 3x + 7$$
$$-2 \,\square\, 7$$
$$-2 < 7$$

The quantity in column A is always less than the quantity in column B for any value of x. The answer is B.

39.
$$-2x + 1 \,\square\, 7x + 1$$
$$-2x + 2x + 1 \,\square\, 7x + 2x + 1$$
$$1 \,\square\, 9x + 1$$
$$1 - 1 \,\square\, 9x + 1 - 1$$
$$0 \,\square\, 9x$$

When $x > 0$, the quantity in column B is greater than the quantity in column A, but when $x < 0$, the quantity in column B is less than the quantity in column A. The answer is D.

40.
$$4x = 25$$
$$\frac{1}{4} \cdot 4x = \frac{1}{4} \cdot 25$$
$$x = 6\frac{1}{4}$$

The solution of the equation in column A is $6\frac{1}{4}$.

$$-3z = -18$$
$$-\frac{1}{3}(-3z) = -\frac{1}{3}(-18)$$
$$z = 6$$

The solution of the equation in column B is 6.

Since $6\frac{1}{4} > 6$, the answer is A.

41.
$$\frac{m}{3} = \frac{5}{12}$$
$$\frac{m}{3} \cdot 3 = \frac{5}{12} \cdot 3$$
$$m = \frac{15}{12} = 1\frac{3}{12} = 1\frac{1}{4}$$

The solution of the equation in column A is $1\frac{1}{4}$.

$$\frac{c}{8} = \frac{4}{15}$$
$$\frac{c}{8} \cdot 8 = \frac{4}{15} \cdot 8$$
$$c = \frac{32}{15} = 2\frac{2}{15}$$

The solution of the equation in column B is $2\frac{2}{15}$.

Since $1\frac{1}{4} < 2\frac{2}{15}$, the answer is B.

CONNECTIONS: DEDUCTIVE REASONING p. 192

1. If we can't play soccer, then it's raining. False
   Counterexample: It is a sunny day but we can't play soccer because no one can find the ball.
2. If a number is even, then it is divisible by 2. True
3. If a number is even, then it is divisible by 4. False
   Counterexample: 10 is even and is not divisible by 4.
4. If $x = 4$, then $5x + 4 = 24$. True
5. If $x < 10$, then $x < 5$. False
   Counterexample: 7 is less than 10 and is not less than 5.

CONNECTIONS: INDUCTIVE REASONING p. 193

TRY THIS p. 193

a. The conjecture is true for all numbers greater than or equal to 1,

EXERCISES p. 193

1. The pattern is that the sum of the first n positive odd integers is n^2, so the sum of the first 25 positive odd integers should be $25^2 = 625$.
   $1 + 3 + 5 + 7 + 9 + 11 + 13 + 15 + 17 + 19 + 21 + 23 + 25 + 27 + 29 + 31 + 33 + 35 + 37 + 39 + 41 + 43 + 45 + 47 + 49 = 625$ ✓
2. The pattern is that the sum of the first n positive integers is the average of n and $n + 1$. The sum of the first 30 positive integers should be $30(31)/2 = 465$.
   $1 + 2 + 3 + 4 + 5 + 6 + 7 + 8 + 9 + 10 + 11 + 12 + 13 + 14 + 15 + 16 + 17 + 18 + 19 + 20 + 21 + 22 + 23 + 24 + 25 + 26 + 27 + 28 + 29 + 30 = 465$ ✓

3–4. Counterexamples may vary. Samples are given.

3. $\frac{1}{2} \cdot \frac{1}{3} = \frac{1}{6}$, and $\frac{1}{6} < \frac{1}{2}, \frac{1}{6} < \frac{1}{3}$

4. $2 - (-4) = 6$, and $6 > 2, 6 > -4$

5. Deductive reasoning uses logic to show that the truth of certain statements follows from the truth of other statements. Inductive reasoning uses observations to read conclusions that seem reasonable based on earlier experience. Check students' work for examples.

LESSON 4-6 PROBLEMS p. 195

1. Strategy: Use logical reasoning

	B	T	R	V
W	no	no		no
C		yes		
L	no	no		
R		no		

William & Lester do not coach basketball. Rosa does not coach tennis, nor does Lester. Therefore, Carrie must be William's sister and she coaches tennis, not William.

	B	T	R	V
W	no	no		
C	no	yes	no	no
L	no	no		yes
R	yes	no		

Thus, Carrie does not coach basketball, racquetball, or volleyball. Rosa must coach basketball. Lester does not like racket sports, so he must coach volleyball.

	B	T	R	V
W	no	no	yes	no
C	no	yes	no	no
L	no	no	no	yes
R	yes	no	no	no

Rosa coaches basketball. Lester coaches volleyball. Carrie coaches tennis. Therefore, William coaches racquetball.

2. Strategy: Make an organized list

0, 1, 2, 3, 7, 9

2 first digit			3 first digit		
201	230	290	301	320	390
203	231	291	302	321	391
207	237	293	307	327	392
209	239	297	309	329	397
210	270		310	370	
213	271		312	371	
217	273		317	372	
219	279		319	379	

2 as first digit—20 combinations
3 as first digit—20 combinations
7 as first digit—20 combinations
9 as first digit—20 combinations
80

There are 80 possible 3-digit telephone prefixes.

3. Strategy: Make an organized list or table

House Number	Number of Houses	Number of Digits	Total Number of Digits
1–9	9	9	9
10–99	90	180	189
100–225	126	378	567

The student painted 567 digits.
$567 \times \$0.50 = \$283.50$
The student earned $283.50 for painting the house numbers.

4. Strategy: Try, test, revise

Try	Test	Revised Try
First Try: Consultant A: $9500	Consultant B: $9500 − 500 = $9000 Total fees: $9000 + $9500 = $18,500	This try is correct.

Consultant A earned $9,000 and consultant B earned $9,500.

5. Strategy: Draw a diagram
Answers may vary.
Here are two ways the tiles could be arranged.

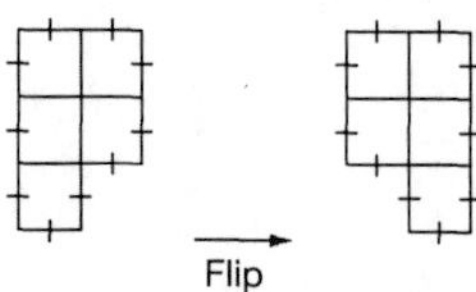

Perimeter is 10.

6. Strategy: Draw a picture

#5 #4 #1 #2 #3
Winner

Car 3 finished first followed by 2, 1, 4, and 5.

7. Strategy: Use logical reasoning

	J	S	N	M
M				no
S		no		
N			no	
J	no			

Meg doesn't live in Mowetown.
Scott doesn't live in Springstown.
Nellie doesn't live in Newton.
Jeff doesn't live in Jackson.

	J	S	N	M
M				no
S	no	no	no	yes
N			no	no
J	no			no

Jeff and Nellie don't live in Mowetown.

Scott must live in Mowetown.
Scott doesn't live anywhere else.

	J	S	N	M
M	no	yes	no	no
S	no	no	no	yes
N	yes	no	no	no
J	no	no	yes	no

If Meg lives in Springstown, no one else lives in Springstown.

If Meg lives in Springstown, she doesn't live anywhere else.

Nellie lives in Jackson, Meg lives in Springstown, Scott lives in Mowetown, and Jeff lives in Newton.

CHAPTER 4 WRAP UP pp. 196–197

1. a. Yes **b.** Yes **c.** Yes **d.** No

2. a. Yes **b.** No **c.** Yes **d.** Yes

3. −1 0

4. 0 5

5. −5 0

6.
$y + 5 > 3$
$y + 5 - 5 > 3 - 5$
$y > -2$

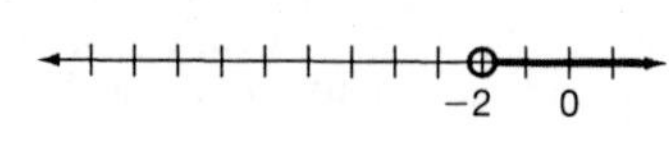

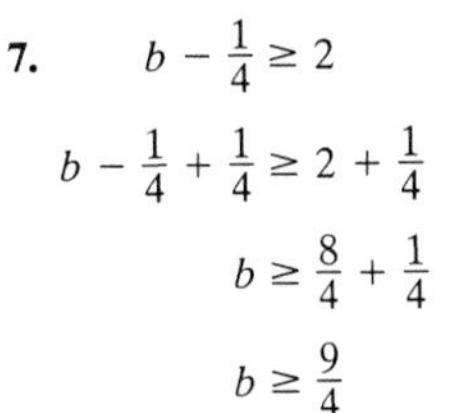

7.
$$b - \frac{1}{4} \geq 2$$
$$b - \frac{1}{4} + \frac{1}{4} \geq 2 + \frac{1}{4}$$
$$b \geq \frac{8}{4} + \frac{1}{4}$$
$$b \geq \frac{9}{4}$$

8.
$$4a + 6 - 3a < 12$$
$$a + 6 < 12$$
$$a + 6 - 6 < 12 - 6$$
$$a < 6$$

0 6

9.
$$4x + 6 - 3x > 2$$
$$x + 6 > 2$$
$$x + 6 - 6 > 2 - 6$$
$$x > -4$$

10.
$$a + \frac{2}{3} \leq \frac{5}{6}$$
$$a + \frac{2}{3} - \frac{2}{3} \leq \frac{5}{6} - \frac{2}{3}$$
$$a \leq \frac{5}{6} - \frac{4}{6}$$
$$a \leq \frac{1}{6}$$

11.
$$-4y + 5y - 8 \leq 12$$
$$y - 8 \leq 12$$
$$y - 8 + 8 \leq 12 + 8$$
$$y \leq 20$$

12.
$$5x < 25$$
$$\frac{1}{5}(5x) < \frac{1}{5}(25)$$
$$x < 5$$

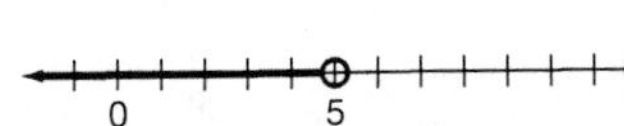

13.
$$-3b \geq 21$$
$$\frac{1}{-3}(-3b) \leq \frac{1}{-3}(21)$$
$$b \leq -7$$

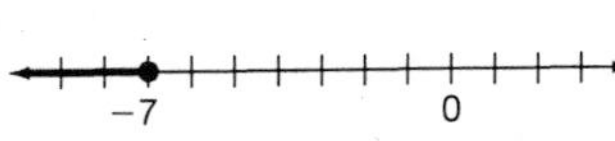

14.
$$-2y > 3$$
$$\frac{1}{-2}(-2y) < \frac{1}{-2}(3)$$
$$y < -\frac{3}{2}$$

−2 −3/2 0

15.
$$3y + 4 < 25$$
$$3y + 4 - 4 < 25 - 4$$
$$3y < 21$$
$$\frac{1}{3}(3y) < \frac{1}{3}(21)$$
$$y < 7$$

16.
$$4a + 9 \leq 2a - 4$$
$$4a - 2a + 9 \leq 2a - 2a - 4$$
$$2a + 9 \leq -4$$
$$2a + 9 - 9 \leq -4 - 9$$
$$2a \leq -13$$
$$\frac{1}{2}(2a) \leq \frac{1}{2}(-13)$$
$$a \leq -\frac{13}{2}$$

17.
$$14 - 8x < 6x + 36$$
$$14 - 8x - 6x < 6x - 6x + 36$$
$$14 - 14x < 36$$
$$14 - 14 - 14x < 36 - 14$$
$$-14x < 22$$
$$\frac{1}{-14}(-14x) > \frac{1}{-14}(22)$$
$$x > -\frac{22}{14} \quad \text{or} \quad -\frac{11}{7}$$

18.
$$7 - 6y > 3y - 20$$
$$7 - 6y - 3y > 3y - 3y - 20$$
$$7 - 9y > -20$$
$$7 - 7 - 9y > -20 - 7$$
$$-9y > -27$$
$$\frac{1}{-9}(-9y) < \frac{1}{-9}(-27)$$
$$y < 3$$

19.
$$6 - 5y > 3 - 4y$$
$$6 - 5y + 4y > 3 - 4y + 4y$$
$$6 - y > 3$$
$$6 - 6 - y > 3 - 6$$
$$-y > -3$$
$$(-1)(-y) < (-1)(-3)$$
$$y < 3$$

20.
$$15a + 3 - 12a \leq 14$$
$$3a + 3 \leq 14$$
$$3a + 3 - 3 \leq 14 - 3$$
$$3a \leq 11$$
$$\frac{1}{3}(3a) \leq \frac{1}{3}(11)$$
$$a \leq \frac{11}{3}$$

21. Let w = Alicia's weight.
$$w + (w + 60) \leq 300$$
$$2w + 60 \leq 300$$
$$2w + 60 - 60 \leq 300 - 60$$
$$2w \leq 240$$
$$\frac{1}{2}(2w) \leq \frac{1}{2}(240)$$
$$w \leq 120$$
The most she could weigh is 120 lb.

22. Let n = grade on next test.
$$\frac{80 + 75 + 86 + n}{4} \geq 82$$
$$4\left(\frac{80 + 75 + 86 + n}{4}\right) \geq 4(82)$$
$$80 + 75 + 86 + n \geq 328$$
$$241 + n \geq 328$$
$$241 - 241 + n \geq 328 - 241$$
$$n \geq 87$$
She must get at least a grade of 87.

23. Let n = first integer.
$$n + (n + 2) + (n + 4) \leq 42$$
$$3n + 6 \leq 42$$
$$3n + 6 - 6 \leq 42 - 6$$
$$3n \leq 36$$
$$\frac{1}{3}(3n) \leq \frac{1}{3}(36)$$
$$n \leq 12$$
The numbers are 12, 14, and 16.

24. Let n = smallest odd whole number.
$$n + (n + 2) + (n + 4) + (n + 6) < 38$$
$$4n + 12 < 38$$
$$4n + 12 - 12 < 38 - 12$$
$$4n < 26$$
$$\frac{1}{4}(4n) < \frac{1}{4}(26)$$
$$n < 6\frac{1}{2}$$

The sets are $\{5, 7, 9, 11\}$, $\{3, 5, 7, 9\}$, and $\{1, 3, 5, 7\}$.

CHAPTER 4 ASSESSMENT

p. 197

1. **a.** Yes **b.** Yes **c.** No **d.** Yes

2. **a.** Yes **b.** Yes **c.** Yes **d.** Yes

3.

−5 0

4. 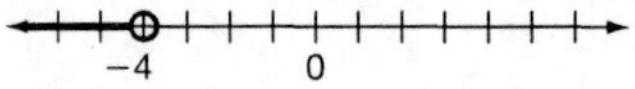

5. 

6. $x - 2 > 5$
$x - 2 + 2 > 5 + 2$
$x > 7$

7. $9x + 2 - 4x > 17$
$5x + 2 > 17$
$5x + 2 - 2 > 17 - 2$
$5x > 15$
$\frac{1}{5}(5x) > \frac{1}{5}(15)$
$x > 3$

8. $x + \frac{1}{3} \geq -5$
$x + \frac{1}{3} - \frac{1}{3} \geq -5 - \frac{1}{3}$
$x \geq -\frac{15}{3} - \frac{1}{3}$
$x \geq -\frac{16}{3}$

9. $7y > -42$
$\frac{1}{7}(7y) > \frac{1}{7}(-42)$
$y > -6$

10. $-6x \leq -24$
$\frac{1}{-6}(-6x) \geq \frac{1}{-6}(-24)$
$x \geq 4$

11. $5x \geq 8x - \frac{3}{2}$
$5x - 8x \geq 8x - 8x - \frac{3}{2}$
$-3x \geq -\frac{3}{2}$
$\frac{1}{-3}(-3x) \leq \frac{1}{-3}\left(-\frac{3}{2}\right)$
$x \leq \frac{1}{2}$

12. $5a - 6 \geq 3a$
$5a - 5a - 6 \geq 3a - 5a$
$-6 \geq -2a$
$\frac{1}{-2}(-6) \leq \frac{1}{-2}(-2a)$
$3 \leq a$

13. $2x - 15 > 5x$
$2x - 2x - 15 > 5x - 2x$
$-15 > 3x$
$\frac{1}{3}(-15) > \frac{1}{3}(3x)$
$-5 > x$

14. $-5y - 34 \geq -19$
$-5y - 34 + 34 \geq -19 + 34$
$-5y \geq 15$
$\frac{1}{-5}(-5y) \leq \frac{1}{-5}(15)$
$y \leq -3$

15. $7 - 6x < 2x + 87$
$7 - 6x + 6x < 2x + 6x + 87$
$7 < 8x + 87$
$7 - 87 < 8x + 87 - 87$
$-80 < 8x$
$\frac{1}{8}(-80) < \frac{1}{8}(8x)$
$-10 < x$

16. $5 - 8y \geq 23$
$5 - 5 - 8y \geq 23 - 5$
$-8y \geq 18$
$\frac{1}{-8}(-8y) \leq \frac{1}{-8}(18)$
$y \leq -\frac{18}{8}$ or $-\frac{9}{4}$

17. $9a - 16 < -52$
$9a - 16 + 16 < -52 + 16$
$9a < -36$
$\frac{1}{9}(9a) < \frac{1}{9}(-36)$
$a < -4$

18. Let n = Bridget's age.
$n + (n + 3) < 16$
$2n + 3 < 16$
$2n + 3 - 3 < 16 - 3$
$2n < 13$
$\frac{1}{2}(2n) < \frac{1}{2}(13)$
$n < 6\frac{1}{2}$
Bridget is 6.

19. Let n = first even integer.
$n + (n + 2) \leq 90$
$2n + 2 \leq 90$
$2n + 2 - 2 \leq 90 - 2$
$2n \leq 88$
$\frac{1}{2}(2n) \leq \frac{1}{2}(88)$
$n \leq 44$
The greatest possible pair is 44 and 46.

CHAPTERS 1–4 CUMULATIVE REVIEW pp. 198–201

1. $\frac{y - x}{4} = \frac{12 - 6}{4} = \frac{6}{4} = \frac{3}{2}$ 2. $\frac{3x}{y} = \frac{3(5)}{4} = \frac{15}{4}$

3. $16 \div (4 \cdot 2) + 9 - 3 = 16 \div 8 + 6 = 2 + 6 = 8$

4. $(48 - 8) \div 5 + 3 = 40 \div 5 + 3 = 8 + 3 = 11$

5. $12 + y = y + 12$ 6. $\frac{5}{6} \cdot \frac{4}{4} = \frac{20}{24}$

7. $\frac{9xy}{12yz} = \frac{3y \cdot 3x}{3y \cdot 4z} = \frac{3x}{4z}$ 8. $\frac{108}{72y} = \frac{36 \cdot 3}{36 \cdot 2y} = \frac{3}{2y}$

9. $y^4 = (2)^4 = 2 \cdot 2 \cdot 2 \cdot 2 = 16$

10. $x^3 + 5 = (3)^3 + 5 = 3 \cdot 3 \cdot 3 + 5 = 27 + 5 = 32$

11. $(2a)^4 = (2 \cdot 5)^4 = (10)^4 = 10 \cdot 10 \cdot 10 \cdot 10 = 10{,}000$

12. $3a^2 = 3(2)^2 = 3 \cdot 2 \cdot 2 = 12$

13. $(3 + 7)^3 = (10)^3 = 10 \cdot 10 \cdot 10 = 1000$

14. $5 + 4^4 = 5 + 4 \cdot 4 \cdot 4 \cdot 4 = 5 + 256 = 261$

15. $(3 \cdot y)z = 3(yz)$ 16. $x + (y + 21) = (x + y) + 21$

17. $5(3x + 5y + 2z) = 15x + 25y + 10z$

18. $8(2w + 4x + 3y) = 16w + 32x + 24y$

19. $54y + 6 = 6 \cdot 9y + 6 \cdot 1 = 6(9y + 1)$

20. $42x + 36y + 12 = 6 \cdot 7x + 6 \cdot 6y + 6 \cdot 2 = 6(7x + 6y + 2)$

21. $9b + 18y + 6b + 4y = 15b + 22y$

22. $3y + 4z + 6z + 6y = 9y + 10z$

23. $2w - 4$ 24. $3(x + y)$

25.

$6(7) = 54$	$6(8) = 54$	$6(9) = 54$
$42 = 54$	$48 = 54$	$54 = 54$
No	No	Yes

{9}

26.

$(1)^2 - 1 = 3$	$(3)^2 - 3 = 3$	$(9)^2 - 9 = 3$
$1 - 1 = 3$	$9 - 3 = 3$	$81 - 9 = 3$
$0 = 3$	$6 = 3$	$72 = 3$

No solution

27.

$2.5(0.6) = 15$	$2.5(6) = 15$	$2.5(60) = 15$
$1.5 = 15$	$15 = 15$	$150 = 15$
No	Yes	No

{6}

28.

$38 - 18 = 56$	$64 - 18 = 56$	$74 - 18 = 56$
$20 = 56$	$46 = 56$	$56 = 56$
No	No	Yes

{74}

29. Both sides were multiplied by 7.

30. 4 was subtracted from both sides, or −4 was added to both sides.

31. $p = 2l + 2w = 2(12) + 2(8.4) = 24 + 16.8 = 40.8$
The perimeter is 40.8 m.

32. $A = l \cdot w = 12(8.4) = 100.8$
The areas is 100.8 m^2.

33. $-4 > -6$ **34.** $-2 < 2$ **35.** $|-14| = 14$

36. $|65| = 65$ **37.** $-2.5 > -4.25$

38. $-\frac{3}{4} = -\frac{6}{8}$

$-\frac{6}{8} < -\frac{3}{8}$,

so $-\frac{3}{4} < -\frac{3}{8}$

39. -3.5

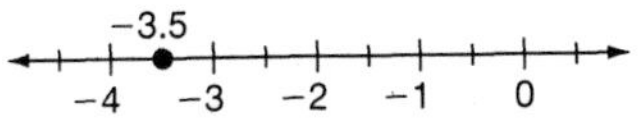

40. $\frac{5}{4}$

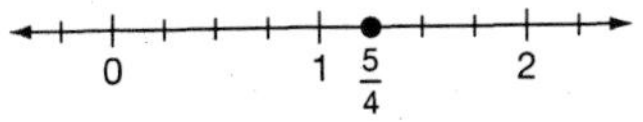

41. $5 + (-9) + 7 = -4 + 7 = 3$ **42.** $-3.5 + 7.2 = 3.7$

43. $-7 - (-8) = -7 + 8 = 1$

44. $-\frac{3}{4} - \frac{2}{3} = -\frac{9}{12} - \frac{8}{12} = -\frac{17}{12}$

45. $-2 - 4x - 6x + 5 = 3 - 10x$

46. $7 - 2x - (-5x) - 8 = 7 - 2x + 5x - 8 = -1 + 3x$

47. $5(-7)(3)(-4) = 420$ **48.** $-\frac{5}{8}\left(-\frac{4}{3}\right) = \frac{20}{24} = \frac{5}{6}$

49. $(-7)(5)(-6)(-0.5) = -105$ **50.** $\frac{-10.8}{36} = -0.3$

51. $\frac{-4}{5} \div \frac{25}{8} = \frac{-4}{5} \cdot \frac{8}{25} = -\frac{32}{125}$

52. $\frac{81}{-90} = \frac{9 \cdot 9}{-9 \cdot 10} = -\frac{9}{10}$ **53.** $4(-3x - 2) = -12x - 8$

54. $-6(2y - 4x) = -12y + 24x$ **55.** $-5(-x - 1) = 5x + 5$

56. $16y - 56 = 8 \cdot 2y - 8 \cdot 7 = 8(2y - 7)$

57. $-2x - 8 = -2 \cdot x + (-2)4 = -2(x + 4)$

58. $5a - 15b + 25 = 5 \cdot a - 5 \cdot 3b + 5 \cdot 5 = 5(a - 3b + 5)$

59. $-4d - 6a + 3a - 5d + 1 = -9d - 3a + 1$

60. $3.2x + 2.9y - 5.8x - 8.1y = -2.6x - 5.2y$

61. $-3x - (-x + y) = -3x + x - y = -2x - y$

62. $-3(x - 2) - 4x = -3x + 6 - 4x = -7x + 6$

63. $10 - 2(5 - 4x) = 10 - 10 + 8x = 8x$

64. Reflexive Property **65.** Transitive Property

66.
$$-2.6x + x = 8.3$$
$$-2.6 + 2.6 + x = 8.3 + 2.6$$
$$x = 10.9$$

67.
$$4\tfrac{1}{2} + y = 8\tfrac{1}{3}$$
$$4\tfrac{1}{2} - 4\tfrac{1}{2} + y = 8\tfrac{1}{3} - 4\tfrac{1}{2}$$
$$y = \frac{25}{3} - \frac{9}{2}$$
$$y = \frac{50}{6} - \frac{27}{6}$$
$$y = \frac{23}{6} \text{ or } 3\tfrac{5}{6}$$

68.
$$-\frac{3}{4}x = 36$$
$$4\left(-\frac{3}{4}x\right) = 4(36)$$
$$-3x = 144$$
$$\frac{1}{-3}(-3x) = \frac{1}{-3}(144)$$
$$x = -48$$

69.
$$-2.2y = -26.4$$
$$\frac{1}{-2.2}(-2.2y) = \frac{1}{-2.2}(-26.4)$$
$$y = 12$$

70.
$$-4x + 3 = 15$$
$$-4x + 3 - 3 = 15 - 3$$
$$-4x = 12$$
$$\frac{1}{-4}(-4x) = \frac{1}{-4}(12)$$
$$x = -3$$

71.
$$-3x + 5 = -8x - 7$$
$$-3x + 3x + 5 = -8x + 3x - 7$$
$$5 = -5x - 7$$
$$5 + 7 = -5x - 7 + 7$$
$$12 = -5x$$
$$\frac{1}{-5}(12) = \frac{1}{-5}(-5x)$$
$$-\frac{12}{5} = x$$

72.
$$4y - 4 + y = 6y + 20 - 4y$$
$$5y - 4 = 2y + 20$$
$$5y - 2y - 4 = 2y - 2y + 20$$
$$3y - 4 = 20$$
$$3y - 4 + 4 = 20 + 4$$
$$3y = 24$$
$$\frac{1}{3}(3y) = \frac{1}{3}(24)$$
$$y = 8$$

73.
$$-3(x - 2) = -15$$
$$-3x + 6 = -15$$
$$-3x + 6 - 6 = -15 - 6$$
$$-3x = -21$$
$$\frac{1}{-3}(-3x) = \frac{1}{-3}(-21)$$
$$x = 7$$

74.
$$\frac{1}{3}x - \frac{5}{6} = \frac{1}{2} + 2x$$
$$6\left(\frac{1}{3}x - \frac{5}{6}\right) = 6\left(\frac{1}{2} + 2x\right)$$
$$2x - 5 = 3 + 12x$$
$$2x - 2x - 5 = 3 + 12x - 2x$$
$$-5 = 3 + 10x$$
$$-5 - 3 = 3 - 3 + 10x$$
$$-8 = 10x$$
$$\frac{1}{10}(-8) = \frac{1}{10}(10x)$$
$$-\frac{8}{10} = x \text{ or } x = -\frac{4}{5}$$

75.
$$-3.7x + 6.2 = -7.3x - 5.8$$
$$10(-3.7x + 6.2) = 10(-7.3x - 5.8)$$
$$-37x + 62 = -73x - 58$$
$$-37x + 73x + 62 = -73x + 73x - 58$$
$$36x + 62 = -58$$
$$36x + 62 - 62 = -58 - 62$$
$$36x = -120$$
$$\frac{1}{36}(36x) = \frac{1}{36}(-120)$$
$$x = -\frac{120}{36} = -3\tfrac{1}{3} \text{ or } -3.\overline{3}$$

76.
$$c = 10d + 5n$$
$$c - 10d = 10d - 10d + 5n$$
$$c - 10d = 5n$$
$$\frac{1}{5}(c - 10d) = \frac{1}{5}(5n)$$
$$\frac{c - 10d}{5} = n$$

77.
$$L = 2rh$$
$$\frac{1}{2h}(L) = \frac{1}{2h}(2rh)$$
$$\frac{L}{2h} = r$$

78.
$$|y| = 7$$
$$y = 7 \text{ or } y = -7$$

79.
$$|x| + 2 = 11$$
$$|x| + 2 - 2 = 11 - 2$$
$$|x| = 9$$
$$x = 9 \text{ or } x = -9$$

80. $3|a| = 27$

$\frac{1}{3}(3|a|) = \frac{1}{3}(27)$

$|a| = 9$

$a = 9$ or $a = -9$

81. $\frac{x}{12} = \frac{16}{18}$

$36\left(\frac{x}{12}\right) = 36\left(\frac{16}{18}\right)$

$3x = 32$

$\frac{1}{3}(3x) = \frac{1}{3}(32)$

$x = \frac{32}{3}$

82. $\frac{16}{6} = \frac{x}{24}$

$24\left(\frac{16}{6}\right) = 24\left(\frac{x}{24}\right)$

$64 = x$

83. $\frac{32}{450} = \frac{x}{800}$

$7200\left(\frac{32}{450}\right) = 7200\left(\frac{x}{800}\right)$

$512 = 9x$

$\frac{1}{9}(512) = \frac{1}{9}(9x)$

$56.9 \approx x$

About 56.9 L will be needed.

84. $\frac{18}{60} = \frac{3}{10} = \frac{30}{100} = 30\%$

85. $2 = 0.04x$

$\frac{1}{0.04}(2) = \frac{1}{0.04}(0.04x)$

$50 = x$

86. $x = 80(0.165) = 13.2$

87. $x + 0.12x = 1680$

$1.12x = 1680$

$\frac{1}{1.12}(1.12x) = \frac{1}{1.12}(1680)$

$x = 1500$

\$1500 was invested.

88. $x + (x + 1) + (x + 2) = 114$

$3x + 3 = 114$

$3x + 3 - 3 = 114 - 3$

$3x = 111$

$\frac{1}{3}(3x) = \frac{1}{3}(111)$

$x = 37$

The integers are 37, 38, and 39.

89. No **90.** Yes **91.** Yes **92.** Yes

93. $x - \frac{1}{6} \geq \frac{2}{3}$

$x - \frac{1}{6} + \frac{1}{6} \geq \frac{2}{3} + \frac{1}{6}$

$x \geq \frac{4}{6} + \frac{1}{6}$

$x \geq \frac{5}{6}$

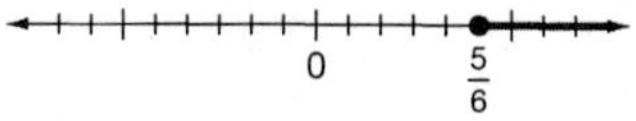

94. $-4x \geq 24$

$\frac{1}{-4}(-4x) \leq \frac{1}{-4}(24)$

$x \leq -6$

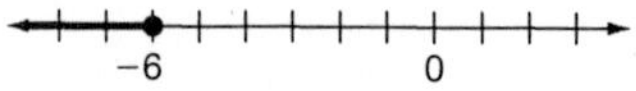

95. $-3x < 30 + 2x$

$-3x - 2x < 30 + 2x - 2x$

$-5x < 30$

$\frac{1}{-5}(-5x) > \frac{1}{-5}(30)$

$x > -6$

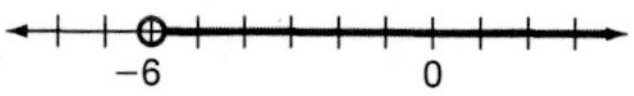

96. $x + 3 \geq 6(x - 4) + 7$

$x + 3 \geq 6x - 24 + 7$

$x + 3 \geq 6x - 17$

$x - 6x + 3 \geq 6x - 6x - 17$

$-5x + 3 \geq -17$

$-5x + 3 - 3 \geq -17 - 3$

$-5x \geq -20$

$\frac{1}{-5}(-5x) \leq \frac{1}{-5}(-20)$

$x \leq 4$

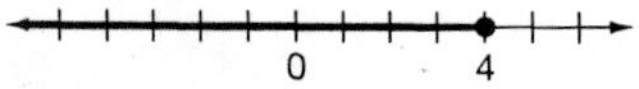

97. Let w = width.

$w + 4$ = length

$2w + 2(w + 4) > 72$

$2w + 2w + 8 > 72$

$4w + 8 > 72$

$4w + 8 - 8 > 72 - 8$

$4w > 64$

$\frac{1}{4}(4w) > \frac{1}{4}(64)$

$w > 16$

The width is greater than 16 ft, the length is greater than 20 ft.

CHAPTER 5

SKILLS & CONCEPTS p. 202

1. 8^4 **2.** $12b^3$

3. $m^4 - 5 = 2^4 - 5 = 2 \cdot 2 \cdot 2 \cdot 2 - 5 = 16 - 5 = 11$

4. $3b^2 = 3(4)^2 = 3 \cdot 4 \cdot 4 = 48$

5. $3(s + t + w) = 3s + 3t + 3w$

6. $-7(x + 4) = -7x - 28$

7. $2x + 8y + 7x + 5y = 9x + 13y$

8. $7b^2 + 9b + 2b^2 + 8 = 9b^2 + 9b + 8$ **9.** $(-6)(-5) = 30$

10. $-\frac{1}{2} \cdot \frac{5}{8} = -\frac{5}{16}$ **11.** $-\frac{16}{-2} = -(-8) = 8$

12. $-\frac{24}{16} = -\frac{8 \cdot 3}{8 \cdot 2} = -\frac{3}{2}$

13. $-(4x - 7y + 2) = -4x + 7y - 2$

14. $-(12r + 7p - 9s) = -12r - 7p + 9s$

15. $5y - 8 - (9y - 6) = 5y - 8 - 9y + 6 = -4y - 2$

16. $5b - 4(6b - 2) = 5b - 24b + 8 = -19b + 8$

LESSON 5-1 TRY THIS pp. 204–206

a. $5^2 \cdot 5^4 = 5^{2+4} = 5^6$ **b.** $a^5 + a^3 = a^{5+3} = a^8$

c. $y^3 \cdot y^2 \cdot y^5 = y^{3+2+5} = y^{10}$

d. $(mn^2)(m^4n^6) = (mm^4)(n^2n^6) = m^{1+4}n^{2+6} = m^5n^8$

e. $\frac{7^6}{7^2} = 7^{6-2} = 7^4$ **f.** $\frac{a^7}{a^2} = a^{7-2} = a^5$

g. $\frac{m^4}{m^2} = m^{4-2} = m^2$ **h.** $\frac{x^4y^3}{x^2y^2} = x^{4-2}y^{3-2} = x^2y$ **i.** $\frac{1}{2^2}$

j. $\frac{1}{y^4}$ **k.** $\frac{3}{c^2}$ **l.** $4^{-2} = \frac{1}{4^2} = \frac{1}{16}$ **m.** $1^{-10} = \frac{1}{1^{10}} = 1$

n. $3^0 = 1$

LESSON 5-1 EXERCISES pp. 207–208

1. $2^4 \cdot 2^3 = 2^{4+3} = 2^7$ **2.** $3^5 \cdot 3^2 = 3^{5+2} = 3^7$

3. $8^5 \cdot 8^9 = 8^{5+9} = 8^{14}$ **4.** $n^3 \cdot n^{20} = n^{3+20} = n^{23}$

5. $x^4 \cdot x^3 = x^{4+3} = x^7$ **6.** $y^7 \cdot y^9 = y^{7+9} = y^{16}$

7. $n^3 \cdot n^1 = n^{3+1} = n^4$ **8.** $z^7 \cdot z^7 = z^{7+7} = z^{14}$

9. $x^3 \cdot x^1 = x^{3+1} = x^4$ **10.** $a^6 \cdot a^8 = a^{6+8} = a^{14}$

11. $m^7 \cdot m^0 = m^{7+0} = m^7$

12. $p^1 \cdot p^1 \cdot p^1 = p^{1+1+1} = p^3$

13. $x^4 \cdot x^2 \cdot x^1 = x^{4+2+1} = x^7$

14. $y^2 \cdot y^4 \cdot y^3 = y^{2+4+3} = y^9$

15. $a^3 \cdot a^4 \cdot a^1 \cdot a^1 = a^{3+4+1+1} = a^9$

16. $b^1 \cdot b^5 \cdot b^2 \cdot b^2 = b^{1+5+2+2} = b^{10}$

17. $(a^3b^6)(a^5b^1) = a^{3+5}b^{6+1} = a^8b^7$

18. $(x^2y^1)(x^5y^2) = x^{2+5}y^{1+2} = x^7y^3$

19. $(p^2q^3r^2)(p^1q^1r^3) = p^{2+1}q^{3+1}r^{2+3} = p^3q^4r^5$

20. $(x^7y^4z^4)(x^2y^5z^8) = x^{7+2}y^{4+5}z^{4+8} = x^9y^9z^{12}$

21. $(5^1s^2t^3)(5^1s^2t^1) = 5^{1+1}s^{2+2}t^{3+1} = 5^2s^4t^4$

22. $(2^1x^1y^2)(2^1x^2y^2) = 2^{1+1}x^{1+2}y^{2+2} = 2^2x^3y^4$

23. $\frac{7^5}{7^2} = 7^{5-2} = 7^3$

24. $\frac{4^7}{4^3} = 4^{7-3} = 4^4$

25. $\frac{8^{12}}{8^6} = 8^{12-6} = 8^6$

26. $\frac{9^{15}}{9^2} = 9^{15-2} = 9^{13}$

27. $\frac{6^4}{6^4} = 6^{4-4} = 6^0 = 1$

28. $\frac{2^7}{2^7} = 2^{7-7} = 2^0 = 1$

29. $\frac{y^9}{y^5} = y^{9-5} = y^4$

30. $\frac{x^{12}}{x^{11}} = x^{12-11} = x^1 = x$

31. $\frac{g^5}{g^5} = g^{5-5} = g^0 = 1$

32. $\frac{h^4}{h^1} = h^{4-1} = h^3$

33. $\frac{m^8}{m^8} = m^{8-8} = m^0 = 1$

34. $\frac{x^7}{x^5} = x^{7-5} = x^2$

35. $\frac{a^3b^4}{a^1b^1} = a^{3-1}b^{4-1} = a^2b^3$

36. $\frac{x^8y^1}{x^7y^1} = x^{8-7}y^{1-1} = x^1y^0 = x^1(1) = x$

37. $\frac{4^3x^3}{4^2x^1} = 4^{3-2}x^{3-1} = 4^1x^2 = 4x^2$

38. $\frac{6^4a^5b^1}{6^2a^2b^1} = 6^{4-2}a^{5-2}b^{1-1} = 6^2a^3b^0 = 6^2a^3$

39. $\frac{1}{3^2}$ 40. $\frac{1}{6^3}$ 41. $\frac{1}{x^4}$ 42. $\frac{1}{n^6}$ 43. $\frac{3}{a}$ 44. $\frac{1}{3x}$

45. $\frac{1}{2y}$ 46. $\frac{4}{x^3}$ 47. $\frac{5}{c^4}$ 48. $\frac{8}{m}$ 49. $\frac{1}{3a}$ 50. $\frac{c}{d^2}$

51. $4^{-2} = \frac{1}{4^2} = \frac{1}{16}$ 52. $8^{-1} = \frac{1}{8^1} = \frac{1}{8}$ 53. $5^{-3} = \frac{1}{5^3} = \frac{1}{125}$

54. $1^{-4} = \frac{1}{1^4} = \frac{1}{1} = 1$ 55. $5^0 = 1$ 56. $2^{-4} = \frac{1}{2^4} = \frac{1}{16}$

57. $10^0 = 1$ 58. $x^0 = 1$

59. $(-2)^4(-2)^2 = (-2)^{4+2} = (-2)^6 = 64$

60. $(-5)^2(-5) = (-5)^{2+1} = (-5)^3 = -125$

61. $\frac{(-3)^6}{(-3)^4} = (-3)^{6-4} = (-3)^2 = 9$

62. $\frac{(-10)^7}{(-10)^6} = (-10)^{7-6} = (-10)^1 = -10$

63. $\frac{4^3}{4^5} = 4^{3-5} = \frac{1}{4^2} = \frac{1}{16}$

64. $\frac{3^4}{3^6} = (3)^{4-6} = 3^{-2} = \frac{1}{3^2} = \frac{1}{9}$

65. $\frac{(-2)^2}{(-2)^5} = (-2)^{2-5} = (-2)^{-3} = \frac{1}{(-2)^3} = -\frac{1}{8}$

66. $\frac{(-5)^3}{(-5)^4} = (-5)^{3-4} = (-5)^{-1} = \frac{1}{(-5)^1} = -\frac{1}{5}$

67. (a) $\frac{x^3}{x^7} = x^{3-7} = x^{-4}$ (b) $x^{-4} = \frac{1}{x^4}$

68. (a) $\frac{y}{y^4} = y^{1-4} = y^{-3}$ (b) $y^{-3} = \frac{1}{y^3}$

69. (a) $\frac{a^2}{a^6} = a^{2-6} = a^{-4}$ (b) $a^{-4} = \frac{1}{a^4}$

70. (a) $\frac{m^5}{m^{10}} = m^{5-10} = m^{-5}$ (b) $m^{-5} = \frac{1}{m^5}$

71. $x^5 \cdot x^3 = x^{5+3} = x^8 = 2^8 = 256$

72. $10^m \cdot 10^n = 10^{m+n} = 10^{2+4} = 10^6 = 1{,}000{,}000$

73. $a^3 \cdot a^2 \cdot a = a^{3+2+1} = a^6 = (-2)^6 = 64$

74. $2^a \cdot 2^b \cdot 2^c = 2^{a+b+c} = 2^{3+2+2} = 2^7 = 128$

75. a. $\frac{1}{2}, \frac{1}{4}, \frac{1}{8}, \frac{1}{16}$
b. $2^{-1}, 2^{-2}, 2^{-3}, 2^{-4}$
c. The portion of the figure that is shaded equals 2 raised to the opposite of the figure number.
d. 2^{-10}

76. The exponents were multiplied when they should have been added. $(3x^2)(2x^5) = 6x^{2+5} = 6x^7$.

77. When the exponents were added, the exponent of the x term, which is 1, was not included. $x^5 \cdot x \cdot x^2 = x^{5+1+2} = x^8$.

78. $5^{x+1} = 125$; $5^{x+1} = 5^3$; $x + 1 = 3$; $x = 2$. The correct choice is **A**.

79. $\frac{4^2 \cdot 4^5}{4^3} = 4^{2+5-3} = 4^4 = 256$

80. $\frac{2^5 \cdot 3^4}{2^2 \cdot 3^2} = 2^{5-2}3^{4-2} = 2^3 \cdot 3^2 = 8 \cdot 9 = 72$

81. $\frac{a^2 \cdot b^3}{a^2 \cdot b^5} = a^{2-2}b^{3-5} = a^0b^{-2} = b^{-2}$ or $\frac{1}{b^2}$

82. $\frac{m^5 \cdot n^6}{m^2 \cdot m^2} = \frac{m^5n^6}{m^4} = m^{5-4}n^6 = mn^6$

83. $4^{-1} \cdot 4^5 = 4^{-1+5} = 4^4 = 256$

84. $\frac{(-3)}{(-3)^{-4}} = (-3)^{1-(-4)} = (-3)^5 = -243$

85. $\frac{x^6 \cdot x^{-2}}{x^2} = x^{6-2-2} = x^2$

86. $\frac{a^{-2} \cdot b^{-3}}{a^4 \cdot b^{-1}} = a^{-2-4}b^{-3-(-1)} = a^{-6}b^{-2}$ or $\frac{1}{a^6b^2}$

87. No; let $a = 1, b = 2, m = 3, 27 \neq 9$.

88. $16 = 2^4$ 89. $4^3 = 64 = 2^6$ 90. $8^2 = 64 = 2^6$

91. $4^3 \cdot 8 \cdot 16 = 64 \cdot 2^3 \cdot 2^4 = 2^6 \cdot 2^3 \cdot 2^4 = 2^{13}$

92. $2^8 \cdot 16^3 \cdot 64 = 256(4^2)^3 4^3 = 4^4(4^2 \cdot 4^2 \cdot 4^2)4^3 = 4^{4+2+2+2+3} = 4^{13}$

93. $9 \cdot 27 \cdot 3 \cdot 81 = 3^2 \cdot 3^3 \cdot 3^1 \cdot 3^4 = 3^{2+3+1+4} = 3^{10}$

94. $\frac{\left(\frac{1}{c}\right)^4}{\left(\frac{1}{c}\right)^5} = \left(\frac{1}{c}\right)^{4-5} = \left(\frac{1}{c}\right)^{-1} = c$

95. $\frac{\left(\frac{a}{b}\right)^3}{\left(\frac{a}{b}\right)^6} = \left(\frac{a}{b}\right)^{3-6} = \left(\frac{a}{b}\right)^{-3} = \left(\frac{b}{a}\right)^3 = \left(\frac{b}{a}\right)\left(\frac{b}{a}\right)\left(\frac{b}{a}\right) = \frac{b^3}{a^3}$

96. $3[8 - 2(t + 3)] = 3[8 - 2t - 6] = 3[2 - 2t] = 6 - 6t$ or $6(1 - t)$

97. $(5m + 6n) - (6m + 9n) = 5m + 6n - 6m - 9n = -m - 3n$ or $-(m + 3n)$

98. $6a - 9a(4a + 3) = 6a - 36a^2 - 27a = -21a - 36a^2$

99. $7a(a + 2) + 3a^2 + 2a^2 = 7a^2 + 14a + 5a^2 = 12a^2 + 14a$

100. $w - 4$ 101. $ac - 8$ 102. $2(m + n)$

103.
$$\begin{aligned} m - 422 &= -53 \\ m - 422 + 422 &= -53 + 422 \\ m &= 369 \end{aligned}$$

104.
$$\begin{aligned} 21t &= -693 \\ \frac{1}{21}\cdot 21t &= \frac{1}{21}\cdot(-693) \\ t &= -33 \end{aligned}$$

105.
$$\begin{aligned} 6(m+3) &= 10m - 2 \\ 6m + 18 &= 10m - 2 \\ 6m - 6m + 18 &= 10m - 6m - 2 \\ 18 &= 4m - 2 \\ 18 + 2 &= 4m - 2 + 2 \\ 20 &= 4m \\ \frac{1}{4}(20) &= \frac{1}{4}\cdot 4m \\ 5 &= m \end{aligned}$$

106.
$$\begin{aligned} \frac{3}{4}c + 4 &= \frac{1}{4}c - 2 \\ \frac{3}{4}c - \frac{1}{4}c + 4 &= \frac{1}{4}c - \frac{1}{4}c - 2 \\ \frac{1}{2}c + 4 &= -2 \\ \frac{1}{2}c + 4 - 4 &= -2 - 4 \\ \frac{1}{2}c &= -6 \\ 2\cdot\frac{1}{2}c &= 2(-6) \\ c &= -12 \end{aligned}$$

107. Let s = cost of sweater.
$$\begin{aligned} 18 + s &\le 45 \\ 18 - 18 + s &\le 45 - 18 \\ s &\le 27 \end{aligned}$$
He can spend \$27 or less.

LESSON 5-2 TRY THIS pp. 209–211

a. $(5^4)^3 = 5^{4\cdot 3} = 5^{12}$ **b.** $(2^2)^5 = 2^{2\cdot 5} = 2^{10}$
c. $(a^6)^3 = a^{6\cdot 3} = a^{18}$ **d.** $(n^4)^4 = n^{4\cdot 4} = n^{16}$
e. $(3y)^2 = (3y)(3y) = 9y^2$
f. $(6m)^4 = (6m)(6m)(6m)(6m) = 1296m^4$
g. $(2a^3)^3 = (2a^3)(2a^3)(2a^3) = 8a^9$
h. $(4x^3)^2 = (4x^3)(4x^3) = 16x^6$ **i.** $(4y^3)^4 = 4^4y^{3\cdot 4} = 256y^{12}$
j. $(3x^4y^7z^6)^5 = 3^5x^{4\cdot 5}y^{7\cdot 5}z^{6\cdot 5} = 243x^{20}y^{35}z^{30}$
k. $(-7x^9y^6)^2 = 7^2x^{9\cdot 2}y^{6\cdot 2} = 49x^{18}y^{12}$
l. $[(-y)^{15}]^3 = (-y)^{15\cdot 3} = -y^{45}$
m. $\left(\frac{y^3}{2}\right)^2 = \frac{y^6}{2^2} = \frac{y^6}{4}$ **n.** $\left(\frac{a^5}{3}\right)^3 = \frac{a^{15}}{3^3} = \frac{a^{15}}{27}$
o. $\left(\frac{x^2}{y^3}\right)^2 = \frac{x^4}{y^6}$

LESSON 5-2 EXERCISES pp. 212–213

1. $(2^5)^2 = 2^{5\cdot 2} = 2^{10}$ **2.** $(3^4)^3 = 3^{4\cdot 3} = 3^{12}$
3. $(5^2)^3 = 5^{2\cdot 3} = 5^6$ **4.** $(6^8)^9 = 6^{8\cdot 9} = 6^{72}$
5. $(y^5)^9 = y^{5\cdot 9} = y^{45}$ **6.** $(x^3)^5 = x^{3\cdot 5} = x^{15}$
7. $(m^8)^4 = m^{8\cdot 4} = m^{32}$ **8.** $(n^5)^{12} = n^{5\cdot 12} = n^{60}$
9. $(a^6)^5 = a^{6\cdot 5} = a^{30}$ **10.** $(y^7)^7 = y^{7\cdot 7} = y^{49}$
11. $(p^{10})^{10} = p^{10\cdot 10} = p^{100}$ **12.** $(w^{12})^7 = w^{12\cdot 7} = w^{84}$
13. $(3y)^4 = 3^4y^4 = 81y^4$ **14.** $(2t)^5 = 2^5t^5 = 32t^5$
15. $(7y)^3 = 7^3y^3 = 343y^3$ **16.** $(8x)^4 = 8^4x^4 = 4096x^4$
17. $(5m)^2 = 5^2m^2 = 25m^2$ **18.** $(4y)^5 = 4^5y^5 = 1024y^5$
19. $(7x)^4 = 7^4x^4 = 2401x^4$ **20.** $(12a)^3 = 12^3a^3 = 1728a^3$
21. $(2m^2)^2 = 2^2m^{2\cdot 2} = 4m^4$ **22.** $(4n^3)^2 = 4^2n^{3\cdot 2} = 16n^6$
23. $(5y^4)^3 = 5^3y^{4\cdot 3} = 125y^{12}$ **24.** $(3x^5)^4 = 3^4x^{5\cdot 4} = 81x^{20}$

25. $(-6t^2)^3 = (-6)^3t^{2\cdot 3} = -216t^6$
26. $(-10b^6)^2 = (-10)^2b^{6\cdot 2} = 100b^{12}$
27. $(8k^4)^3 = 8^3k^{4\cdot 3} = 512k^{12}$ **28.** $(7x^5)^3 = 7^3x^{5\cdot 3} = 343x^{15}$
29. $(2x^8y^3)^2 = 2^2x^{8\cdot 2}y^{3\cdot 2} = 4x^{16}y^6$
30. $(3mn^4)^3 = 3^3m^3n^{4\cdot 3} = 27m^3n^{12}$
31. $(-2x^2y^4)^3 = (-2)^3x^{2\cdot 3}y^{4\cdot 3} = -8x^6y^{12}$
32. $(-3m^4n^2)^2 = (-3)^2m^{4\cdot 2}n^{2\cdot 2} = 9m^8n^4$
33. $(4x^2y^3z)^4 = 4^4x^{2\cdot 4}y^{3\cdot 4}z^4 = 256x^8y^{12}z^4$
34. $(2m^5n^4p^3)^3 = 2^3m^{5\cdot 3}n^{4\cdot 3}p^{3\cdot 3} = 8m^{15}n^{12}p^9$
35. $\left(\frac{3}{a^2}\right)^3 = \frac{3^3}{a^{2\cdot 3}} = \frac{27}{a^6}$ **36.** $\left(\frac{7}{x^7}\right)^2 = \frac{7^2}{x^{7\cdot 2}} = \frac{49}{x^{14}}$
37. $\left(\frac{x^2}{4}\right)^4 = \frac{x^{2\cdot 4}}{4^4} = \frac{x^8}{256}$ **38.** $\left(\frac{y^5}{3}\right)^2 = \frac{y^{5\cdot 2}}{3^2} = \frac{y^{10}}{9}$
39. $\left(\frac{m^4}{n^2}\right)^3 = \frac{m^{4\cdot 3}}{n^{2\cdot 3}} = \frac{m^{12}}{n^6}$ **40.** $\left(\frac{a^8}{b^4}\right)^3 = \frac{a^{8\cdot 3}}{b^{4\cdot 3}} = \frac{a^{24}}{b^{12}}$
41. $\left(\frac{3\cdot 2^2}{5}\right)^3 = \frac{3^3\cdot 2^{2\cdot 3}}{5^3} = \frac{3^3\cdot 2^6}{5^3} = \frac{27\cdot 64}{125} = \frac{1728}{125}$
42. $\left(\frac{5\cdot 2^4}{3}\right)^2 = \frac{5^2\cdot 2^{4\cdot 2}}{3^2} = \frac{5^2\cdot 2^8}{3^2} = \frac{25\cdot 256}{9} = \frac{6400}{9}$
43. $\left(\frac{xy^2}{z}\right)^3 = \frac{x^3y^{2\cdot 3}}{z^3} = \frac{x^3y^6}{z^3}$ **44.** $\left(\frac{ab^4}{c}\right)^3 = \frac{a^3b^{4\cdot 3}}{c^3} = \frac{a^3b^{12}}{c^3}$
45. $\left(\frac{-2x^2y^6}{5}\right)^2 = \frac{(-2)^2x^{2\cdot 2}y^{6\cdot 2}}{5^2} = \frac{4x^4y^{12}}{25}$
46. $\left(\frac{3x^3y^3}{2}\right)^4 = \frac{3^4x^{3\cdot 4}y^{3\cdot 4}}{2^4} = \frac{81x^{12}y^{12}}{16}$
47. $\left(\frac{-4m^2n^5}{3}\right)^3 = \frac{(-4)^3m^{3\cdot 2}n^{5\cdot 3}}{3^3} = -\frac{64m^6n^{15}}{27}$
48. $\left(\frac{-5p^4q^3}{2}\right)^3 = \frac{(-5)^3p^{4\cdot 3}q^{3\cdot 3}}{2^3} = -\frac{125p^{12}q^9}{8}$
49. $[(-x^5)]^6 = (-1)^6x^{5\cdot 6} = x^{30}$
50. $[(-y)^{18}]^2 = (-1)^{18\cdot 2}y^{18\cdot 2} = y^{36}$
51. $\left(\frac{-x}{3y}\right)^3 = -\frac{x^3}{3^3y^3} = -\frac{x^3}{27y^3}$ **52.** $\left(\frac{2c}{-y}\right)^4 = \frac{2^4c^4}{(-y)^4} = \frac{16c^4}{y^4}$
53. $\left(\frac{x^2y}{z}\right)^3 = \frac{x^{2\cdot 3}y^3}{z^3} = \frac{x^6y^3}{z^3}$ **54.** $\left(\frac{m}{n^4p}\right)^3 = \frac{m^3}{n^{4\cdot 3}p^3} = \frac{m^3}{n^{12}p^3}$
55. $\left(\frac{-3a^2b^4}{4c^3}\right)^2 = \frac{(-3)^2a^{2\cdot 2}b^{4\cdot 2}}{4^2c^{3\cdot 2}} = \frac{9a^4b^8}{16c^6}$
56. $\left(\frac{2m^5n^5}{p^4}\right)^3 = \frac{2^3m^{5\cdot 3}n^{5\cdot 3}}{p^{4\cdot 3}} = \frac{8m^{15}n^{15}}{p^{12}}$
57. $(2n)^4\left(\frac{3}{2}n\right)^3 = 2^4n^4\left(\frac{3}{2}\right)^3n^3 = 16n^4\left(\frac{27}{8}\right)n^3 = 54n^7$
58. $(4x^3)^2 + (2x^2)^3 = 4^2x^{3\cdot 2} + 2^3x^{2\cdot 3} = 16x^6 + 8x^6 = 24x^6$
59. $(7a)(4a) - (3a)^2 = 28a^2 - 3^2a^2 = 28a^2 - 9a^2 = 19a^2$
60. $(-2y^2)^3 + 4y(2y^5) = (-2)^3y^{2\cdot 3} + 8y^{1+5} = -8y^6 + 8y^6 = 0$
61. $(-3z^4)^2 - (z^2)^4 = (-3)^2z^{4\cdot 2} - z^{2\cdot 4} = 9z^8 - z^8 = 8z^8$
62. $(6cd^2)^2 + 3cd(cd^3) = 6^2c^2d^{2\cdot 2} + 3c^{1+1}d^{1+3} = 36c^2d^4 + 3c^2d^4$
$= 39c^2d^4$
63. $3z^3(2z^4) - (-5z^3)^2 = 6z^{3+4} - (-5)^2z^{3\cdot 2} = 6z^7 - 25z^6$
64.
$$\begin{aligned} b^2(a^3b)^2 + a^2(a^2b^2)^2 &= b^2(a^{3\cdot 2}b^2) + a^2(a^{2\cdot 2}b^{2\cdot 2}) \\ &= b^2(a^6b^2) + a^2(a^4b^4) \\ &= a^6b^{2+2} + a^{2+4}b^4 \\ &= a^6b^4 + a^6b^4 \\ &= 2a^6b^4 \end{aligned}$$
65. $(3c^4)^2(2c) = 3^2c^{4\cdot 2}(2c) = 9c^8(2c) = 18c^{8+1} = 18c^9$

66. $(-2x^2y^3)^4(xy)^3 = (-2)^4x^{2\cdot 4}y^{3\cdot 4}\cdot x^3y^3 = 16x^8y^{12}(x^3y^3)$
$= 16x^{8+3}y^{12+3} = 16x^{11}y^{15}$

67. $(-3a^2b^4)^3(4a^3b)^2 = (-3)^3a^{2\cdot 3}b^{4\cdot 3}(4^2a^{3\cdot 2}b^2)$
$= -27a^6b^{12}(16a^6b^2)$
$= -432a^{6+6}b^{12+2} = -432a^{12}b^{14}$

68. Yes. We know $(a^m)^n = a^{mn}$.
By the commutative property, $mn = nm$, so $a^{mn} = a^{nm}$. Since $a^{nm} = (a^n)^m$, $(a^m)^n = (a^n)^m$.

69. $y = 2^x$, so $4y = 4\cdot 2^x = 2^2\cdot 2^x = 2^{2+x}$
The correct choice is **B.**

70. $x^{2a}x^4 = x^{2a+4}$ 71. $x^{3a}x^{2b} = x^{3a+2b}$

72. $x^{a+4}x^3 = x^{a+4+3} = x^{a+7}$

73. $x^5x^{2a-4} = x^{5+2a-4} = x^{2a+1}$

74. $(a^{n+1}b^{m+2})^3 = a^{3(n+1)}b^{3(m+2)}$
$= a^{3n+3}b^{3m+6}$

75. $(x^ay^{a-3})^3 = x^{3a}y^{3(a-3)} = x^{3a}y^{3a-9}$

76. $(c^3d)^a(cd^7)^a = c^{3a}d^ac^ad^{7a} = c^{3a+a}d^{a+7a} = c^{4a}d^{8a}$

77. $x^2(x^{a+2})y^3 = x^{a+2+2}y^3 = x^{a+4}y^3$

78. $x^{a+4} = x^4x^8$
$x^{a+4} = x^{12}$
$a + 4 = 12$
$a = 8$

79. $x^{a-3} = x^5x^3$
$x^{a-3} = x^8$
$a - 3 = 8$
$a = 11$

80. $x^{2a} = \frac{x^{12}}{x^9}$
$x^{2a} = x^3$
$2a = 3$
$a = \frac{3}{2}$

81. $x^{3a} = x^4x^6$
$x^{3a} = x^{10}$
$3a = 10$
$a = \frac{10}{3}$

82. $6c + (-9m) - 5c + m = c - 8m$

83. $21 - 8x - 9 - (-7x) = 12 - 8x + 7x = 12 - x$

84. $\frac{y}{x}$ 85. $\frac{8}{5c}$ 86. $-\frac{2a}{5}$ 87. $\frac{2}{m}$ 88. $\frac{t}{7}$

89. $m + 4 = -3m$
$m - m + 4 = -3m - m$
$4 = -4m$
$-\frac{1}{4}\cdot 4 = -\frac{1}{4}\cdot(-4m)$
$-1 = m$

90. $4x + 2x = 9x - 6$
$6x = 9x - 6$
$6x - 9x = 9x - 9x - 6$
$-3x = -6$
$-\frac{1}{3}(-3x) = -\frac{1}{3}(-6)$
$x = 2$

CONNECTIONS: GEOMETRY p. 213

1. $V = (2x)(2x)(2x) = (2x)^3$ or $8x^3$
2. $V = (4x)(4x)(4x) = (4x)^3$ or $64x^3$
3. $V = (8x)(8x)(8x) = (8x)^3$ or $512x^3$
4. $64x^3 = 8(8x^3)$
$216x^3 = 8(64x^3)$
The volume is multiplied by 8.

LESSON 5-3 TRY THIS pp. 214–215

a. $-15x$ b. $-m^2$ c. y^2 d. $(-x)^2(x^3) = x^2x^3 = x^5$
e. $(3p^5q^2)(4p^2q^3) = 12p^7q^5$ f. $(4x^5y^5)(-2x^6y^4) = -8x^{11}y^9$
g. $(-7y^4)(-y)(2y^3) = 14y^8$ h. $(7a^5)(3a^3)(-a^5) = -21a^{13}$
i. $\frac{x^8}{x^5} = x^{8-5} = x^3$ j. $\frac{12m^5}{8m^8} = \frac{4\cdot 3}{4\cdot 2}\cdot m^{5-8} = \frac{3}{2}m^{-3} = \frac{3}{2m^3}$
k. $\frac{-5x^3y^4}{-5x^2y} = \frac{-5}{-5}\cdot x^{3-2}y^{4-1} = xy^3$
l. $\frac{-32x^{15}y^7}{8x^{14}y^6} = \frac{-32}{8}\cdot x^{15-14}y^{7-6} = -4xy$

LESSON 5-3 EXERCISES pp. 215–216

1. $(6x^2)(7) = 6\cdot 7x^2 = 42x^2$
2. $(5y^3)(-2) = 5(-2)y^3 = -10y^3$
3. $(-x^3)(-x^1) = x^{3+1} = x^4$ 4. $(-y^4)(y^2) = -y^{4+2} = -y^6$
5. $(-x^5)(x^3) = -x^{5+3} = -x^8$
6. $(-m^6)(-m^2) = m^{6+2} = m^8$
7. $(3a^4)(2a^2) = 3\cdot 2a^{4+2} = 6a^6$
8. $(5x^3)(4x^5) = 5\cdot 4x^{3+5} = 20x^8$
9. $(7t^5)(4t^3) = 7\cdot 4t^{5+3} = 28t^8$
10. $(-3b^3)(5b^5) = -3\cdot 5b^{3+5} = -15b^8$
11. $(3g^4)(-6g^3) = -18g^{4+3} = -18g^7$
12. $(h^5)(-7h^3) = -7h^{5+3} = -7h^8$
13. $(-6x^3)(x^8) = -6x^{3+8} = -6x^{11}$
14. $(-8m^7)(-4m^3) = -8(-4)m^{7+3} = 32m^{10}$
15. $(-5n^4)(-5n^4) = -5(-5)n^{4+4} = 25n^8$
16. $(-x^7)(5x^{12}) = -5x^{7+12} = -5x^{19}$
17. $(x^3y^4)(x^4y^2) = x^{3+4}y^{4+2} = x^7y^6$
18. $(2m^3n^2)(-3m^6n^5) = 2(-3)m^{3+6}n^{2+5} = -6m^9n^7$
19. $(4a^4b^8)(2a^4b^2) = 4\cdot 2a^{4+4}b^{8+2} = 8a^8b^{10}$
20. $(-2x^3y)(-6x^9y^8) = -2(-6)x^{3+9}y^{1+8} = 12x^{12}y^9$
21. $(y^5)(2y)(3y^2) = 2\cdot 3y^{5+1+2} = 6y^8$
22. $(3x^4)(x^4)(5x^2) = 3\cdot 5x^{4+4+2} = 15x^{10}$
23. $(-4m^2)(5m^4)(-2m^3) = -4(5)(-2)m^{2+4+3} = 40m^9$
24. $(9b^2)(2b^5)(-3b^7) = 9(2)(-3)b^{2+5+7} = -54b^{14}$
25. $\frac{x^6}{x^2} = x^{6-2} = x^4$ 26. $\frac{a^7}{a} = a^{7-1} = a^6$
27. $\frac{4x^5}{2x^2} = \frac{4}{2}\cdot x^{5-2} = 2x^3$
28. $\frac{-6a^3}{6a} = -\frac{6}{6}\cdot a^{3-1} = -a^2$
29. $\frac{12m^4}{4m^4} = \frac{12}{4}\cdot m^{4-4} = 3m^0 = 3$
30. $\frac{-4x^6}{-2x^6} = \frac{-4}{-2}\cdot x^{6-6} = 2x^0 = 2$
31. $\frac{5a^3}{a^7} = 5\cdot a^{3-7} = 5a^{-4} = \frac{5}{a^4}$
32. $\frac{15y^8}{3} = \frac{15}{3}\cdot y^8 = 5y^8$
33. $\frac{-h^5}{2h^4} = \frac{-1}{2}\cdot h^{5-4} = -\frac{1}{2}h^1 = -\frac{1}{2}h$
34. $\frac{k^3}{3k^8} = \frac{1}{3}\cdot k^{3-8} = \frac{1}{3}k^{-5} = \frac{1}{3k^5}$
35. $\frac{2x^{10}}{8x^5} = \frac{2}{8}\cdot x^{10-5} = \frac{1}{4}x^5$
36. $\frac{3m^5}{6m^7} = \frac{3}{6}\cdot m^{5-7} = \frac{1}{2}m^{-2} = \frac{1}{2m^2}$
37. $\frac{16x^2}{-4x^2} = -\frac{16}{4}\cdot x^{2-2} = -4x^0 = -4$

38. $\frac{-25a^7}{-25} = \frac{-25}{-25} \cdot a^7 = a^7$

39. $\frac{45x^3}{15x^2} = \frac{45}{15} \cdot x^{3-2} = 3x^1 = 3x$

40. $\frac{6m^6}{2m^2} = \frac{6}{2} \cdot m^{6-2} = 3m^4$

41. $\frac{10x^5y^4}{2x^3y} = \frac{10}{2} \cdot x^{5-3}y^{4-1} = 5x^2y^3$

42. $\frac{-12m^7n^8}{4m^2n^5} = -\frac{12}{4} \cdot m^{7-2}n^{8-5} = -3m^5n^3$

43. $\frac{24a^6b^9}{-6a^6b^3} = -\frac{24}{6} \cdot a^{6-6}b^{9-3} = -4a^0b^6 = -4b^6$

44. $\frac{48x^6y^7}{12xy^5} = \frac{48}{12} \cdot x^{6-1}y^{7-5} = 4x^5y^2$

45. $\frac{-12p^8r^3}{4p^6r^4} = -\frac{12}{4} \cdot p^{8-6}r^{3-4} = -3p^2r^{-1} = \frac{-3p^2}{r}$

46. $\frac{2x^{12}y^5}{3x^4y^2} = \frac{2}{3} \cdot x^{12-4}y^{5-2} = \frac{2}{3}x^8y^3$ or $\frac{2x^8y^3}{3}$

47. $\frac{5a^{11}b^7}{-7a^5b^9} = -\frac{5}{7} \cdot a^{11-5}b^{7-9} = -\frac{5}{7}a^6b^{-2} = \frac{-5a^6}{7b^2}$

48. $\frac{6x^{13}y^4}{24x^5y^7} = \frac{6}{24} \cdot x^{13-5}y^{4-7} = \frac{1}{4}x^8y^{-3} = \frac{x^8}{4y^3}$

49. $x^3(x^4)^2 = x^3 \cdot x^8 = x^{11}$

50. $p(p^4)^3 = p \cdot p^{12} = p^{13}$ **51.** $(a^3)^2(a^4)^3 = a^6a^{12} = a^{18}$

52. $(m^2)^4(m^3)^2 = m^8m^6 = m^{14}$

53. $(2x^2)(3x^3)^2 = 2x^2(9x^6) = 18x^8$

54. $(3y^4)(5y^4)^2 = 3y^4(25y^8) = 75y^{12}$

55. $(3x^4)^2(2x^5)^2 = 9x^8 \cdot 4x^{10} = 36x^{18}$

56. $(4y)^3(-2y^2)^2 = 64y^3 \cdot 4y^4 = 256y^7$

57. $(2x^2y)(3x^4y^5) = 6x^6y^6$ **58.** $(-3mn^4)(4mn^2) = -12m^2n^6$

59. $(ab^2)^3(a^3b^4)^2 = a^3b^6a^6b^8 = a^9b^{14}$

60. $(m^3n)^2(mn^5)^3 = m^6n^2m^3n^{15} = m^9n^{17}$

61. $\frac{(-2x^2)^2}{x^3} = \frac{4x^4}{x^3} = 4x^{4-3} = 4x$

62. $\frac{(3a^3)^2}{18a^2} = \frac{9a^6}{18a^2} = \frac{1}{2} \cdot a^{6-2} = \frac{a^4}{2}$

63. $\frac{(4y^3)^2}{(4y^2)^2} = \frac{16y^6}{16y^4} = y^{6-4} = y^2$ **64.** $\frac{(-5m)^4}{(-25m^2)^2} = \frac{625m^4}{625m^4} = 1$

65. $\frac{a^4b^5}{3a^2b^6} = \frac{1}{3} \cdot a^{4-2}b^{5-6} = \frac{1}{3}a^2b^{-1} = \frac{a^2}{3b}$

66. $\frac{2x^6y^4}{8x^4y^7} = \frac{1}{4}x^{6-4}y^{4-7} = \frac{1}{4}x^2y^{-3} = \frac{x^2}{4y^3}$

67. $\frac{-2m^3}{-4m^4n^6} = \frac{-2}{-4} \cdot m^{3-4}n^{-6} = \frac{1}{2}m^{-1}n^{-6} = \frac{1}{2mn^6}$

68. $\frac{-4ab^3}{-8a^2b^4} = \frac{-4}{-8} \cdot a^{1-2}b^{3-4} = \frac{1}{2}a^{-1}b^{-1} = \frac{1}{2ab}$

69. It must be equal to one.

70. $(5x^{-2})(2x^{-4}) = 10x^{-2-4} = 10x^{-6} = \frac{10}{x^6}$

71. $(8m^{-3})(-4m^4)(m^{-4}) = -32m^{-3+4-4} = -32m^{-3} = \frac{-32}{m^3}$

72. $\frac{25b^{16}}{5b^{-12}} = \frac{25}{5} \cdot b^{16-(-12)} = 5b^{28}$

73. $\frac{12m^{-10}}{-4m^5} = \frac{12}{-4} \cdot m^{-10-5} = -3m^{-15} = -\frac{3}{m^{15}}$

74. $(3a^{-2}b^4)(-4a^6b^{-7}) = -12a^4b^{-3} = -\frac{12a^4}{b^3}$

75. $(5x^6y^7)(3x^{-6}y^{-7}) = 15x^0y^0 = 15$

76. $(5x^{-4}y^{-6}z^5)(-4x^5y^5z^{-3})(-4x^2yz^{-1}) = 80x^3y^0z = 80x^3z$

77. $(qrs)(-qrs^3)(-5q^{-3}r^4s^{-5}) = 5q^{-1}r^6s^{-1} = \frac{5r^6}{qs}$

78. $3x + 2y + 4x = (3 + 4)x + 2y = 7x + 2y$

79. $7x + 3y^2 + y^2 = 7x + (3 + 1)y^2 = 7x + 4y^2$

80. $8pt + 4t + 2pt + t = (8 + 2)pt + (4 + 1)t = 10pt + 5t$

81. $5m - 7m = (5 - 7)m = -2m$

82. $m - 3n - 2n = m + (-3 - 2)n = m - 5n$

83. $14a + b - 5a - 3b = (14 - 5)a + (1 - 3)b = 9a - 2b$

84. $15\% = 0.15$ **85.** $0.04\% = 0.0004$ **86.** $125\% = 1.25$

87.
$$\begin{aligned} x + 4 - 6x &< -10 \\ 2x + 4 &< -10 \\ 2x + 4 - 4 &< -10 - 4 \\ 2x &< -14 \\ \tfrac{1}{2}(2x) &< \tfrac{1}{2}(-14) \\ x &< -7 \end{aligned}$$

88.
$$\begin{aligned} 6x &\le -36 \\ \tfrac{1}{6} \cdot 6x &\le \tfrac{1}{6}(-36) \\ x &\le -6 \end{aligned}$$

89.
$$\begin{aligned} 3 - 6x &< 9 \\ 3 - 3 - 6x &< 9 - 3 \\ -6x &< 6 \\ -\tfrac{1}{6}(-6x) &> -\tfrac{1}{6} \cdot 6 \\ x &> -1 \end{aligned}$$

90. Let n = number of books left.
$n = 407 + 23 - 17 + 15 - 29 - 26 + 30$
$n = 403$
403 books were left.

LESSON 5-4 TRY THIS p. 218

a. 1250 **b.** 700,000 **c.** 0.0048
d. 0.00018 **e.** 3.2×10^3 **f.** 1.39×10^5
g. 3.07×10^{-2} **h.** 2.004×10^{-1}
i. $(1.1 \times 10^{-8})(5 \times 10^{-7}) = (1.1 \times 5)(10^{-8} \times 10^{-7})$
$= 5.5 \times 10^{-15}$

j. $\frac{4.2 \times 10^5}{2.1 \times 10^2} = \frac{4.2}{2.1} \times \frac{10^5}{10^2} = 2.0 \times 10^{5-2} = 2.0 \times 10^3$

LESSON 5-4 EXERCISES pp. 219–220

1. 5543 **2.** 329 **3.** 0.00235 **4.** 0.0001743

5. 57,000 **6.** 489,000 **7.** 0.000034 **8.** 4000

9. 0.0006 **10.** 120.6 **11.** 0.003007 **12.** 0.0000804

13. 4.25×10^2 **14.** 4.78×10^{-1} **15.** 1.24×10^4

16. 3.206×10^4 **17.** 4.5×10^{-2} **18.** 3×10^{-5}

19. 1.25×10^5 **20.** 1.2×10 **21.** 5.2×10^6

22. 1.24×10^7 **23.** 5.6×10^{-6} **24.** 3.2×10^{-8}

25. $(7 \times 10^4)(2 \times 10^2) = (7 \times 2)(10^4 \times 10^2)$
$= 14 \times 10^6 = 1.4 \times 10^7$

26. $(2.2 \times 10^{-3})(3.0 \times 10^5) = (2.2 \times 3)(10^{-3} \times 10^5)$
$= 6.6 \times 10^2$

27. $(4.0 \times 10^7)(8.0 \times 10^3) = (4 \times 8)(10^7 \times 10^3)$
$= 32 \times 10^{10} = 3.2 \times 10^{11}$

28. $(6.1 \times 10^9)(2.5 \times 10^{-4}) = (6.1 \times 2.5)(10^9 \times 10^{-4})$
$= 15.25 \times 10^5$
$= 1.525 \times 10^6$

29. $(2.5 \times 10^{-3})(4.0 \times 10^{-8}) = (2.5 \times 4.0)(10^{-3} \times 10^{-8})$
$= 10 \times 10^{-11}$
$= 1.0 \times 10^{-10}$

30. $(5.4 \times 10^{-6})(5.1 \times 10^{-8}) = (5.4 \times 5.1)(10^{-6} \times 10^{-8})$
$= 27.54 \times 10^{-14}$
$= 2.754 \times 10^{-13}$

31. $\dfrac{(6.0 \times 10^7)}{(3.0 \times 10^2)} = \dfrac{6.0}{3.0} \times \dfrac{10^7}{10^2} = 2.0 \times 10^5$

32. $\dfrac{(9.0 \times 10^8)}{(3.0 \times 10^2)} = \dfrac{9.0}{3.0} \times \dfrac{10^8}{10^2} = 3.0 \times 10^6$

33. $\dfrac{(8.4 \times 10^6)}{(2.0 \times 10^8)} = \dfrac{8.4}{2.0} \times \dfrac{10^6}{10^8} = 4.2 \times 10^{-2}$

34. $\dfrac{(6.9 \times 10^4)}{(3.0 \times 10^8)} = \dfrac{6.9}{3.0} \times \dfrac{10^4}{10^8} = 2.3 \times 10^{-4}$

35. $\dfrac{(1.5 \times 10^{-2})}{(3 \times 10^{-4})} = \dfrac{1.5}{3} \times \dfrac{10^{-2}}{10^{-4}} = 0.5 \times 10^{-2-(-4)}$
$= 0.5 \times 10^{-2+4}$
$= 0.5 \times 10^2$
$= 5.0 \times 10^1$

36. $\dfrac{(2.7 \times 10^{12})}{(9.0 \times 10^{12})} = \dfrac{2.7}{9.0} \times \dfrac{10^{12}}{10^{12}} = 0.3 \times 10^0 = 3.0 \times 10^{-1}$

37. $\dfrac{(3.4 \times 10^6)(6 \times 10^3)}{(5 \times 10^5)} = \dfrac{3.4 \times 6}{5} \times \dfrac{10^6 \times 10^3}{10^5}$
$= 4.08 \times 10^4 = 40{,}800$

38. $\dfrac{(4.55 \times 10^3)(2.6 \times 10^5)}{(2 \times 10^{-2})} = \dfrac{4.55 \times 2.6}{2} \times \dfrac{10^3 \times 10^5}{10^{-2}}$
$= 5.915 \times 10^{3+5-(-2)}$
$= 5.915 \times 10^{8+2}$
$= 5.915 \times 10^{10}$
$= 59{,}150{,}000{,}000$

39. $\dfrac{(5.2 \times 10^{-4})(4 \times 10^5)}{(2.5 \times 10^9)} = \dfrac{5.2 \times 4}{2.5} \times \dfrac{10^{-4} \times 10^5}{10^9}$
$= 8.32 \times 10^{-4+5-9}$
$= 8.32 \times 10^{-8}$
$= 0.0000000832$

40. $\dfrac{(5 \times 10^{-3})(3.26 \times 10^{-4})}{(4 \times 10^2)} = \dfrac{5 \times 3.26}{4} \times \dfrac{10^{-3} \times 10^{-4}}{10^2}$
$= 4.075 \times 10^{-3-4-2}$
$= 4.075 \times 10^{-9}$
$= 0.000000004075$

41. $d = rt; d = (3.0 \times 10^5)(5.0 \times 10^2)$
$= 15 \times 10^7$
$= 1.5 \times 10^8$ km or 150,000,000 km

42. $(2000 \text{ years})\left(365\dfrac{\text{days}}{\text{year}}\right)\left(24\dfrac{\text{hours}}{\text{day}}\right)\left(60\dfrac{\text{minutes}}{\text{hour}}\right)\left(60\dfrac{\text{seconds}}{\text{minute}}\right)$
$= 6.3072 \times 10^{10}$ seconds or 63,072,000,000 seconds

43. Answers may vary.

44. $(3.01 \times 10^{-23})(1.3 \times 10^{21}) = (3.01 \times 1.3)(10^{-23} \times 10^{21})$
$= 3.913 \times 10^{-2}$ g
$= 0.03913$ g

45. three times $(3.6 \times 10^{-3}) = 10.8 \times 10^{-3} = 1.08 \times 10^{-2}$
half of $(2.16 \times 10^{-2}) = 1.08 \times 10^{-2}$
The quantities are equal. The correct choice is **C.**

46. $1.86 \times 10^5 \times 60 \times 60 \times 24 \times 365$
$= 58{,}656{,}960 \times 10^5$
$\approx 5.8657 \times 10^7 \times 10^5$
$= 5.8657 \times 10^{12}$ mi
$= 5{,}865{,}700{,}000{,}000$ mi

47. $\dfrac{2.79 \times 10^9}{1.86 \times 10^5} = 1.5 \times 10^4$ seconds
$= 15{,}000$ seconds

48. $1.24 \times 10^{-3} = 0.00124$

49. $(8 \times 10^4)y = 6.4 \times 10^7$
$y = \dfrac{6.4 \times 10^7}{8 \times 10^4}$
$y = 0.8 \times 10^3 = 8 \times 10^2$ or 800

50. $(3.1 \times 10^5)y = 9.3 \times 10^3$
$y = \dfrac{9.3 \times 10^3}{3.1 \times 10^5}$
$y = 3 \times 10^{-2}$ or 0.03

51. $\dfrac{(3.6 \times 10^6)(4 \times 10^{-3})}{(4.8 \times 10^{-2})(1.2 \times 10^6)} = \dfrac{3.6 \times 4}{4.8 \times 1.2} \times \dfrac{10^6 \times 10^{-3}}{10^{-2} \times 10^6}$
$= 2.5 \times 10^{6-3-(-2)-6}$
$= 2.5 \times 10^{3+2-6}$
$= 2.5 \times 10^{-1}$ or 0.25

52. $21 - 15t = 3(7 - 5t)$ 53. $9a + 6 = 3(3a + 2)$

54. $30 + 15k = 15(2 + k)$ 55. $12m - 4n = 4(3m - n)$

56. $3a^2 + 6a + 9 = 3(a^2 + 2a + 3)$

57. $5x + (2x - 6) = 5x + 2x - 6 = 7x - 6$

58. $(11y + 9) - 6y = 11y + 9 - 6y = 5y + 9$

59. $4a - (3a + 15) = 4a - 3a - 15 = a - 15$

60. $(4x - 7) - (3x - 7) = 4x - 7 - 3x + 7 = x$

LESSON 5-5 TRY THIS pp. 222–224

a. No b. Yes; binomial
c. Terms: $5y^3, 6y, -3$; Coefficients: $5, 6, -3$
d. Terms: $m^4, -3m, -6$; Coefficients: $1, -3, -6$
e. Terms: $-3m^4n^2, -m^2n, 2n$; Coefficients: $-3, -1, 2$
f. $2x - 4x^3 - 24 - 6x^3 = 2x - (4 + 6)x^3 - 24$
$= 2x - 10x^3 - 24$
g. $7m^2 - m - m^2 - 7 = (7 - 1)m^2 - m - 7$
$= 6m^2 - m - 7$
h. $8x^2y^2 - y^2 + y^3 - 1 - 4x^2y^2 = (8 - 4)x^2y^2 - y^2 + y^3 - 1$
$= 4x^2y^2 - y^2 + y^3 - 1$
i. $4b^5 - 2ab^3 - 3b^5 + 7ab^3 = (4 - 3)b^5 + (-2 + 7)ab^3$
$= b^5 + 5ab^3$
j. 4, 2, 1, 0; 4 k. 11, 7, 7, 1; 11

LESSON 5-5 EXERCISES pp. 224–225

1. no 2. yes; trinomial 3. yes; binomial
4. yes; monomial 5. no 6. yes; trinomial
7. yes; binomial 8. yes; binomial 9. yes; monomial
10. yes; trinomial 11. yes; trinomial 12. yes; trinomial
13. yes; monomial 14. no

15. Terms: $-4m^9, 6m, -1$
Coefficients: $-4, 6, -1$

16. Terms: $a^5, 4a^3, -3a^2, a$
Coefficients: $1, 4, -3, 1$

17. Terms: $2x^2y, 5xy^2, -6y^4$
Coefficients: $2, 5, -6$

18. Terms: $m^4n^3, -3m^3n^2, 6m^2n^4$
Coefficients: $1, -3, 6$

19. Terms: $8p^3, 2pq, -4$
Coefficients: $8, 2, -4$

20. Terms: $a^4b^6, -2a^6b^4$
Coefficients: $1, -2$

21. Terms: $-3n^6, 3n, -3$
Coefficients: $-3, 3, -3$

22. Terms: $x^6, -2x^5, 3x^2, -2x, -4$
Coefficients: $1, -2, 3, -2, -4$

23. Terms: $x^8y^6, -2x^6y^6, 8x^4y^7, -4xy^8$
Coefficients: $1, -2, 8, -4$

24. Terms: $12m^{12}, -8m^{11}n^{10}, 5m^5n^{11}, -m^4n^{12}, n^{14}$
Coefficients: $12, -8, 5, -1, 1$

25. $2x - 5x = (2 - 5)x = -3x$

26. $x - 9x = (1 - 9)x = -8x$

27. $2x^2 + 8x^2 = (2 + 8)x^2 = 10x^2$

28. $3x^2 - 4x^2 = (3 - 4)x^2 = -x^2$

29. $x^3 - 5x - 2x^3 = (1 - 2)x^3 - 5x = -x^3 - 5x$

30. $5x^3 + 6x^3 + 4 = (5 + 6)x^3 + 4 = 11x^3 + 4$

31. $6x^4 - 3x^4 + 7 = (6 - 3)x^4 + 7 = 3x^4 + 7$

32. $6x^4 - 2x^4 + 5 = (6 - 2)x^4 + 5 = 4x^4 + 5$

33. $5x^3 - 3 - 2x^3 = (5 - 2)x^3 - 3 = 3x^3 - 3$

34. $-3x^4 - 6x^4 + 5 = (3 - 6)x^4 + 5 = -9x^4 + 5$

35. $3a^4 - 2a + 2a + a^4 = (3 + 1)a^4 + (-2 + 2)a$
$= 4a^4$

36. $2x^2 - 6x + 3x + 4x^2 = (2 + 4)x^2 + (-6 + 3)x$
$= 6x^2 - 3x$

37. $4xy^2 + 2x^2y - xy^2 + 3x^2y$
$= (4 - 1)xy^2 + (2 + 3)x^2y$
$= 3xy^2 + 5x^2y$

38. $-7m^2n^2 + 2mn - 2m^2n^2 - 4mn$
$= (-7 - 2)m^2n^2 + (2 - 4)mn$
$= -9m^2n^2 - 2mn$

39. $2ab^2 + 3ab - 5a^2b + 4ab^2$
$= (2 + 4)ab^2 + 3ab - 5a^2b$
$= 6ab^2 + 3ab - 5a^2b$

40. $6x^2 + 5xy^2 + 2x^2 - 3xy^2$
$= (6 + 2)x^2 + (5 - 3)xy^2$
$= 8x^2 + 2xy^2$

41. The student should have subtracted the coefficients of the like terms. $7x^3 - x^3 = 7x^3 - 1x^3 = (7 - 1)x^3 = 6x^3$

42. 1, 0; 1 **43.** 2, 1, 0; 2 **44.** 3, 2, 1, 0; 3 **45.** 2, 1, 6, 4; 6

46. 6, 4, 2, 0; 6 **47.** 9, 9, 4; 9

48. Sometimes. For example, the degree of $4x + 1$ equals the sum of the degrees of the terms. The degree of $x^2 + x$ is less than the sum of the degrees of the terms.

49. $\frac{1}{4}x^5 - 5 + \frac{1}{2}x^5 - 2x = \frac{3}{4}x^5 - 2x - 5$

50. $\frac{1}{3}x^3 + 2x - \frac{1}{6}x^3 + 4 = \left(\frac{2}{6} - \frac{1}{6}\right)x^3 + 2x + 4$
$= \frac{1}{6}x^3 + 2x + 4$

51. $\frac{1}{2}a^4 - 4a^2 + \frac{2}{3}a^4 - 3 = \left(\frac{3}{6} + \frac{4}{6}\right)a^4 - 4a^2 - 3$
$= \frac{7}{6}a^4 - 4a^2 - 3$

52. $\frac{2}{5}r^5 - \frac{1}{2}r^3 + \frac{7}{2}r^3 = \frac{2}{5}r^5 + \left(-\frac{1}{2} + \frac{7}{2}\right)r^3$
$= \frac{2}{5}r^5 + 3r^3$

53. a. $3y + 2y + 4 + 2y + 4 + 3y + (2y + 4) + 7y$
$= (3 + 2 + 2 + 3 + 2 + 7)y + (4 + 4 + 4)$
$= 19y + 12$

b. $4a + 7 + a + \frac{1}{2}a + 3 + a + 2a + 3a$
$= \left(4 + 1 + \frac{1}{2} + 1 + 2 + 3\right)a + (7 + 3)$
$= 11\frac{1}{2}a + 10$

54. $\frac{1}{x}$ is not a monomial; $\frac{5}{y}$ is not a monomial; $\sqrt{x}$ is not a monomial;
$\frac{y^2 + 3}{y} = y + \frac{3}{y}$, $\frac{3}{y}$ is not a monomial.

55. $n(n + 2) - 3 = n^2 + 2n - 3$

56. Let n = coefficient of x^3,
$n - 3$ = coefficient of x^2,
$3(n - 3)$ = coefficient of x,
$n + 2$ = last coefficient.
$n + (n - 3) + 3(n - 3) + n + 2 = -4$
$n + n - 3 + 3n - 9 + n + 2 = -4$
$6n - 10 = -4$
$6n - 10 + 10 = -4 + 10$
$6n = 6$
$n = 1$
So the coefficients are 1, − 2, − 6, and 3 and the polynomial is $x^3 - 2x^2 - 6x + 3$.

57. $c^2 \cdot c^5 \cdot c^3 = c^{2+5+3} = c^{10}$ **58.** $3(m^2)^3 = 3^3m^{2 \cdot 3} = 27m^6$

59. $(x^3y^2)(x^4y^9) = x^{3+4}y^{2+9} = x^7y^{11}$

60. $(-2ab)^3 = (-2)^3a^3b^3 = -8a^3b^3$

61. $(3c^{-2})^2 = 9c^{-4}$ or $\frac{9}{c^4}$ **62.** $(3c)^{-2} = \frac{1}{(3c)^2} = \frac{1}{9c^2}$

63. $y\left(y + \frac{2}{3}\right) = \left(-\frac{1}{2}\right)\left(-\frac{1}{2} + \frac{2}{3}\right) = \left(-\frac{1}{2}\right)\left(-\frac{3}{6} + \frac{4}{6}\right)$
$= \left(-\frac{1}{2}\right)\left(\frac{1}{6}\right)$
$= -\frac{1}{12}$

64. $y^4 = \left(-\frac{1}{2}\right)^4 = \frac{1}{2^4} = \frac{1}{16}$

65. $1 - \frac{3}{4}y = 1 - \frac{3}{4}\left(-\frac{1}{2}\right) = 1 + \frac{3}{8} = \frac{11}{8}$

66. $-6x \le 12$
$\frac{1}{-6}(-6x) \ge \frac{1}{-6}(12)$
$x \ge -2$

67. $2 + 9a \ge 29$
$2 - 2 + 9a \ge 29 - 2$
$9a \ge 27$
$\frac{1}{9}(9a) \ge \frac{1}{9}(27)$
$a \ge 3$

68. $9 - 6c = 3c + 54$
$9 - 6c + 6c = 3c + 6c + 54$
$9 = 9c + 54$
$9 - 54 = 9c + 54 - 54$
$-45 = 9c$
$\frac{1}{9}(-45) = \frac{1}{9}(9c)$
$-5 = c$

LESSON 5-6 TRY THIS pp. 226–228

a. $6x^7 + 3x^5 - 2x^4 + 4x^3 + 5x^2 + x$
b. $7x^5 - 5x^4 + 2x^3 + 4x^2 - 3$
c. $-14x^7 - 10x^3y^2 + 7x^2y^3 - 14y$
d. $3m^2 - 2m + 3 - 5m^2 - 1 - m = -2m^2 - 3m + 2$
e. $-4m^2y + my - 2m^2y - my + 3m^3y$
$= -6m^2y + 3m^3y = 3m^3y - 6m^2y$
f. $-4x - 7 = -4(3) - 7 = -12 - 7 = -19$
g. $-5x^2 + 7x + 10 = -5(3)^2 + 7(3) + 10$
$= -5(9) + 21 + 10$
$= -45 + 21 + 10$
$= -14$
h. $2x^2y + 5xy - 4 = 2(-4)^2(5) + 5(-4)(5) - 4$
$= 2(16)(5) - 100 - 4$
$= 160 - 100 - 4$
$= 56$
i. $-16t^2 + 140t = -16(7)^2 + 140(7)$
$= -16(49) + 980$
$= -784 + 980$
$= 196$ ft
j. $0.005s^2 - 0.35s + 37$
$= 0.005(55)^2 - 0.35(55) + 37$
$= 0.005(3025) - 19.25 + 37$
$= 15.125 + 17.75$
$= 32.875$
≈ 32.9¢ per mile

k. $0.041h - 0.018A - 2.69$
$= 0.041(170) - 0.018(25) - 2.69$
$= 6.97 - 0.45 - 2.69$
$= 3.83$ L

LESSON 5-6 EXERCISES pp. 229–230

1. $x^5 + 6x^3 + 2x^2 + x + 1$ **2.** $-5x^6 - 2x^3 + 2x^2 + 3x + 3$

3. $15x^9 + 7x^8 + 5x^3 - x^2 + x$ **4.** $x^5 - 5x^4 + 6x^3 + 9x - 5$

5. $-5y^8 - y^7 + 9y^6 + 8y^3 - 7y^2$ **6.** $p^8 - 7p^4 + p^2 + p - 4$

7. $m^6 + m^4$ **8.** $m^4 - 2m^3 + 1$

9. $13m^3 - 9m + 8$ **10.** $m^2 - 4m + 1$

11. $-3m^2 + 9mp$ **12.** $-6m^3p^4 - 2mp - 4m$

13. $12m^4 - 2m + \frac{1}{4}$ **14.** $4m^3 + m - \frac{1}{2}$

15. $x^3 - 27 = (5)^3 - 27 = 125 - 27 = 98$

16. $x^5 + x = (-2)^5 + (-2) = -32 - 2 = -34$

17. $x^4 - x = (3)^4 - 3 = 81 - 3 = 78$

18. $5x^4 - 7x + 2 = 5(-2)^4 - 7(-2) + 2$
$= 5(16) + 14 + 2$
$= 80 + 16$
$= 96$

19. $2x^3 - 5x^2 + x - 3 = 2(3)^3 - 5(3)^2 + 3 - 3$
$= 2(27) - 5(9)$
$= 54 - 45$
$= 9$

20. $2x - 5 + 4x^3 + x + x^2 - 2x = 4x^3 + x^2 + x - 5$
$= 4(-4)^3 + (-4)^2 + (-4) - 5$
$= 4(-64) + 16 - 4 - 5$
$= -256 + 7$
$= -249$

21. $-4x^3 + 2x^2 + x - 3 = -4(5)^3 + 2(5)^2 + 5 - 3$
$= -4(125) + 2(25) + 2$
$= -500 + 50 + 2$
$= -448$

22. $x^5 - x^4 + x^3 - x^2 + x - 1$
$= (-1)^5 - (-1)^4 + (-1)^3 - (-1)^2 + (-1) - 1$
$= -1 - 1 - 1 - 1 - 1 - 1$
$= -6$

23. $-5x + 2 = -5(4) + 2 = -20 + 2 = -18$

24. $-3x + 1 = -3(4) + 1 = -12 + 1 = -11$

25. $2x^2 - 5x + 7 = 2(4)^2 - 5(4) + 7$
$= 2(16) - 20 + 7$
$= 32 - 3$
$= 19$

26. $3x^2 + x - 7 = 3(4)^2 + 4 - 7$
$= 3(16) - 3$
$= 48 - 3$
$= 45$

27. $x^3 - 5x^2 + x = (4)^3 - 5(4)^2 + (4)$
$= 64 - 5(16) + 4$
$= 64 - 80 + 4$
$= -12$

28. $7 - x + 3x^2 = 7 - 4 + 3(4)^2$
$= 3 + 3(16)$
$= 3 + 48$
$= 51$

29. $3a + 5ab = 3(-1) + 5(-1)(2)$
$= -3 - 10 = -13$

30. $6 - 2ab = 6 - 2(-1)(2)$
$= 6 + 4$
$= 10$

31. $a^2 - 2a + b = (-1)^2 - 2(-1) + 2$
$= 1 + 2 + 2 = 5$

32. $5a - 6 + a^2b = 5(-1) - 6 + (-1)^2(2)$
$= -5 - 6 + 1(2)$
$= -11 + 2 = -9$

33. $-3a^3 + 7a^2 - 3b - 2 = -3(-1)^3 + 7(-1)^2 - 3(2) - 2$
$= -3(-1) + 7(1) - 6 - 2$
$= 3 + 7 + 8$
$= 2$

34. $-2a^3 - 5a^2 + 4a + 3b$
$= -2(-1)^3 - 5(-1)^2 + 4(-1) + 3(2)$
$= -2(-1) - 5(1) - 4 + 6$
$= 2 - 5 + 2$
$= -1$

35. $0.4x^2 - 40x + 1039 = 0.4(18)^2 - 40(18) + 1039$
$= 0.4(324) - 720 + 1039$
$= 129.6 + 319$
$= 448.6$ or 449 accidents

36. $0.4x^2 - 40x + 1039 = 0.4(20)^2 - 40(20) + 1039$
$= 0.4(400) - 800 + 1039$
$= 160 + 239$
$= 399$ accidents

37. $x \cdot x - 4 \cdot 4 = x^2 - 16$

38. $\pi \cdot r \cdot r - \pi \cdot 3 \cdot 3 = \pi r^2 - 9\pi$

39. $ax^2 + 3x + 7 = 15$ when $x = 1$
$a(1)^2 + 3(1) + 7 = 15$
$a + 3 + 7 = 15$
$a + 10 = 15$
$a + 10 - 10 = 15 - 10$
$a = 5$

40. $(-5x^3 + 3x^2 + 6)(7x - 12)$
$= (-5[3]^3 + 3[3]^2 + 6)(7[3] - 12)$
$= (-5[27] + 3[9] + 6)(21 - 12)$
$= (-135 + 27 + 6)(9)$
$= (-102)9$
$= -918$

41. $(2x^3 + 3x^2 - 4x + 8)(x^4 - x^2 + 5x)$
$= (2[-2]^3 + 3[-2]^2 - 4[-2] + 8)([-2]^4 - [-2]^2 + 5[-2])$
$= (2[-8] + 3[4] + 8 + 8)(16 - [4] - 10)$
$= (-16 + 12 + 8 + 8)(2)$
$= 12(2) = 24$

42. $(4x^5 - 4x^3 + 5x^2 - 4x + 6)(-3x^3 + 6x^2 - x + 8)$
$= (4[-1]^5 - 4[-1]^3 + 5[-1]^2 - 4[-1] + 6)(-3[-1]^3$
$+ 6[-1]^2 - [-1] + 8)$
$= (-4 + 4 + 5 + 4 + 6)(3 + 6 + 1 + 8) = 15(18) = 270$

43. $0.4x^2 - 40x + 1039$: $a = 0.4$, $b = -40$
$2ax = -b$
$2(0.4)x = -(-40)$
$0.8x = 40$
$\frac{1}{0.8}(0.8x) = \frac{1}{0.8}(40)$
$x = 50$
The age with the lowest daily accidents is 50.

44. $\frac{x^2y^4}{xy} = xy^3$ **45.** $\left(\frac{x^3}{2}\right)^3 = \frac{x^9}{2^3} = \frac{x^9}{8}$ **46.** $\frac{4a^9}{a^7} = 4a^2$

47. $\frac{21c^3}{7a^3} = \frac{3c^3}{a^3}$ **48.** $1.603 \times 10^4 = 16{,}030$

49. $7.662 \times 10^{-3} = 0.007662$

50. Let the integer $= n$.
$n + (n + 1) = 67$
$2n + 1 = 67$
$2n + 1 - 1 = 67 - 1$
$2n = 66$
$n = 33$
The integers are 33 and 34.

LESSON 5-7 TRY THIS pp. 231–233

a. $2x(x) - 4(1) = 2x^2 - 4; 6(x) + 3(1) = 6x + 3; 2x^2 - 4 + 6x + 3 = 2x^2 + 6x - 1$
b. $(2x + 1) + (x^2 - x + 4) + (3x^2 - 5) = 4x^2 + x$

c. $x^2 + 7x + 3$ **d.** $24m^4 + 5m^3 + m^2 + 1$

e. $2a^2b - 7a - 1$ **f.** $8n^3 - m^3n^2 - 7n - 3m - 5$

g.
$$\begin{array}{r} -2m^3 - 5m^2 - 2m - 4 \\ m^4 \qquad\quad - 6m^2 + 7m - 10 \\ \hline m^4 - 2m^3 - 11m^2 + 5m - 14 \end{array}$$

h.
$$\begin{array}{r} -3x^4y^3 \qquad\quad - 5xy + 2 \\ x^4y^3 + x^2 + 2xy + 5 \\ \hline -2x^4y^3 + x^2 - 3xy + 7 \end{array}$$

LESSON 5-7 EXERCISES pp. 233–235

1. $2x(x) - 2(1) + 6(x) + 2(x) = 2x^2 - 2 + 6x + 2x$
$= 2x^2 + 8x - 2$

2. $x(x) + 3(2) + x(x) - 1(1) = x^2 + 6 + x^2 - 1 = 2x^2 + 5$

3. $(3x - 1) + (3x - 1) + (3x^2 - x - 12) = 3x^2 + 5x - 14$

4. $(10x^2 - 2x + 7) + (15x - 3) + (3x^2 + 4) = 13x^2 + 13x + 8$

5. $-x + 5$ **6.** $5x^2 - x + 3$ **7.** $-4x^4 + 6x^3 + 6x^2 + 2x + 4$

8. $5x^4 - x^3 + 6x^2 - x - 4$ **9.** $12x^2 + 6$

10. $3x^4 - 4x^3 + x^2 + x + 4$ **11.** $5x^4 - 2x^3 - 7x^2 - 5x$

12. $8x^5 - 4x^4 - 3x^3 - x + 5$

13. $9x^8 + 8x^7 - 3x^4 + 2x^2 - 2x + 5$ **14.** $4x^5 + 9x^2 + 1$

15. $-3cd^4 + 3d^2 + 4cd$

16.
$$\begin{array}{r} 4m^4 - 3m^3 + 6m^2 + 5m - 4 \\ 6m^3 - 8m^2 - 3m + 1 \\ \hline 4m^4 + 3m^3 - 2m^2 + 2m - 3 \end{array}$$

17.
$$\begin{array}{r} 5a^4 - 2a^3 + 4a^2 + 5a \quad\; \\ 5a^3 - 5a^2 \qquad\quad + 2 \\ \hline 5a^4 + 3a^3 - a^2 + 5a + 2 \end{array}$$

18.
$$\begin{array}{r} 5t^2 - 2t + 3 \\ -3t^4 + 3t^2 + 5t - 3 \\ \hline -3t^4 + 8t^2 + 3t \quad\; \end{array}$$

19.
$$\begin{array}{r} 7y^5 - 6y^4 + 3y^3 \qquad\quad - 1 \\ 6y^4 - 4y^3 + 6y^2 + 5 \\ \hline 7y^5 \qquad\quad - y^3 + 6y^2 + 4 \end{array}$$

20.
$$\begin{array}{r} -x^3y^2 + 6x^2 + 3x + 5 \\ x^4 + 2x^3y^2 - 3x^2 \qquad\quad + 2 \\ \hline x^4 + x^3y^2 + 3x^2 + 3x + 7 \end{array}$$

21.
$$\begin{array}{r} -2h^3 + 3h^2k + 5hk + 3 \\ -5h^2k - 2hk + 1 \\ \hline -2h^3 - 2h^2k + 3hk + 4 \end{array}$$

22.
$$\begin{array}{r} -3x^4y^3 + 6x^3y^3 - 6x^2 + 5xy^5 + 1 \\ 5x^5 \qquad\quad - 3x^3y^3 \qquad\quad - 5xy^5 \qquad \\ \hline 5x^5 - 3x^4y^3 + 3x^3y^3 - 6x^2 \qquad\quad + 1 \end{array}$$

23.
$$\begin{array}{r} 4x^2y \qquad\qquad - 5xy + 7 \\ 8x^2y + 7xy^2 + 3xy - 2 \\ \hline 12x^2y + 7xy^2 - 2xy + 5 \end{array}$$

24.
$$\begin{array}{r} 4x^3y^4 + 7x^4y^3 - 4x^5 - 6x^4 \qquad \\ -6x^3y^4 - 3x^4y^3 \qquad\quad + 2x^4 - x^3 \\ \hline -2x^3y^4 + 4x^4y^3 - 4x^5 - 4x^4 - x^3 \end{array}$$

25. a. $3x^2 + x^2 + x^2 + 4x = 5x^2 + 4x$
b. $5x^2 + 4x = 5(3^2) + 4(3) = 5(9) + 12 = 45 + 12 = 57$
c. $5x^2 + 4x = 5(8^2) + 4(8) = 5(64) + 32$
$= 320 + 32 = 352$

26. a. $\pi r^2 + 9\pi + 4\pi = \pi r^2 + 13\pi$
b. $\pi r^2 + 13\pi = \pi(5^2) + 13\pi = 25\pi + 13\pi = 38\pi$
c. $\pi r^2 + 13\pi = \pi(11.3^2) + 13\pi = 127.69\pi + 13\pi$
$= 140.69\pi$

27. a. $n + 5, n + 10$
b. $n - 2, n + 3, n + 8$
c. $3n + 9$
d. $3n + 9 = 69; 3n = 60; n = 20$
e. $n = 20, n + 5 = 25, n + 10 = 30$. The brothers are now 20, 25, and 30.
f. Each age is a multiple of 5: $\frac{20}{5} = 4, \frac{25}{5} = 5, \frac{30}{5} = 6$.
Subtracting 2 from each age gives the ages two years ago: 18, 23, and 28, $18 + 23 + 28 = 69$.

28. a. The length of a side must be greater than 0. $n^2 - 4 > 0$ when $n > 2$ and when $n < -2$. But n cannot be less than -2 because then $3n + 2$ would be negative.
b. $n^2 - 4 + 3n + 2 + n^2 - 4 + 3n + 2 = 2n^2 + 6n - 4$
c. When $n = 2, 2n^2 + 6n - 4 = 16$. When $n > 2, 2n^2 + 6n - 4 > 16$.

29. Answers may vary. Some differences are that coefficients of polynomials cannot be carried and that adding polynomials can involve adding negative coefficients.

30. Let y = second polynomial.
$$x^2 + 3 + y = 2x^2 + x + 8$$
$$x^2 - x^2 + 3 - 3 + y = 2x^2 - x^2 + x + 8 - 3$$
$$y = x^2 + x + 5$$

31.
$$\begin{array}{l} \quad ax + b \\ + cx + d \\ \hline (a + c)x + (b + d) \end{array}$$
$$\begin{array}{l} \quad cx + d \\ + ax + b \\ \hline (c + a)x + (d + b) \end{array}$$
Since $a + c = c + a$ and $b + d = d + b$, these are equal, so addition of binomials is commutative.

32.
$$\begin{array}{l} \quad ax^2 + bx + c \\ + dx^2 + ex + f \\ \hline (a + d)x^2 + (b + e)x + (c + f) \end{array}$$
$$\begin{array}{l} \quad dx^2 + ex + f \\ + ax^2 + bx + c \\ \hline (d + a)x^2 + (e + b)x + (f + c) \end{array}$$
Since $a + d = d + a, b + e = e + b$, and $e + f = f + e$, these are equal, so addition of trinomials is commutative.

33.
$$\begin{array}{l} \quad a_nx^n + a_{n-1}x^{n-1} + \ldots a_1x + a_0 \\ + b_nx^n + b_{n-1}x^{n-1} + \ldots b_1x + b_0 \\ \hline (a_n + b_n)x^n + (a_{n-1} + b_{n-1})x^{n-1} + \ldots (a_1 + b_1)x \\ + (a_0 + b_0) \end{array}$$
When added in the opposite order, we get
$(b_n + a_n)x^n + (b_{n-1} + a_{n-1})x^{n-1} + \ldots (b_1 + a_1)x + (b_0 + a_0)$.
Since $a_n + b_n = b_n + a_n$, and $\cdots a_0 + b_0 = b_0 + a_0$, these are equal, so addition of polynomials is commutative.

34. Distributive property of multiplication over addition

35. Additive inverse **36.** Multiplicative identity

37. Commutative property of multiplication

38. Additive identity **39.** Commutative property of addition

40. $32t^{15}$ **41.** $18a^7$ **42.** x **43.** $12m^2n^2$ **44.** $a(5c + 12)$

45. $y(xz + 5 - 9z)$ **46.** $a(a + 1 + b)$

LESSON 5-8 TRY THIS pp. 236–237

a. $-12x^4 + 3x^2 - 4x$

b. $13x^6y^4 - 2x^4y + 3x^2 - xy + \frac{5}{13}$

c. $(5x^4 + 4) - (2x^2 - 1) = 5x^4 + 4 + (-2x^2 + 1)$
$= 5x^4 - 2x^2 + 5$

d. $(-7m^3 + 2m + 4) - (-2m^3 - 4)$
$= -7m^3 + 2m + 4 + (2m^3 + 4)$
$= -5m^3 + 2m + 8$

e. $(-3a^2b^4 + 5ab - 4) - (-4a^3 + 11a^2b^4 - 2a - 6)$
$= -3a^2b^4 + 5ab - 4 + (4a^3 - 11a^2b^4 + 2a + 6)$
$= 4a^3 - 14a^2b^4 + 5ab + 2a + 2$

f. (a)
$$\begin{array}{r} 4x^3 + 2x^2 - 2x - 3 \\ -(2x^3 - 3x^2 \qquad\quad + 2) \\ \hline \end{array}$$
(b)
$$\begin{array}{r} 4x^3 + 2x^2 - 2x - 3 \\ +(-2x^3 + 3x^2 \qquad\quad - 2) \\ \hline 2x^3 + 5x^2 - 2x - 5 \end{array}$$

g. (a)
$$\begin{array}{r} -3ab^2 + 4ab - 7a \qquad \\ -(-2ab^2 \qquad\quad - 3a + 4) \\ \hline \end{array}$$
(b)
$$\begin{array}{r} -3ab^2 + 4ab - 7a \qquad \\ +(+2ab^2 \qquad\quad + 3a - 4) \\ \hline -ab^2 + 4ab - 4a - 4 \end{array}$$

LESSON 5-8 EXERCISES pp. 238–239

1. $5x$ **2.** $-x^2 + 3x$ **3.** $x^2 - 10x + 2$

4. $4x^3 + x^2 + x$ **5.** $-12x^4y + 3x^3 - 3$

6. $-4x^3 + 6x^2y^2 + 8xy - 1$

7. $(5x^2 + 6) - (3x^2 - 8) = 5x^2 + 6 + (-3x^2 + 8)$
$= 2x^2 + 14$

8. $(7a^3 - 2a^2 + 6) - (7a^2 + 2a - 4)$
$= 7a^3 - 2a^2 + 6 + (-7a^2 - 2a + 4)$
$= 7a^3 - 9a^2 - 2a + 10$

9. $(6x^5 - 3x^4 + x + 1) - (8x^5 + 3x^4 - 1)$
$= 6x^5 - 3x^4 + x + 1 + (-8x^5 - 3x^4 + 1)$
$= -2x^5 - 6x^4 + x + 2$

10. $\left(\frac{1}{2}x^2 - \frac{3}{2}x + 2\right) - \left(\frac{3}{2}x^2 + \frac{1}{2}x - 2\right)$
$= \frac{1}{2}x^2 - \frac{3}{2}x + 2 + \left(-\frac{3}{2}x^2 - \frac{1}{2}x + 2\right)$
$= -x^2 - 2x + 4$

11. $(6b^2 + 2b) - (-3b^2 - 7b + 8)$
$= 6b^2 + 2b + (3b^2 + 7b - 8)$
$= 9b^2 + 9b - 8$

12. $7x^3 - (-3x^2 - 2x + 1)$
$= 7x^3 + (3x^2 + 2x - 1)$
$= 7x^3 + 3x^2 + 2x - 1$

13. $(5m^3 - 3m - 6) - (-2m^3 + 5)$
$= 5m^3 - 3m - 6 + (2m^3 - 5)$
$= 7m^3 - 3m - 11$

14. $(-4n^4 + n^3 + 2n^2) - (n^4 - 3n^3 - n^2 + 4)$
$= -4n^4 + n^3 + 2n^2 + (-n^4 + 3n^3 + n^2 - 4)$
$= -5n^4 + 4n^3 + 3n^2 - 4$

15. $(6y^3 - 4y - 7) - (-3y^4 - 2y^3 + y - 4)$
$= 6y^3 - 4y - 7 + (3y^4 + 2y^3 - y + 4)$
$= 3y^4 + 8y^3 - 5y - 3$

16. $(7t^4 + 4t) - (6t^5 - 3t^4 + 2t^2 + 3t - 1)$
$= 7t^4 + 4t + (-6t^5 + 3t^4 - 2t^2 - 3t + 1)$
$= -6t^5 + 10t^4 - 2t^2 + t + 1$

17. $(8v^4u + 6v^2 - 5) - (2v^4u - 3v^2 + 2)$
$= 8v^4u + 6v^2 - 5 + (-2v^4u + 3v^2 - 2)$
$= 6v^4u + 9v^2 - 7$

18. $(-3m^3n^2 + 2m^2 - mn - 4) - (-5m^3n^2 - 4m^2 + 3mn + 2)$
$= -3m^3n^2 + 2m^2 - mn - 4 + (5m^3n^2 + 4m^2 - 3mn - 2)$
$= 2m^3n^2 + 6m^2 - 4mn - 6$

19. $(8mn^5 + n^4 - 3mn^3 + 2n^2) - (-mn^5 - mn^4 - n^2 - 1)$
$= 8mn^5 + n^4 - 3mn^3 + 2n^2 + (mn^5 + mn^4 + n^2 + 1)$
$= 9mn^5 + n^4 + mn^4 - 3mn^3 + 3n^2 + 1$

20. $(3x^4y + 2x^3y - x^2 - 7) - (-2x^6 - 3x^4y + 2x^3y - x^2 - 7)$
$= 3x^4y + 2x^3y - x^2 - 7 + (2x^6 + 3x^4y - 2x^3y + x^2 + 7)$
$= 2x^6 + 6x^4y$

21. (a) $x^2 + 5x + 6$
$-(x^2 + 2x\quad)$
(b) $x^2 + 5x + 6$
$+(-x^2 - 2x\quad)$
$3x + 6$

22. (a) $x^3 \quad + 1$
$-(x^3 + x^2\quad)$
(b) $x^3 \quad + 1$
$+(-x^3 - x^2\quad)$
$-x^2 + 1$

23. (a) $c^4 \quad - 3c^2 + c + 1$
$-(c^4 - 4c^3\quad)$
(b) $c^4 \quad - 3c^2 + c + 1$
$+(c^4 + 4c^3\quad)$
$4c^3 - 3c^2 + c + 1$

24. (a) $3x^2 - 6x + 1$
$-(6x^2 + 8x - 3)$
(b) $3x^2 - 6x + 1$
$+(-6x^2 - 8x + 3)$
$-3x^2 - 14x + 4$

25. (a) $5x^4 + 6x^3 - 9x^2$
$-(-6x^4 - 6x^3 + \quad + 8x)$
(b) $5x^4 + 6x^3 - 9x^2$
$+(6x^4 + 6x^3 \quad - 8x)$
$11x^4 + 12x^3 - 9x^2 - 8x$

26. (a) $5x^4 \quad + 6x^2 - 3x + 6$
$-(\quad 6x^3 + 7x^2 - 8x - 9)$
(b) $5x^4 \quad + 6x^2 - 3x + 6$
$+(\quad - 6x^3 - 7x^2 + 8x + 9)$
$5x^4 - 6x^3 - x^2 + 5x + 15$

27. (a) $3m^4 + 6m^2 + 8m - 1$
$-(4m^5 - 6m^4 \quad - 8m - 7)$
(b) $3m^4 + 6m^2 + 8m - 1$
$+(-4m^5 + 6m^4 \quad + 8m + 7)$
$-4m^5 + 9m^4 + 6m^2 + 16m + 6$

28. (a) $6x^5 \quad + 3x^2 - 7x + 2$
$-(10x^5 + 6x^3 - 5x^2 - 2x + 4)$
(b) $6x^5 \quad + 3x^2 - 7x + 2$
$+(-10x^5 - 6x^3 + 5x^2 + 2x - 4)$
$-4x^5 - 6x^3 + 8x^2 - 5x - 2$

29. (a) $x^5y^2 \quad - x^3y^2 \quad + xy - 1$
$-(x^5y^2 - x^4y^2 - x^3y^2 - x^2y + xy - 1)$
(b) $x^5y^2 \quad - x^3y^2 \quad + xy - 1$
$+(-x^5y^2 + x^4y^2 + x^3y^2 + x^2y - xy + 1)$
$x^4y^2 \quad + x^2y$

30. (a) $x^5 + x^4y^2 - x^3 + x^2y - xy + 2$
$-(x^5 + x^4y^2 + x^3 - x^2y - xy + 2)$
(b) $x^5 + x^4y^2 - x^3 + x^2y - xy + 2$
$+(-x^5 - x^4y^2 - x^3 + x^2y + xy - 2)$
$-2x^3 + 2x^2y$

31. $(y + 4) + (y - 5) - (y + 8)$
$= y + 4 + y - 5 - y - 8 = y - 9$

32. $(7y^2 - 5y + 6) - (3y^2 + 8y - 12) + (8y^2 - 10y + 3)$
$= 7y^2 - 5y + 6 - 3y^2 - 8y + 12 + 8y^2 - 10y + 3$
$= 12y^2 - 23y + 21$

33. $(4a^2 - 3a) + (7a^2 - 9a - 13) - (6a - 9)$
$= 4a^2 - 3a + 7a^2 - 9a - 13 - 6a + 9$
$= 11a^2 - 18a - 4$

34. $(3x^2 - 4x + 6) - (-2x^2 + 4) + (-5x - 3)$
$= 3x^2 - 4x + 6 + 2x^2 - 4 - 5x - 3$
$= 5x^2 - 9x - 1$

35. $(-8y^2 - 4) - (3y + 6) - (2y^2 - y)$
$= -8y^2 - 4 - 3y - 6 - 2y^2 + y$
$= -10y^2 - 2y - 10$

36. $(5x^3 - 4x^2 + 6) - (2x^3 + x^2 - x) + (x^3 - x)$
$= 5x^3 - 4x^2 + 6 - 2x^3 - x^2 + x + x^3 - x$
$= 4x^3 - 5x^2 + 6$

37. $(-xy^4 - 7y^3 + xy^2) + (-2xy^4 + 5y - 2) - (-6y^3 + xy^2)$
$= -xy^4 - 7y^3 + xy^2 - 2xy^4 + 5y - 2 + 6y^3 - xy^2$
$= -3xy^4 - y^3 + 5y - 2$

38. Let y = the other polynomial.
Either $y - (3x^2 + x) = 2x^2 + x + 4$
or $(3x^2 + x) - (y) = 2x^2 + x + 4$
(a) $y - (3x^2 + x) = 2x^2 + x + 4$
$y - (3x^2 + x) + (3x^2 + x) = 2x^2 + x + 4 + (3x^2 + x)$
$y = 5x^2 + 2x + 4$
(b) $(3x^2 + x) - y = 2x^2 + x + 4$
$(3x^2 + x) - (3x^2 + x) - y = 2x^2 + x + 4 - (3x^2 + x)$
$-y = 2x^2 + x + 4 + (-3x^2 - x)$
$-y = -x^2 + 4$
$(-1)(-y) = (-1)(-x^2 + 4)$
$y = x^2 - 4$
Either $y = 5x^2 + 2x + 4$ or $y = x^2 - 4$

39. $6x + 3 - (2x + 1 + 2x + 1) = 6x + 3 - 2x - 1 - 2x - 1 = 2x + 1$

40. $3x^2 - 6 - (x^2 + 2 + x^2 + 2) = 3x^2 - 6 - x^2 - 2 - x^2 - 2 = x^2 - 10$

41. $4x^2 - x - 16 - (x - 10 + 2x^2 - 14) = 4x^2 - x - 16 - x + 10 - 2x^2 + 14 = 2x^2 - 2x + 8$

42. $11x^2 + 10 - (5x^2 - 13x + 24 + x^2 + 7x + 9) = 11x^2 + 10 - 5x^2 + 13x - 24 - x^2 - 7x - 9 = 5x^2 + 6x - 23$

43. No, $5(-x)^3 - 3(-x)^2 + 2(-x) = -5x^3 - 3x^2 - 2x$; the additive inverse of the polynomial has a $+ 3x^2$ term.

44. a. A zero polynomial, or 0

b. For each term, the coefficients are rational numbers; subtraction of rational numbers is not commutative, so $a_nx^n - b_nx^n = (a_n - b_n)x^n$, which $\neq (b_n - a_n)x^n$, since $a - b \neq b - a$.

c. No, $a_n - (b_n - c_n) = a_n - b_n + c_n$. $(a_n - b_n) - c_n = a_n - b_n - c_n$. Since $c_n \neq -c_n$, these are not equal.

45. 1.594×10^3 **46.** 7.72×10^{-1} **47.** 9.361×10^4

48. Terms: $5x^3, 3x^2, -2x, 1$
Coefficients: $5, 3, -2, 1$

49. Terms: $5n^4m, 7n^2m^2, -2m, 3$
Coefficients: $5, 7, -2, 3$

50.
$$\begin{aligned} 16 - 3a &< 5a \\ 16 - 3a + 3a &< 5a + 3a \\ 16 &< 8a \\ 2 &< a \end{aligned}$$

51.
$$\begin{aligned} 21 + 4h &= 11h \\ 21 + 4h - 4h &= 11h - 4h \\ 21 &= 7h \\ 3 &= h \end{aligned}$$

LESSON 5-9 TRY THIS pp. 240–242

a. $4x(2x + 4) = (4x)(2x) + (4x)(4) = 8x^2 + 16x$

b. $3a^2(-5a^3 + 2a - 7)$
$= (3a^2)(-5a^3) + (3a^2)(2a) + (3a^2)(-7)$
$= -15a^5 + 6a^3 - 21a^2$

c. $5s(8t^4 - 4s^2 - 9t - 11)$
$= (5s)(8t^4) + (5s)(-4s^2) + (5s)(-9t) + (5s)(-11)$
$= 40st^4 - 20s^3 - 45st - 55s$

d. $(x + 3)(x + 4) = x^2 + 4x + 3x + 12 = x^2 + 7x + 12$

e. $(x + 3)(x - 5) = x^2 - 5x + 3x - 15 = x^2 - 2x - 15$

f. $(2x + 1)(x + 4) = 2x^2 + 8x + x + 4 = 2x^2 + 9x + 4$

g. $(2x^2 - 3)(x - 2) = 2x^3 - 4x^2 - 3x + 6$

h. $(6x^2 + 5)(2x^3 + 1) = 12x^5 + 10x^3 + 6x^2 + 5$

i. $(y^3 + 7)(y^3 - 7) = y^6 - 7y^3 + 7y^3 - 49 = y^6 - 49$

j. $(2x^5 + x^2)(-x^3 + x) = -2x^8 + 2x^6 - x^5 + x^3$

k. $(3a + b)(-2a - 4b) = -6a^2 - 12ab - 2ab - 4b^2$
$= -6a^2 - 14ab - 4b^2$

l. $(2xy + 4x)(-2y + y^2) = -4xy^2 + 2xy^3 - 8xy + 4xy^2$
$= 2xy^3 - 8xy$

m. $(3rs + 2r)(r^2 + 2rs^2) = 3r^3s + 2r^3 + 6r^2s^3 + 4r^2s^2$

n.
$$\begin{array}{r} 5x + 3 \\ \underline{x - 4} \\ 5x^2 + 3x \\ \underline{-20x - 12} \\ 5x^2 - 17x - 12 \end{array}$$

o.
$$\begin{array}{r} 2y^2 - 3 \\ \underline{3y - 5} \\ 6y^3 \qquad - 9y \\ \underline{-10y^2 \qquad + 15} \\ 6y^3 - 10y^2 - 9y + 15 \end{array}$$

p.
$$\begin{array}{r} 3a + b \\ \underline{2a - b} \\ 6a^2 + 2ab \\ \underline{-3ab - b^2} \\ 6a^2 - ab - b^2 \end{array}$$

q.
$$\begin{array}{r} 6m^2 + n \\ \underline{3m - n^2} \\ 18m^3 \qquad + 3mn \\ \underline{-6m^2n^2 \qquad - n^3} \\ 18m^3 - 6m^2n^2 + 3mn - n^3 \end{array}$$

r.
$$\begin{array}{r} 4pq - p^2 \\ \underline{pq + p^2} \\ 4p^2q^2 - p^3q \\ \underline{4p^3q - p^4} \\ 4p^2q^2 + 3p^3q - p^4 \end{array}$$

s.
$$\begin{array}{r} \frac{1}{2}r^2s + s \\ \underline{\frac{1}{2}r^2s - s} \\ \frac{1}{4}r^4s^2 + \frac{1}{2}r^2s^2 \\ \underline{-\frac{1}{2}r^2s^2 - s^2} \\ \frac{1}{4}r^4s^2 \qquad - s^2 \end{array}$$

LESSON 5-9 EXERCISES pp. 242–244

1. $-3x^2 + 15x$ **2.** $8y^2 - 12y$ **3.** $12x^3 + 24x^2$

4. $-10a^3 + 5a^2$ **5.** $-6m^4 - 6m^2x$ **6.** $-4x^4 + 4x^3$

7. $3x^6 + 15x^3$ **8.** $15m^6 + 20m^3$ **9.** $18y^6 + 24y^5$

10. $4y^7 - 24y^6$ **11.** $6x^3 + 8x^2 - 6x$

12. $30x^4 + 6x^3 - 24x$ **13.** $15a^4 + 30a^3 - 35a^2$

14. $-24b^6 + 12b^4 - 16b^2$ **15.** $-8y^9 - 8y^8 + 4y^7 - 20y^6$

16. $-2x^9 - 4x^8 + 2x^7 + 2x^6 - 6x^5$

17. $-7h^4k^6 + 7h^4k^4 + 7h^4k^3 - 7h^4k$

18. $-x^3y^7 + x^3y^4 - x^3y^3 + x^3y^2 - x^3y$

19. $-10a^9b + 2a^3 - 24a^2b$ **20.** $-10xy^5 - 10x^2y^3 + 120x^2$

21. $(x + 1)(x^2 + 3) = x^3 + 3x + x^2 + 3$
$= x^3 + x^2 + 3x + 3$

22. $(x^2 - 3)(x - 1) = x^3 - x^2 - 3x + 3$

23. $(x^3 + 2)(x + 1) = x^4 + x^3 + 2x + 2$

24. $(x^4 + 2)(x + 12) = x^5 + 12x^4 + 2x + 24$

25. $(a + 2)(a - 3) = a^2 - 3a + 2a - 6$
$= a^2 - a - 6$

26. $(x + 2)(x + 2) = x^2 + 2x + 2x + 4$
$= x^2 + 4x + 4$

27. $(3x + 2)(3x + 3) = 9x^2 + 9x + 6x + 6$
$= 9x^2 + 15x + 6$

28. $(4x + 1)(2x + 2) = 8x^2 + 8x + 2x + 2$
$= 8x^2 + 10x + 2$

29. $(5x - 6)(x + 2) = 5x^2 + 10x - 6x - 12$
$= 5x^2 + 4x - 12$

30. $(x - 8)(x + 8) = x^2 + 8x - 8x - 64$
$= x^2 - 64$

31. $(3x - 1)(3x + 1) = 9x^2 + 3x - 3x - 1$
$= 9x^2 - 1$

32. $(2x + 3)(2x + 3) = 4x^2 + 6x + 6x + 9$
$= 4x^2 + 12x + 9$

33. $(4x - 2y)(x - y) = 4x^2 - 4xy - 2xy + 2y^2$
$= 4x^2 - 6xy + 2y^2$

34. $(2x - y)(3x + y) = 6x^2 + 2xy - 3xy - y^2$
$= 6x^2 - xy - y^2$

35. $\left(x - \frac{1}{4}\right)\left(x + \frac{1}{4}\right) = x^2 + \frac{1}{4}x - \frac{1}{4}x - \frac{1}{16}$
$= x^2 - \frac{1}{16}$

36. $\left(x + \frac{3}{4}\right)\left(x + \frac{3}{4}\right) = x^2 + \frac{3}{4}x + \frac{3}{4}x + \frac{9}{16}$
$= x^2 + \frac{3}{2}x + \frac{9}{16}$

37. $(x - 0.1)(x + 0.1) = x^2 + 0.1x - 0.1x - 0.01$
$= x^2 - 0.01$

38. $(3x^2 + 1)(x + 1) = 3x^3 + 3x^2 + x + 1$

39. $(2x^2 + 6)(x + 1) = 2x^3 + 2x^2 + 6x + 6$

40. $(2b^2 + 3)(2b - 1) = 4b^3 - 2b^2 + 6b - 3$

41. $(-2x + 1)(x - 6) = -2x^2 + 12x + x - 6$
$= -2x^2 + 13x - 6$

42. $(3x + 4)(2x - 4) = 6x^2 - 12x + 8x - 16$
$= 6x^2 - 4x - 16$

43. $(x + 7y)(x + 7y) = x^2 + 7xy + 7xy + 49y^2$
$= x^2 + 14xy + 49y^2$

44. $(2x + 5y)(2x + 5y) = 4x^2 + 10xy + 10xy + 25y^2$
$= 4x^2 + 20xy + 25y^2$

45. $(3x^5 + 2)(2x^2 + 6) = 6x^7 + 18x^5 + 4x^2 + 12$

46. $(1 - 2x)(1 + 3x^2) = 1 + 3x^2 - 2x - 6x^3$
$= 1 - 2x + 3x^2 - 6x^3$

47. $(8x^3 + 1)(x^3 + 8) = 8x^6 + 64x^3 + x^3 + 8$
$= 8x^6 + 65x^3 + 8$

48. $(4 - 2x)(5 - 2x^2) = 20 - 8x^2 - 10x + 4x^3$
$= 20 - 10x - 8x^2 + 4x^3$

49. $(4x^2 + 3)(x - 3) = 4x^3 - 12x^2 + 3x - 9$

50. $(7x - 2)(2x - 7) = 14x^2 - 49x - 4x + 14$
$= 14x^2 - 53x + 14$

51. $(4x^4 + x^2)(x^2 + x) = 4x^6 + 4x^5 + x^4 + x^3$

52. $(5x^6 + 3x^3)(2x^6 + 2x^3) = 10x^{12} + 10x^9 + 6x^9 + 6x^6$
$= 10x^{12} + 16x^9 + 6x^6$

53. $(ab + 3b^2)(ab - 3b^2) = a^2b^2 + 3ab^3 - 3ab^3 - 9b^4$
$= a^2b^2 - 9b^4$

54. $(m^2n - 5n)(m^2n + 5n) = m^4n^2 + 5m^2n^2 - 5m^2n^2 - 25n^2$
$= m^4n^2 - 25n^2$

55. $(a + b)(a + b) = a^2 + ab + ab + b^2$
$= a^2 + 2ab + b^2$

56. $(a - b)(a - b) = a^2 - ab - ab + b^2$
$= a^2 - 2ab + b^2$

57. $(2x + 3)(2x + 3) = 4x^2 + 6x + 6x + 9$
$= 4x^2 + 12x + 9$

58. $(5y + 6)(5y + 6) = 25y^2 + 30y + 30y + 36$
$= 25y^2 + 60y + 36$

59. $6y(14y - 5) = 84y^2 - 30y$

60. $4t(21t + 8) - 2t(3t - 4) = 84t^2 + 32t - 6t^2 + 8t$
$= 78t^2 + 40t$

61. $m^2 - 28$

62. $z^2 - 24(z - 3) - 3z$
$= z^2 - 24z + 72 - 3z$
$= z^2 - 27z + 72$

63. Let $(m + n)$ = the other binomial.
$(x + 2)(m + n) = 2x^2 + 5x + 2$
Since $x \cdot m = 2x^2$, $m = 2x$.
Since $2 \cdot n = 2$, $n = 1$.
The binomial is $2x + 1$.

64. The exponents were not added. The correct solution is $2x^4 - x^2y + 6x^2y^3 - 3y^4$.

65. Correct

66. The second term should be negative. The correct solution is $a^2b^2 - 4b^4$.

67. The exponents were multiplied instead of added. The correct solution is $-2x^5 - 6x^4 + 6x^3 - 4x^2$.

68. Possible answer: $(x - 2)(x + 2) = x^2 - 4$

69. $V = (12 - 2x)^2 \cdot x$
$= (144 - 48x + 4x^2)x$
$= 4x^3 - 48x^2 + 144x$
$S = 4x(12 - 2x) + (12 - 2x)^2$
$= 48x - 8x^2 + 144 - 48x + 4x^2$
$= -4x^2 + 144$

70. a. $(x + 3)(x + 6) + (x + 3)(x + 6)$
$= x^2 + 9x + 18 + x^2 + 9x + 18$
$= 2x^2 + 18x + 36$

b. $(x + 4)(x + 5) - (x + 4)(x + 5)$
$= x^2 + 9x + 20 - x^2 - 9x - 20$
$= 0$

71. a. $(x - 2)(x - 7) + (x - 2)(x - 7)$
$= x^2 - 9x + 14 + x^2 - 9x + 14$
$= 2x^2 - 18x + 28$

b. $(x - 6)(x - 2) - (x - 6)(x - 2)$
$= x^2 - 8x + 12 - x^2 + 8x - 12$
$= 0$

72. a. $(x + 5)(x - 3) + (x + 5)(x - 3)$
$= x^2 + 2x - 15 + x^2 + 2x - 15$
$= 2x^2 + 4x - 30$

b. $(x + 9)(x - 4) - (x + 9)(x - 4)$
$= x^2 + 5x - 36 - x^2 - 5x + 36$
$= 0$

73. a. $(x + 7)(x - 8) + (x - 7)(x + 8)$
$= x^2 - x - 56 + x^2 + x - 56$
$= 2x^2 - 112$

b. $(x + 2)(x - 5) - (x - 2)(x + 5)$
$= x^2 - 3x - 10 - x^2 - 3x + 10$
$= -6x$

74. From Exercise 71, 3 75. From Exercise 73, 2

76. From Exercise 72, 1 77. $\frac{1}{2}(n + 3)$ or $\frac{n + 3}{2}$

78. $6n + 9$ 79. $3(7 - n)$ 80. $n + (n + 1)$

81.
$15r = 3(r + 28)$
$15r = 3r + 84$
$15r - 3r = 3r - 3r + 84$
$12r = 84$
$r = \frac{84}{12}$
$r = 7$

82.
$25 = 4(m - 3) - 3$
$25 = 4m - 12 - 3$
$25 = 4m - 15$
$25 + 15 = 4m - 15 + 15$
$40 = 4m$
$\frac{40}{4} = m$
$10 = m$

83.
$13k = 19k + 12$
$13k - 19k = 19k - 19k + 12$
$-6k = 12$
$k = \frac{12}{-6}$
$k = -2$

84.
$12x = 16(x - 2) + 48$
$12x = 16x - 32 + 48$
$12x = 16x + 16$
$12x - 16x = 16x - 16x + 16$
$-4x = 16$
$x = \frac{16}{-4}$
$x = -4$

LESSON 5-10 TRY THIS pp. 245–246

a. $(x + 2)(x - 2) = x^2 - 2^2 = x^2 - 4$
b. $(x^2 + 7)(x^2 - 7) = (x^2)^2 - 7^2 = x^4 - 49$
c. $(3t + 5)(3t - 5) = (3t)^2 - 5^2 = 9t^2 - 25$
d. $(2x^3 + y)(2x^3 - y) = (2x^3)^2 - y^2 = 4x^6 - y^2$
e. $(x + 2)(x + 2) = x^2 + 2 \cdot x \cdot 2 + 2^2 = x^2 + 4x + 4$
f. $(y - 9)(y - 9) = y^2 - 2 \cdot y \cdot 9 + 9^2 = y^2 - 18y + 81$
g. $(4x - 5)^2 = (4x)^2 - 2 \cdot 4x \cdot 5 + 5^2 = 16x^2 - 40x + 25$
h. $(a - 4)^2 = a^2 - 2 \cdot a \cdot 4 + 4^2 = a^2 - 8a + 16$
i. $(5x^2 + 4)(5x^2 + 4) = (5x^2)^2 + 2 \cdot 5x^2 \cdot 4 + 4^2$
$= 25x^4 + 40x^2 + 16$
j. $(4x^2 - 3x)^2 = (4x^2)^2 - 2 \cdot 4x^2 \cdot 3x + (3x)^2$
$= 16x^4 - 24x^3 + 9x^2$

LESSON 5-10 EXERCISES pp. 247–248

1. $(x + 4)(x - 4) = x^2 - 4^2 = x^2 - 16$
2. $(a + 1)(a - 1) = a^2 - 1^2 = a^2 - 1$
3. $(d - 6)(d + 6) = d^2 - 6^2 = d^2 - 36$
4. $(y - 5)(y + 5) = y^2 - 5^2 = y^2 - 25$
5. $(6 - m)(6 + m) = 6^2 - m^2 = 36 - m^2$
6. $(8 + m)(8 - m) = 8^2 - m^2 = 64 - m^2$
7. $(2x + 1)(2x - 1) = (2x)^2 - 1^2 = 4x^2 - 1$
8. $(3y - 1)(3y + 1) = (3y)^2 - 1^2 = 9y^2 - 1$
9. $(4a - 7)(4a + 7) = (4a)^2 - 7^2 = 16a^2 - 49$
10. $(5b - 2)(5b + 2) = (5b)^2 - 2^2 = 25b^2 - 4$
11. $(4x^2 - 3)(4x^2 + 3) = (4x^2)^2 - 3^2 = 16x^4 - 9$
12. $(2x^2 + 3)(2x^2 - 3) = (2x^2)^2 - 3^2 = 4x^4 - 9$
13. $(3x^4 + 2)(3x^4 - 2) = (3x^4)^2 - 2^2 = 9x^8 - 4$
14. $(6t^5 - 5)(6t^5 + 5) = (6t^5)^2 - 5^2 = 36t^{10} - 25$
15. $(x^6 - x^2)(x^6 + x^2) = (x^6)^2 - (x^2)^2 = x^{12} - x^4$
16. $(3a - 4b)(3a + 4b) = (3a)^2 - (4b)^2 = 9a^2 - 16b^2$
17. $(7c - 2d)(7c + 2d) = (7c)^2 - (2d)^2 = 49c^2 - 4d^2$

18. $(-3m + 2n)(-3m - 2n) = (-3m)^2 - (2n)^2 = 9m^2 - 4n^2$

19. $(-6t + s)(-6t - s) = (-6t)^2 - s^2 = 36t^2 - s^2$

20. $(x^2 + y^2)(x^2 - y^2) = (x^2)^2 - (y^2)^2 = x^4 - y^4$

21. $(x + 2)^2 = x^2 + 2 \cdot x \cdot 2 + 2^2 = x^2 + 4x + 4$

22. $(a + 3)^2 = a^2 + 2 \cdot a \cdot 3 + 3^2 = a^2 + 6a + 9$

23. $(t - 3)^2 = t^2 - 2 \cdot t \cdot 3 + 3^2 = t^2 - 6t + 9$

24. $(r - 2)^2 = r^2 - 2 \cdot r \cdot 2 + 2^2 = r^2 - 4r + 4$

25. $(2x - 1)^2 = (2x)^2 - 2 \cdot 2x \cdot 1 + 1^2 = 4x^2 - 4x + 1$

26. $(3c - 1)^2 = (3c)^2 - 2 \cdot 3c \cdot 1 + 1^2 = 9c^2 - 6c + 1$

27. $(4a - 3b)^2 = (4a)^2 - 2(4a)(3b) + (3b^2)$
$= 16a^2 - 24ab + 9b^2$

28. $(7a - 2b)^2 = (7a)^2 - 2(7a)(2b) + (2b)^2$
$= 49a^2 - 28ab + 4b^2$

29. $(4s + 5t)^2 = (4s)^2 + 2(4s)(5t) + (5t)^2 = 16s^2 + 40st + 25t^2$

30. $\left(x - \frac{1}{2}\right)^2 = x^2 - 2(x)\left(\frac{1}{2}\right) + \left(\frac{1}{2}\right)^2 = x^2 - x + \frac{1}{4}$

31. $\left(x - \frac{1}{4}\right)^2 = x^2 - 2(x)\left(\frac{1}{4}\right) + \left(\frac{1}{4}\right)^2 = x^2 - \frac{1}{2}x + \frac{1}{16}$

32. $\left(a + \frac{2}{3}\right)^2 = a^2 + 2(a)\left(\frac{2}{3}\right) + \left(\frac{2}{3}\right)^2 = a^2 + \frac{4}{3}a + \frac{4}{9}$

33. $(2x + 7)(2x + 7) = (2x)^2 + 2(2x)(7) + 7^2$
$= 4x^2 + 28x + 49$

34. $(4x + 3)(4x + 3) = (4x)^2 + 2(4x)(3) + 3^2 = 16x^2 + 24x + 9$

35. $(3x - 2y)(3x + 2y) = (3x)^2 - (2y)^2 = 9x^2 - 4y^2$

36. $(7x - 5y)(7x + 5y) = (7x)^2 - (5y)^2 = 49x^2 - 25y^2$

37. $(5x^2 - 1)(5x^2 - 1) = (5x^2)^2 - 2(5x^2)(1) + 1^2$
$= 25x^4 - 10x^2 + 1$

38. $(12 - 3x^2)(12 + 3x^2) = 12^2 - (3x^2)^2 = 144 - 9x^4$

39. $\left(2x - \frac{1}{5}\right)\left(2x - \frac{1}{5}\right) = 2(x)^2 - 2(2x)\left(\frac{1}{5}\right) + \left(\frac{1}{5}\right)^2$
$= 4x^2 - \frac{4}{5}x + \frac{1}{25}$

40. $\left(3x + \frac{3}{4}\right)\left(3x - \frac{3}{4}\right) = (3x)^2 - \left(\frac{3}{4}\right)^2 = 9x^2 - \frac{9}{16}$

41. $(2x^3 - 0.3)(2x^3 + 0.3) = (2x^3)^2 - (0.3)^2$
$= 4x^6 - 0.09$

42. $(t^2 - 0.2)(t^2 + 0.2) = (t^2)^2 - (0.2)^2$
$= t^4 - 0.04$

43. a. ac, ad, bc, bd
b. $ac + ad + bc + bd$
c. $ac + ad + bc + bd$. Results are the same.

44. a. $a^2 + ab$
b. $ab + b^2$
c. $a^2 + ab - (ab + b^2) = a^2 + ab - ab - b^2 = a^2 - b^2$
d. $a(a - b) + b(a - b) = a^2 - ab + ab - b^2 = a^2 - b^2$
Results are the same.

45. Let a = smallest integer.
$a^2 + (a + 1)^2 + (a + 2)^2 = 3a^2 + 65$
$a^2 + a^2 + 2a + 1 + a^2 + 4a + 4 = 3a^2 + 65$
$3a^2 + 6a + 5 = 3a^2 + 65$
$3a^2 - 3a^2 + 6a + 5 = 3a^2 - 3a^2 + 65$
$6a + 5 = 65$
$6a = 60$
$a = 10$
The integers are 10, 11, and 12.

46. $m = k^2 + 10k + 25 = (k + 5)^2$
If k is an integer, $k + 5$ is an integer and m is the square of an integer. The correct choice is **E**.

47. $a^2 - 2ab + b^2 = (a - b)^2 = 0$
$a - b = 0$ if $a = b$. The correct choice is **D**.

48. Never; $x^2 - 6x + 9 = (x - 3)^2$ and the square of a real number is never negative.

49. a. Additive inverses
b. $(x - y)^2 = x^2 - 2xy + y^2$
$(y - x)^2 = y^2 - 2xy + x^2$
c. Results are the same because the squares of additive inverses are equal.

50. $(10x + 5)^2 = (10x)^2 + 2 \cdot 10x \cdot 5 + 5^2$
$= 100x^2 + 100x + 25$
$= 100(x^2 + x) + 25$
Add the first digit to its square; multiply by 100; add 25.

51. $25a^2 - 49 = (5a + 7)(5a - 7)$

52. a. $V = w(w + 1)(w + 2)$
$= w(w^2 + 3w + 2)$
$= w^3 + 3w^2 + 2w$
b. $V = l(l + 1)(l - 1)$
$= l(l^2 - 1)$
$= l^3 - l$
c. $V = h(h - 1)(h - 2)$
$= h(h^2 - 3h + 2)$
$= h^3 - 3h^2 + 2h$

53. $(9x - 7) + (11x - 6) = 9x - 7 + 11x - 6 = 20x - 13$

54. $(4y^3 - 7y) - (2y^3 - 5y^2) = 4y^3 - 7y - 2y^3 + 5y^2$
$= 2y^3 + 5y^2 - 7y$

55. $(3m^5)^3 = 3^3(m^5)^3 = 27m^{15}$

56. $(a^3b^2c)(a^2b^4c^2) = a^5b^6c^3$ 57. $15(2y^2)(y^5) = 30y^7$

58. $-9a^2 + 8 = -9(3^2) + 8 = -9 \cdot 9 + 8 = -81 + 8 = -73$

59. $2a^2 - 9a + 15 = 2(3^2) - 9(3) + 15 = 2 \cdot 9 - 27 + 15$
$= 18 - 27 + 15$
$= 6$

60. $7 - 9a + a^2 = 7 - 9 \cdot 3 + 3^2 = 7 - 27 + 9 = -11$

61. $15a - 3a^2 - 7 = 15 \cdot 3 - 3 \cdot 3^2 - 7 = 45 - 27 - 7 = 11$

62. $5a^2 - 9a - 18 = 5 \cdot 3^2 - 9 \cdot 3 - 18 = 45 - 27 - 18 = 0$

63. $17 = 0.25n$
$\frac{17}{0.25} = n$
$68 = n$

64. $n = 0.08(750)$
$n = 60$

LESSON 5-11 TRY THIS pp. 249–250

a. $(b^2 + 3b - 4)(b^2 + 5)$
$= (b^2 + 3b - 4)b^2 + (b^2 + 3b - 4)5$
$= b^4 + 3b^3 - 4b^2 + 5b^2 + 15b - 20$
$= b^4 + 3b^3 + b^2 + 15b - 20$

b. $(2x - 3y + 5)(3x + 4y)$
$= (2x - 3y + 5)3x + (2x - 3y + 5)4y$
$= 6x^2 - 9xy + 15x + 8xy - 12y^2 + 20y$
$= 6x^2 - xy - 12y^2 + 15x + 20y$

c.
$$\begin{array}{r} 3a^2 - 2a + 4 \\ a^2 + 5a + 1 \\ \hline 3a^4 - 2a^3 + 4a^2 \qquad\qquad \\ + 15a^3 - 10a^2 + 20a \qquad \\ + 3a^2 - 2a + 4 \\ \hline 3a^4 + 13a^3 - 3a^2 + 18a + 4 \end{array}$$

d.
$$\begin{array}{r} 5x^2 + 4x + 2 \\ -4x^2 + x - 8 \\ \hline -20x^4 - 16x^3 - 8x^2 \qquad\qquad \\ + 5x^3 + 4x^2 + 2x \qquad \\ - 40x^2 - 32x - 16 \\ \hline -20x^4 - 11x^3 - 44x^2 - 30x - 16 \end{array}$$

e.
$$\begin{array}{r} 4n^3 - 6n - 5 \\ 2n^2 + n - 2 \\ \hline 8n^5 - 12n^3 - 10n^2 \qquad\qquad \\ + 4n^4 - 6n^2 - 5n \qquad \\ - 8n^3 + 12n + 10 \\ \hline 8n^5 + 4n^4 - 20n^3 - 16n^2 + 7n + 10 \end{array}$$

f. $(3x^4y^2 - 4x^2 - 5)(x^3 + x^2y)$
$= (3x^4y^2 - 4x^2 - 5)x^3 + (3x^4y^2 - 4x^2 - 5)x^2y$
$= 3x^7y^2 + 3x^6y^3 - 4x^5 - 4x^4y - 5x^3 - 5x^2y$

g. $(x + 5)(x + 6) = x^2 + 6x + 5x + 30 = x^2 + 11x + 30$

h. $(x-4)(x+4) = x^2 - 4^2 = x^2 - 16$

i. $4x^2(-2x^3 + 5x^2 + 10) = -8x^5 + 20x^4 + 40x^2$

j. $(9x^2+1)^2 = (9x^2)^2 + 2\cdot 9x^2 \cdot 1 + 1^2 = 81x^4 + 18x^2 + 1$

k. $(2x-5)(2x+8) = 4x^2 + 16x - 10x - 40$
$= 4x^2 + 6x - 40$

l. $(x^2 - 4x - 3)(3x - 2) = (x^2 - 4x - 3)3x - (x^2 - 4x - 3)2$
$= 3x^3 - 12x^2 - 9x - 2x^2 + 8x + 6$
$= 3x^3 - 14x^2 - x + 6$

LESSON 5-11 EXERCISES pp. 251–252

1. $(x^2 + x + 1)(x - 1) = x(x^2 + x + 1) - 1(x^2 + x + 1)$
$= x^3 + x^2 + x - x^2 - x - 1$
$= x^3 - 1$

2. $(n^2 - n + 2)(n + 2) = n(n^2 - n + 2) + 2(n^2 - n + 2)$
$= n^3 - n^2 + 2n + 2n^2 - 2n + 4$
$= n^3 + n^2 + 4$

3. $(2x^2 + 6x + 1)(2x + 1) = 2x(2x^2 + 6x + 1) + 1(2x^2 + 6x + 1)$
$= 4x^3 + 12x^2 + 2x + 2x^2 + 6x + 1$
$= 4x^3 + 14x^2 + 8x + 1$

4. $(4x^2 - 2x - 1)(3x - 1) = 3x(4x^2 - 2x - 1) - 1(4x^2 - 2x - 1)$
$= 12x^3 - 6x^2 - 3x - 4x^2 + 2x + 1$
$= 12x^3 - 10x^2 - x + 1$

5. $(3y^2 + 6y + 2)(y^2 - 3) = 3y^2(y^2 - 3) + 6y(y^2 - 3) + 2(y^2 - 3)$
$= 3y^4 - 6y^3 + 2y^2 - 9y^2 + 18y - 6$
$= 3y^4 - 6y^3 - 7y^2 + 18y - 6$

6. $(y^2 + 6y + 1)(3y^2 - 3) = 3y^2(y^2 + 6y + 1) - 3(y^2 + 6y + 1)$
$= 3y^4 + 18y^3 + 3y^2 - 3y^2 - 18y - 3$
$= 3y^4 + 18y^3 - 18y - 3$

7. $(x^3 + x^2 - x)(x^3 + x^2) = x^3(x^3 + x^2 - x) + x^2(x^3 + x^2 - x)$
$= x^6 + x^5 - x^4 + x^5 + x^4 - x^3$
$= x^6 + 2x^5 - x^3$

8. $(x^3 - x^2 + x)(x^3 - x^2) = x^3(x^3 - x^2 + x) - x^2(x^3 - x^2 + x)$
$= x^6 - x^5 + x^4 - x^5 + x^4 - x^3$
$= x^6 - 2x^5 + 2x^4 - x^3$

9. $(a - b)(a^3 + a^2b + ab^2 + b^3)$
$= a(a^3 + a^2b + b^3) - b(a^3 + a^2b + b^3)$
$= a^4 + a^3b + a^2b^2 + ab^3 - a^3b - a^2b^2 - ab^3 - b^4$
$= a^4 - b^4$

10. $(c + d)(c^3 - c^2d + cd^2 - d^3)$
$= c(c^3 - c^2d + cd^2 - d^3) + d(c^3 - c^2d + cd^2 - d^3)$
$= c^4 - c^3d + c^2d^2 - cd^3 + c^3d - c^2d^2 + cd^3 - d^4$
$= c^4 - d^4$

11. $(x^2 + x + 1)(x^2 - x - 1)$
$= x^2(x^2 + x + 1) - x(x^2 + x + 1) - 1(x^2 + x + 1)$
$= x^4 + x^3 + x^2 - x^3 - x^2 - x - x^2 - x - 1$
$= x^4 - x^2 - 2x - 1$

12. $(x^2 - x + 1)(x^2 - x + 1)$
$= x^2(x^2 - x + 1) - x(x^2 - x + 1) + 1(x^2 - x + 1)$
$= x^4 - x^3 + x^2 - x^3 + x^2 - x + x^2 - x + 1$
$= x^4 - 2x^3 + 3x^2 - 2x + 1$

13. $(2x^2 + 3x - 4)(2x^2 + x - 2)$
$= 2x^2(2x^2 + 3x - 4) + x(2x^2 + 3x - 4) - 2(2x^2 + 3x - 4)$
$= 4x^4 + 6x^3 - 8x^2 + 2x^3 + 3x^2 - 4x - 4x^2 - 6x + 8$
$= 4x^4 + 8x^3 - 9x^2 - 10x + 8$

14. $(2x^2 - x - 3)(2x^2 - 5x - 2)$
$= 2x^2(2x^2 - x - 3) - 5x(2x^2 - x - 3) - 2(2x^2 - x - 3)$
$= 4x^4 - 2x^3 - 6x^2 - 10x^3 + 5x^2 + 15x - 4x^2 + 2x + 6$
$= 4x^4 - 12x^3 - 5x^2 + 17x + 6$

15. $(2t^2 - t - 4)(3t^2 + 2t - 1)$
$= 3t^2(2t^2 - t - 4) + 2t(2t^2 - t - 4) - 1(2t^2 - t - 4)$
$= 6t^4 - 3t^3 - 12t^2 + 4t^3 - 2t^2 - 8t - 2t^2 + t + 4$
$= 6t^4 + t^3 - 16t^2 - 7t + 4$

16. $(3a^2 - 5a + 2)(2a^2 - 3a + 4)$
$= 2a^2(3a^2 - 5a + 2) - 3a(3a^2 - 5a + 2) + 4(3a^2 - 5a + 2)$
$= 6a^4 - 10a^3 + 4a^2 - 9a^3 + 15a^2 - 6a + 12a^2 - 20a + 8$
$= 6a^4 - 19a^3 + 31a^2 - 26a + 8$

17. $(2x^2 + x - 2)(-2x^2 + 4x - 5)$
$= -2x^2(2x^2 + x - 2) + 4x(2x^2 + x - 2) - 5(2x^2 + x - 2)$
$= -4x^4 - 2x^3 + 4x^2 + 8x^3 + 4x^2 - 8x - 10x^2 - 5x + 10$
$= -4x^4 + 6x^3 - 2x^2 - 13x + 10$

18. $(3x^2 - 8x + 1)(-2x^2 - 4x + 2)$
$= -2x^2(3x^2 - 8x + 1) - 4x(3x^2 - 8x + 1) + 2(3x^2 - 8x + 1)$
$= -6x^4 + 16x^3 - 2x^2 - 12x^3 + 32x^2 - 4x + 6x^2 - 16x + 2$
$= -6x^4 + 4x^3 + 36x^2 - 20x + 2$

19. $(x^5 - x^3 + x)(x^4 + x^2 - 1)$
$= x^4(x^5 - x^3 + x) + x^2(x^5 - x^3 + x) - 1(x^5 - x^3 + x)$
$= x^9 - x^7 + x^5 + x^7 - x^5 + x^3 - x^5 + x^3 - x$
$= x^9 - x^5 + 2x^3 - x$

20. $(3x^6 + 3x^4 + 3x^2)(x^5 - x^3 + x)$
$= x^5(3x^6 + 3x^4 + 3x^2) - x^3(3x^6 + 3x^4 + 3x^2)$
$+ x(3x^6 + 3x^4 + 3x^2)$
$= 3x^{11} + 3x^9 + 3x^7 - 3x^9 - 3x^7 - 3x^5 + 3x^7 + 3x^5 + 3x^3$
$= 3x^{11} + 3x^7 + 3x^3$

21. $(b^3 + b^2 + b + 1)(b - 1)$
$= b(b^3 + b^2 + b + 1) - 1(b^3 + b^2 + b + 1)$
$= b^4 + b^3 + b^2 + b - b^3 - b^2 - b - 1$
$= b^4 - 1$

22. $(x^3 + x^2 + x - 2)(x - 2)$
$= x(x^3 + x^2 + x - 2) - 2(x^3 + x^2 + x - 2)$
$= x^4 + x^3 + x^2 - 2x - 2x^3 - 2x^2 - 2x + 4$
$= x^4 - x^3 - x^2 - 4x + 4$

23. $(x^3 + x^2 - x - 3)(xy - 3y)$
$= xy(x^3 + x^2 - x - 3) - 3y(x^3 + x^2 - x - 3)$
$= x^4y + x^3y - x^2y - 3xy - 3x^3y - 3x^2y + 3xy + 9y$
$= x^4y - 2x^3y - 4x^2y + 9y$

24. $(x^3 - x^2 - x + 4)(xy + 4y)$
$= xy(x^3 - x^2 - x + 4) + 4y(x^3 - x^2 - x + 4)$
$= x^4y - x^3y - x^2y + 4xy + 4x^3y - 4x^2y - 4xy + 16y$
$= x^4y + 3x^3y - 5x^2y + 16y$

25. $(x - 8)(x - 8) = x^2 - 2\cdot x\cdot 8 + 8^2 = x^2 - 16x + 64$

26. $(x + 7)(x + 7) = x^2 + 2\cdot x\cdot 7 + 7^2 = x^2 + 14x + 49$

27. $(x - 8)(x + 8) = x^2 - 8^2 = x^2 - 64$

28. $(x + 7)(x - 7) = x^2 - 7^2 = x^2 - 49$

29. $(x - 8)(x + 5) = x^2 + 5x - 8x - 40 = x^2 - 3x - 40$

30. $(x + 7)(x - 4) = x^2 - 4x + 7x - 28 = x^2 + 3x - 28$

31. $4x(x^2 + 6x - 3) = 4x^3 + 24x^2 - 12x$

32. $8x(-x^2 - 4x + 3) = -8x^3 - 32x^2 + 24x$

33. $\left(2x^2 - \frac{1}{2}\right)\left(2x^2 - \frac{1}{2}\right) = (2x^2)^2 - 2(2x^2)\left(\frac{1}{2}\right) + \left(\frac{1}{2}\right)^2$
$= 4x^4 - 2x^2 + \frac{1}{4}$

34. $(1 - x^2)(1 - x^2) = 1^2 - 2(1)(x^2) + (x^2)^2$
$= 1 - 2x^2 + x^4$ or $x^4 - 2x^2 + 1$

35. $(6a^3 - 1)(6a^3 + 1) = (6a^3)^2 - 1^2$
$= 36a^6 - 1$

36. $(2b^2 - 7)(3b^2 + 9) = 6b^4 + 18b^2 - 21b^2 - 63$
$= 6b^4 - 3b^2 - 63$

37. $(2 - 3x)(2 + 3x) = 2^2 - (3x)^2 = 4 - 9x^2$ or $-9x^2 + 4$

38. $(4 + 5x)(4 - 5x) = 4^2 - (5x)^2 = 16 - 25x^2$ or $-25x^2 + 16$

39. $(6x^4 + 4)^2 = (6x^4)^2 + 2(6x^4)(4) + 4^2$
$= 36x^8 + 48x^4 + 16$

40. $(8 - 6x^4)^2 = 8^2 - 2(8)(6x^4) + (6x^4)^2$
$= 64 - 96x^4 + 36x^8$ or $36x^8 - 96x^4 + 64$

41. $-6x^2(x^3 + 8x - 9) = -6x^5 - 48x^3 + 54x^2$

42. $-5x^2(x^3 - 2x + 4) = -5x^5 + 10x^3 - 20x^2$

43. $(6q^3 - 1)(2q^2 + 1) = 12q^5 + 6q^3 - 2q^2 - 1$

44. $(7p^2 + 4)(5p^2 - 8) = 35p^4 - 56p^2 + 20p^2 - 32$
$= 35p^4 - 36p^2 - 32$

45. $\left(\frac{3}{4}x + 1\right)\left(\frac{3}{4}x + 2\right) = \frac{9}{16}x^2 + \frac{3}{2}x + \frac{3}{4}x + 2$
$= \frac{9}{16}x^2 + \frac{9}{4}x + 2$

46. $\left(\frac{1}{5}x^2 + 9\right)\left(\frac{3}{5}x^2 - 7\right) = \frac{3}{25}x^4 - \frac{7}{5}x^2 + \frac{27}{5}x^2 - 63$
$= \frac{3}{25}x^4 + 4x^2 - 63$

47. $(x^2 + 2x + 3)(4x + 5)$
$= 4x(x^2 + 2x + 3) + 5(x^2 + 2x + 3)$
$= 4x^3 + 8x^2 + 12x + 5x^2 + 10x + 15$
$= 4x^3 + 13x^2 + 22x + 15$

48. $(x^2 + 2x)(3x^2 + 4x + 5)$
$= x^2(3x^2 + 4x + 5) + 2x(3x^2 + 4x + 5)$
$= 3x^4 + 4x^3 + 5x^2 + 6x^3 + 8x^2 + 10x$
$= 3x^4 + 10x^3 + 13x^2 + 10x$

49. $(x^3 - 4x^2)(3x^2 - 2x + 5)$
$= x^3(3x^2 - 2x + 5) - 4x^2(3x^2 - 2x + 5)$
$= 3x^5 - 2x^4 + 5x^3 - 12x^4 + 8x^3 - 20x^2$
$= 3x^5 - 14x^4 + 13x^3 - 20x^2$

50. $(x^3 - 4x^2 + 5)(3x^2 - 2x)$
$= 3x^2(x^3 - 4x^2 + 5) - 2x(x^3 - 4x^2 + 5)$
$= 3x^5 - 12x^4 + 15x^2 - 2x^4 + 8x^3 - 10x$
$= 3x^5 - 14x^4 + 8x^3 + 15x^2 - 10x$

51. $(x + y)^3 = (x + y)^2(x + y) = (x^2 + 2xy + y^2)(x + y)$
$= x(x^2 + 2xy + y^2) + y(x^2 + 2xy + y^2)$
$= x^3 + 2x^2y + xy^2 + x^2y + 2xy^2 + y^3$
$= x^3 + 3x^2y + 3xy^2 + y^3$

52. $(x + y)^4 = (x + y)^3(x + y)$
$= (x^3 + 3x^2y + 3xy^2 + y^3)(x + y)$
$= x(x^3 + 3x^2y + 3xy^2 + y^3)$
$+ y(x^3 + 3x^2y + 3xy^2 + y^3)$
$= (x^4 + 3x^3y + 3x^2y^2 + xy^3 + x^3y + 3x^2y^2$
$+ 3xy^3 + y^4$
$= x^4 + 4x^3y + 6x^2y^2 + 4xy^3 + y^4$

53. Coefficients are from Pascal's triangle.
$x^5 + 5x^4y + 10x^3y^2 + 10x^2y^3 + 5xy^4 + y^5$

54. a. $(x^2 + x + 1)(x - 1) = x(x^2 + x + 1) - (x^2 + x + 1)$
$= x^3 + x^2 + x - x^2 - x - 1 = x^3 - 1$
b. $(x^2 + x + 1)(x + 1) = x(x^2 + x + 1) + x^2 + x + 1$
$= x^3 + x^2 + x + x^2 + x + 1 = x^3 + 2x^2 + 2x + 1$
c. $(x^2 - x + 1)(x - 1) = x(x^2 - x + 1) - 1(x^2 - x + 1)$
$= x^3 - x^2 + x - x^2 + x - 1 = x^3 - 2x^2 + 2x - 1$
d. $(x^2 - x + 1)(x + 1) = x(x^2 - x + 1) + 1(x^2 - x + 1)$
$= x^3 - x^2 + x + x^2 - x + 1 = x^3 + 1$
e. $(-x^2 + x - 1)(x - 1) = x(-x^2 + x - 1) - 1(-x^2 + x - 1)$
$= -x^3 + x^2 - x + x^2 - x + 1 = -x^3 + 2x^2 - 2x + 1$
f. $(-x^2 + x - 1)(x + 1) = x(-x^2 + x - 1) + 1(-x^2 + x -$
$1) = -x^3 + x^2 - x - x^2 + x - 1 = -x^3 - 1$
g. $(x^3 + x^2 + x + 1)(x - 1)$
$= x(x^3 + x^2 + x + 1) - 1(x^3 + x^2 + x + 1)$
$= x^4 + x^3 + x^2 + x - x^3 - x^2 - x - 1 = x^4 - 1$
h. $(x^3 + x^2 + x + 1)(x + 1)$
$= x(x^3 + x^2 + x + 1) + 1(x^3 + x^2 + x + 1)$
$= x^4 + x^3 + x^2 + x + x^3 + x^2 + x + 1$
$= x^4 + 2x^3 + 2x^2 + 2x + 1$
i. $(x^3 - x^2 + x - 1)(x - 1)$
$= x(x^3 - x^2 + x - 1) - 1(x^3 - x^2 + x - 1)$
$= x^4 - x^3 + x^2 - x - x^3 + x^2 - x + 1$
$= x^4 - 2x^3 + 2x^2 - 2x + 1$
j. $(x^3 - x^2 + x - 1)(x + 1)$
$= x(x^3 - x^2 + x - 1) + 1(x^3 - x^2 + x - 1)$
$= x^4 - x^3 + x^2 - x + x^3 - x^2 + x - 1 = x^4 + 1$
k. $(-x^3 + x^2 - x + 1)(x - 1)$
$= x(-x^3 + x^2 - x + 1) - 1(-x^3 + x^2 - x + 1)$
$= -x^4 + x^3 - x^2 + x + x^3 - x^2 + x - 1$
$= -x^4 + 2x^3 - 2x^2 + 2x - 1$
l. $(-x^3 + x^2 - x + 1)(x + 1)$
$= x(-x^3 + x^2 - x + 1) + 1(-x^3 + x^2 - x + 1)$
$= -x^4 + x^3 - x^2 + x - x^3 + x^2 - x + 1 = -x^4 + 1$

55. $x^4 + x^3 + x^2 + x + 1$

56. $x^4 - x^3 + x^2 - x + 1$

57. $x^5 + x^4 + x^3 + x^2 + x + 1$

58. $x^2(x^2 + xy + y^2) + xy(x^2 + xy + y^2) + y^2(x^2 + xy + y^2)$
$= x^4 + x^3y + x^2y^2 + x^3y + x^2y^2 + xy^3 + x^2y^2 + xy^3 + y^4$
$= x^4 + 2x^3y + 3x^2y^2 + 2xy^3 + y^4$

59. The products that yield x-terms are $c \cdot dx + e \cdot bx$.
$cdx + ebx = 1x$
$x(cd + eb) = 1x$
So any 4 coefficients b, c, d, and e such that $cd + eb = 1$ will work, e.g., $b = -1, c = 1, d = 1, e = 1$.

60. $(x - 3)^2 = x^2 - 2 \cdot x \cdot 3 + 3^2 = x^2 - 6x + 9$

61. $(x + 3)^3 = (x^2 + 2 \cdot x \cdot 3 + 3^2)(x + 3) = (x^2 + 6x + 9)(x + 3)$
$= x(x^2 + 6x + 9) + 3(x^2 + 6x + 9)$
$= x^3 + 6x^2 + 9x + 3x^2 + 18x + 27 = x^3 + 9x^2 + 27x + 27$

62. $(x - 3)(x + 3) = x^2 - 3^2 = x^2 - 9$ 63. $-7a$ 64. $21n$

65. $-3y^2 + 9y - 1$ 66. 0.000011 67. 21,000,000

68. 2, 1, 0; 2 69. 7, 3, 0; 7 70. 1, 0; 1

71. $\frac{1}{2.5} = \frac{3.6}{n}$

$2.5n \cdot \frac{1}{2.5} = \frac{3.6}{n} \cdot 2.5n$

$n = 3.6 \times 2.5$
$n = 9$ ft

PROBLEMS p. 253

1. $0.49W + 0.45P - 6.36R + 8.7$
$= 0.49(86.2) + 0.45(4.8) - 6.36(6.0) + 8.7$
$= 42.238 + 2.16 - 38.16 + 8.7$
$= 14.938\% \approx 15\%$

2. $0.49W + 0.45P - 6.36R + 8.7$
$= 0.49(95.8) + 0.45(5.1) - 6.36(7.2) + 8.7$
$= 46.942 + 2.295 - 45.792 + 8.7$
$= 12.145\% \approx 12\%$

3. $0.041h - 0.018A - 2.69$
$= 0.041(170) - 0.018(29) - 2.69$
$= 6.97 - 0.522 - 2.69$
$= 3.758$ Liters ≈ 3.8 Liters

4. $0.041h - 0.018A - 2.69$
$= 0.041(156) - 0.018(18) - 2.69$
$= 6.396 - 0.324 - 2.69$
$= 3.382$ Liters ≈ 3.4 Liters

LESSON 5-12 PROBLEMS p. 255

1. Strategy: Make a table

Job A

Year	1	2	3	4	5	6	7	8	9	10
Amount (1000)	30	33	36	39	42	45	48	51	54	57
Total	30	63	99	138	180	225	273	324	378	435

$435,000

Job B

Year	1	2	3	4	5	6	7	8	9	10
Amount (1000)	37	39	41	43	45	47	49	51	53	55
Total	37	76	117	160	205	252	301	352	405	460

$460,000

Job B will pay more money altogether for the 10-year period.

2. Strategies: Make a table. Look for a pattern

Year	1	2	3	4	5	6	7	8	9	10
Amount (million)	1	3	5	7	9	11	13	15	17	19
Total	1	4	9	16	25	36	49	64	81	100

$100 million

The family gave a total of $100 million for the 10-year period.

3. Strategy: Use logical reasoning
If each person paid the same amount, then the amount paid must be a factor of 203. The factors of 203 are 1, 7, 29, 203. Since each person paid more than $10, we rule out $1 and $7. If the stamp sold for $203 only one person bought the stamp. Seven people bought the stamp with each person paying $29.

4. Strategy: Draw a diagram.

	5			
*	O	O	O	*
O	X	X	X	O
O	X	X	X	O 5
O	X	X	X	O
*	O	O	O	*

X–Base price—no fence ($1200) – 9 lots
O–One side fenced ($1350) – 12 lots
*–2 sides fenced ($1500) – 4 lots

Nine lots were priced at $1200—no fence.
Twelve lots were priced at $1350—one side fenced.
Four lots were priced at $1500—two sides fenced.

5. Strategies: Make a table. Look for a pattern
Make a table where the first row is No. of people doing hiring & training, the second row is No. of new sales people, and the third row is Total number of sales people.

1st week	2nd week	3rd week	4th week
25	50	100	200
50	100	200	400
75	175	375	775
↓	↓	↓	↓
(25 × 3)	(25 × 7)	(25 × 15)	(25 × 31)
↓	↓	↓	↓
$(2^2 - 1)$	$(2^3 - 1)$	$(2^4 - 1)$	$(2^5 - 1)$

8192
12th week → $25 \times (2^{13} - 1)$
$25 \times (8192 - 1) = 204{,}775$

The company would have 204,775 members after 12 weeks.

6. Strategy: Try, test, revise

Try	Test	Revised Try
First try: Good pieces: 10	Bad pieces: 25 − 10 = 15 10 × $10 = $100 15 × $5 = $75 Amount earned: $100 − $75 = $25	$25 is more than $10 Revise try down Revised try: 9
Second try: Good pieces: 9	Bad pieces: 25 − 9 = 16 9 × $10 = $90 16 × $5 = $80 Amount earned: $90 − $80 = $10	This is correct.

The painter completed 9 doors that did not need to be repainted and 16 that did need repainting.

CHAPTER 5 WRAP UP pp. 256–258

1. $7^2 \cdot 7^4 = 7^{2+4} = 7^6$ **2.** $y^3 \cdot y^5 = y^{3+5} = y^8$

3. $x^7 \cdot x^3 \cdot x^1 = x^{7+3+1} = x^{11}$

4. $(a^2b^4)(a^3b^1) = a^{2+3}b^{4+1} = a^5b^5$

5. $(x^4y^5)(x^4y^5) = x^{4+4}y^{5+5} = x^8y^{10}$

6. $(l^1m^7n^5)(l^2m^6n^1) = l^{1+2}m^{7+6}n^{5+1} = l^3m^{13}n^6$

7. $\frac{7^5}{7^3} = 7^{5-3} = 7^2$ **8.** $\frac{a^9}{a^4} = a^{9-4} = a^5$

9. $\frac{x^9y^7}{x^2y^3} = x^{9-2}y^{7-3} = x^7y^4$ **10.** $7^{-3} = \frac{1}{7^3}$ **11.** $y^{-2} = \frac{1}{y^2}$

12. $a^0 = 1$ **13.** $(5^3)^2 = 5^{3 \cdot 2} = 5^6$ **14.** $(3^4)^4 = 3^{4 \cdot 4} = 3^{16}$

15. $(x^6)^2 = x^{6 \cdot 2} = x^{12}$ **16.** $(a^3)^3 = a^{3 \cdot 3} = a^9$

17. $(3a)^2 = 3^2a^2 = 9a^2$ **18.** $(2b)^3 = 2^3b^3 = 8b^3$

19. $(2x^3)^3 = 2^3(x^3)^3 = 8x^9$ **20.** $(4p^2)^3 = 4^3(p^2)^3 = 64p^6$

21. $(3x^2yz^4)^2 = 3^2(x^2)^2y^2(z^4)^2 = 9x^4y^2z^8$

22. $(-2x^6y^2)^3 = (-2)^3(x^6)^3(y^2)^3 = -8x^{18}y^6$

23. $[(-n)^{15}]^2 = (-n)^{30} = n^{30}$ **24.** $\left(\frac{y^3}{3}\right)^4 = \frac{y^{12}}{3^4} = \frac{y^{12}}{81}$

25. $6a^2$ **26.** $-6x^3$ **27.** $-20b^3c^6$ **28.** $10y^8$

29. $15w^3z^7$ **30.** $32x^3y^4$ **31.** $\frac{a^6}{a^3} = a^{6-3} = a^3$

32. $\frac{15n^5}{-15n} = \frac{15}{-15} \cdot \frac{n^5}{n^1} = (-1)n^{5-1} = -n^4$

33. $\frac{-15x^3y^6}{5xy^3} = -\frac{15}{5} \cdot \frac{x^3y^6}{x^1y^3} = -3x^{3-1}y^{6-3} = -3x^2y^3$

34. $\frac{-24m^{12}n^2}{-6m^5n} = \frac{-24}{-6} \cdot \frac{m^{12}n^2}{m^5n^1} = 4m^{12-5}n^{2-1} = 4m^7n$

35. $\frac{18b^{14}c^6}{-3b^7c^2} = \frac{18}{-3} \cdot \frac{b^{14}c^6}{b^7c^2} = -6b^{14-7}c^{6-2} = -6b^7c^4$

36. $\frac{-28x^4y^8}{-7x^2y^6} = \frac{-28}{-7} \cdot \frac{x^4y^8}{x^2y^6} = 4x^{4-2}y^{8-6} = 4x^2y^2$

37. 3250 **38.** 0.0057 **39.** 2.426×10^6 **40.** 4.5×10^{-5}

41. $4x^3 + 4$ **42.** $-3x^5 + 25$ **43.** 5, 3, 0; 5 **44.** 2, 1, 0; 2

45. $7x^5 - 2x^4 + 3x^2 - 2x + 5$

46. $-4x^5 - 2x^3y^2 + 7x^2y^3 + 3y$

47. $-x^5 + 10x^4 - 7x - 1$

48. $8x^4y^3 + 3x^3 - 7xy^2 + 6y$

49. $7x - 10 = 7(5) - 10 = 35 - 10 = 25$

50. $x^2 - 3x + 6x = (5)^2 - 3(5) + 6 = 25 - 15 + 6 = 16$

51. $(5x^3 - 2x^2 + 3x) + (2x^3 + 6x^2 + x)$
$= (5 + 2)x^3 + (-2 + 6)x^2 + (3 + 1)x$
$= 7x^3 + 4x^2 + 4x$

52. $(3x^4 - x^3 + x - 4) + (3x^4 - 5x^3 + 3x^2 - 5)$
$= (3 + 3)x^4 + (-1 - 5)x^3 + 3x^2 + x - 4 - 5$
$= 6x^4 - 6x^3 + 3x^2 + x - 9$

53. $(3x^5 - 4x^4 + x^3 - 3) + (3x^4 - 5x^3 + 3x^2)$
$= 3x^5 + (-4 + 3)x^4 + (1 - 5)x^3 + 3x^2 - 3$
$= 3x^5 - x^4 - 4x^3 + 3x^2 - 3$

54. $(a^3 + 7a^2b - ab^2 - 2b^3) + (2a^3 - 3ab^2 + 2b^3)$
$= (1 + 2)a^3 + 7a^2b + (-1 - 3)ab^2 + (-2 + 2)b^3$
$= 3a^3 + 7a^2b - 4ab^2$

55. $(7y^3 + 8) - (3y^3 - 6) = 7y^3 + 8 + (-3y^3 + 6)$
$= 4y^3 + 14$

56. $(5x^2 - 4x + 1) - (3x^2 + 7)$
$= 5x^2 - 4x + 1 + (-3x^2 - 7)$
$= 2x^2 - 4x - 6$

57. $(3x^5 + 4x^4 + 2x^2 + 3) - (2x^5 - 4x^4 + 3x^3 + 4x^2 - 5)$
$= 3x^5 + 4x^4 + 2x^2 + 3 + (-2x^5 + 4x^4 - 3x^3 - 4x^2 + 5)$
$= x^5 + 8x^4 - 3x^3 - 2x^2 + 8$

58. (a)
$$\begin{array}{r} 6y^2 - 5y + 3 \\ \underline{-(8y^2 - 3y - 8)} \end{array}$$
(b)
$$\begin{array}{r} 6y^2 - 5y + 3 \\ \underline{+(-8y^2 + 3y + 8)} \\ -2y^2 - 2y + 11 \end{array}$$

59. (a)
$$\begin{array}{r} 2x^5 \qquad - x^3 \qquad + x + 3 \\ \underline{-(3x^5 - x^4 + 4x^3 + 2x^2 - x + 3)} \end{array}$$
(b)
$$\begin{array}{r} 2x^5 \qquad - x^3 \qquad + x + 3 \\ \underline{+(-3x^5 + x^4 - 4x^3 - 2x^2 + x - 3)} \\ -x^5 + x^4 - 5x^3 - 2x^2 + 2x \end{array}$$

60. $3x(5x + 6) = 3x(5x) + 3x(6) = 15x^2 + 18x$

61. $5x^3(3x^3 - 8x^2 + 10x + 2)$
$= 5x^3(3x^3) + 5x^3(-8x^2) + 5x^3(10x) + 5x^3(2)$
$= 15x^6 - 40x^5 + 50x^4 + 10x^3$

62. $(x + 4)(x - 7) = x^2 - 7x + 4x - 28$
$= x^2 - 3x - 28$

63. $(a-3)(a+3)=a^2-3^2=a^2-9$

64. $(b^2+3)(b^2+2)=b^4+2b^2+3b^2+6$
$=b^4+5b^2+6$

65. $(2x^2+5xy)(3x^2-3)=6x^4-6x^2+15x^3y-15xy$

66. $(x-3)(x+3)=x^2-3^2=x^2-9$

67. $(a-8)(a+8)=a^2-8^2=a^2-64$

68. $(2y+3)(2y-3)=(2y)^2-3^2=4y^2-9$

69. $(3x^2-4)(3x^2+4)=(3x^2)^2-4^2=9x^4-16$

70. $(-2y+7x)(-2y-7x)=(-2y)^2-(7x)^2$
$=4y^2-49x^2$

71. $(2+3y)(2-3y)=2^2-(3y)^2=4-9y^2$

72. $(a+4)^2=a^2+2\cdot a\cdot 4+4^2=a^2+8a+16$

73. $(3x+6)^2=(3x)^2+2\cdot 3x\cdot 6+6^2=9x^2+36x+36$

74. $(4x^2-5x+1)(3x-2)$
$=3x(4x^2-5x+1)-2(4x^2-5x+1)$
$=12x^3-15x^2+3x-8x^2+10x-2$
$=12x^3-23x^2+13x-2$

75. $(2a^2+3a-2)(a^2-4)$
$=a^2(2a^2+3a-2)-4(2a^2+3a-2)$
$=2a^4+3a^3-2a^2-8a^2-12a+8$
$=2a^4+3a^3-10a^2-12a+8$

76. $(2b^2+5b-3)(2b^2-2b+1)$
$=2b^2(2b^2+5b-3)-2b(2b^2+5b-3)+1(2b^2+5b-3)$
$=4b^4+10b^3-6b^2-4b^3-10b^2+6b+2b^2+5b-3$
$=4b^4+6b^3-14b^2+11b-3$

77. $(x^4-2x+3)(x^3+x-1)$
$x^3(x^4-2x+3)+x(x^4-2x+3)-1(x^4-2x+3)$
$=x^7-2x^4+3x^3+x^5-2x^2+3x-x^4+2x-3$
$=x^7+x^5-3x^4+3x^3-2x^2+5x-3$

CHAPTER 5 ASSESSMENT p. 259

1. $6^2\cdot 6^3=6^{2+3}=6^5$ 2. $x^6\cdot x^2=x^{6+2}=x^8$

3. $a^8\cdot a^3=a^{8+3}=a^{11}$ 4. $(r^2s^3)(rs^4)=r^{2+1}s^{3+4}=r^3s^7$

5. $\frac{3^5}{3^2}=3^{5-2}=3^3$ 6. $\frac{a^4b^5}{ab^3}=a^{4-1}b^{5-3}=a^3b^2$

7. $6^{-2}=\frac{1}{6^2}$ 8. $y^{-4}=\frac{1}{y^4}$

9. $3^0=1$ 10. $(x^3)^2=x^{3\cdot 2}=x^6$

11. $(-3y^2)^3=(-3)^3(y^2)^3=-27y^6$ 12. $\left(\frac{a^4}{3}\right)^3=\frac{(a^4)^3}{3^3}=\frac{a^{12}}{27}$

13. $(-2y^2)(4y)=-2(4)y^{2+1}=-8y^3$

14. $(6x^2)(-2x^3)(-2x^5)=24x^{2+3+5}=24x^{10}$

15. $(-4n^3)(-4n^3)=16n^{3+3}=16n^6$ 16. $\frac{b^3}{b}=b^{3-1}=b^2$

17. $\frac{7a^4}{a^4}=7a^{4-4}=7a^0=7$

18. $\frac{4x^5}{12x^3}=\frac{4}{12}\cdot x^{5-3}=\frac{1}{3}x^2$ or $\frac{x^2}{3}$ 19. 326,500

20. 0.00207 21. 2.46×10^5 22. 3.85×10^{-3}

23. $5a^2-6$ 24. $3y^2-4y$

25. $3-x^2+2x+5x^2-6x=3+4x^2-4x=4x^2-4x+3$

26. $x^2-5x-1=(-2)^2-5(-2)-1=4+10-1=13$

27. $(5x^4+7x^3-8)+(3x^4-5x^3+6x^2)$
$=8x^4+2x^3+6x^2-8$

28. $(12x^2-3x-8)-(4x^2+5)$
$=12x^2-3x-8+(-4x^2-5)$
$=8x^2-3x-13$

29. $-3x^2(4x^2-3x-5)=-3x^2(4x^2)-3x^2(-3x)-3x^2(-5)$
$=-12x^4+9x^3+15x^2$

30. $(3b+5)(b-3)=3b^2-9b+5b-15=3b^2-4b-15$

31. $(6a^2-2)(a^2-1)=6a^4-6a^2-2a^2+2=6a^4-8a^2+2$

32. $(3p-2)(3p+2)=(3p)^2-(2)^2=9p^2-4$

33. $(3x^2+4)(3x^2-4)=(3x^2)^2-(4)^2=9x^4-16$

34. $(x-9)^2=x^2-2\cdot x\cdot 9+9^2=x^2-18x+81$

35. $(4x^7+3)(4x^7-3)=(4x^7)^2-3^2=16x^{14}-9$

36. $(3x^2-2x)^2=(3x^2)^2-2\cdot(3x^2)(2x)+(2x)^2$
$=9x^4-12x^3+4x^2$

37. $(2x+1)(3x^2-5x-3)$
$=2x(3x^2-5x-3)+1(3x^2-5x-3)$
$=6x^3-10x^2-6x+3x^2-5x-3$
$=6x^3-7x^2-11x-3$

38. $(-2a^3+5a^2-3)(3a^2+1)$
$=3a^2(-2a^3+5a^2-3)+1(-2a^3+5a^2-3)$
$=-6a^5+15a^4-9a^2-2a^3+5a^2-3$
$=-6a^5+15a^4-2a^3-4a^2-3$

CHAPTER 6

SKILLS & CONCEPTS p. 260

1. $6x+6y=6(x+y)$ 2. $24w+24z=24(w+z)$

3. $4y+28+12z=4\cdot y+4\cdot 7+4\cdot 3z$
$=4(y+7+3z)$

4. $2n+10$ 5. $2(n+6)$

6.
$$\begin{aligned}6y+4&=2y+8\\6y-2y+4&=2y-2y+8\\4y+4&=8\\4y+4-4&=8-4\\4y&=4\\\tfrac{1}{4}(4y)&=\tfrac{1}{4}(4)\\y&=1\end{aligned}$$

7.
$$\begin{aligned}3(2a+4)&=20\\6a+12&=20\\6a+12-12&=20-12\\6a&=8\\\tfrac{1}{6}(6a)&=\tfrac{1}{6}(8)\\a&=\tfrac{8}{6}=\tfrac{4}{3}\end{aligned}$$

8. Let w = width of the rectangle.
$w+20$ = length
$$\begin{aligned}2w+2(w+20)&=280\\2w+2w+40&=280\\4w+40&=280\\4w+40-40&=280-40\\4w&=240\\\tfrac{1}{4}(4w)&=\tfrac{1}{4}(240)\\w&=60\end{aligned}$$
The width is 60 cm, the length 80 cm.

9. $(-6x^8)(2x^5)=-12x^{8+5}=-12x^{13}$

10. $(-6x^2y^2)(4xy^4)=-24x^{2+1}y^{2+4}=-24x^3y^6$

11. $9x(4x+7)=36x^2+63x$

12. $3s(6t^4-2s^2-3t-6)=18st^4-6s^3-9st-18s$

13. $(3x+8)(x-7)=3x^2-21x+8x-56$
$=3x^2-13x-56$

14. $(x+3)(5x-7)=5x^2-7x+15x-21$
$=5x^2+8x-21$

15. $8x(2x^2-6x+1)=16x^3-48x^2+8x$

16. $(x+6)(x-4)=x^2-4x+6x-24$
$=x^2+2x-24$

17. $(y-8)(y+3)=y^2+3y-8y-24$
$=y^2-5y-24$

18. $(7w + 6)(4w - 1) = 28w^2 - 7w + 24w - 6$
$= 28w^2 + 17w - 6$

19. $(x - 9)^2 = x^2 - 2 \cdot x \cdot 9 + 9^2$
$= x^2 - 18x + 81$

20. $(5x + 3)^2 = (5x)^2 + 2 \cdot 5x \cdot 3 + 3^2$
$= 25x^2 + 30x + 9$

21. $(a - 7)(a + 7) = a^2 - 7^2 = a^2 - 49$

22. $(2 - 5y)(2 + 5y) = 2^2 - (5y)^2 = 4 - 25y^2$

INTRODUCING THE CONCEPT p. 262

13 pairs; 1 and $16x^4$, 2 and $8x^4$, 4 and $4x^4$, 8 and $2x^4$, 16 and x^4, x and $16x^3$, $2x$ and $8x^3$, $4x$ and $4x^3$, $8x$ and $2x^3$, $16x$ and x^3, x^2 and $16x^2$, $2x^2$ and $8x^2$, $4x^2$ and $4x^2$

LESSON 6-1 TRY THIS pp. 262–263

a. $(4x^2)(2x^2)$, $(4x)(2x^3)$, $(8x)(x^3)$ Answers may vary.
b. $(2m)(3m^4)$, $(m^2)(6m^3)$, $(2m^3)(3m^2)$ Answers may vary.
c. $(6ab)(2ab)$, $(6a^2)(2b^2)$, $(12)(a^2b^2)$ Answers may vary.
d. $x^2 + 3x = x(x + 3)$ e. $a^2b + 2ab = ab(a + 2)$
f. $3x^6 - 5x^3 + 2x^2 = x^2(3x^4 - 5x + 2)$
g. $9x^4 - 15x^3 + 3x^2 = 3x^2(3x^2 - 5x + 1)$
h. $2p^3q^2 + p^2q + pq = pq(2p^2q + p + 1)$
i. $12m^4n^4 + 3m^3n^2 + 6m^2n^2 = 3m^2n^2(4m^2n^2 + m + 2)$

LESSON 6-1 EXERCISES pp. 264–265

1–9. Answers may vary.

10. $x(x - 4)$ 11. $y(y + 8)$ 12. $2a(a + 3)$
13. $3p(p - 1)$ 14. $3(y^4 + 2y^2 + 2)$ 15. $5(x^2 + 2x + 6)$
16. $2m(7m^3 - 6)$ 17. $7y^2(4 + 3y^2)$ 18. $x^4(32x - 17)$
19. $x^3(9 + 25x^4)$ 20. a^2 21. $18y^4$ 22. $2(x^2 + x - 4)$
23. $3(2x^2 + x - 5)$
24. $x^2y(x + 6)$ 25. $a^2b(4a^2b + 1)$ 26. $8x^2y(x^2y - 3)$
27. $5m^3(m^2n + 2)$ 28. $3m^3n(4m^2n + 3m + 2n)$
29. $2xy^2(x^2 + 3y + 4)$ 30. $17x(x^4 + 2x^2 + 3)$
31. $16x(x^5 - 2x^4 - 3)$ 32. $x^2(6x^2 - 10x + 3)$
33. $x(5x^4 + 10x - 8)$ 34. $x^2(x^3 + x^2 + x - 1)$
35. $x^3(x^6 - x^4 + x + 1)$ 36. $2x^3(x^4 - x^3 - 32x^2 + 2)$
37. $5(2x^3 + 5x^2 + 3x - 4)$ 38. $2a^2(2a^2b^4 - ab^2 + 3)$
39. $5pq^2(p^2 + 2p - 4)$
40. $x^2(2xy - 4y + 1)$ 41. $m^2n^2(6mn + 3m + 1)$

42. A: $3x$ is not a factor of $13x$, so $3x$ is not a factor of $15x^3 - 9x^2 + 13x$.
B: $3x$ is not a factor of $24y^2$, so $3x$ is not a factor of $-21x^2 + 24y^2$.
C: $3x$ is not a factor of x^3, so $3x$ is not a factor of $9x - x^3$.
D: $3x$ is a factor of $6x^2$ and $15x$, so $3x$ is a factor of $6x^2 + 15x$.
The correct choice is **D**.

43. $5x = 5 \cdot x$
$x^2 = x \cdot x$
Common factor: x

44. $3x = 3 \cdot x$
$ax - 3$ is factored
Relatively prime

45. $x + x^2 = x(x + 1)$
$3x^3 = 3 \cdot x \cdot x \cdot x$
Common factor: x

46. $y - 6$ is factored
y is factored
Relatively prime

47. $7a = 7 \cdot a$
a is factored
Common factor: a

48. $2p^2 + 2 = 2(p^2 + 1)$
$2p = 2 \cdot p$
Relatively prime (constant is only common factor)

49. $t^2 - 4t = t(t - 4)$
$t^2 - 4 = (t + 2)(t - 2)$
Relatively prime

50. $3a^2 - a = a(3a - 1)$
$a^3 - 2a = a(a^2 - 2)$
Common factor: a

51. $2x + 4 = 2(x + 2)$
$2x^2 - 4 = 2(x^2 - 2)$
Relatively prime (constant is only common factor)

52. $m^2 + 4mn = m(m + 4n)$
$3mn + 2m = m(3n + 2)$
Common factor: m

53. $4x^5 + 8x^3 - 6x = x(4x^4 + 8x^2 - 6)$
$8x^3 + 12x^2 + 24x - 16$ is factored
Relatively prime

54. $6x^2y + 4xy + 2x = 2x(3xy + 2y + 1)$
$2x^3 + 8x^2y + 14x = 2x(x^2 + 4xy + 7)$
Common factors: 2 and x

55. $a^3 + a^2b + ab^2 + b^3$ is factored.
$a^2 - ab^2 = a(a - b^2)$
Relatively prime

56. Side of square $= 2r$
Area of square $= (\text{side})^2 = (2r)^2 = 4r^2$
Area of circle $= \pi r^2$
Shaded area $=$ (area of square) $-$ (area of circle)
$= 4r^2 - \pi r^2$
$= r^2(4 - \pi)$

57. $3t$; $6t^3 + 30t^2 = 3t[2t^2 + 10t]$;
$9t^3 + 27t^2 + 9t = 3t[3t^2 + 9t + 3]$

58. No common factor

59. $24t^2$; $192t^6 - 480t^4 = 24t^2[8t^4 - 20t^2]$;
$144t^8 + 72t^2 = 24t^2[6t^6 + 3]$

60. No common factor 61. $x^7 \cdot x^5 \cdot x = x^{7+5+1} = x^{13}$

62. $(3m^2n^3)^2 = 3^2m^{2\cdot2}n^{3\cdot2} = 9m^4n^6$

63. $(9t^2)(-2t^5) = -18t^{2+5} = -18t^7$

64. 4.37×10^{-3} 65. 3.075×10^2 66. 5.613×10^3

67. $12 - 9m^3 + 6m^2 + 4m^3 - 8m^2 = -5m^3 - 2m^2 + 12$

68. $5m^2 + 116 - 4m^2 + 3 = m^2 + 119$

CONNECTIONS: GEOMETRY p. 265

1. Let n = length of each missing side.
$$2(x + y) + 2n = 8x + 4y$$
$$2x + 2y + 2n = 8x + 4y$$
$$2x - 2x + 2y - 2y + 2n = 8x - 2x + 4y - 2y$$
$$2n = 6x + 2y$$
$$\frac{1}{2}(2n) = \frac{1}{2}(6x + 2y)$$
$$n = 3x + y$$
The lengths are each $3x + y$.

2. Let n = top missing side
$2n + 1$ = bottom missing side
$$n + (2n + 1) + 2(2x + 1) = 16x + 3$$
$$3n + 1 + 4x + 2 = 16x + 3$$
$$3n + 4x + 3 = 16x + 3$$
$$3n + 4x - 4x + 3 - 3 = 16x - 4x + 3 - 3$$
$$3n = 12x$$
$$\frac{1}{3}(3n) = \frac{1}{3}(12x)$$
$$n = 4x$$
The sides are $4x$ and $8x + 1$.

LESSON 6-2 TRY THIS pp. 266–268

a. Yes b. No c. No d. No e. Yes f. Yes
g. $x^2 - 9 = (x + 3)(x - 3)$ h. $y^2 - 64 = (y + 8)(y - 8)$
i. $4y^2 - 49 = (2y)^2 - 7^2 = (2y + 7)(2y - 7)$
j. $16x^2 - 25y^2 = (4x)^2 - (5y)^2 = (4x - 5y)(4x + 5y)$
k. $a^8b^4 - 4 = (a^4b^2)^2 - 2^2 = (a^4b^2 + 2)(a^4b^2 - 2)$
l. $25a^{10} - 36b^8 = (5a^5)^2 - (6b^4)^2 = (5a^5 + 6b^4)(5a^5 - 6b^4)$

m. $32y^2 - 8y^6 = 8y^2(4 - y^4)$
$= 8y^2(2 + y^2)(2 - y^2)$

n. $5 - 20y^6 = 5(1 - 4y^6)$
$= 5(1 + 2y^3)(1 - 2y^3)$

o. $a^3b - 4ab^3 = ab(a^2 - 4b^2)$
$= ab(a + 2b)(a - 2b)$

p. $64x^4y^4 - 25x^6y^8 = x^4y^4(64 - 25x^2y^4)$
$= x^4y^4(8 + 5xy^2)(8 - 5xy^2)$

q. $81x^4 - 1 = (9x^2 + 1)(9x^2 - 1)$
$= (9x^2 + 1)(3x + 1)(3x - 1)$

r. $16m^4 - n^8 = (4m^2 + n^4)(4m^2 - n^4)$
$= (4m^2 + n^4)(2m + n^2)(2m - n^2)$

LESSON 6-2 EXERCISES pp. 268–269

1. Yes **2.** Yes **3.** No **4.** No **5.** No **6.** No

7. Yes **8.** Yes **9.** $(x + 2)(x - 2)$

10. $(x + 6)(x - 6)$ **11.** $(x + 3y)(x - 3y)$

12. $(m + y)(m - y)$ **13.** $(4a + 3)(4a - 3)$

14. $(5x + 2)(5x - 2)$ **15.** $(2x + 5)(2x - 5)$

16. $(3a + 4)(3a - 4)$ **17.** $(5m + 7)(5m - 7)$

18. $25(2x + 1)(2x - 1)$ **19.** $(x^2 + 3)(x^2 - 3)$

20. $(y^3 + 2)(y^3 - 2)$ **21.** $(m^8 + 5)(m^8 - 5)$

22. $(a^6 + 4)(a^3 + 2)(a^3 - 2)$ **23.** $4(x^2 + 2)(x^2 - 2)$

24. $(4x^3 + 5)(4x^3 - 5)$ **25.** $(8y^2 + 9)(8y^2 - 9)$

26. $(2x^5 + 5)(2x^5 - 5)$ **27.** $(6x^6 + 7)(6x^6 - 7)$

28. $(4y + 5)(4y - 5)$

29. $36x - 49x^3 = x(36 - 49x^2) = x(6 + 7x)(6 - 7x)$

30. $121a^8 - 100 = (11a^4 + 10)(11a^4 - 10)$

31. $81y^6 - 25y^2 = y^2(81y^4 - 25) = y^2(9y^2 - 5)(9y^2 + 5)$

32. $100y^6 - 49y^4 = y^4(100y^2 - 49) = y^4(10y + 7)(10y - 7)$

33. $8x^2 - 98y^2 = 2(4x^2 - 49y^2) = 2(2x + 7y)(2x - 7y)$

34. $-54y^4 + 24x^2 = 6(4x^2 - 9y^4) = 6(2x + 3y^2)(2x - 3y^2)$

35. $-50y^2 + 32x^2 = 2(16x^2 - 50y^2) = 2(4x + 5y)(4x - 5y)$

36. $27y^2 - 48y^4 = 3y^2(9 - 16y^2) = 3y^2(3 + 4y)(3 - 4y)$

37. $75m^6n^2 - 147 = 3(25m^6n^2 - 49) = 3(5m^3n - 7)(5m^3n + 7)$

38. $50a^{10}b^4 - 72 = 2(25a^{10}b^4 - 36) = 2(5a^5b^2 - 6)(5a^5b^2 + 6)$

39. $x^4 - 1 = (x^2 + 1)(x^2 - 1) = (x^2 + 1)(x + 1)(x - 1)$

40. $x^4 - 16 = (x^2 + 4)(x^2 - 4) = (x^2 + 4)(x + 2)(x - 2)$

41. $4x^4 - 64 = 4(x^4 - 16) = 4(x^2 + 4)(x^2 - 4)$
$= 4(x^2 + 4)(x + 2)(x - 2)$

42. $5x^4 - 80 = 5(x^4 - 16) = 5(x^2 + 4)(x^2 - 4)$
$= 5(x^2 + 4)(x + 2)(x - 2)$

43. $16 - y^4 = (4 + y^2)(4 - y^2) = (4 + y^2)(2 + y)(2 - y)$

44. $25 - x^4 = (5 + x^2)(5 - x^2)$

45. $625 - m^4 = (25 + m^2)(25 - m^2)$
$= (25 + m^2)(5 + m)(5 - m)$

46. $4 - 9y^2 = (2 + 3y)(2 - 3y)$

47. $16x - 81x^3 = x(16 - 81x^2) = x(4 + 9x)(4 - 9x)$

48. $1 - y^8 = (1 + y^4)(1 - y^4) = (1 + y^4)(1 + y^2)(1 - y^2)$
$= (1 + y^4)(1 + y^2)(1 + y)(1 - y)$

49. $b^8 - a^4 = (b^4 + a^2)(b^4 - a^2)$
$= (b^4 + a^2)(b^2 + a)(b^2 - a)$

50. $16x^2 - 25x^4 = x^2(16 - 25x^2)$
$= x^2(4 + 5x)(4 - 5x)$

51. $x^{16} - 9x^2 = x^2(x^{14} - 9) = x^2(x^7 + 3)(x^7 - 3)$

52. $-16 + x^6 = (x^3 + 4)(x^3 - 4)$

53. $-81 + 49a^4 = (7a^2 + 9)(7a^2 - 9)$

54. $-64 + c^{14} = (c^7 + 8)(c^7 - 8)$

55. $x^{12} - 16 = (x^6 + 4)(x^6 - 4)$
$= (x^6 + 4)(x^3 + 2)(x^3 - 2)$

56. $x^8 - 1 = (x^4 + 1)(x^4 - 1)$
$= (x^4 + 1)(x^2 + 1)(x^2 - 1)$
$= (x^4 + 1)(x^2 + 1)(x + 1)(x - 1)$

57. $a^{12} - 4a^2 = a^2(a^{10} - 4) = a^2(a^5 + 2)(a^5 - 2)$

58. $16p^8 - t^4 = (4p^4 + t^2)(4p^4 - t^2)$
$= (4p^4 + t^2)(2p^2 + t)(2p^2 - t)$

59. $-9 + 25a^4 = (5a^2 + 3)(5a^2 - 3)$

60. $x^8 - 81 = (x^4 + 9)(x^4 - 9)$
$= (x^4 + 9)(x^2 + 3)(x^2 - 3)$

61. $-49 + 9c^8 = (3c^4 + 7)(3c^4 - 7)$

62. $4x^4 - 4x^2 = 4x^2(x^2 - 1)$
$= 4x^2(x + 1)(x - 1)$

63. $3x^5 - 12x^3 = 3x^3(x^2 - 4)$
$= 3x^3(x + 2)(x - 2)$

64. $3x^2 - \frac{1}{3} = 3\left(x^2 - \frac{1}{9}\right)$
$= 3\left(x + \frac{1}{3}\right)\left(x - \frac{1}{3}\right)$

65. $18x^3 - \frac{8}{25}x = 2x\left(9x^2 - \frac{4}{25}\right)$
$= 2x\left(3x + \frac{2}{5}\right)\left(3x - \frac{2}{5}\right)$

66. $x^2 - 2.25 = (x + 1.5)(x - 1.5)$

67. $x^3 - \frac{x}{16} = x\left(x^2 - \frac{1}{16}\right)$
$= x\left(x + \frac{1}{4}\right)\left(x - \frac{1}{4}\right)$

68. $3.24x^2 - 0.81 = (1.8x + 0.9)(1.8x - 0.9)$

69. $0.64x^2 - 1.21 = (0.8x + 1.1)(0.8x - 1.1)$

70. $1.28x^2 - 2 = 2(0.64x^2 - 1)$
$= 2(0.8x + 1)(0.8x - 1)$

71. $(x + 3)^2 - 9 = (x + 3)^2 - 3^2$
$= (x + 3 - 3)(x + 3 + 3)$
$= x(x + 6)$

72. $(y - 5)^2 - 36 = (y - 5)^2 - 6^2$
$= (y - 5 + 6)(y - 5 - 6)$
$= (y + 1)(y - 11)$

73. $(3a + 4)^2 - 49 = (3a + 4)^2 - 7^2$
$= (3a + 4 - 7)(3a + 4 + 7)$
$= (3a - 3)(3a + 11)$
$= 3(a - 1)(3a + 11)$

74. $(2y - 7)^2 - 1 = (2y - 7)^2 - 1^2$
$= (2y - 7 - 1)(2y - 7 + 1)$
$= (2y - 8)(2y - 6)$
$= 4(y - 4)(y - 3)$

75. $y^8 - 256 = (y^4 + 16)(y^4 - 16)$
$= (y^4 + 16)(y^2 + 4)(y^2 - 4)$
$= (y^4 + 16)(y^2 + 4)(y + 2)(y - 2)$

76. $x^{16} - 1 = (x^8 + 1)(x^8 - 1)$
$= (x^8 + 1)(x^4 + 1)(x^4 - 1)$
$= (x^8 + 1)(x^4 + 1)(x^2 + 1)(x^2 - 1)$
$= (x^8 + 1)(x^4 + 1)(x^2 + 1)(x + 1)(x - 1)$

77. No; any product of the form $(x + a)(x + c)$ has 3 terms: $x^2 + (a + c)x + ac$. For the product to have 2 terms, a and c must be opposites; but if a and c are opposites, then ac must be negative, and ac cannot equal b^2 for any value of b.

78. $x(x + 2)(x + 1) = x^3 + 3x^2 + 2x$
$(x - 2)(x + 2)(x - 1) = x^3 - x^2 - 4x + 4$
Answers may vary.

79. $(x^2 - 2)(x^2 + 2) = x^4 - 4$ Answers may vary.

80. $(x + 5)(x + 1)(x - 1) = (x + 5)(x^2 - 1)$
$= x^3 + 5x^2 - x - 5$
Answers may vary.

81. $(a + 2b)(a + b)(a - b) = (a + 2b)(a^2 - b^2)$
$= a^3 - ab^2 + 2a^2b - 2b^3$
Answers may vary.

82. $(x^2 - 5)(x + 1)(x - 1) = (x^2 - 5)(x^2 - 1)$
$= x^4 - 6x^2 + 5$
Answers may vary.

83. $(x + 7)(x + 7) = x^2 + 2 \cdot 7x + 7^2 = x^2 + 14x + 49$

84. $(2a - 3)(2a - 3) = (2a)^2 - 2 \cdot 2a \cdot 3 + 3^2 = 4a^2 - 12a + 9$

85. 1, 0; 1 86. 3, 2, 1, 0; 3 87. 5, 2, 0; 5 88. 0.2

89. 0.08 90. 4.3 91. 0.065

92. $26 - 3c = 10c$
$26 = 13c$
$\frac{26}{13} = c$
$2 = c$

93. $4t - 12 = t + 3$
$4t - t - 12 = t - t + 3$
$3t - 12 = 3$
$3t = 3 + 12$
$3t = 15$
$t = \frac{15}{3}$
$t = 5$

94. Let n = amount needed.
$68 + n = 200$
$n = 200 - 68$
$n = 132$
Ana needs $132.

95. Let b = length of base.
$b + (b + 3) + (b - 5) = 52$
$3b - 2 = 52$
$3b = 54$
$b = \frac{54}{3}$
$b = 18$
The length of the base is 18 cm.

LESSON 6-3 TRY THIS pp. 270–271

a. Yes b. Yes c. No d. Yes e. No f. Yes
g. $x^2 + 2x + 1 = (x + 1)^2$ h. $x^2 - 2x + 1 = (x - 1)^2$
i. $25x^2 - 70x + 49 = (5x - 7)^2$
j. $48m^2 + 120mn + 75n^2 = 3(16m^2 + 40mn + 25n^2)$
$= 3(4m + 5n)^2$

LESSON 6-3 EXERCISES pp. 271–272

1. Yes 2. Yes 3. No 4. No 5. Yes 6. No

7. No 8. Yes 9. No 10. Yes 11. $(x - 7)^2$

12. $(x - 8)^2$ 13. $(x + 8)^2$ 14. $(x + 7)^2$

15. $(x - 1)^2$ 16. $(x + 1)^2$ 17. $(x + 2y)^2$

18. $(x - 2y)^2$ 19. $(y - 3x)^2$ 20. $(y + 3x)^2$

21. $2x^2 - 4x + 2 = 2(x^2 - 2x + 1) = 2(x - 1)^2$

22. $2x^2 - 40x + 200 = 2(x^2 - 20x + 100) = 2(x - 10)^2$

23. $x^3 - 18x^2 + 81x = x(x^2 - 18x + 81) = x(x - 9)^2$

24. $x^3 + 24x^2 + 144x = x(x^2 + 24x + 144) = x(x + 12)^2$

25. $20x^2 + 100x + 125 = 5(4x^2 + 20x + 25) = 5(2x + 5)^2$

26. $12x^2 + 36xy + 27y^2 = 3(4x^2 + 12xy + 9y^2)$
$= 3(2x + 3y)^2$

27. $49y^2 - 42xy + 9x^2 = (7y - 3x)^2$

28. $64y^2 - 112xy + 49x^2 = (8y - 7x)^2$

29. $5y^4 + 10y^2 + 5 = 5(y^4 + 2y^2 + 1)$
$= 5(y^2 + 1)^2$

30. $a^4 + 14a^2 + 49 = (a^2 + 7)^2$

31. $y^6 + 26y^3 + 169 = (y^3 + 13)^2$

32. $y^6 - 16y^3 + 64 = (y^3 - 8)^2$

33. $16x^{10} - 8x^5 + 1 = (4x^5 - 1)^2$

34. $9x^{10} + 12x^5 + 4 = (3x^5 + 2)^2$

35. $4x^4 + 4x^2 + 1 = (2x^2 + 1)^2$

36. $1 - 2a^4 + a^8 = (1 + a^4)^2$

37. $81x^6 + 72x^3y + 16y^2 = (9x^3 + 4y)^2$

38. $9a^8 - 30a^4b + 25b^2 = (3a^4 - 5b)^2$

39. Not possible 40. $27x^3 - 13x = x(27x^2 - 13)$

41. $x^2 + 22x + 121 = (x + 11)^2$

42. Not possible 43. Not possible

44. $18x^3 + 12x^2 + 2x = 2x(9x^2 + 6x + 1) = 2x(3x + 1)^2$

45. $63x - 28 = 7(9x - 4)$

46. $162x^2 - 82x = 2x(81x - 41)$

47. $x^4y^4 - 9y^4 = y^4(x^4 - 9)$
$= y^4(x^2 + 3)(x^2 - 3)$

48. $81x^2 - 64x = x(81x - 64)$

49. $x^8 - 2^8 = (x^4 + 16)(x^4 - 16)$
$= (x^4 + 16)(x^2 + 4)(x^2 - 4)$
$= (x^4 + 16)(x^2 + 4)(x + 2)(x - 2)$

50. $3^4 - x^4 = (9 + x^2)(9 - x^2)$
$= (9 + x^2)(3 + x)(3 - x)$

51. $(y + 3)^2 + 2(y + 3) + 1$
$= (y^2 + 6y + 9) + (2y + 6) + 1$
$= y^2 + 8y + 16 = (y + 4)^2$

52. $(a + 4)^2 - 2(a + 4) + 1$
$= (a^2 + 8a + 16) - (2a + 8) + 1$
$= a^2 + 6a + 9 = (a + 3)^2$

53. $4(a + 5)^2 + 20(a + 5) + 25$
$= (4a^2 + 40a + 100) + (20a + 100) + 25$
$= 4a^2 + 60a + 225 = (2a + 15)^2$

54. $49(x + 1)^2 - 42(x + 1) + 9$
$= (49x^2 + 98x + 49) - (42x + 42) + 9$
$= 49x^2 + 56x + 16 = (7x + 4)^2$

55. $(x + 7)^2 - 4x - 24 = x^2 + 14x + 49 - 4x - 24$
$= x^2 + 10x + 25$
$= (x + 5)^2$

56. $(a + 4)^2 - 6a - 15 = a^2 + 8a + 16 - 6a - 15$
$= a^2 + 2a + 1$
$= (a + 1)^2$

57. $x^2 + a^2x + a^2 = x^2 + 2ax + a^2$
$a^2x = 2ax$
$a = 2$

58. $9x^8 + 48x^9 + 64 = (3x^9 + 8)^2$

59. $x^{2n} + 10x^n + 25 = (x^n + 5)^2$

60. $a^2 + 2a + 1 - 9 = (a + 1)^2 - 3^2$
$= (a + 4)(a - 2)$

61. $y^2 + 6y + 9 - x^2 - 8x - 16 = (y + 3)^2 - (x + 4)^2$
$= (y + x + 7)(y - x - 1)$

62. $2 \cdot a \cdot 1 = 6$
$a = 3$
$c = a^2 = 9$

63. $2 \cdot a \cdot 3 = -24$
$a = \frac{-24}{6} = -4$
$c = a^2 = 16$

64. $(x + 1)^2 - x^2 = x^2 + 2x + 1 - x^2$
$= 2x + 1 = x + (x + 1)$

65. $(9 - x^2)(1 + 2x) = -2x^3 - x^2 + 18x + 9$

66. $(y^3 + y^2)(y^3 - 4) = y^6 + y^5 - 4y^3 - 4y^2$

67. $6x^2 - 9x = 3x(2x - 3)$ **68.** $24a^2 - 12a = 12a(2a - 1)$

69. $9y^3 + 3y = 3y(3y^2 + 1)$ **70.** 0.001667 **71.** 359,400

LESSON 6-4 TRY THIS pp. 274–276

a. $(x + 4)(x + 3)$ **b.** $(x + 9)(x + 4)$
c. $(x - 5)(x - 3)$ **d.** $(x - 4)(x - 5)$
e. $(x - 3)(x - 4)$ **f.** $(m + 3n)(m + 5n)$
g. $(a + 3b)(a + 2b)$ **h.** $(p + 4q)(p + 2q)$
i. $(x + 6)(x - 2)$ **j.** $(x - 6)(x + 2)$
k. $(a + 7b)(a - 2b)$ **l.** $(x - 6y)(x + 5y)$

LESSON 6-4 EXERCISES pp. 276–277

1. $(x + 5)(x + 3)$ **2.** $(x + 3)(x + 2)$

3. $(x + 4)(x + 3)$ **4.** $(x + 8)(x + 1)$

5. $(x - 3)^2$ **6.** $(y + 7)(y + 4)$

7. $(x + 7)(x + 2)$ **8.** $(a + 6)(a + 5)$

9. $(b + 4)(b + 1)$ **10.** $(x - 7)(x - 4)$

11. $(a - 8)(a - 6)$ **12.** $(z - 1)(z - 7)$

13. $(m + 7)(m + 3)$ **14.** $(a - 9)(a - 5)$

15. $(z - 4)(z - 6)$ **16.** $(t + 6p)^2$

17. $(a - 5b)(a - 4b)$ **18.** $(x - 4y)(x - y)$

19. $(c - 5d)(c - 2d)$ **20.** $(x - 5y)(x - 3y)$

21. $(y - 10z)(y - z)$ **22.** $(x - 5)(x + 3)$

23. $(x + 7)(x - 6)$ **24.** $(x + 5)(x - 3)$

25. $(x - 9)(x + 2)$ **26.** $(y - 7)(y + 4)$

27. $(x - 8)(x + 2)$ **28.** $(x - 7)(x + 6)$

29. $(y - 9)(y + 5)$ **30.** $(x - 12)(x + 5)$

31. $(x - 11y)(x + 9y)$ **32.** $(x + 12y)(x - 6y)$

33. $(c + 8d)(c - 7d)$ **34.** $(b + 8c)(b - 3c)$

35. $(a + 7b)(a - 5b)$ **36.** $(y + x)(y - 2x)$

37. $x^2 + 20x + 100 = (x + 10)^2$

38. $x^2 + 20x + 99 = (x + 11)(x + 9)$

39. $x^2 - 21x - 100 = (x - 25)(x + 4)$

40. $x^2 - 20x + 96 = (x - 12)(x - 8)$

41. $x^2 - 21x - 72 = (x - 24)(x + 3)$

42. $4x^2 + 40x + 100 = 4(x^2 + 10x + 25) = 4(x + 5)^2$

43. $x^2 - 25x + 144 = (x - 16)(x - 9)$

44. $y^2 - 21y + 108 = (y - 12)(y - 9)$

45. $a^2 + a - 132 = (a + 12)(a - 11)$

46. $a^2 + 9a - 90 = (a + 15)(a - 6)$

47. $120y^2 - 23xy + x^2 = (15y - x)(8y - x)$

48. $96e^2 + 22de + d^2 = (16e + d)(6e + d)$

49. $108y^2 - 3xy - x^2 = (12y + x)(9y - x)$

50. $112z^2 + 9yz - y^2 = (7z + y)(16z - y)$

51. $D = rt$
$n^2 + 5n - 24 = (n + 8)t$
Let the time, t, be the binomial $(x + y)$.
$n^2 + 5n - 24 = (n + 8)(x + y)$
The first term, n^2, must equal nx, so $x = n$.
The last term, -24, must equal $8y$, so $y = -3$.
The time is $(x + y) = (n - 3)$ hours.
Check: $(n + 8)(n - 3) = n^2 + 8n - 3n - 24$
$= n^2 + 5n - 24$

52. a. The signs of a and b must be opposite.
b. Since the middle term is negative, the number with the larger absolute value must be negative. Therefore, a must be a negative integer.

53. a. The signs of a and b must be opposite.
b. Since the middle term is positive, the number with the larger absolute value must be positive. Therefore, b is a negative integer.

54. Factors of 50: (1, 50), (2, 25), (5, 10), (−1, −50), (−2, −25), (−5, −10). Hence, m can be $50 + 1 = 51$, $2 + 25 = 27$, $5 + 10 = 15$, and −51, −27, −15.

55. −50 has factors (1, −50), (2, −25), (5, −10), (−1, 50), (−2, 25), (−5, 10); and hence, b can be $1 - 50 = -49$, $2 - 25 = -23$, $5 - 10 = -5$, as well as 5, 23, and 49.

56. $x^3 - x^2 - 6x = x(x^2 - x - 6) = x(x - 3)(x + 2)$

57. $-x^3 + 22x^2 + 23x = -x(x^2 - 22x - 23)$
$= -x(x - 23)(x + 1)$

58. $(12x)(x^2)$; $(6x^2)(2x)$; $(4x)(3x^2)$ Answers may vary.

59. $8y(y^2)$; $(4y^2)(2y)$; $(2y^2)(4y)$ Answers may vary.

60. $(3m + 14) - (m + 9) = 3m + 14 - m - 9 = 2m + 5$

61. $\frac{a^6b^3}{a^2b^2} = a^{6-2}b^{3-2} = a^4b$ **62.** $\frac{6m^6}{3m^6} = \frac{6}{3} \cdot m^{6-6} = 2$

63. $(4y^2 - 3) + (y^2 + 11) = 4y^2 - 3 + y^2 + 11$
$= 5y^2 + 8$

64. $\frac{5t^3}{11t} = \frac{5}{11}t^{3-1} = \frac{5t^2}{11}$ **65.** $\frac{4c^3}{4c^2} = \frac{4}{4} \cdot c^{3-2} = c$

66. $|x| + 3 = 7$
$|x| = 7 - 3$
$|x| = 4$
$x = 4$ or -4

67. $3|c| - 2 = 4$
$3|c| = 6$
$|c| = 2$
$c = 2$ or -2

68. $4 - |m| = -2$
$-|m| = -2 - 4$
$-|m| = -6$
$|m| = 6$
$m = 6$ or -6

LESSON 6-5 TRY THIS pp. 278–279

a. $6x^2 + 7x + 2 = (3x + 2)(2x + 1)$
b. $8x^2 + 10x - 3 = (4x - 1)(2x + 3)$
c. $6x^2 - 41x - 7 = (6x + 1)(x - 7)$
d. $3x^2 - 2x + 36 = 3(x - 3)(x - 4)$
e. $8x^2 - 2 = 2(2x + 1)(2x - 1)$
f. $9a^2 - 15a - 6 = 3(3a + 1)(a - 2)$
g. $2x^2 + 4x - 6 = 2(x^2 + 2x - 3)$
$= 2(x + 3)(x - 1)$
h. $4a^2 + 2a - 6 = 2(2a^2 + a - 3)$
$= 2(2a + 3)(a - 1)$
i. $6m^2 + 15mn - 9n^2 = 3(2m^2 + 5mn - 3n^2)$
$= 3(2m - n)(m + 3n)$

LESSON 6-5 EXERCISES pp. 279–280

1. $(2x + 1)(x - 4)$ **2.** $(3x - 4)(x + 1)$

3. $(5x - 9)(x + 2)$ **4.** $(3x + 5)(x - 3)$

5. $(2x + 7)(3x + 1)$ **6.** $(2x + 3)(3x + 2)$

7. $(3x + 1)(x + 1)$ **8.** $(7x + 1)(x + 2)$

9. $(2x + 5)(2x - 3)$ **10.** $(3a - 2)(3a + 4)$

11. $(2x + 1)(x - 1)$ **12.** $(3n - 5)(5n + 2)$

13. $(3x + 8)(3x - 2)$ **14.** $(2y + 1)(y + 2)$

15. $(3x + 1)(x - 2)$ **16.** $(6c - 5)(3c + 2)$

17. $(3x + 4)(4x + 5)$ **18.** $(3x + 5)(5x - 2)$

19. $(7x - 1)(2x + 3)$ **20.** $(7x + 4)(5x + 2)$

21. $(3p + 4)(3p + 2)$ **22.** $(2 - 3x)(3 - 2x)$

23. $(7 - 3b)^2$ **24.** $(3x - 2)(5x - 3)$

25. $(x + 2)(24x - 1)$ **26.** $(8a + 3)(2a + 9)$

27. $(7x + 4)(5x - 11)$ **28.** $(3a - 1)(3a + 5)$

29. $2(5 - x)(2 + x)$ **30.** $(5 + 2x)(3 - x)$

31. $4(3x - 2)(x + 3)$ **32.** $3(2c - 1)(c - 5)$

33. $6(5x - 9)(x + 1)$ **34.** $5(4x - 1)(x - 1)$

35. $2(3x + 5)(x - 1)$ **36.** $3(2y - 3)(3y + 1)$

37. $(3a - 1)(a - 1)$ **38.** $(2x + 3)(3x + 2)$

39. $4(3x + 2)(x - 3)$ **40.** $3(2x + 1)(x + 5)$

41. $(2x - 1)(x + 1)$ **42.** $(5s + 3)(3s + 2)$

43. $(3b - 8)(3b + 2)$ **44.** $7(2x + 1)(x + 2)$

45. $5(3x + 1)(x - 2)$ **46.** $(6b - 5)(5b + 4)$

47. $(6x + 5y)(3x - 2y)$ **48.** $(3a - 4b)(4a - 5b)$

49. $(5m + 2n)(3m - 5n)$ **50.** $(7p + q)(2p - 3q)$

51. $(5x - 2y)(7x - 4y)$ **52.** $(8a - b)(7a - b)$

53. $(3x^2 + 2)(3x^2 + 4)$ **54.** $(3 - 2y)(2 - 3y)$

55. $(3x - 7)^2$ **56.** $(5x^2 - 3)(3x^2 - 2)$

57. $6a^3 + 4a^2 - 10a = 2a(3a^2 + 2a - 5)$
$= 2a(3a + 5)(a - 1)$

58. $18x^3 - 21x^2 - 9x = 3x(6x^2 - 7x - 3)$
$= 3x(2x - 3)(3x + 1)$

59. Not factorable **60.** Not factorable

61. $x^5 + x^3 - 6x = x(x^4 + x^2 - 6) = x(x^2 + 3)(x^2 - 2)$

62. $x^5 - 6x^3 + 5x = x(x^4 - 6x^2 + 5) = x(x^2 - 5)(x^2 - 1)$
$= x(x^2 - 5)(x + 1)(x - 1)$

63. Let $(mx + n)$ = the binomial that, when squared, equals $ax^2 + 12x + c$.
$(mx + n)^2 = m^2x^2 + 2mnx + n^2 = ax^2 + 12x + c$
The coefficients of x must be equal.
$2mn = 12$
$mn = 6$
Possible whole number pairs for m and n:
1) $m = 1, n = 6 \rightarrow a = 1, c = 36$
2) $m = 6, n = 1 \rightarrow a = 36, c = 1$
3) $m = 2, n = 3 \rightarrow a = 4, c = 9$
4) $m = 3, n = 2 \rightarrow a = 9, c = 4$
Since $a \neq 1$ and $c > a$, only 3) holds.
Thus, $a = 4$ and $c = 9$.

64. Answers may vary, but students should recognize that Bobbi should have factored 4 out of the polynomial.
$(2y + 10)(2y + 8) = 2(y + 5)2(y + 4)$
$= 4(y + 5)(y + 4)$

65. $20x^{2n} + 16x^n + 3 = (10x^n + 3)(2x^n + 1)$

66. $-15x^{2m} + 26x^m - 8 = (-3x^m + 4)(5x^m - 2)$

67. $x^{6a} - x^{3a} - 6 = (x^{3a} - 3)(x^{3a} + 2)$

68. $x^{4n+1} + 2x^{2n+1} + x = x(x^{4n} + 2x^{2n} + 1)$
$= x(x^{2n} + 1)^2$

69. $3(a + 1)^{n+1}(a + 3)^2 - 5(a + 1)^n(a + 3)^3$
$= (a + 1)^n(a + 3)^2[3(a + 1) - 5(a + 3)]$
$= (a + 1)^n(a + 3)^2[-2a - 12]$
$= (a + 1)^n(a + 3)^2(-2)(a + 6)$
$= -2(a + 1)^n(a + 3)^2(a + 6)$

70. $mn + 11$ **71.** $\frac{a + b}{2}$ **72.** $(x - y)^2$ **73.** $\frac{r}{s + t}$

74. $3 - 4y < 7$
$-4y < 4$
$y > -1$

75. $6t > 9 + 9t$
$-3t > 9$
$t < -3$

76. $8 - 3y \leq 2$
$-3y \leq -6$
$y \geq 2$

LESSON 6-6 TRY THIS p. 281

a. $8x^3 + 2x^2 + 12x + 3 = 2x^2(4x + 1) + 3(4x + 1)$
$= (2x^2 + 3)(4x + 1)$

b. $4x^3 - 6x^2 - 6x + 9 = 2x^2(2x - 3) - 3(2x - 3)$
$= (2x^2 - 3)(2x - 3)$

c. $x^3 + x^2 - x - 1 = x^2(x + 1) - 1(x + 1)$
$= (x^2 - 1)(x + 1)$
$= (x + 1)(x - 1)(x + 1)$

d. $3a - 6b + 5a^2 - 10ab = 3(a - 2b) + 5a(a - 2b)$
$= (3 + 5a)(a - 2b)$

LESSON 6-6 EXERCISES p. 282

1. $x^3 + 3x^2 + 2x + 6 = x^2(x + 3) + 2(x + 3)$
$= (x + 3)(x^2 + 2)$

2. $6z^3 + 3z^2 + 2z + 1 = 3z^2(2z + 1) + 1(2z + 1)$
$= (2z + 1)(3z^2 + 1)$

3. $2y^3 + 6y^2 + y + 3 = 2y^2(y + 3) + 1(y + 3)$
$= (y + 3)(2y^2 + 1)$

4. $3x^3 + 2x^2 + 3x + 2 = x^2(3x + 2) + 1(3x + 2)$
$= (3x + 2)(x^2 + 1)$

5. $8a^3 - 12a^2 + 6a - 9 = 4a^2(2a - 3) + 3(2a - 3)$
$= (2a - 3)(4a^2 + 3)$

6. $10p^3 - 25p^2 + 4p - 10 = 5p^2(2p - 5) + 2(2p - 5)$
$= (2p - 5)(5p^2 + 2)$

7. $12x^3 - 16x^2 + 3x - 4 = 4x^2(3x - 4) + 1(3x - 4)$
$= (3x - 4)(4x^2 + 1)$

8. $18c^3 - 21c^2 + 30c - 35 = 3c^2(6c - 7) + 5(6c - 7)$
$= (6c - 7)(3c^2 + 5)$

9. $b^3 + 8b^2 - 3b - 24 = b^2(b + 8) - 3(b + 8)$
$= (b + 8)(b^2 - 3)$

10. $2x^3 + 12x^2 - 5x - 30 = 2x^2(x + 6) - 5(x + 6)$
$= (x + 6)(2x^2 - 5)$

11. Not factorable

12. $24x^3 + 27x^2 - 8x - 9 = 3x^2(8x + 9) - 1(8x + 9)$
$= (8x + 9)(3x^2 - 1)$

13. $2x^3 - 8x^2 - 9x + 36 = 2x^2(x - 4) - 9(x - 4)$
$= (x - 4)(2x^2 - 9)$

14. $20g^3 - 4g^2 - 25g + 5 = 4g^2(5g - 1) - 5(5g - 1)$
$= (5g - 1)(4g^2 - 5)$

15. $ax - bx + ay - by = x(a - b) + y(a - b)$
$= (a - b)(x + y)$

16. $bx + 2b + cx + 2c = b(x + 2) + c(x + 2)$
$= (x + 2)(b + c)$

17. $n^2 + 2n + np + 2p = n(n + 2) + p(n + 2)$
$= (n + 2)(n + p)$

18. $2x^2 - 4x + xz - 2z = 2x(x - 2) + z(x - 2)$
$= (x - 2)(2x + z)$

19. $a^2 - 3a + ay - 3y = a(a - 3) + y(a - 3)$
$= (a - 3)(a + y)$

20. $6y^2 - 3y + 2py - p = 3y(2y - 1) + p(2y - 1)$
$= (2y - 1)(3y + p)$

21. $4x^5 + 6x^3 + 6x^2 + 9 = 2x^3(2x^2 + 3) + 3(2x^2 + 3)$
$= (2x^3 + 3)(2x^2 + 3)$

22. $4y^5 + 6y^4 + 6y^3 + 9y^2 = y^2(4y^3 + 6y^2 + 6y + 9)$
$= y^2[2y^2(2y + 3) + 3(2y + 3)]$
$= y^2(2y^2 + 3)(2y + 3)$

23. $c^6 - c^4 - c^2 + 1 = c^4(c^2 - 1) - 1(c^2 - 1)$
$= (c^4 - 1)(c^2 - 1)$
$= (c^2 + 1)(c^2 - 1)(c + 1)(c - 1)$
$= (c^2 + 1)(c + 1)(c - 1)(c + 1)(c - 1)$

24. $x^{13} + x^7 + 2x^6 + 2 = x^7(x^6 + 1) + 2(x^6 + 1)$
$= (x^7 + 2)(x^6 + 1)$

25. $(x - y)^2 - z^2 = (x - y + z)(x - y - z)$

26. $4 - (2a + 3b)^2 = (2 + 2a + 3b)(2 - [2a + 3b])$
$= (2 + 2a + 3b)(2 - 2a - 3b)$

27. $a^2 + 2ab + b^2 - 1 = (a + b)^2 - 1$
$= (a + b + 1)(a + b - 1)$

28. $c^2 - 6cd + 9d^2 - 4 = (c - 3d)^2 - 4$
$= (c - 3d + 2)(c - 3d - 2)$

29. $D = abc$

30. $(acx^{m+n} + adx^n) + (bcx^m + bd) = ax^n(cx^m + d) + b(cx^m + d)$
$= (ax^n + b)(cx^m + d)$

31. $28x^3 + 20x^2 + 7x + 5 = (28x^3 + 20x^2) + (7x + 5)$
$= 4x^2(7x + 5) + 1(7x + 5)$
$= (7x + 5)(4x^2 + 1)$

32. $x^2(x + 1)^2 - (x^2 + 1)^2 = x^2(x^2 + 2x + 1) - (x^4 + 2x^2 + 1)$
$= x^4 + 2x^3 + x^2 - x^4 - 2x^2 - 1$
$= 2x^3 - 2x^2 + x^2 - 1$
$= 2x^2(x - 1) + (x + 1)(x - 1)$
$= (x - 1)(2x^2 + x + 1)$

33. $m^2 + 2mn + n^2$ 34. $m^2 - 2mn + n^2$

35. $m^2 - n^2$ 36. $(x + 4)(x - 4)$

37. $(y + 3)(y + 3)$ or $(y + 3)^2$

38. $3a^2 - 6a + 3 = 3(a^2 - 2a + 1) = 3(a - 1)^2$

39. $(c - 10)(c + 9)$ 40. $(n - 6)(n - 9)$

41. $20 - 4x - 5y + xy = 4(5 - x) - y(5 - x)$
$= (4 - y)(5 - x)$

42. $(x + 1)(x + 2)$ 43. $(3a^2 + b)(3a^2 - b)$ 44. $(5 - 4a)^2$

LESSON 6-7 TRY THIS p. 283

a. $3m^4 - 3 = 3(m^4 - 1) = 3(m^2 + 1)(m^2 - 1)$
$= 3(m^2 + 1)(m + 1)(m - 1)$
b. $x^6 + 8x^3 + 16 = (x^3 + 4)^2$
c. $2x^4 + 8x^3 + 6x^2 = 2x^2(x^2 + 4x + 3)$
$= 2x^2(x + 1)(x + 3)$
d. $3x^3 + 12x^2 - 2x - 8 = 3x^2(x + 4) - 2(x + 4)$
$= (3x^2 - 2)(x + 4)$
e. $8x^3 - 200x = 8x(x^2 - 25)$
$= 8x(x + 5)(x - 5)$
f. $y^5 - 2y^4 - 35y^3 = y^3(y^2 - 2y - 35)$
$= y^3(y - 7)(y + 5)$

LESSON 6-7 EXERCISES p. 284

1. $2x^2 - 128 = 2(x^2 - 64)$
$= 2(x + 8)(x - 8)$

2. $3t^2 - 27 = 3(t^2 - 9)$
$= 3(t + 3)(t - 3)$

3. $a^2 + 25 - 10a = a^2 - 10a + 25$
$= (a - 5)^2$

4. $y^2 + 49 + 14y = y^2 + 14y + 49$
$= (y + 7)^2$

5. $2x^2 - 11x + 12 = (2x - 3)(x - 4)$

6. $8y^2 - 18y - 5 = (2y - 5)(4y + 1)$

7. $x^3 + 24x^2 + 144x = x(x^2 + 24x + 144)$
$= x(x + 12)^2$

8. $x^3 - 18x^2 + 81x = x(x^2 - 18x + 81)$
$= x(x - 9)^2$

9. $24x^2 - 54 = 6(4x^2 - 9)$
$= 6(2x - 3)(2x + 3)$

10. $8x^2 - 98 = 2(4x^2 - 49)$
$= 2(2x + 7)(2x - 7)$

11. $20x^3 - 4x^2 - 72x = 4x(5x^2 - x - 18)$
$= 4x(5x + 9)(x - 2)$

12. $9x^3 + 12x^2 - 45x = 3x(3x^2 + 4x - 15)$
$= 3x(3x - 5)(x + 3)$

13. Not factorable 14. Not factorable

15. $x^5 - 14x^4 + 49x^3 = x^3(x^2 - 14x + 49)$
$= x^3(x - 7)^2$

16. $2x^6 + 8x^5 + 8x^4 = 2x^4(x^2 + 4x + 4)$
$= 2x^4(x + 2)^2$

17. Not factorable 18. Not factorable

19. $4x^4 - 64 = 4(x^4 - 16)$
$= 4(x^2 + 4)(x^2 - 4)$
$= 4(x^2 + 4)(x + 2)(x - 2)$

20. $5x^5 - 80x = 5x(x^4 - 16)$
$= 5x(x^2 + 4)(x^2 - 4)$
$= 5x(x^2 + 4)(x + 2)(x - 2)$

21. $1 - y^8 = (1 + y^4)(1 - y^4)$
$= (1 + y^4)(1 + y^2)(1 - y^2)$
$= (1 + y^4)(1 + y^2)(1 + y)(1 - y)$

22. $t^8 - 1 = (t^4 + 1)(t^4 - 1)$
$= (t^4 + 1)(t^2 + 1)(t^2 - 1)$
$= (t^4 + 1)(t^2 + 1)(t + 1)(t - 1)$

23. $x^5 - 4x^4 + 3x^3 = x^3(x^2 - 4x + 3)$
$= x^3(x - 1)(x - 3)$

24. $x^6 - 2x^5 + 7x^4 = x^4(x^2 - 2x + 7)$

25. $x^3 + 3x^2 - 4x - 12 = x^2(x + 3) - 4(x + 3)$
$= (x + 3)(x^2 - 4)$
$= (x + 3)(x + 2)(x - 2)$

26. $x^3 - 5x^2 - 25x + 125 = x^2(x - 5) - 25(x - 5)$
$= (x - 5)(x^2 - 25)$
$= (x - 5)(x - 5)(x + 5)$
or $(x - 5)^2(x + 5)$

27. $x^4 + 7x^2 - 3x^3 - 21x = x(x^3 + 7x - 3x^2 - 21)$
$= x[x(x^2 + 7) - 3(x^2 + 7)]$
$= x(x^2 + 7)(x - 3)$

28. $m^4 + 8m^3 + 8m^2 + 64m = m(m^3 + 8m^2 + 8m + 64)$
$= m[m^2(m + 8) + 8(m + 8)]$
$= m(m + 8)(m^2 + 8)$

29. $a^4 - 2a^2 + 1 = (a^2 - 1)(a^2 - 1)$
$= (a + 1)(a - 1)(a + 1)(a - 1)$
$= (a + 1)^2(a - 1)^2$

30. Not factorable

31. $20 - 6x - 2x^2 = 2(10 - 3x - x^2) = 2(5 + x)(2 - x)$
or $-2(x^2 + 3x - 10) = -2(x + 5)(x - 2)$

32. $45 - 3x - 6x^2 = 3(15 - x - 2x^2) = 3(5 - 2x)(3 + x)$
or $-3(2x^2 + x - 15) = -3(2x - 5)(x + 3)$

33. $18 + y^3 - 9y - 2y^2 = (-9y + 18) + (y^3 - 2y^2)$
$= -9(y - 2) + y^2(y - 2)$
$= (y - 2)(y^2 - 9)$
$= (y - 2)(y + 3)(y - 3)$

34. $-(x^4 - 7x^2 - 18) = -(x^2 - 9)(x^2 + 2)$
$= -(x + 3)(x - 3)(x^2 + 2)$

35. $a^3 + 4a^2 + a + 4 = a^2(a + 4) + 1(a + 4)$
$= (a^2 + 1)(a + 4)$

36. $x^3 + x^2 - (4x + 4) = x^2(x + 1) - 4(x + 1)$
$= (x^2 - 4)(x + 1)$
$= (x + 2)(x - 2)(x + 1)$

37. $12a^3b^2 - 6a^2b + 4a^2b^2 - 2ab$
$= 2ab(6a^2b - 3a + 2ab - 1)$
$= 2ab[3a(2ab - 1) + 1(2ab - 1)]$
$= 2ab(3a + 1)(2ab - 1)$

38. $a^3 - 5a^2b - 14ab^2 = a(a^2 - 5ab - 14b^2)$
$= a(a - 7b)(a + 2b)$

39. $3x^3y - 2x^2y^2 + 3x^4y - 2x^3y^2 = x^2y(3x - 2y + 3x^2 - 2xy)$
$= x^2y(1[3x - 2y] + x[3x - 2y])$
$= x^2y(x + 1)(3x - 2y)$

40. $m^2n^2 + 7mn^3 + 10n^4 = n^2(m^2 + 7mn + 10n^2)$
$= n^2(m + 5n)(m + 2n)$

41. The factors of $x^2 + 7x + 10$ are $(x + 2)$ and $(x + 5)$. $(x + 5)$ cannot be a factor of $x^6 + 4x^4 - 31x^2 + 28$, because 28 is not divisible by 5. Thus the common binomial factor must be $(x + 2)$.

42. $64a^4 + 1 = 64a^4 + 16a^2 + 1 - 16a^2$
$= (8a^2 + 1)^2 - 16a^2$
$= (8a^2 + 4a + 1)(8a^2 - 4a + 1)$

43. $x^{2h} - 2^{2h} = x^8 - 2^8 = (x^4 + 2^4)(x^4 - 2^4)$
$= (x^4 + 2^4)(x^2 + 2^2)(x^2 - 2^2)$
$= (x^4 + 2^4)(x^2 + 2^2)(x + 2)(x - 2)$
$= (x^4 + 16)(x^2 + 4)(x + 2)(x - 2)$

44. $\frac{1}{m^2}$ **45.** $\frac{1}{x}$ **46.** $\frac{3}{c^2}$

47. $(8a^5 + a^3 - 1) - (2a^5 + 4a^3 - 1)$
$= 8a^5 + a^3 - 1 - 2a^5 - 4a^3 + 1$
$= 6a^5 - 3a^3$

48. $(-3a^2b + 7ab - 4a) - (-2a^2b - 4a + 3ab)$
$= -3a^2b + 7ab - 4a + 2a^2b + 4a - 3ab$
$= -a^2b + 4ab$

CONNECTIONS: DISCRETE MATH p. 285

1. $m^5 + 5m^4n + 10m^3n^2 + 10m^2n^3 + 5mn^4 + n^5$
2. $x^3 + 3x^2 + 3x + 1$
3. $a^4 + 4a^3(4) + 6a^2(4)^2 + 4a(4)^3 + 4^4$
$= a^4 + 16a^3 + 96a^2 + 256a + 256$
4. 1 6 15 20 15 6 1
5. $a^6 + 6a^5b + 15a^4b^2 + 20a^3b^3 + 15a^2b^4 + 6ab^5 + b^6$

LESSON 6-8 TRY THIS pp. 287–288

a. $x - 3 = 0$ or $x + 4 = 0$
$x = 3$ or $x = -4$
Check: 3 | -4
$(3 - 3)(3 + 4)$ | $(-4 - 3)(-4 + 4)$
$0(1)$ | $(-7)0$
0 | 0

b. $x - 7 = 0$ or $x - 3 = 0$
$x = 7$ or $x = 3$
Check: 7 | 3
$(7 - 7)(7 - 3)$ | $(3 - 7)(3 - 3)$
$0(4)$ | $-4(0)$
0 | 0

c. $y = 0$ or $3y - 17 = 0$
$3y = 17$
$y = \frac{17}{3}$
Check: 0 | $\frac{17}{3}$
$0(3(0) - 17)$ | $\frac{17}{3}\left(3\left(\frac{17}{3}\right) - 17\right)$
$0(0 - 17)$ | $\frac{17}{3}(17 - 17)$
$0(-17)$ | $\frac{17}{3}(0)$
0 | 0

d. $4t + 1 = 0$ or $3t - 2 = 0$
$4t = -1$ or $3t = 2$
$t = -\frac{1}{4}$ or $t = \frac{2}{3}$
Check: $-\frac{1}{4}$ | $\frac{2}{3}$
$\left(4\left(-\frac{1}{4}\right) + 1\right)\left(3\left(-\frac{1}{4}\right) - 2\right)$ | $\left(4\left(\frac{2}{3}\right) + 1\right)\left(3\left(\frac{2}{3}\right) - 2\right)$
$-1 + 1\left(-\frac{3}{4} - 2\right)$ | $\left(\frac{8}{3} + 1\right)(2 - 2)$
$0\left(-\frac{11}{4}\right)$ | $\left(\frac{11}{3}\right)0$
0 | 0

e. $x^2 - x - 6 = 0$
$(x - 3)(x + 2) = 0$
$x - 3 = 0$ or $x + 2 = 0$
$x = 3$ or $x = -2$

f. $m^2 - m = 56$
$m^2 - m - 56 = 0$
$(m - 8)(m + 7) = 0$
$m - 8 = 0$ or $m + 7 = 0$
$m = 8$ or $m = -7$

g. $x^2 - 3x = 28$
$x^2 - 3x - 28 = 0$
$(x - 7)(x + 4) = 0$
$x - 7 = 0$ or $x + 4 = 0$
$x = 7$ or $x = -4$

h. $x^2 + 6x + 9 = 0$
$(x + 3)^2 = 0$
$x + 3 = 0$
$x = -3$
The root is -3.

i. $x^2 + 4x = 0$
$x(x + 4) = 0$
$x = 0$ or $x + 4 = 0$
$x = 0$ or $x = -4$
The roots are 0 and -4.

j. $25x^2 - 16 = 0$
$(5x + 4)(5x - 4) = 0$
$5x + 4 = 0$ or $5x - 4 = 0$
$5x = -4$ or $5x = 4$
$x = \frac{-4}{5}$ or $x = \frac{4}{5}$
The roots are $\frac{-4}{5}$ and $\frac{4}{5}$.

LESSON 6-8 EXERCISES pp. 289–290

1. $x + 8 = 0$ or $x + 6 = 0$
$x = -8$ or $x = -6$

2. $c + 3 = 0$ or $c + 2 = 0$
$c = -3$ or $c = -2$

3. $a - 3 = 0$ or $a + 5 = 0$
$a = 3$ or $a = -5$

4. $x + 9 = 0$ or $x - 3 = 0$
$x = -9$ or $x = 3$

5. $x + 12 = 0$ or $x - 11 = 0$
$x = -12$ or $x = 11$

6. $x - 13 = 0$ or $x + 53 = 0$
$x = 13$ or $x = -53$

7. $x = 0$ or $x + 5 = 0$
$x = 0$ or $x = -5$

or less than or equal to 0. The conjecture is false for all numbers between 0 and 1. Check students' work for examples and counterexamples.

8. $y = 0$ or $y + 7 = 0$
$y = 0$ or $y = -7$

9. $y = 0$ or $y - 13 = 0$
$y = 0$ or $y = 13$

10. $v = 0$ or $v - 4 = 0$
$v = 0$ or $v = 4$

11. $y = 0$ or $y + 10 = 0$
$y = 0$ or $y = -10$

12. $x = 0$ or $x - 21 = 0$
$x = 0$ or $x = 21$

13. $7x - 28 = 0$ or $28x - 7 = 0$
$7x = 28$ or $28x = 7$
$x = 4$ or $x = \frac{7}{28}$ or $\frac{1}{4}$

14. $12x - 11 = 0$ or $8x - 5 = 0$
$12x = 11$ or $8x = 5$
$x = \frac{11}{12}$ or $x = \frac{5}{8}$

15. $2x = 0$ or $3x - 2 = 0$
$x = 0$ or $3x = 2$
$x = 0$ or $x = \frac{2}{3}$

16. $75x = 0$ or $8x - 9 = 0$
$x = 0$ or $8x = 9$
$x = 0$ or $x = \frac{9}{8}$

17. $\frac{1}{2}x = 0$ or $\frac{2}{3}x - 12 = 0$
$x = 0$ or $\frac{2}{3}x = 12$
$\frac{3}{2}\left(\frac{2}{3}x\right) = \frac{3}{2}(12)$
$x = 0$ or $x = 18$

18. $\frac{5}{7}d = 0$ or $\frac{3}{4}d - 6 = 0$
$d = 0$ or $\frac{3}{4}d = 6$
$\frac{4}{3}\left(\frac{3}{4}d\right) = \frac{4}{3}(6)$
$d = 0$ or $d = 8$

19. $\frac{1}{3} - 3x = 0$ or $\frac{1}{5} - 2x = 0$
$\frac{1}{3} = 3x$ or $\frac{1}{5} = 2x$
$\frac{1}{9} = x$ or $\frac{1}{10} = x$

20. $\frac{1}{5} + 2x = 0$ or $\frac{1}{9} - 3x = 0$
$\frac{1}{5} = -2x$ or $\frac{1}{9} = 3x$
$-\frac{1}{10} = x$ or $\frac{1}{27} = x$

21. $\frac{1}{3}y - \frac{2}{3} = 0$ or $\frac{1}{4}y - \frac{3}{2} = 0$
$\frac{1}{3}y = \frac{2}{3}$ or $\frac{1}{4}y = \frac{3}{2}$
$y = 2$ or $y = 6$

22. $\frac{7}{4}x - \frac{1}{12} = 0$ or $\frac{2}{3}x - \frac{12}{11} = 0$
$\frac{7}{4}x = \frac{1}{12}$ or $\frac{2}{3}x = \frac{12}{11}$
$\frac{4}{7}\left(\frac{7}{4}x\right) = \frac{4}{7}\left(\frac{1}{12}\right)$ $\frac{3}{2}\left(\frac{2}{3}x\right) = \frac{3}{2}\left(\frac{12}{11}\right)$
$x = \frac{1}{21}$ or $x = \frac{18}{11}$

23. $0.3x - 0.1 = 0$ or $0.05x - 1 = 0$
$3x - 1 = 0$ $5x - 100 = 0$
$3x = 1$ $5x = 100$
$x = \frac{1}{3}$ or $x = 20$

24. $0.1x - 0.3 = 0$ or $0.4x - 20 = 0$
$x - 3 = 0$ $4x - 200 = 0$
$x = 3$ $4x = 200$
$x = 3$ or $x = 50$

25. $9x = 0$ or $3x - 2 = 0$ or $2x - 1 = 0$
$x = 0$ $3x = 2$ $2x = 1$
$x = 0$ or $x = \frac{2}{3}$ or $x = \frac{1}{2}$

26. $x - 5 = 0$ or $x + 55 = 0$ or $5x - 1 = 0$
$x = 5$ $x = -55$ $5x = 1$
$x = 5$ or $x = -55$ or $x = \frac{1}{5}$

27. $x^2 + 6x + 5 = 0$
$(x + 5)(x + 1) = 0$
$x + 5 = 0$ or $x + 1 = 0$
$x = -5$ or $x = -1$

28. $x^2 + 7x - 18 = 0$
$(x + 9)(x - 2) = 0$
$x + 9 = 0$ or $x - 2 = 0$
$x = -9$ or $x = 2$

29. $x^2 + 4x - 21 = 0$
$(x + 7)(x - 3) = 0$
$x + 7 = 0$ or $x - 3 = 0$
$x = -7$ or $x = 3$

30. $b^2 - 8b + 15 = 0$
$(b - 5)(b - 3) = 0$
$b - 5 = 0$ or $b - 3 = 0$
$b = 5$ or $b = 3$

31. $x^2 - 8x = 0$
$x(x - 8) = 0$
$x = 0$ or $x - 8 = 0$
$x = 0$ or $x = 8$

32. $x^2 - 3x = 0$
$x(x - 3) = 0$
$x = 0$ or $x - 3 = 0$
$x = 0$ or $x = 3$

33. $x^2 + 19x = 0$
$x(x + 19) = 0$
$x = 0$ or $x + 19 = 0$
$x = 0$ or $x = -19$

34. $x^2 - 100 = 0$
$(x + 10)(x - 10) = 0$
$x + 10 = 0$ or $x - 10 = 0$
$x = -10$ or $x = 10$

35. $9x^2 - 4 = 0$
$(3x + 2)(3x - 2) = 0$
$3x + 2 = 0$ or $3x - 2 = 0$
$3x = -2$ $3x = 2$
$x = -\frac{2}{3}$ or $x = \frac{2}{3}$

36. $4a^2 - 9 = 0$
$(2a + 3)(2a - 3) = 0$
$2a + 3 = 0$ or $2a - 3 = 0$
$2a = -3$ $2a = 3$
$a = -\frac{3}{2}$ or $a = \frac{3}{2}$

37. $x^2 + 6x + 9 = 0$
$(x + 3)^2 = 0$
$x + 3 = 0$
$x = -3$

38. $x^2 + 10x + 25 = 0$
$(x + 5)^2 = 0$
$x + 5 = 0$
$x = -5$

39. $12y^2 - 5y = 2$
$12y^2 - 5y - 2 = 0$
$(4y + 1)(3y - 2) = 0$
$4y + 1 = 0$ or $3y - 2 = 0$
$4y = -1$ $3y = 2$
$y = -\frac{1}{4}$ or $y = \frac{2}{3}$

40. $2y^2 + 12y = -10$
$2y^2 + 12y + 10 = 0$
$2(y^2 + 6y + 5) = 0$
$2(y + 5)(y + 1) = 0$
$y + 5 = 0$ or $y + 1 = 0$
$y = -5$ or $y = -1$

41. $x(x-5)=14$
$x^2-5x=14$
$x^2-5x-14=0$
$(x-7)(x+2)=0$
$x-7=0$ or $x+2=0$
$x=7$ or $x=-2$

42. $t(3t+1)=2$
$3t^2+t=2$
$3t^2+t-2=0$
$(3t-2)(t+1)=0$
$3t-2=0$ or $t+1=0$
$3t=2$ or $t=-1$
$t=\frac{2}{3}$ or $t=-1$

43. $64m^2=81$
$64m^2-81=0$
$(8m+9)(8m-9)=0$
$8m+9=0$ or $8m-9=0$
$8m=-9$ or $8m=9$
$m=-\frac{9}{8}$ or $m=\frac{9}{8}$

44. $100t^2=49$
$100t^2-49=0$
$(10t+7)(10t-7)=0$
$10t+7=0$ or $10t-7=0$
$10t=-7$ $\quad 10t=7$
$t=-\frac{7}{10}$ or $t=\frac{7}{10}$

45. $4x+9=0$ or $14x-7=0$
$4x=-9$ $\quad 14x=7$
$x=-\frac{9}{4}$ $\quad x=\frac{7}{14}$ or $\frac{1}{2}$

46. $3w-1=0$ or $w+2=0$
$3w=1$ or $w=-2$
$w=\frac{1}{3}$ or $w=-2$

47. $5x^2=6x$
$5x^2-6x=0$
$x(5x-6)=0$
$x=0$ or $5x-6=0$
$x=0$ or $5x=6$
$x=0$ or $x=\frac{6}{5}$

48. $(5x+1)(4x-12)=0$
$5x+1=0$ or $4x-12=0$
$5x=-1$ $\quad 4x=12$
$x=-\frac{1}{5}$ or $x=3$

49. $x^2-2x+1=0$
$(x-1)^2=0$
$x-1=0$
$x=1$

50. $(3x-9)(x+3)=0$
$3x-9=0$ or $x+3=0$
$3x=9$ or $x=-3$
$x=3$ or $x=-3$

51. $6x^2-4x=10$
$6x^2-4x-10=0$
$2(3x^2-2x-5)=0$
$2(3x-5)(x+1)=0$
$3x-5=0$ or $x+1=0$
$3x=5$ or $x=-1$
$x=\frac{5}{3}$ or $x=-1$

52. $(2x+5)(x+4)=0$
$2x+5=0$ or $x+4=0$
$2x=-5$ or $x=-4$
$x=-\frac{5}{2}$ or $x=-4$

53. $(2x+9)(x+8)=0$
$2x+9=0$ or $x+8=0$
$2x=-9$ or $x=-8$
$x=-\frac{9}{2}$ or $x=-8$

54. $v^2-6v-16=0$
$(v-8)(v+2)=0$
$v-8=0$ or $v+2=0$
$v=8$ or $v=-2$

55. $c^2-16=0$
$(c+4)(c-4)=0$
$c+4=0$ or $c-4=0$
$c=-4$ or $c=4$

56. $d^2+7d+6=0$
$(d+6)(d+1)=0$
$d+6=0$ or $d+1=0$
$d=-6$ or $d=-1$

57. $x^2-9x+14=0$
$(x-7)(x-2)=0$
$x-7=0$ or $x-2=0$
$x=7$ or $x=2$

58. $x^2+12x=0$
$x(x+12)=0$
$x=0$ or $x+12=0$
$x=0$ or $x=-12$

59. $3x^2-7x=20$
$3x^2-7x-20=0$
$(3x+5)(x-4)=0$
$3x+5=0$ or $x-4=0$
$3x=-5$ or $x=4$
$x=-\frac{5}{3}$ or $x=4$

60. $7x^2=8x$
$7x^2-8x=0$
$x(7x-8)=0$
$x=0$ or $7x-8=0$
$x=0$ or $7x=8$
$x=0$ or $x=\frac{8}{7}$

61. $b^2+9b=20+8b$
$b^2+9b-20-8b=0$
$b^2+b-20=0$
$(b+5)(b-4)=0$
$b+5=0$ or $b-4=0$
$b=-5$ or $b=4$

62. $y^2+8y=16y-16$
$y^2-8y+16=0$
$(y-4)^2=0$
$y-4=0$
$y=4$

63. $t^2-6t+9=36$
$t^2-6t-27=0$
$(t-9)(t+3)=0$
$t-9=0$ or $t+3=0$
$t=9$ or $t=-3$

64. $t^2-10t+25=10-2t$
$t^2-8t+15=0$
$(t-5)(t-3)=0$
$t-3=0$ or $t-5=0$
$t=3$ or $t=5$

65. $\left(x+\frac{1}{8}\right)\left(x-\frac{1}{8}\right)=0$
$x+\frac{1}{8}=0$ or $x-\frac{1}{8}=0$
$x=-\frac{1}{8}$ or $x=\frac{1}{8}$

66. $\left(x + \frac{5}{6}\right)\left(x - \frac{5}{6}\right) = 0$

$x + \frac{5}{6} = 0$ or $x - \frac{5}{6} = 0$

$x = -\frac{5}{6}$ or $x = \frac{5}{6}$

67. $5\left(\frac{1}{16}x^2 - 1\right) = 0$

$5\left(\frac{1}{4}x + 1\right)\left(\frac{1}{4}x - 1\right) = 0$

$\frac{1}{4}x + 1 = 0$ or $\frac{1}{4}x - 1 = 0$

$\frac{1}{4}x = -1$ or $\frac{1}{4}x = 1$

$x = -4$ or $x = 4$

68. $\frac{27}{25}x^2 - \frac{1}{3} = 0$

$3\left(\frac{9}{25}x^2 - \frac{1}{9}\right) = 0$

$3\left(\frac{3}{5}x + \frac{1}{3}\right)\left(\frac{3}{5}x - \frac{1}{3}\right) = 0$

$\frac{3}{5}x + \frac{1}{3} = 0$ or $\frac{3}{5}x - \frac{1}{3} = 0$

$\frac{3}{5}x = -\frac{1}{3}$ or $\frac{3}{5}x = \frac{1}{3}$

$x = -\frac{5}{9}$ or $x = \frac{5}{9}$

69. Possible pairs of constants in the monomial factors are $(+1, -16), (-1, +16), (+4, -4), (+8, -2)$, and $(-8, +2)$. The corresponding trinomials are:
$(x + 1)(x - 16) = x^2 - 15x - 16$
$(x - 1)(x + 16) = x^2 + 15x - 16$
$(x + 8)(x - 2) = x^2 + 6x - 16$
$(x - 8)(x + 2) = x^2 - 6x - 16$

70. An equation has -1 as a solution when $x + 1$ is one of the factors of the equation, so A and D have -1 as a solution. The equation $x^2 - x = -2x$ becomes $x^2 + x = 0$, which factors to $x(x + 1) = 0$. So -1 is a solution of C. B does not have $x + 1$ as a factor. The correct choice is B.

71. a. $(x - 1)(x + 3) = 0, x^2 + 2x - 3 = 0$
b. $(x - 3)(x + 1) = 0, x^2 - 2x - 3 = 0$
c. $(x - 2)^2 = 0, x^2 - 4x + 4 = 0$
d. $(x - 3)(x - 4) = 0, x^2 - 7x + 12 = 0$
e. $(x - 3)(x + 4) = 0, x^2 + x - 12 = 0$
f. $(x + 3)(x - 4) = 0, x^2 - x - 12 = 0$
g. $(x + 3)(x + 4) = 0, x^2 + 7x + 12 = 0$
h. $\left(x - \frac{1}{2}\right)^2 = 0$ or $(2x - 1)^2 = 0$,

$x^2 - x + \frac{1}{4} = 0$ or $4x^2 - 4x + 1 = 0$

i. $(x - 5)(x + 5) = 0, x^2 - 25 = 0$
j. $x(x - 0.1)\left(x - \frac{1}{4}\right) = 0$ or $x(10x - 1)(4x - 1) = 0$,

$x\left(x - \frac{1}{10}\right)\left(x - \frac{1}{4}\right) = 0, x\left(x^2 - \frac{14}{40}x + \frac{1}{40}\right) = 0,$

$x^3 - \frac{14}{40}x^2 + \frac{1}{40}x = 0,$ or $40x^3 - 14x^2 + x = 0$

72. a. (3) b. (5) c. (1) d. (2) e. (4) f. (6)

73. $3(n + 8)$ 74. $3(n + 8)$ 75. $\frac{1}{2}(n - 15)$ or $\frac{n - 15}{2}$

76. $(a + b)^2$ 77. $a^2 + b^2$ 78. $a^2 - b^2$

79. $4y^2 + 10y - 6 = 2(2y^2 + 5y - 3)$
$= 2(2y - 1)(y + 3)$

80. $4x^2 - y^2 = (2x - y)(2x + y)$

81. $6y^2 - 5y - 6 = (2y - 3)(3y + 2)$

LESSON 6-9 TRY THIS pp. 292–293

a. $(x - 7)(x - 8) = 0$
$x - 7 = 0$ or $x - 8 = 0$
$x = 7$ or $x = 8$

b. $x(x - 1) = 0$
$x = 0$ or $x - 1 = 0$
$x = 0$ or $x = 1$

c. $(x + 1)(x - 1) = 24$
$x^2 - 1 - 24 = 0$
$x^2 - 25 = 0$
$(x - 5)(x + 5) = 0$
$x - 5 = 0$ or $x + 5 = 0$
$x = 5$ or $x = -5$

d. $x^2 - x = 20$
$x^2 - x - 20 = 0$
$(x - 5)(x + 4) = 0$
$x - 5 = 0$ or $x + 4 = 0$
$x = 5$ or $x = -4$

e. $2x^2 + 1 = 73$
$2x^2 - 72 = 0$
$2(x^2 - 36) = 0$
$2(x + 6)(x - 6) = 0$
$x + 6 = 0$ or $x - 6 = 0$
$x = -6$ or $x = 6$

f. $l(l - 2) = 15$
$l^2 - 2l - 15 = 0$
$(l - 5)(l + 3) = 0$
$l - 5 = 0$ or $l + 3 = 0$
$l = 5$ or $l = -3$
Since length cannot be negative, $l = -3$ is not a solution.
$l = 5$ cm, $w = l - 2 = 5 - 2 = 3$ cm

g. $x(x + 1) = 462$
$x^2 + x - 462 = 0$
$(x - 21)(x + 22) = 0$
$x - 21 = 0$ or $x + 22 = 0$
$x = 21$ or $x = -22$
$x + 1 = 22$ or $x + 1 = -21$
There are two pairs: 21 and 22, or -22 and -21.

LESSON 6-9 EXERCISES pp. 294–296

1. $4n^2 - n = 3$
$4n^2 - n - 3 = 0$
$(4n + 3)(n - 1) = 0$
$4n + 3 = 0$ or $n - 1 = 0$
$4n = -3$ or $n = 1$
$n = -\frac{3}{4}$ or $n = 1$

2. $x^2 + 15 = 8x$
$x^2 - 8x + 15 = 0$
$(x - 5)(x - 3) = 0$
$x - 5 = 0$ or $x - 3 = 0$
$x = 5$ or $x = 3$

3. $n^2 + 8 = 6n$
$n^2 - 6n + 8 = 0$
$(n - 4)(n - 2) = 0$
$n - 4 = 0$ or $n - 2 = 0$
$n = 4$ or $n = 2$

4. $n^2 + 7 = 32$
$n^2 - 25 = 0$
$(n + 5)(n - 5) = 0$
$n + 5 = 0$ or $n - 5 = 0$
$n = -5$ or $n = 5$

5. $n(n + 1) = 182$
$n^2 + n = 182$
$n^2 + n - 182 = 0$
$(n + 14)(n - 13) = 0$
$n + 14 = 0$ or $n - 13 = 0$
$n = -14$ or $n = 13$
If $n = -14, n + 1 = -13$.
If $n = 13, n + 1 = 14$.

6. $n(n + 1) = 56$
$n^2 + n = 56$
$n^2 + n - 56 = 0$
$(n + 8)(n - 7) = 0$
$n + 8 = 0$ or $n - 7 = 0$
$n = -8$ or $n = 7$
If $n = -8, n + 1 = -7$.
If $n = 7, n + 1 = 8$.

7. $n(n + 2) = 168$
$n^2 + 2n = 168$
$n^2 + 2n - 168 = 0$
$(n + 14)(n - 12) = 0$
$n + 14 = 0$ or $n - 12 = 0$
$n = -14$ or $n = 12$
If $n = -14, n + 2 = -12$.
If $n = 12, n + 2 = 14$.

8. $n(n + 2) = 224$
$n^2 + 2n = 224$
$n^2 + 2n - 224 = 0$
$(n + 16)(n - 14) = 0$
$n + 16 = 0$ or $n - 14 = 0$
$n = -16$ or $n = 14$
If $n = -16, n + 2 = -14$.
If $n = 14, n + 2 = 16$.

9. $n(n + 2) = 255$
$n^2 + 2n = 255$
$n^2 + 2n - 255 = 0$
$(n + 17)(n - 15) = 0$
$n + 17 = 0$ or $n - 15 = 0$
$n = -17$ or $n = 15$
If $n = -17, n + 2 = -15$.
If $n = 15, n + 2 = 17$.

10. $n(n + 2) = 143$
$n^2 + 2n = 143$
$n^2 + 2n - 143 = 0$
$(n + 13)(n - 11) = 0$
$n + 13 = 0$ or $n - 11 = 0$
$n = -13$ or $n = 11$
If $n = -13, n + 2 = -11$.
If $n = 11, n + 2 = 13$.

11. $w(w + 4) = 96$
$w^2 + 4w = 96$
$w^2 + 4w - 96 = 0$
$(w + 12)(w - 8) = 0$
$w + 12 = 0$ or $w - 8 = 0$
$w = -12$ or $w = 8$
Width cannot be negative, so -12 is not a solution.
$w = 8$ m, $l = 12$ m

12. $w(w + 5) = 84$
$w^2 + 5w = 84$
$w^2 + 5w - 84 = 0$
$(w + 12)(w - 7) = 0$
$w + 12 = 0$ or $w - 7 = 0$
$w = -12$ or $w = 7$
Width cannot be negative, so -12 is not a solution.
$w = 7$ cm, $l = 12$ cm

13. $s^2 - 5 = 4s$
$s^2 - 4s - 5 = 0$
$(s - 5)(s + 1) = 0$
$s - 5 = 0$ or $s + 1 = 0$
$s = 5$ or $s = -1$
Length cannot be negative, so $s = -1$ is not a solution. $s = 5$ ft

14. $4s - 3 = s^2$
$0 = s^2 - 4s + 3$
$0 = (s - 3)(s - 1)$
$s - 3 = 0$ or $s - 1 = 0$
$s = 3$ or $s = 1$
The length is 3 in. or 1 in.

15. $A = \frac{1}{2}bh$
$28 = \frac{1}{2}(h + 10)h$
$56 = (h + 10)h$
$56 = h^2 + 10h$
$0 = h^2 + 10h - 56$
$0 = (h + 14)(h - 4)$
$h + 14 = 0$ or $h - 4 = 0$
$h = -14$ or $h = 4$
Height cannot be negative so -14 is not a solution.
$h = 4$ cm, $b = 14$ cm

16. $10 = \frac{1}{2}(h + 8)h$
$20 = (h + 8)h$
$20 = h^2 + 8h$
$0 = h^2 + 8h - 20$
$0 = (h + 10)(h - 2)$
$h + 10 = 0$ or $h - 2 = 0$
$h = -10$ or $h = 2$
Height cannot be negative, so $h = -10$ is not a solution.
$h = 2$ m, $b = 10$ m

17. $(s + 3)(s + 3) = 81$
$s^2 + 6s + 9 = 81$
$s^2 + 6s - 72 = 0$
$(s + 12)(s - 6) = 0$
$s + 12 = 0$ or $s - 6 = 0$
$s = -12$ or $s = 6$
Length cannot be negative, so $s = -12$ is not a solution. $s = 6$ m

18. $(s + 7)(s + 7) = 121$
$s^2 + 14s + 49 = 121$
$s^2 + 14s - 72 = 0$
$(s + 18)(s - 4) = 0$
$s + 18 = 0$ or $s - 4 = 0$
$s = -18$ or $s = 4$
Length cannot be negative, so $s = -18$ is not a solution.
$s = 4$ in.

19. $n^2 + (n + 2)^2 = 74$
$n^2 + n^2 + 4n + 4 = 74$
$2n^2 + 4n - 70 = 0$
$2(n^2 + 2n - 35) = 0$
$2(n + 7)(n - 5) = 0$
$n + 7 = 0$ or $n - 5 = 0$
$n = -7$ or $n = 5$
Since n is positive, $n = -7$ is not a solution.
The integers are 5 and 7.

20. $n^2 + (n + 2)^2 = 130$
$n^2 + n^2 + 4n + 4 = 130$
$2n^2 + 4n - 126 = 0$
$2(n^2 + 2n - 63) = 0$
$2(n + 9)(n - 7) = 0$
$n + 9 = 0$ or $n - 7 = 0$
$n = -9$ or $n = 7$
Since n is positive, $n = -9$ is not a solution.
The integers are 7 and 9.

21. Let x be the smaller of the two consecutive even integers. Then $x + 2$ is the larger of the two even integers. The sum of the squares of two consecutive even integers is 52 then can be written $x^2 + (x + 2)^2 = 52$. The correct choice is **D**.

22. $7x + 1 = (x + 1)^2$
$7x + 1 = x^2 + 2x + 1$
$0 = x^2 - 5x$
$0 = x(x - 5)$
$x = 0$ or $x - 5 = 0$
$x = 5$
Since x is positive, $x = 5$.

23. $6x + 1 = (x - 1)^2$
$6x + 1 = x^2 - 2x + 1$
$0 = x^2 - 8x$
$0 = x(x - 8)$
$x = 0$ or $x - 8 = 0$
$x = 8$
Since x is positive, $x = 8$.

24. $x^3 = 2x^2$
$x^3 - 2x^2 = 0$
$x^2(x - 2) = 0$
$x^2 = 0$ or $x - 2 = 0$
$x = 0$ or $x = 2$

25. The student subtracted two from the number before squaring instead of squaring the number, then subtracting two.

26. **a.** $464 = 180t - 16t^2$
b. $16t^2 - 180t + 464 = 0$
$4t^2 - 45t + 116 = 0$
$(4t - 29)(t - 4) = 0$
$4t - 29 = 0$ or $t - 4 = 0$
$4t = 29$ or $t = 4$
$t = \frac{29}{4}$ or $t = 4$

It will reach 464 ft after 4 sec.

c. It will again reach 464 ft after $\frac{29}{4} = 7\frac{1}{4}$ sec.

27. a.
$$\begin{aligned} h &= rt - 4.9t^2 \\ 4.9 &= (9.8)t - 4.9t^2 \\ 4.9t^2 - 9.8t + 4.9 &= 0 \\ 49t^2 - 98t + 49 &= 0 \\ (7t - 7)^2 &= 0 \\ 7t - 7 &= 0 \\ 7t &= 7 \\ t &= 1 \end{aligned}$$
Height will be reached at 1 second.

b. $h = 0$
$$\begin{aligned} 0 &= 9.8t - 4.9t^2 \\ &= 98t - 49t^2 \\ &= 49t(2 - t) \end{aligned}$$
$49t = 0$ or $2 - t = 0$
$t = 0$ or $t = 2$
Ball will be at $h = 0$ at $t = 0$ (beginning) and after 2 sec.

28. a.

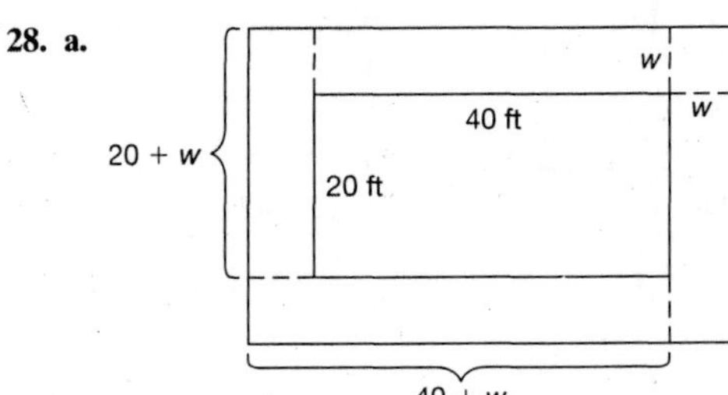

b. $1500 - (40 \cdot 20) = 1500 - 800 = 700\ \text{ft}^2$
c. $w(20 + w)$
d. $w(40 + w)$
e. $2[w(20 + w) + w(40 + w)]$
f.
$$\begin{aligned} 2[w(20 + w) + w(40 + w)] &= 700 \\ 2(20w + w^2 + 40w + w^2) &= 700 \\ 2(2w^2 + 60w) &= 700 \\ 4w^2 + 120w &= 700 \\ 4w^2 + 120w - 700 &= 0 \\ 4(w^2 + 30w - 175) &= 0 \\ 4(w - 5)(w - 25) &= 0 \end{aligned}$$
$w - 5 = 0$ or $w - 25 = 0$
$w = 5$ or $w = 25$
The sidewalk cannot be 25 ft wide, so the width is 5 ft.

29. Let l be the length of the side of the base. Then surface area =
$$\begin{aligned} 2l^2 + 4(9l) &= 350 \\ 2l^2 + 36l - 350 &= 0 \\ 2(l^2 + 18l - 175) &= 0 \\ 2(l + 25)(l - 7) &= 0 \end{aligned}$$
$l + 25 = 0$ or $l - 7 = 0$
$l = -25$ or $l = 7$
Since length must be positive, the length is 7 in.

30.
$$\begin{aligned} (x + (x + 1))((x + 1) - x) + 8 &= x^2 + (x + 1)^2 \\ (2x + 1) + 8 &= x^2 + x^2 + 2x + 1 \\ 2x + 9 &= 2x^2 + 2x + 1 \\ -2x^2 + 8 &= 0 \\ 2x^2 &= 8 \\ x^2 &= 4 \end{aligned}$$
$x = 2$ or $x = -2$. We are looking for positive numbers, so $x = 2$ and $x + 1 = 3$.

31.
$$\begin{aligned} x^2 + (x + 1)^2 &= 1 + x(x + 1) + 8(x + 1) \\ x^2 + x^2 + 2x + 1 &= 1 + x^2 + x + 8x + 8 \\ x^2 + 2x &= 9x + 8 \\ x^2 - 7x - 8 &= 0 \\ (x + 1)(x - 8) &= 0 \end{aligned}$$
$x = -1$ or $x = 8$
Since the numbers are positive, 8 is one of the numbers, and 9 is the other number.

32. Since the margins account for half the page area, so does the print. Hence, if x is margin width,
$$(15 - 2x)(20 - 2x) = \tfrac{1}{2}(15 \cdot 20)$$
$$\begin{aligned} 4x^2 - 30x - 40x + 300 &= 150 \\ 4x^2 - 70x + 150 &= 0 \\ 2(2x^2 - 35x + 75) &= 0 \\ 2(2x - 5)(x - 15) &= 0 \end{aligned}$$
$2x = 5$ or $x = 15$
$x = \frac{5}{2}$

The margins cannot be 15 cm wide, so they are $\frac{5}{2}$ or $2\frac{1}{2}$ cm wide.

33. Width = w, length = $2w$
$$\begin{aligned} 4(w - 2(4))(2w - 2(4)) &= 616 \\ 4(w - 8)(2w - 8) - 616 &= 0 \\ 8w^2 - 96w + 256 - 616 &= 0 \\ 8w^2 - 96w - 360 &= 0 \\ 8(w^2 - 12w - 45) &= 0 \\ 8(w^2 - 15)(w + 3) &= 0 \end{aligned}$$
$w = 15$ or $w = -3$
The width must be 15 cm, so the length is 30 cm, and the volume of the box is 616 cm^3.

34. $d(20 - 2d) = 50$, where d is the depth.
$$\begin{aligned} 20d - 2d^2 - 50 &= 0 \\ 2d^2 - 20d + 50 &= 0 \\ 2(d^2 - 10d + 25) &= 0 \\ 2(d - 5)(d - 5) &= 0 \\ d - 5 &= 0 \\ d &= 5 \end{aligned}$$
Depth is 5 in. The area is 10×5.

35. 1.17203×10^5 **36.** 5.59×10^{-3}

37. $(10m^2)^4 = 10^4 m^{2 \cdot 4} = 10{,}000m^8$

38. $(5x^5)(x^2)(16x) = 5 \cdot 16x^{5+2+1} = 80x^8$

39. $(3a^3b^2)(-5ab^3) = 3(-5)a^{3+1}b^{2+3} = -15a^4b^5$

40. $n = 0.80(30)$
$n = 24$

41. $35 = 0.05n$
$\frac{34}{0.05} = n$
$n = 680$

42. $a^2 - 8a + 16 = (a - 4)^2$

43. $6c^2 - 15c - 9 = 3(2c^2 - 5c - 3)$
$= 3(2c + 1)(c - 3)$

44. $x^4 - x^2 = x^2(x^2 - 1)$
$= x^2(x + 1)(x - 1)$

45. $2m^3 - 4m^2 - m + 2 = 2m^2(m - 2) - 1(m - 2)$
$= (2m^2 - 1)(m - 2)$

46. $36y^4 - 63 = 9(4y^4 - 7)$

47. $5x^2 + 70x + 245 = 5(x^2 + 14x + 49)$
$= 5(x + 7)^2$

PREPARING FOR STANDARDIZED TESTS p. 298

1. $(x + y)(x - y) = x^2 - y^2$
$(4)(6) = 24$
The correct choice is **C**.

2. $(r + 2)\left(\frac{1}{r}\right) = 0$
$r\left[(r + 2)\left(\frac{1}{r}\right) = 0\right]$
$r + 2 = 0$
$r = -2$
The correct choice is **D**.

3. $0.53^2 - 0.52^2 = (0.53 - 0.52)(0.53 + 0.52)$
$= (0.01)(1.05)$
$= 0.0105$
The correct choice is **B**.

4. $x + 3x = y + 3y + 7$
$4x = 4y + 7$
$x = y + \frac{7}{4}$
$x - y = \frac{7}{4}$
The correct choice is **E**.

5. $x^2 - 16 = (8)(16)$
$x^2 - (9)(16) = 0$
$(x + 12)(x - 12) = 0$
$x = 12$
The correct choice is **C**.

6. $(23)^2 - 2(23)(13) + (13)^2 = (23 - 13)^2$
$= 10^2$
$= 100$
The correct choice is **C**.

7. $ab = 2 \quad (a + b)^2 = 10$
$(a + b)^2 = a^2 + 2ab + b^2$
So, $a^2 + 2ab + b^2 = 10$
$a^2 + 2(2) + b^2 = 10$
$a^2 + b^2 = 10 - 4$
$= 6$
The correct choice is **B**.

8. $xy - 2y + 7x - 14 = 12$ and $x - 2 = 4$
$x = 6$
If $x = 6, 6y - 2y + 7(6) - 14 = 12$
$4y + 28 = 12$
$y + 7 = 3$
The correct choice is **D**.

9. $x + y = m \quad x - y = \frac{1}{m}$
$(x + y)(x - y) = x^2 - y^2$
So, $m \cdot \frac{1}{m} = x^2 - y^2$
$1 = x^2 - y^2$
The correct choice is **D**.

10. $m = 11$
$\frac{m^2 + 3m}{m} = \frac{m(m + 3)}{m} = m + 3$
$11 + 3 = 14$
The correct choice is **C**.

CHAPTER 6 WRAP UP pp. 299–301

1. Answers may vary. **2.** Answers may vary.

3. $x^2 - 3x = x(x - 3)$

4. $6y^3 + 12y^2 + 3y = 3y(2y^2 + 4y + 1)$

5. $8x^6 - 32x^5 + 4x^4 = 4x^4(2x^2 - 8x + 1)$

6. $6a^4b^4 - 2a^3b + 8a^2 = 2a^2(3a^2b^4 - ab + 4)$

7. No **8.** Yes **9.** $(3x + 2)(3x - 2)$

10. $(2x + 5)(2x - 5)$

11. $2x^2 - 50 = 2(x^2 - 25)$
$= 2(x + 5)(x - 5)$

12. $3x^2 - 27 = 3(x^2 - 9)$
$= 3(x + 3)(x - 3)$

13. $x^4 - 81 = (x^2 + 9)(x^2 - 9)$
$= (x^2 + 9)(x + 3)(x - 3)$

14. $16x^4 - 1 = (4x^2 + 1)(4x^2 - 1)$
$= (4x^2 + 1)(2x + 1)(2x - 1)$

15. No. **16.** No. **17.** Yes. **18.** No. **19.** $(x - 3)^2$

20. $(x + 7)^2$ **21.** $(3x - 5)^2$ **22.** $(5x - 2)^2$

23. $18x^2 - 12x + 2 = 2(9x^2 - 6x + 1)$
$= 2(3x - 1)^2$

24. $12x^2 + 60x + 75 = 3(4x^2 + 20x + 25)$
$= 3(2x + 5)^2$

25. $(x - 5)(x - 3)$ **26.** $(x + 6)(x - 2)$

27. $(y + 4)(y + 5)$ **28.** $(b - 6)(b + 3)$

29. $(m + 7)(m + 8)$ **30.** $(p - 8)(p + 1)$

31. $(2x + 1)(x - 4)$ **32.** $(2y - 1)(3y - 1)$

33. $6a^2 - 28a - 48 = 2(3a^2 - 14a - 24)$
$= 2(a - 6)(3a + 4)$

34. $x^3 + x^2 + 3x + 3 = x^2(x + 1) + 3(x + 1)$
$= (x + 1)(x^2 + 3)$

35. $x^4 + 4x^3 - 2x - 8 = x^3(x + 4) - 2(x + 4)$
$= (x + 4)(x^3 - 2)$

36. $x^3 + 3x^2 - x - 3 = x^2(x + 3) - 1(x + 3)$
$= (x + 3)(x^2 - 1)$
$= (x + 3)(x + 1)(x - 1)$

37. $6x^3 + 4x^2 + 3x + 2 = 2x^2(3x + 2) + 1(3x + 2)$
$= (3x + 2)(2x^2 + 1)$

38. $7x^2 - 7 = 7(x^2 - 1)$
$= 7(x + 1)(x - 1)$

39. $-75x^3 + 60x^2 - 12x = -3x(25x^2 - 20x + 4)$
$= -3x(5x - 2)^2$

40. $a^2 - 4a - 21 = (a - 7)(a + 3)$

41. $x^2 + 2x - 195 = (x + 15)(x - 13)$

42. $x^3 - 3x + 4x^2 - 12 = x(x^2 - 3) + 4(x^2 - 3)$
$= (x^2 - 3)(x + 4)$

43. $1 - a^8 = (1 + a^4)(1 - a^4)$
$= (1 + a^4)(1 + a^2)(1 - a^2)$
$= (1 + a^4)(1 + a^2)(1 + a)(1 - a)$

44. $(x - 1)(x + 3) = 0$
$x - 1 = 0$ or $x + 3 = 0$
$x = 1$ or $x = -3$

45. $y(4y - 6) = 0$
$y = 0$ or $4y - 6 = 0$
$4y = 6$
$y = 0$ or $y = \frac{6}{4}$ or $\frac{3}{2}$

46. $x^2 + 2x - 35 = 0$
$(x + 7)(x - 5) = 0$
$x + 7 = 0$ or $x - 5 = 0$
$x = -7$ or $x = 5$

47. $x^2 + x - 12 = 0$
$(x + 4)(x - 3) = 0$
$x + 4 = 0$ or $x - 3 = 0$
$x = -4$ or $x = 3$

48. $3x^2 - 2 = 5x$
$3x^2 - 5x - 2 = 0$
$(3x + 1)(x - 2) = 0$
$3x + 1 = 0$ or $x - 2 = 0$
$3x = -1$ or $x = 2$
$x = -\frac{1}{3}$ or $x = 2$

49. $9x^2 = 16$
$9x^2 - 16 = 0$
$(3x + 4)(3x - 4) = 0$
$3x + 4 = 0$ or $3x - 4 = 0$
$3x = -4$ or $3x = 4$
$x = -\frac{4}{3}$ or $x = \frac{4}{3}$

50. $n^2 - n = 6$
$n^2 - n - 6 = 0$
$(n - 3)(n + 2) = 0$
$n - 3 = 0$ or $n + 2 = 0$
$n = 3$ or $n = -2$

51. $n(n + 2) = 288$
$n^2 + 2n = 288$
$n^2 + 2n - 288 = 0$
$(n + 18)(n - 16) = 0$
$n + 18 = 0$ or $n - 16 = 0$
$n = -18$ or $n = 16$
If $n = -18, n + 2 = -16$.
If $n = 16, n + 2 = 18$.

52.
$$\begin{aligned} n(n+2) &= 323 \\ n^2 + 2n &= 323 \\ n^2 + 2n - 323 &= 0 \\ (n+19)(n-17) &= 0 \\ n + 19 = 0 \quad &\text{or} \quad n - 17 = 0 \\ n = -19 \quad &\text{or} \quad n = 17 \end{aligned}$$
If $n = -19, n + 2 = -17$.
If $n = 17, n + 2 = 19$.

53.
$$\begin{aligned} 2n^2 - 10 &= n \\ 2n^2 - n - 10 &= 0 \\ (2n-5)(n+2) &= 0 \\ 2n - 5 = 0 \quad &\text{or} \quad n + 2 = 0 \\ 2n = 5 \quad &\text{or} \quad n = -2 \\ n = \frac{5}{2} \quad &\text{or} \quad n = -2 \end{aligned}$$

54.
$$\begin{aligned} (s+5)^2 &= 289 \\ s^2 + 10s + 25 &= 289 \\ s^2 + 10s - 264 &= 0 \\ (s+22)(s-12) &= 0 \\ s + 22 = 0 \quad &\text{or} \quad s - 12 = 0 \\ s = -22 \quad &\text{or} \quad s = 12 \end{aligned}$$
Length is positive, so $s = 12$ cm.

CHAPTER 6 ASSESSMENT p. 301

1. $x^2 - 5x = x(x-5)$

2. $6x^3 + 9x^2 - 3x = 3x(2x^2 + 3x - 1)$

3. $4y^4 - 8y^3 + 6y^2 = 2y^2(2y^2 - 4y + 3)$

4. $4x^2 - 9 = (2x+3)(2x-3)$

5. $3x^2 - 75 = 3(x^2 - 25)$
$= 3(x+5)(x-5)$

6. $3x^4 - 48 = 3(x^4 - 16)$
$= 3(x^2 + 4)(x^2 - 4)$
$= 3(x^2 + 4)(x+2)(x-2)$

7. $x^2 - 10x + 25 = (x-5)^2$

8. $49x^2 - 84x + 36 = (7x-6)^2$

9. $45x^2 + 60x + 20 = 5(9x^2 + 12x + 4)$
$= 5(3x+2)^2$

10. $x^2 - 7x + 10 = (x-5)(x-2)$

11. $x^2 - x - 12 = (x-4)(x+3)$

12. $x^3 + 2x^2 - 3x = x(x^2 + 2x - 3)$
$= x(x+3)(x-1)$

13. $4x^2 - 4x - 15 = (2x-5)(2x+3)$

14. $5x^2 - 26x + 5 = (5x-1)(x-5)$

15. $10x^2 + 28x - 48 = 2(5x^2 + 14x - 24)$
$= 2(5x-6)(x+4)$

16. $x^3 + x^2 + 2x + 2 = x^2(x+1) + 2(x+1)$
$= (x+1)(x^2+2)$

17. $x^4 + 2x^3 - 3x - 6 = x^3(x+2) - 3(x+2)$
$= (x+2)(x^3 - 3)$

18. $6x^3 + 9x^2 - 15x = 3x(2x^2 + 3x - 5)$
$= 3x(2x+5)(x-1)$

19. $80 - 5x^4 = 5(16 - x^4)$
$= 5(4 + x^2)(4 - x^2)$
$= 5(4 + x^2)(2 + x)(2 - x)$

20. $y^5 - 8y^4 + 15y^3 = y^3(y^2 - 8y + 15)$
$= y^3(y-5)(y-3)$

21.
$$\begin{aligned} x^2 - x - 20 &= 0 \\ (x-5)(x+4) &= 0 \\ x - 5 = 0 \quad &\text{or} \quad x + 4 = 0 \\ x = 5 \quad &\text{or} \quad x = -4 \end{aligned}$$

22.
$$\begin{aligned} 2x^2 + 7x &= 15 \\ 2x^2 + 7x - 15 &= 0 \\ (2x-3)(x+5) &= 0 \\ 2x - 3 = 0 \quad &\text{or} \quad x + 5 = 0 \\ 2x = 3 \quad &\text{or} \quad x = -5 \\ x = \frac{3}{2} \quad &\text{or} \quad x = -5 \end{aligned}$$

23.
$$\begin{aligned} 4a^2 &= 25 \\ 4a^2 - 25 &= 0 \\ (2a+5)(2a-5) &= 0 \\ 2a + 5 = 0 \quad &\text{or} \quad 2a - 5 = 0 \\ 2a = -5 \quad &\text{or} \quad 2a = 5 \\ a = -\frac{5}{2} \quad &\text{or} \quad a = \frac{5}{2} \end{aligned}$$

24.
$$\begin{aligned} x(x-3) &= 28 \\ x^2 - 3x &= 28 \\ x^2 - 3x - 28 &= 0 \\ (x-7)(x+4) &= 0 \\ x - 7 = 0 \quad &\text{or} \quad x + 4 = 0 \\ x = 7 \quad &\text{or} \quad x = -4 \end{aligned}$$

25.
$$\begin{aligned} n^2 - 24 &= 5n \\ n^2 - 5n - 24 &= 0 \\ (n-8)(n+3) &= 0 \\ n - 8 = 0 \quad &\text{or} \quad n + 3 = 0 \\ n = 8 \quad &\text{or} \quad n = -3 \end{aligned}$$

26.
$$\begin{aligned} w(w+6) &= 40 \\ w^2 + 6w &= 40 \\ w^2 + 6w - 40 &= 0 \\ (w+10)(w-4) &= 0 \\ w + 10 = 0 \quad &\text{or} \quad w - 4 = 0 \\ w = -10 \quad &\text{or} \quad w = 4 \end{aligned}$$
Width is positive, so $w = 4$ m and $l = 10$ m.

27.
$$\begin{aligned} n(n+2) &= 528 \\ n^2 + 2n &= 528 \\ n^2 + 2n - 528 &= 0 \\ (n+24)(n-22) &= 0 \\ n + 24 = 0 \quad &\text{or} \quad n - 22 = 0 \\ n = -24 \quad &\text{or} \quad n = 22 \end{aligned}$$
If $n = -24, n + 2 = -22$.
If $n = 22, n + 2 = 24$.

CHAPTER 7

SKILLS & CONCEPTS p. 302

1. $3x + y = 3(4) + 3 = 12 + 3 = 15$

2. $\dfrac{3m+1}{2n} = \dfrac{3(5)+1}{2(2)} = \dfrac{15+1}{4} = \dfrac{16}{4} = 4$

3. $y^2 + 2 = 6^2 + 2 = 36 + 2 = 38$

4. $m^2 + 7 = 7^2 + 7 = 49 + 7 = 56$

5. $-3 < 2$ **6.** $-2 > -6$

7. $0 > -8$ **8.** $5 > -2$

9.
$$\begin{aligned} \frac{5}{2} - y &= \frac{1}{3} \\ 6\left(\frac{5}{2} - y\right) &= 6\left(\frac{1}{3}\right) \\ 15 - 6y &= 2 \\ -6y &= -13 \\ y &= \frac{13}{6} \end{aligned}$$

10.
$$\begin{aligned} w + 8 &= -3 \\ w &= -3 - 8 \\ w &= -11 \end{aligned}$$

11.
$$\begin{aligned} -4 + x &= 8 \\ x &= 8 + 4 \\ x &= 12 \end{aligned}$$

12. $6x = -12$

$x = -\frac{12}{6} = -2$

13. $\frac{7}{8}w = -\frac{2}{3}$

$24\left(\frac{7}{8}w\right) = 24\left(-\frac{2}{3}\right)$

$21w = -16$

$w = -\frac{16}{21}$

14. $\frac{2}{3}t = \frac{1}{8}$

$24\left(\frac{2}{3}t\right) = 24\left(\frac{1}{8}\right)$

$16t = 3$

$t = \frac{3}{16}$

15. $5x + 8 = 43$

$5x = 35$

$x = 7$

16. $-2x + 9 = -11$

$-2x = -11 - 9$

$-2x = -20$

$x = \frac{20}{2} = 10$

17. $-8x + 3x = 25$

$-5x = 25$

$x = \frac{25}{-5} = -5$

18. $5x + 6 = -2x - 8$

$7x + 6 = -8$

$7x = -14$

$x = -2$

19. $6(x - 6) = 3(x - 4)$

$6x - 36 = 3x - 12$

$3x - 36 = -12$

$3x = 24$

$x = 8$

20. $d = \frac{5k}{s}$

$ds = 5k$

$\frac{ds}{5} = k$

21. $S = \frac{Mp^2}{mv}$

$mvS = Mp^2$

$v = \frac{Mp^2}{mS}$

LESSON 7-1 TRY THIS pp. 305–307

a–i.

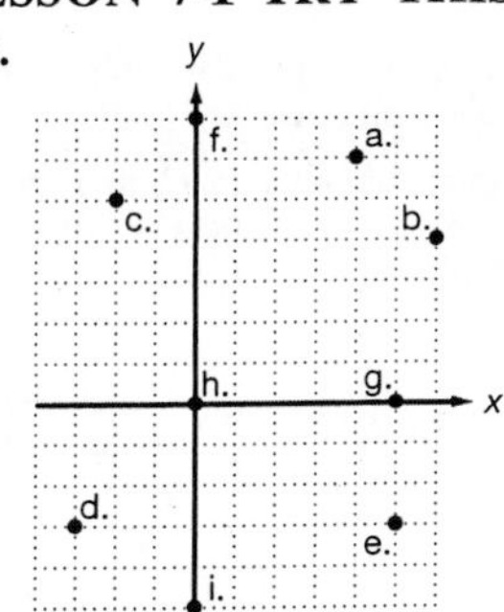

j. I **k.** III **l.** IV **m.** II

n. (4, 3), (−4, −3), (2, −4), (1, 5), (−2, 0), (0, 3)

LESSON 7-1 EXERCISES pp. 307–308

1–15. Odd

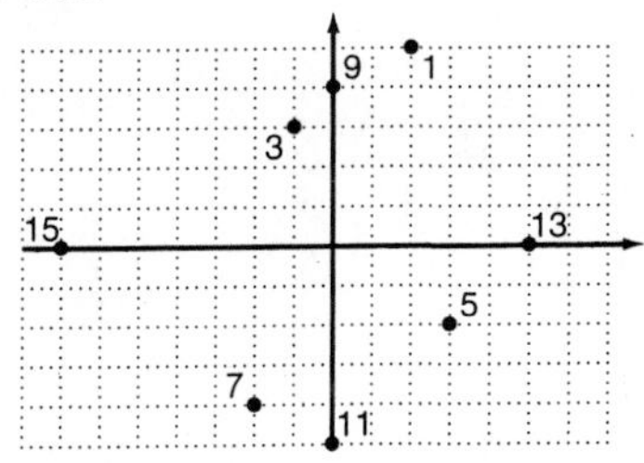

2–16. Even

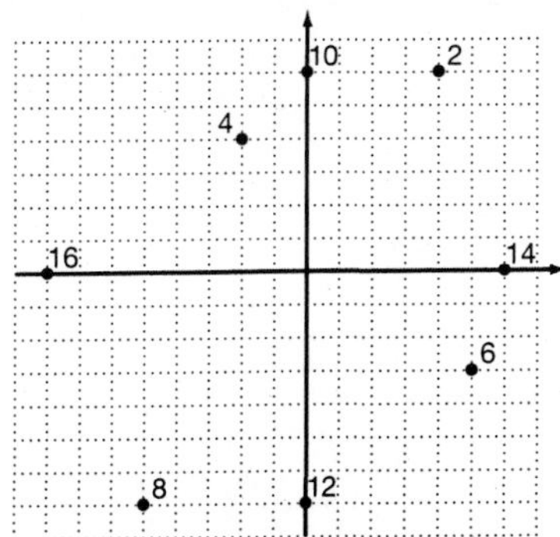

17. II **18.** III **19.** IV **20.** IV **21.** III **22.** II

23. I **24.** I

25. **a.** $y; x$

b. positive; negative

26. Answers may vary. Samples are given.

a. Phoenix, Arizona, and Tucson, Arizona, are different communities in the same state.

b. Concord, Massachusetts, and Concord, California, are communities in different states.

27. $A(3, 3), B(0, -4), C(-5, 0), D(-1, -1), E(2, 0)$

28. $A(4, 1), B(0, -5), C(-4, 0), D(-3, -2), E(2, 0)$

29. $|x| = |y|$, Ex. $(-3, 3), (-4, 4), (5, 5)$

30. $y = -x$, Ex. $(-1, 1), (0, 0), (2, -2)$

31. $x = y^2$, Ex. $(4, -2), (9, 3), (1, -1)$

32. $x - y = 1$, Ex. $(-2, -3), (0, -1), (2, 1)$

$y - x = 1$, Ex. $(-1, 0), (0, 1), (2, 3)$

33. (q, r) and (r, q) are symmetric about the line $y = x$.

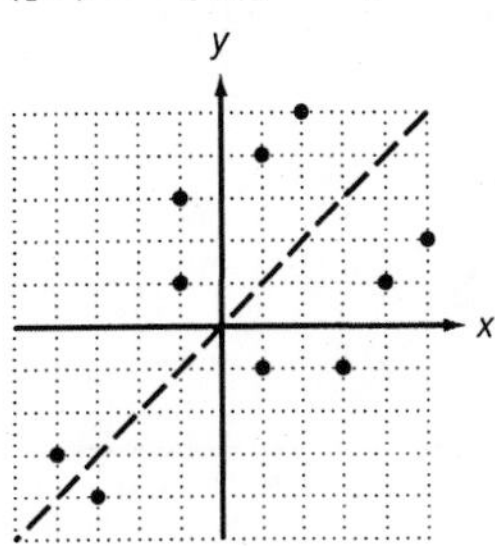

34. $xy = 2$

$y = \frac{2}{x}$

Ex. $(1, 2), (-2, -1), \left(\frac{2}{7}, 7\right)$

35. $x + y = 5$, Ex. $(2, 3), (4, 1), (0, 5)$

36. The width of the rectangle is from (5, 3) to (5, −2), which is 3 − (−2) or 5 units. The length is from (−3, 3) to (5, 3), or 5 − (−3) = 8 units. Perimeter = 2(5 + 8) = 26 units.

37. Base from (0, 9) to (0, −4) is of length 13. Altitude from (0, −4) to (5, −4) is of length 5.

Area $= \frac{1}{2}(5 \cdot 13) = \frac{65}{2} = 32.5$

38. $54m^2 - 24n^2 = 6(9m^2 - 4n^2)$

$= 6(3m - 2n)(3m + 2n)$

39. $x^3 - 5x^2 + 2x - 10 = x^2(x - 5) + 2(x - 5)$

$= (x - 5)(x^2 + 2)$

40. $(xy - 4yz) + 6yz = xy + 2yz$

41. $(ab - bc) + (3ab - 2bc) = 4ab - 3bc$

42. $(xy + 3yz) - (2xy - 5yz) = xy + 3yz - 2xy + 5yz$

$= -xy + 8yz$

43. $(mn - pq) - (2pq + 5mn) = mn - pq - 2pq - 5mn$

$= -4mn - 3pq$

LESSON 7-2 TRY THIS pp. 309–311

a. $y = 2x + 3$; $(3) = 2(2) + 3$; $3 = 7$; no

b. $4y - 3x = 22$; $4(4) - 3(-2) = 22$; $22 = 22$; yes

c. $y - 2x = 3$. Let $x = 0, y - 2 \cdot 0 = 3; y = 3; (0, 3)$.

Let $x = 1, y - 2 \cdot 1 = 3; y = 5; (1, 5)$.

Let $x = -2, y - 2 \cdot (-2) = 3;$

$y = -1; (-2, -1)$.

Answers may vary.

d.

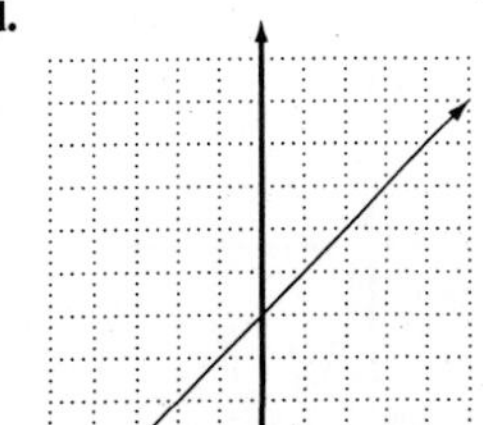

e.

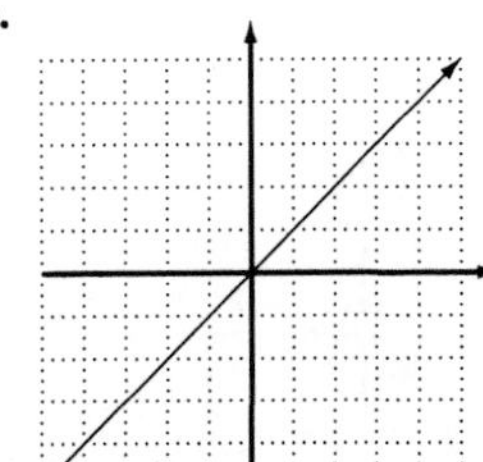

LESSON 7-2 EXERCISES pp. 311–312

1. $y = 3x - 1; (5) = 3(2) - 1; 5 = 5$; yes

2. $y = 2x + 5; (7) = 2(1) + 5; 7 = 7$; yes

3. $3x - y = 3; 3(2) - (-3) = 3; 9 = 3$; no

4. $2x + y = 2; 2(-1) + (4) = 2; 2 = 2$; yes

5. $2x + 3y = -7; 2(-2) + 3(-1) = -7; -7 = -7$; yes

6. $4x + 2y = 8; 4(0) + 2(-4) = 8; -8 = 8$; no

7. Ex. $(2, 5), (1, 3), (0, 1)$ **8.** Ex. $(2, 8), (1, 5), (0, 2)$

9. Ex. $(2, 4)$ $(3, 3), (4, 2)$ **10.** Ex. $(1, 7), (4, 4), (7, 1)$

11. Ex. $(6, -2), (5, 0), (4, 2)$ **12.** Ex. $(2, -5), (3, -2), (4, 1)$

13. Ex. $(-1, 6), (2, 2), (5, -2)$ **14.** Ex. $(-6, 7), (1, 2), (8, -3)$

15. Ex. $(-2, -7), (3, -1), (8, 5)$

16.

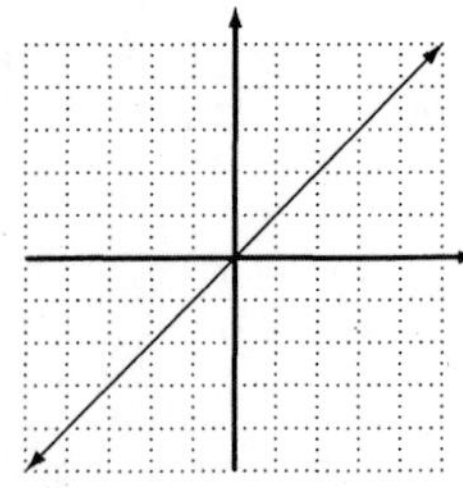

17.

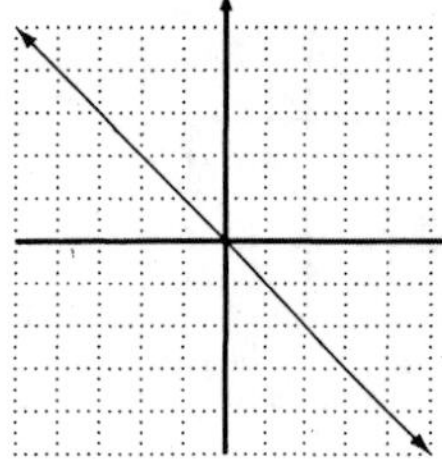

18.

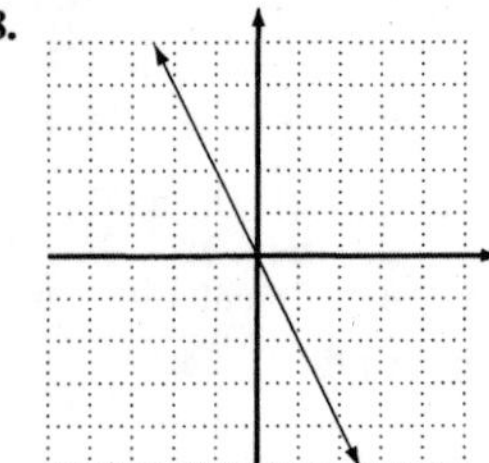

19.

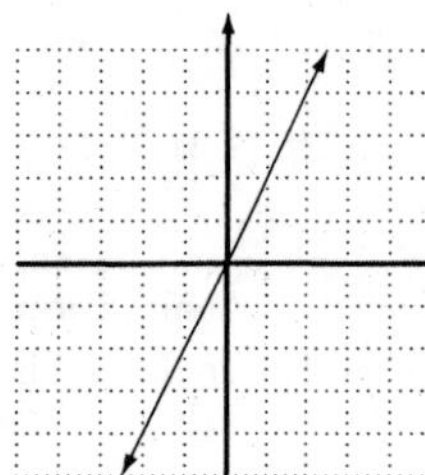

20.

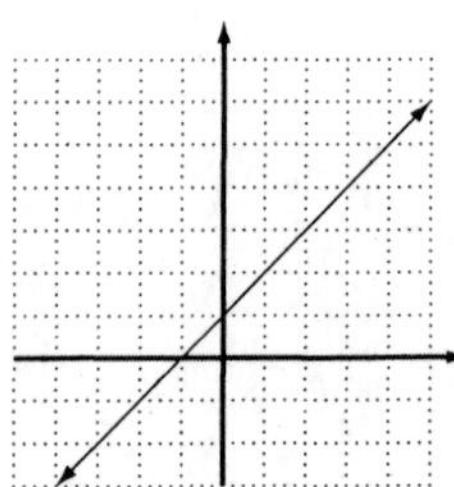

21.

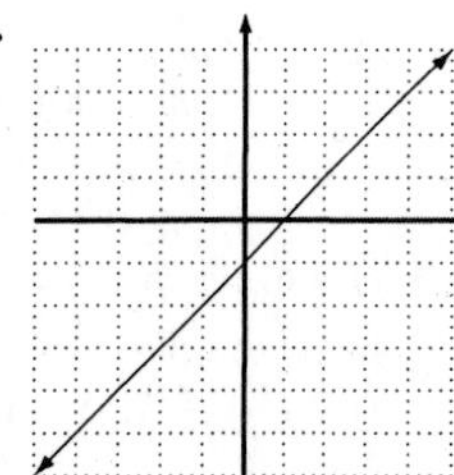

22.

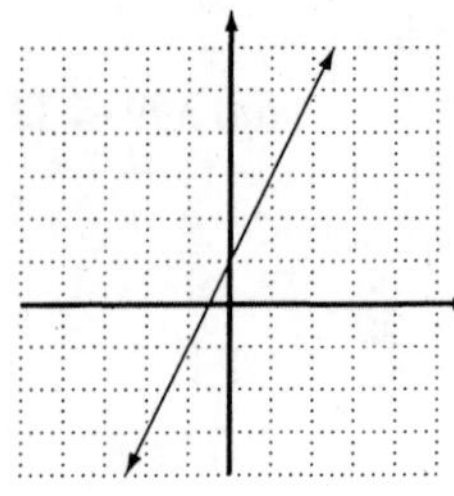

23.

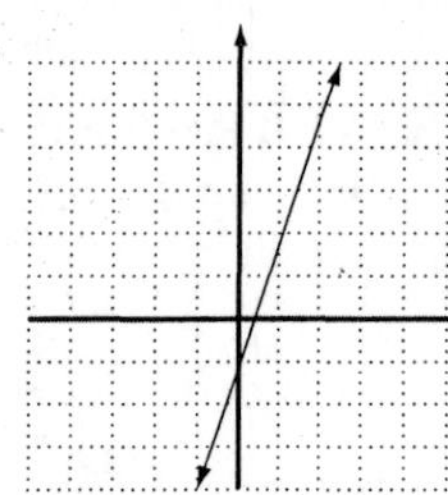

24.

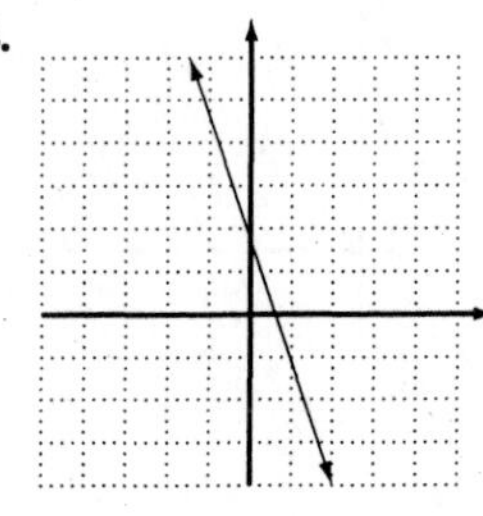

25.

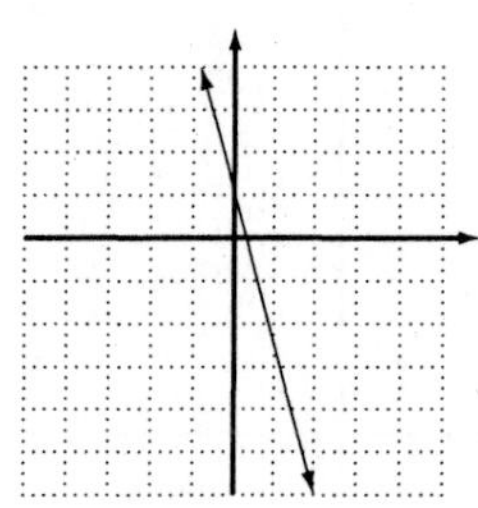

26.

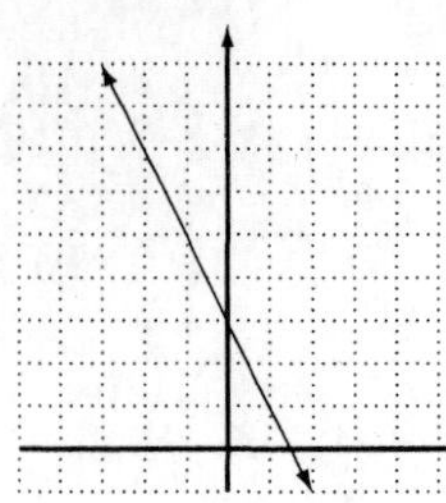

27.

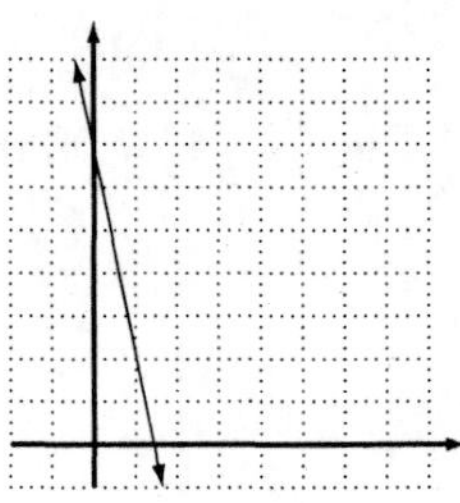

28.

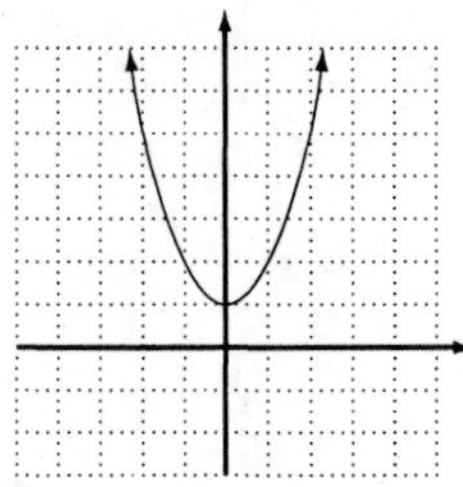

29.

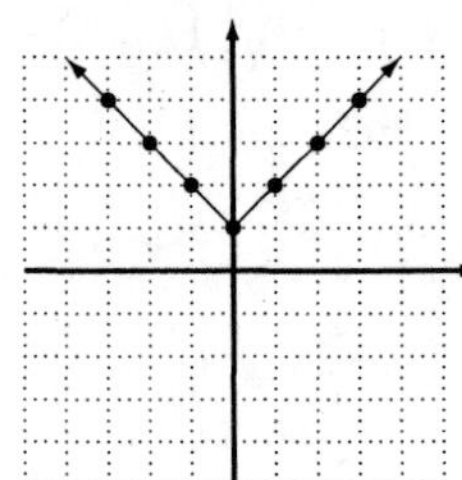

30.

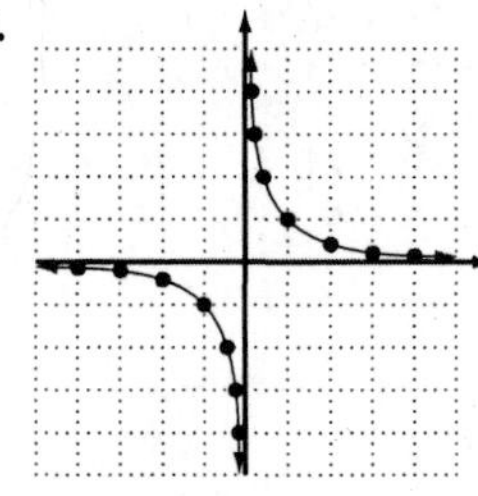

31. Yes; no; no; no

32. **a.** $6x + 9y$
b. 2 h on Friday and 5 h on Saturday or 5 h on Friday and 3 h on Saturday or 8 h on Friday and 1 h on Saturday

33. $68x + 76y = 864$; one solution assumes that each machine runs the same hours, or $x = y$. Then $68x + 76x = 864$, $144x = 864$, $x = 6$, so $y = 6$ and $(6, 6)$ is a solution.
6 hours for each machine.

34. $4^{-3} = \frac{1}{4^3} = \frac{1}{64}$ **35.** $m^0 = 1$ **36.** $(y^2)^3 = y^6$

37. $8x^4 - (x^4 + 2x) + 3x = 8x^4 - x^4 - 2x + 3x$
$= 7x^4 + x$ or $x(7x^3 + 1)$

38.
$$\begin{aligned} (2y + 3)(y + 3) &= 0 \\ 2y + 3 = 0 \quad &\text{or} \quad y + 3 = 0 \\ 2y = -3 \quad &\text{or} \quad y = -3 \\ y = -\tfrac{3}{2} \quad &\text{or} \quad y = -3 \end{aligned}$$

39.
$$\begin{aligned} 36c^2 &= 0 \\ c^2 &= 0 \\ c &= 0 \end{aligned}$$

40.
$$\begin{aligned} 9x^2 &= 25 \\ 9x^2 - 25 &= 0 \\ (3x + 5)(3x - 5) &= 0 \\ 3x + 5 = 0 \quad &\text{or} \quad 3x - 5 = 0 \\ 3x = -5 \quad &\text{or} \quad 3x = 5 \\ x = -\tfrac{5}{3} \quad &\text{or} \quad x = \tfrac{5}{3} \end{aligned}$$

41.
$$\begin{aligned} y^2 + 3y - 18 &= 0 \\ (y + 6)(y - 3) &= 0 \\ y + 6 = 0 \quad &\text{or} \quad y - 3 = 0 \\ y = -6 \quad &\text{or} \quad y = 3 \end{aligned}$$

42.
$$\begin{aligned} 5x^2 &= 7x \\ 5x^2 - 7x &= 0 \\ x(5x - 7) &= 0 \\ x = 0 \quad &\text{or} \quad 5x - 7 = 0 \\ x = 0 \quad &\text{or} \quad 5x = 7 \\ x = 0 \quad &\text{or} \quad x = \tfrac{7}{5} \end{aligned}$$

43.
$$\begin{aligned} 3x^2 + 14x + 9 &= 2x \\ 3x^2 + 12x + 9 &= 0 \\ 3(x^2 + 4x + 3) &= 0 \\ 3(x + 1)(x + 3) &= 0 \\ x + 1 = 0 \quad &\text{or} \quad x + 3 = 0 \\ x = -1 \quad &\text{or} \quad x = -3 \end{aligned}$$

44. $16 - 12c = 4(4 - 3c)$

45. $m^2n^3 + 2mn^2 = mn^2(mn + 2)$

46. $9a^4 - 9b^4 = 9(a^4 - b^4)$
$= 9(a^2 + b^2)(a^2 - b^2)$
$= 9(a^2 + b^2)(a + b)(a - b)$

47. $x^2 + 6xy + 9y^2 = (x + 3y)(x + 3y)$ or $(x + 3y)^2$

48. $x^2 + 7x - 18 = (x + 9)(x - 2)$

49. $6x^2 - 7x + 2 = (3x - 2)(2x - 1)$

50.
$$\begin{aligned} \frac{9}{5}C + 32 &= F \\ 5\left(\frac{9}{5}C + 32\right) &= 5F \\ 9C + 160 &= 5F \\ 9C &= 5F - 160 \\ C &= \frac{5F - 160}{9} = \frac{5}{9}(F - 32) \end{aligned}$$

51.
$$\begin{aligned} A &= P(1 + rt) \\ A &= P + Prt \\ A - P &= Prt \\ \frac{A - P}{Pt} &= r \end{aligned}$$

52.
$$\begin{aligned} A &= \frac{1}{2}h(b_1 + b_2) \\ 2A &= hb_1 + hb_2 \\ 2A - hb_1 &= hb_2 \\ \frac{2A - hb_1}{h} &= b_2 \end{aligned}$$

LESSON 7-3 INTRODUCING THE CONCEPT p. 313

From Exercise 31 on page 312, the equations whose graphs are straight lines are $y = 3x - 4$, $y - 4x = 2$, and $2x - 3y = 0$.

LESSON 7-3 TRY THIS pp. 314–315

a.

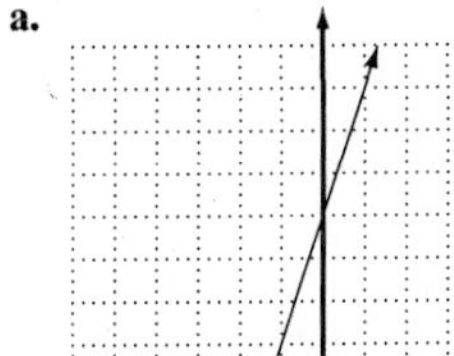

b.

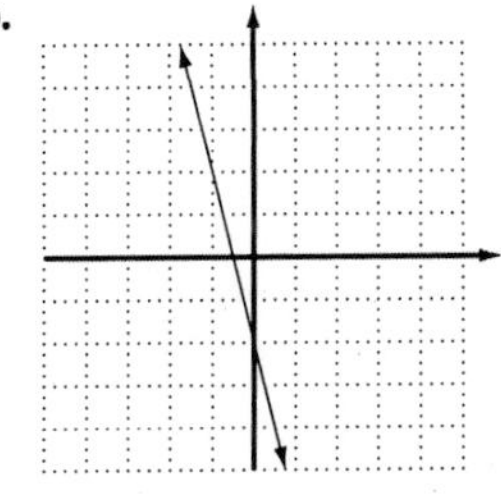

c.

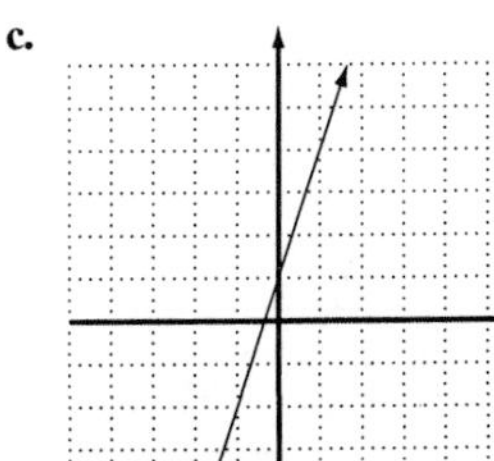

d.

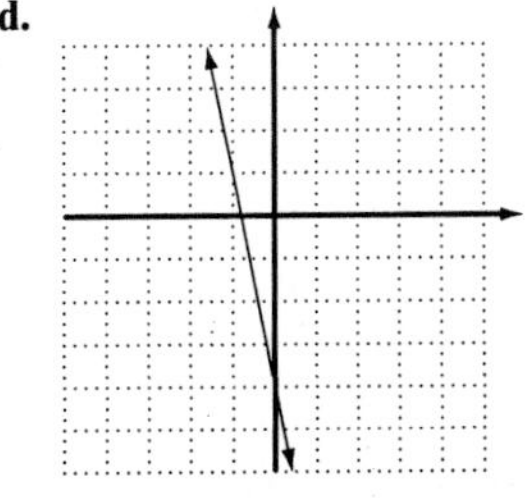

e.

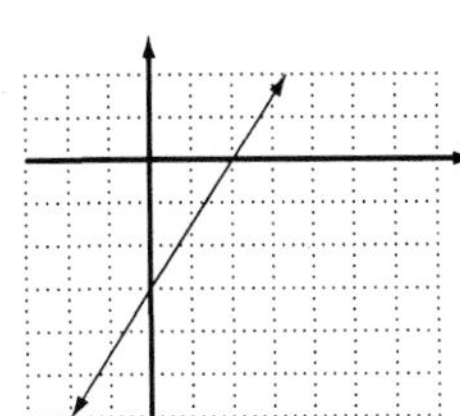

f.

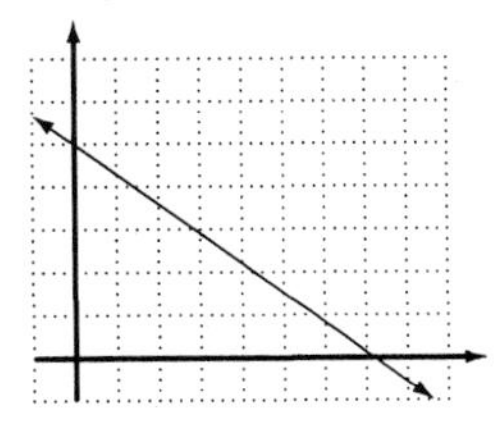

g.

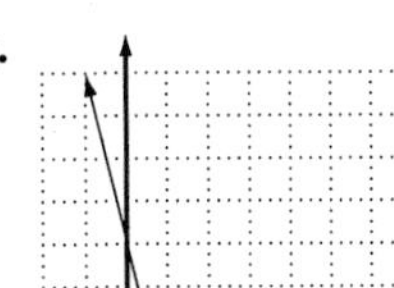

h.

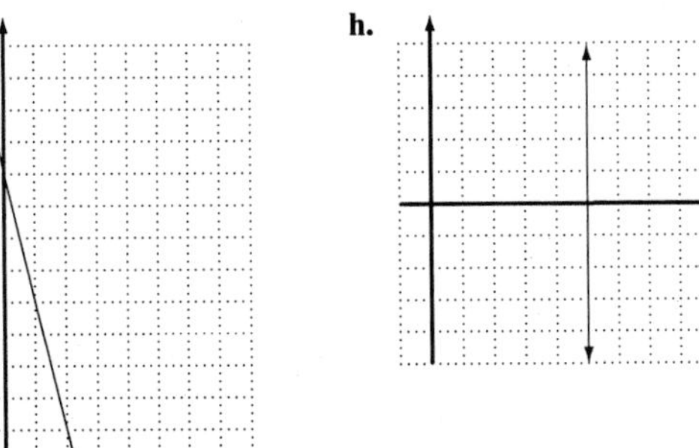

i.

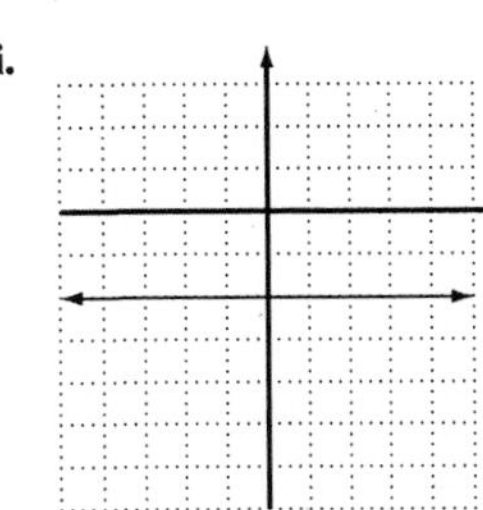

j.

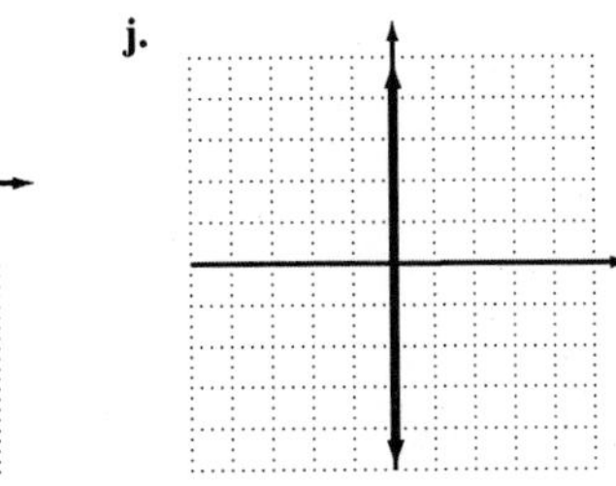

k.

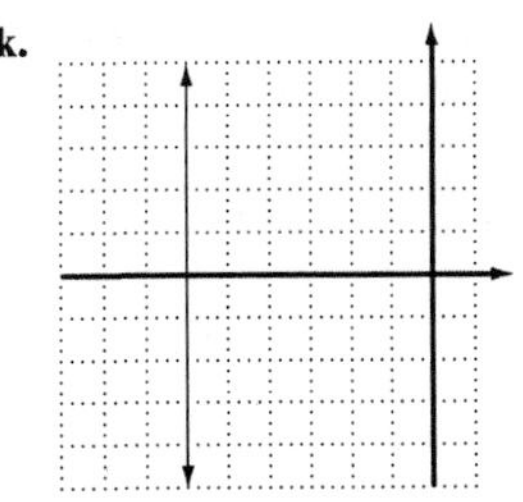

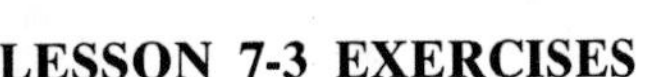

LESSON 7-3 EXERCISES pp. 316–317

1.

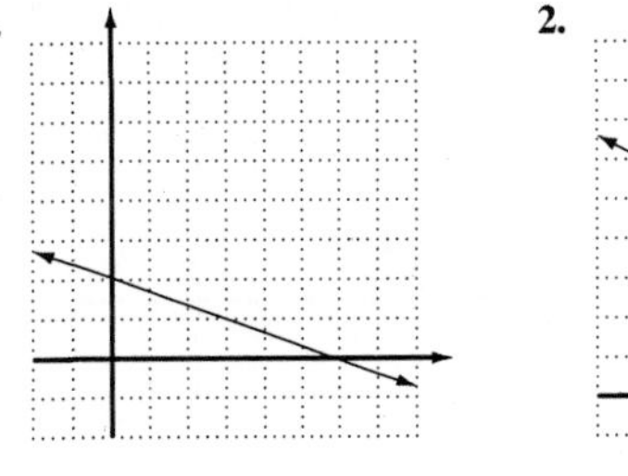

2.

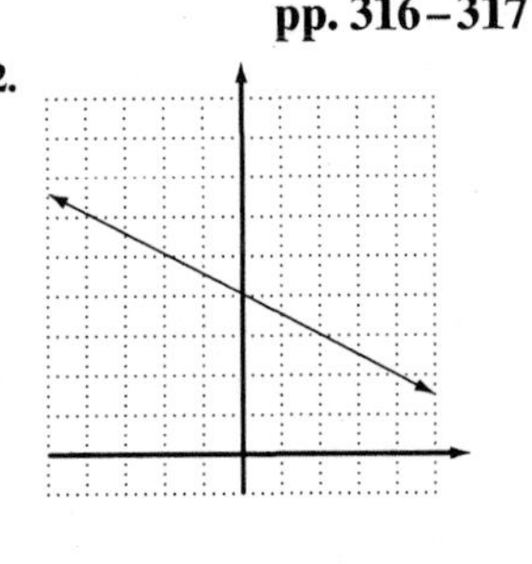

3.

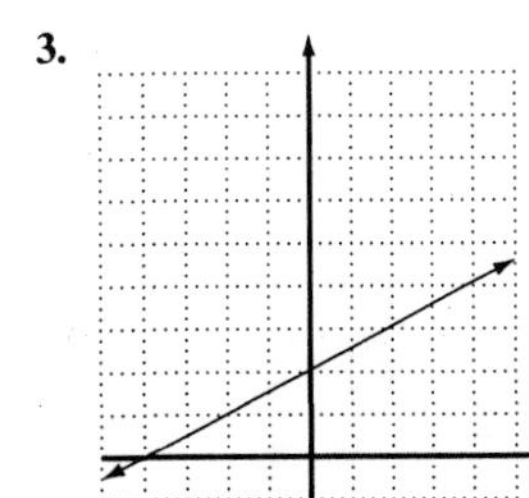

4.

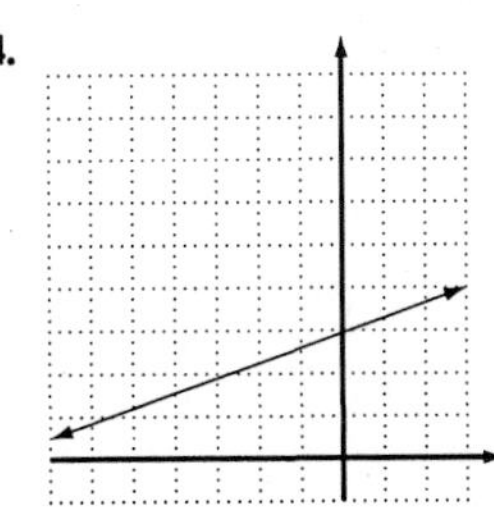

5.

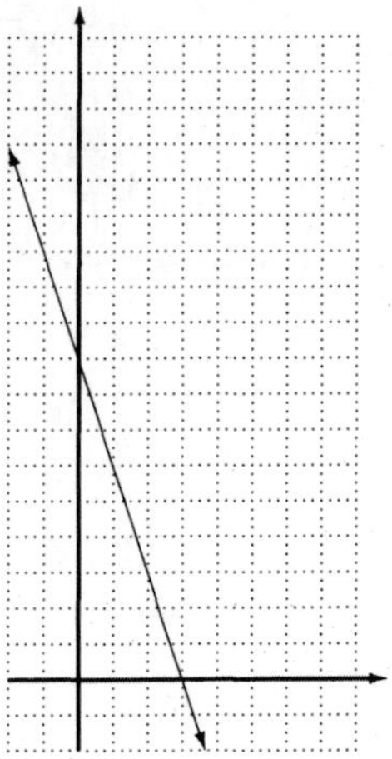

6.

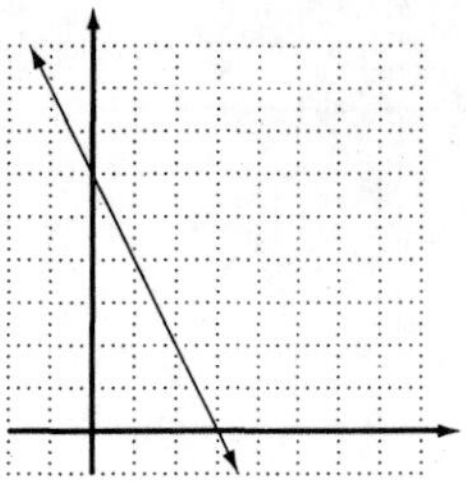

7.

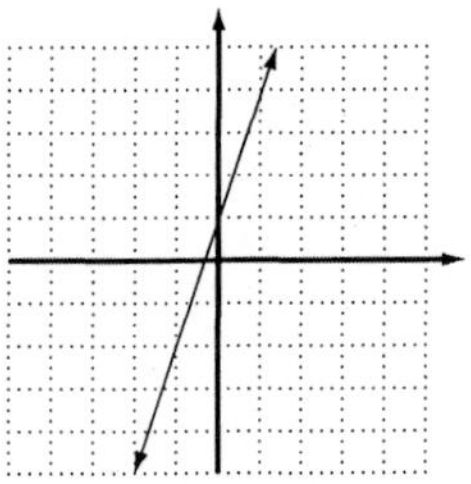

8.

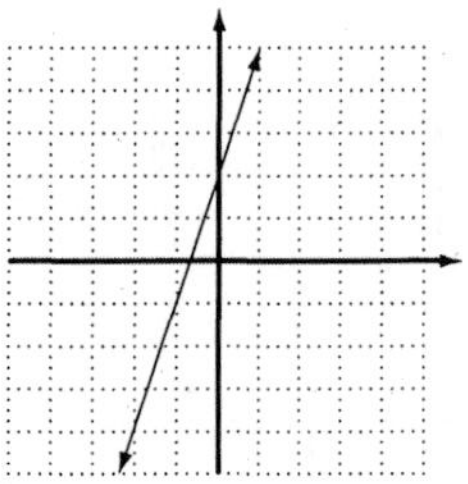

9.

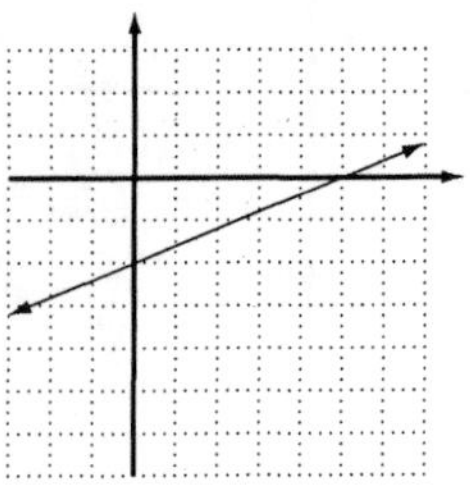

10.

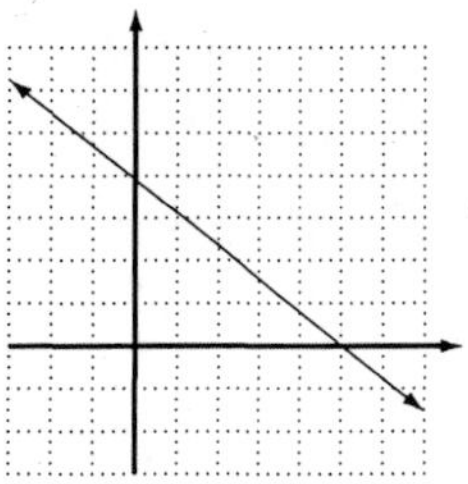

11.

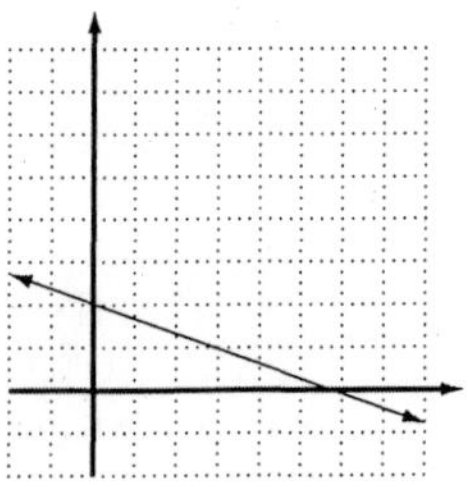

12.

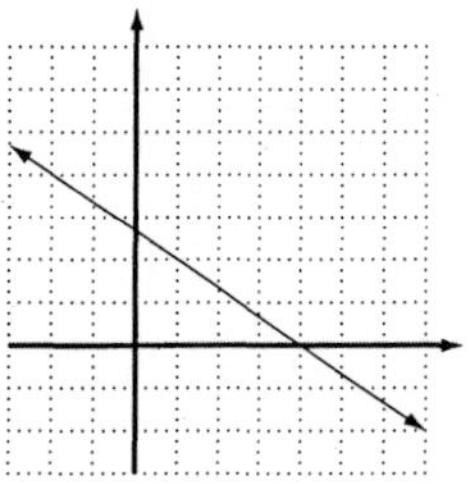

13.

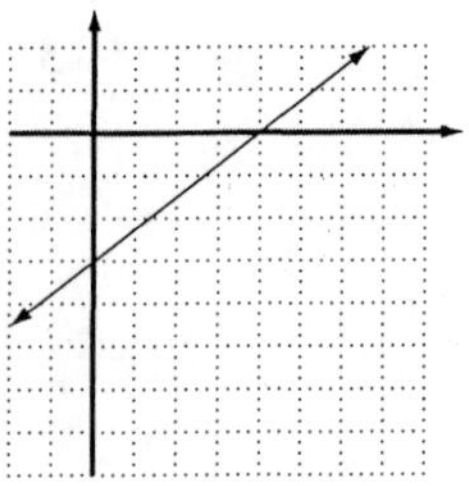

14.

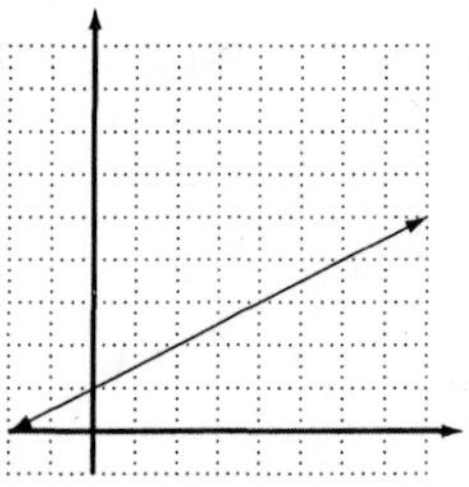

15.

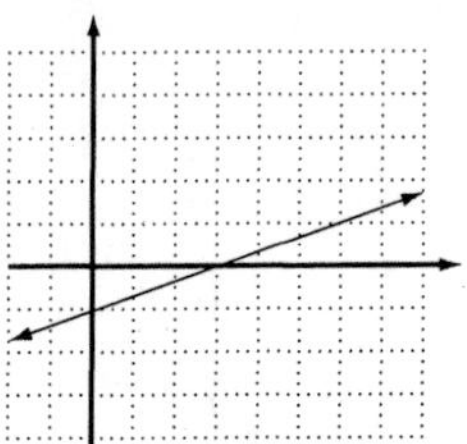

16.

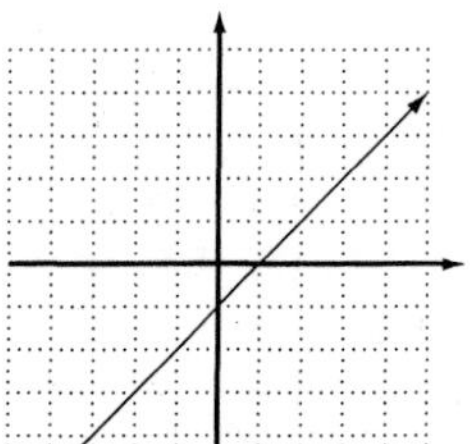

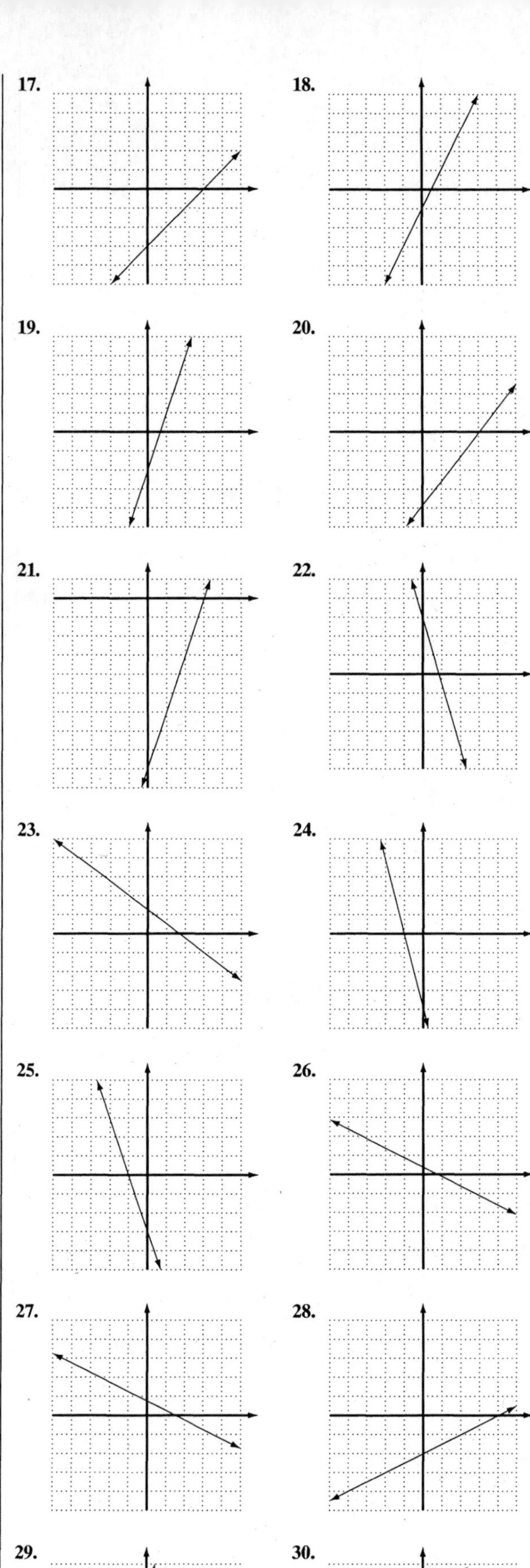

17.

18.

19.

20.

21.

22.

23.

24.

25.

26.

27.

28.

29.

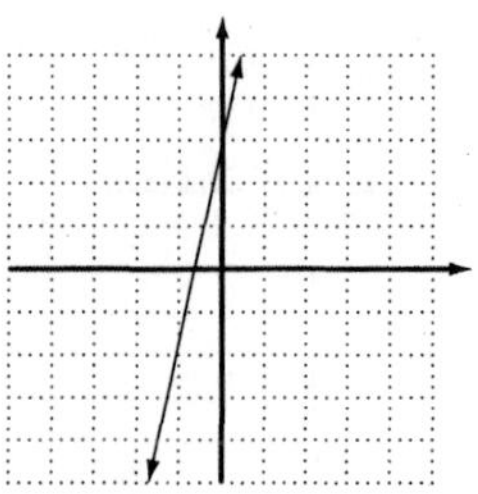

30.

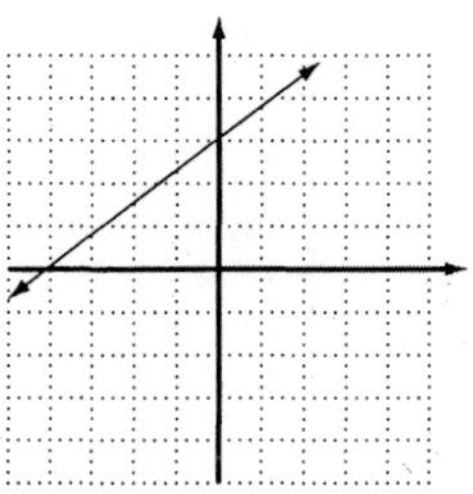

31. 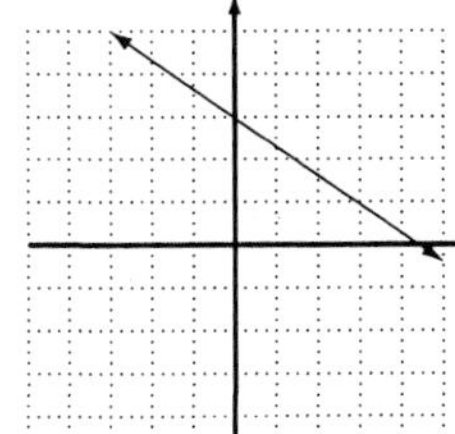

32. 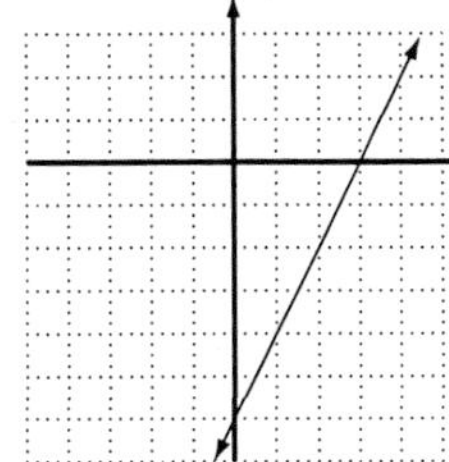

33. 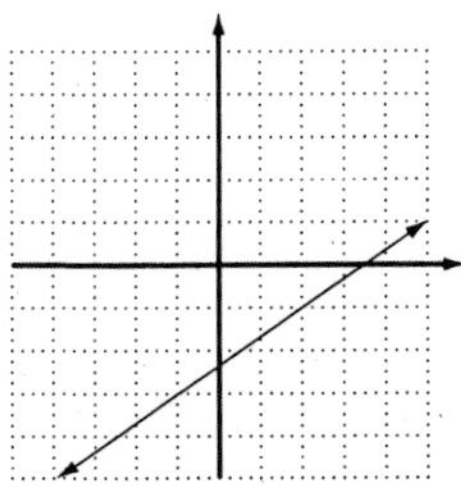

34. 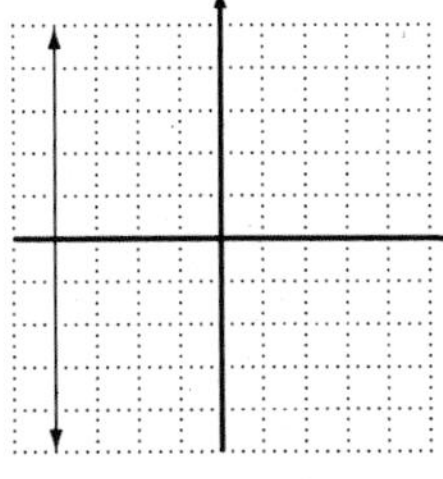

35. 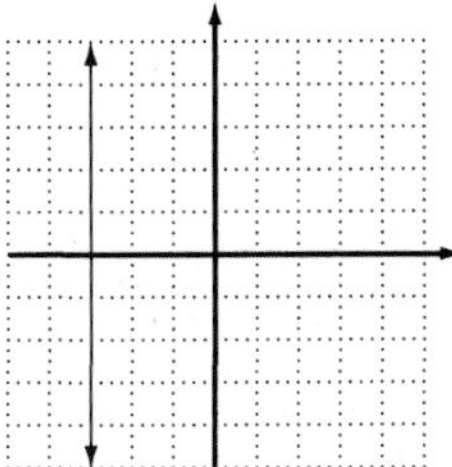

36. 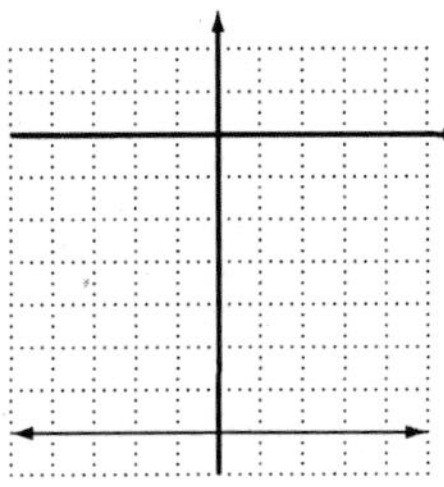

37. 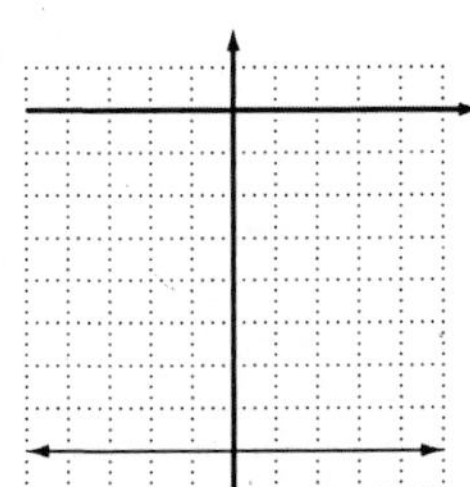

38. 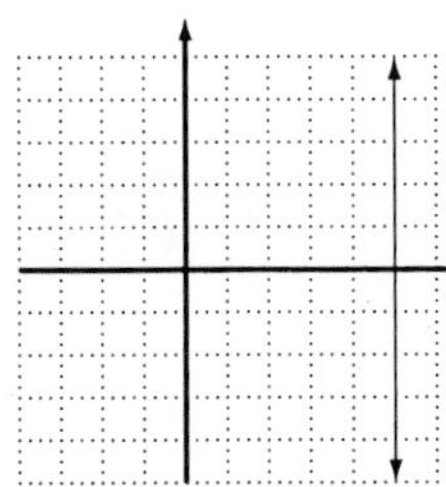

39. 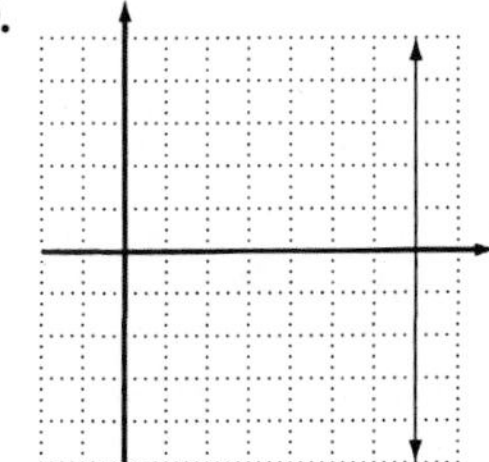

40. 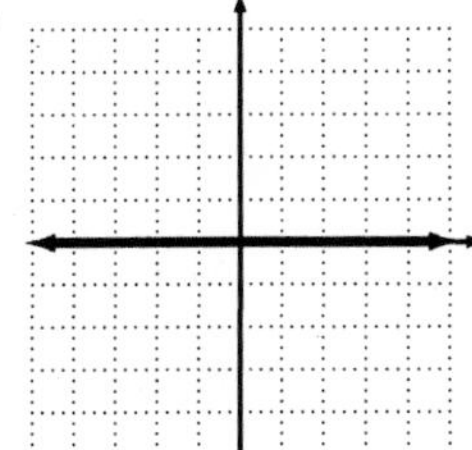

41. 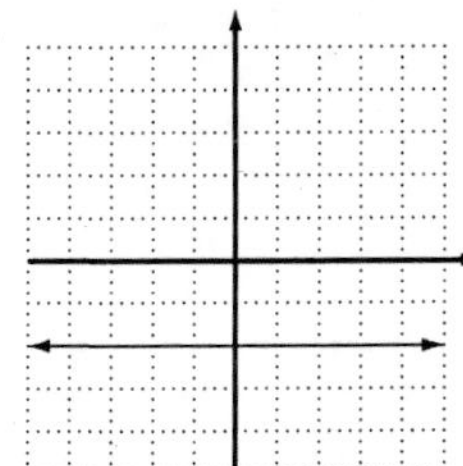

42. $x = 0$ **43.** $(-3, 6)$

44. The graph of $x = -2$ comes within 2 units of the origin at $(0, -2)$. The closest that the graph of $x = 3$ comes to the origin is 3 units at $(0, 3)$.

45. *c* **46.** *b* **47.** *d* **48.** *a* **49.** *e*

50. $2y - x = 0$ is an equation for line c in the graph, but it is not in standard form. The answer is A.

51. Changing the constant raises or lowers the graph.

52. $y = -5$ **53.** $x = 13$ **54.** $y = 2.8$ **55.** $x = -3\frac{1}{2}$

56. 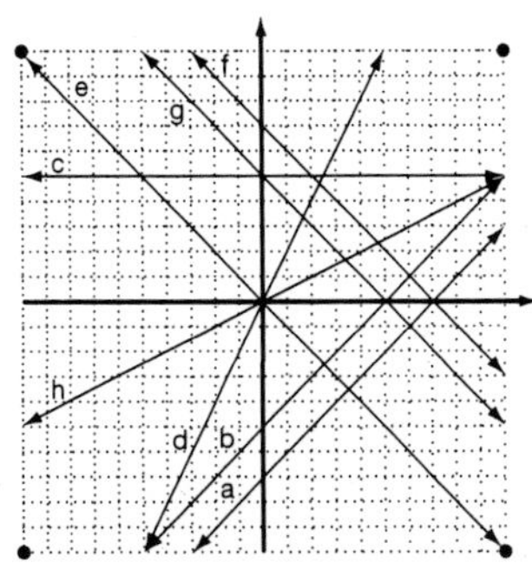

57. e; b and g, a and f, d and h

58. Always true; the x term, y term, and constant term are in the correct positions, $-A$, $-B$, and $-C$ are constants, and $-A$ and $-B$ are not both 0. So $-Ax - By = -C$ is in standard form by definition.

59. $x^2 + 24x + 144 = (x + 12)^2$ Yes

60. $m^2 - 24m - 144$ No

61. $a^2 - 2ac + c^2 = (a - c)^2$ Yes

62. $a^2c - ac^2 = ac(a - c)$

63. $x^2y^2 - 2xy - 8 = (xy - 4)(xy + 2)$

64. $a^2 - 3ab - 4b^2 = (a - 4b)(a + b)$

65. $a = \frac{v^2}{r}$, $ar = v^2$, $r = \frac{v^2}{a}$

66. $K = \frac{1}{2}Iw^2$, $2K = Iw^2$, $\frac{2K}{w^2} = I$

67. $\frac{2500}{65} \approx 38.5$ minutes

CONNECTIONS: REASONING p. 317

1. *D* **2.** *C* **3.** *F* **4.** *B*

LESSON 7-4 TRY THIS pp. 319–320

a. 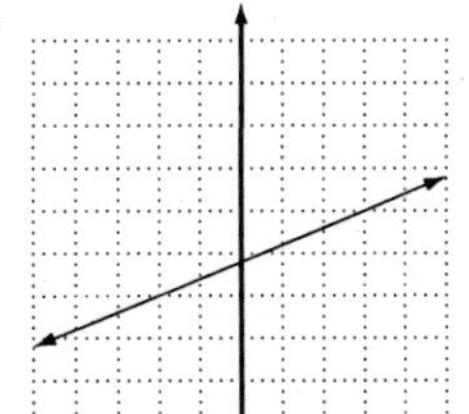

slope $= \frac{2}{5}$

b. 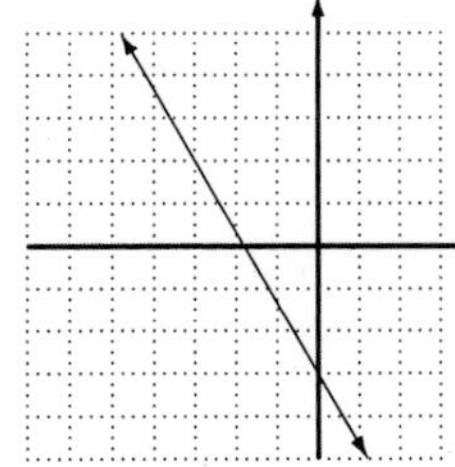

slope $= -\frac{5}{3}$

c. $\frac{9 - 2}{8 - 2} = \frac{7}{6}$ **d.** $\frac{-2 - (-6)}{3 - (-4)} = \frac{4}{7}$

e. $\frac{1 - 3}{2 - (-2)} = \frac{-2}{4} = -\frac{1}{2}$ **f.** $\frac{4 - (-11)}{-9 - 5} = -\frac{15}{14}$

g. $\frac{7 - 7}{3 - 9} = \frac{0}{-6} = 0$ **h.** $\frac{0 - (-6)}{4 - 4} = \frac{6}{0}$ No slope

i. $\frac{5 - 4}{-1 - 2} = \frac{1}{-3} = -\frac{1}{3}$

LESSON 7-4 EXERCISES pp. 321–322

1. $m = \frac{5 - (-1)}{3 - 1} = \frac{6}{2} = 3$

2. $m = \frac{3 - (-2)}{2 - (-2)} = \frac{5}{4}$

3. $m = \frac{7 - (-2)}{-2 - 5} = \frac{9}{-7} = -\frac{9}{7}$

4. $m = \frac{7 - 4}{4 - (-3)} = \frac{3}{7}$

5.

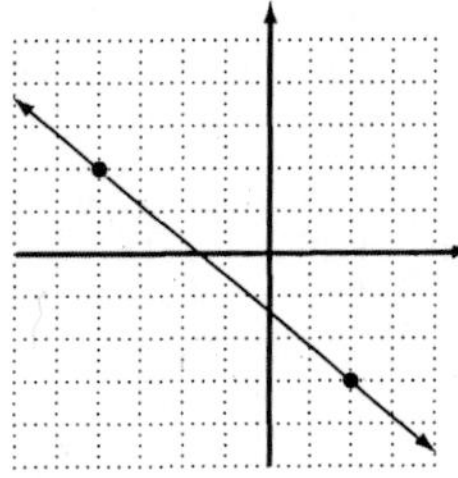

slope $= -\frac{5}{6}$

6.

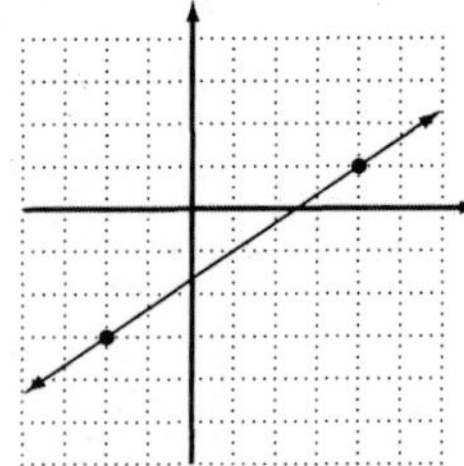

slope $= \frac{4}{6} = \frac{2}{3}$

7.

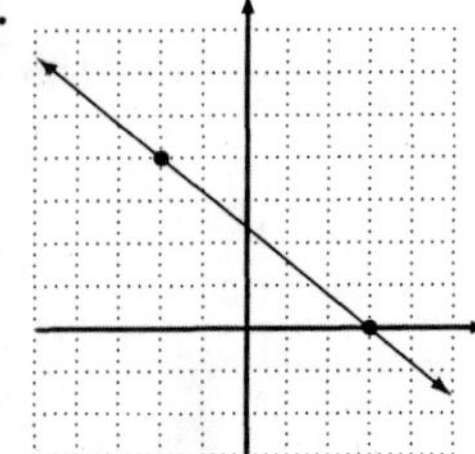

slope $= -\frac{4}{5}$

8.

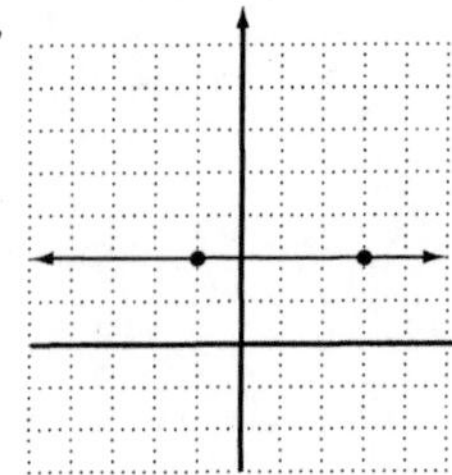

slope $= 0$

9.

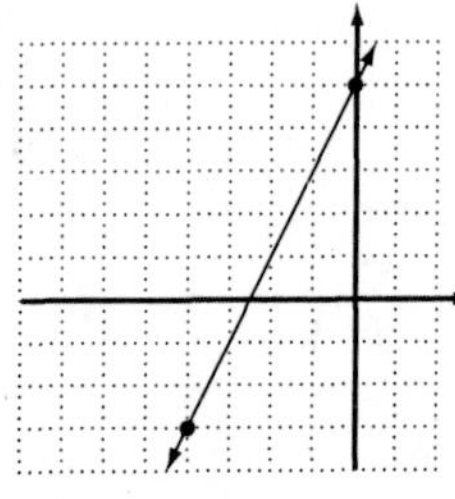

slope $= \frac{8}{4} = 2$

10.

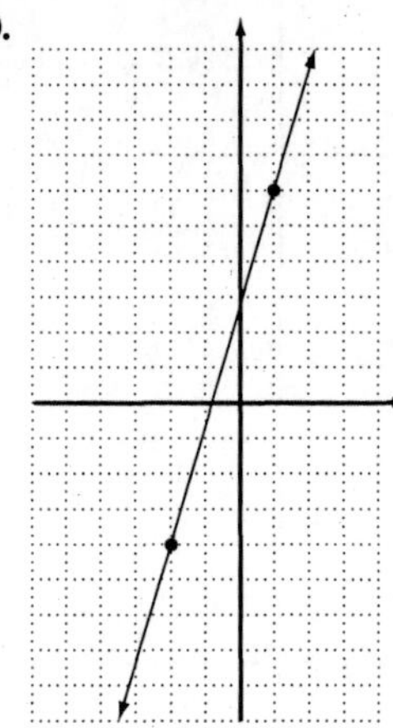

slope $= \frac{10}{3}$

11. $m = \frac{7 - 0}{5 - 4} = \frac{7}{1} = 7$ 12. $m = \frac{2 - 0}{6 - 3} = \frac{2}{3}$

13. $m = \frac{10 - 8}{-3 - 0} = \frac{2}{-3} = -\frac{2}{3}$ 14. $m = \frac{9 - 7}{0 - 4} = \frac{2}{-4} = -\frac{1}{2}$

15. $m = \frac{-2 - (-6)}{3 - 5} = \frac{4}{-2} = -2$

16. $m = \frac{4 - (-7)}{-2 - 6} = \frac{11}{-8} = -\frac{11}{8}$

17. $m = \frac{0 - (-9)}{0 - (-3)} = \frac{9}{3} = 3$

18. $m = \frac{0 - (-8)}{0 - (-4)} = \frac{8}{4} = 2$

19. $m = \frac{\frac{1}{2} - \left(-\frac{1}{2}\right)}{\frac{3}{4} - \frac{1}{4}} = \frac{1}{\frac{1}{2}} = 1 \cdot \frac{2}{1} = 2$

20. $m = \frac{\frac{3}{4} - \frac{1}{8}}{\frac{1}{2} - \frac{1}{4}} = \frac{\frac{6}{8} - \frac{1}{8}}{\frac{2}{4} - \frac{1}{4}} = \frac{\frac{5}{8}}{\frac{1}{4}} = \frac{5}{8} \cdot \frac{4}{1} = \frac{20}{8} = \frac{5}{2}$

21. No slope 22. No slope 23. Zero slope 24. Zero slope

25. No slope 26. No slope 27. Zero slope 28. Zero slope

29. $\frac{7 - 3}{x - 4} = 2$

$7 - 3 = 2(x - 4)$

$4 = 2x - 8$

$12 = 2x; \quad x = 6$

30. $\frac{3 - y}{-6 - 9} = \frac{2}{3}$

$-15 \cdot \frac{3 - y}{-15} = -15 \cdot \frac{2}{3}$

$3 - y = -10$

$-y = -13$

31. $\frac{4y - y}{2 - (-4)} = 6$

$3y = 6(6) = 36$

$y = \frac{36}{3} = 12$

32. $7\% = \frac{7}{100}$ 33. $\frac{11.7}{30} = 0.39, 0.39 \times 100\% = 39\%$

34. $XY: m = \frac{4 - 2}{-1 - 2} = \frac{2}{-3} = -\frac{2}{3}$

$XZ: m = \frac{4 - (-2)}{-1 - 2} = \frac{6}{-3} = -2$

$YZ: m = \frac{2 - (-2)}{2 - 2} = \frac{4}{0}$ No slope

35. a. $\frac{\text{rise}}{\text{run}} = \frac{12}{5}; \frac{\text{rise}}{\text{run}} = \frac{18}{5}; \frac{\text{rise}}{\text{run}} = \frac{24}{5}$

b. Greatest slope $= \frac{20}{5} = 4$. From that position, the rise decreased to 0 while the run increased to 20. Thus all slope values from 4 down to $m = \frac{0}{20} = 0$ occurred during the slide.

36. $\frac{1 - 3}{1 - (-1)} = \frac{-2}{2} = -1$

$\frac{-8 - 1}{10 - 1} = \frac{-9}{9} = -1$

Thus the lines through (1, 1) and (−1, 3) and through (1, 1) and (10, −8) have the same slope, −1. Since they have the same slope and contain the same point, (1, 1), they must be the same line, and all three points are on that line.

37. slope $= \frac{p - q}{q - p} = \frac{-(q - p)}{q - p} = -1$

38. Up 2, right 1 or down 2, left 1: slope = 2
Up 2, left 1 or down 2, right 1: slope = −2
Up 1, right 2 or down 1, left 2: slope $= \frac{1}{2}$
Up 1, left 2 or down 1, right 2: slope $= -\frac{1}{2}$

39. In using the slope formula, Garth subtracted the y-coordinates (numerator) and the x-coordinates (denominator) in opposite orders.

40. $9m^4n^2 - 16 = (3m^2n + 4)(3m^2n - 4)$

41. $a^2b^2 + ab - 2 = (ab + 2)(ab - 1)$

42. $3x^2 + 2xy - y^2 = (3x - y)(x + y)$

43.
$$\begin{aligned} 3x - y &= 2 \\ 3(0) - (-2) &= 2 \\ 0 + 2 &= 2 \\ 2 &= 2 \quad \text{Yes} \end{aligned}$$

44.
$$\begin{aligned} 3x - 2y &= 2 \\ 3(2) - 2(3) &= 2 \\ 6 - 6 & \\ 0 & \quad \text{No} \end{aligned}$$

45. $2.575 \times 10^{-3} = 0.002575$

46. $1.004 \times 10^5 = 100{,}400$

47.
$$\begin{aligned} y^2 - 7y - 18 &= 0 \\ (y - 9)(y + 2) &= 0 \\ y - 9 = 0 \quad &\text{or} \quad y + 2 = 0 \\ y = 9 \quad &\text{or} \quad y = -2 \end{aligned}$$

48.
$$\begin{aligned} m^2 + 3m - 10 &= 0 \\ (m + 5)(m - 2) &= 0 \\ m + 5 = 0 \quad &\text{or} \quad m - 2 = 0 \\ m = -5 \quad &\text{or} \quad m = 2 \end{aligned}$$

49.
$$\begin{aligned} a^2 + 4a + 4 &= 0 \\ (a + 2)(a + 2) &= 0 \\ a + 2 &= 0 \\ a &= -2 \end{aligned}$$

LESSON 7-5 TRY THIS pp. 324–325

a. $5y = -4x + 7$

$y = -\frac{4}{5}x + \frac{7}{5}$; the slope is $-\frac{4}{5}$

b. $8y = -3x + 9$

$y = -\frac{3}{8}x + \frac{9}{8}$; the slope is $-\frac{3}{8}$

c. $5y = -x + 7$

$y = -\frac{1}{5}x + \frac{7}{5}$; the slope is $-\frac{1}{5}$

d. $-4y = -5x + 8$

$y = \frac{5}{4}x - \frac{8}{4}$; the slope is $\frac{5}{4}$

e. $y = 5x + 0$ slope is 5, y-intercept 0

f. $y = -\frac{3}{2}x - 6$ slope is $-\frac{3}{2}$, y-intercept −6

g. $3x + 4y = 16$
$4y = -3x + 16$
$y = -\frac{3}{4}x + 4$ slope is $-\frac{3}{4}$, y-intercept 4

h. $-7x - 5y = 25$
$-5y = 7x + 25$
$y = -\frac{7}{5}x - 5$ slope is $-\frac{7}{5}$, y-intercept −5

i.

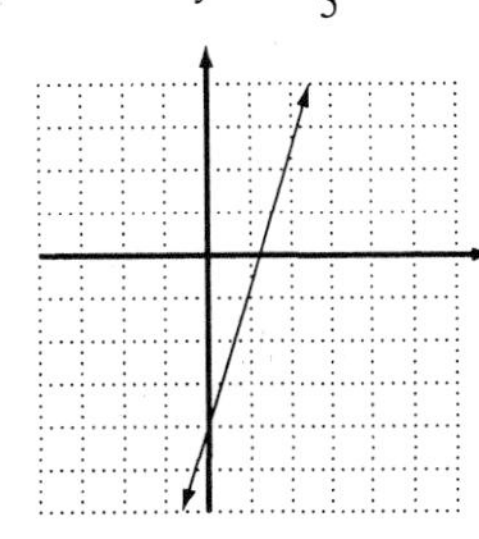

j.

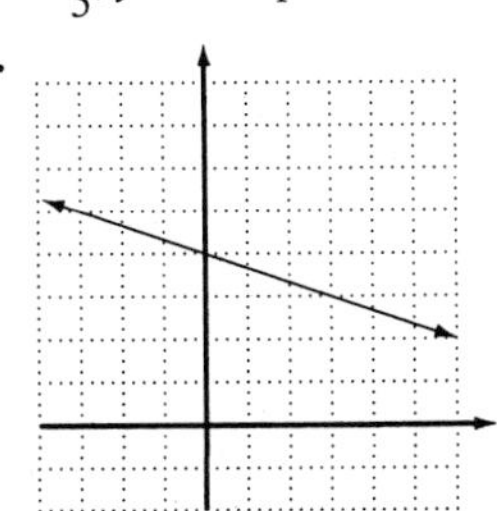

k.

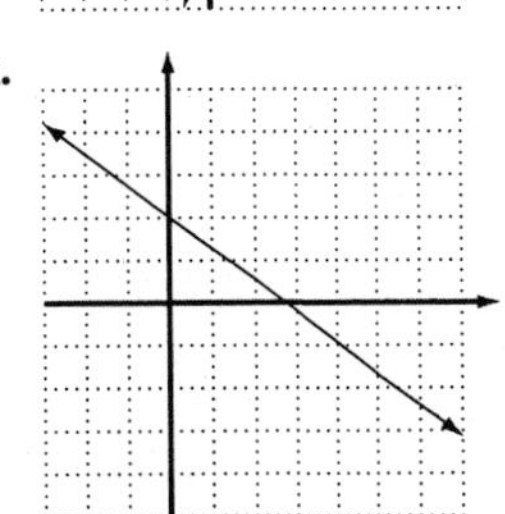

LESSON 7-5 EXERCISES pp. 326–327

1. $3x + 2y = 6$
$2y = -3x + 6$
$y = -\frac{3}{2}x + 3 \qquad m = -\frac{3}{2}$

2. $4x - y = 5$
$4x - 5 = y \qquad m = 4$

3. $x + 4y = 8$
$4y = -x + 8$
$y = -\frac{1}{4}x + 2 \qquad m = -\frac{1}{4}$

4. $x + 3y = 6$
$3y = -x + 6$
$y = -\frac{1}{3}x + 2 \qquad m = -\frac{1}{3}$

5. $-2x + y = 4$
$y = 2x + 4 \qquad m = 2$

6. $-5x + y = 5$
$y = 5x + 5 \qquad m = 5$

7. $4x - 3y = -12$
$-3y = -4x - 12$
$y = \frac{4}{3}x + 4 \qquad m = \frac{4}{3}$

8. $3x - 4y = -12$
$-4y = -3x - 12$
$y = \frac{3}{4}x + 3 \qquad m = \frac{3}{4}$

9. $x - 2y = 9$
$-2y = -x + 9$
$y = \frac{1}{2}x - \frac{9}{2} \qquad m = \frac{1}{2}$

10. $x - 3y = -2$
$-3y = -x - 2$
$y = \frac{1}{3}x + \frac{2}{3} \qquad m = \frac{1}{3}$

11. $-2x + 4y = 8$
$4y = 2x + 8$
$y = \frac{1}{2}x + 2 \qquad m = \frac{1}{2}$

12. $-5x + 7y = 2$
$7y = 5x + 2$
$y = \frac{5}{7}x + \frac{2}{7} \qquad m = \frac{5}{7}$

13. $-7x + 5y = 16$
$5y = 7x + 16$
$y = \frac{7}{5}x + \frac{16}{5} \qquad m = \frac{7}{5}$

14. $-3x + 2y = 9$
$2y = 3x + 9$
$y = \frac{3}{2}x + \frac{9}{2} \qquad m = \frac{3}{2}$

15. $-6x - 9y = 13$
$-9y = 6x + 13$
$y = -\frac{2}{3}x - \frac{13}{9} \qquad m = -\frac{2}{3}$

16. $-8x - 5y = 18$
$-5y = 8x + 18$
$y = -\frac{8}{5}x - \frac{18}{5} \qquad m = -\frac{8}{5}$

17. $8x + 9y = 10$
$9y = -8x + 10$
$y = -\frac{8}{9}x + \frac{10}{9} \qquad m = -\frac{8}{9}$

18. $7x + 4y = 13$
$4y = -7x + 13$
$y = -\frac{7}{4}x + \frac{13}{4} \qquad m = -\frac{7}{4}$

19. $y = -4x - 9 \qquad m = -4$, y-intercept $= -9$

20. $y = -3x - 5 \qquad m = -3$, y-intercept $= -5$

21. $2x + 3y = 9$
$3y = -2x + 9$
$y = -\frac{2}{3}x + 3 \qquad m = -\frac{2}{3}$, y-intercept $= 3$

22. $5x + 4y = 12$
$4y = -5x + 12$
$y = -\frac{5}{4}x + 3 \qquad m = -\frac{5}{4}$, y-intercept $= 3$

23. $-8x - 7y = 21$
$-7y = 8x + 21$
$y = -\frac{8}{7}x - 3 \qquad m = -\frac{8}{7}$, y-intercept $= -3$

24. $-2x - 9y = 13$
$-9y = 2x + 13$
$y = -\frac{2}{9}x - \frac{13}{9} \qquad m = -\frac{2}{9}$, y-intercept $= -\frac{13}{9}$

25. $9x = 3y + 5$
$9x - 5 = 3y$
$3x - \frac{5}{3} = y \qquad m = 3$, y-intercept $= -\frac{5}{3}$

26. $4x = 9y + 7$
$4x - 7 = 9y$
$\frac{4}{9}x - \frac{7}{9} = y \qquad m = \frac{4}{9}$, y-intercept $= -\frac{7}{9}$

27. $-6x = 4y + 2$
$-6x - 2 = 4y$
$-\frac{3}{2}x - \frac{1}{2} = y \qquad m = -\frac{3}{2}$, y-intercept $= -\frac{1}{2}$

28.

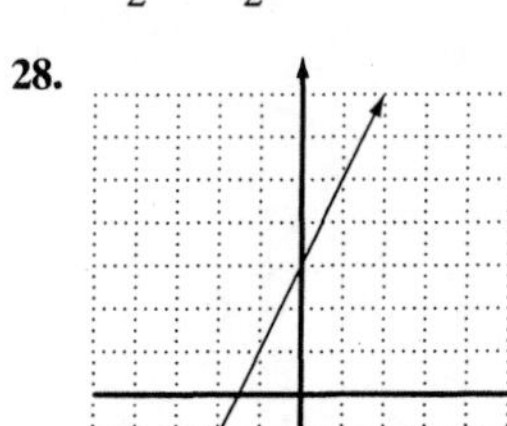

29.

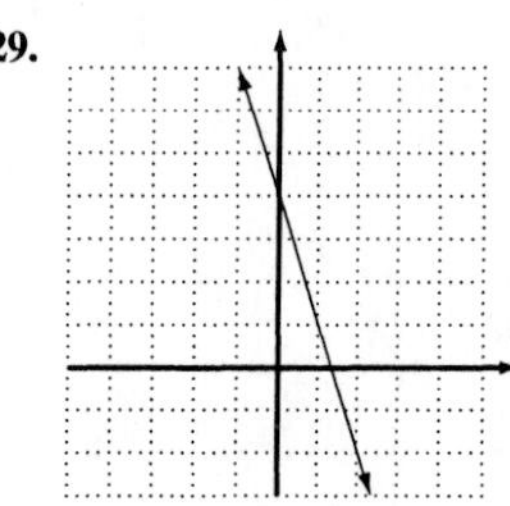

30.

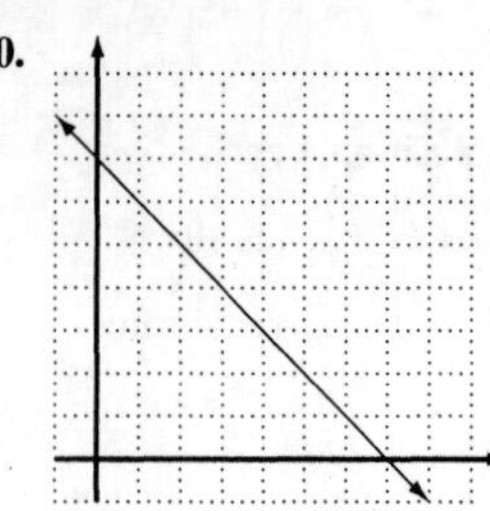

31.

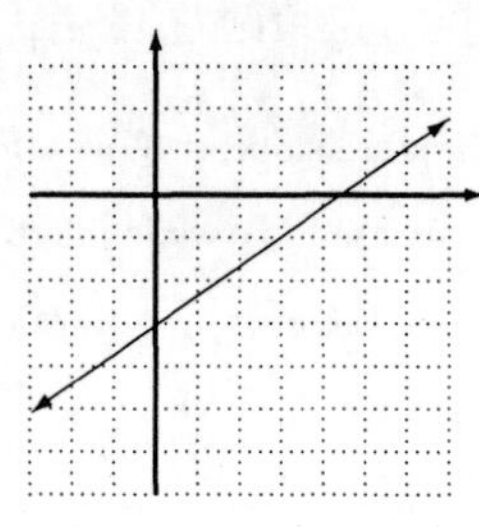

32.

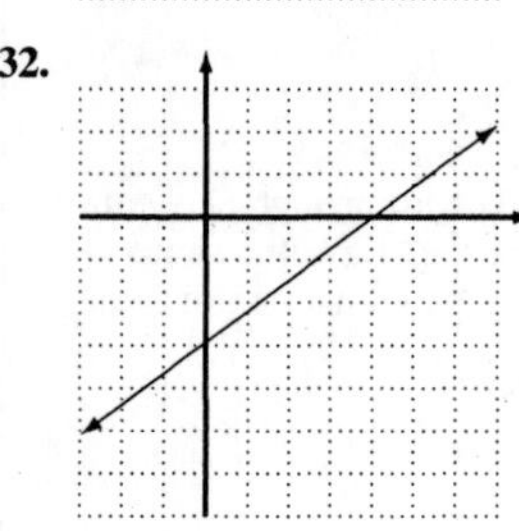

33.

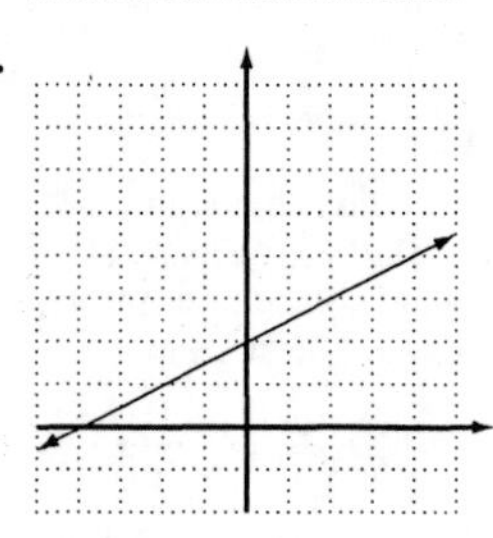

34.

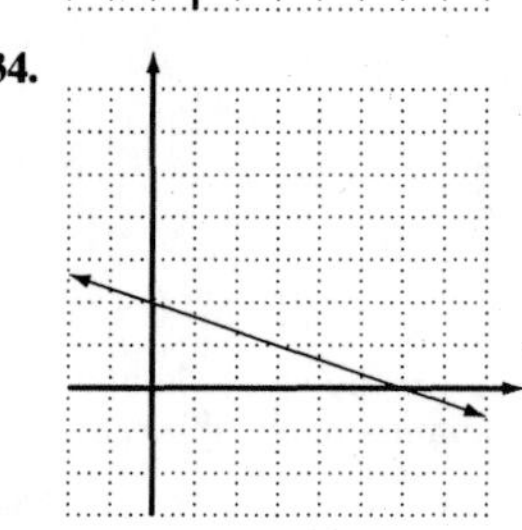

35.

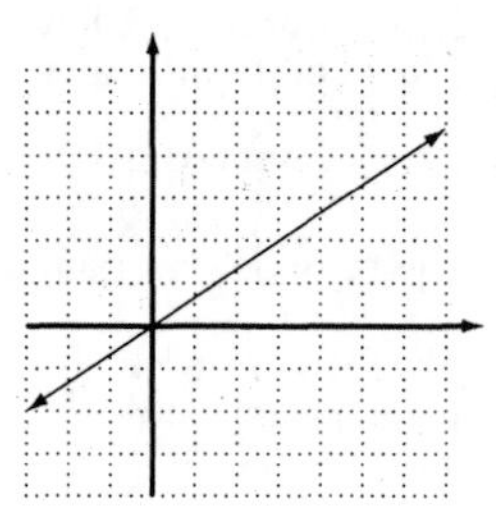

36.

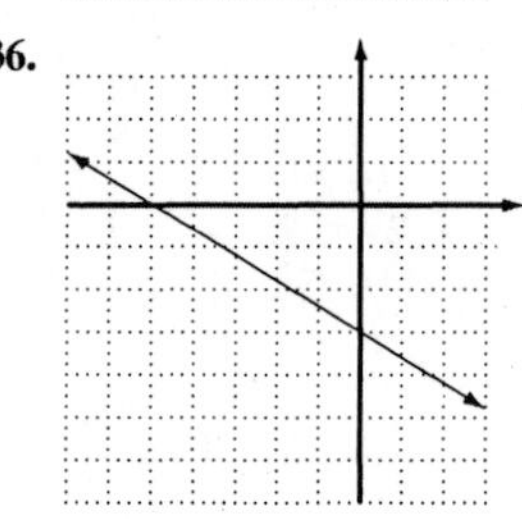

37.

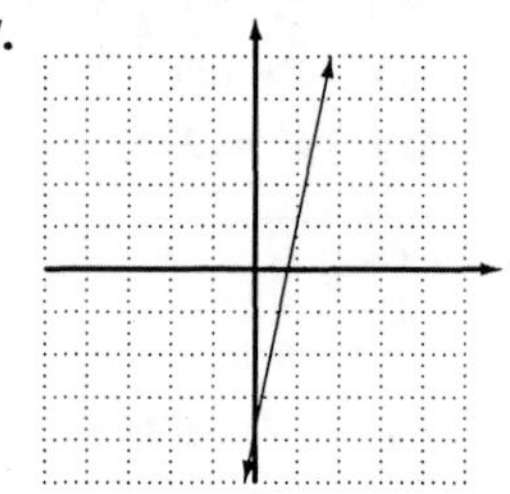

38.

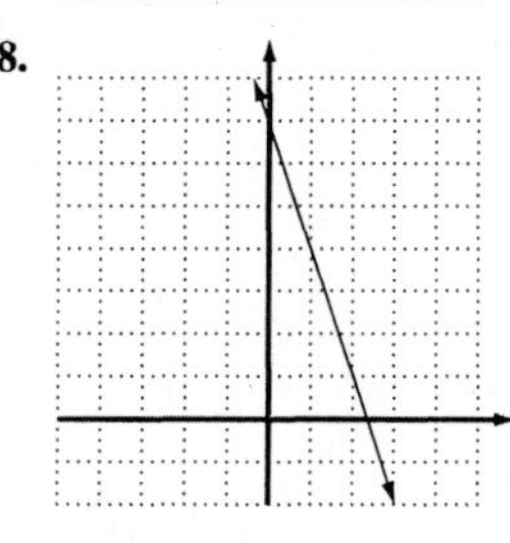

39.

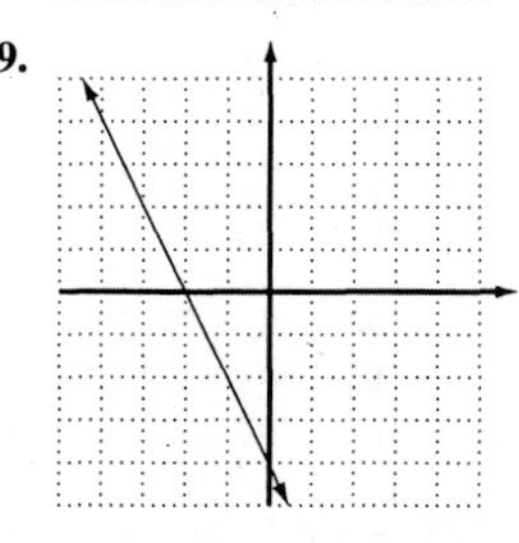

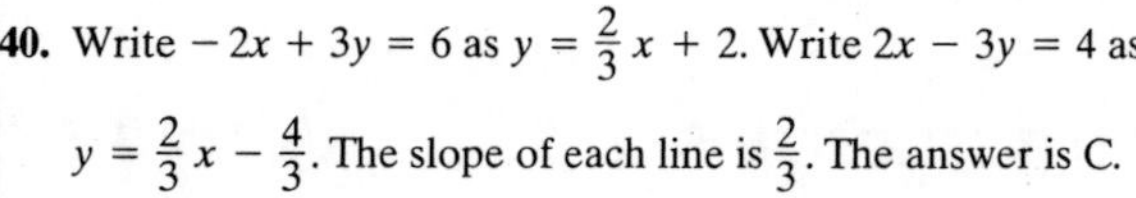

40. Write $-2x + 3y = 6$ as $y = \frac{2}{3}x + 2$. Write $2x - 3y = 4$ as $y = \frac{2}{3}x - \frac{4}{3}$. The slope of each line is $\frac{2}{3}$. The answer is C.

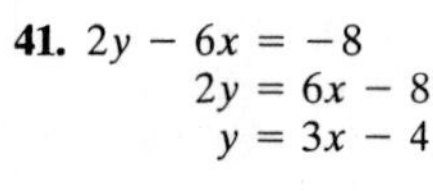

41. $2y - 6x = -8$
$2y = 6x - 8$
$y = 3x - 4$

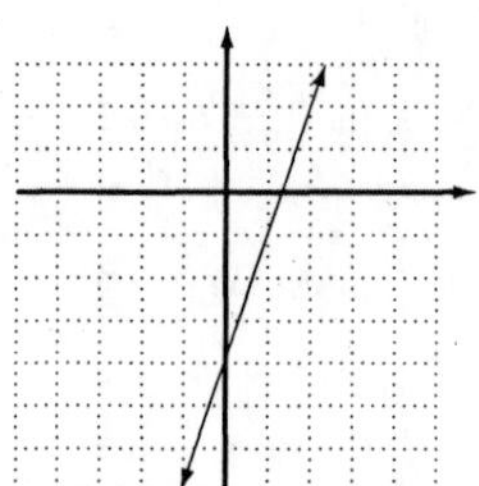

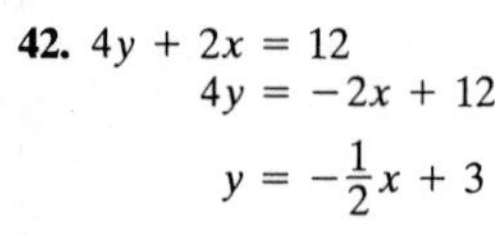

42. $4y + 2x = 12$
$4y = -2x + 12$
$y = -\frac{1}{2}x + 3$

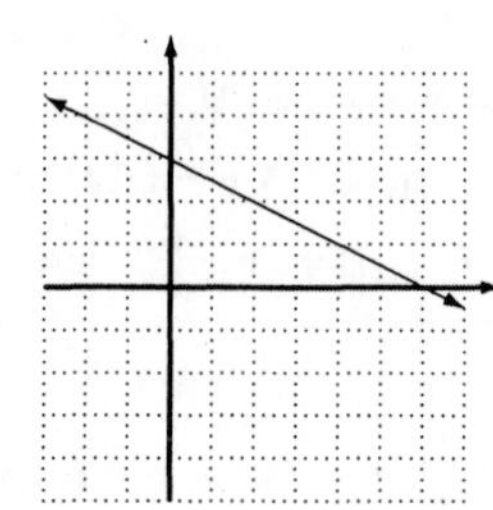

43. $2x - 5y = 15$
$-5y = -2x + 15$
$y = \frac{2}{5}x - 3$

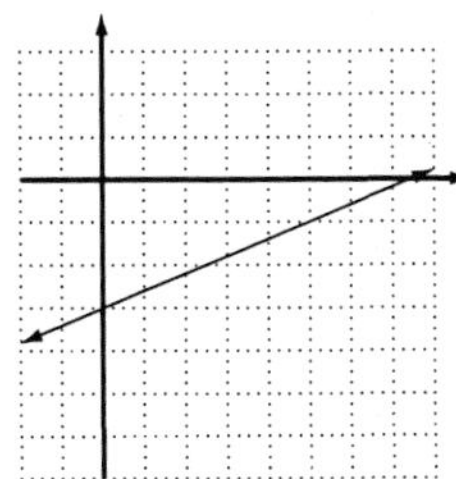

44. $6x + 3y = -12$
$3y = -6x - 12$
$y = -2x - 4$

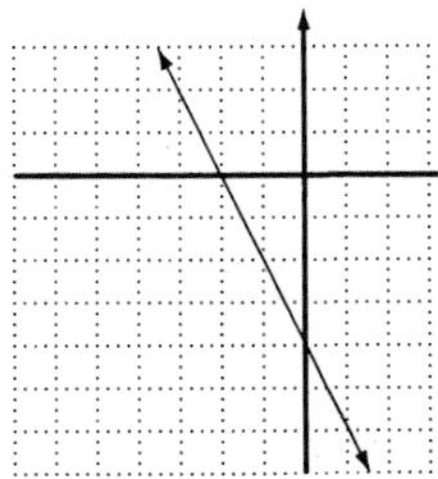

45. $8x - 3y = 15$
$-3y = -8x + 15$
$y = \frac{8}{3}x - 5$

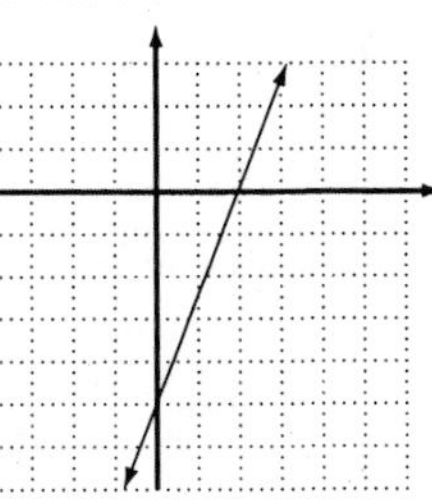

46. $-2x = -4y + 16$
$-2x - 16 = -4y$
$\frac{1}{2}x + 4 = y$

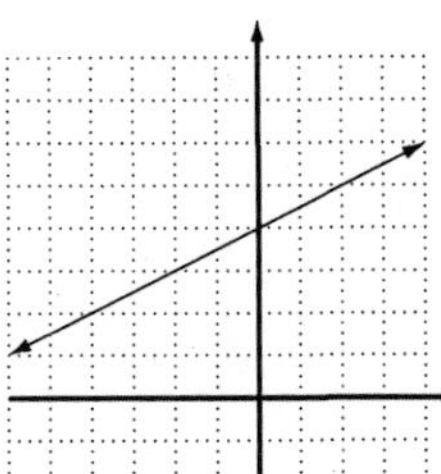

47. $ky + 2x = 7$
$ky = -2x + 7$
$y = -\frac{2}{k}x + \frac{7}{k}$

The slope is $-\frac{2}{k} = 1$.
$-2 = k$

48. $y = 3x - 2$ **49.** $y = 8x$ **50.** $y = -5$

51. $y = -7x + 4$ **52.** $y = \frac{1}{2}x + 1$ **53.** $y = -6x + \frac{3}{4}$

54. $y = \frac{2}{3}x - 8$

55. $3(x + 4) = y - 8x + 3$
$3x + 12 = y - 8x + 3$
$11x + 12 = y + 3$
$11x + 9 = y$ $m = 11, b = 9$

56. $2y + 4x = 3(y - x) + 8$
$2y + 4x = 3y - 3x + 8$
$2y + 7x = 3y + 8$
$7x = y + 8$
$7x - 8 = y$ $m = 7, b = -8$

57.

slopes: $-3, 3$; vertex $(0, 5)$

58. First row:
$Ax + By = C$
$By = -Ax + C$
$y = -\frac{A}{B}x + \frac{C}{B}$ (slope-intercept form)

The y-intercept is $\frac{C}{B}$.

In $Ax + By = C$, if $y = 0$, then
$Ax + B(0) = C$
$Ax = C$
$x = \frac{C}{A}$

The x-intercept is $\frac{C}{A}$.

Second row:
$y = mx + b$ (The y-intercept is b.)
$-mx + y = b$ (standard form)
If $y = 0$, then
$-mx + 0 = b$ (standard form)
$-mx = b$
$x = -\frac{b}{m}$ $\left(\text{The } x\text{-intercept is } -\frac{b}{m}.\right)$

Third row:

Slope $= \frac{b - 0}{0 - a} = -\frac{b}{a}$, y-intercept $= b$, so

$y = -\frac{b}{a}x + b$ (slope-intercept form)

$\frac{b}{a}x + y = b$ or $bx + ay = ab$ (standard form)

The completed table:

Standard Form	Slope-Intercept Form	x- and y-Intercepts
$Ax + By = C$, $A \neq 0$, $B \neq 0$	$y = -\frac{A}{B}x + \frac{C}{B}$	$\left(\frac{C}{A}, 0\right)$ and $\left(0, \frac{C}{B}\right)$
$-mx + y = b$	$y = mx + b$	$\left(-\frac{b}{m}, 0\right)$ and $(0, b)$
$\frac{b}{a}x + y = b$	$y = -\frac{b}{a}x + b$	$(a, 0)$ and $(0, b)$ $a \neq 0$, $b \neq 0$

59. IV **60.** II **61.** I **62.** III **63.** IV **64.** II

65. Answers may vary. $(-1, 3), (1, 2), \left(2, \frac{3}{2}\right)$

66. Answers may vary. $(-2, -1), (2, 1), (4, 2)$

67. Answers may vary. $(0, 2), (1, -1), (-1, 5)$

68. Answers may vary. $(2, 0), (0, -2), (1, -1)$

69. $25b^2 - 16a^2 = (5b + 4a)(5b - 4a)$

70. $a^4 + 4a^3b + 4a^2b^2 = a^2(a^2 + 4ab + 4b^2) = a^2(a + 2b)^2$

71. $mn + 5m + 3n + 15 = m(n + 5) + 3(n + 5)$
$= (m + 3)(n + 5)$

72. $6x^2 + 14x + 8 = 2(3x^2 + 7x + 4) = 2(x + 1)(3x + 4)$

73. $12y^2 - 108 = 0$
$12(y^2 - 9) = 0$
$12(y + 3)(y - 3) = 0$
$y + 3 = 0$ or $y - 3 = 0$
$y = -3$ or $y = 3$

74. $a^2 - 3a - 10 = 0$
$(a - 5)(a + 2) = 0$
$a - 5 = 0$ or $a + 2 = 0$
$a = 5$ or $a = -2$

75. $x^2 - 25 = 0$
$(x + 5)(x - 5) = 0$
$x + 5 = 0$ or $x - 5 = 0$
$x = -5$ or $x = 5$

76. Let n = number of erasers.
$n = 144 \times 31 + 4$
$n = 4468$
4468 erasers were produced.

CONNECTIONS: REASONING p. 327

a. Same slope, but $b = 6$
b. Same y-intercept, but $m = 6$
c. $2y = 6x - 8$
$y = 3x - 4$ Same line
d. $4 = 3x - y$
$y = 3x - 4$ Same line
e. $y = \frac{-x}{3} - 4$

$y = -\frac{1}{3}x - 4$

Same y-intercept, but $m = -\frac{1}{3}$

f. $-y = -3x + 4$
$y = 3x - 4$ Same line

LESSON 7-6 TRY THIS pp. 328–330

a. $y = mx + b$
$2 = 5 \cdot 4 + b; -18 = b$ so $y = 5x - 18$
b. $y = mx + b$
$1 = -3 \cdot -2 + b; -5 = b$ so $y = -3x - 5$
c. $\frac{6-2}{2-8} = -\frac{4}{6} = -\frac{2}{3} = m$

$2 = -\frac{2}{3}(8) + b; \frac{22}{3} = b$

$y = -\frac{2}{3}x + \frac{22}{3}$

d. $\frac{-5-4}{-3-(-1)} = \frac{9}{2} = m$

$4 = \frac{9}{2}(-1) + b; \frac{17}{2} = b$

$y = \frac{9}{2}x + \frac{17}{2}$

e. $y - 5 = 6(x - 3)$
$y - 5 = 6x - 18$
$y = 6x - 13$

f. $y - 4 = -\frac{2}{3}(x - 1)$

$y - 4 = -\frac{2}{3}x + \frac{2}{3}$

$y = -\frac{2}{3}x + \frac{14}{3}$

g. $y = x + 2$

h. $y = mx + b$

$4 = -\frac{7}{6}(-4) + b$

$-\frac{2}{3} = b$

$y = -\frac{7}{6}x - \frac{2}{3}$

LESSON 7-6 EXERCISES pp. 331–332

1. $y = 5x + b$
$5 = 5(2) + b$
$5 = 10 + b$
$-5 = b$ $y = 5x - 5$

2. $y = -2x + b$
$0 = -2(-3) + b$
$0 = 6 + b$
$-6 = b$ $y = -2x - 6$

3. $y = \frac{3}{4}x + b$

$4 = \frac{3}{4}(2) + b$

$4 = \frac{3}{2} + b$

$\frac{5}{2} = b$ $y = \frac{3}{4}x + \frac{5}{2}$

4. $y = -x + b$

$2 = -\frac{1}{2} + b$

$2\frac{1}{2} = b$ $y = -x + 2\frac{1}{2}$ or $y = -x + \frac{5}{2}$

5. $y = x + b$
$-6 = 2 + b$
$-8 = b$ $y = x - 8$

6. $y = -3x + b$
$0 = -3(-3) + b$
$0 = 9 + b$
$-9 = b$ $y = -3x - 9$

7. $y = -3x + 3$

8. $y = \frac{3}{4}x + b$

$3 = \frac{3}{4}(4) + b$

$3 = 3 + b$

$0 = b$ $y = \frac{3}{4}x$

9. $y = \frac{1}{2}x + b$

$1 = \frac{1}{2}(-2) + b$

$1 = -1 + b$

$2 = b$ $y = \frac{1}{2}x + 2$

10. $y = -\frac{3}{5}x + b$

$-5 = -\frac{3}{5}(-3) + b$

$-5 = \frac{9}{5} + b$

$-\frac{34}{5} = b$ $y = -\frac{3}{5}x - \frac{34}{5}$

11. $y = \frac{5}{2}x + b$

$-2 = \frac{5}{2}(-6) + b$

$-2 = -15 + b$

$13 = b$ $y = \frac{5}{2}x + 13$

12. $y = 3x + b$

$0 = 3\left(-\frac{1}{2}\right) + b$

$0 = -\frac{3}{2} + b$

$\frac{3}{2} = b$ $y = 3x + \frac{3}{2}$

13. $m = \frac{3-1}{2-(-6)} = \frac{2}{8} = \frac{1}{4}$

$y = \frac{1}{4}x + b$

$3 = \frac{1}{4}(2) + b$

$3 = \frac{1}{2} + b$

$\frac{5}{2} = b$ $y = \frac{1}{4}x + \frac{5}{2}$

14. $m = \frac{16-5}{12-1} = \frac{11}{11} = 1$
$y = x + b$
$5 = 1 + b$
$4 = b$ $y = x + 4$

15. $m = \frac{4-2}{0-4} = \frac{2}{-4} = -\frac{1}{2}$

$y = -\frac{1}{2}x + b$

$4 = -\frac{1}{2}(0) + b$

$4 = b$ $y = -\frac{1}{2}x + 4$

16. $m = \frac{2-0}{4-0} = \frac{2}{4} = \frac{1}{2}$

$y = \frac{1}{2}x + b$

$0 = \frac{1}{2}(0) + b$

$0 = b$ $y = \frac{1}{2}x$

17. $m = \frac{5-2}{1-3} = \frac{3}{-2} = -\frac{3}{2}$

$y = -\frac{3}{2}x + b$

$5 = -\frac{3}{2}(1) + b$

$\frac{10}{2} = -\frac{3}{2} + b$

$\frac{13}{2} = b$ $y = -\frac{3}{2}x + \frac{13}{2}$

18. $m = \frac{4-1}{-1-(-4)} = \frac{3}{3} = 1$
$y = x + b$
$4 = -1 + b$
$5 = b$ $y = x + 5$

19. $m = \frac{0-(-2)}{5-0} = \frac{2}{5}$

$y = \frac{2}{5}x + b$

$0 = \frac{2}{5}(5) + b$

$0 = 2 + b$

$-2 = b$ $y = \frac{2}{5}x - 2$

20. $m = \frac{3-(-2)}{1-(-2)} = \frac{5}{3}$

$y = \frac{5}{3}x + b$

$3 = \frac{5}{3}(1) + b$

$\frac{9}{3} = \frac{5}{3} + b$

$\frac{4}{3} = b$ $y = \frac{5}{3}x + \frac{4}{3}$

21. $m = \frac{-1 - (-4)}{2 - (-2)} = \frac{3}{4}$

$m = \frac{3}{4}x + b$

$-1 = \frac{3}{4}(2) + b$

$-\frac{2}{2} = \frac{3}{2} + b$

$-\frac{5}{2} = b \qquad y = \frac{3}{4}x - \frac{5}{2}$

22. $m = \frac{5 - (-3)}{-3 - (-1)} = \frac{8}{-2} = -4$

$y = -4x + b$
$-3 = -4(-1) + b$
$-3 = 4 + b$
$-7 = b \qquad y = -4x - 7$

23. $(5, 1)$ and $(0, -3)$ are on line.
$b = -3$

$m = \frac{1 - (-3)}{5 - 0} = \frac{4}{5}$

$y = \frac{4}{5}x - 3$

24. $(-2, 6)$ and $(4, 2)$ are on line.

$m = \frac{6 - 2}{-2 - 4} = \frac{4}{-6} = -\frac{2}{3}$

$y = -\frac{2}{3}x + b$

$6 = -\frac{2}{3}(-2) + b$

$\frac{18}{3} = \frac{4}{3} + b$

$\frac{14}{3} = b \qquad y = -\frac{2}{3}x + \frac{14}{3}$

25. $(0, 6)$ and $(-4, 0)$ are on line.
$b = 6$

$m = \frac{6 - 0}{0 - (-4)} = \frac{6}{4} = \frac{3}{2}$

$y = \frac{3}{2}x + 6$

26. $(4, 0)$ and $(-3, 2)$ are on line.

$m = \frac{2 - 0}{-3 - 4} = \frac{2}{-7} = -\frac{2}{7}$

$y = -\frac{2}{7}x + b$

$0 = -\frac{2}{7}(4) + b$

$0 = -\frac{8}{7} + b$

$\frac{8}{7} = b$

$y = -\frac{2}{7}x + \frac{8}{7}$

27. Check students' work.

28. $-y = -3x - 4$
$y = 3x + 4$; slope is 3.
$y - (-3) = 3(x - 2)$
$y + 3 = 3x - 6$
$y = 3x - 9$

29. $-3y = -x + 6$

$y = \frac{x}{3} - 2$; y-intercept is -2.

$m = \frac{-1 - (-2)}{5 - 0} = \frac{1}{5}$

$y = \frac{1}{5}x - 2$

30. $-2y = -3x + 8$

$y = \frac{3}{2}x - 4$; slope is $\frac{3}{2}$.

$2y = -3x - 4$

$y = -\frac{3}{2}x - 2$; intercept is -2.

$y = \frac{3}{2}x - 2$

31. $3y = 2x + 1$

$y = \frac{2}{3}x + \frac{1}{3}$; slope is $\frac{2}{3}$.

$y - (-5) = \frac{2}{3}(x - 8)$

$y + 5 = \frac{2}{3}x - \frac{16}{3}$

$y = \frac{2}{3}x - \frac{31}{3}$

32. $m = \frac{9 - 8}{14 - 12} = \frac{1}{2}$

$y = \frac{1}{2}x + b$

$8 = \frac{1}{2}(12) + b$

$8 = 6 + b$
$2 = b$
The y-intercept is 2, so the line intercepts the y-axis at $(0, 2)$.

33. a. $\left(\frac{x_1 + x_2}{2}, \frac{y_1 + y_2}{2}\right) = \left(\frac{-4 + 6}{2}, \frac{3 + (-9)}{2}\right) = (1, -3)$

b. $\left(\frac{x_1 + x_2}{2}, \frac{y_1 + y_2}{2}\right) = \left(\frac{-4 + 4}{2}, \frac{0 + 0}{2}\right) = (0, 0)$

c. $\left(\frac{x_1 + x_2}{2}, \frac{y_1 + y_2}{2}\right) = \left(\frac{-2 + 4}{2}, \frac{1 + 3}{2}\right) = (1, 2)$

d. $\left(\frac{x_1 + x_2}{2}, \frac{y_1 + y_2}{2}\right) = \left(\frac{-4 + 4}{2}, \frac{3 + (-3)}{2}\right) = (0, 0)$

34. Midpoints are $(3, 7), (7, 6), (5, 3)$.

Second midpoints are $\left(5, 6\frac{1}{2}\right), \left(6, 4\frac{1}{2}\right), (4, 5)$.

Original slopes are $\frac{7 - 6}{3 - 7} = -\frac{1}{4}, \frac{6 - 3}{7 - 5} = \frac{3}{2}$,

and $\frac{7 - 3}{3 - 5} = -2$.

Slopes of third triangle are $\frac{6\frac{1}{2} - 4\frac{1}{2}}{5 - 6} = -2, \frac{5 - 4\frac{1}{2}}{4 - 6} = -\frac{1}{4}$,

and $\frac{6\frac{1}{2} - 5}{5 - 4} = \frac{3}{2}$.

The corresponding sides have the same slope.

35. Midpoint $= \left(\frac{3 + 10}{2}, \frac{6 - 2}{2}\right) = \left(\frac{13}{2}, 2\right)$

$m = \frac{5 - 2}{2 - \frac{13}{2}} = -\frac{2}{3}$

$y = -\frac{2}{3}x + b$

$(5) = -\frac{2}{3}(2) + b$

$\frac{15}{3} = -\frac{4}{3} + b$

$\frac{19}{3} = b$

36.

37.

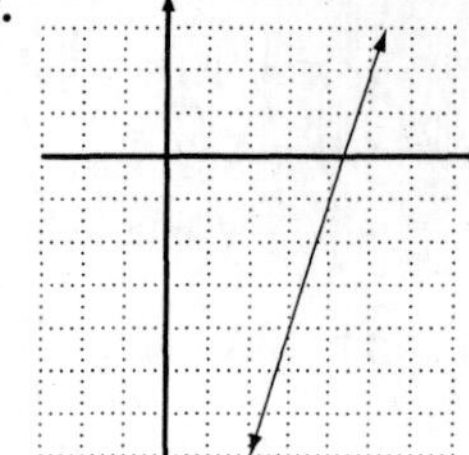

38.

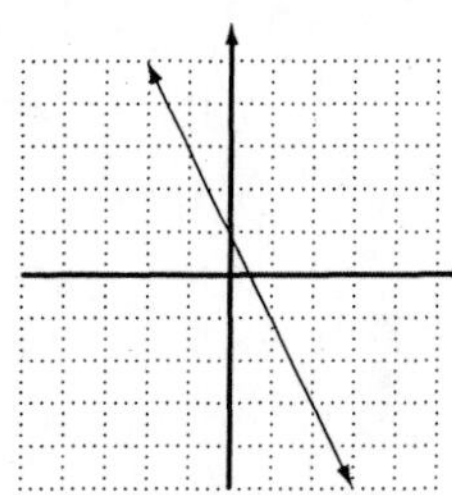

39. $n = 0.68 \times 240 = 163.2$

40.
$$54 = 0.12n$$
$$\frac{54}{0.12} = n$$
$$450 = n$$

41.
$$x^2 - 49 = 0$$
$$(x + 7)(x - 7) = 0$$
$$x + 7 = 0 \quad \text{or} \quad x - 7 = 0$$
$$x = -7 \quad \text{or} \quad x = 7$$

42.
$$a^2 - a - 6 = 0$$
$$(a - 3)(a + 2) = 0$$
$$a - 3 = 0 \quad \text{or} \quad a + 2 = 0$$
$$a = 3 \quad \text{or} \quad a = -2$$

43.
$$m^2 + 5m - 36 = 0$$
$$(m + 9)(m - 4) = 0$$
$$m + 9 = 0 \quad \text{or} \quad m - 4 = 0$$
$$m = -9 \quad \text{or} \quad m = 4$$

44.
$$c(c + 7) = 0$$
$$c = 0 \quad \text{or} \quad c + 7 = 0$$
$$c = 0 \quad \text{or} \quad c = -7$$

45.
$$(x - 9)(3x + 5) = 0$$
$$x - 9 = 0 \quad \text{or} \quad 3x + 5 = 0$$
$$x = 9 \quad \text{or} \quad 3x = -5$$
$$x = 9 \quad \text{or} \quad x = -\frac{5}{3}$$

46.
$$81x^2 = 16$$
$$81x^2 - 16 = 0$$
$$(9x + 4)(9x - 4) = 0$$
$$9x + 4 = 0 \quad \text{or} \quad 9x - 4 = 0$$
$$9x = -4 \quad \text{or} \quad 9x = 4$$
$$x = -\frac{4}{9} \quad \text{or} \quad x = \frac{4}{9}$$

47. $4m^2 - 36m + 80 = 4(m^2 - 9m + 20) = 4(m - 5)(m - 4)$

48. $x^5 + 4x^4 + 4x^3 = x^3(x^2 + 4x + 4) = x^3(x + 2)^2$

49.
$$9c^3 - 3c^2 - 3c + 1 = 3c^2(3c - 1) - 1(3c - 1)$$
$$= (3c^2 - 1)(3c - 1)$$

50. $y^3 - 2y^2 - 8y = y(y^2 - 2y - 8) = y(y - 4)(y + 2)$

51. $x^2y^2 - z^2 = (xy + z)(xy - z)$

52. $\frac{4^7}{4^4} = 4^{7-4} = 4^3$

53. $\frac{p^{18}}{p^{16}} = p^{18-16} = p^2$

54. $(5^3)^4 = 5^{3 \cdot 4} = 5^{12}$

55. Let p = population (in millions) in 1990.
$$p = 151 + (0.65)151$$
$$p = (1 + 0.65)151$$
$$p = (1.65)151$$
$$p \approx 249$$
The 1990 population was about 249 million.

LESSON 7-7 TRY THIS p. 335

a. (1)
$$m = \frac{10.5 - 10.2}{1960 - 1990} = \frac{0.3}{-30} = -0.01$$
$$r = -0.01t + b$$
$$10.5 = 0.01(1960) + b$$
$$10.5 = -19.6 + b$$
$$30.1 = b \quad \text{so} \quad r = -0.01t + 30.1$$
(2)
$$r = -0.01t + 30.1$$
$$r = -0.01(2000) + 30.1$$
$$r = -20.0 + 30.1$$
$$r = 10.1$$
The record in 2000 should be 10.1 s.

b.

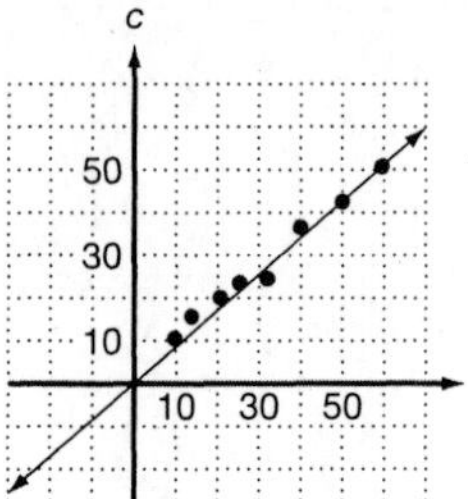

Answers may vary.

$$c = \frac{5}{6}d$$

LESSON 7-7 EXERCISES pp. 335–337

1. a.
$$\text{slope} = \frac{1.10 - 0.85}{10 - 5} = \frac{0.25}{5} = 0.05$$
$$p = 0.05m + b$$
$$(1.1) = 0.05(10) + b$$
$$1.1 = 0.5 + b$$
$$0.6 = b$$
$$p = 0.05m + 0.6$$

b.
$$p = 0.05(20) + 0.6$$
$$p = 1 + 0.6$$
$$p = 1.6$$
The cost is \$1.60.

2. a.
$$m = \frac{50 - 32}{10 - 0}$$
$$m = \frac{18}{10} = 1.8$$
$$F = 1.8C + b$$
$$(32) = 1.8(0) + b$$
$$32 = b$$
$$F = 1.8C + 32$$
Since $1.8 = 1\frac{8}{10} = \frac{18}{10} = \frac{9}{5}$, this can be written $F = \frac{9}{5}C + 32$.

b.
$$F = 1.8(30) + 32$$
$$F = 54 + 32$$
$$F = 86$$
The temperature is 86°F.

3. a.
$$m = \frac{10 - (-5)}{500 - 2000} = \frac{15}{-1500} = -\frac{1}{100}$$
$$t = -\frac{1}{100}h + b$$
$$(10) = -\frac{1}{100}(500) + b$$
$$10 = -5 + b$$
$$15 = b$$
$$t = -\frac{1}{100}h + 15$$

b.
$$t = -\frac{1}{100}(1500) + 15$$
$$t = -15 + 15$$
$$t = 0$$
The temperature is 0°C.

4. a. $m = \frac{127 - 100}{680 - 500} = \frac{27}{180} = \frac{3}{20}$

$b = \frac{3}{20}a + k \quad (k = y\text{-intercept})$

$100 = \frac{3}{20}(500) + k$

$100 = 75 + k$
$25 = k$

$b = \frac{3}{20}a + 25$

b. $b = \frac{3}{20}(700) + 25$

$b = 105 + 25$
$b = 130$
The test score is 130.

5. a. $m = \frac{3.8 - 3.65}{1970 - 1990} = \frac{0.15}{-20} = -0.0075$

$r = -0.0075t + b$
$(3.8) = -0.0075(1970) + b$
$3.8 = -14.775 + b$
$18.575 = b$
$r = -0.0075t + 18.575$

b. $r = -0.0075(2000) + 18.575$
$r = -15 + 18.575$
$r = 3.575$
The record should be 3.575 minutes.

6. a. $m = \frac{40 - 19}{300 - 150} = \frac{21}{150} = \frac{7}{50}$

$t = \frac{7}{50}l + b$

$(19) = \frac{7}{50}(150) + b$

$19 = 21 + b$
$-2 = b$

$t = \frac{7}{50}l - 2$

b. $t = \frac{7}{50}(200) - 2$

$t = 28 - 2$
$t = 26$

The length is 26 mm.

c. $t = \frac{7}{50}(350) - 2$

$t = 49 - 2$
$t = 47$

The length is 47 mm.

7.

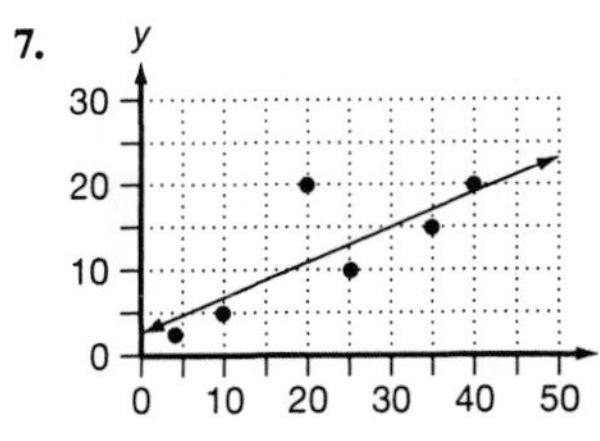

Answers may vary. Using (10, 5) and (40, 20):

$m = \frac{20 - 5}{40 - 10} = \frac{15}{30} = \frac{1}{2}$

$y = \frac{1}{2}d + b$

$(20) = \frac{1}{2}(40) + b$

$20 = 20 + b$
$0 = b$

$y = \frac{1}{2}d$

8.

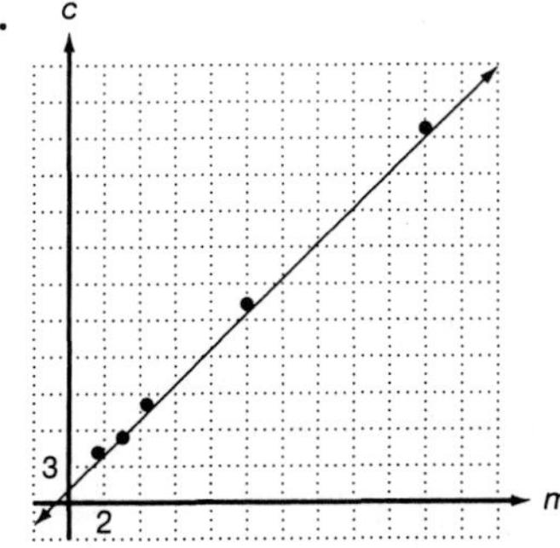

Answers may vary. Using (2, 4) and (20, 31):

$\text{slope} = \frac{31 - 4}{20 - 2} = \frac{27}{18} = \frac{3}{2}$

$c = \frac{3}{2}m + b$

$(4) = \frac{3}{2}(2) + b$

$4 = 3 + b$
$1 = b$

$c = \frac{3}{2}m + 1$

9.

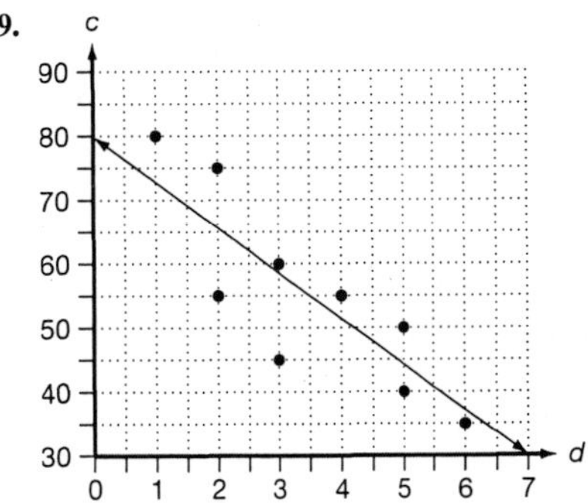

Answers may vary. Using (3, 60) and (6, 35):

$m = \frac{60 - 35}{3 - 6} = \frac{25}{-3} = -\frac{25}{3}$

$c = -\frac{25}{3}d + b$

$(60) = -\frac{25}{3}(3) + b$

$60 = -25 + b$
$85 = b$

$c = -\frac{25}{3}d + 85$

10.

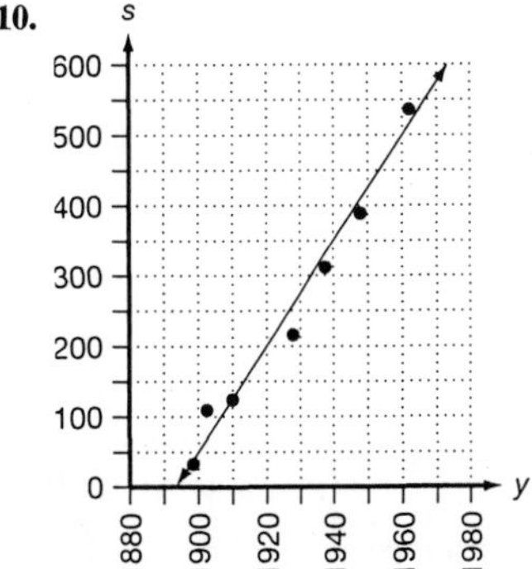

Answers may vary. Using the points (1898, 39) and (1910, 132):

$m = \frac{132 - 39}{1910 - 1898} = \frac{93}{12}$

$s = \frac{93}{12}y + b$

$(39) = \frac{93}{12}(1898) + b$

$39 = \frac{176,514}{12} + b$

$39 = 14,709.5 + b$
$-14,670.5 = b$

$s = \frac{93}{12}y - 14,670.5$

$s = \frac{93}{12}(2000) - 14,670.5$

$s = 15,500 - 14,670.5$
$s = 829.5$
The estimate is 829.5 mi/h.

11. Two points on the graph are (0, 3500) and (2, 2200).

$$m = \frac{3500 - 2200}{0 - 2} = \frac{1300}{-2} = -650$$

$$\begin{aligned} y &= -650x + b \\ 3500 &= -650(0) + b \\ 3500 &= b \\ y &= -650x + 3500 \text{ is the equation of the line.} \\ y &= -650(5) + 3500 \\ y &= -3250 + 3500 \\ y &= 250 \end{aligned}$$

The value will be $250.

12. Two points on the graph are (0, 14,000) and (2, 9000).

$$m = \frac{14{,}000 - 9000}{0 - 2} = \frac{5000}{-2} = -2500$$

$$y = -2500x + b$$

Since (0, 14,000) is on graph, $b = 14{,}000$.

$$\begin{aligned} y &= -2500x + 14{,}000 \text{ is the equation of the line.} \\ y &= -2500(5) + 14{,}000 \\ y &= -12{,}500 + 14{,}000 \\ y &= 1500 \end{aligned}$$

The value will be $1500.

13. Two points on the graph are (8, 7) and (20, 10).

$$m = \frac{10 - 7}{20 - 8} = \frac{3}{12} = \frac{1}{4}$$

$$y = \frac{1}{4}x + b$$

$$10 = \frac{1}{4}(20) + b$$

$$5 = b$$

The equation of the line is $y = \frac{1}{4}x + 5$.

$$y = \frac{1}{4}(200) + 5$$

$$y = 50 + 5 = 55$$

The height will be 55 feet.

14. Let c = number of children.
Let a = number of adults.
Their combined weight exceeds the weight limit:

$$34c + 75a > 500.$$

It exceeds the limit by no more than 50 kg:

$$34c + 75a \le 550.$$

Together:

$$500 < 34c + 75a \le 550.$$

Make an organized list:

Number of Children	Number of Adults	Combined Weight
17	0	578 (No)
16	0	544 (Yes)
15	0	510 (Yes)
15	1	585 (No)
14	1	551 (No)
13	1	517 (Yes)
12	2	558 (No)
11	2	524 (Yes)
10	3	565 (No)
9	3	531 (Yes)
8	4	572 (No)
7	4	538 (Yes)
6	4	504 (Yes)
5	5	545 (Yes)
4	5	511 (Yes)
3	6	552 (No)
2	6	518 (Yes)
1	7	559 (No)
0	7	525 (Yes)

The (children, adult) ordered pairs for which $500 < 34c + 75a \le 550$ are (16, 0), (15, 0), (13, 1), (11, 2), (9, 3), (7, 4), (6, 4), (5, 5), (4, 5), (2, 6), (0, 7)

15. Answers may vary.

$(0, 0), \left(1, \frac{21}{20}\right), \left(2, \frac{11}{5}\right), \left(3, \frac{69}{20}\right), \left(4, \frac{24}{5}\right), \left(5, \frac{25}{4}\right)$

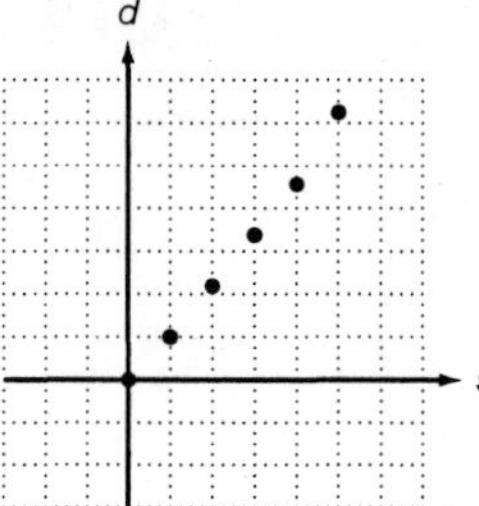

The relationship is not linear.

16. $2y = 6x + 5$

$$y = 3x + \frac{5}{2}$$

$$m = 3$$

17. $4x + y = 7$

$$\begin{aligned} y &= -4x + 7 \\ m &= -4 \end{aligned}$$

18. $(x^3 - 2)(x^2 + 2) = x^5 + 2x^3 - 2x^2 - 4$

19. $3y^3(y^2 - 2y) = 3y^5 - 6y^4$

20. $(a^2 - 2a)^2 = a^4 - 4a^3 + 4a^2$

21. $50y^4 - 72y^2 = 2y^2(25y^2 - 36)$
$= 2y^2(5y + 6)(5y - 6)$

22. $16 - 9m^2 = (4 + 3m)(4 - 3m)$

23. $ab + 3a - 6b - 18 = a(b + 3) - 6(b + 3)$
$= (a - 6)(b + 3)$

24.

$$\begin{aligned} n^2 - 1 &= 143 \\ n^2 - 144 &= 0 \\ (n + 12)(n - 12) &= 0 \\ n + 12 &= 0 \quad \text{or} \quad n - 12 = 0 \\ n &= -12 \quad \text{or} \quad n = 12 \end{aligned}$$

25.

$$\begin{aligned} n(n + 1) &= 110 \\ n^2 + n &= 110 \\ n^2 + n - 110 &= 0 \\ (n + 11)(n - 10) &= 0 \\ n + 11 &= 0 \quad \text{or} \quad n - 10 = 0 \\ n &= -11 \quad \text{or} \quad n = 10 \end{aligned}$$

The integers are 10, 11 or -11, -10.

26.

$$\begin{aligned} 3(n^2 - 1) &= 72 \\ 3n^2 - 3 &= 72 \\ n^2 - 1 &= 24 \\ n^2 - 25 &= 0 \\ (n + 5)(n - 5) &= 0 \\ n + 5 &= 0 \quad \text{or} \quad n - 5 = 0 \\ n &= -5 \quad \text{or} \quad n = 5 \end{aligned}$$

LESSON 7-8 TRY THIS pp. 338–340

a. Yes. $3x - y = -5$ is the same line as $y = 3x + 5$ and $5y - 15x = 10$ is the same line as $y = 3x + 2$. Both have $m = 3$.

b. No. $4y = -12x + 16$ is the same line as $y = -3x + 4$. Slopes are different.

c. Yes. Slopes are $\frac{1}{2}$ and -2, and product of slopes is -1.

d. No. Slopes are $\frac{3}{4}$ and $\frac{3}{4}$, and product of slopes is $\frac{9}{16}$.

e. $y = 2x + 4$ has slope 2, so a perpendicular line has slope $-\frac{1}{2}$.

$$y - 0 = -\frac{1}{2}(x - 0)$$
$$y = -\frac{1}{2}x$$

f. $2y = -x + 8$

$y = -\frac{1}{2}x + 4$ has slope $-\frac{1}{2}$, so a perpendicular line has slope 2.

$$y - (-3) = 2(x - (-1))$$
$$y + 3 = 2(x + 1)$$
$$y + 3 = 2x + 2$$
$$y = 2x - 1$$

LESSON 7-8 EXERCISES pp. 340–341

1. $x + 4 = y$ $\quad$ $y - x = -3$; $y = x - 3$

Yes

2. $3x - 4 = y$ $\quad$ $y - 3x = 8$; $y = 3x + 8$

Yes

3. $y + 3 = 6x$; $y = 6x - 3$ $\quad$ $-6x - y = 2$; $-y = 6x + 2$; $y = -6x - 2$

No

4. $y = -4x + 2$ $\quad$ $-5 = -2y + 8x$; $-8x - 5 = -2y$; $4x + \frac{5}{2} = y$

No

5. $y = 2x + 7$ $\quad$ $5y + 10x = 20$; $5y = -10x + 20$; $y = -2x + 4$

No

6. $y = -7x - 5$ $\quad$ $2y = -7x - 10$; $y = -\frac{7}{2}x - 5$

No

7. $3x - y = -9$; $y = -3x - 9$; $y = 3x + 9$ $\quad$ $2y - 6x = -2$; $2y = 6x - 2$; $y = 3x - 1$

Yes

8. $y - 6 = -6x$; $y = -6x + 6$ $\quad$ $-2x + y = 5$; $y = 2x + 5$

No

9. $-3x + y = 4$; $y = 3x + 4$ $\quad$ $3x - y = -6$; $-y = -3x - 6$; $y = 3x + 6$

Yes

10. $-4 = y + 2x$; $-2x - 4 = y$ $\quad$ $6x + 3y = 4$; $3y = -6x + 4$; $y = -2x + \frac{4}{3}$

Yes

11. $8x - 4y = 16$; $-4y = -8x + 16$; $y = 2x - 4$ $\quad$ $5y - 10x = 3$; $5y = 10x + 3$; $y = 2x + \frac{3}{5}$

Yes

12. $-4x = 3y + 5$; $-4x - 5 = 3y$; $-\frac{4}{3}x - \frac{5}{3} = y$ $\quad$ $8x + 6y = -1$; $6y = -8x - 1$; $y = -\frac{8}{6}x - \frac{1}{6}$; $y = -\frac{4}{3}x - \frac{1}{6}$

Yes

13. $y = -4x + 3$ $\quad$ $4y + x = -1$; $4y = -x - 1$; $y = -\frac{1}{4}x - \frac{1}{4}$

$(-4)\left(-\frac{1}{4}\right) = 1$

No

14. $y = -\frac{2}{3}x + 4$ $\quad$ $3x + 2y = 1$; $2y = -3x + 1$; $y = -\frac{3}{2}x + \frac{1}{2}$

$\left(-\frac{2}{3}\right)\left(-\frac{3}{2}\right) = 1$

No

15. $x + y = 6$; $y = -x + 6$ $\quad$ $4y - 4x = 12$; $4y = 4x + 12$; $y = x + 3$

$(-1)(1) = -1$

Yes

16. $2x - 5y = -3$; $-5y = -2x - 3$; $y = \frac{2}{5}x + \frac{3}{5}$ $\quad$ $5x + 2y = 6$; $2y = -5x + 6$; $y = -\frac{5}{2}x + 3$

$\left(\frac{2}{5}\right)\left(-\frac{5}{2}\right) = -1$

Yes

17. $y = -x + 8$ $\quad$ $x - y = -1$; $-y = -x - 1$; $y = x + 1$

$(-1)(1) = -1$

Yes

18. $2x + 6y = -3$; $6y = -2x - 3$; $y = -\frac{1}{3}x - \frac{1}{2}$ $\quad$ $12y = 4x + 20$; $y = \frac{1}{3}x + \frac{5}{3}$

$\left(-\frac{1}{3}\right)\left(\frac{1}{3}\right) = -\frac{1}{9}$

No

19. $6x + y = -4$; $y = -6x - 4$ $\quad$ $6x - y = 4$; $-y = -6x + 4$; $y = 6x - 4$

$(-6)(6) = -36$

No

20. $4y = x + 5$; $y = \frac{1}{4}x + \frac{5}{4}$ $\quad$ $9y + 3x = 2$; $9y = -3x + 2$; $y = -\frac{1}{3}x + \frac{2}{9}$

$\left(\frac{1}{4}\right)\left(-\frac{1}{3}\right) = -\frac{1}{12}$

No

21. $6y - x = -12$; $6y = x - 12$; $y = \frac{1}{6}x - 2$ $\quad$ $\frac{1}{6}x + y = 3$; $y = -\frac{1}{6}x + 3$

$\left(\frac{1}{6}\right)\left(-\frac{1}{6}\right) = -\frac{1}{36}$

No

22. $\frac{2}{3}x + y = 6$

$y = -\frac{2}{3}x + 6$

$8y - 12x - 12 = 0$
$8y = 12x + 12$
$y = \frac{12}{8}x + \frac{12}{8}$
$y = \frac{3}{2}x + \frac{3}{2}$

$\left(-\frac{2}{3}\right)\left(\frac{3}{2}\right) = -1$

Yes

23. $\frac{2}{5}x - \frac{1}{10}y = 20$

$10\left(\frac{2}{5}x - \frac{1}{10}y\right) = 10(20)$
$4x - y = 200$
$-y = -4x + 200$
$y = 4x - 200$

$5x + 10y = -5$
$10y = -5x - 5$
$y = -\frac{1}{2}x - \frac{1}{2}$

$(4)\left(-\frac{1}{2}\right) = -2$

No

24. $\frac{1}{2}x + \frac{3}{4}y = 6$

$4\left(\frac{1}{2}x + \frac{3}{4}y\right) = 4(6)$
$2x + 3y = 24$
$3y = -2x + 24$
$y = -\frac{2}{3}x + 8$

$-\frac{3}{2}x + y = 4$
$y = \frac{3}{2}x + 4$

$\left(-\frac{2}{3}\right)\left(\frac{3}{2}\right) = -1$

Yes

25. $\frac{3}{8}x - \frac{y}{2} = 1$

$2\left(\frac{3}{8}x - \frac{y}{2}\right) = 2(1)$
$\frac{3}{4}x - y = 2$
$y = \frac{3}{4}x - 2$

$\frac{4}{3}x - y + 1 = 0$
$-y = -\frac{4}{3}x - 1$
$y = \frac{4}{3}x + 1$

$\left(\frac{3}{4}\right)\left(\frac{4}{3}\right) = 1$

No

26. $3x + 4y = 4$
$4y = -3x + 4$
$y = -\frac{3}{4}x + 1$

$4y = 3x + 4$
$y = \frac{3}{4}x + 1$

The slopes, $-\frac{3}{4}$ and $\frac{3}{4}$ are neither equal nor negative reciprocals of each other. The graphs are neither parallel nor perpendicular. The answer is C.

27. $y = 3x + 4$ has slope 3,

so a perpendicular line has slope $-\frac{1}{3}$.

$y - 6 = -\frac{1}{3}(x - 0)$

$y = -\frac{1}{3}x + 6$

28. $y = 2x - 3$ has slope 2,

so a perpendicular line has slope $-\frac{1}{2}$.

$y - 4 = -\frac{1}{2}(x - (-2))$

$y - 4 = -\frac{1}{2}(x + 2)$

$y - 4 = -\frac{1}{2}x - 1$

$y = -\frac{1}{2}x + 3$

29. $3y = x$
$y = \frac{1}{3}x$ has slope $\frac{1}{3}$,
so a perpendicular line has slope -3.
$y - 2 = -3(x - 0)$
$y - 2 = -3x$
$y = -3x + 2$

30. $y = -2x - 4$ has slope -2,

so a perpendicular line has slope $\frac{1}{2}$.

$y - 0 = \frac{1}{2}(x - 1)$

$y = \frac{1}{2}x - \frac{1}{2}$

31. $y = 3x + 4$
has slope 3, so a parallel line has slope 3.
$y - 6 = 3(x - 0)$
$y = 3x + 6$

32. $y = 2x - 3$
has slope 2, so a parallel line has slope 2.
$y - 4 = 2(x - (-2))$
$y - 4 = 2(x + 2)$
$y - 4 = 2x + 4$
$y = 2x + 8$

33. $3y = x$
$y = \frac{1}{3}x$ has slope $\frac{1}{3}$,

so a parallel line has slope $\frac{1}{3}$.

$y - 2 = \frac{1}{3}(x - 0)$

$y - 2 = \frac{1}{3}x$

$y = \frac{1}{3}x + 2$

34. $y = -2x - 4$ has slope -2,
so a parallel line has slope -2.
$y - 0 = -2(x - 1)$
$y = -2x + 2$

35. a. $x - 2y = 6$
$2y = x - 6$
$y = \frac{1}{2}x - 3$ has slope $\frac{1}{2}$,
so a perpendicular line has slope -2.
$y - (-1) = -2(x - 4)$
$y + 1 = -2x + 8$
$y = -2x + 7$

b. No; the line $x - 2y = 6$ contains the point $(4, -1)$.

36. $ax + by = c$
$by = -ax + c$
$y = -\frac{a}{b}x + \frac{c}{b}$

A line parallel to this has slope $-\frac{a}{b}$.

A line perpendicular to this has slope $\frac{b}{a}$.

Equation of parallel line: $y = \left(-\frac{a}{b}\right)x + \text{constant}$

Rewriting: $by = -ax + \text{constant}$
$ax + by = \text{constant}$ (different from c)

Equation of perpendicular line: $y = \left(\frac{b}{a}\right)x + \text{constant}$

Rewriting: $ay = bx + \text{constant}$
$ay - bx = \text{constant}$

37. Answers may vary.

38. Slope of $5x + 20y = 12$ is $-\frac{5}{20} = -\frac{1}{4}$.

Slope of $4y = kx - 6$ is $\frac{k}{4}$.

Slopes must be equal, so $-\frac{1}{4} = \frac{k}{4}$

$k = -1$

39. Product of slopes must equal -1, so $\left(-\frac{1}{4}\right)\left(\frac{k}{4}\right) = -1$.

$$-\frac{k}{16} = -1$$
$$k = 16$$

40. Points $(-1, -1)$ and $(1, 2)$ are on line ①.

Slope: $\frac{2-(-1)}{1-(-1)} = \frac{3}{2}$

So $y = \frac{3}{2}x + b$.

$2 = \frac{3}{2}(1) + b$

$\frac{1}{2} = b$ Equation ①: $y = \frac{3}{2}x + \frac{1}{2}$ or $2y - 3x = 1$

Since line ② is perpendicular, slope is $-\frac{2}{3}$.

$y = -\frac{2}{3}x + b$

$-1 = -\frac{2}{3}(-1) + b$

$-1 = \frac{2}{3} + b$

$-\frac{5}{3} = b$

Equation ②: $y = -\frac{2}{3}x - \frac{5}{3}$ or $3y + 2x = -5$

41. Points $(-3, 2)$ and $(1, -1)$ are on line ①.

$m = \frac{2-(-1)}{-3-1} = \frac{3}{-4}$

So $y = -\frac{3}{4}x + b$

$-1 = -\frac{3}{4}(1) + b$

$-\frac{1}{4} = b$

Equation ①: $y = -\frac{3}{4}x - \frac{1}{4}$ or $4y + 3x = -1$

Since line ② is perpendicular, slope $= \frac{4}{3}$.

$y = \frac{4}{3}x + b$

$-1 = \frac{4}{3}(1) + b$

$-\frac{7}{3} = b$

Equation ②: $y = \frac{4}{3}x - \frac{7}{3}$ or $3y - 4x = -7$

42. $y = 3x + 5 \qquad m = 3, b = 5$

43. $2x + 4y = 5$
$4y = -2x + 5$
$y = -\frac{1}{2}x + \frac{5}{4} \qquad m = -\frac{1}{2}, b = \frac{5}{4}$

44. $6x = 2y + 3$
$y = 3x - \frac{3}{2} \qquad m = 3, b = -\frac{3}{2}$

45. $6x = 3y - 2$
$y = 2x - \frac{2}{3} \qquad m = 2, b = \frac{2}{3}$

46. $5y - 3x = 15$
$y = \frac{3}{5}x + 3 \qquad m = \frac{3}{5}, b = 3$

47. $2x = 3y + 4$
$y = \frac{2}{3}x - \frac{4}{3} \qquad m = \frac{2}{3}, b = -\frac{4}{3}$

48. $3x + 4y = 8$
$y = -\frac{3}{4}x + 2 \qquad m = -\frac{3}{4}, b = 2$

49. $y = -2x + b$
$3 = -2(1) + b$
$b = 5,$ so $y = -2x + 5$

50. $y = 9x + b$
$4 = 9(-1) + b$
$b = 13,$ so $y = 9x + 13$

51. $9a^2 - 49b^2 = (3a + 7b)(3a - 7b)$

52. $5x^2 + 70x + 245 = 5(x^2 + 14x + 49) = 5(x + 7)^2$

53. $2m^3 + 3m^2 - 18m - 27 = m^2(2m + 3) - 9(2m + 3)$
$= (2m + 3)(m^2 - 9)$
$= (2m + 3)(m + 3)(m - 3)$

54. $3x^2 - 3x - 90 = 3(x^2 - x - 30) = 3(x - 6)(x + 5)$

55. $(3t^3)^2 = 3^2t^{3\cdot 2} = 9t^6$

56. $(4ab^2c)(3abc^3) = 4\cdot 3a^{1+1}b^{2+1}c^{1+3} = 12a^2b^3c^4$

57. $(2x^2yz)(3x^3yz^2) = 2\cdot 3x^{2+3}y^{1+1}z^{1+2} = 6x^5y^2z^3$

58. $(y + 11)(y - 11) + 121 = y^2 - 121 + 121 = y^2$

59. $(2x + y)(3x + 3y) = 6x^2 + 6xy + 3xy + 3y^2$
$= 6x^2 + 9xy + 3y^2$

LESSON 7-9 TRY THIS pp. 342–343

a. The y-intercept of a line occurs at the point where the line crosses the y-axis. Thus, the x-coordinate of the point is zero. Let $x = 0$ in the equation $y = mx + b$. $y = m\cdot 0 + b$, $y = 0 + b$, $y = b$. Thus, b is the y-intercept.

b. Suppose that (x_1, y_1) and (x_2, y_2) are any two points on a vertical line. The slope of the line would be $\frac{y_2 - y_1}{x_2 - x_1}$. Since the line is vertical, the x-coordinates are the same, so the slope would be $\frac{y_2 - y_1}{0}$. Division by 0 is not defined, so the line has no slope.

LESSON 7-9 EXERCISES p. 343

1. First, show that a point (x_2, y_2) on a nonvertical line with slope m and containing (x_1, y_1) must satisfy the equation $y - y_1 = m(x - x_1)$. By the slope formula,

$$\frac{y_2 - y_1}{x_2 - x_1} = m$$

Multiplying each side of the equation by $x_2 - x_1$, we have

$$(x_2 - x_1)\left(\frac{y_2 - y_1}{x_2 - x_1}\right) = m(x_2 - x_1)$$
$$y_2 - y_1 = m(x_2 - x_1)$$

Thus, the point (x_2, y_2) satisfies the equation $y - y_1 = m(x - x_1)$.
Next, show that a point that satisfies the equation $y - y_1 = m(x - x_1)$ lies on a nonvertical line with slope m and containing (x_1, y_1). Suppose (x_2, y_2) is such a point. Then,
$y_2 - y_1 = m(x_2 - x_1)$.
If $x_2 = x_1$, then $y_2 - y_1 = m(x_2 - x_1) = 0$, so $y_2 = y_1$. This means that (x_1, y_1) and (x_2, y_2) are one and the same point, a point that does indeed lie on the desired line. Now suppose $x_2 \neq x_1$. Then $x_2 - x_1 \neq 0$, so multiply both sides of the equation

by $\frac{1}{x_2 - x_1}$ to get $\frac{y_2 - y_1}{x_2 - x_1} = m$.

Thus, the line through (x_1, y_1) and (x_2, y_2) is nonvertical with slope m. (x_2, y_2) lies on this line and the proof is complete.

2. If a line has slope m and y-intercept b at $(0, b)$, then by the point-slope equation theorem,

$y - b = m(x - 0)$	Substitution
$y - b = mx$	Addition property of zero
$y = mx + b$	Addition property of equality

3. 2, 0; 2 **4.** 6, 4, 1; 6 **5.** 6, 3; 6

6. $-ax^2 - bx - c$ **7.** $-35 + 8c$ **8.** $-y + 9$

9. Answers may vary. $3(a^3), (3a)(a^2), (3a^2)(a)$

10. Answers may vary. $3(5a)(ab), (5a^2)(3b), (a^2)(15b)$

11. Answers may vary. $\left(-4, -\frac{3}{4}\right), (3, 1), \left(4, \frac{5}{4}\right)$

12. $4a^2b + 2a = 2a(2ab + 1)$ **13.** $4y^2 - 9 = (2y + 3)(2y - 3)$

14. $10c^2 + 28c - 6 = 2(5c^2 + 14c - 3) = 2(5c - 1)(c + 3)$

LESSON 7-10 PROBLEMS p. 345

1. Strategies: Simplify the problem
Make a table
Look for a pattern
Draw a diagram

Number of Triangles	Perimeter
1	3 m
2	4 m
3	5 m
4	6 m
⋮	
70	72 m

The perimeter of figure made with 70 triangles would be 72 meters.

2. Strategies: Simplify the problem
Make a table
Look for a pattern

Number of Teams	Games Needed
1	0
2	1
3	2
4	3
⋮	⋮
12	11

Eleven games are needed to determine a winner.

3. Strategy: Make an organized list

M1W1 M2W1 M3W1
M1W2 M2W2 M3W2 } Couple combinations
M1W3 M2W3 M3W3

Match combinations

M1W1 vs M2W2, M2W3, M3W2, M3W3

M2W1 vs M3W2, M3W3

M2W2 vs M3W1, M3W3

M1W2 vs M2W1, M2W3, M3W1, M3W3

M3W1 vs M2W3

M3W2 vs M2W3

M1W3 vs M2W1, M2W2, M3W1, M3W2

Eighteen different mixed-doubles matches could be played.

4. Strategy: Make an organized list

P—pocket or D—desk
O—orange, B—black, R—red, T—tan
G—gold, S—silver

POG, POS, PBG, PBS, PRG, PRS, PTG, PTS
DOG, DOS, DBG, DBS, DRG, DRS, DTG, DTS

There are 16 different choices for checkbook covers.

5. Strategies: Draw a diagram
Use logical reasoning

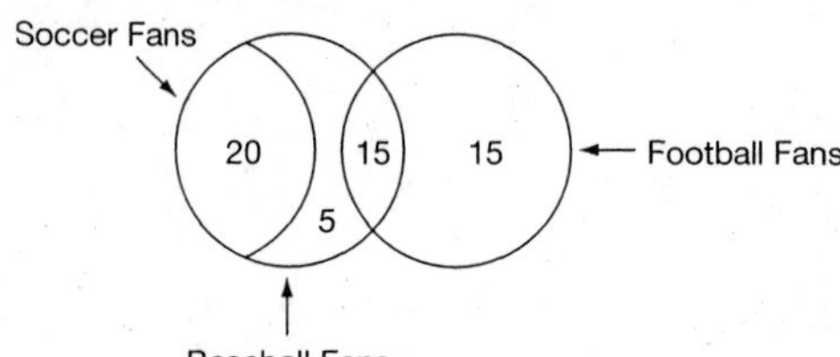

(1) 20 soccer fans (3) $\frac{1}{2}$ baseball fans are soccer fans

(2) 30 football fans (4) 40 baseball fans

(5) $\frac{1}{2}$ football fans are also baseball fans

There are 5 baseball fans who are neither soccer fans nor football fans.

6. Strategies: Simplify the problem
Draw a diagram

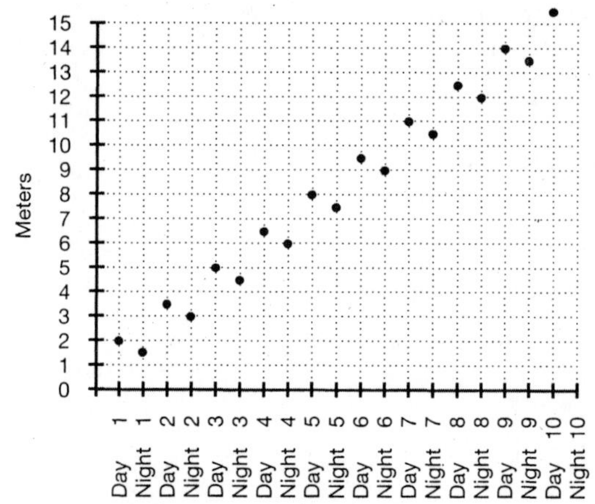

The pump takes 10 days to raise the water level to a height of 15 m.

7. Strategies: Simplify the problem
Make a table
Look for a pattern

Size of Square	Number of Squares
7 × 7	1
6 × 6	4 → (2 × 2)
5 × 5	9 → (3 × 3)
4 × 4	16 → (4 × 4)
3 × 3	25 → (5 × 5)
2 × 2	36 → (6 × 6)
1 × 1	49 → (7 × 7)
	Total 140

There are 140 different squares in the grid.

8. The simpler form has value -1 whether it is computed as $(3/1) - 4$ or $3/(1 - 4)$. Julie should have tried simple numbers a, b, and c for which $(a/b) - c \neq a/(b - c)$.

APPLICATION PROBLEM p. 346

a. $10{,}000\left(1 + \frac{0.11}{1}\right)^{2 \cdot 1} = \$12{,}321$

b. $10{,}000\left(1 + \frac{0.11}{2}\right)^{2\cdot 2} = \$12{,}388.25$

c. $10{,}000\left(1 + \frac{0.11}{4}\right)^{2\cdot 4} = \$12{,}423.81$

d. $10{,}000\left(1 + \frac{0.11}{12}\right)^{2\cdot 12} = \$12{,}448.29$

e. $10{,}000\left(1 + \frac{0.11}{365}\right)^{2\cdot 365} = \$12{,}460.35$

f. $10{,}000\left(1 + \frac{0.11}{24 \cdot 365}\right)^{2\cdot 24\cdot 365} \approx \$12{,}460.72$

CHAPTER 7 WRAP UP pp. 347–349

1–6.

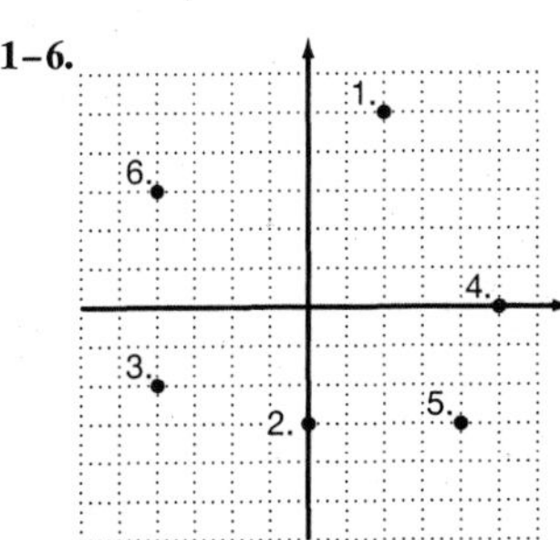

7. IV 8. III 9. I 10. II 11. (4, 3) 12. (−3, 5)

13. (−4, −3)

14. $3x + y = 4$
$3(0) + 4 = 4$
$0 + 4 = 4$
Yes

15. $3x + y = 4$
$3(1) + (-1) = 4$
$3 - 1 = 4$
$2 = 4$
No

16.

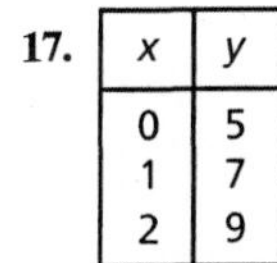

x	y
0	−1
1	1
2	3

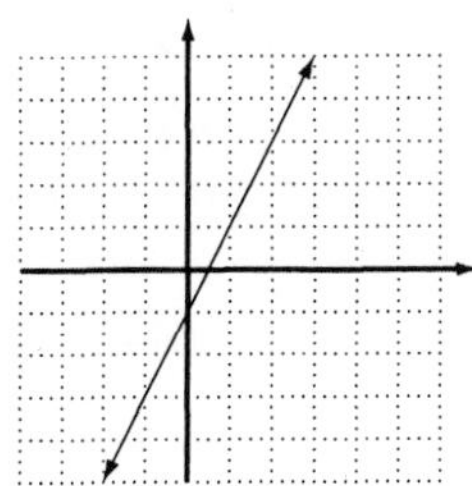

17.

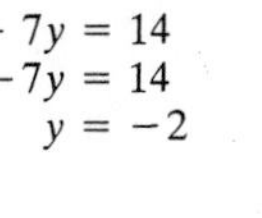

x	y
0	5
1	7
2	9

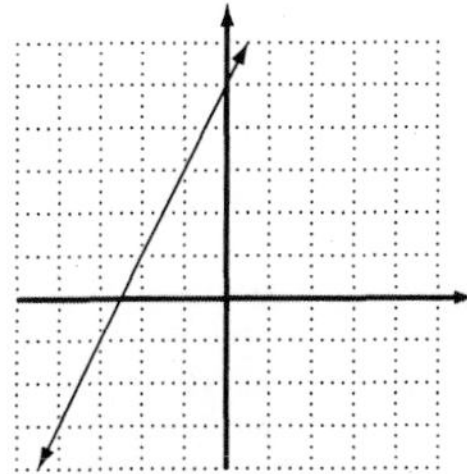

18. $2x - 7y = 14$
x-intercept: $2x - 7(0) = 14$
$2x = 14$
$x = 7$
y-intercept: $2(0) - 7y = 14$
$-7y = 14$
$y = -2$

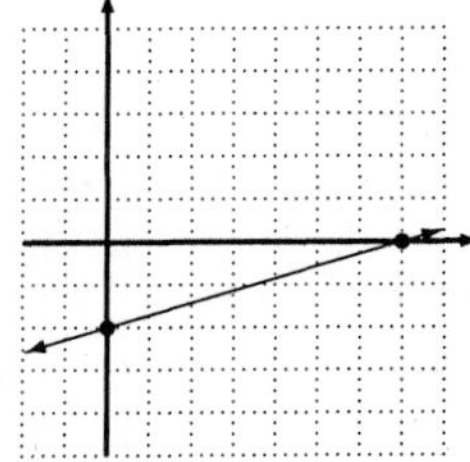

19. $3x - 2y = -6$
x-intercept: $3x - 2(0) = -6$
$3x = -6$
$x = -2$
y-intercept: $3(0) - 2y = -6$
$-2y = -6$
$y = 3$

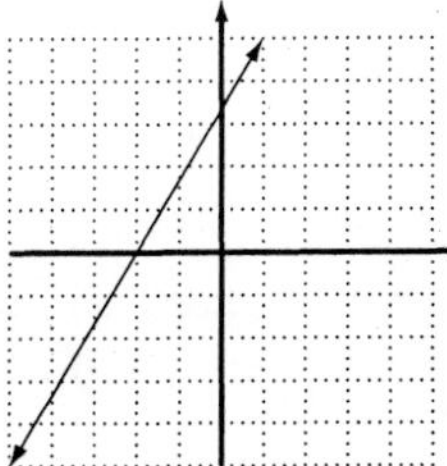

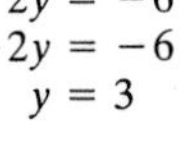

20.

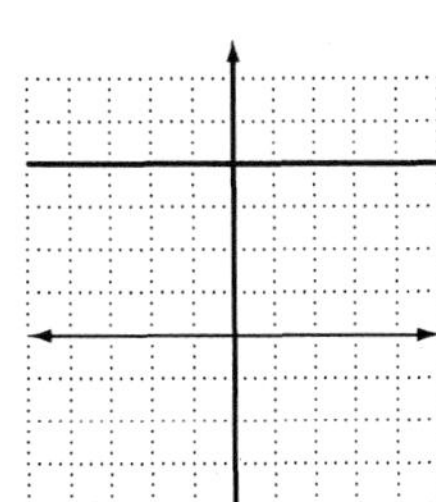

21.

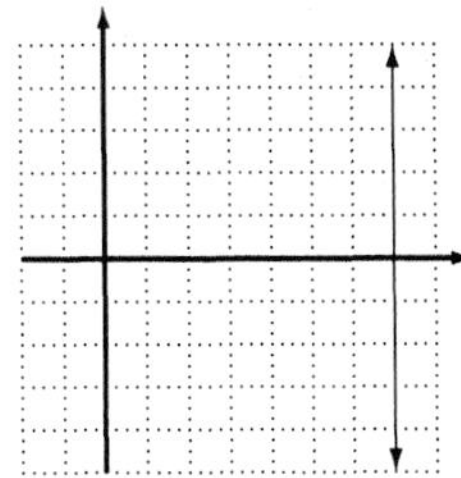

22. $m = \frac{8 - (-4)}{6 - (-2)} = \frac{12}{8} = \frac{3}{2}$

23. $m = \frac{1 - 1}{5 - (-1)} = \frac{0}{6} = 0$

24. $m = \frac{5 - 0}{(-3) - (-3)} = \frac{5}{-3 + 3} = \frac{5}{0}$ No slope

25. $m = \frac{4 - (-8)}{3 - 5} = \frac{12}{-2} = -6$

26. $3x - 2y = -6$
$-2y = -3x - 6$
$y = \frac{3}{2}x + 3$ slope $= \frac{3}{2}$

27. $5x + 3y = 4$
$3y = -5x + 4$
$y = -\frac{5}{3}x + \frac{4}{3}$ slope $= -\frac{5}{3}$

28. $3x - 5y = 4$
$-5y = -3x + 4$
$y = \frac{3}{5}x - \frac{4}{5}$ slope $= \frac{3}{5}$
y-intercept $= -\frac{4}{5}$

29. $2x = 6y + 12$
$2x - 12 = 6y$
$\frac{1}{3}x - 2 = y$ slope $= \frac{1}{3}$
y-intercept $= -2$

30.

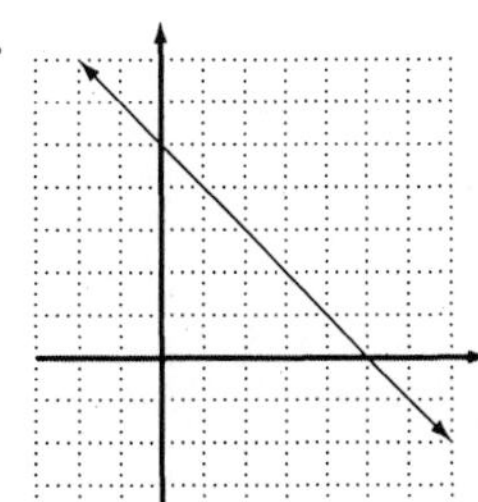

31.

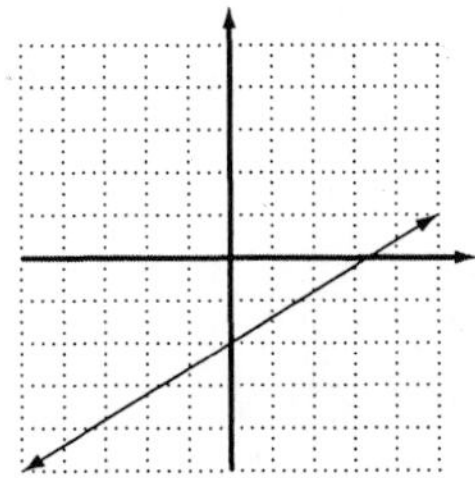

32.

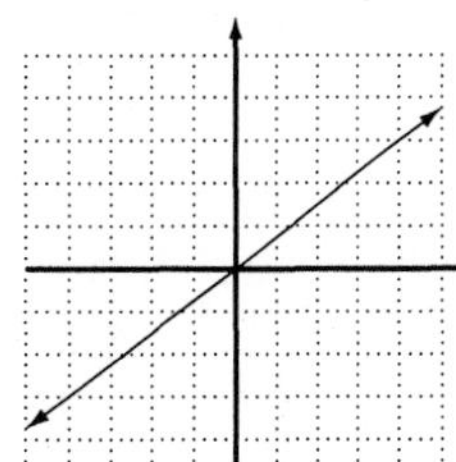

33. $y = 3x - 4$ 34. $y = 5x$

35. $y = 3x + b$
$(2) = 3(1) + b$
$2 = 3 + b$
$-1 = b$
$y = 3x - 1$

36. $y = -2x + b$
$(4) = -2(0) + b$
$4 = b$
$y = -2x + 4$

37. $y = -\frac{1}{2}x + b$

$(4) = -\frac{1}{2}(-2) + b$

$4 = 1 + b$

$3 = b$

$y = -\frac{1}{2}x + 3$

38. $m = \frac{7-1}{5-(-1)} = \frac{6}{6} = 1$

$y = x + b$

$(7) = (5) + b$

$2 = b$

$y = x + 2$

39. $m = \frac{0-(-3)}{2-(-4)} = \frac{3}{6} = \frac{1}{2}$

$y = \frac{1}{2}x + b$

$(0) = \frac{1}{2}(2) + b$

$0 = 1 + b$

$-1 = b$

$y = \frac{1}{2}x - 1$

40. Points on graph: (2, 0) and (0, − 3)

$m = \frac{0-(-3)}{2-0} = \frac{3}{2}$

$y = \frac{3}{2}x + b$

$(-3) = \frac{3}{2}(0) + b$

$-3 = b$

$y = \frac{3}{2}x - 3$

41. Points on graph: (3, 0) and (0, 2)

$m = \frac{2-0}{0-3} = -\frac{2}{3}$

$y = -\frac{2}{3}x + b$

$2 = -\frac{2}{3}(0) + b$

$2 = b$

$y = -\frac{2}{3}x + 2$

42. $m = \frac{20-15}{68-59} = \frac{5}{9}$

$C = \frac{5}{9}F + b$

$(20) = \frac{5}{9}(68) + b$

$20 = \frac{340}{9} + b$

$-\frac{160}{9} = b$

$C = \frac{5}{9}F - \frac{160}{9}$ or

$C = \frac{5}{9}(F - 32)$

43. $C = \frac{5}{9}(77) - \frac{160}{9}$

$C = \frac{385}{9} - \frac{160}{9}$

$C = \frac{225}{9}$

$C = 25°$

44. $y - 5 = -2x$ $y + 2x = -3$

$y = -2x + 5$ $y = -2x - 3$

Yes

45. $y = 3x - 4$ $y + 3x = 2$

$y = -3x + 2$

No

46. $y = \frac{2}{3}x$ $2y = -3x + 8$

$y = -\frac{3}{2}x + 4$

$\left(\frac{2}{3}\right)\left(-\frac{3}{2}\right) = -1$

Yes

47. $6y = -x + 18$ $y = -6x - 4$

$y = -\frac{1}{6}x + 3$

$\left(-\frac{1}{6}\right)(-6) = 1$

No

48. $4x + y = 6$ $4x + y = 8$

$y = -4x + 6$ $y = -4x + 8$

Parallel

49. $2x + y = 10$ $y = \frac{1}{2}x - 4$

$y = -2x + 10$

$(-2)\left(\frac{1}{2}\right) = -1$

Perpendicular

50. $x + 4y = 8$ $x = -4y - 10$

$4y = -x + 8$ $x + 10 = -4y$

$y = -\frac{1}{4}x + 8$ $-\frac{1}{4}x - \frac{5}{2} = y$

Parallel

51. $3x - y = 6$ $3x + y = 8$

$3x - 6 = y$ $y = -3x + 8$

$(3)(-3) = -9$

Neither

CHAPTER 7 ASSESSMENT p. 350

1–2.

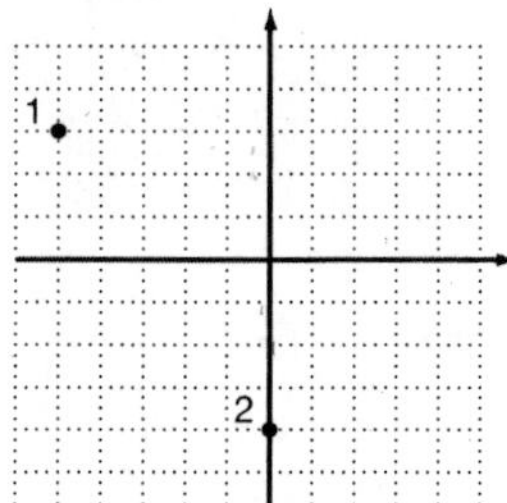

3. III **4.** II **5.** (3, 3) **6.** (0, − 4)

7. (− 5, 0) **8.** (− 1, 1)

9. $2x + 3y = 12$

$2(2) + 3(3) = 12$

$4 + 9 = 12$

$13 = 12$

No

10. $2x + 3y = 12$

$2(3) + 3(2) = 12$

$6 + 6 = 12$

$12 = 12$

Yes

11.

x	y
1	7
2	4
3	1

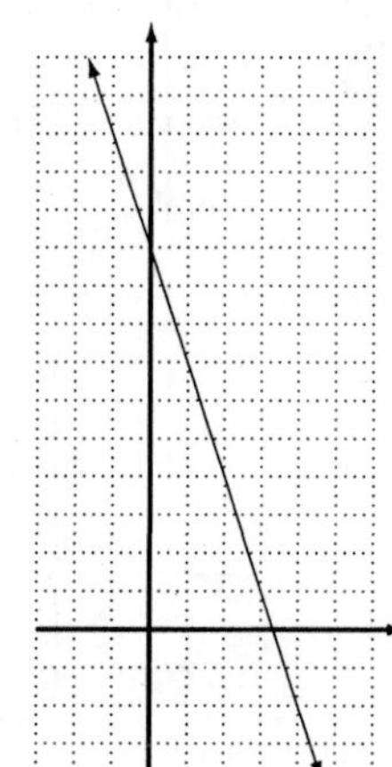

12. $2x - 3y = -6$
x-intercept: $2x - 3(0) = -6$
$2x = -6$
$x = -3$
y-intercept: $2(0) - 3y = -6$
$-3y = -6$
$y = 2$

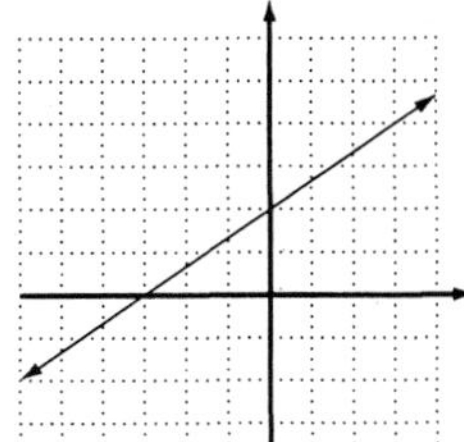

13.

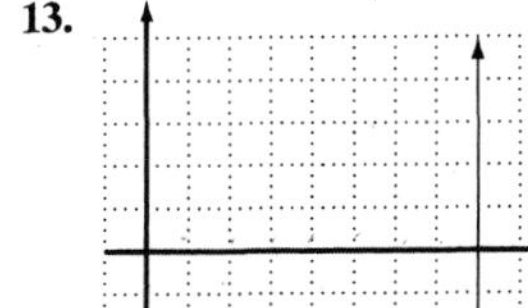

14.

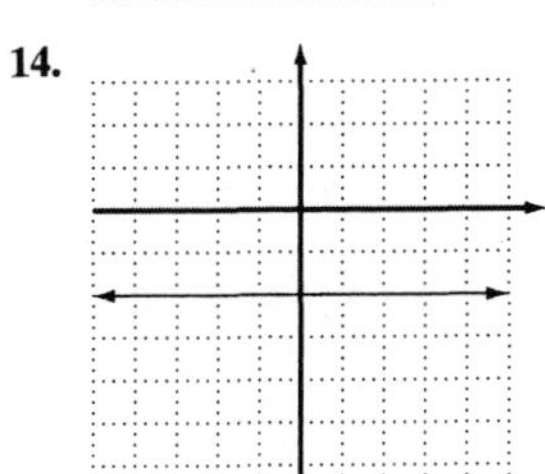

15. $m = \dfrac{2 - (-5)}{9 - (-3)} = \dfrac{7}{12}$

16. $m = \dfrac{7 - (-1)}{4 - 4} = \dfrac{8}{0}$ No slope

17. $-4x + 3y = -6$
$3y = 4x - 6$
$y = \frac{4}{3}x - 2$

slope $= \frac{4}{3}$ y-intercept $= -2$

18.

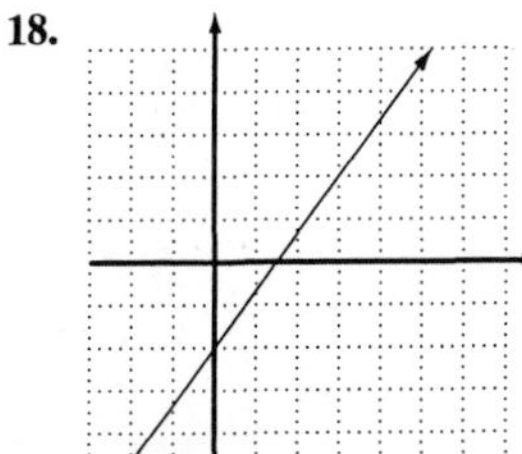

19. $y = x + b$
$(5) = (3) + b$
$2 = b$
$y = x + 2$

20. $y = -3x + b$
$(0) = -3(-2) + b$
$0 = 6 + b$
$-6 = b$
$y = -3x - 6$

21. $m = \dfrac{1 - (-2)}{1 - 2} = \dfrac{3}{-1} = -3$
$y = -3x + b$
$(1) = -3(1) + b$
$1 = -3 + b$
$4 = b$
$y = -3x + 4$

22. $m = \dfrac{-1 - (-3)}{4 - (-4)} = \dfrac{-1 + 3}{4 + 4} = \dfrac{2}{8} = \dfrac{1}{4}$
$y = \frac{1}{4}x + b$
$(-1) = \frac{1}{4}(4) + b$
$-1 = 1 + b$
$-2 = b$
$y = \frac{1}{4}x - 2$

23. $m = \dfrac{30 - 10}{5000 - 1000} = \dfrac{20}{4000} = \dfrac{1}{200}$
$p = \frac{1}{200}n + b$
$(10) = \frac{1}{200}(1000) + b$
$10 = 5 + b$
$5 = b$
$p = \frac{1}{200}n + 5$

24. $p = \frac{1}{200}(10{,}000) + 5$
$p = 50 + 5$
$p = 55$
The profit is \$55 per unit.

25. $2x + y = 8$ $\quad$ $2x + y = 4$
$y = -2x + 8$ $\quad$ $y = -2x + 4$
Parallel

26. $2x + 5y = 2$ $\quad$ $y = 2x + 4$
$5y = -2x + 2$
$y = -\frac{2}{5}x + \frac{2}{5}$
$\left(-\frac{2}{5}\right)(2) = -\frac{4}{5}$
Neither

27. $x + 2y = 8$ $\quad$ $-2x + y = 8$
$2y = -x + 8$ $\quad$ $y = 2x + 8$
$y = -\frac{1}{2}x + 4$
$\left(-\frac{1}{2}\right)(2) = -1$
Perpendicular

CHAPTERS 1-7 CUMULATIVE REVIEW pp. 351–355

1. $y + 6 + y = 8 + 6 + 8 = 22$ **2.** $\frac{x}{18} = \frac{24}{18} = \frac{6 \cdot 4}{6 \cdot 3} = \frac{4}{3}$

3. Answers may vary. Ex. $4x + y \cdot 3, x \cdot 4 + 3y, 3y + 4x$

4. $\dfrac{16}{48} = \dfrac{16 \cdot 1}{16 \cdot 3} = \dfrac{1}{3}$ **5.** $\dfrac{q}{12pq} = \dfrac{1}{12p}$ **6.** $\dfrac{51s}{3st} = \dfrac{17}{t}$

7. $x^2 - 5 = 3^2 - 5 = 9 - 5 = 4$

8. $(4y)^3 = (4 \cdot 3)^3 = 12^3 = 1728$

9. $(y - 1)^2 = (6 - 1)^2 = 5^2 = 25$ **10.** $3(2x + y) = 6x + 3y$

11. $4(3x + 4y + z) = 12x + 16y + 4z$

12. $7a + 7b + a + 7c = (7 + 1)a + 7b + 7c$
$= 8a + 7b + 7c$

13. $6x^2 + 2y + 2z + 3x^2 = (6 + 3)x^2 + 2y + 2z$
$= 9x^2 + 2y + 2z$

14. $2y - 7$ **15.** $x - 3y$ **16.** $s + 5$

17. a. Open **b.** $9 \cdot 8 - 5 = 27$
$72 - 5 = 27$
$67 = 27$
False
c. Open

18. $5.4 + 2.7 = 8.5$ $\quad$ $5.8 + 2.7 = 8.5$ $\quad$ $6.2 + 2.7 = 8.5$
$8.1 = 8.5$ $\quad$ $8.5 = 8.5$ $\quad$ $8.9 = 8.5$
False $\quad$ True $\quad$ False
$x = 5.8$

19. $112(35) = 4256$ $\quad$ $112(37) = 4256$
$3920 = 4256$ $\quad$ $4144 = 4256$
False $\quad$ False
No solution

20. $D = rt$

$t = 270 \text{ min} = 4\frac{1}{2}h$

$D = 55\left(4\frac{1}{2}\right)$

$D = 247\frac{1}{2} \text{ mi}$

21. $F = \frac{9}{5}C + 32$

$F = \frac{9}{5}(15) + 32$

$F = 27 + 32$

$F = 59°$

22. $-10 > -14$ **23.** $-3.1 > -3.15$ **24.** $0.01 < 0.1$

25. $-\frac{2}{3} = -\frac{8}{12}$

$-\frac{3}{4} = -\frac{9}{12}$

$-\frac{8}{12} > -\frac{9}{12}$

so $-\frac{2}{3} > -\frac{3}{4}$

26. $\frac{7}{8} = \frac{63}{72}$

$\frac{8}{9} = \frac{64}{72}$

$\frac{63}{72} < \frac{64}{72}$

so $\frac{7}{8} < \frac{8}{9}$

27. $-\frac{4}{10} < 0$

$\frac{5}{7} > 0$

so $-\frac{4}{10} < \frac{5}{7}$

28. 18 **29.** 25

30. $-\frac{1}{2} + \frac{3}{8} + (-6) + \frac{3}{4} = -\frac{4}{8} + \frac{3}{8} - \frac{48}{8} + \frac{6}{8} = -\frac{43}{8}$

31. $-2.6 + (-7.5) + 2.6 + (-7.5) = -15$

32. $-6.1 - (-3.1) + 7.9 - 3.1 + 1.8$
$= -6.1 + 3.1 + 7.9 - 3.1 + 1.8 = 3.6$

33. $-\frac{5}{9} - \frac{2}{18} = -\frac{5}{9} - \frac{1}{9} = -\frac{6}{9} = -\frac{2}{3}$

34. $\left(-\frac{2}{3}\right)\left(\frac{18}{15}\right) = \left(-\frac{2}{3}\right)\left(\frac{6}{5}\right) = -\frac{12}{15} = -\frac{4}{5}$

35. $\frac{3}{5}\left(-\frac{3}{5}\right)\left(-\frac{25}{9}\right) = \frac{225}{225} = 1$ **36.** $-2(-7)(-3) = -42$

37. $-\frac{4}{3} \div \frac{-2}{9} = -\frac{4}{3}\left(-\frac{9}{2}\right) = \frac{36}{6} = 6$

38. $-6.262 \div 1.01 = -6.2$

39. $-\frac{72}{108} \div -\frac{2}{3} = -\frac{72}{108}\left(-\frac{3}{2}\right) = \frac{216}{216} = 1$

40. $121x - 55 = 11 \cdot 11x - 11 \cdot 5 = 11(11x - 5)$

41. $-6 - 2x - 12y = -2 \cdot 3 + (-2)x + (-2)6y$
$= -2(3 + x + 6y)$
or $2(-3 - x - 6y)$

42. $-8x - (9 - 4x) = -8x - 9 + 4x = -4x - 9$

43. $-2(y + 3) - 3y = -2y - 6 - 3y = -5y - 6$

44. Additive inverse property **45.** Distributive property

46. $x - \frac{3}{8} = \frac{1}{2}$

$x - \frac{3}{8} + \frac{3}{8} = \frac{1}{2} + \frac{3}{8}$

$x = \frac{4}{8} + \frac{3}{8}$

$x = \frac{7}{8}$

47. $-3.2 = y - 5.8$

$-3.2 + 5.8 = y - 5.8 + 5.8$

$2.6 = y$

48. $-\frac{2}{3} = x - \frac{8}{12}$

$-\frac{2}{3} + \frac{8}{12} = x - \frac{8}{12} + \frac{8}{12}$

$-\frac{8}{12} + \frac{8}{12} = x$

$0 = x$

49. $-4x = -18$

$\frac{1}{-4}(-4x) = \frac{1}{-4}(-18)$

$x = \frac{18}{4} = \frac{9}{2}$

50. $-\frac{x}{3} = -16$

$-3\left(-\frac{x}{3}\right) = -3(-16)$

$x = 48$

51. $-\frac{5}{6} = x - \frac{1}{3}$

$6\left(-\frac{5}{6}\right) = 6\left(x - \frac{1}{3}\right)$

$-5 = 6x - 2$

$-5 + 2 = 6x - 2 + 2$

$-3 = 6x$

$\frac{1}{6}(-3) = \frac{1}{6}(6x)$

$-\frac{3}{6} = x$

$-\frac{1}{2} = x$

52. $6y + 3 = -15$

$6y + 3 - 3 = -15 - 3$

$6y = -18$

$\frac{1}{6}(6y) = \frac{1}{6}(-18)$

$y = -3$

53. $3(x - 2) = 24$

$3x - 6 = 24$

$3x - 6 + 6 = 24 + 6$

$3x = 30$

$\frac{1}{3}(3x) = \frac{1}{3}(30)$

$x = 10$

54. $-2(x - 4) = 10$

$-2x + 8 = 10$

$-2x + 8 - 8 = 10 - 8$

$-2x = 2$

$\frac{1}{-2}(-2x) = \frac{1}{-2}(2)$

$x = -1$

55. Let d = cost of one disk.

$12d = 9$

$\frac{1}{12}(12d) = \frac{1}{12}(9)$

$d = \frac{9}{12} = 0.75$

The cost is \$0.75.

56. Let b = number of boys.

$b + (2b + 1) = 19$

$3b + 1 = 19$

$3b + 1 - 1 = 19 - 1$

$3b = 18$

$\frac{1}{3}(3b) = \frac{1}{3}(18)$

$b = 6$

There are 6 boys.

57. $9(t + 2) = 5(t - 3)$

$9t + 18 = 5t - 15$

$9t - 5t + 18 = 5t - 5t - 15$

$4t + 18 = -15$

$4t + 18 - 18 = -15 - 18$

$4t = -33$

$\frac{1}{4}(4t) = \frac{1}{4}(-33)$

$t = -\frac{33}{4}$

58. $4 + 3x - 2 = 5x + 8 - x$

$2 + 3x = 4x + 8$

$2 + 3x - 3x = 4x - 3x + 8$

$2 = x + 8$

$2 - 8 = x + 8 - 8$

$-6 = x$

59. $\frac{5}{3} + \frac{2}{3}x = \frac{13}{12} + \frac{5}{4}x + \frac{3}{4}$

$12\left(\frac{5}{3} + \frac{2}{3}x\right) = 12\left(\frac{13}{12} + \frac{5}{4}x + \frac{3}{4}\right)$

$20 + 8x = 13 + 15x + 9$

$20 + 8x = 22 + 15x$

$20 + 8x - 8x = 22 + 15x - 8x$

$20 = 22 + 7x$

$20 - 22 = 22 - 22 + 7x$

$-2 = 7x$

$\frac{1}{7}(-2) = \frac{1}{7}(7x)$

$-\frac{2}{7} = x$

60. $\frac{1}{3}x - \frac{2}{9} = \frac{2}{3} + \frac{4}{9}x$
$9\left(\frac{1}{3}x - \frac{2}{9}\right) = 9\left(\frac{2}{3} + \frac{4}{9}x\right)$
$3x - 2 = 6 + 4x$
$3x - 3x - 2 = 6 + 4x - 3x$
$-2 = 6 + x$
$-2 - 6 = 6 - 6 + x$
$-8 = x$

61. $C = 2\pi r$
$\frac{1}{2\pi}(C) = \frac{1}{2\pi}(2\pi r)$
$\frac{C}{2\pi} = r$

62. $4|x| = 28$
$\frac{1}{4}(4|x|) = \frac{1}{4}(28)$
$|x| = 7$
$x = 7$ or $x = -7$

63. $|x| - 16 = 45$
$|x| - 16 + 16 = 45 + 16$
$|x| = 61$
$x = 61$ or $x = -61$

64. $\frac{24}{x} = \frac{8}{3}$
$3x\left(\frac{24}{x}\right) = 3x\left(\frac{8}{3}\right)$
$72 = 8x$
$\frac{1}{8}(72) = \frac{1}{8}(8x)$
$9 = x$

65. $\frac{12}{15} = \frac{t}{35}$
$\frac{4}{5} = \frac{t}{35}$
$35\left(\frac{4}{5}\right) = 35\left(\frac{t}{35}\right)$
$28 = t$

66. $I = prt$
$I = 300(0.06)(1)$
$I = \$18$

67. $n = \frac{21}{35}$
$n = 0.6 = \frac{60}{100} = 60\%$

68. **a.** Yes **b.** Yes **c.** No

69. $4y + 4 - 2y \leq 12$
$2y + 4 \leq 12$
$2y + 4 - 4 \leq 12 - 4$
$2y \leq 8$
$\frac{1}{2}(2y) \leq \frac{1}{2}(8)$
$y \leq 4$

0 4

70. $4x + 3 - 3x > 2$
$x + 3 > 2$
$x + 3 - 3 > 2 - 3$
$x > -1$

−1 0

71. $-2y > 3$
$\frac{1}{-2}(-2y) < \frac{1}{-2}(3)$
$y < -\frac{3}{2}$

$-\frac{3}{2}$ 0

72. $6 - 5y > 8 - 4y$
$6 - 5y + 5y > 8 - 4y + 5y$
$6 > 8 + y$
$6 - 8 > 8 - 8 + y$
$-2 > y$

−2 0

73. $n + (n + 2) + (n + 4) < 100$
$3n + 6 < 100$
$3n + 6 - 6 < 100 - 6$
$3n < 94$
$\frac{1}{3}(3n) < \frac{1}{3}(94)$
$n < 31\frac{1}{3}$

The numbers are 31, 33, and 35.

74. $x^8 \cdot x^2 = x^{8+2} = x^{10}$

75. $\frac{z^4}{z^7} = \frac{1}{z^{7-4}} = \frac{1}{z^3}$

76. $(4y^3)^2 = 4^2(y^3)^2 = 4^2y^{3 \cdot 2} = 16y^6$

77. $(3x^2y)^3 = 3^3(x^2)^3y^3 = 3^3x^{2 \cdot 3}y^3 = 27x^6y^3$

78. $(-2x)(4x^3) = -8x^{1+3} = -8x^4$

79. $(3b^2c^3)(-4bc^4)(-2b^2) = 24b^{2+1+2}c^{3+4}$
$= 24b^5c^7$

80. $\frac{-25n^6}{-5n^3} = 5n^{6-3} = 5n^3$

81. $\frac{-48m^6n^8}{8m^4n^8} = -6m^{6-4}n^{8-8} = -6m^2n^0 = -6m^2$

82. $\frac{36a^4b^7}{-3a^6b^2} = \frac{-12b^{7-2}}{a^{6-4}} = \frac{-12b^5}{a^2}$

83. $\frac{4p^2r^4}{12p^5r^9} = \frac{1}{3p^{5-2}r^{9-4}} = \frac{1}{3p^3r^5}$

84. $248{,}000 = 2.48 \times 10^5$

85. $0.0000375 = 3.75 \times 10^{-5}$

86. $-3x^2 + 4x - 5x^3 - 6x^2 + 2 - 3x = -5x^3 - 9x^2 + x + 2$

87. $2x^3 - 7 + 3x^2 - 6x^3 - 4x^2 + 5 = -4x^3 - x^2 - 2$

88. $x^2 - 6x + 8 = 4^2 - 6(4) + 8 = 16 - 24 + 8 = 0$

89. $(3x^4 + 2x^3 - 6x^2) + (-2x^4 - 3x^2 - 7)$
$= 3x^4 + 2x^3 - 6x^2 - 2x^4 - 3x^2 - 7$
$= x^4 + 2x^3 - 9x^2 - 7$

90. $(a^4b^2 - 3a^2b + 4b^3) + (5a^4b^2 + 6a^2b - 9b^3)$
$= a^4b^2 - 3a^2b + 4b^3 + 5a^4b^2 + 6a^2b - 9b^3$
$= 6a^4b^2 + 3a^2b - 5b^3$

91. $(-8y^2 - y + 2) - (-y^3 - 6y^2 + y - 5)$
$= -8y^2 - y + 2 + y^3 + 6y^2 - y + 5$
$= y^3 - 2y^2 - 2y + 7$

92. $(14v^3u + 4u^2 - 3v^2) - (8v^3u - 6u^2 + 5v^2)$
$= 14v^3u + 4u^2 - 3v^2 - 8v^3u + 6u^2 - 5v^2$
$= 6v^3u + 10u^2 - 8v^2$

93. $4x^3(2x^2 - x + 7) = 8x^5 - 4x^4 + 28x^3$

94. $(2x - 5)(3x + 4) = 6x^2 + 8x - 15x - 20$
$= 6x^2 - 7x - 20$

95. $(xy - 7y^2)(xy + 7y^2) = (xy)^2 - (7y^2)^2$
$= x^2y^2 - 49y^4$

96. $3m(-m^7 + 4m^2n + 3n^3) = -3m^8 + 12m^3n + 9mn^3$

97. $(2a - 5b)^2 = (2a)^2 - 2 \cdot 2a \cdot 5b + (5b)^2$
$= 4a^2 - 20ab + 25b^2$

98. $(4x - 5y)(x + 6y) = 4x^2 + 24xy - 5xy - 30y^2$
$= 4x^2 + 19xy - 30y^2$

99. $(1 - 3x^2)(2 - 4x^2) = 2 - 4x^2 - 6x^2 + 12x^4$
$= 2 - 10x^2 + 12x^4$

100. $(2x^5 + 3)(3x^2 - 6) = 6x^7 - 12x^5 + 9x^2 - 18$

101. $(2x^3 + 1)(2x^3 - 1) = (2x^3)^2 - 1^2 = 4x^6 - 1$

102. $(8x + 3)^2 = (8x)^2 + 2 \cdot 8x \cdot 3 + 3^2$
$= 64x^2 + 48x + 9$

103. $(6x - 5)^2 = (6x)^2 - 2 \cdot 6x \cdot 5 + 5^2$
$= 36x^2 - 60x + 25$

104. $(4x^3 - x + 1)(x - 1) = 4x^4 - 4x^3 - x^2 + x + x - 1$
$= 4x^4 - 4x^3 - x^2 + 2x - 1$

105. $x^2 - 4x = x(x - 4)$

106. $6x^5 - 36x^3 + 9x^2 = 3x^2(2x^3 - 12x + 3)$

107. $12x - 4x^2 - 48x^4 = 4x(3 - x - 12x^3)$

108. $9x^2 - 1 = (3x + 1)(3x - 1)$

109. $2x^2 - 8 = 2(x^2 - 4) = 2(x + 2)(x - 2)$

110. $16x^4 - 81 = (4x^2 + 9)(4x^2 - 9)$
$= (4x^2 + 9)(2x + 3)(2x - 3)$

111. $x^2 - 14x + 49 = (x - 7)^2$

112. $16x^2 + 40x + 25 = (4x + 5)^2$

113. $x^2 - 8xy + 16y^2 = (x - 4y)^2$

114. $c^2 - 7cd + 6d^2 = (c - d)(c - 6d)$

115. $18x^2 - 48x + 32 = 2(9x^2 - 24x + 16)$
$= 2(3x - 4)^2$

116. $x^2 - 10x + 24 = (x - 6)(x - 4)$

117. $x^2 - 2x - 35 = (x - 7)(x + 5)$

118. $x^3 - 4x^2 - 21x = x(x^2 - 4x - 21)$
$= x(x - 7)(x + 3)$

119. $8x^2 + 10x + 3 = (2x + 1)(4x + 3)$

120. $3x^2 + 10x - 8 = (3x - 2)(x + 4)$

121. $6x^2 - 28x + 16 = 2(3x^2 - 14x + 8)$
$= 2(3x - 2)(x - 4)$

122. $x^3 + x^2 + 2x + 2 = x^2(x + 1) + 2(x + 1)$
$= (x + 1)(x^2 + 2)$

123. $x^4 + 2x^3 - 3x - 6 = x^3(x + 2) - 3(x + 2)$
$= (x + 2)(x^3 - 3)$

124. $3 - 12x^6 = 3(1 - 4x^6)$
$= 3(1 + 2x^3)(1 - 2x^3)$

125. $x^2 + 5x + xy + 5y = x(x + 5) + y(x + 5)$
$= (x + 5)(x + y)$

126. $am + an - bm - bn = a(m + n) - b(m + n)$
$= (m + n)(a - b)$

127. $x^2 + 4x - 12 = 0$
$(x + 6)(x - 2) = 0$
$x + 6 = 0$ or $x - 2 = 0$
$x = -6$ or $x = 2$

128. $2x^2 + 7x - 4 = 0$
$(2x - 1)(x + 4) = 0$
$2x - 1 = 0$ or $x + 4 = 0$
$2x = 1$ or $x = -4$
$x = \frac{1}{2}$ or $x = -4$

129. Let n = the first integer.
$n(n + 2) = 224$
$n^2 + 2n = 224$
$n^2 + 2n - 224 = 0$
$(n - 14)(n + 16) = 0$
$n - 14 = 0$ or $n + 16 = 0$
$n = 14$ or $n = -16$
If $n = 14, n + 2 = 16$.
If $n = -16, n + 2 = -14$.

130. I 131. II 132. IV

133.
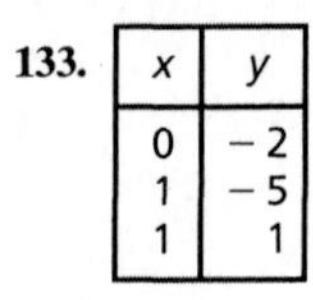

x	y
0	−2
1	−5
1	1

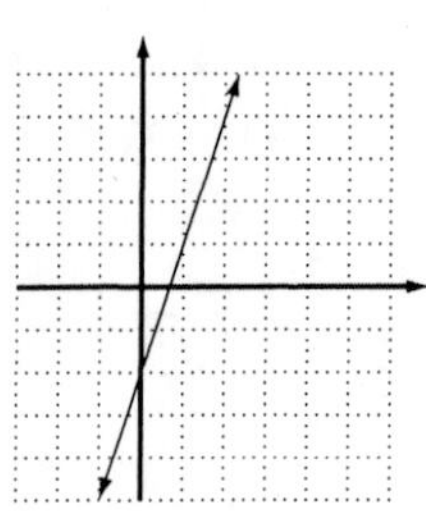

134.
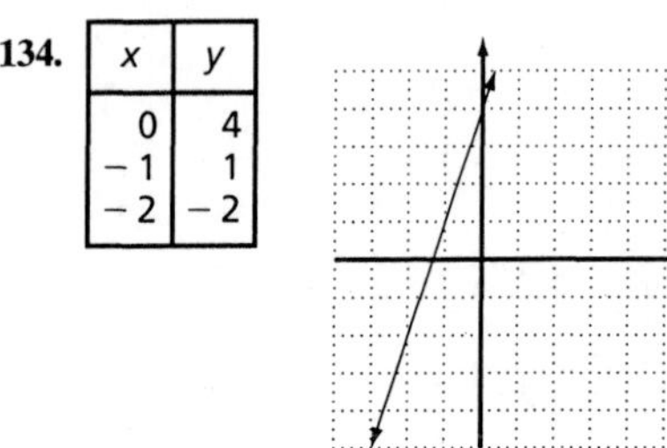

x	y
0	4
−1	1
−2	−2

135. $3y = x + 6$
x-intercept: $3(0) = x + 6$
$0 = x + 6$
$-6 = x$
y-intercept: $3y = (0) + 6$
$y = 2$

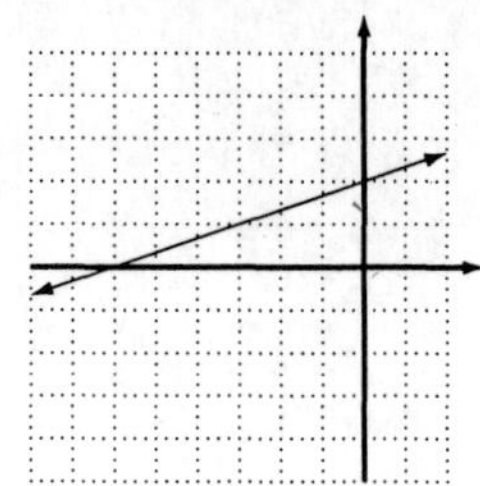

136. $2x = 3y + 9$
x-intercept: $2x = 3(0) + 9$
$2x = 9$
$x = \frac{9}{2}$
y-intercept: $2(0) = 3y + 9$
$0 = 3y + 9$
$-9 = 3y$
$-3 = 0$

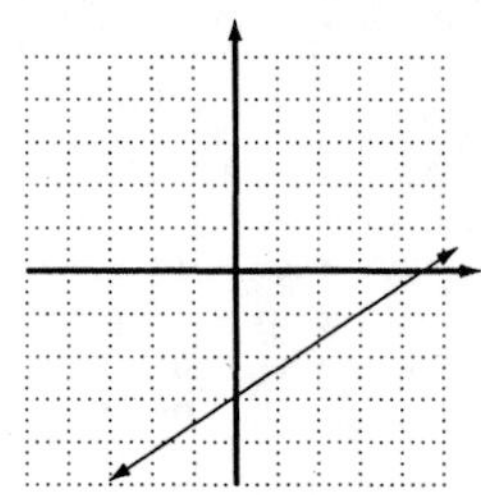

137. $m = \frac{0 - (-3)}{4 - 0} = \frac{3}{4}$

138. $m = \frac{8 - 2}{-1 - 2} = \frac{6}{-3} = -2$

139. $2y = -4x + 8$
$y = -2x + 4$
slope $= -2$, y-intercept $= 4$

140. $4x = 9y - 7$
$4x + 7 = 9y$
$\frac{4}{9}x + \frac{7}{9} = y$
slope $= \frac{4}{9}$, y-intercept $= \frac{7}{9}$

141. $y = -x + 3$

142. $y = 5x + b$
$(2) = 5(5) + b$
$2 = 25 + b$
$-23 = b$
$y = 5x - 23$

143. $y = \frac{2}{3}x + b$
$(5) = \frac{2}{3}(2) + b$
$5 = \frac{4}{3} + b$
$\frac{15}{3} - \frac{4}{3} = b$
$\frac{11}{3} = b$
$y = \frac{2}{3}x + \frac{11}{3}$

144. $m = \frac{4 - 0}{6 - (-2)} = \frac{4}{8} = \frac{1}{2}$
$y = \frac{1}{2}x + b$
$0 = \frac{1}{2}(-2) + b$
$0 = -1 + b$
$1 = b$
$y = \frac{1}{2}x + 1$

145. $y = -\frac{1}{2}x - \frac{1}{2}$ $-2y = x + 6$
$y = -\frac{1}{2}x - 3$
Parallel

146. $6x + y = -4$ $6y = x + 8$
$y = -6x - 4$ $y = \frac{1}{6}x + \frac{4}{3}$
$(-6)\left(\frac{1}{6}\right) = -1$
Perpendicular

CHAPTER 8

SKILLS & CONCEPTS p. 356

1. $y + 3 = -2$
$y + 3 - 3 = -2 - 3$
$y = -5$

2. $9y = 2$
$\frac{1}{9}(9y) = \frac{1}{9}(2)$
$y = \frac{2}{9}$

3. $-3x + 2 = -10$
$-3x + 2 - 2 = -10 - 2$
$-3x = -12$
$\frac{1}{-3}(-3x) = \frac{1}{-3}(-12)$
$x = 4$

4. $3x + 4 = 19$
$3x + 4 - 4 = 19 - 4$
$3x = 15$
$\frac{1}{3}(3x) = \frac{1}{3}(15)$
$x = 5$

5. $6x + 2x = 45$
$8x = 45$
$\frac{1}{8}(8x) = \frac{1}{8}(45)$
$x = \frac{45}{8}$

6. $-7y - 8y = -30$
$-15y = -30$
$\frac{1}{-15}(-15y) = \frac{1}{-15}(-30)$
$y = 2$

7. $2n + 8$ **8.** $10x + 5y$

9. $6x + 5 = 2x + 13$
$6x - 2x + 5 = 2x - 2x + 13$
$4x + 5 = 13$
$4x + 5 - 5 = 13 - 5$
$4x = 8$
$\frac{1}{4}(4x) = \frac{1}{4}(8)$
$x = 2$

10. $9(t + 2) = 6(t - 2)$
$9t + 18 = 6t - 12$
$9t - 6t + 18 = 6t - 6t - 12$
$3t + 18 = -12$
$3t + 18 - 18 = -12 - 18$
$3t = -30$
$\frac{1}{3}(3t) = \frac{1}{3}(-30)$
$t = -10$

11. $3 + 4w = 3 + 4(-2) = 3 - 8 = -5$

12. $-7w - 8 = -7(-2) - 8 = 14 - 8 = 6$

13. $w^2 - 2w + 3 = (-2)^2 - 2(-2) + 3$
$= 4 + 4 + 3$
$= 11$

14. $y = 4x - 14$
$-2 = 4(3) - 14$
$-2 = 12 - 14$
$-2 = -2$
Yes

15. $y = -3x - 2$
$5 = -3(-1) - 2$
$5 = 3 - 2$
$5 = 1$
No

16. Answers may vary.

17. Answers may vary.

18. Answers may vary.

19. $2x - 4y = 1$
$-4y = -2x + 1$
$y = \frac{1}{2}x - \frac{1}{4}$

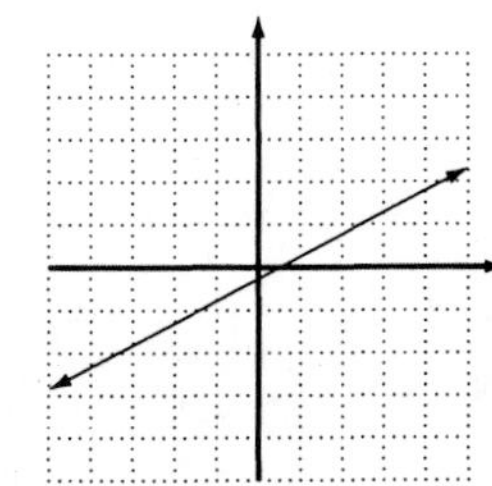

20. $-x + 3y = 5$
$3y = x + 5$
$y = \frac{1}{3}x + \frac{5}{3}$

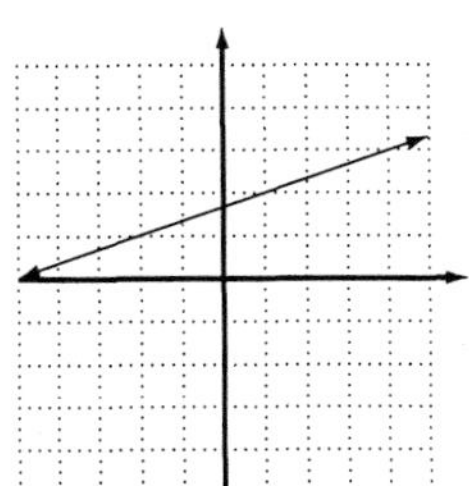

21.

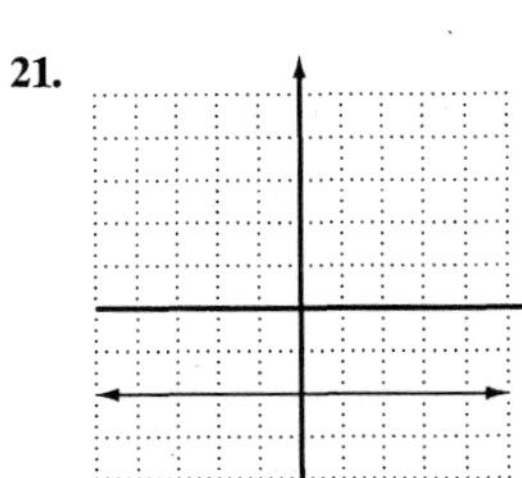

22.

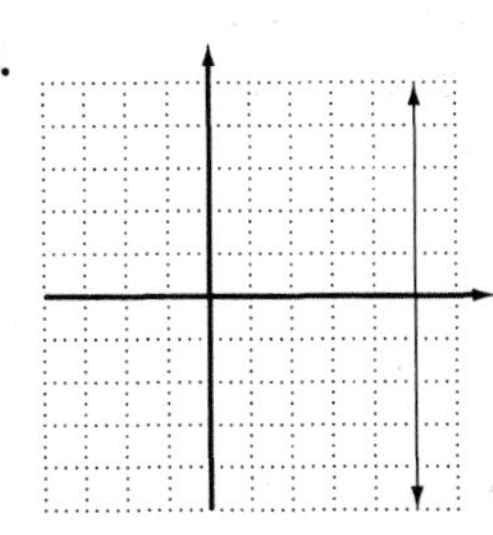

INTRODUCING THE CONCEPT p. 358

Set 1: $2x + 3y = 12$
$3y = -2x + 12$
$y = -\frac{2}{3}x + 4$

$x - 4y = -5$
$-4y = -x - 5$
$y = \frac{1}{4}x + \frac{5}{4}$

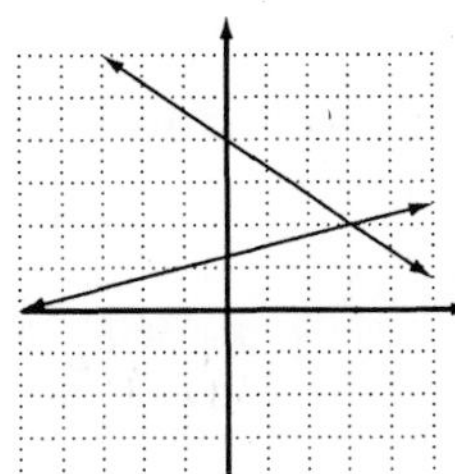

The lines intersect. They have one solution in common.

Set 2: $x = 2y + 1$
$x - 1 = 2y$
$\frac{1}{2}x - \frac{1}{2} = y$

$3x - 6y = 9$
$-6y = -3x + 9$
$y = \frac{1}{2}x - \frac{3}{2}$

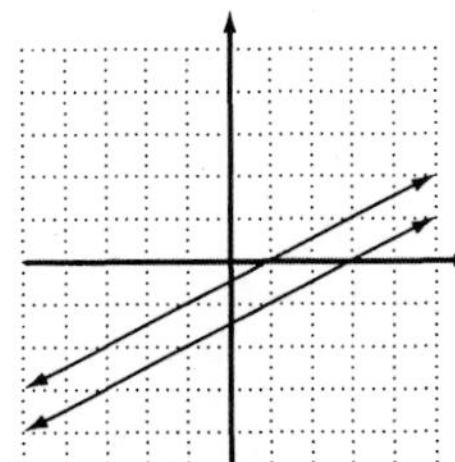

The lines are parallel. They have no solutions in common.

Set 3: $2x = 4 - y$
$2x - 4 = -y$
$-2x + 4 = y$

$6x + 3y = 12$
$3y = -6x + 12$
$y = -2x + 4$

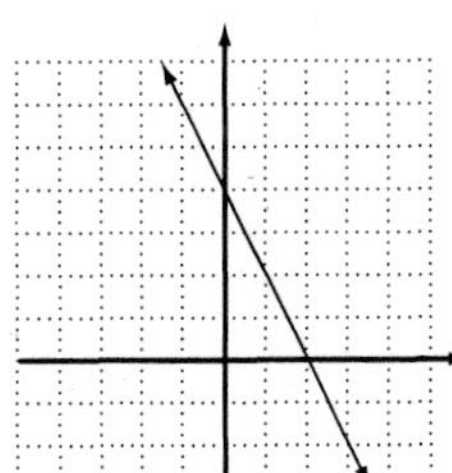

These are the same lines. They have an infinite number of solutions in common.

LESSON 8-1 TRY THIS pp. 359–360

a.

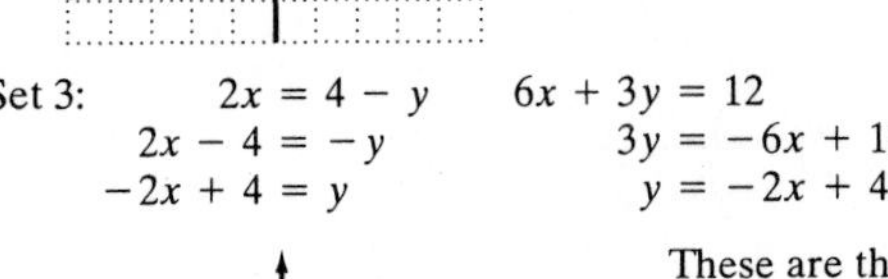

	$x = 2y + 8$	$2x + y = 1$	
2	$2(-3) + 8$	$2(2) + (-3)$	1
	$-6 + 8$	$4 - 3$	
	2	1	

Yes, $(2, -3)$ is a solution of the system.

b.

$a = \frac{1}{4}b + 10$	
20	$\frac{1}{4}(40) + 10$
	$10 + 10$
	20

$b - a = -20$	
$40 - 20$	-20
20	

No, (20, 40) is not a solution of $b - a = -20$, so it is not a solution of the system.

c.

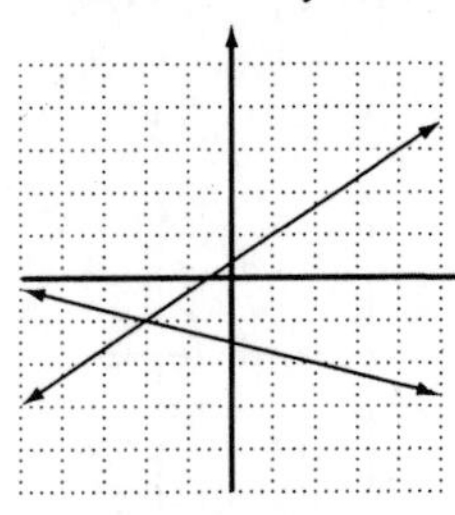

$(-2, -1)$

d.

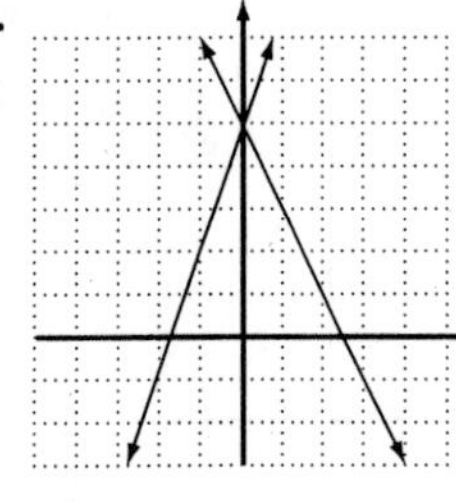

$(0, 5)$

e.

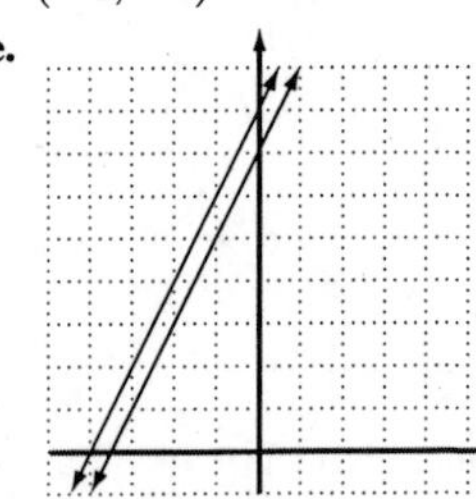

No solution

f.

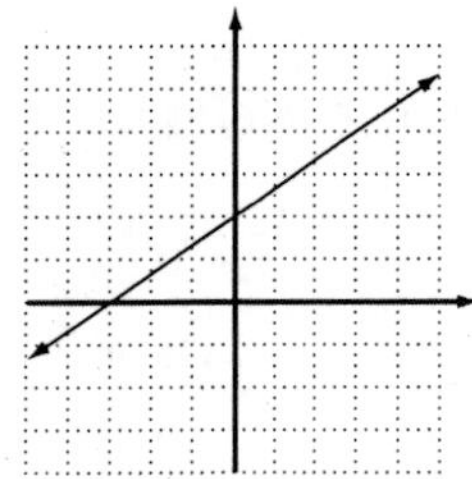

Infinitely many solutions

LESSON 8-1 EXERCISES pp. 360–361

1.

$2x + 3y = 12$	
$2(3) + 3(2)$	12
$6 + 6$	
12	

$x - 4y = -5$	
$3 - 4(2)$	-5
$3 - 8$	-5
-5	

Yes

2.

$5x - 2y = -5$	
$5(1) - 2(5)$	-5
$5 - 10$	
-5	

$3x - 7y = -32$	
$3(1) - 7(5)$	-32
$3 - 35$	
-32	

Yes

3.

$3t - 2s = 0$	
$3(3) - 2(2)$	0
$9 - 4$	
5	

$t + 2s = 15$	
$3 + 2(2)$	15
$3 + 4$	
7	

No

4.

$b + 2a = 2$	
$(-2) + 2(2)$	2
$-2 + 4$	
2	

$b - a = -4$	
$(-2) - (2)$	-4
-4	

Yes

5.

$x = -1$	
(-1)	-1

$x - y = -2$	
$(-1) - (1)$	-2
-2	-2

Yes

6.

$2x = -y - 2$	
$2(-3)$	$-(4) - 2$
-6	-6

$y = -4$	
(4)	-4

No

7.

$y = \frac{1}{4}x$	
(3)	$\frac{1}{4}(12)$
3	3

$3x - y = 33$	
$3(12) - (3)$	33
$36 - 3$	
33	

Yes

8.

$y = -\frac{1}{3}x$	
(1)	$-\frac{1}{3}(-3)$
	1

$3y = -5x - 12$	
3(1)	$-5(-3) - 12$
3	$15 - 12$
	3

Yes

9.

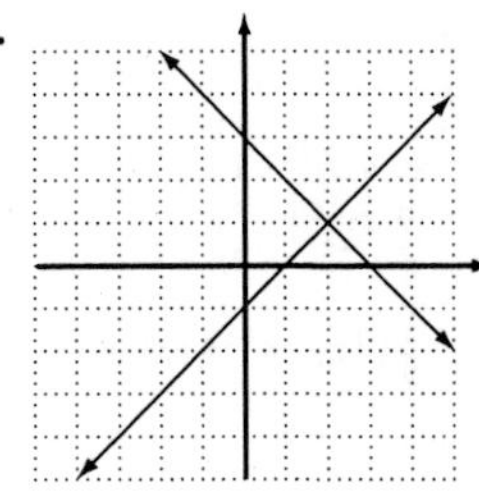

(2, 1)

10.

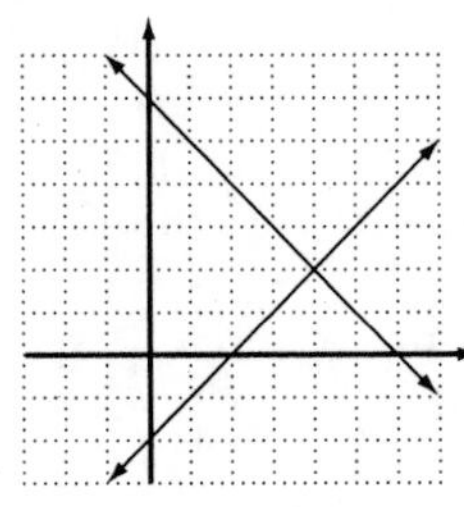

(4, 2)

11.

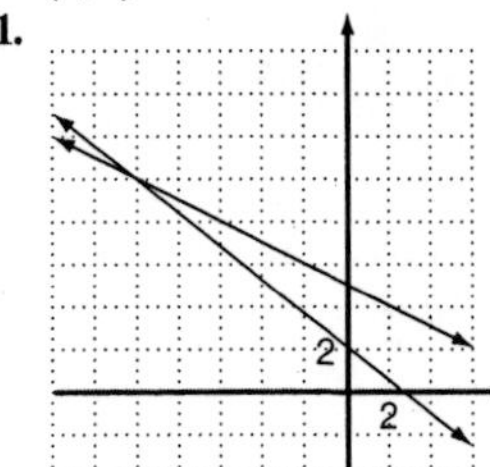

$(-12, 11)$

12.

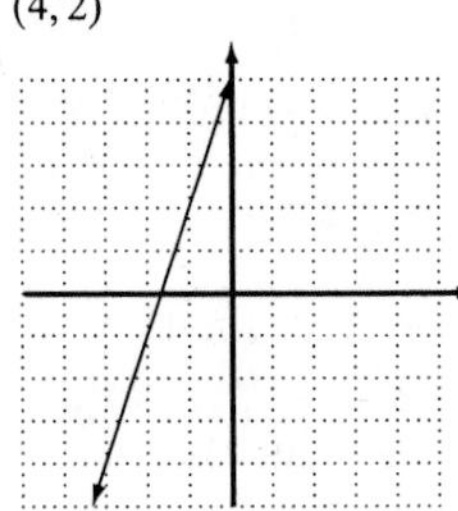

Infinitely many solutions

13.

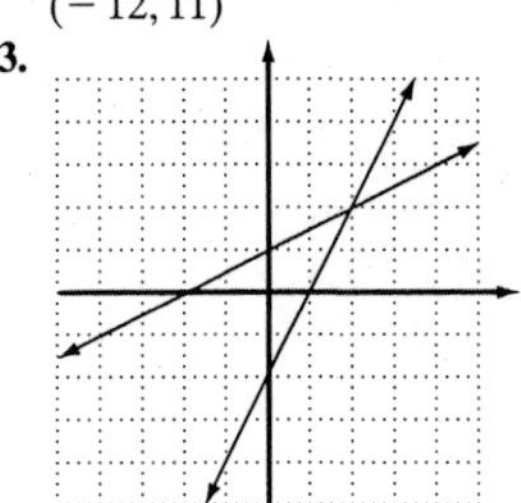

(2, 2)

14.

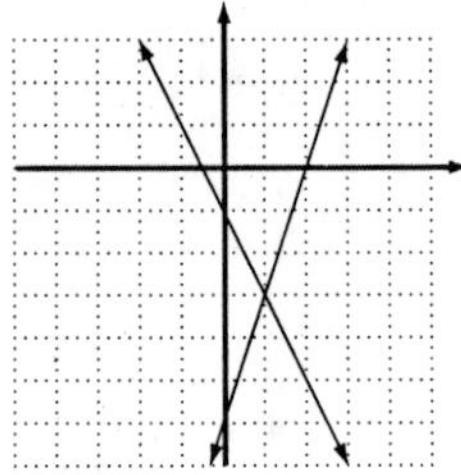

$(1, -3)$

15.

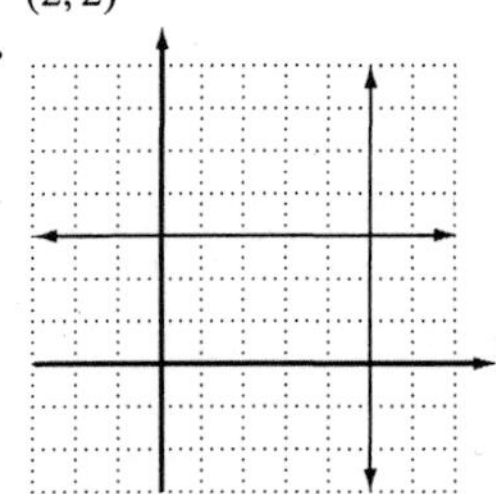

(5, 3)

16.

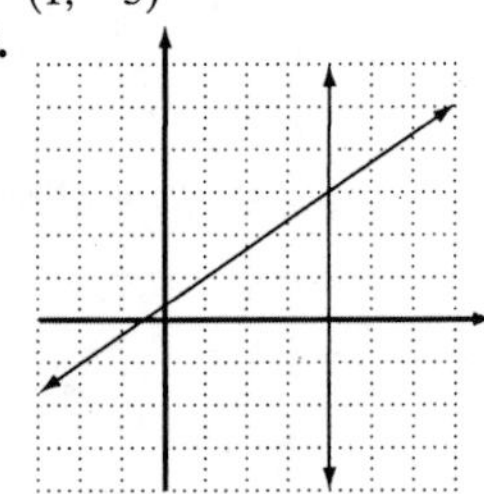

(4, 3)

17.

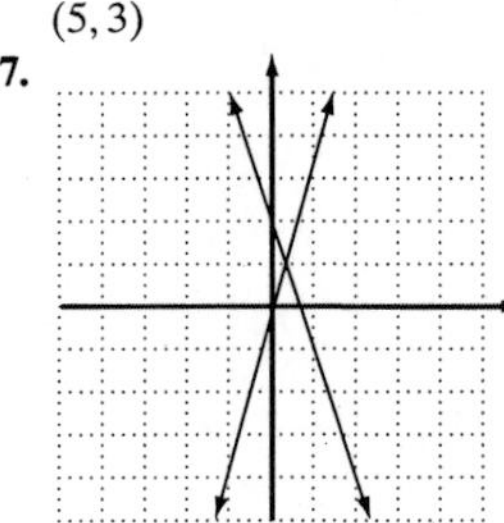

$\left(\frac{1}{3}, 1\right)$

18.

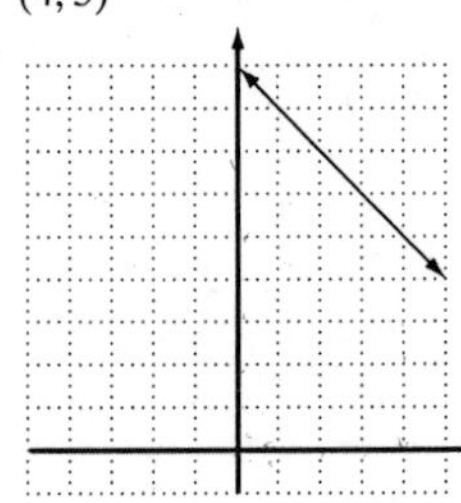

Infinitely many solutions

19.

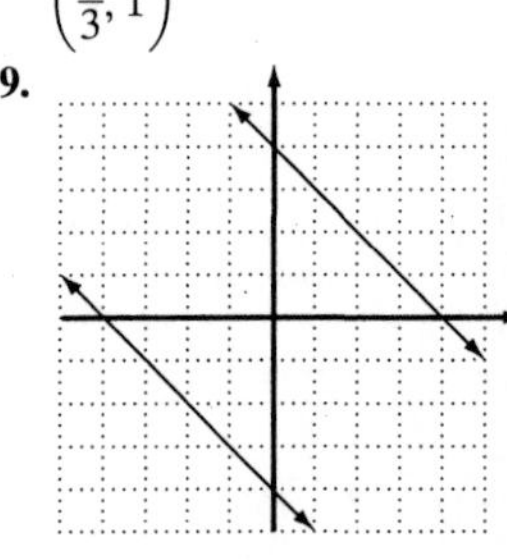

No solution

20.

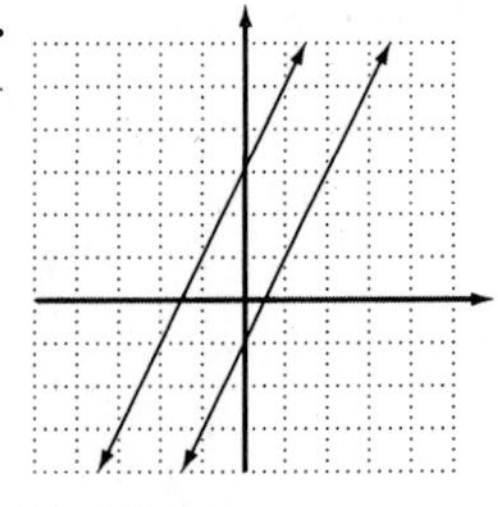

No solution

21. All except 19 and 20

22. Exercises 12 and 18

23. Exercises 19 and 20

24. A system is consistent if it has one or more solutions. So the graphs of the equations must intersect in one or more points. In I they intersect in one point. In II the graphs coincide and so intersect in an infinite number of points. In III the lines are parallel and have no intersection. The answer is B.

25. Estimated solutions: (0, 1) and (2, 1)
Checking (0, 1):

$y = -2x^2 + 4x + 1$		$y = x^2 - 2x + 1$	
1	$-2(0)^2 + 4(0) + 1$	1	$(0)^2 - 2(0) + 1$
	$0 + 0 + 1$		$0 - 0 + 1$
	1		1

Yes

Checking (2, 1):

1	$-2(2)^2 + 4(2) + 1$	1	$(2)^2 - 2(2) + 1$
	$-8 + 8 + 1$		$4 - 4 + 1$
	1		1

Yes

26.
$$Ax - 3y = 13 \qquad x - By = 8$$
$$A(2) - 3(-3) = 13 \qquad 2 - B(-3) = 8$$
$$2A + 9 = 13 \qquad 2 + 3B = 8$$
$$2A = 4 \qquad 3B = 6$$
$$A = 2 \qquad B = 2$$

27.

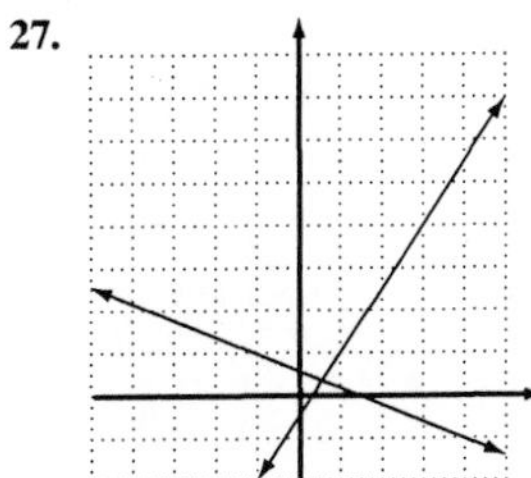

$\left(\frac{2}{3}, \frac{3}{7}\right)$
Noninteger solutions are difficult to approximate from graphs. Other methods are needed.

28. Answers may vary.
$x + y = -2$
$x - y = 6$

29. Answers may vary.
$x + y = 1$

30. $x - y = 3$
$-y = -x + 3$
$y = x - 3$
Slope $= 1$, y-intercept $= -3$

31. $2x = y + 1$
$2x - 1 = y$
Slope $= 2$, y-intercept $= -1$

32. $y = -3x + 2$

33. Since $(0, -2)$ is on the line, the y-intercept is -2.
So $y = mx - 2$ is a partial solution.
$4 = m(2) - 2$
$6 = m(2)$
$3 = m$
The equation is $y = 3x - 2$.

34. $4a^2 - 14a - 18 = 2(2a^2 - 7a - 9)$
$= 2(2a - 9)(a + 1)$

35. $y^3 + 2y^2 + 5y = y(y^2 + 2y + 5)$

36. $16m^4 - 1 = (4m^2 + 1)(4m^2 - 1)$
$= (4m^2 + 1)(2m + 1)(2m - 1)$

37. $m^2 + 5m - 14 = 0$
$(m + 7)(m - 2) = 0$
$m + 7 = 0$ or $m - 2 = 0$
$m = -7$ or $m = 2$

38. $2x^2 - 9x - 5 = 0$
$(2x + 1)(x - 5) = 0$
$2x + 1 = 0$ or $x - 5 = 0$
$2x = -1$ or $x = 5$
$x = -\frac{1}{2}$ or $x = 5$

39. Let $n =$ the first integer.
$(n + 2)^2 - n^2 = 40$
$n^2 + 4n + 4 - n^2 = 40$
$4n + 4 = 40$
$4n = 36$
$n = 9$
The integers are 9 and 11.

LESSON 8-2 TRY THIS — pp. 362–364

a. $x + y = 5$
$x = y + 1$
Substitute $y + 1$ for x in the first equation.
$(y + 1) + y = 5$
$2y + 1 = 5$
$2y = 4$, so $y = 2$
Substitute 2 for y in the second equation.
$x = 2 + 1$, so $x = 3$
Checking (3, 2): $3 + 2 = 5$ and $3 = 2 + 1$, so the solution is (3, 2).

b. $a - b = 4$
$b = 2 - 5a$
Substitute $2 - 5a$ for b in the first equation.
$a - (2 - 5a) = 4, a - 2 + 5a = 4, 6a = 6, a = 1$
Substitute 1 for a in the second equation.
$b = 2 - 5(1), b = 2 - 5, b = -3$
Checking: $1 - (-3) = 4$ and $-3 = 2 - 5(1)$, so $(1, -3)$ is the solution.

c. $y = x + 2$
$y = 2x - 1$
Substitute $2x - 1$ for y in the first equation.
$2x - 1 = x + 2$
$x - 1 = 2$
$x = 3$
Substitute 3 for x in the first equation.
$y = 3 + 2 = 5$
Checking $x = 3$ and $y = 5$ in both equations:

$y = x + 2$		$y = 2x - 1$	
5	$3 + 2$	5	$2(3) - 1$
	5		$6 - 1$
			5

The solution is (3, 5).

d. $x - 2y = 8$
$2x + y = 8$
Solving the first equation for x, $x = 2y + 8$.
Substituting in the second equation,
$2(2y + 8) + y = 8, 4y + 16 + y = 8, 5y = -8, y = -\frac{8}{5}$.
Substituting for y in the first equation,
$x - 2\left(-\frac{8}{5}\right) = 8, x + \frac{16}{5} = 8, 5x + 16 = 40, 5x = 24,$
$x = \frac{24}{5}$.
The solution is $\left(\frac{24}{5}, -\frac{8}{5}\right)$.

e. $4x - y = 5$
$2x + y = 10$
Solving the second equation for y, $y = 10 - 2x$.
Substituting $10 - 2x$ for y in the first equation,
$4x - (10 - 2x) = 5, 4x - 10 + 2x = 5, 6x = 15,$
$x = \frac{15}{6} = \frac{5}{2}$. Substituting $\frac{5}{2}$ for x in the second equation,
$2\left(\frac{5}{2}\right) + y = 10, 5 + y = 10, y = 5.$
$\left(\frac{5}{2}, 5\right)$ checks and is the solution.

f. $y = x + 5$
$2x + y = 8$
Substitute $x + 5$ for y in the second equation.
$2x + (x + 5) = 8$
$2x + x + 5 = 8$
$3x + 5 = 8$
$3x = 3$
$x = 1$
Substitute 1 for x in the first equation.
$y = 1 + 5$
$y = 6$
Checking $x = 1$ and $y = 6$ in both equations:

$y = x + 5$		$2x + y = 8$	
6	$1 + 5$	$2(1) + 6$	8
	6	$2 + 6$	
		8	

The solution is $(1, 6)$.

g. $3x + 4y = 2$
$2x - y = 5$
Solve the second equation for y.
$-y = -2x + 5$
$y = 2x - 5$
Substitute $2x - 5$ for y in the first equation.
$3x + 4(2x - 5) = 2$
$3x + 8x - 20 = 2$
$11x - 20 = 2$
$11x = 22$
$x = 2$
Substitute 2 for x in the second equation.
$2(2) - y = 5$
$4 - y = 5$
$-y = 1$
$y = -1$
Checking $x = 2$ and $y = -1$ in both equations:

$3x + 4y = 2$		$2x - y = 5$	
$3(2) + 4(-1)$	2	$2(2) - (-1)$	5
$6 - 4$		$4 + 1$	
2		5	

The solution is $(2, -1)$.

h. Let x = one number and y = the other number.
$x + y = 84$
$x = 3y$
Substitute $3y$ for x in the first equation.
$(3y) + y = 84$
$4y = 84$
$y = 21$
Substitute 21 for y in the second equation.
$x = 3(21)$
$x = 63$
The numbers are 63 and 21.

LESSON 8-2 EXERCISES pp. 365–366

1. $x + y = 4$
$y = 2x + 1$
Substitute $2x + 1$ for y in first equation.
$x + (2x + 1) = 4$
$3x + 1 = 4$
$3x = 3$
$x = 1$
Substitute 1 for x in second equation.
$y = 2(1) + 1$
$y = 2 + 1$
$y = 3$
The solution is $(1, 3)$.

2. $x + y = 10$
$y = x + 8$
Substitute $x + 8$ for y in first equation.
$x + (x + 8) = 10$
$2x + 8 = 10$
$2x = 2$
$x = 1$
Substitute 1 for x in second equation.
$y = 1 + 8$
$y = 9$
The solution is $(1, 9)$.

3. $x = y - 1$
$y = 4 - 2x$
Substitute $(y - 1)$ for x in second equation.
$y = 4 - 2(y - 1)$
$y = 4 - 2y + 2$
$y = 6 - 2y$
$3y = 6$
$y = 2$
Substitute 2 for y in first equation.
$x = 2 - 1$
$x = 1$
The solution is $(1, 2)$.

4. $x = y + 6$
$y = -2 - x$
Substitute $(-2 - x)$ for y in first equation.
$x = (-2 - x) + 6$
$x = 4 - x$
$2x = 4$
$x = 2$
Substitute 2 for x in second equation.
$y = -2 - 2$
$y = -4$
The solution is $(2, -4)$.

5. $y = 2x - 5$
$3y - x = 5$
Substitute $2x - 5$ for y in second equation.
$3(2x - 5) - x = 5$
$6x - 15 - x = 5$
$5x - 15 = 5$
$5x = 20$
$x = 4$
Substitute 4 for x in first equation.
$y = 2(4) - 5$
$y = 8 - 5$
$y = 3$
The solution is $(4, 3)$.

6. $y = 2x + 1$
$x + y = -2$
Substitute $2x + 1$ for y in second equation.
$x + (2x + 1) = -2$
$3x + 1 = -2$
$3x = -3$
$x = -1$
Substitute -1 for x in first equation.
$y = 2(-1) + 1$
$y = -2 + 1$
$y = -1$
The solution is $(-1, -1)$.

7. $x = -2y$
$x = 2 - 4y$
Substitute $-2y$ for x in second equation.
$(-2y) = 2 - 4y$
$2y = 2$
$y = 1$
Substitute 1 for y in first equation.
$x = -2(1)$
$x = -2$
The solution is $(-2, 1)$.

8. $r = -3s$
$r = 10 - 4s$
Substitute $(-3s)$ for r in second equation.
$-3s = 10 - 4s$
$s = 10$
Substitute 10 for s in first equation.
$r = -3(10)$
$r = -30$
The solution is $(-30, 10)$.

9. $x = 3y - 4$
$2x - y = 7$
Substitute $3y - 4$ for x in second equation.
$2(3y - 4) - y = 7$
$6y - 8 - y = 7$
$5y - 8 = 7$
$5y = 15$
$y = 3$
Substitute 3 for y in first equation.
$x = 3(3) - 4$
$x = 9 - 4$
$x = 5$
The solution is $(5, 3)$.

10. $s + t = -4$
$s - t = 2$
Solve second equation for s.
$s = t + 2$
Substitute $t + 2$ for s in first equation.
$(t + 2) + t = -4$
$2t + 2 = -4$
$2t = -6$
$t = -3$
Substitute -3 for t in $s = t + 2$.
$s = -3 + 2$
$s = -1$
The solution is $(-1, -3)$.

11. $x - y = 6$
$x + y = -2$
Solve first equation for x.
$x = y + 6$
Substitute $y + 6$ for x in second equation.
$(y + 6) + y = -2$
$2y + 6 = -2$
$2y = -8$
$y = -4$
Substitute -4 for y in $x = y + 6$.
$x = -4 + 6 = 2$
The solution is $(2, -4)$.

12. $y - 2x = -6$
$2y - x = 5$
Solve first equation for y.
$y = 2x - 6$
Substitute $2x - 6$ for y in second equation.
$2(2x - 6) - x = 5$
$4x - 12 - x = 5$
$3x - 12 = 5$
$3x = 17$
$x = \frac{17}{3}$
Substitute $\frac{17}{3}$ for x in $y = 2x - 6$.
$y = 2\left(\frac{17}{3}\right) - 6$
$y = \frac{34}{3} - \frac{18}{3}$
$y = \frac{16}{3}$
The solution is $\left(\frac{17}{3}, \frac{16}{3}\right)$.

13. $x - y = 5$
$x + 2y = 7$
Solve first equation for x.
$x = y + 5$
Substitute $y + 5$ for x in second equation.
$(y + 5) + 2y = 7$
$3y + 5 = 7$
$3y = 2$
$y = \frac{2}{3}$
Substitute $\frac{2}{3}$ for y in $x = y + 5$.
$x = \frac{2}{3} + 5$
$x = \frac{17}{3}$
The solution is $\left(\frac{17}{3}, \frac{2}{3}\right)$.

14. $2x + 3y = -2$
$2x - y = 9$
Solve second equation for y.
$2x - 9 = y$
Substitute $2x - 9$ for y in first equation.
$2x + 3(2x - 9) = -2$
$2x + 6x - 27 = -2$
$8x - 27 = -2$
$8x = 25$
$x = \frac{25}{8}$
Substitute $\frac{25}{8}$ for x in $y = 2x - 9$.
$y = 2\left(\frac{25}{8}\right) - 9$
$y = \frac{50}{8} - \frac{72}{8} = \frac{-22}{8} = \frac{-11}{4}$
The solution is $\left(\frac{25}{8}, \frac{-11}{4}\right)$.

15. $x + 2y = 10$
$3x + 4y = 8$
Solve first equation for x.
$x = 10 - 2y$
Substitute $10 - 2y$ for x in second equation.
$3(10 - 2y) + 4y = 8$
$30 - 6y + 4y = 8$
$30 - 2y = 8$
$-2y = -22$
$y = 11$
Substitute 11 for y in $x = 10 - 2y$.
$x = 10 - 2(11) = 10 - 22 = -12$
The solution is $(-12, 11)$.

16. $x - y = -3$
$2x + 3y = -6$
Solve first equation for x.
$x = y - 3$
Substitute $y - 3$ for x in second equation.
$2(y - 3) + 3y = -6$
$2y - 6 + 3y = -6$
$5y - 6 = -6$
$5y = 0$
$y = 0$
Substitute 0 for y in $x = y - 3$.
$x = 0 - 3$
$x = -3$
The solution is $(-3, 0)$.

17. $3b + 2a = 2$
$-2b + a = 8$
Solve second equation for a.
$a = 8 + 2b$
Substitute $8 + 2b$ for a in first equation.
$3b + 2(8 + 2b) = 2$
$3b + 16 + 4b = 2$
$7b + 16 = 2$
$7b = -14$
$b = -2$
Substitute -2 for b in $a = 8 + 2b$.
$a = 8 + 2(-2) = 8 - 4 = 4$
The solution is $(4, -2)$.

18. $r - 2s = 0$
$4r - 3s = 15$
Solve first equation for r.
$r = 2s$
Substitute $2s$ for r in second equation.
$4(2s) - 3s = 15$
$8s - 3s = 15$
$5s = 15$
$s = 3$
Substitute 3 for s in $r = 2s$.
$r = 2(3) = 6$
The solution is $(6, 3)$.

19. $y - 2x = 0$
$3x + 7y = 17$
Solve first equation for y.
$y = 2x$
Substitute $2x$ for y in second equation.
$3x + 7(2x) = 17$
$3x + 14x = 17$
$17x = 17$
$x = 1$
Substitute 1 for x in $y = 2x$.
$y = 2(1) = 2$
The solution is $(1, 2)$.

20. $x - 3y = 7$
$-3x + 16y = 28$
Solve first equation for x.
$x = 7 + 3y$
Substitute $7 + 3y$ for x in second equation.
$-3(7 + 3y) + 16y = 28$
$-21 - 9y + 16y = 28$
$-21 + 7y = 28$
$7y = 49$
$y = 7$
Substitute 7 for y in $x = 7 + 3y$.
$x = 7 + 3(7) = 7 + 21 = 28$
The solution is $(28, 7)$.

21. $8x + 4y = 6$
$4x = 3 - y$
Solve second equation for y.
$y = 3 - 4x$
Substitute $3 - 4x$ for y in first equation.
$8x + 4(3 - 4x) = 6$
$8x + 12 - 16x = 6$
$-8x = -6$
$x = \frac{-6}{-8} = \frac{3}{4}$
Substitute $\frac{3}{4}$ for x in $y = 3 - 4x$.
$y = 3 - 4\left(\frac{3}{4}\right) = 3 - 3 = 0$
The solution is $\left(\frac{3}{4}, 0\right)$.

22. Let x = one number and y = the other number.
$x + y = 27$
$x = y + 3$
Substitute $y + 3$ for x in first equation.
$(y + 3) + y = 27$
$2y + 3 = 27$
$2y = 24$
$y = 12$
Substitute 12 for y in second equation.
$x = 12 + 3 = 15$
The numbers are 15 and 12.

23. Let x = one number and y = the other number.
$x + y = 36$
$x = y + 2$
Substitute $y + 2$ for x in first equation.
$(y + 2) + y = 36$
$2y + 2 = 36$
$2y = 34$
$y = 17$
Substitute 17 for y in $x = y + 2$.
$x = 17 + 2 = 19$
The numbers are 19 and 17.

24. Let x = one number and y = the other number.
$x + y = 58$
$x = y + 16$
Substitute $y + 16$ for x in first equation.
$(y + 16) + y = 58$
$2y + 16 = 58$
$2y = 42$
$y = 21$
Substitute 21 for y in $x = y + 16$.
$x = 21 + 16 = 37$
The numbers are 37 and 21.

25. Let x = one number and y = the other number.
$x + y = 66$
$x = y + 8$
Substitute $y + 8$ for x in first equation.
$(y + 8) + y = 66$
$2y + 8 = 66$
$2y = 58$
$y = 29$
Substitute 29 for y in $x = y + 8$.
$x = 29 + 8 = 37$
The numbers are 37 and 29.

26. Let x = one number and y = the other number.
$x - y = 16$
$3x = 7y$
Solve first equation for x.
$x = 16 + y$
Substitute $16 + y$ for x in second equation.
$3(16 + y) = 7y$
$48 + 3y = 7y$
$48 = 4y$
$12 = y$
Substitute 12 for y in $x = 16 + y$.
$x = 16 + 12 = 28$
The numbers are 28 and 12.

27. Let x = one number and y = the other number.
$x - y = 18$
$2y + 3x = 74$
Solve first equation for x.
$x = 18 + y$
Substitute $18 + y$ for x in second equation.
$2y + 3(18 + y) = 74$
$2y + 54 + 3y = 74$
$5y + 54 = 74$
$5y = 20$
$y = 4$
Substitute 4 for y in $x = 18 + y$.
$x = 18 + 4 = 22$
The numbers are 22 and 4.

28. $3y + 3x = 14$
$y = -x + 4$
Substitute $(-x + 4)$ for y in first equation.
$3(-x + 4) + 3x = 14$
$-3x + 12 + 3x = 14$
$12 = 14$
False, so there are no solutions.

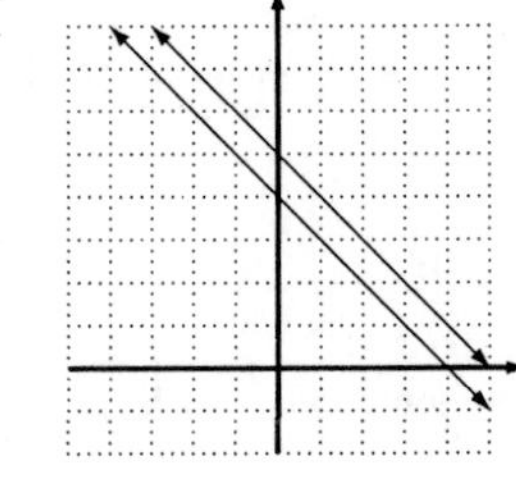

29. $y = x + 5$
$-3x + 3y = 15$
Substitute $x + 5$ for y in second equation.
$-3x + 3(x + 5) = 15$
$-3x + 3x + 15 = 15$
$15 = 15$
True, so there are infinitely many solutions.

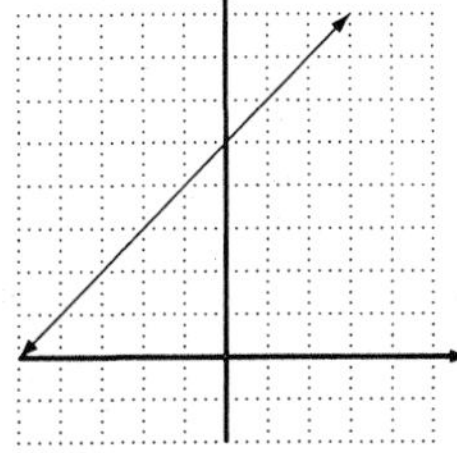

30. For the third equation, $2(2) - (-3) = 1$
$4 + 3 = 1$
$7 = 1$
False; $(2, -3)$ is not a solution of the system.

31. Solve first system for x and y:
$x = 2 - 2y$
$5(2 - 2y) - 3y = -29$
$10 - 10y - 3y = -29$
$10 - 13y = -29$
$-13y = -39$
$y = 3$
$x = 2 - 2y = 2 - 2(3) = 2 - 6 = -4$
Substitute $x = -4$ and $y = 3$ in second system:
$A(-4) + 5(3) = -9$ $\quad (-4) + B(3) = 8$
$-4A + 15 = -9$ $\quad 3B = 12$
$-4A = -24$ $\quad B = 4$
$A = 6$

32. Substituting $5 + y$ for x in the first equation
Collecting like terms
Subtracting 5 from both sides of the equation
Dividing both sides of the equation by 2
Substituting 7 for y in the first equation

33. $y = -1$; substituting into equation ①,
$x + (-1) + z = 4$
$x = 5 - z$;
substituting both into equation ②,
$(5 - z) - 2(-1) - z = 1$
$5 - z + 2 - z = 1$
$-2z = -6$
$z = 3$
Substituting into $x = 5 - z$, $x = 5 - 3 = 2$
Solution: $(2, -1, 3)$

34. $x = z - 70$ equation ②
$y = \frac{z}{2}$ from equation ③
Substituting both into equation ①
$(z - 70) + \left(\frac{z}{2}\right) + z = 180$
$\frac{5}{2}z = 250$
$z = 100$
Substituting into equation ②, $x = 100 - 70 = 30$
Substituting into equation ③, $y = \frac{100}{2} = 50$
Solution: $(30, 50, 100)$

35. Answers may vary.
Substitute 10 for $x + y$ in fourth equation.
$(10) + z = 10$
$z = 0$
Substitute 0 for z in second and third equations.
$y + (0) = 10$ $\quad x + (0) = 10$
$y = 10$ $\quad x = 10$
Substitute $x = 10$ and $y = 10$ in first equation.
$(10) + (10) = 10$
$20 = 10$
False, so there is no solution.

36. $y = 2x - 9$
$y - 2x = 11$
Rewriting equation ②: $y = 2x + 11$
The slope of each line is 2 and the intercepts are different so the lines are parallel.

37. $6y - 21x = 3$
$8y - 5 = 28x$
Equation ①: $6y = 21x + 3$
$y = \frac{7}{2}x + \frac{1}{2}$
Equation ②: $8y = 28x + 5$
$y = \frac{7}{2}x + \frac{5}{8}$
The slope of each line is $\frac{7}{2}$ and the intercepts are different so the lines are parallel.

38. $4y + 9 = x$
$5 - 2y = 8x$
Equation ①: $4y = x - 9$
$y = \frac{1}{4}x - \frac{9}{4}$
Equation ②: $-2y = 8x - 5$
$y = -4x + \frac{5}{2}$
The slopes are different so the lines are not parallel.

39. $9a^2 - 6ab + b^2 = (3a - b)^2$

40. $36y^4 - 25y^2 = y^2(36y^2 - 25)$
$= y^2(6y + 5)(6y - 5)$

41. $x^2 - 4xyz^2 + 4y^2z^4 = x^2 - 2 \cdot x \cdot 2yz^2 + 2y^2z^4 = (x - 2yz^2)^2$

42. $9x^2 + 12xz^3 + 4z^6 = 9x^2 + 2 \cdot 3x \cdot 2z^3 + 4z^6 = (3x + 2z^3)^2$

43. $n^2 + 10n + 25 = 0$
$(n + 5)^2 = 0$
$n + 5 = 0$
$n = -5$

44. $n^2 - 10n + 25 = 0$
$(n - 5)^2 = 0$
$n - 5 = 0$
$n = 5$

45. $n^2 - 25 = 0$
$(n + 5)(n - 5) = 0$
$n + 5 = 0$ or $n - 5 = 0$
$n = -5$ or $n = 5$

46. $4n^2 - 49 = 0$
$(2n + 7)(2n - 7) = 0$
$2n + 7 = 0$ or $2n - 7 = 0$
$2n = -7$ or $2n = 7$
$n = -\frac{7}{2}$ or $n = \frac{7}{2}$

47. Let w = width.
$2(w + 15) + 2w = 350$
$2w + 30 + 2w = 350$
$4w + 30 = 350$
$4w = 320$
$w = 80$
The width is 80 cm; the length is 95 cm.

48. Let l = length.
$(l + 8)^2 = 169$
$l^2 + 16l + 64 = 169$
$l^2 + 16l - 105 = 0$
$(l + 21)(l - 5) = 0$
$l + 21 = 0$ or $l - 5 = 0$
$l = -21$ or $l = 5$
The length is 5 in.

LESSON 8-3 TRY THIS

pp. 367–370

a. $x + y = 5$
$2x - y = 4$
$3x + 0y = 9$
$3x = 9$, so $x = 3$
$2(3) - y = 4$
$6 - y = 4$
$-y = -2$, so $y = 2$
$(3, 2)$ is the solution.

b. $3x - 3y = 6$
$\underline{3x + 3y = 0}$
$6x + 0y = 6$
$6x = 6, \text{ so } x = 1$
$3(1) + 3y = 0, 3y = -3, \text{ so } y = -1$
$(1, -1)$ is the solution.

c. $5x + 3y = 17$
$\underline{-5x + 2y = 3}$ Multiplied by -1
$5y = 20$
$y = 4$
$5x + 3(4) = 17, 5x + 12 = 17, 5x = 5, x = 1$
$(1, 4)$ is the solution.

d. $8x + 11y = 37$
$\underline{2x - 11y = -7}$ Multiplied by -1
$10x = 30$
$x = 3$

$8(3) + 11y = 37, 24 + 11y = 37, 11y = 13, y = \frac{13}{11}$

$\left(3, \frac{13}{11}\right)$ is the solution.

e. $4a + 7b = 11$
$\underline{-4a - 6b = -10}$ Multiplied by -1
$b = 1$
$4a + 7(1) = 11, 4a + 7 = 11, 4a = 4, a = 1$
$(1, 1)$ is the solution.

f. $7x - 5y = 76$
$\underline{20x + 5y = 275}$ Multiplied by 5
$27x = 351$
$x = 13$
$7(13) - 5y = 76, 91 - 5y = 76, -5y = -15,$
$y = \frac{-15}{-5} = 3$
$(13, 3)$ is the solution.

g. $5b + 10c = 15$
$\underline{15b - 10c = -35}$ Multiplied by 5
$20b = -20$
$b = -1$
$5(-1) + 10c = 15, -5 + 10c = 15, 10c = 20, c = 2$
$(-1, 2)$ is the solution.

h. $15x + 9y = 6$ Multiplied by 3
$\underline{-15x - 25y = 10}$ Multiplied by -5
$-16y = 16$
$y = -1$
$5x + 3(-1) = 2, 5x - 3 = 2, 5x = 5, x = 1$
$(1, -1)$ is the solution.

i. $42x + 14y = 28$ Multiplied by 7
$\underline{-20x - 14y = 16}$ Multiplied by -2
$22x = 44$
$x = 2$
$6(2) + 2y = 4, 12 + 2y = 4, 2y = -8, y = -4$
$(2, -4)$ is the solution.

j. $x - y = 36$
$\frac{1}{6}x - \frac{1}{9}y = 11$
$3x - 2y = 198$ Multiplied the second equation by 18
$\underline{-3x + 3y = -108}$ Multiplied the first equation by -3
$y = 90$
$x - 90 = 36, x = 126$
The numbers are 126 and 90.

LESSON 8-3 EXERCISES pp. 371–372

1. $x + y = 10$
$\underline{x - y = 8}$
$2x = 18$
$x = 9$
$(9) + y = 10$
$y = 1$
$(9, 1)$ is the solution.

2. $x - y = 7$
$\underline{x + y = 3}$
$2x = 10$
$x = 5$
$(5) + y = 3$
$y = -2$
$(5, -2)$ is the solution.

3. $x + y = 8$
$\underline{-x + 2y = 7}$
$3y = 15$
$y = 5$
$x + (5) = 8$
$x = 3$
$(3, 5)$ is the solution.

4. $x + y = 6$
$\underline{-x + 3y = -2}$
$4y = 4$
$y = 1$
$x + (1) = 6$
$x = 5$
$(5, 1)$ is the solution.

5. $3x - y = 9$
$\underline{2x + y = 6}$
$5x = 15$
$x = 3$
$3(3) - y = 9$
$9 - y = 9$
$-y = 0$
$y = 0$
$(3, 0)$ is the solution.

6. $4x - y = 1$
$\underline{3x + y = 13}$
$7x = 14$
$x = 2$
$3(2) + y = 13$
$6 + y = 13$
$y = 7$
$(2, 7)$ is the solution.

7. $4a + 3b = 7$
$\underline{-4a + b = 5}$
$4b = 12$
$b = 3$
$-4a + (3) = 5$
$-4a = 2$
$a = -\frac{2}{4} = -\frac{1}{2}$
$\left(-\frac{1}{2}, 3\right)$ is the solution.

8. $7c + 5d = 18$
$\underline{c - 5d = -2}$
$8c = 16$
$c = 2$
$7(2) + 5d = 18$
$14 + 5d = 18$
$5d = 4$
$d = \frac{4}{5}$
$\left(2, \frac{4}{5}\right)$ is the solution.

9. $8x - 5y = -9$
$\underline{3x + 5y = -2}$
$11x = -11$
$x = -1$
$3(-1) + 5y = -2$
$-3 + 5y = -2$
$5y = 1$
$y = \frac{1}{5}$
$\left(-1, \frac{1}{5}\right)$ is the solution.

10. $3a - 3b = -15$
$\underline{-3a - 3b = -3}$
$-6b = -18$
$b = 3$
$3a - 3(3) = -15$
$3a = -6$
$a = -2$
$(-2, 3)$ is the solution.

11. $4x - 5y = 7$
$\underline{-4x + 5y = 7}$
$0 = 14$
No solution

12. $2x + 3y = 4$
$\underline{-2x - 3y = -4}$
$0 = 0$
Infinitely many solutions

13. $-2x - 2y = 16$ Multiplied by 2
$\underline{2x - y = -1}$
$-3y = 15$
$y = -5$
$2x - (-5) = -1$
$2x + 5 = -1$
$2x = -6$
$x = -3$
$(-3, -5)$ is the solution.

14. $x + y = -7$
$\underline{-3x - y = 9}$ Multiplied by -1
$-2x = 2$
$x = -1$
$(-1) + y = -7$
$y = -6$
$(-1, -6)$ is the solution.

15. $-x - 3y = -19$ Multiplied by -1
$\underline{x - y = -1}$
$-4y = -20$
$y = 5$
$x - (5) = -1$
$x = 4$
$(4, 5)$ is the solution.

16. $6x - 2y = 16$ Multiplied by 2
$\underline{x + 2y = 5}$
$7x = 21$
$x = 3$
$(3) + 2y = 5$
$2y = 2$
$y = 1$
$(3, 1)$ is the solution.

17. $3x + 3y = 15$ Multiplied by 3
$\underline{5x - 3y = 17}$
$8x \quad = 32$
$x = 4$
$(4) + y = 5$
$y = 1$
(4, 1) is the solution.

18. $-4x + 4y = -28$ Multiplied by -4
$\underline{4x - 5y = 25}$
$-y = -3$
$y = 3$
$x - (3) = 7$
$x = 10$
(10, 3) is the solution.

19. $-6w - 9z = -51$ Multiplied by -3
$\underline{6w + 8z = 48}$ Multiplied by 2
$-z = -3$
$z = 3$
$2w + 3(3) = 17$
$2w = 8$
$w = 4$
(4, 3) is the solution.

20. $63p + 45q = 18$ Multiplied by 9
$\underline{40p - 45q = 85}$ Multiplied by 5
$103p \quad = 103$
$p = 1$
$7(1) + 5q = 2$
$5q = -5$
$q = -1$
(1, −1) is the solution.

21. $-6a - 9b = 3$ Multiplied by -3
$\underline{6a + 10b = -4}$ Multiplied by 2
$b = -1$
$2a + 3(-1) = -1$
$2a - 3 = -1$
$2a = 2$
$a = 1$
(1, −1) is the solution.

22. $18x - 24y = 96$ Multiplied by 6
$\underline{20x + 24y = 56}$ Multiplied by 4
$38x \quad = 152$
$x = 4$
$3(4) - 4y = 16$
$12 - 4y = 16$
$-4y = 4$
$y = -1$
(4, −1) is the solution.

23. $-5x + 15y = 0$ Multiplied by -5
$\underline{5x - y = -14}$
$14y = -14$
$y = -1$
$x - 3(-1) = 0$
$x + 3 = 0$
$x = -3$
(−3, −1) is the solution.

24. $-15a + 6b = 0$ Multiplied by -3
$\underline{4a - 6b = -22}$ Multiplied by 2
$-11a \quad = -22$
$a = 2$
$5(2) - 2b = 0$
$10 - 2b = 0$
$-2b = -10$
$b = 5$
(2, 5) is the solution.

25. $9x - 6y = 30$ Multiplied by 3
$\underline{10x + 6y = 8}$ Multiplied by 2
$19x \quad = 38$
$x = 2$
$3(2) - 2y = 10$
$6 - 2y = 10$
$-2y = 4$
$y = -2$
(2, −2) is the solution.

26. $4p + 10q = 18$ Multiplied by 2
$\underline{15p - 10q = 20}$ Multiplied by 5
$19p \quad = 38$
$p = 2$
$2(2) + 5q = 9$
$4 + 5q = 9$
$5q = 5$
$q = 1$
(2, 1) is the solution.

27. $3x - 8y = 11$
$\underline{-3x - 18y = -24}$ Multiplied by -3
$-26y = -13$
$y = \frac{1}{2}$
$x + 6\left(\frac{1}{2}\right) = 8$
$x + 3 = 8$
$x = 5$
$\left(5, \frac{1}{2}\right)$ is the solution.

28. $-3m + 3n = -96$ Multiplied by -3
$\underline{3m - 8n = 6}$
$-5n = -90$
$n = 18$
$m - (18) = 32$
$m = 50$
(50, 18) is the solution.

29. $a + b = 12$
$\underline{-a - \frac{1}{2}b = -8}$ Multiplied by -2
$\frac{1}{2}b = 4$
$b = 8$
$a + (8) = 12$
$a = 4$
(4, 8) is the solution.

30. $2p - q = 8$
$\underline{\frac{4}{3}p + q = 12}$ Multiplied by 4
$\frac{10}{3}p \quad = 20$
$10p = 60$
$p = 6$
$2(6) - q = 8$
$12 - q = 8$
$-q = -4$
$q = 4$
(6, 4) is the solution.

31. Let x = one number and y = the other number.
$x + y = 115$
$\underline{x - y = 21}$
$2x \quad = 136$
$x = 68$
$(68) + y = 115$
$y = 47$
The numbers are 68 and 47.

32. Let x = one number and y = the other number.
$x + y = 26.4$
$x = 5y$
Substitute $5y$ for x in first equation.
$5y + y = 26.4$
$6y = 26.4$
$y = 4.4$
$x = 5(4.4)$
$x = 22$
The numbers are 22 and 4.4.

33. $l + w = 19$
$l = 2w - 1$
Substitute $2w - 1$ for l in first equation.
$(2w - 1) + w = 19$
$3w - 1 = 19$
$3w = 20$
$$w = \frac{20}{3}$$
Substitute $\frac{20}{3}$ for w in second equation.
$$l = 2\left(\frac{20}{3}\right) - 1 = \frac{40}{3} - \frac{3}{3} = \frac{37}{3}$$
The length is $\frac{37}{3}$ in., the width $\frac{20}{3}$ in.

34. $2l + 2w = 48$
$$w = \frac{1}{2}l + 2$$
Substitute $\frac{1}{2}l + 2$ for w in first equation.
$$2l + 2\left(\frac{1}{2}l + 2\right) = 48$$
$2l + l + 4 = 48$
$3l + 4 = 48$
$3l = 44$
$$l = \frac{44}{3}$$
Substitute $\frac{44}{3}$ for l in second equation.
$$w = \frac{1}{2}\left(\frac{44}{3}\right) + 2 = \frac{22}{3} + \frac{6}{3} = \frac{28}{3}$$
The length is $\frac{44}{3}$ in., the width $\frac{28}{3}$ in.

35. Let x = first angle and y = second angle.
$$\begin{array}{r} x + y = 90 \\ \underline{x - y = 34} \\ 2x \quad = 124 \end{array}$$
$x = 62$
$(62) + y = 90$
$y = 28$
The angles measure 62° and 28°.

36. Let x = first angle and y = second angle.
$x + y = 90$
$$y = \frac{1}{2}x + 42$$
Substitute $\frac{1}{2}x + 42$ for y in first equation.
$$x + \left(\frac{1}{2}x + 42\right) = 90$$
$$\frac{3}{2}x + 42 = 90$$
$$\frac{3}{2}x = 48$$
$x = 32$
$(32) + y = 90$
$y = 58$
The angles measure 32° and 58°.

37. Graphs of the two equations coincide (they both have slope 2 and y-intercept -10) so a solution of the first equation must be a solution of the second.
I. Check $(0, -10)$ in the first equation.
$2x - y = 10$
$2(0) - (-10) = 10$
$10 = 10$ ✔
II. Check $(2, 6)$.
$2x - y = 10$
$2(2) - 6 = 10$
$-2 = 10$
III. Check $(5, 0)$.
$2x - y = 10$
$2(5) - 0 = 10$
$10 = 10$ ✔
IV. Check $(-10, -30)$.
$2x - y = 10$
$2(-10) - (-30) = 10$
$10 = 10$ ✔
The answer is C.

38. $3(x - y) = 9$
$x + y = 7$
Divide both sides of first equation by 3 and add.
$$\begin{array}{r} x - y = 3 \\ \underline{x + y = 7} \\ 2x \quad = 10 \end{array}$$
$x = 5$
$(5) + y = 7, y = 2$
$(5, 2)$ is the solution.

39. $5(a - b) = 10$
$a + b = 2$
Divide both sides of first equation by 5 and add.
$$\begin{array}{r} a - b = 2 \\ \underline{a + b = 2} \\ 2a \quad = 4 \end{array}$$
$a = 2$
$(2) + b = 2, b = 0$
$(2, 0)$ is the solution.

40. $2x - 2y = 3 + x$
$x = 3y + 4$
Rearranging both equations, multiplying the second by -1 and adding
$$\begin{array}{r} x - 2y = 3 \\ \underline{-x + 3y = -4} \\ y = -1 \end{array}$$
$x = 3(-1) + 4, x = 1$
$(1, -1)$ is the solution.

41. $2(5a - 5b) = 10$
$-5(6a + 2b) = 10$
Rearranging both equations
$10a - 10b = 10$
$-30a - 10b = 10$
Multiplying the second equation by -1 and adding
$$\begin{array}{r} 10a - 10b = 10 \\ \underline{30a + 10b = -10} \\ 40a \quad = 0 \end{array}$$
$a = 0$
$10(0) - 10b = 10, -10b = 10, b = -1$
$(0, -1)$ is the solution.

42. Multiplying each equation by 100
$150x + 85y = 163{,}750$
$x + y = 1525$
Multiply second equation by -85 and add.
$$\begin{array}{r} 150x + 85y = 163{,}750 \\ \underline{-85x - 85y = -129{,}625} \\ 65x \quad = 34{,}125 \end{array}$$
$x = 525$
$525 + y = 1525$
$y = 1000$
$(525, 1000)$ is the solution.

43. $ax + by = c$
$dx + ey = f$
Solving for y,
$$\begin{array}{rl} adx + bdy = cd & \text{Multiplying by } d \\ \underline{-adx - aey = -af} & \text{Multiplying by } -a \\ bdy - aey = cd - af & \\ (bd - ae)y = cd - af & \end{array}$$
$$y = \frac{cd - af}{bd - ae} \text{ or } \frac{af - cd}{ae - bd}$$
Solving for x,
$$\begin{array}{rl} aex + bey = ce & \text{Multiplying by } e \\ \underline{-bdx - bey = -bf} & \\ (ae - bd)x = ce - bf & \end{array}$$
$$x = \frac{ce - bf}{ae - bd}$$

44. $$\begin{aligned} y &= ax + b \\ -y &= -x - c \quad \text{Multiplying by } -1 \\ \hline 0 &= ax - x + b - c \\ 0 &= x(a-1) + b - c \\ c - b &= x(a-1) \\ \frac{c-b}{a-1} &= x \end{aligned}$$

Substituting in $y = x + c$,

$$y = \frac{c-b}{a-1} + c,$$

$$y = \frac{c-b}{a-1} + \frac{c(a-1)}{a-1},$$

$$y = \frac{c - b + ac - c}{a-1} = \frac{ac-b}{a-1}$$

The solution is $\left(\frac{c-b}{a-1}, \frac{ac-b}{a-1}\right)$ or $\left(\frac{b-c}{1-a}, \frac{b-ac}{1-a}\right)$.

45. $$\begin{aligned} ax + by + c &= 0 \\ -ax - cy - b &= 0 \quad \text{Multiplying by } -1 \\ \hline by - cy + c - b &= 0 \\ (b-c)y &= b - c \\ y &= \frac{b-c}{b-c} = 1 \end{aligned}$$

Substituting in $ax + by + c = 0, ax + b(1) + c = 0,$

$ax + b + c = 0, ax = -b - c, x = \frac{-b-c}{a}$

The solution is $\left(\frac{-b-c}{a}, 1\right)$.

46. $3(7 - a) - 2(1 + 2b) + 5 = 0$

$3a + 2b - 18 = 0$

Simplify.

$$\begin{aligned} -3a - 4b &= -24 \\ 3a + 2b &= 18 \quad \text{Adding} \\ \hline -2b &= -6 \\ b &= 3 \end{aligned}$$

$3a + 2(3) = 18, 3a = 12, a = 4$

(4, 3) is the solution.

47. $\frac{2}{x} - \frac{3}{y} = -\frac{1}{2}$

$\frac{1}{x} + \frac{2}{y} = \frac{11}{12}$

Multiply first equation by 2, second by 3:

$$\begin{aligned} \frac{4}{x} - \frac{6}{y} &= -1 \\ \frac{3}{x} + \frac{6}{y} &= \frac{11}{4} \quad \text{Adding} \\ \hline \frac{7}{x} &= \frac{7}{4} \\ 7x &= 28 \\ x &= 4 \end{aligned}$$

$$\begin{aligned} \frac{2}{4} - \frac{3}{y} &= -\frac{1}{2} \\ -\frac{3}{y} &= -1 \\ -3 &= -y \\ y &= 3 \end{aligned}$$

(4, 3) is the solution.

48. $a = 14, b = -10, c = 2600, d = 24, e = 20, f = 520$

$$x = \frac{ce - bf}{ae - bd} = \frac{20(2600) - (-10)(520)}{14(20) - (-10)(24)} = \frac{52{,}000 + 5200}{280 + 240}$$

$$= \frac{57{,}200}{520} = 110$$

$$y = \frac{af - cd}{ae - bd} = \frac{14(520) - 2600(24)}{14(20) - (-10)(24)} = \frac{7280 - 62{,}400}{280 + 240}$$

$$= \frac{-55{,}120}{520} = -106$$

(110, −106) is the solution.

49. $8y - 3x = 10$

$-6y - 3x = 4$

First equation: $8y = 3x + 10$

$y = \frac{3}{8}x + \frac{5}{4}$

Second equation: $-6y = 3x + 4$

$y = -\frac{1}{2}x - \frac{2}{3}$

$\frac{3}{8}\left(-\frac{1}{2}\right) = -\frac{3}{16}$

Slopes are not negative reciprocals, so lines are not perpendicular.

50. $3x + 2y = 1$

$2x - 3y = 4$

First equation: $2y = -3x + 1$

$y = -\frac{3}{2}x + \frac{1}{2}$

Second equation: $-3y = -2x + 4$

$y = \frac{2}{3}x - \frac{4}{3}$

$-\frac{3}{2} \cdot \frac{2}{3} = -1$

Slopes are negative reciprocals and intercepts are different, so lines are perpendicular.

51. $8x + y = 10$

$x - 8y = 0$

First equation: $y = -8x + 10$

Second equation: $-8y = -x$

$y = \frac{1}{8}x$

$-8\left(\frac{1}{8}\right) = -1$

Slopes are negative reciprocals, so lines are perpendicular.

52. **53.**

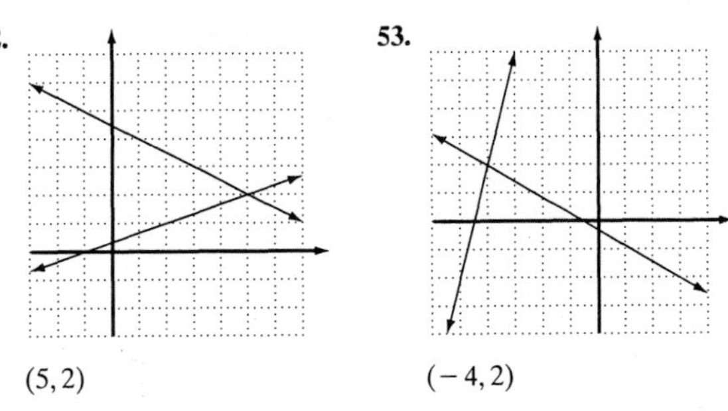

(5, 2) (−4, 2)

54. $2m^3 - 4m^2 - m + 2 = 2m^2(m - 2) - 1 \cdot (m - 2)$

$= (2m^2 - 1)(m - 2)$

55. $3y^2 - 12 = 3(y^2 - 4)$

$= 3(y + 2)(y - 2)$

56. $x^2z - xz^2 = xz(x - z)$

57. $(a^2b + 2ab^2) - (3a^2b + ab^2) = a^2b + 2ab^2 - 3a^2b - ab^2$

$= ab^2 - 2a^2b$

or $ab(-2a + b)$

58. $(3y^2 - xy + 2x) + (5xy - 2y^2 + x)$

$= 3y^2 - xy + 2x + 5xy - 2y^2 + x$

$= y^2 + 4xy + 3x$

LESSON 8-4 TRY THIS pp. 374–376

a. Let x = number of vans sold and y = number of trucks sold.

$$\begin{aligned} x + y &= 180 \\ x - y &= 40 \\ \hline 2x &= 220 \\ x &= 110 \\ 110 + y &= 180 \\ y &= 70 \end{aligned}$$

He sold 110 vans and 70 trucks.

b. Let x = miles driven, y = miles walked.
$x + y = 45$
$x = 13 + y$
By substitution,
$(13 + y) + y = 45$
$13 + 2y = 45$
$2y = 32$
$y = 16$ km walked

c. Let x = Wilma's age now, y = Bev's age now.
$x = 13 + y$
$x + 9 = 2(y + 9) = 2y + 18$ or
$x = 2y + 9$
Then $(2y + 9) = 13 + y$
$y = 4$
Bev is 4 years old.

d. Let x = Stan's age, y = Adam's age now.

$$x = \frac{2}{3}y$$

$$x + 7 = \frac{3}{4}(y + 7) \quad \text{or}$$

$$x = \frac{3}{4}y - \frac{7}{4}$$

$$\left(\frac{3}{4}y - \frac{7}{4}\right) = \frac{2}{3}y$$

$$\frac{1}{12}y = \frac{7}{4}$$

$$y = 21 \qquad x = \frac{2}{3}(21) = 14$$

Stan is 14 years old; Adam is 21 years old.

e. Let x = cost of pencil and y = cost of pen.
$4x + 2y = 74$
$6x + 5y = 153$
$12x + 6y = 222$ Multiplying first equation by 3
$-12x - 10y = -306$ Multiplying second equation by -2
$-4y = -84$
$y = 21$
$4x + 2(21) = 74$
$4x + 42 = 74$
$4x = 32$
$x = 8$
A pencil costs 8¢ and a pen costs 21¢.

f. Let m = mileage.
$3195 + 33m = c$
$-3495 - 29m = -c$
$-300 + 4m = 0$
$4m = 300$
$m = 75$
The cost is the same for 75 miles.

LESSON 8-4 EXERCISES pp. 377–379

1. a. $n + d = 150$
b. $n + 12 = d$
c. $n + d = 150$
$n + 12 = d$
d. $n + (n + 12) = 150$
$2n + 12 = 150$
$2n = 138$
$n = 69$
$(69) + 12 = d$
$81 = d$
He has 69 nickels and 81 dimes.

2. a. $t + m = 2.1$ **b.** $2t$
c. $3m$ **d.** $2t + 3m = 5.15$
e. $t + m = 2.1$
$2t + 3m = 5.15$
f. $-2t - 2m = -4.2$
$2t + 3m = 5.15$
$m = 0.95$
$t + (0.95) = 2.1$
$t = 1.15$
Milk costs \$0.95, a taco \$1.15.

3. Let x = cost of orange, y = cost of apple.
$4x + 5y = 3.56$
$3x + 4y = 2.76$
$12x + 15y = 10.68$
$-12x - 16y = -11.04$
$-y = -0.36$
$y = 0.36$
$4x + 5(0.36) = 3.56$
$4x + 1.8 = 3.56$
$4x = 1.76$
$x = 0.44$
An orange costs \$0.44, an apple \$0.36.

4. Let x = son's age, y = Zelma's age.
$x + 18 = y$
$y - 1 = 3(x - 1)$
$y - 1 = 3x - 3$
$y = 3x - 2$
$x + 18 = (3x - 2)$
$20 = 2x$
$10 = x$
$(10) + 18 = y$
$28 = y$
Zelma is 28; her son is 10.

5. Let x = Tyrone's age, y = daughter's age.
$x = 2y$
$x + 6 = 3(y - 6)$
$x + 6 = 3y - 18$
$x = 3y - 24$
$(2y) = 3y - 24$
$-y = -24$
$y = 24$
$x = 2(24) = 48$
Tyrone is 48; his daughter is 24.

6. Let x = Frederique's age, y = brother's age.
$x = y + 2$
$x - 12 = 2(y - 12)$
$x - 12 = 2y - 24$
$x = 2y - 12$
$(y + 2) = 2y - 12$
$-y + 2 = -12$
$-y = -14$
$y = 14$
$x = (14) + 2 = 16$
Frederique is 16; her brother is 14.

7. Let l = length, w = width.
$2l + 2w = 160$

$$\frac{1}{4}l = 2w$$

$$2l + \left(\frac{1}{4}l\right) = 160$$

$$2\frac{1}{4}l = 160$$

$$\frac{9}{4}l = 160$$

$$l = \frac{4}{9}(160) = \frac{640}{9} \quad \text{or} \quad 71\frac{1}{9}$$

$$\frac{1}{4}\left(\frac{640}{9}\right) = 2w$$

$$\frac{160}{9} = 2w$$

$$\frac{80}{9} \quad \text{or} \quad 8\frac{8}{9} = w$$

The length is $71\frac{1}{9}$ ft $\left(\frac{640}{9}\right)$; the width $8\frac{8}{9}$ ft $\left(\frac{80}{9}\right)$.

8. Let x = number of rockfish,
y = number of bluefish.
$x + y = 24$
$2.5x + 8y = 137$
$-8x - 8y = -192$ Multiply by -8.
$-5.5x = -55$
$x = 10$
$(10) + y = 24$
$y = 14$
She caught 10 rockfish, 14 bluefish.

9. Let m = mileage.
$$41.95 + 0.29m = 38.95 + 0.31m$$
$$100(41.95 + 0.29m) = 100(38.95 + 0.31m)$$
$$4195 + 29m = 3895 + 31m$$
$$300 = 2m$$
$$150 = m$$
The mileage is 150 miles.

10. Let m = mileage.
$$57.99 + 0.48m = 58.95 + 0.46m$$
$$100(57.99 + 0.48m) = 100(58.95 + 0.46m)$$
$$5799 + 48m = 5895 + 46m$$
$$2m = 96$$
$$m = 48$$
The mileage is 48 miles.

11. Let x = cost of apple, y = cost of orange.
$$6x + 3y = 3.36$$
$$2x + 5y = 3.04$$
$$-6x - 15y = -3.36$$
$$6x + 3y = 9.12$$
$$-12y = -5.76$$
$$y = 0.48$$
$$2x + 5(0.48) = 3.04$$
$$2x + 2.40 = 3.04$$
$$2x = 0.64$$
$$x = 0.32$$
An apple costs \$0.32, an orange \$0.48.

12. Let n = number of cards.
$$25 + 0.02n = 10 + 0.05n$$
$$15 + 0.02n = 0.05n$$
$$15 = 0.03n$$
$$500 = n$$
The cost will be the same for 500 cards.

13. Let x = number of \$21 tickets,
y = number of \$27 tickets.
$$x + y = 29$$
$$21x + 27y = 675$$
$$-21x - 21y = -609$$
$$6y = 66$$
$$y = 11$$
$$x + (11) = 29$$
$$x = 18$$
They bought eighteen \$21 tickets and eleven \$27 tickets.

14. Let x = number of $\frac{1}{2}$-gal cartons,
y = number of gal cartons.
$$x + y = 21$$
$$1.46x + 2.39y = 41.82$$
$$-1.46x - 1.46y = -30.66$$
$$0.93y = 11.16$$
$$y = 12$$
$$x + (12) = 21$$
$$x = 9$$
He bought 9 half-gal cartons and 12 gal cartons.

15. Let x = number of 12-oz packs,
y = number of 16-oz packs.
$$x + y = 10$$
$$1.8x + 2.4y = 21.6$$
$$-1.8x - 1.8y = -18$$
$$0.6y = 3.6$$
$$y = 6$$
$$x + (6) = 10$$
$$x = 4$$
She bought four 12-oz packs and six 16-oz packs.

16. Let x = number of adults,
y = number of children.
$$x + y = 38$$
$$5.25x + 4y = 179.50$$
$$-\ 4x - 4y = -152$$
$$1.25x = 27.50$$
$$x = 22$$
$$(22) + y = 38$$
$$y = 16$$
There were 22 adults and 16 children.

17. Let a = Tweedledee's weight, b = Tweedledum's.
$$a + 2b = 361$$
$$2a + b = 362$$
Multiplying the first equation by -2 and adding
$$-2a - 4b = -722$$
$$2a + b = 362$$
$$-3b = -360$$
$$b = 120$$
$$a + 2(120) = 361$$
$$a = 361 - 240 = 121$$
Tweedledum weighs 120 lb, Tweedledee 121 lb.

18. $c + b = 5000$
$$63c + 52b = 279{,}800$$
Multiplying the first equation by -52 and adding
$$-52c - 52b = -260{,}000$$
$$63c + 52b = 279{,}800$$
$$11c = 19{,}800$$
$c = 1800$ cycles
$$(1800) + b = 5000$$
$b = 3200$ bumper stickers

19. $3285 + 49x = c$
$$3195 + 48x = c$$
$$3285 + 49x = 3195 + 48x$$
$$x = -90$$
Mileage cannot be negative. No solution.

20. $r + p = 35$
$$4r + 2p = 94$$
Multiplying the first equation by -2 and adding
$$-2r - 2p = -70$$
$$4r + 2p = 94$$
$$2r = 24$$
$$r = 12$$
$$(12) + p = 35$$
$$p = 23$$
12 rabbits, 23 pheasants

21. Let x = rate for \$1100,
y = rate for \$1800.
$$y = 0.015 + x$$
$$1100x + 1800y = 288$$
Substituting,
$$1100x + 1800(x + 0.015) = 288$$
$$1100x + 1800x + 27 = 288$$
$$2900x = 261$$
$$x = 0.09$$
$$y = 0.015 + 0.09 = 0.105$$
9%, 10.5%

22. x = price of bat, y = price of ball, z = price of glove.
$$x + y + z = 99.00$$
$$x = y + 9.95$$
$$z = x + 65.45$$
Solve the second equation for y.
$$y = x - 9.95$$
Substitute $x - 9.95$ for y and $x + 65.45$ for z in the first equation.
$$x + (x - 9.95) + (x + 65.45) = 99.00$$
$$3x + 55.50 = 99.00$$
$$3x = 43.50,\ x = \$14.50$$
$$y = (14.50) - 9.95 = \$4.55$$
$$z = (14.50) + 65.45 = \$79.95$$
The glove costs \$79.95, the bat costs \$14.50, and the ball costs \$4.55.

23.

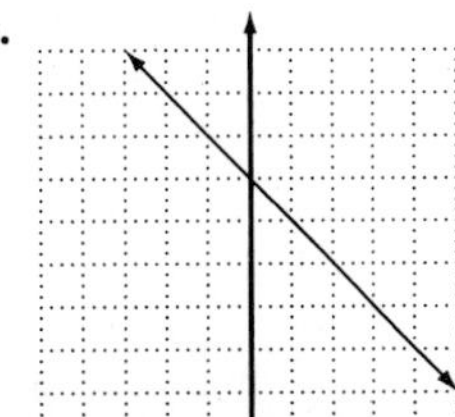

slope = -1

24.

slope = 2

25.

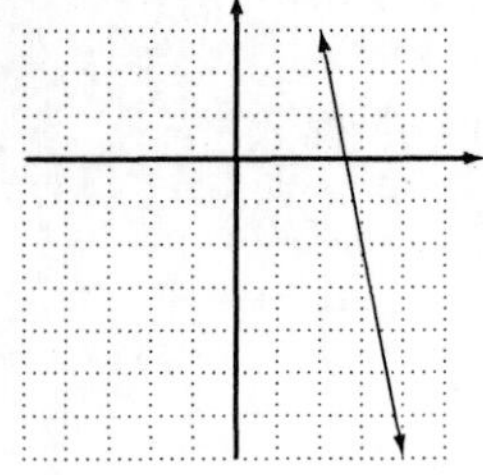

slope = -5

26. $m = \frac{7-2}{3-(-2)} = \frac{5}{5} = 1$
$y = x + b$
$2 = -2 + b$
$4 = b$
Equation is $y = x + 4$.

27. $y = 6x + 7$ 28. $\frac{x^6}{x^2} = x^{6-2} = x^4$ 29. $\frac{t^9}{t^8} = t^{9-8} = t$

30. $\frac{n^4}{n^4} = 1$ 31. $\frac{x^3y^5}{x^3y^4} = x^{3-3}y^{5-4} = x^0y^1 = y$

32. $7m^4n^2 - 7m^2n^4 = 7m^2n^2(m^2 - n^2)$
$= 7m^2n^2(m+n)(m-n)$

33. $81x^2 - 126xy + 49y^2 = (9x - 7y)^2$

LESSON 8-5 TRY THIS pp. 381–383

a. $d = 56(t+1)$ and $d = 84t$.
$84t = 56(t+1)$
$84t = 56t + 56$
$28t = 56$
$t = 2$
$d = 84t = 2(84) = 168$ km

b. $d = (r+25)5$ and $d = (r-25)6$.
$(r+25)5 = (r-25)6$
$5r + 125 = 6r - 150$
$-r = -275$
275 km/h

c. $35t + 40t = 200$
$75t = 200$
$t = 2\frac{2}{3}$ h

d. $d = 35t$
$d + 15 = 40t$
$t = 3$ h

LESSON 8-5 EXERCISES pp. 383–386

1. a.

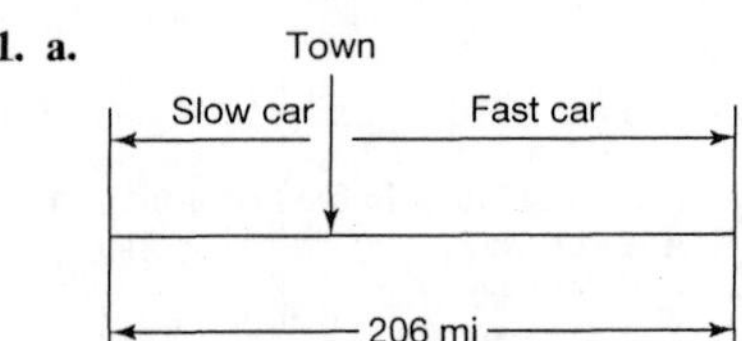

b.

	Distance	Rate	Time
Slow Car	d	48	t
Fast Car	$206 - d$	55	t

c. $48t + 55t = 206$

d. $103t = 206$
$t = 2$
In 2 hours the cars will be 206 miles apart.

2. a.

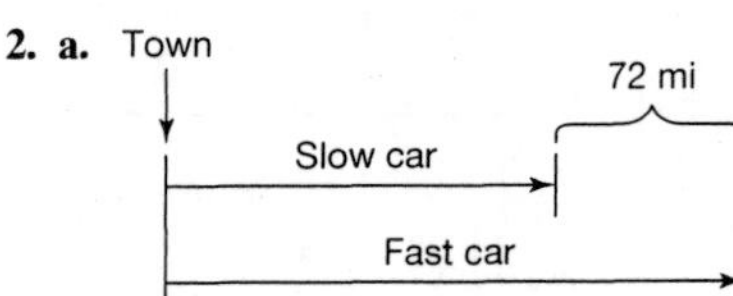

b.

	Distance	Rate	Time
Slow car	d	30	t
Fast car	$d + 72$	46	t

c. $d = 30t$
$d + 72 = 46t$

d. $(30t) + 72 = 46t$
$72 = 16t$
$4.5 = t$
In 4.5 hours the cars will be 72 miles apart.

3. a.

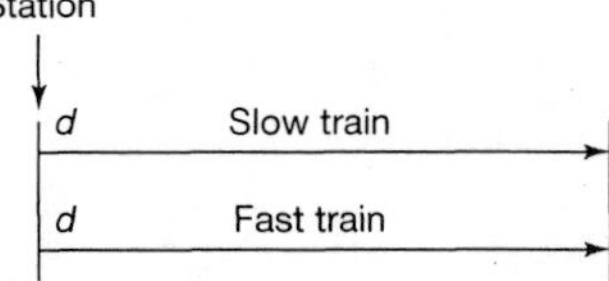

b.

	Distance	Rate	Time
1st train	d	72	$t + 3$
2nd train	d	120	t

c. $d = 72(t+3)$
$d = 120t$

d. $d = 72t + 216$
$120t = 72t + 216$
$48t = 216$
$t = 4.5$
The second train overtakes the first train 4.5 hours after it leaves.

4. $44t + 55t = 297$
$99t = 297$
$t = 3$ h

5. $47t = 32t + 69$
$15t = 69$
$t = 4.6$ h

6. $d = 192(t+2)$
$d = 960t$
$960t = 192(t+2)$
$960t = 192t + 384$
$768t = 384$
$t = 0.5$ h after jet leaves

7. $d = 4(r+6)$
$d = 10(r-6)$
$4(r+6) = 10(r-6)$
$4r + 24 = 10r - 60$
$24 = 6r - 60$
$84 = 6r$
$14 = r$
$r = 14$ km/h

8. $d = 4(r+20)$
$d = 5(r-20)$
$4(r+20) = 5(r-20)$
$4r + 80 = 5r - 100$
$80 = r - 100$
$180 = r$
$r = 180$ km/h

9. $d = 96t$
$d = 64(t+2)$
$96t = 64t + 128$
$32t = 128$
$t = 4$
$d = 96(4)$
$d = 384$ km

10. $d = 637t$
$d = 273(t+4)$
$637t = 273t + 1092$
$364t = 1092$
$t = 3$
$d = 637(3)$
$d = 1911$ km

11. $2(r-w) = 600$
$\frac{5}{3}(r+w) = 600$
$2r - 2w = 600$
$\frac{5}{3}r + \frac{5}{3}w = 600$
$3\left(\frac{5}{3}r + \frac{5}{3}w\right) = 3(600)$
$5r + 5w = 1800$
$10r + 10w = 3600$
$10r - 10w = 3000$
$20r = 6600$
$r = 330$ km/h

12. $3(r-w) = 18$
$\frac{3}{2}(r+w) = 18$
$3r - 3w = 18$
$\frac{3}{2}r + \frac{3}{2}w = 18$
$2\left(\frac{3}{2}r + \frac{3}{2}w\right) = 2(18)$
$3r + 3w = 36$
$3r - 3w = 18$
$6r = 54$
$r = 9$ km/h

13.
$$\begin{aligned} 45t &= d \\ 6(2 - t) &= 25 - d \\ 12 - 6t &= 25 - d \\ -6t &= 13 - d \\ 45t &= \phantom{13 -{}} d \\ \hline 39t &= 13 \\ t &= \frac{1}{3} \\ 45\left(\frac{1}{3}\right) &= d \\ d &= 15 \text{ mi} \end{aligned}$$

14.
$$\begin{aligned} 9t &= d \\ 5(1 - t) &= 8 - d \\ 5 - 5t &= 8 - d \\ -5t &= 3 - d \\ 9t &= \phantom{3 -{}} d \\ \hline 4t &= 3 \\ t &= \frac{3}{4} \\ 9\left(\frac{3}{4}\right) &= d \\ d &= 6\tfrac{3}{4} \text{ km} \end{aligned}$$

15.
$$\begin{aligned} (r + 25.5)4.23 &= d \\ (r - 25.5)4.97 &= d \\ (r + 25.5)4.23 &= (r - 25.5)4.97 \\ 4.23r + 107.865 &= 4.97r - 126.735 \\ 234.6 &= 0.74r \\ 317.03 \text{ km/h} &\approx r \end{aligned}$$

16. $2\frac{1}{2}(r + w) = 625$, or $\frac{5}{2}(r + w) = 625$, so

$$r + w = \frac{2}{5}(625) = 250$$

$4\frac{1}{6}(r - w) = 625$, or $\frac{25}{6}(r - w) = 625$, so

$$r - w = \frac{6}{25}(625) = 150$$

Adding
$$\begin{aligned} r + w &= 250 \\ r - w &= 150 \\ \hline 2r \phantom{{}- w} &= 400 \\ r &= 200 \end{aligned}$$

$200 + w = 250$, so $w = 50$

The wind speed is 50 mi/h, and the speed of the plane in still air is 200 mi/h.

17. Let t = time spent on land in one direction.
Let d = distance traveled in water. Then
$$\begin{aligned} d &= (20 - 4)(4.5 - t) \\ d &= (20 + 4)(3.5 - t) \\ 16(4.5 - t) &= 24(3.5 - t) \\ 72 - 16t &= 84 - 24t \\ 8t &= 12; t = 1.5 \end{aligned}$$
Then $d = 16(4.5 - 1.5) = 16(3) = 48$ mi.
Distance on land $= rt = 60(1.5) = 90$ mi.
Land 90 mi, water 48 mi

18. r = plane's air speed, w = wind speed

Then $2900 = (r - w)5$ and $2900 = \left(r - \frac{w}{2}\right) \cdot 4\frac{5}{6}$

$$5r - 5w = 4\frac{5}{6}r - \frac{1}{2} \cdot \frac{29}{6} \cdot w$$

$$\frac{1}{6}r = \left(5 - \frac{29}{12}\right)w = \frac{31}{12}w$$

$r = \frac{31}{2}w$. Therefore

$$2900 = 5\left(\frac{31}{2}w - w\right)$$

$$580 = \frac{31}{2}w - \frac{2}{2}w$$

$$580 = \frac{29}{2}w; w = 40 \text{ mph}$$

$2900 = 5(r - 40)$, $580 = r - 40$, $620 = r$
40 mi/h, 620 mi/h

19.
$$\begin{aligned} d &= 55t \\ d - 10 &= 40t \\ 55t &= 40t + 10 \\ 15t &= 10 \\ t &= \frac{2}{3} \text{hr} = 40 \text{ min} \end{aligned}$$

After 40 min

20. $d = 107.4t$

$$d = 217.1\left(t - 16\frac{57}{60}\right) = 217.1(t - 16.95)$$

$$\begin{aligned} 107.4t &= 217.1t - 3679.845 \\ 3679.845 &= 109.7t \\ t &\approx 33.54 \end{aligned}$$

Since $d = 107.4t$,
$$\begin{aligned} d &\approx 107.4(33.54) \\ d &\approx 3603 \text{ mi} \end{aligned}$$

21. Ingrid must arrive at the station by 7:10 A.M. in order to have 5 minutes to get on the 7:15 train, the last one that will give her the 35 minutes she needs to get to her office. To travel the 18 miles to the station at the rush hour rate of 12 miles per 24 minutes she needs 36 minutes. Thirty-six minutes before 7:10 A.M. is 6:34 A.M., the time she must leave her house.

22.

$x - 7y$	2
$6 - 7(1)$	2
$6 - 7$	
-1	

No

23.

$y - 4x$	-3
$5 - 4(2)$	-3
$5 - 8$	
-3	

$2x - y$	-1
$2(2) - 5$	-1
$4 - 5$	
-1	

Yes

24.
$$\begin{aligned} x^2 - 3x &= 4 \\ x^2 - 3x - 4 &= 0 \\ (x - 4)(x + 1) &= 0 \\ x - 4 = 0 \quad &\text{or} \quad x + 1 = 0 \\ x = 4 \quad &\text{or} \quad x = -1 \end{aligned}$$

25.
$$\begin{aligned} y^2 - 7y - 18 &= 0 \\ (y - 9)(y + 2) &= 0 \\ y - 9 = 0 \quad &\text{or} \quad y + 2 = 0 \\ y = 9 \quad &\text{or} \quad y = -2 \end{aligned}$$

26. $\frac{x^4y^7}{xy^3} = x^{4-1}y^{7-3} = x^3y^4$ **27.** $\frac{a^9b^8}{a^4b^2} = a^{9-4}b^{8-2} = a^5b^6$

28. $\left(\frac{q^3s^5}{qs^2}\right)^3 = (q^2s^3)^3 = q^{2\cdot3}s^{3\cdot3} = q^6s^9$

29. $\frac{x^{12}y^3z^5}{x^3yz^3} = x^{12-3}y^{3-1}z^{5-3} = x^9y^2z^2$

ERROR ANALYSIS p. 386

1.
$$\begin{aligned} 3(4) - y &= 4 \\ -y &= 4 - 12 \\ -y &= -8 \\ y &= 8 \end{aligned}$$
The correct solution is (4, 8).

2.
$$\begin{aligned} 4x - y &= 17 \\ -x - y &= 7 \\ \hline 5x &= 10 \\ x &= 2 \\ 4(2) - y &= 17 \\ 8 - y &= 17 \\ -y &= 9 \\ y &= -9 \end{aligned}$$
The correct solution is (2, – 9).

LESSON 8-6 TRY THIS pp. 388–389

a. Let x = the tens digit and y = the ones digit.

① $x + y = 5$

② $(10y + x) - (10x + y) = 27$

$$\begin{aligned} 10y + x - 10x - y &= 27 && \text{Simplifying ②} \\ 9y - 9x &= 27 \\ y - x &= 3 \\ y + x &= 5 && \text{Equation ①} \\ \hline 2y \phantom{{}+ x} &= 8 && \text{Adding} \\ y &= 4 \end{aligned}$$

Since $x + y = 5, x + 4 = 5, x = 1$.
The number is 14.

b. Let x = the tens digit and y = the ones digit.

① $x + y = 7$

② $(10x + y) - (10y + x) = 9$

$10x + y - 10y - x = 9$ Simplifying ②

$9x - 9y = 9$

$x - y = 1$

$x + y = 7$ Equation ①

$2x = 8$ Adding

$x = 4$

Since $x + y = 7, 4 + y = 7, y = 3$.

The number is 43.

c. Let q = the number of quarters and d = the number of dimes.
$q + d = 20$. Hence $q = 20 - d$. Also, $25q + 10d = 305$.
By substitution, $25(20 - d) + 10d = 305$

$500 - 25d + 10d = 305$

$-15d = -195$

$d = 13, q = 20 - (13) = 7$

7 quarters, 13 dimes

d. Let d = the number of dimes and n = the number of nickels.

$d + n = 19$, and $d = 19 - n$

$10d + 5n = 135$

$10(19 - n) + 5n = 135$

$190 - 10n + 5n = 135$

$-5n = -55$

$n = 11, d = 19 - (11) = 8$

8 dimes, 11 nickels

e. Let a = the number of adults and c = the number of children.

$a + c = 166$

$200a + 75c = 29{,}325$

Multiplying the first by -75 and adding,

$-75a - 75c = -12{,}450$

$200a + 75c = 29{,}325$

$125a = 16{,}875$

$a = 135$

$c = 166 - (135) = 31$

135 adults, 31 children

LESSON 8-6 EXERCISES pp. 390–391

1. Let x = tens digit and y = ones digit.

$x + y = 9$

$(10y + x) - (10x + y) = 63$

$10y + x - 10x - y = 63$

$9y - 9x = 63$

$9y + 9x = 81$

$18y = 144$

$y = 8$

$x + (8) = 9$

$x = 1$

The number is 18.

2. Let x = tens digit and y = ones digit.

$x + y = 10$

$(10y + x) - (10x + y) = 36$

$10y + x - 10x - y = 36$

$9y - 9x = 36$

$9y + 9x = 90$

$18y = 126$

$y = 7$

$x + (7) = 10$

$x = 3$

The number is 37.

3. Let x = tens digit and y = ones digit.

$x + y = 12$

$(10x + y) - (10y + x) = 18$

$10x + y - 10y - x = 18$

$9x - 9y = 18$

$\frac{1}{9}(9x - 9y) = \frac{1}{9}(18)$

$x - y = 2$

$x + y = 12$

$2x = 14$

$x = 7$

$(7) + y = 12$

$y = 5$

The number is 75.

4. Let x = tens digit and y = ones digit.

$x + y = 16$

$(10x + y) - (10y + x) = 18$

$10x + y - 10y - x = 18$

$9x - 9y = 18$

$9x + 9y = 144$

$18x = 162$

$x = 9$

$(9) + y = 16$

$y = 7$

The number is 97.

5. Let x = number of dimes, y = number of quarters.

$x + y = 103$

$10x + 25y = 1525$

$-10x - 10y = -1030$

$15y = 495$

$y = 33$

$x + (33) = 103$

$x = 70$

There are 70 dimes and 33 quarters.

6. Let x = number of nickels, y = number of quarters.

$x + y = 13$

$5x + 25y = 125$

$-5x - 5y = -65$

$20y = 60$

$y = 3$

$x + (3) = 13$

$x = 10$

There are 10 nickels and 3 quarters.

7. Let x = number of nickels, y = number of dimes.

$y = 5x$

$5x + 10y = 440$

$5x + 10(5x) = 440$

$5x + 50x = 440$

$55x = 440$

$x = 8$

$y = 5(8) = 40$

There are 8 nickels and 40 dimes.

8. Let x = number of nickels, y = number of dimes.

$x = 3y$

$5x + 10y = 2500$

$5(3y) + 10y = 2500$

$15y + 10y = 2500$

$25y = 2500$

$y = 100$

$x = 3(100) = 300$

There are 300 nickels and 100 dimes.

9. Let x = number of adults, y = number of children.

$x + y = 429$

$x + 0.75y = 372.50$

$-x - y = -429$

$-0.25y = -56.5$

$y = 226$

$x + (226) = 429$

$x = 203$

203 adults and 226 children attended.

10. Let x = number of adults, y = number of children.

$x + y = 578$

$2x + 1.5y = 985$

$-2x - 2y = -1156$

$-0.5y = -171$

$y = 342$

$x + (342) = 578$

$x = 236$

236 adults and 342 children attended.

11. Let x = number of adults, y = number of students.

$x + y = 200$

$9x + 4.5y = 1485$

$-9x - 9y = -1800$

$-4.5y = -315$

$y = 70$

$x + (70) = 200$

$x = 130$

130 adults and 70 students attended.

12. Let x = number at \$2.50, y = number at \$4.00.

$$\begin{aligned} x + y &= 203 \\ 2.5x + 4y &= 620 \\ -4x - 4y &= -812 \\ \hline -1.5x \quad &= -192 \\ x &= 128 \\ (128) + y &= 203 \\ y &= 75 \end{aligned}$$

128 at \$2.50 and 75 at \$4.00 were sold.

13. Let x = number of 5-g bolts, y = number of 10-g bolts.

$$\begin{aligned} x + y &= 300 \\ 5x + 10y &= 2350 \\ -5x - 5y &= -1500 \\ \hline 5y &= 850 \\ y &= 170 \\ x + (170) &= 300 \\ x &= 130 \end{aligned}$$

There are 130 5-g bolts and 170 10-g bolts.

14. Let x = number of 5-g bolts, y = number of 10-g bolts.

$$\begin{aligned} x + y &= 460 \\ 5x + 10y &= 3800 \\ -5x - 5y &= -2300 \\ \hline 5y &= 1500 \\ y &= 300 \\ x + (300) &= 460 \\ x &= 160 \end{aligned}$$

There are 160 5-g bolts and 300 10-g bolts.

15. Let x = the tens digit and y = the ones digit.

① $x + y = 14$

② $(10x + y) - (10y + x) = 18$

$10x + y - 10y - x = 18$ Simplifying ②

$9x - 9y = 18$

$x - y = 2$

$x + y = 14$ Equation ①

$2x = 16$ Adding

$x = 8$

Since $x + y = 14, 8 + y = 14, y = 6$. The number is 86.

16. Let x = the tens digit and y = the ones digit.

① $10x + y + 27 = 10y + x$

② $x + y = 11$

$9x - 9y = -27$ Simplifying ①

$x - y = -3$

$x + y = 11$ Equation ②

$2x = 8$ Adding

$x = 4$

Since $x + y = 11, 4 + y = 11, y = 7$. The number is 47.

17. Let t = tens digit and u = ones digit.

① $t = u + 1$

② $10t + u = 6(t + u)$

$10(u + 1) + u = 6[(u + 1) + u]$ Substitution

$11u + 10 = 12u + 6$

$u = 4$

Since $t = u + 1, t = 4 + 1, t = 5$.
The number is 54.

18. Let x = ones and hundreds digits, y = tens digit

① $x + x + y = 5$

② $100x + 10y + x - (100y + 10x + x) = 90$

$100x + 10y + x - 100y - 10x - x = 90$

Simplifying ② $90x - 90y = 90$

$x - y = 1$

Simplifying ① $2x + y = 5$

Adding $3x = 6$

$x = 2$

Since $x - y = 1, 2 - y = 1, y = 1$.
The number is 212.

19. Let x = hundreds digit, y = tens digit, z = ones digit

① $100x + 10y + z = 28(x + y + z)$

② $z = 2y$

③ $z = x + 3$

Substituting ② in ③:

$$\begin{aligned} 2y &= x + 3 \\ 2y - 3 &= x \end{aligned}$$

Substituting this and ② in ①:

$$\begin{aligned} 100(2y - 3) + 10y + (2y) &= 28([2y - 3] + y + [2y]) \\ 200y - 300 + 10y + 2y &= 28(5y - 3) \\ 212y - 300 &= 140y - 84 \\ 72y &= 216 \\ y &= 3 \end{aligned}$$

Since $z = 2y, z = 6$. Since $x = 2y - 3, x = 2(3) - 3 = 3$.
The number is 336.

20. Let q = the number of quarters and d = the number of dimes.
$25q + 10d = 220$
We have only one equation. Dividing by 5,

$$\begin{aligned} 5q + 2d &= 44 \\ 2d &= 44 - 5q \\ d &= \frac{44 - 5q}{2} \end{aligned}$$

If q is odd, $44 - 5q$ is odd and not divisible by 2. If q is 9 or more, d is negative. So $q = 0, 2, 4, 6$, or 8, and $d = 22, 17, 12, 7$, or 2. The (d, q) solutions are $(22, 0), (17, 2), (12, 4), (7, 6), (2, 8)$. The fewest coins are $2 + 8 = 10$ coins.

21. Let d = number of dimes, q = number of quarters.

① $10d + 25q = 2000$

② $25d + 10q = 2900$

$20d + 50q = 4000$ Multiplying ① by 2

$-125d - 50q = -14{,}500$ Multiplying ② by -5

$-105d = -10{,}500$ Adding

$d = 100$

$10(100) + 25q = 2000$ Substituting $d = 100$ in ①

$1000 + 25q = 2000$

$25q = 1000$

$q = 40$

She asked for 100 dimes and 40 quarters.

22. Let x = tens digit and y = ones digit.
Amount Glenda paid − true cost = 36

$$\begin{aligned} (10y + x) - (10x + y) &= 36 \\ 10y + x - 10x - y &= 36 \\ 9y - 9x &= 36 \\ y - x &= 4 \end{aligned}$$

Possible costs are \$15, \$26, \$37, \$48, and \$59.

23. $16a^8 - 36 = 4(4a^8 - 9)$
$= 4(2a^4 - 3)(2a^4 + 3)$

24. $8x^3 + 10x^2 - 6x = 2x(4x^2 + 5x - 3)$

25. $c^2 - 5c = c(c - 5)$ **26.** $y^2 - 10y + 25 = (y - 5)^2$

27. $45m^2 - 106m + 45 = (5m - 9)(9m - 5)$

28. $2t^3 - 2t^2 - 4t = 2t(t^2 - t - 2)$
$= 2t(t - 2)(t + 1)$

29. $c^2 + 4c = 0$

$c(c + 4) = 0$

$c = 0$ or $c + 4 = 0$

$c = 0$ or $c = -4$

30. $a^2 - 7a = -12$

$a^2 - 7a + 12 = 0$

$(a - 4)(a - 3) = 0$

$a - 4 = 0$ or $a - 3 = 0$

$a = 4$ or $a = 3$

31. $x^2 + 3x = 10$

$x^2 + 3x - 10 = 0$

$(x + 5)(x - 2) = 0$

$x + 5 = 0$ or $x - 2 = 0$

$x = -5$ or $x = 2$

32. $\frac{x^4y^7}{x^2y^5} = x^{4-2}y^{7-5} = x^2y^2$

33. $\frac{x^9y^5z^4}{x^6y^2z} = x^{9-6}y^{5-2}z^{4-1} = x^3y^3z^3$

34. $\left(\frac{a^3b^7c}{a^3b}\right)^3 = (b^6c)^3 = b^{6\cdot3}c^3 = b^{18}c^3$

35. $(x+1)^2 = x^2 + 2x + 1$ 36. $(x-3)^2 = x^2 - 6x + 9$

37. $(a+7)^2 = a^2 + 14a + 49$ 38. $(r+3)(r-3) = r^2 - 9$

39. $(2a+4)(a-5) = 2a^2 - 10a + 4a - 20 = 2a^2 - 6a - 20$

40. $(m-4)^2 = m^2 - 8m + 16$

41. ① $3x + y = 5$
② $x + 2y = 0$
$-6x - 2y = -10$ Multiplying ① by -2
$-5x = -10$ Adding
$x = 2$
$3(2) + y = 5$ Substituting $x = 2$ in ①
$6 + y = 5$
$y = -1$
$x = 2, y = -1$

42. ① $2x + 3y = -2$
② $3x + 2y = 7$
$-6x - 9y = 6$ Multiplying ① by -3
$6x + 4y = 14$ Multiplying ② by 2
$-5y = 20$ Adding
$y = -4$
$2x + 3(-4) = -2$ Substituting $y = -4$ in ①
$2x - 12 = -2$
$x = 5$
$x = 5, y = -4$

PREPARING FOR STANDARDIZED TESTS p. 393

1–8. Methods may vary.

1. $x + 2y = 6$
$+(3x + y = 4)$
$4x + 3y = 10$
(C), variation

2. $5x - 3y = 8$
$x = \frac{4y}{5}$
$5\left(\frac{4y}{5}\right) - 3y = 8$
$y = 8$
(E), substitution

3. $x + 4y = 9$
$+(4x + 3y = 7)$
$5x + 7y = 16$
(C), variation

4. $3x + 3y = 17$
$+(x + 4y = 3)$
$4x + 7y = 20$
$\frac{4x + 7y}{4} = \frac{20}{4} = 5$
(A), variation

5. $4x - 3y = 12$
$x = \frac{7y}{4}$
$4\left(\frac{7y}{4}\right) - 3y = 12$
$7y - 3y = 12$
$4y = 12$
$y = 3$
(B), substitution

6. $x + y = 3$
$+(x - y = 2)$
$2x = 5$
$x = 2.5$
$4x = 10$
(D), addition

7. $5x + 2y = 6$
$-(2x + y = 4)$
$3x + y = 2$
(D), variation

8. $x + 2y = 4$
$+(2x + y = 2)$
$3x + 3y = 6$
$2(3x + 3y) = 2(6)$
$6x + 6y = 12$
(E), variation

9. $3x - 2y = 13$
$+(5x + 4y = 11)$
$8x + 2y = 24$
$\frac{8x + 2y}{6} = \frac{24}{6} = 4$
(C), variation

10. $5x + 2y = 12$
$-(3x - 2y = 4)$
$2x + 4y = 8$
$\frac{2x + 4y}{4} = \frac{8}{4} = 2$
(E), variation

11. $3x + 2y = 10$
$5x - 2y = 6$
$8x = 16$
$\frac{8x}{4} = \frac{16}{4}$
$2x = 4$
(D), variation

APPLICATION p. 394

1. $1.68 + 0.06(1.68) = $1.78; No

2. $29.98 + 0.06(29.98) = $31.78; No

3. $33.00 + 0.06(33.00) = $34.98; Yes

4. $249.50 + 0.06(249.50) = $264.47; Yes

5. $x + 0.055x = \$1.50$
$1.055x = \$1.50$
$x = \$1.42$

6. $x + 0.055a = \$2.00$
$1.055x = \$2.00$
$x = \$1.90$

7. $x + 0.055x = \$3.00$
$1.055x = \$3.00$
$x = \$2.84$

8. $x + 0.055x = \$2.50$
$1.055x = \$2.50$
$x = \$2.37$

9. $x + 0.055x = \$0.75$
$1.055x = \$0.75$
$x = \$0.71$

10. $x + 0.055x = \$1.00$
$1.055x = \$1.00$
$x = \$0.95$

CHAPTER 8 WRAP UP pp. 395–396

1. $x - y = 3$
$6 - (-1) = 3$
$6 + 1 = 3$
No

2. $2x + y = 1$ $x - y = 5$
$2(2) + (-3) = 1$ $2 - (-3) = 5$
$4 - 3 = 1$ $2 + 3 = 5$
$1 = 1$ $5 = 5$
Yes

3. $x + 3y = 1$ $2x - y = -5$
$-2 + 3(1) = 1$ $2(-2) - 1 = -5$
$-2 + 3 = 1$ $-4 - 1 = -5$
$1 = 1$ $-5 = -5$
Yes

4. $x - y = 3$
$-4 - (-1) = 3$
$-4 + 1 = 3$
$-3 = 3$
No

5.
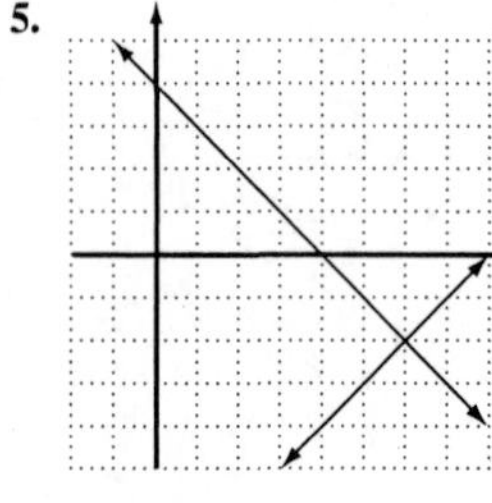
(6, −2)

6.
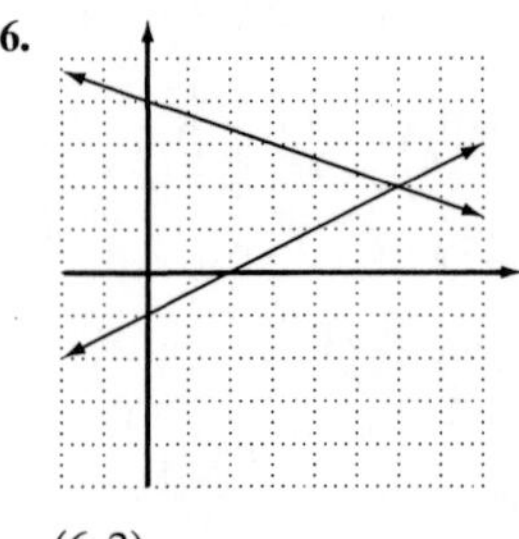
(6, 2)

7.

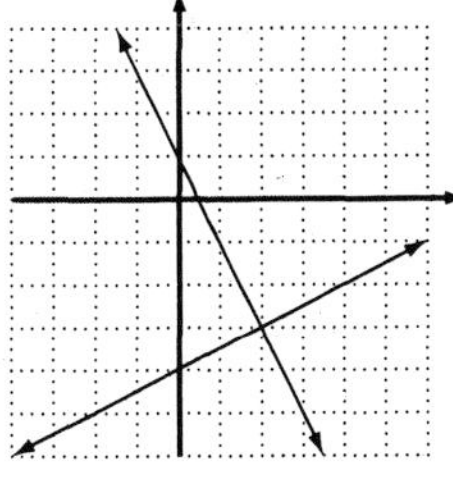

(2, −3)

8.

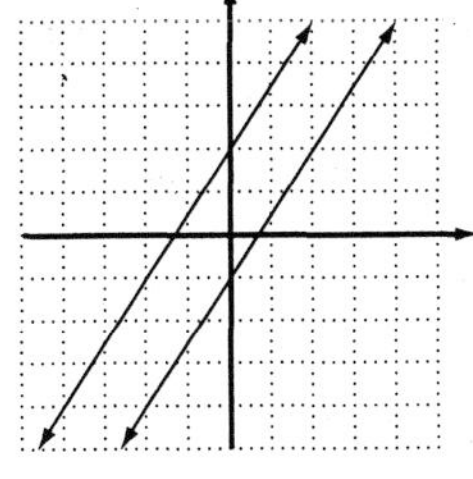

No solution; lines are parallel.

9. $y = 5 - x$
$3x - 4y = -20$
$3x - 4(5 - x) = -20$
$3x - 20 + 4x = -20$
$7x - 20 = -20$
$7x = 0$
$x = 0$
$y = 5 - (0) = 5$
(0, 5) is the solution.

10. $x + 2y = 6 \rightarrow x = 6 - 2y$
$2x + 3y = 8$
$2(6 - 2y) + 3y = 8$
$12 - 4y + 3y = 8$
$12 - y = 8$
$-y = -4$
$y = 4$
$x = 6 - 2(4) = 6 - 8 = -2$
(−2, 4) is the solution.

11. $3x + y = 1$
$x = 2y + 5$
$3(2y + 5) + y = 1$
$6y + 15 + y = 1$
$7y + 15 = 1$
$7y = -14$
$y = -2$
$x = 2(-2) + 5 = -4 + 5 = 1$
(1, −2) is the solution.

12. $x + y = 6$
$y = 3 - 2x$
$x + (3 - 2x) = 6$
$x + 3 - 2x = 6$
$3 - x = 6$
$-x = 3$
$x = -3$
$y = 3 - 2(-3) = 3 + 6 = 9$
(−3, 9) is the solution.

13. $s + t = 5$
$s = 13 - 3t$
$(13 - 3t) + t = 5$
$13 - 2t = 5$
$-2t = -8$
$t = 4$
$s = 13 - 3(4) = 13 - 12 = 1$
(1, 4) is the solution.

14. $x - y = 4$
$y = 2 - x$
$x - (2 - x) = 4$
$x - 2 + x = 4$
$2x - 2 = 4$
$2x = 6$
$x = 3$
$y = 2 - (3) = -1$
(3, −1) is the solution.

15. $x + y = 30 \rightarrow x = 30 - y$
$x - y = 40$
$(30 - y) - y = 40$
$30 - 2y = 40$
$-2y = 10$
$y = -5$
$x = 30 - (-5) = 35$
The numbers are 35 and −5.

16.
$$\begin{array}{r} x + y = 4 \\ \underline{2x - y = 5} \\ 3x \quad = 9 \end{array}$$
$x = 3$
$(3) + y = 4$
$y = 1$
(3, 1) is the solution.

17.
$$\begin{array}{r} x + 2y = 9 \\ \underline{3x - 2y = -5} \\ 4x \quad = 4 \end{array}$$
$x = 1$
$(1) + 2y = 9$
$2y = 8$
$y = 4$
(1, 4) is the solution.

18.
$$\begin{array}{r} x - y = 8 \\ \underline{2x + y = 7} \\ 3x \quad = 15 \end{array}$$
$x = 5$
$(5) - y = 8$
$-y = 3$
$y = -3$
(5, −3) is the solution.

19. $3x - y = -13 \rightarrow 9x - 3y = -39$
$$\begin{array}{r} \underline{2x + 3y = -5} \\ 11x \quad = -44 \end{array}$$
$x = -4$
$3(-4) - y = -13$
$-12 - y = -13$
$-y = -1$
$y = 1$
(−4, 1) is the solution.

20. $2x + 3y = 8 \rightarrow 10x + 15y = 40$
$5x + 2y = -2 \rightarrow \underline{-10x - 4y = 4}$
$11y = 44$
$y = 4$
$2x + 3(4) = 8$
$2x + 12 = 8$
$2x = -4$
$x = -2$
(−2, 4) is the solution.

21. $5x - 2y = 2 \rightarrow 15x - 6y = 6$
$3x - 7y = 36 \rightarrow \underline{-15x + 35y = -180}$
$29y = -174$
$y = -6$
$5x - 2(-6) = 2$
$5x + 12 = 2$
$5x = -10$
$x = -2$
(−2, −6) is the solution.

22. $-x - y = -5 \rightarrow x + y = 5$
$2x - y = 4 \rightarrow \underline{2x - y = 4}$
$3x \quad = 9$
$x = 3$
$(3) + y = 5$
$y = 2$
(3, 2) is the solution.

23. $6x + 2y = 4 \rightarrow 42x + 14y = 28$
$10x + 7y = -8 \rightarrow \underline{-20x - 14y = 16}$
$22x \quad = 44$
$x = 2$
$6(2) + 2y = 4$
$12 + 2y = 4$
$2y = -8$
$y = -4$
(2, −4) is the solution.

24. Let x = one number, y = the other.
$x + y = 27$
$\frac{1}{2}x + \frac{1}{3}y = 11$
$6\left(\frac{1}{2}x + \frac{1}{3}y\right) = 6(11)$
$$\begin{array}{r} 3x + 2y = 66 \\ \underline{-3x - 3y = -81} \\ -y = -15 \end{array}$$
$y = 15$
$x + (15) = 27$
$x = 12$
The numbers are 12 and 15.

25. Let x = Roberta's age, y = Cindy's age.

$$\begin{aligned} x - y &= 25 \\ x + 4 &= 2(y + 4) \\ x + 4 &= 2y + 8 \\ x - 2y &= 4 \\ \underline{-x + y} &\underline{= -25} \\ -y &= -21 \\ y &= 21 \\ x - (21) &= 25 \\ x &= 46 \end{aligned}$$

Roberta is 46; Cindy is 21.

26.

$$\begin{aligned} l - w &= 17 \\ 2l + 2w &= 76 \\ \underline{2l - 2w} &\underline{= 34} \\ 4l &= 110 \\ l &= 27.5 \\ (27.5) - w &= 17 \\ -w &= -10.5 \\ w &= 10.5 \end{aligned}$$

The length is 27.5 cm, the width 10.5 cm.

27. Let r = speed in still air.

$$\begin{aligned} 4(r + 15) &= 5(r - 15) \\ 4r + 60 &= 5r - 75 \\ 60 &= r - 75 \\ 135 &= r \end{aligned}$$

The rate is 135 mi/h.

28. Let x = the tens digit, y = the ones digit.

$$\begin{aligned} x + y &= 6 \\ (10y + x) - (10x + y) &= 36 \\ 10y + x - 10x - y &= 36 \\ 9y - 9x &= 36 \\ \underline{9y + 9x} &\underline{= 54} \\ 18y &= 90 \\ y &= 5 \\ x + (5) &= 6 \\ x &= 1 \end{aligned}$$

The number is 15.

29. Let x = number of dimes, y = number of quarters.

$$\begin{aligned} x - y &= 40 \\ 10x + 25y &= 2500 \\ \underline{25x - 25y} &\underline{= 1000} \\ 35x &= 3500 \\ x &= 100 \\ (100) - y &= 40 \\ -y &= -60 \\ y &= 60 \end{aligned}$$

There are 100 dimes and 60 quarters.

CHAPTER 8 ASSESSMENT p. 397

1.

$$\begin{aligned} x - y &= 2 & x + y &= 6 \\ (4) - (2) &= 2 & (4) + (2) &= 6 \\ 2 &= 2 & 6 &= 6 \end{aligned}$$

Yes

2.

$$\begin{aligned} x - 2y &= 6 & 2x - 3y &= 5 \\ (-8) - 2(-7) &= 6 & 2(-8) - 3(-7) &= 5 \\ -8 + 14 &= 6 & -16 + 21 &= 5 \\ 6 &= 6 & 5 &= 5 \end{aligned}$$

Yes

3.

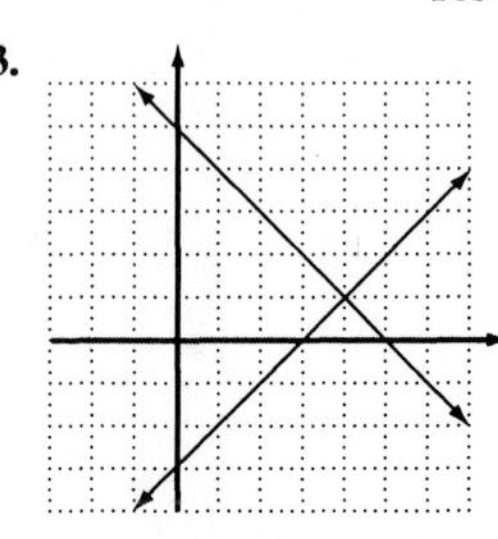

$(4, 1)$

4.

$(10, -2)$

5.

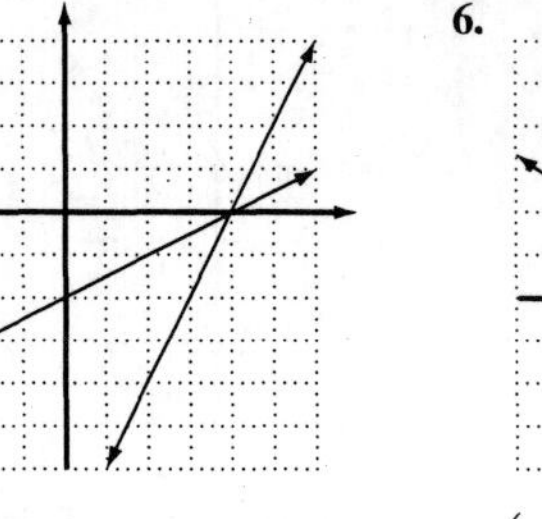

$(4, 0)$

6.

$(-1, 0)$

7.

$$\begin{aligned} y &= 6 - x \\ 2x - 3y &= 22 \\ 2x - 3(6 - x) &= 22 \\ 2x - 18 + 3x &= 22 \\ 5x - 18 &= 22 \\ 5x &= 40 \\ x &= 8 \\ y = 6 - (8) &= -2 \end{aligned}$$

$(8, -2)$ is the solution.

8.

$$\begin{aligned} x + 2y = 5 &\rightarrow x = 5 - 2y \\ x + y &= 2 \\ (5 - 2y) + y &= 2 \\ 5 - y &= 2 \\ -y &= -3 \\ y &= 3 \\ x = 5 - 2(3) &= 5 - 6 = -1 \end{aligned}$$

$(-1, 3)$ is the solution.

9.

$$\begin{aligned} x + y = 31 &\rightarrow x = 31 - y \\ x - y &= 17 \\ (31 - y) - y &= 17 \\ 31 - 2y &= 17 \\ -2y &= -14 \\ y &= 7 \\ x = 31 - (7) &= 24 \end{aligned}$$

$(24, 7)$ is the solution.

10.

$$\begin{aligned} 7x + y = 10 &\rightarrow y = 10 - 7x \\ 2y + 5x &= 11 \\ 2(10 - 7x) + 5x &= 11 \\ 20 - 14x + 5x &= 11 \\ 20 - 9x &= 11 \\ -9x &= -9 \\ x &= 1 \\ y = 10 - 7(1) &= 10 - 7 = 3 \end{aligned}$$

$(1, 3)$ is the solution.

11.

$$\begin{aligned} x - y &= 6 \\ \underline{3x + y} &\underline{= -2} \\ 4x &= 4 \\ x &= 1 \\ (1) - y &= 6 \\ -y &= 5 \\ y &= -5 \end{aligned}$$

$(1, -5)$ is the solution.

12.

$$\begin{aligned} 3x - 4y &= 7 \\ \underline{x + 4y} &\underline{= 5} \\ 4x &= 12 \\ x &= 3 \\ (3) + 4y &= 5 \\ 4y &= 2 \\ y &= \frac{1}{2} \end{aligned}$$

$\left(3, \frac{1}{2}\right)$ is the solution.

13.

$$\begin{aligned} 4x + 5y = 5 &\rightarrow & 12x + 15y &= 15 \\ 6x + 7y = 7 &\rightarrow & \underline{-12x - 14y} &\underline{= -14} \\ & & y &= 1 \end{aligned}$$

$$\begin{aligned} 4x + 5(1) &= 5 \\ 4x + 5 &= 5 \\ 4x &= 0 \\ x &= 0 \end{aligned}$$

$(0, 1)$ is the solution.

14. $2x + 3y = 13 \rightarrow 10x + 15y = 65$
$3x - 5y = 10 \rightarrow \underline{9x - 15y = 30}$
$19x = 95$
$x = 5$

$2(5) + 3y = 13$
$10 + 3y = 13$
$3y = 3$
$y = 1$
(5, 1) is the solution.

15. $x + y = 4 \rightarrow -2x - 2y = -8$
$\underline{2x + 3y = 7}$
$y = -1$
$x + (-1) = 4$
$x = 5$
(5, −1) is the solution.

16. $7x - 5y = 13 \rightarrow -14x + 10y = -26$
$\underline{8x - 10y = 2}$
$-6x = -24$
$x = 4$

$7(4) - 5y = 13$
$28 - 5y = 13$
$-5y = -15$
$y = 3$
(4, 3) is the solution.

17. Let r = rate of boat.
$2(r + 8) = 3(r - 8)$
$2r + 16 = 3r - 24$
$16 = r - 24$
$40 = r$
$r = 40$ km/h

18. Let x = one number, y = the other.
$x + y = 8$
$\underline{x - y = 12}$
$2x = 20$
$x = 10$
$(10) + y = 8$
$y = -2$
The numbers are 10 and −2.

19. Let x = number of dimes, y = number of quarters.
$x + y = 25$
$10x + 25y = 355$
$\underline{-10x - 10y = -250}$
$15y = 105$
$y = 7$
There are 7 quarters.

20. Let x = number of adult tickets, y = number of child tickets.
$x + y = 360$
$110x + 40y = 28{,}260$
$\underline{-40x - 40y = -14{,}400}$
$70x = 13{,}860$
$x = 198$
$(198) + y = 360$
$y = 162$
198 adult tickets and 162 child tickets were sold.

21. Let r = rate of first train and $r + 15$ = rate of second.
Time of first train = 8, time of second = 6.
$8r + 6(r + 15) = 580$
$8r + 6r + 90 = 580$
$14r + 90 = 580$
$14r = 490$
$r = 35$
The first train travels 35 mi/h, the second 50 mi/h.

CHAPTER 9

SKILLS & CONCEPTS YOU NEED FOR CHAPTER 9 — p. 398

1. $-6 < -4$ **2.** $4.5 > -4.5$

3. **(a)** Yes **(b)** Yes **(c)** Yes

4. −3 0

5. 0 1

6. $2 - 3x > 20$
$-3x > 18$
$x < -6$
−6 0

7. $28x + 18 > 26x - 8$
$2x + 18 > -8$
$2x > -26$
$x > -13$

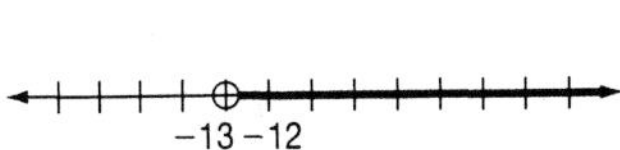

8. $8x - 10 > 7x - 4$
$8x > 7x + 6$
$x > 6$
0 6

9. $8x - 13 \leq -13$
$8x \leq 0$
$x \leq 0$

10. **a.** $2x - y = 6$
$2(1) - 4 = 6$
$2 - 4 = 6$
$-2 = 6$
No

b. $2x - y = 6$
$2(1) - (-4) = 6$
$2 + 4 = 6$
$6 = 6$
Yes

c. $2x - y = 6$
$2(2) - (-2) = 6$
$4 + 2 = 6$
$6 = 6$
Yes

11. $2y - x = 2$
$2(-1) - (-4) = 2$
$-2 + 4 = 2$
$2 = 2$

$x = 4y$
$(-4) = 4(-1)$
$-4 = -4$
Yes

12. $y + 2 = x$
$(2) + 2 = (0)$
$4 = 0$

$y - 2 = -x - 4$
$(2) - 2 = -(0) - 4$
$0 = -4$
No

13. 

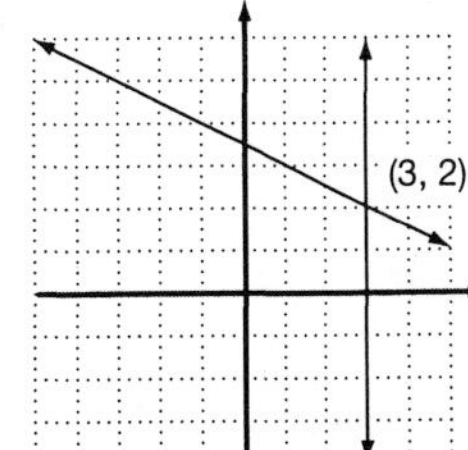

14. 

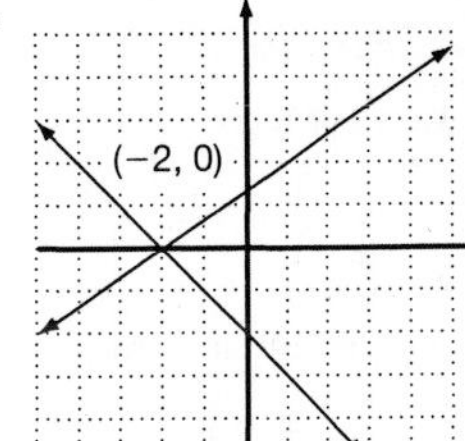

LESSON 9-1 TRY THIS — pp. 400–402

a. **(a)** $G = \{6, 7, 8 \ldots\}$
(b) $G = \{x \mid x$ is a whole number and $x > 5\}$

b. **(a)** $T = \{20, 15, 10, 5, 0, -5, \ldots\}$
(b) $T = \{x \mid x$ is a multiple of 5 and $x < 24\}$

c. **(a)** $P = \{2, 3, 5, 7, 11, 13, 17, 19\}$
(b) $P = \{x \mid x$ is a prime number and $x < 20\}$

d. $P \cap T = \{0, 1\}$ **e.** $T \cap S = \{1, 6\}$

f. $P \cap S = \{-3, 1\}$ **g.** ∅ **h.** E

i. $\{0, 2\}$ or T **j.** ∅ **k.** S **l.** T

m. $\{-4, -3, -2, 0, 4, 5, 6\}$

n. $\{-3, -2, 0, 1, 3, 4, 5\}$

o. D
p. $\{x \mid x \text{ is a whole number}\}$
q. M

LESSON 9-1 EXERCISES pp. 403–404

1. (a) $A = \{0, 1, 2, 3\}$
(b) $A = \{x \mid x \text{ is a whole number and } x < 4\}$

2. (a) $F = \{12, 13, 14, \ldots\}$
(b) $F = \{x \mid x \text{ is an integer and } x \geq 12\}$

3. (a) $N = \{-1, -2, -3, -4\}$
(b) $N = \{x \mid x \text{ is an integer and } -5 < x < 0\}$

4. (a) $P = \{2, 3, 5, 7, 11, 13, 17, 19, 23, 29\}$
(b) $P = \{x \mid x \text{ is a prime number and } x < 30\}$

5. (a) $H = \{3, 6, 9, 12, 15, 18, 21\}$
(b) $H = \{x \mid x \text{ is a multiple of 3 and } 0 < x \leq 21\}$

6. (a) $R = \{4, 8, 12, 16, \ldots\}$
(b) $R = \{x \mid x \text{ is a multiple of 4 and } x > 0\}$

7. (a) $E = \{2, 4, 6, 8, \ldots\}$
(b) $E = \{x \mid x \text{ is an even integer and } x > 0\}$

8. (a) $T = \{1, 2, 3, 4, 6, 12\}$
(b) $T = \{x \mid x \text{ is a factor of 12 and } x > 0\}$

9. (a) $m = \{2\}$
(b) $m = \{x \mid x \text{ is an even prime number}\}$

10. (a) $s = \{0, 1, 4, 9, 16\}$
(b) $s = \{x \mid x \text{ is an integer, a perfect square, and } x < 20\}$

11. $\{1, 2\}$ **12.** $\{0\}$ **13.** $\{4, 5\}$ **14.** $\{1, 2\}$

15. $\varnothing$ **16.** $\varnothing$ **17.** $\varnothing$ **18.** $\varnothing$

19. $\{0, 2, 4, 6, 8, \ldots\}$ or E **20.** $\{1, 3, 5, 7, 9, \ldots\}$ or D

21. $\{-5, -4, -3, -2, -1, 0\}$ or P

22. $\{-2, -1, 0, 1, 2, 3, 4\}$

23. $\{-5, -4, -3, -2, -1, 0, 5, 6, 7, 8\}$

24. $\{-2, -1, 0, 5, 6, 7, 8\}$

25. $\{-1, 0, 1, 2, 3, 4, 5, 6, 7, 8\}$

26. $\{-5, -4, -3, -2, -1, 0, 1, 2, 3, 4\}$

27. $\{-5, -4, -3, -2, -1, 0\}$ or P

28. $\{5, 6, 7, 8\}$ or S **29.** $\{0, 1, 2, 3, \ldots\}$ or W

30. $\{\ldots -2, -1, 0, 1, 2, \ldots\}$ or Z

31. True **32.** False **33.** True **34.** False

35. True **36.** True **37.** True **38.** False

39. False **40.** True **41.** True **42.** False

43. A **44.** A **45.** A **46.** $\varnothing$ **47.** $\{2, 4, 6, 8 \ldots\}$

48. $\{\ldots -2, -1, 0, 1, 2, \ldots\}$

49. Answers may vary. Ex: $\{5, 1, 0\}$ and $\{1, 9\}$

50. $n(A \cup B) = n(A) + k$, where k is the number of elements in B that are not also in A.
$k = n(B) - n(A \cap B)$. Thus,
$n(A \cup B) = n(A) + n(B) - n(A \cap B)$.

51.

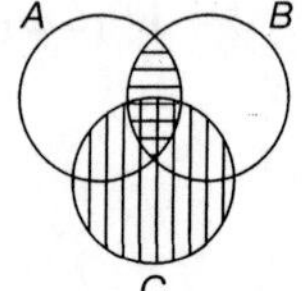

A B C

52.

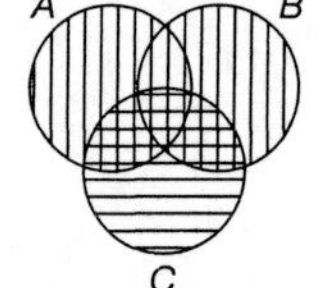

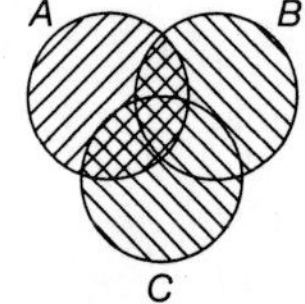

53. $B = \{3, 7, 10, 15\}$

54. $18a^2 - 21a - 9 = 3(6a^2 - 7a - 3)$
$= 3(3a + 1)(2a - 3)$

55. $49 - 4c^2 = (7 + 2c)(7 - 2c)$

56. $5m^2 - 125 = 5(m^2 - 25) = 5(m + 5)(m - 5)$

57. $4a^2 - 12a + 9 = 4a^2 - 2 \cdot 2a \cdot 3 + 9 = (2a - 3)^2$

58. $4y^2 + 28y + 49 = 4y^2 + 2 \cdot 2y \cdot 7 + 49 = (2y + 7)^2$

59. $8x^2 + 18xy - 18y^2 = 2(4x^2 + 9xy - 9y^2)$
$= 2(x + 3y)(4x - 3y)$

60.
$y = x - 5$
$y = 11 - 7x$
$(x - 5) = 11 - 7x$ Substituting first equation in second
$8x = 16$
$x = 2$
$y = 2 - 5 = -3$

61.
$x = y + 2$
$x + y = 8$
$(y + 2) + y = 8$ Substituting first equation in second
$2y + 2 = 8$
$2y = 6$
$y = 3$
$x = 3 + 2 = 5$

62.
$2x - y = -1$
$2y - x = -4$
$2x + 1 = y$ Solving first equation for y
$2(2x + 1) - x = -4$ Substituting in second equation
$4x + 2 - x = -4$
$3x = -6$
$x = -2$
$y = 2(-2) + 1 = -3$

63. $y = mx + b$
$0 = b$ Substituting $(0, 0)$ in $y = mx + b$
So $y = mx$
$3 = m$ Substituting $(1, 3)$ in $y = mx$
The equation is $y = 3x$.

64. $y = mx + b$
$m = \dfrac{1 - (-1)}{1 - 3} = \dfrac{2}{-2} = -1$
$y = -x + b$
$1 = -1 + b$
$2 = b$
The equation is $y = -x + 2$.

65. $y = mx + b$
$m = \dfrac{-5 - (-3)}{-3 - 3} = \dfrac{-2}{-6} = \dfrac{1}{3}$
$y = \dfrac{1}{3}x + b$
$-3 = \dfrac{1}{3}(3) + b$
$-4 = b$
The equation is $y = \dfrac{1}{3}x - 4$.

66.
$x + y = 31$
$\underline{x - y = 5}$
$2x = 36$ Adding
$x = 18$
$18 + y = 31$
$y = 13$
The numbers are 13 and 18.

67.
$x + y = 13$
$xy = 36$
$y = 13 - x$ Solving first equation for y
$x(13 - x) = 36$ Substituting in second equation
$13x - x^2 = 36$
$x^2 - 13x + 36 = 0$
$(x - 9)(x - 4) = 0$
$x = 9$ or $x = 4$
When $x = 9$, $y = 4$; when $x = 4$, $y = 9$.
The numbers are 4 and 9.

68.

$$p + h = 86$$
$$595p + 1975h = 93{,}950$$
$$p = 86 - h \quad \text{Solving first equation for } p$$
$$595(86 - h) + 1975h = 93{,}950 \quad \text{Substituting in second equation}$$
$$51{,}170 - 595h + 1975h = 93{,}950$$
$$1380h = 42{,}780$$
$$h = 31$$
$$p = 86 - 31 = 55$$

55 paperbacks and 31 hardcovers were sold.

CONNECTIONS: REASONING — p. 404

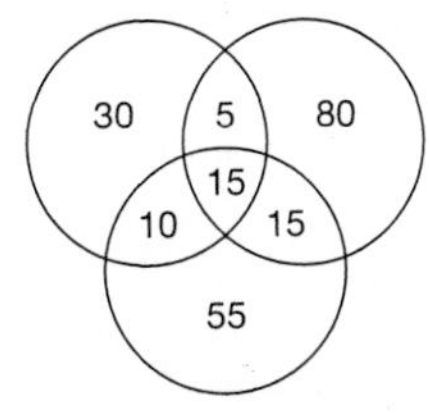

$80 + 30 + 55 = 165$ students

LESSON 9-2 TRY THIS — pp. 406–407

a. 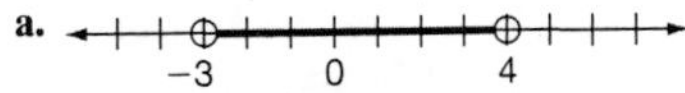

b.

c.

d.

e. $\{x \mid -4 < x \leq 1\}$

f. $5 \not< 3$

$\varnothing$

g.

h. $-2x - 6 > 4$ or $x + 5 > 8$

$-2x > 10$ $\quad x > 3$

$x < -5$ or $x > 3$

$\{x \mid x < -5 \text{ or } x > 3\}$

i. $-5x + 2 > 27$ or $x - 3 > 2$

$-5x > 5$ $\quad x > 5$

$x < -5$ or $x > 5$

$\{x \mid x < -5 \text{ or } x > 5\}$

LESSON 9-2 EXERCISES — pp. 408–409

1.

2.

3.

4.

5.

6.

7. $3 < x + 2$ and $x + 2 < 5$

$1 < x$ and $x < 3$

$\{x \mid 1 < x < 3\}$

8. $-4 \leq x - 3$ and $x - 3 < 1$

$-1 \leq x$ and $x < 4$

$\{x \mid -1 \leq x < 4\}$

9. $12 < 2x$ and $2x < 20$

$6 < x$ and $x < 10$

$\{x \mid 6 < x < 10\}$

10. $-18 < 3x$ and $3x < 3$

$-6 < x$ and $x < 1$

$\{x \mid -6 < x < 1\}$

11. $-20 \leq 5x$ and $5x \leq 15$

$-4 \leq x$ and $x \leq 3$

$\{x \mid -4 \leq x \leq 3\}$

12. $7 < 2x + 5$ and $2x + 5 < 17$

$2 < 2x$ and $2x < 12$

$1 < x$ and $x < 6$

$\{x \mid 1 < x < 6\}$

13. $19 \leq 5x + 4$ and $5x + 4 \leq 24$

$15 \leq 5x$ and $5x \leq 20$

$3 \leq x$ and $x \leq 4$

$\{x \mid 3 \leq x \leq 4\}$

14. $-5 < 7x - 5$ and $7x - 5 \leq 16$

$0 < 7x$ and $7x \leq 21$

$0 < x$ $\quad x \leq 3$

$\{x \mid 0 < x \leq 3\}$

15. $-11 \leq -2x + 1$ and $-2x + 1 \leq -3$

$-12 \leq -2x$ and $-2x \leq -4$

$6 \geq x$ and $x \geq 2$

$\{x \mid 2 \leq x \leq 6\}$

16. $-19 \leq 5x + 6$ and $5x + 6 < -4$

$-25 \leq 5x$ and $5x < -10$

$-5 \leq x$ and $x < -2$

$\{x \mid -5 \leq x < -2\}$

17.

18.

19.

20.

21.

22.

23. $x + 8 < 10$ or $x - 5 > 2$

$x < 2$ or $x > 7$

$\{x \mid x < 2 \text{ or } x > 7\}$

24. $x - 2 < 3$ or $x + 3 > 9$

$x < 5$ or $x > 6$

$\{x \mid x < 5 \text{ or } x > 6\}$

25. $x + 1 \le 0$ or $x - 6 > 3$
$x \le -1$ or $x > 9$
$\{x \mid x \le -1 \text{ or } x > 9\}$

26. $5x < -20$ or $3x > 12$
$x < -4$ or $x > 4$
$\{x \mid x < -4 \text{ or } x > 4\}$

27. $4x < 16$ or $3x > 15$
$x < 4$ or $x > 5$
$\{x \mid x < 4 \text{ or } x > 5\}$

28. $-2x > -14$ or $3x > 21$
$x < 7$ or $x > 7$
$\{x \mid x < 7 \text{ or } x > 7\}$ or $\{x \mid x \neq 7\}$

29. $2x + 7 \le -3$ or $5x - 9 > 6$
$2x \le -10$ or $5x > 15$
$x \le -5$ or $x > 3$
$\{x \mid x \le -5 \text{ or } x > 3\}$

30. $4x - 9 \le -17$ or $2x + 6 > 8$
$4x \le -8$ or $2x > 2$
$x \le -2$ or $x > 1$
$\{x \mid x \le -2 \text{ or } x > 1\}$

31. A: $5x > 20$ or $2x < -20$ becomes $x > 4$ or $x < -10$.
B: $-15 < x + 5 < 9$ becomes $-20 < x < 4$.
C: $x + 3 > 7$ and $x + 10 < 0$ becomes $x > 4$ and $x < -10$.
D: $-3x < -30$ or $x - 7 > -3$ becomes $x > -10$ or $x > 4$.
The answer is A.

32. $x + 2 < 7$ or $x - 1 > -4$
$x < 5$ or $x > -3$
These conditions are satisfied by all numbers on the number line.

33. $x - 5 < -3$ or $x + 8 > 7$
$x < 2$ or $x > -1$
These conditions are satisfied by all numbers on the number line.

34. $3x + 12 \le 6$ and $2x - 4 > 2$
$3x \le -6$ and $2x > 6$
$x \le -2$ and $x > 3$
$\varnothing$
No rational numbers satisfy these conditions.

35. $-2x + 1 > 5$ and $-2x + 10 > 2$
$-2x > 4$ and $-2x > -8$
$x < -2$ and $x < 4$
Solution: $\{x \mid x < -2\}$

36. $-6 > -3x - 6$ and $-3x - 6 \ge 6$
$0 > -3x$ and $-3x \ge 12$
$0 < x$ and $x \le -4$
$\varnothing$
No rational numbers satisfy these conditions.

37. $3x - 8 < 13$ or $-3x + 10 > 5$
$3x < 21$ or $-3x > -5$
$x < 7$ or $x < \frac{5}{3}$
Solution: $\{x \mid x < 7\}$

38. $-5 < x \le 2$ 39. $x \le -5$ or $x > 5$

40. $x \le -2$ or $x > 1$ 41. $4 \le x \le 9$

42. $x < 0$ or $x > 6$ 43. $x < 1$ or $x > 1$

44. $20 < l < 25$ 45. $-230{,}000{,}000 \le M \le -60{,}000{,}000$

46. $1063 \le G \le 2808$ 47. $L < -39$ or $L > 357$

48. No. Let $a = -1$, $b = -2$, $c = 1$, and $d = 0$.
$ac = -1$ and $bd = 0$
-1 is not greater than 0.

49. $x \le 2$ and $x \neq -3$
or $x < -3$ or $(-3 < x$ and $x \le 2)$

50. $x = -4$ or $x > 4$

51. $(x - 3)(x + 5) \ge 0$
$x - 3 \ge 0$ and $x + 5 \ge 0$ or $x - 3 \le 0$ and $x + 5 \le 0$
$x \ge 3$ and $x \ge -5$ or $x \le 3$ and $x \le -5$
$x \ge 3$ or $x \le -5$

52. $(x + 8)(x - 4) < 0$
$x + 8 < 0$ and $x - 4 > 0$ or $x + 8 > 0$ and $x - 4 < 0$
$x < -8$ and $x > 4$ or $x > -8$ and $x < 4$
The first possibility is impossible,
so $x > -8$ and $x < 4$.

53. $x^2 + x - 2 > 0$
$(x + 2)(x - 1) > 0$
$x + 2 > 0$ and $x - 1 > 0$ or $x + 2 < 0$ and $x - 1 < 0$
$x > -2$ and $x > 1$ or $x < -2$ and $x < 1$
$x > 1$ or $x < -2$

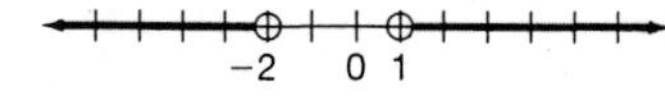

54. $x^2 - x - 6 \le 0$
$(x - 3)(x + 2) \le 0$
$x - 3 \le 0$ and $x + 2 \ge 0$ or $x - 3 \ge 0$ and $x + 2 \le 0$
$x \le 3$ and $x \ge -2$ or $x \ge 3$ and $x \le -2$
The second possibility is impossible,
so $x \le 3$ and $x \ge -2$.

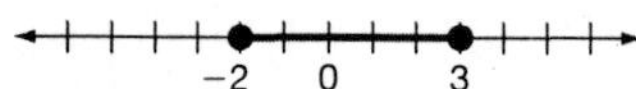

55. 2, 0; 2

56. 5, 3, 1, 0; 5

57. 9, 6; 9

58. $m = \frac{2 - 1}{4 - (-3)} = \frac{1}{7}$
$y = \frac{1}{7}x + b$
$1 = \frac{1}{7}(-3) + b$
$\frac{10}{7} = b$
Equation: $y = \frac{1}{7}x + \frac{10}{7}$

59. $m = \frac{1 - 5}{-2 - 0} = \frac{-4}{-2} = 2$
$y = 2x + b$
$5 = 2 \cdot 0 + b$
$5 = b$
Equation: $y = 2x + 5$

60. $x + y = -1$
$x - y = 3$
$2x = 2$ Adding
$x = 1$
$1 + y = -1$
$y = -2$ $(1, -2)$

61. $4x - 2y = 18$ ①
$x + 3y = -20$ ②
$x = -3y - 20$ Solving ② for x
$4(-3y - 20) - 2y = 18$ Substituting in ①
$-12y - 80 - 2y = 18$
$-14y = 98$
$y = -7$
$x = -3(-7) - 20 = 1$ $(1, -7)$

62. $4x + 5y = -1$ ①
$2x - 3y = 5$ ②
$-4x + 6y = -10$ Multiplying ② by -2
$4x + 5y = -1$ ①
$11y = -11$ Adding
$y = -1$
$2x - 3(-1) = 5$
$2x + 3 = 5$
$2x = 2$
$x = 1$ $(1, -1)$

63. $n + d = 41$ ①
$5n + 10d = 340$ ②
$-5n - 5d = -205$ Multiplying ① by -5
$5d = 135$
$d = 27$
$n + 27 = 41$
$n = 14$
14 nickels and 27 dimes

64. Let x = first number, y = second number.
$x - y = 8$
$x = 8 + y$
$xy = 65$
$(8 + y)y = 65$
$8y + y^2 = 65$
$y^2 + 8y - 65 = 0$
$(y + 13)(y - 5) = 0$
$y + 13 = 0$ or $y - 5 = 0$
$y = -13$ or $y = 5$
If $y = -13$, $x = 8 + (-13) = -5$.
If $y = 5$, $x = 8 + 5 = 13$.
The solutions are $(5, 13)$ and $(-5, -13)$.

CONNECTIONS: REASONING p. 410

1. False **2.** True **3.** True **4.** False **5.** True

LESSON 9-3 TRY THIS p. 411

a. $|x + 8| = 6$
$x + 8 = 6$ or $x + 8 = -6$
$x = -2$ or $x = -14$

b. $|x - 6| = 10$
$x - 6 = 10$ or $x - 6 = -10$
$x = 16$ or $x = -4$

c. $|4x + 9| = -7$
Absolute value is positive or zero.
Solution: ∅

LESSON 9-3 EXERCISES p. 412

1. $|x + 9| = 18$
$x + 9 = 18$ or $x + 9 = -18$
$x = 9$ or $x = -27$

2. $|x - 4| = 9$
$x - 4 = 9$ or $x - 4 = -9$
$x = 13$ or $x = -5$

3. $|x + 11| = 6$
$x + 11 = 6$ or $x + 11 = -6$
$x = -5$ or $x = -17$

4. $|m - 7| = 23$
$m - 7 = 23$ or $m - 7 = -23$
$m = 30$ or $m = -16$

5. $|x - 10| = -8$
Absolute value is positive or zero.
Solution: ∅

6. $|x + 17| = 2$
$x + 17 = 2$ or $x + 17 = -2$
$x = -15$ or $x = -19$

7. $|2x - 4| = 6$
$2x - 4 = 6$ or $2x - 4 = -6$
$2x = 10$ $2x = -2$
$x = 5$ or $x = -1$

8. $|4b - 11| = 5$
$4b - 11 = 5$ or $4b - 11 = -5$
$4b = 16$ $4b = 6$
$b = 4$ or $b = \frac{3}{2}$

9. $|7x - 2| = 5$
$7x - 2 = 5$ or $7x - 2 = -5$
$7x = 7$ $7x = -3$
$x = 1$ or $x = -\frac{3}{7}$

10. $|8x + 3| = -27$
Absolute value is positive or zero.
Solution: ∅

11. $|5x - 9| = 1$
$5x - 9 = 1$ or $5x - 9 = -1$
$5x = 10$ $5x = 8$
$x = 2$ or $x = \frac{8}{5}$

12. $|4x + 3| = 67$
$4x + 3 = 67$ or $4x + 3 = -67$
$4x = 64$ $4x = -70$
$x = 16$ or $x = -\frac{70}{4} = -\frac{35}{2}$

13. $|2y - 6| = -9$
Absolute value is positive or zero.
Solution: ∅

14. $|4x + 3| = -5$
Absolute value is positive or zero.
Solution: ∅

15. $|3x + 1| = 0.5$
$3x + 1 = 0.5$ or $3x + 1 = -0.5$
$3x = -0.5$ $3x = -1.5$
$x = -\frac{0.5}{3} = -\frac{1}{6}$ or $x = -\frac{1.5}{3} = -\frac{1}{2}$

16. $|5x + 8| = \frac{1}{2}$
$5x + 8 = \frac{1}{2}$ or $5x + 8 = -\frac{1}{2}$
$5x = -\frac{15}{2}$ $5x = -\frac{17}{2}$
$x = -\frac{3}{2}$ or $x = -\frac{17}{10}$

17. $|2r - 1| = \frac{1}{4}$
$2r - 1 = \frac{1}{4}$ or $2r - 1 = -\frac{1}{4}$
$2r = \frac{5}{4}$ or $2r = \frac{3}{4}$
$r = \frac{5}{8}$ or $r = \frac{3}{8}$

18. $\left|\frac{1}{3}x - 9\right| = 10$
$\frac{1}{3}x - 9 = 10$ or $\frac{1}{3}x - 9 = -10$
$\frac{1}{3}x = 19$ $\frac{1}{3}x = -1$
$x = 57$ or $x = -3$

19. $|0.2x + 1| = 0.8$
$0.2x + 1 = 0.8$ or $0.2x + 1 = -0.8$
$0.2x = -0.2$ $0.2x = -1.8$
$x = -1$ or $x = -9$

20. $|4.2x - 1.4| = 7$
$4.2x - 1.4 = 7$ or $4.2x - 1.4 = -7$
$4.2x = 8.4$ $\quad 4.2x = -5.6$
$x = 2$ or $x = -\frac{4}{3}$

21. $|5x + 0.2| = 1.2$
$5x + 0.2 = 1.2$ or $5x + 0.2 = -1.2$
$5x = 1$ $\quad 5x = -1.4$
$x = 0.2$ or $x = -0.28$

22. $|2x + 5| - 9 = 12$
$2x + 5 = 21$ or $2x + 5 = -21$
$2x = 16$ $\quad 2x = -26$
$x = 8$ or $x = -13$ $\quad \{8, -13\}$

23. $|3y - 2| + 4 = 21$
$3y - 2 = 17$ or $3y - 2 = -17$
$3y = 19$ $\quad 3y = -15$
$y = \frac{19}{3}$ or $y = -5$ $\quad \left\{\frac{19}{3}, -5\right\}$

24. $|2 - a| - 3 = 1$
$|2 - a| = 4$
$2 - a = 4$ or $2 - a = -4$
$a = -2$ or $a = 6$ $\quad \{6, -2\}$

25. $8 - |1 - y| = 7$
$1 = |1 - y|$
$1 - y = 1$ or $1 - y = -1$
$y = 0$ or $y = 2$ $\quad \{0, 2\}$

26. $3|y + 6| = 6$
$y + 6 = 2$ or $y + 6 = -2$
$y = -4$ or $y = -8$ $\quad \{-4, -8\}$

27. $4|t + 3| = 16$
$t + 3 = 4$ or $t + 3 = -4$
$t = 1$ or $t = -7$ $\quad \{1, -7\}$

28. $8 + |2c - 1| = 4$
$|2c - 1| = -4$
$\varnothing$

29. $3|b - 2| + 7 = 10$
$3|b - 2| = 3$
$b - 2 = 1$ or $b - 2 = -1$
$b = 3$ or $b = 1$ $\quad \{3, 1\}$

30. $4|3 - z| - 8 = 8$
$4|3 - z| = 16$
$3 - z = 4$ or $3 - z = -4$
$z = -1$ or $z = 7$ $\quad \{-1, 7\}$

31. $10 + |5x + 2| = 7$
$|5x + 2| = -3$
$\varnothing$

32. $6 - |3y - 2| = 10$
$-4 = |3y - 2|$
$\varnothing$

33. $-|x + 1| = -2$
$|x + 1| = 2$
$x + 1 = 2$ or $x + 1 = -2$
$x = 1$ or $x = -3$ $\quad \{1, -3\}$

34. $|x + 3| = 3$

35. ① If $x - 4 \geq 0$, $x - 4 = x - 4$
$x \geq 4$, $\quad$ So $x \geq 4$
or ② If $x - 4 \leq 0$, $x - 4 = -(x - 4)$
$x \leq 4$, $x - 4 = -x + 4$
$2x = 8$
$x = 4$

Solution: $\{x | x \geq 4\}$

36. $|3x| = |4x - 1|$
① $3x = 4x - 1$
$x = 1$
or ② $3x = -(4x - 1)$
$3x = -4x + 1$
$7x = 2$
$x = \frac{1}{7}$

Solution: $\left\{1, \frac{1}{7}\right\}$

37. $|2y| = |3y + 2| + 1$
① If $2y \geq 0$ ($y \geq 0$), then $|2y| = 2y$.
$2y = |3y + 2| + 1$
$2y - 1 = |3y + 2|$
$3y + 2 = 2y - 1$ or $3y + 2 = -(2y - 1)$
$y = -3$ or $3y + 2 = -2y + 1$
$5y = -1$
$y = -\frac{1}{5}$

Neither solution is correct because $y \geq 0$.
② If $2y < 0$ ($y < 0$), then $|2y| = -2y$.
$-2y = |3y + 2| + 1$
$-2y - 1 = |3y + 2|$
$3y + 2 = -2y - 1$ or $3y + 2 = -(-2y - 1)$
$5y = -3$ or $3y + 1 = 2y + 1$
$y = -\frac{3}{5}$ or $y = -1$

Both values are less than zero, so the solution is $\left\{\frac{-3}{5}, -1\right\}$.

38. $x - 2y = 1$
$-2y = -x + 1$
$y = \frac{1}{2}x - \frac{1}{2}$
$m = \frac{1}{2}, b = -\frac{1}{2}$

39. $-4x - y = 7$
$-y = 4x + 7$
$y = -4x - 7$
$m = -4, b = -7$

40. $3x = y - 4$
$y = 3x + 4$
$m = 3, b = 4$

41. $5y + 4 = 2x - 1$
$5y = 2x - 5$
$y = \frac{2}{5}x - 1$
$m = \frac{2}{5}, b = -1$

42. $3x - 5 = -4y + 7$
$4y = -3x + 12$
$y = -\frac{3}{4}x + 3$
$m = -\frac{3}{4}, b = 3$

43. $2x^3 - 4x^2 - 6x = 2x(x^2 - 2x - 3)$
$= 2x(x - 3)(x + 1)$

44. $2y^2 - 9y + 4 = (2y - 1)(y - 4)$

45. $9a^2 - 4 = (3a + 2)(3a - 2)$

46. $3y + 4x = -5$ ①
$x = y + 4$ ②
$3y + 4(y + 4) = -5$ $\quad$ Substituting ② in ①
$3y + 4y + 16 = -5$
$7y + 16 = -5$
$7y = -21$
$y = -3$
$x = -3 + 4 = 1$ $\quad \{1, -3\}$

47. $2x + y = -2$ ①
$y - x = -5$ ②
$y = x - 5$ $\quad$ Solving ② for y
$2x + (x - 5) = -2$ $\quad$ Substituting in ①
$3x - 5 = -2$
$3x = 3$
$x = 1$
$y = 1 - 5 = -4$ $\quad \{1, -4\}$

48. $3x - y = 2$
$\underline{2x + y = 3}$
$5x \quad = 5$ $\quad$ Adding
$x = 1$
$2(1) + y = 3$
$y = 1$ $\quad \{1, 1\}$

49. $(m + 2)(m - 1) = 0$

$m + 2 = 0$ or $m - 1 = 0$

$m = -2$ or $m = 1$ $\{1, -2\}$

50. $a(2a + 6)(a - 5) = 0$

$a = 0$ or $2a + 6 = 0$ or $a - 5 = 0$

$a = 0$ or $2a = -6$ or $a = 5$

$a = 0$ or $a = -3$ or $a = 5$

51. Let R = Roy's age.

$2(R - 8) = 42 - 8$

$2R - 16 = 34$

$2R = 50$

$R = 25$

Roy is 25.

LESSON 9-4 TRY THIS pp. 414–415

a. $\{x \mid -7 < x < 7\}$

b. $\{x \mid -6 < x < 6\}$

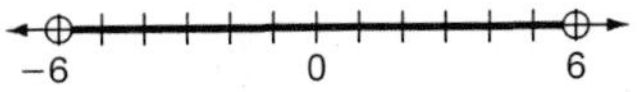

c. $\{x \mid -14 \le x \le 4\}$

d. $-2 \le 3x - 4 \le 2$

$-2 \le 3x - 4$ or $3x - 4 \le 2$

$2 \le 3x$ $\quad 3x \le 6$

$\frac{3}{2} \le x$ or $x \le 2$

$\left\{x \middle| \frac{2}{3} \le x \le 2\right\}$

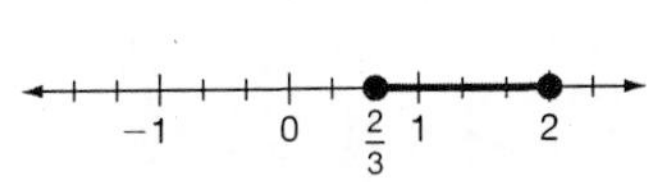

e. $\{x \mid x < -1$ or $x > 1\}$

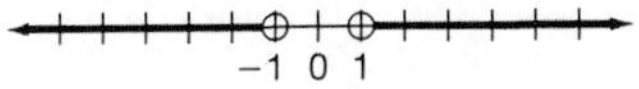

f. $\{x \mid x \le -3$ or $x \ge 3\}$

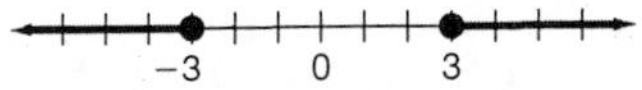

g. $\{x \mid x < -5$ or $x > 5\}$

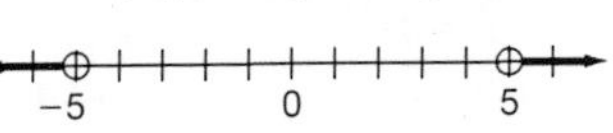

h. $2x > 10$ or $-10 > 2x$

$x > 5$ or $-5 > x$

$\{x \mid x < -5$ or $x > 5\}$

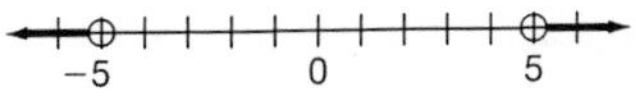

i. $x - 4 \ge 5$ or $-5 \ge x - 4$

$x \ge 9$ or $-1 \ge x$

$\{x \mid x \le -1$ or $x \ge 9\}$

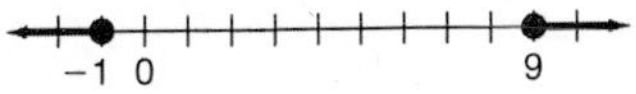

j. $2x + 4 \ge 16$ or $-16 \ge 2x + 4$

$2x \ge 12$ $\quad -20 \ge 2x$

$x \ge 6$ or $-10 \ge x$

$\{x \mid x \le -10$ or $x \ge 6\}$

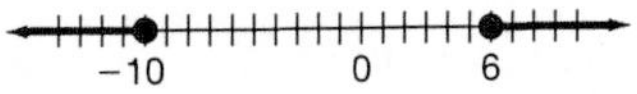

LESSON 9-4 EXERCISES pp. 415–416

1. $|x| < 1$

$x < 1$ and $x > -1$

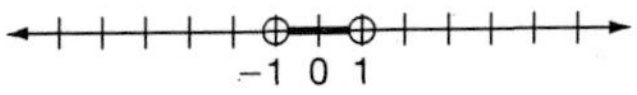

2. $|t| \le 4.5$

$t \le 4.5$ and $t \ge -4.5$

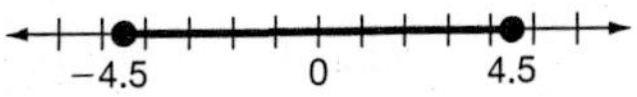

3. $|5x| \le 20$

$5x \le 20$ and $5x \ge -20$

$x \le 4$ and $x \ge -4$

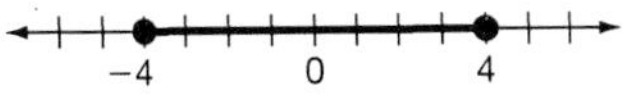

4. $|6x| \le 24$

$6x \le 24$ and $6x \ge -24$

$x \le 4$ and $x \ge -4$

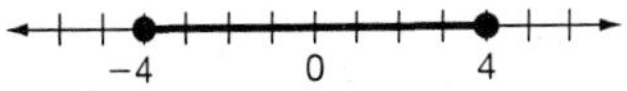

5. $|2x| < 11$

$2x < 11$ and $2x > -11$

$x < \frac{11}{2}$ and $x > -\frac{11}{2}$

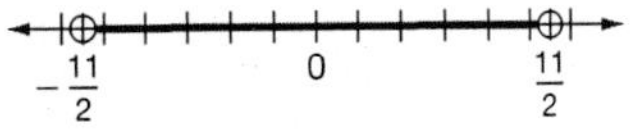

6. $|5y| \le 5$

$5y \le 5$ and $5y \ge -5$

$y \le 1$ and $y \ge -1$

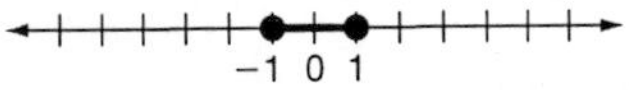

7. $|4t| < 28$

$4t < 28$ and $4t > -28$

$t < 7$ and $t > -7$

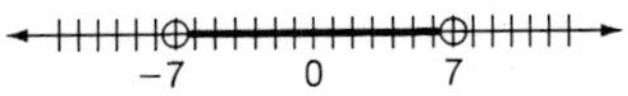

8. $|6x| \le 36$

$6x \le 36$ and $6x \ge -36$

$x \le 6$ and $x \ge -6$

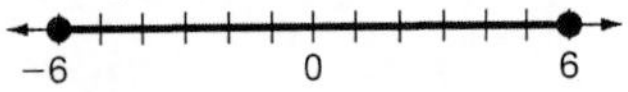

9. $|7x| \le 35$

$7x \le 35$ and $7x \ge -35$

$x \le 5$ and $x \ge -5$

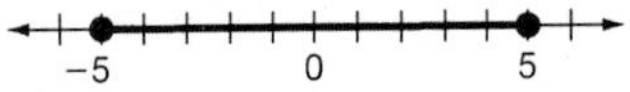

10. $|x - 3| < 12$

$x - 3 < 12$ and $x - 3 > -12$

$x < 15$ and $x > -9$

11. $|x + 2| \le 5$

$x + 2 \le 5$ and $x + 2 \ge -5$

$x \le 3$ and $x \ge -7$

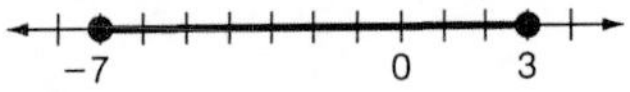

12. $|x - 5| \le 7$

$x - 5 \le 7$ and $x - 5 \ge -7$

$x \le 12$ and $x \ge -2$

13. $|x + 6| < 2$

$x + 6 < 2$ and $x + 6 > -2$

$x < -4$ and $x > -8$

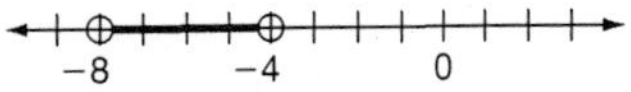

14. $|2y - 4| < 7$

$2y - 4 < 7$ and $2y - 4 > -7$

$2y < 11$ $\quad 2y > -3$

$y < \frac{11}{2}$ and $y > -\frac{3}{2}$

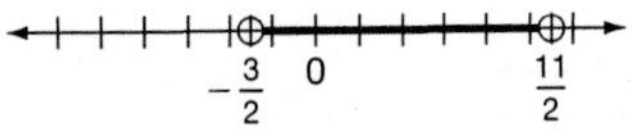

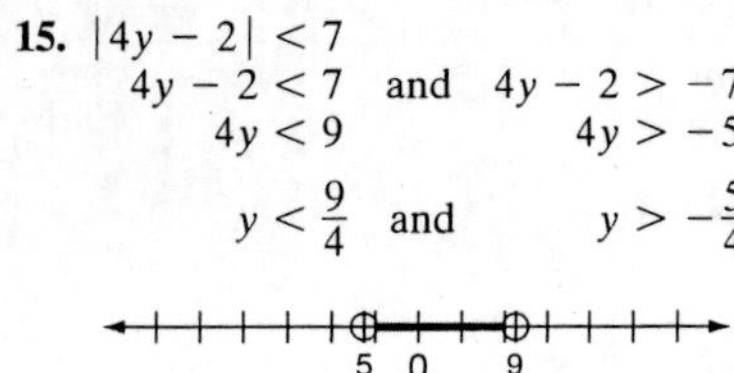

15. $|4y - 2| < 7$
$4y - 2 < 7$ and $4y - 2 > -7$
$4y < 9$ $\quad$ $4y > -5$
$y < \frac{9}{4}$ and $y > -\frac{5}{4}$

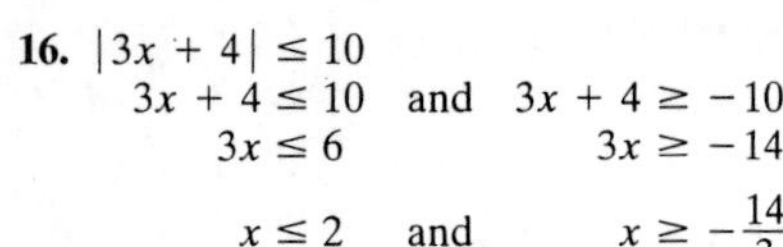

16. $|3x + 4| \leq 10$
$3x + 4 \leq 10$ and $3x + 4 \geq -10$
$3x \leq 6$ $\quad$ $3x \geq -14$
$x \leq 2$ and $x \geq -\frac{14}{3}$

17. $|2x + 1| \leq 5$
$2x + 1 \leq 5$ and $2x + 1 \geq -5$
$2x \leq 4$ $\quad$ $2x \geq -6$
$x \leq 2$ and $x \geq -3$

18. $|4z + 3| \leq 15$
$4z + 3 \leq 15$ and $4z + 3 \geq -15$
$4z \leq 12$ $\quad$ $4z \geq -18$
$z \leq 3$ and $z \geq -\frac{9}{2}$

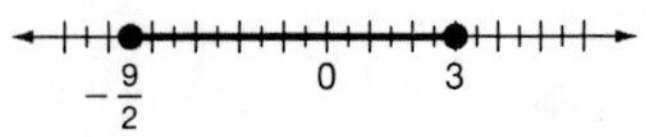

19. $|d - 1| < 0.011$
$d - 1 < 0.011$ and $d - 1 > -0.011$
$d < 1.011$ and $d > 0.989$

20. $|2d - 2| \leq 1.1$
$2d - 2 \leq 1.1$ and $2d - 2 \geq -1.1$
$2d \leq 3.1$ $\quad$ $2d \geq 0.9$
$d \leq 1.55$ and $d \geq 0.45$

21. $|2d - 4| \leq 0.002$
$2d - 4 \leq 0.002$ and $2d - 4 \geq -0.002$
$2d \leq 4.002$ $\quad$ $2d \geq 3.998$
$d \leq 2.001$ and $d \geq 1.999$

22. $|y| > 3$
$y > 3$ or $y < -3$

23. $|t| > 4$
$t > 4$ or $t < -4$

24. $|y| \geq 7$
$y \geq 7$ or $y \leq -7$

25. $|x| \geq 9$
$x \geq 9$ or $x \leq -9$

26. A: $|t + 1| < 5$
$t + 1 < 5$ and $t + 1 > -5$
$t < 4$ and $t > -6$, which can be written $-6 < t < 4$.
B: $|t + 1| > 5$
$t + 1 > 5$ or $t + 1 < -5$
$t > 4$ or $t < -6$
C: $|t - 1| < 5$
$t - 1 < 5$ and $t - 1 > -5$
$t < 6$ and $t > -4$, which can be written $-4 < t < 6$.
D: $|t - 1| > 5$
$t - 1 > 5$ or $t - 1 < -5$
$t > 6$ or $t < -4$
The answer is A.

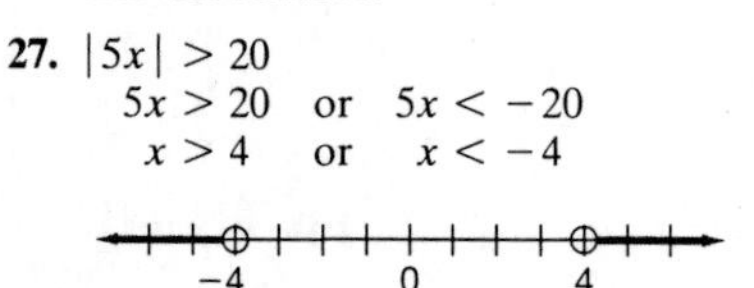

27. $|5x| > 20$
$5x > 20$ or $5x < -20$
$x > 4$ or $x < -4$

28. $|3x| \geq 18$
$3x \geq 18$ or $3x \leq -18$
$x \geq 6$ or $x \leq -6$

29. $|9t| \geq 27$
$9t \geq 27$ or $9t \leq -27$
$t \geq 3$ or $t \leq -3$

30. $|0.5x| > 1$
$0.5x > 1$ or $0.5x < -1$
$x > 2$ or $x < -2$

31. $|x - 1| \geq 6$
$x - 1 \geq 6$ or $x - 1 \leq -6$
$x \geq 7$ or $x \leq -5$

32. $|x + 5| > 9$
$x + 5 > 9$ or $x + 5 < -9$
$x > 4$ or $x < -14$

33. $|x - 9| \geq 11$
$x - 9 \geq 11$ or $x - 9 \leq -11$
$x \geq 20$ or $x \leq -2$

34. $\left|t - \frac{1}{2}\right| \geq 3$
$t - \frac{1}{2} \geq 3$ or $t - \frac{1}{2} \leq -3$
$t \geq 3\frac{1}{2}$ or $t \leq -2\frac{1}{2}$
$t \geq \frac{7}{2}$ or $t \leq -\frac{5}{2}$

35. $|3y + 1| > 4$
$3y + 1 > 4$ or $3y + 1 < -4$
$3y > 3$ $\quad$ $3y < -5$
$y > 1$ or $y < -\frac{5}{3}$

36. $|4x - 3| \geq 13$

$4x - 3 \geq 13$ or $4x - 3 \leq -13$

$4x \geq 16$ $\qquad$ $4x \leq -10$

$x \geq 4$ or $x \leq -\frac{5}{2}$

37. $|6x + 1| \geq 11$

$6x + 1 \geq 11$ or $6x + 1 \leq -11$

$6x \geq 10$ $\qquad$ $6x \leq -12$

$x \geq \frac{5}{3}$ or $x \leq -2$

38. $\left|\frac{1}{5}x - \frac{1}{4}\right| > 1$

$\frac{1}{5}x - \frac{1}{4} > 1$ or $\frac{1}{5}x - \frac{1}{4} < -1$

$20\left(\frac{1}{5}x - \frac{1}{4}\right) > 20$ or $20\left(\frac{1}{5}x - \frac{1}{4}\right) < -20$

$4x - 5 > 20$ $\qquad$ $4x - 5 < -20$

$4x > 25$ $\qquad$ $4x < -15$

$x > \frac{25}{4}$ or $x < -\frac{15}{4}$

39. The second line is not correct. If $|x - 3| > 5$, then $x - 3 > 5$ or $x - 3 < -5$.

40. $|4x - 1| = 7$

$4x - 1 = 7$ or $4x - 1 = -7$

$4x = 8$ or $4x = -6$

$x = 2$ or $x = \frac{-3}{2}$ $\qquad$ $\left\{2, -\frac{3}{2}\right\}$

41. $|2x + 3| \leq 9$

$2x + 3 \leq 9$ and $2x + 3 \geq -9$

$2x \leq 6$ and $2x \geq -12$

$x \leq 3$ and $x \geq -6$ $\qquad$ $\{x \mid -6 \leq x \leq 3\}$

42. $|7x - 4| > 8$

$7x - 4 > 8$ or $7x - 4 < -8$

$7x > 12$ or $7x < -4$

$x > \frac{12}{7}$ or $x < -\frac{4}{7}$

$\left\{x \middle| x < -\frac{4}{7} \text{ or } x > \frac{12}{7}\right\}$

43. $\left|\frac{2y + 1}{3}\right| \geq 5$

$\frac{2y + 1}{3} \geq 5$ or $\frac{2y + 1}{3} \leq -5$

$2y + 1 \geq 15$ or $2y + 1 \leq -15$

$2y \geq 14$ or $2y \leq -16$

$y \geq 7$ or $y \leq -8$

$\{y \mid y \leq -8 \text{ or } y \geq 7\}$

44. $\left|\frac{3x + 2}{4}\right| \leq 5$

$\frac{3x + 2}{4} \leq 5$ and $\frac{3x + 2}{4} \geq -5$

$3x + 2 \leq 20$ and $3x + 2 \geq -20$

$3x \leq 18$ and $3x \geq -22$

$x \leq 6$ and $x \geq -\frac{22}{3}$

$\left\{x \middle| -\frac{22}{3} \leq x \leq 6\right\}$

45. $\left|\frac{13}{4} + 2t\right| = \frac{1}{4}$

$\frac{13}{4} + 2t = \frac{1}{4}$ or $\frac{13}{4} + 2t = -\frac{1}{4}$

$2t = -\frac{12}{4}$ or $2t = -\frac{14}{4}$

$2t = -3$ or $2t = -\frac{7}{2}$

$t = -\frac{3}{2}$ or $t = -\frac{7}{4}$ $\qquad$ $\left\{-\frac{3}{2}, -\frac{7}{4}\right\}$

46. $|3x + 2| + 2 = 3$

$|3x + 2| = 1$

$3x + 2 = 1$ or $3x + 2 = -1$

$3x = -1$ or $3x = -3$

$x = -\frac{1}{3}$ or $x = -1$ $\qquad$ $\left\{-1, -\frac{1}{3}\right\}$

47. $|2b - 4| < -5$

Absolute value always ≥ 0.

Solution: $\varnothing$

48. $|3x + 5| > 0$

$3x + 5 > 0$ or $3x + 5 < 0$

$3x > -5$ or $3x < -5$

$x > -\frac{5}{3}$ or $x < -\frac{5}{3}$ $\qquad$ $\left\{x \middle| x \neq -\frac{5}{3}\right\}$

49. a. $|x + 1| \leq 3$ $\qquad$ **b.** $\left|x - \frac{1}{2}\right| > \frac{5}{2}$

50. $|5x| \geq 20$ or $|2x| \leq 4$

$5x \geq 20$ or $5x \leq -20$ $\qquad$ $2x \leq 4$ and $2x \geq -4$

$x \geq 4$ or $x \leq -4$ or $x \leq 2$ and $x \geq -2$

$\{x \mid x \leq -4$ or $-2 \leq x \leq 2$ or $x \geq 4\}$

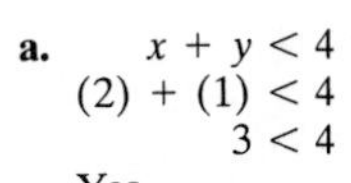

51. $\{11, 13, 17, 19, 23, 29\}$ $\qquad$ **52.** $\{4, 8, 12, 16, 20, 24\}$

53. $\{0, 2\}$ $\qquad$ **54.** $\{-6, -4, -2, 0, 2, 4, 6\}$

55. $\{-2, -1, 0, 1, 2, 4, 6\}$ $\qquad$ **56.** $\{0, 2\}$

57. $\{-6, -4, -2, -1, 0, 1, 2\}$ $\qquad$ **58.** $\{-2, 0, 2\}$

LESSON 9-5 TRY THIS $\qquad$ pp. 417–419

a. $x + y < 4$

$(2) + (1) < 4$

$3 < 4$

Yes

b. $y > 2x + 1$

$(8) > 2(4) + 1$

$8 > 8 + 1$

$8 > 9$

No

c.

d.

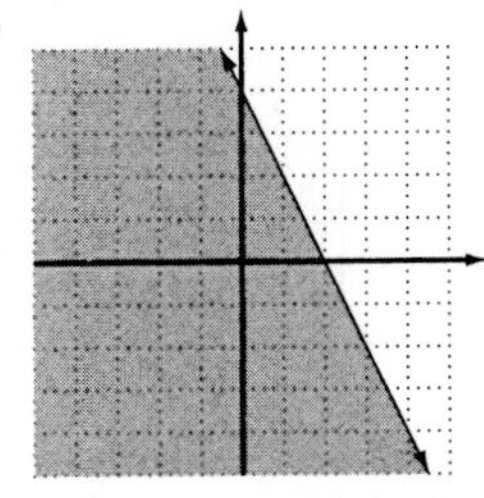

e.

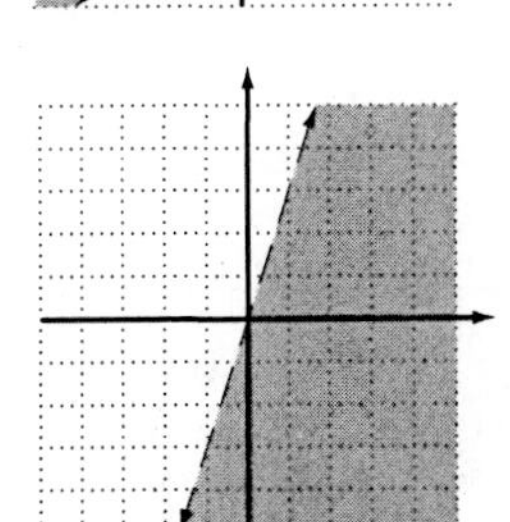

f.

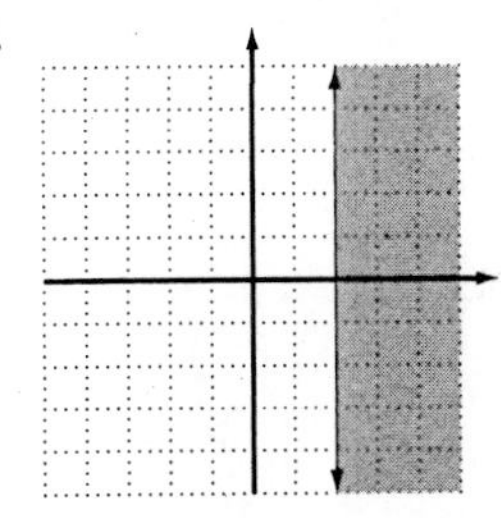

LESSON 9-5 EXERCISES pp. 419–420

1.
$$-x - 3y < 18$$
$$-(-3) - 3(-5) < 18$$
$$3 + 15 < 18$$
$$18 < 18$$
No

2.
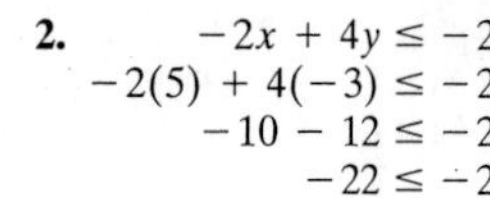
$$-2x + 4y \le -2$$
$$-2(5) + 4(-3) \le -2$$
$$-10 - 12 \le -2$$
$$-22 \le -2$$
Yes

3.
$$7y - 9x > -3$$
$$7\left(-\frac{1}{4}\right) - 9\left(\frac{1}{2}\right) > -3$$
$$-\frac{7}{4} - \frac{9}{2} > -3$$
$$-\frac{7}{4} - \frac{18}{4} > -3$$
$$-\frac{25}{4} > -3$$
$$-6\frac{1}{4} > -3$$
No

4.
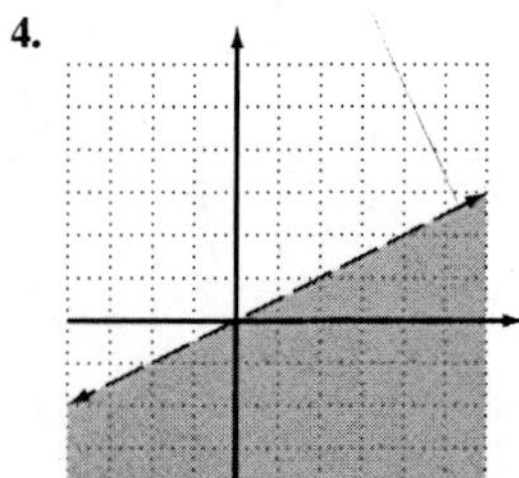

5.
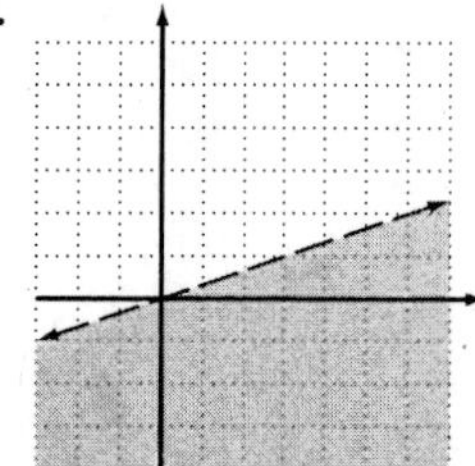

6.
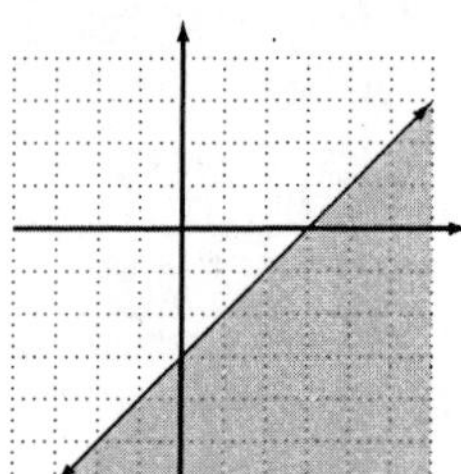

7.
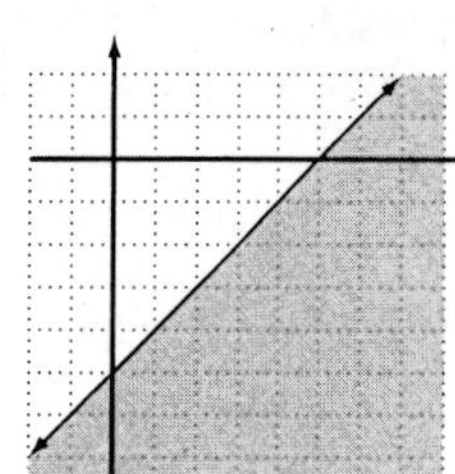

8.
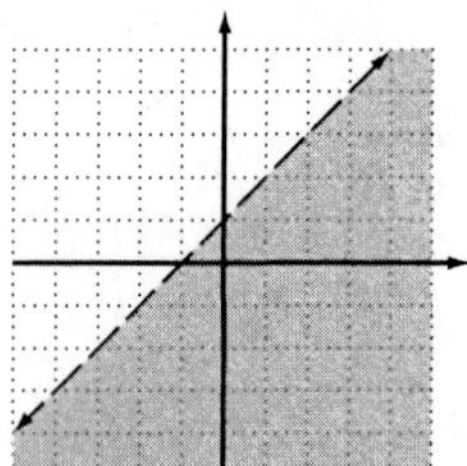

9.
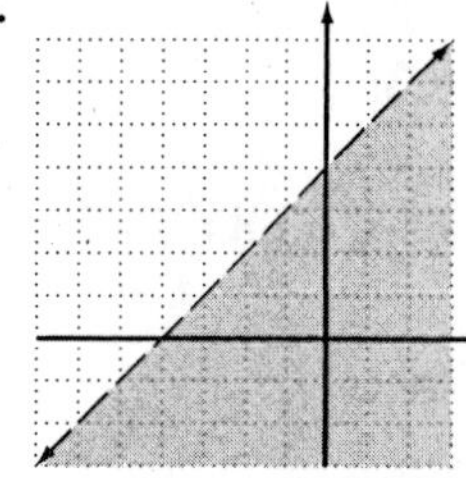

10.
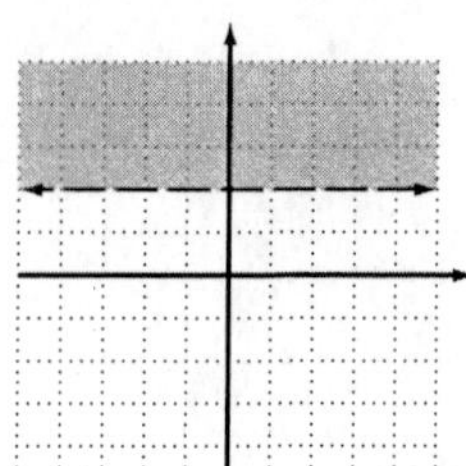

11.
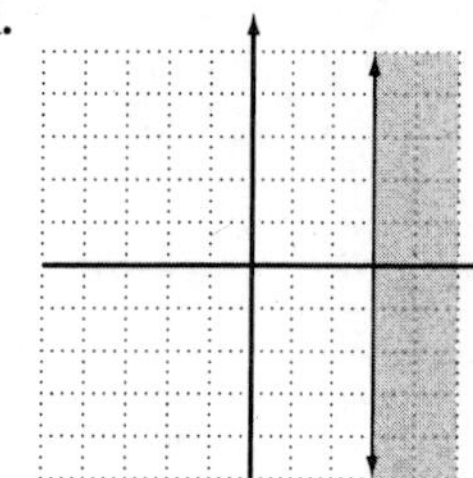

12.
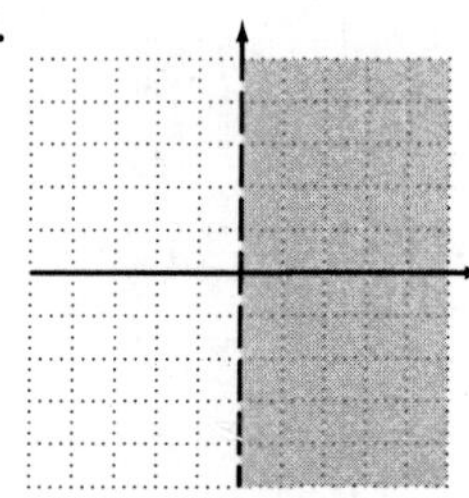

13.
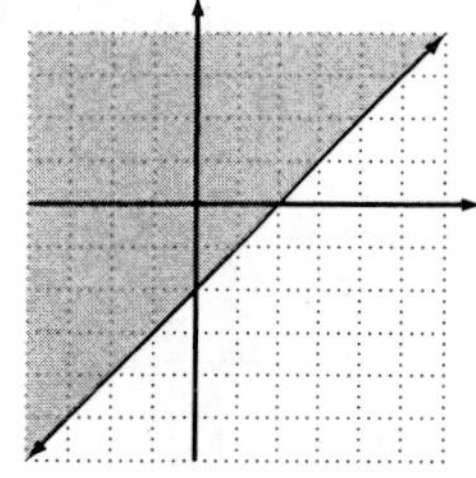

14.
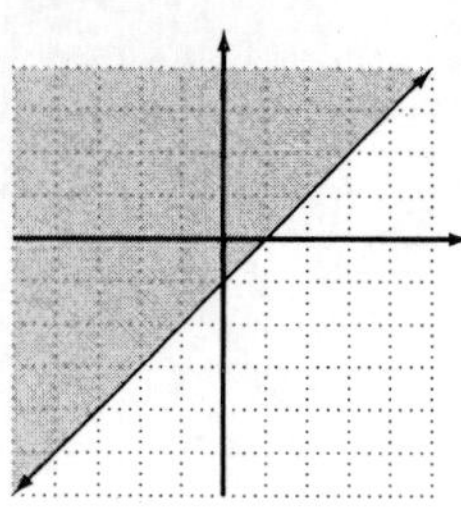

15.
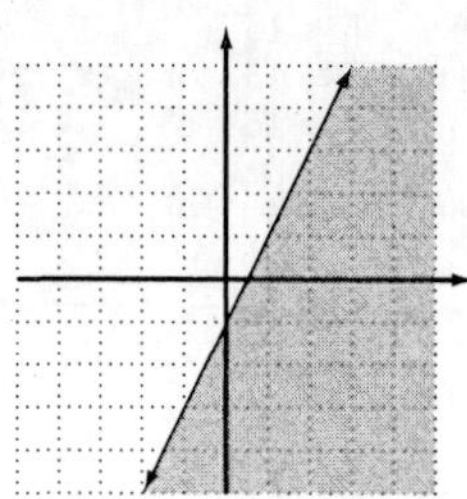

16.
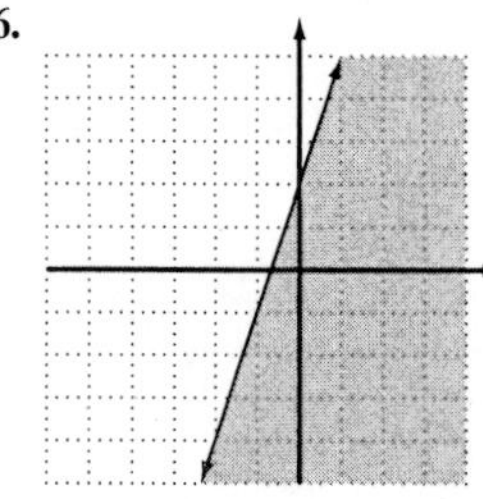

17.
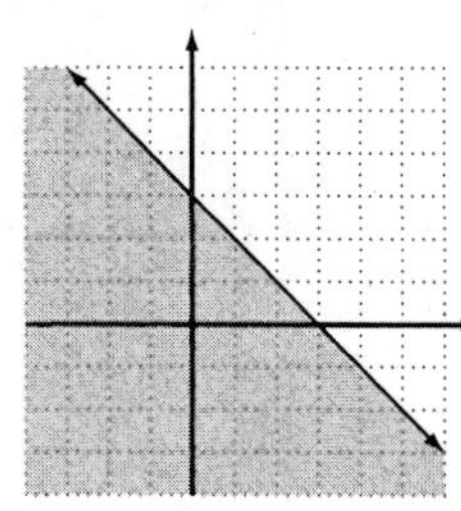

18.
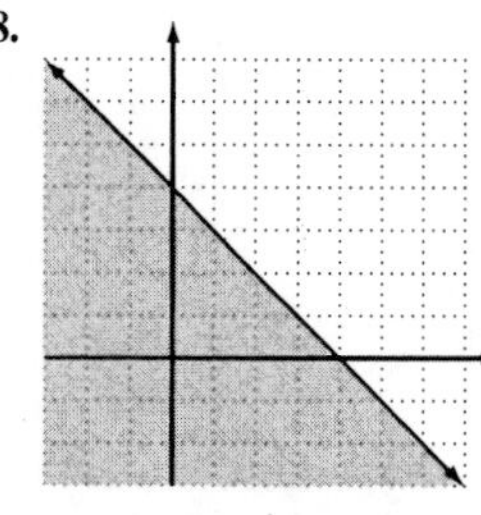

19.
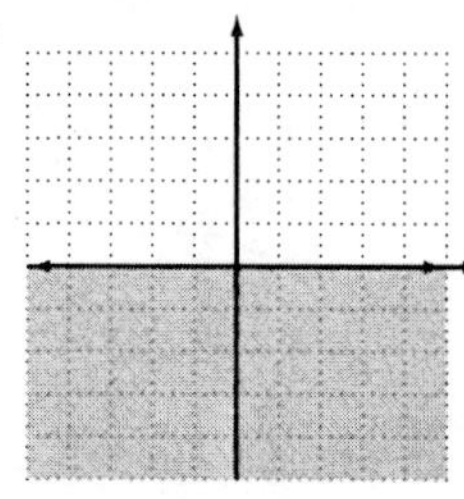

20.
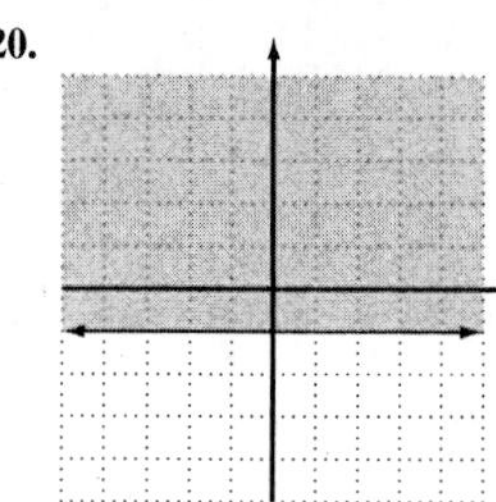

21.
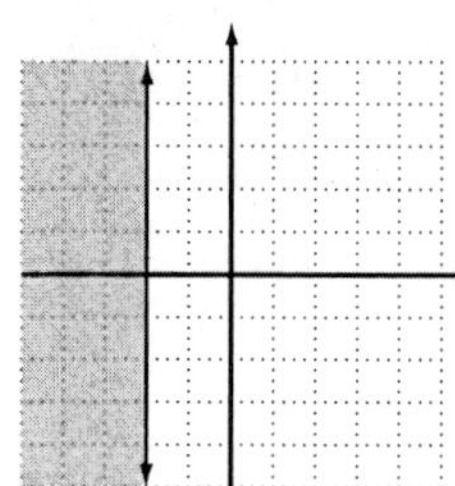

22.
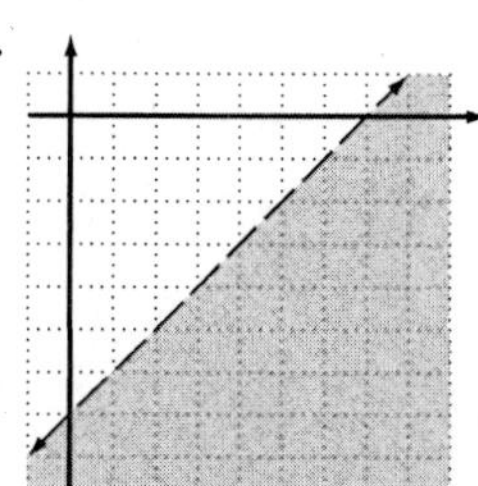

23.
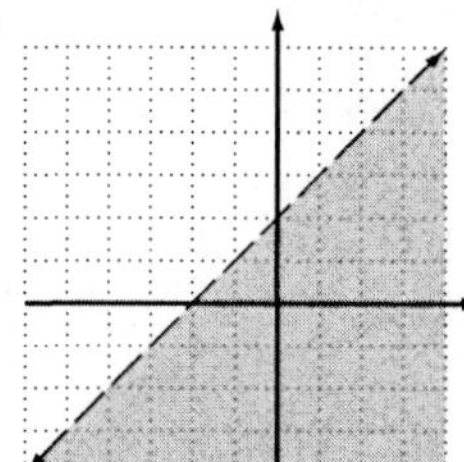

24.
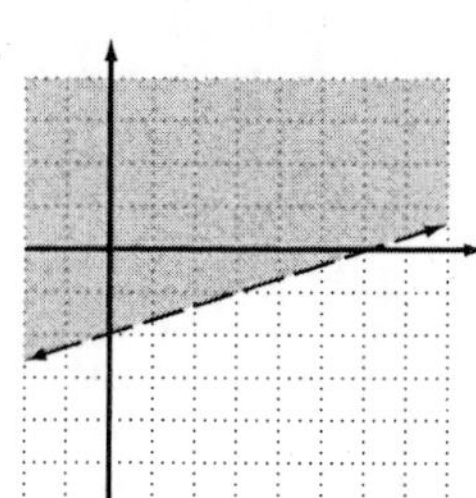

25.
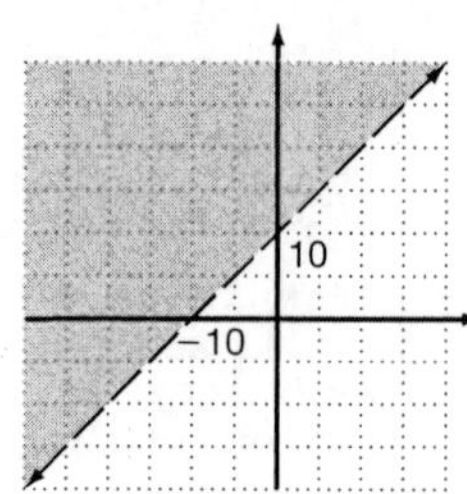

26.
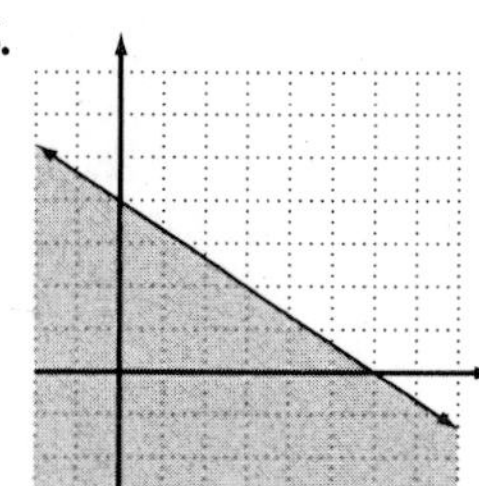

27.
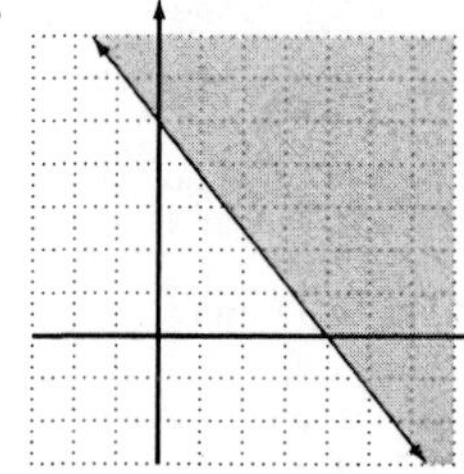

28.

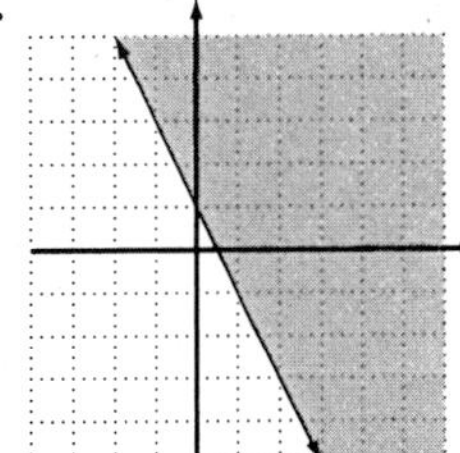

29.

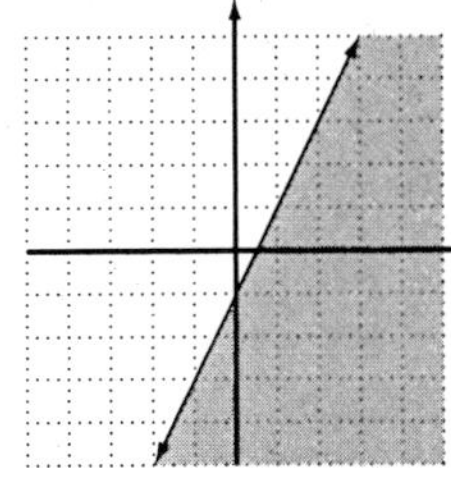

30.

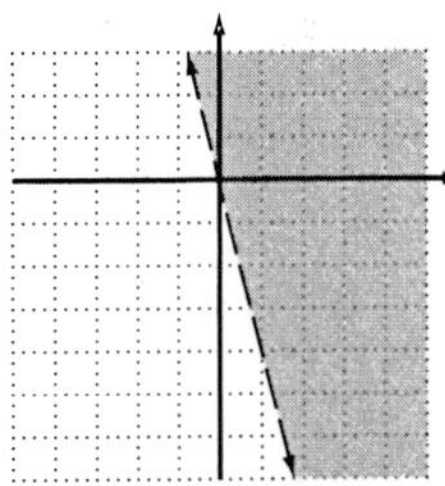

31.

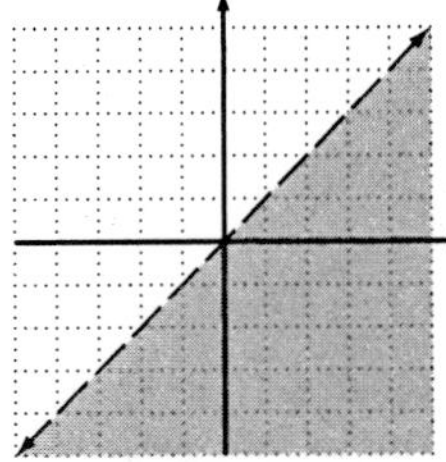

32.

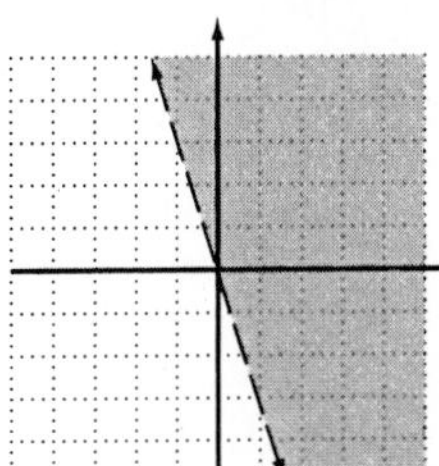

33.

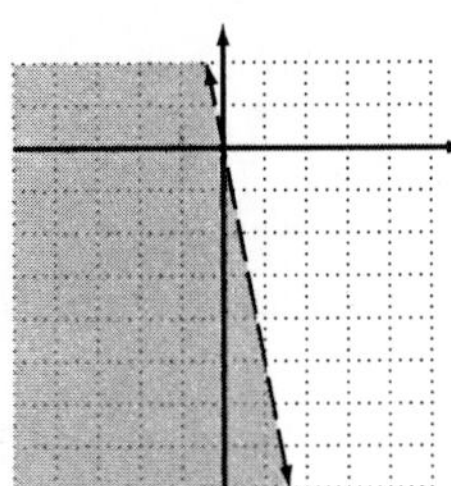

34. The boundary line is $y = 2x - 3$. The inequality $y - 2x > -3$ solved for y becomes $y > 2x - 3$, which has the boundary line $y = 2x - 3$. The answer is D.

35. $y < x + 1$ **36.** $y \leq x - 4$

37. $y > x - 2$ **38.** $y \geq x + 4$

39. $y \leq x - 3$ **40.** $x > -2$

41. $(x \geq 0 \text{ and } y \leq 0)$ or $(x \leq 0 \text{ and } y \geq 0)$; $xy \leq 0$

42.

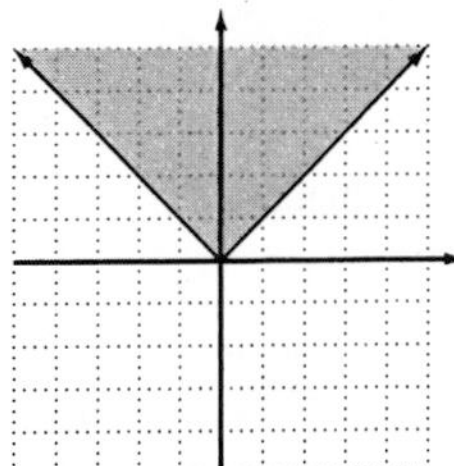

43.

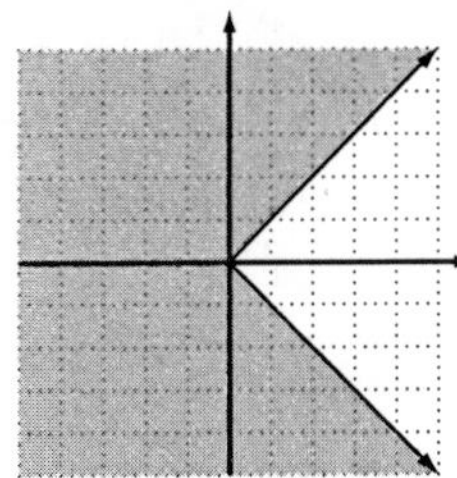

44.

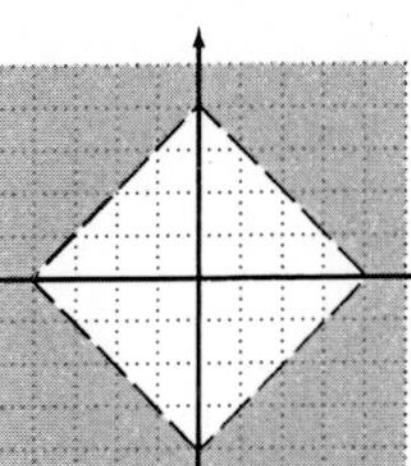

45.

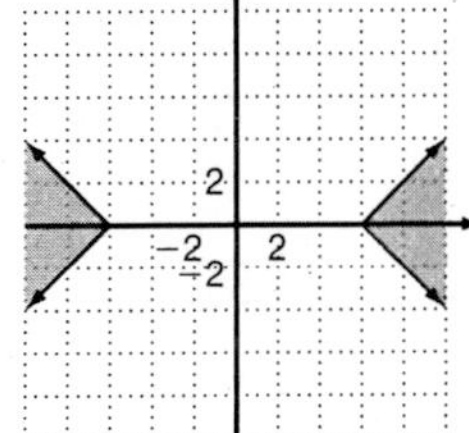

46. −5 0 2

47. −4 −1 0

48. 0 3

49. $5 < x + 8 \leq 13$
$-3 < x \leq 5$

50. $2x + 1 \leq -7$ or $3x - 5 > 4$
$2x \leq -8$ or $3x > 9$
$x \leq -4$ or $x > 3$

51. $m^2 - 15m + 50 = (m - 5)(m - 10)$

52. $2a^2 - 5a - 42 = (2a + 7)(a - 6)$

53. $2x^2 + 3xa + a^2 = (2x + a)(x + a)$

54. $6x^2 + 19x + 15 = (3x + 5)(2x + 3)$

LESSON 9-6 TRY THIS p. 422

a.

b.

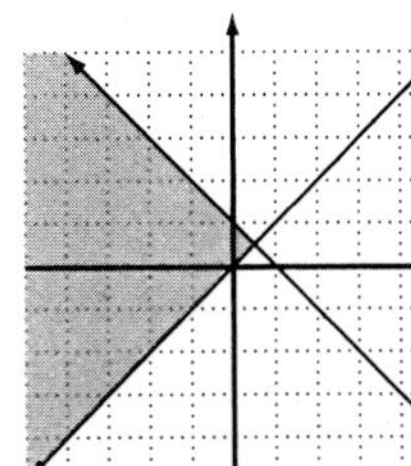

c.

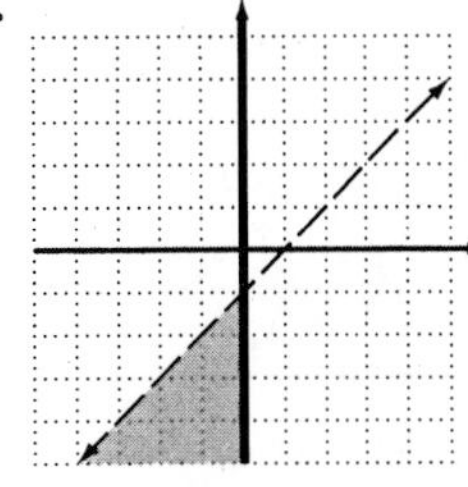

d.

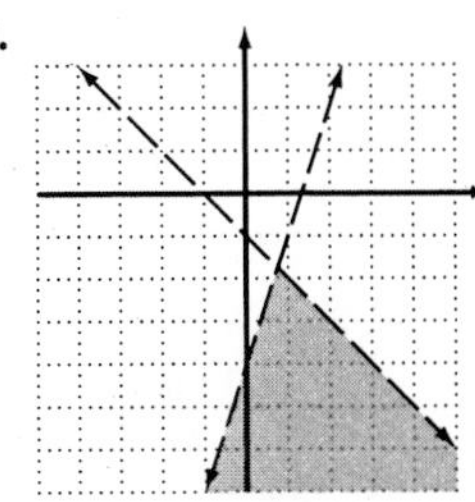

e. i. $0 \leq b \leq 300$
$0 \leq r \leq 400$
$b + r \geq 100$
$b + r \geq 200$

iii. Yes

ii.

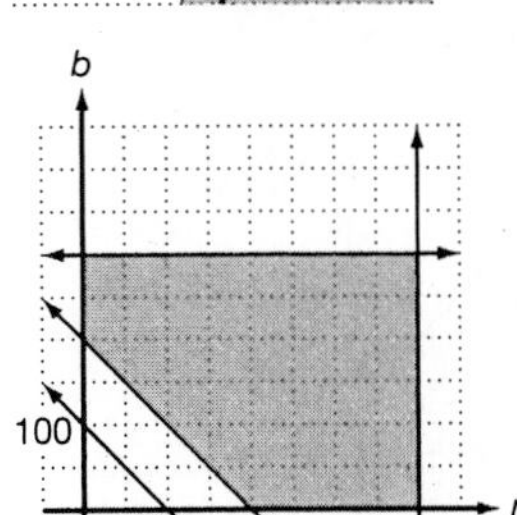

LESSON 9-6 EXERCISES pp. 423–424

1.

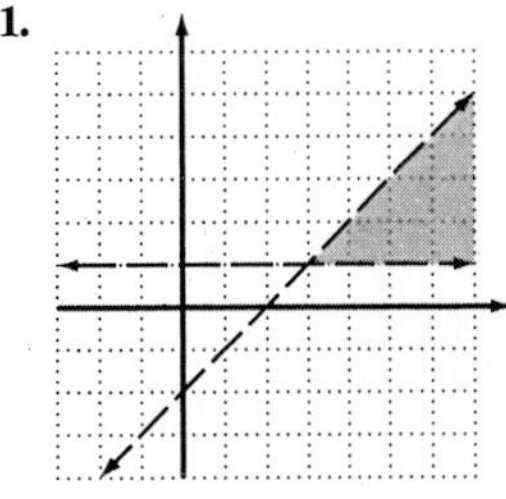

2.

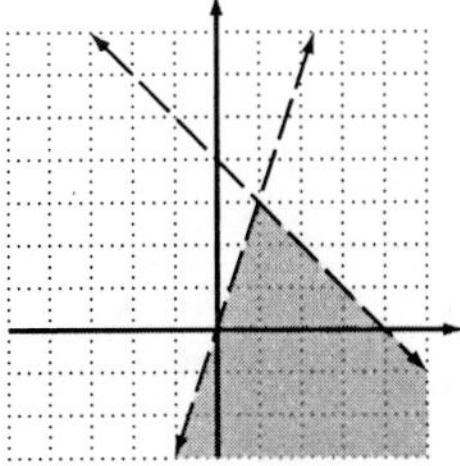

3.

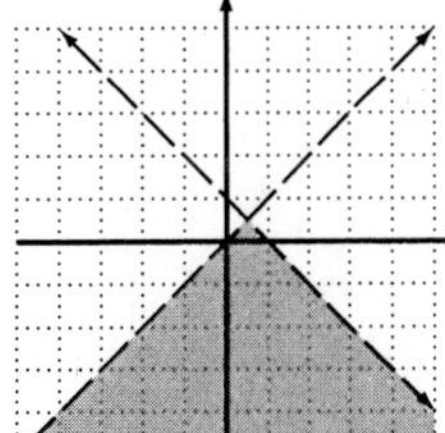

4.

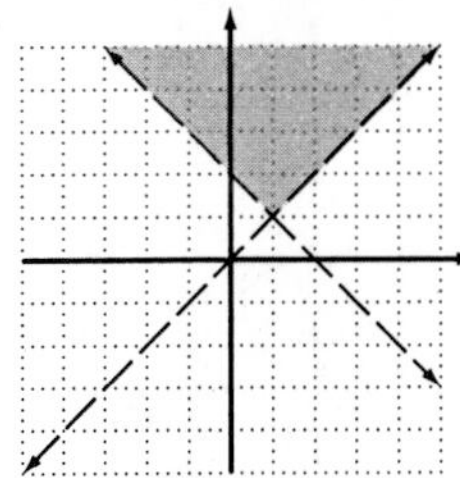

5.

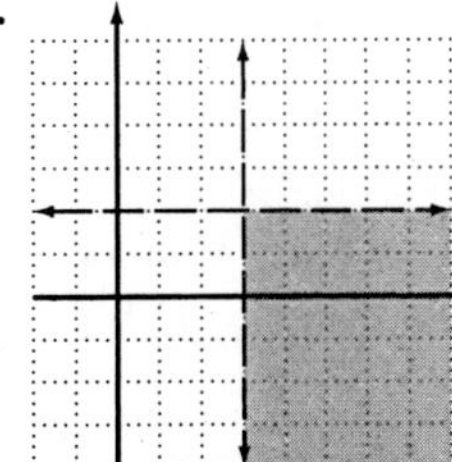

6.

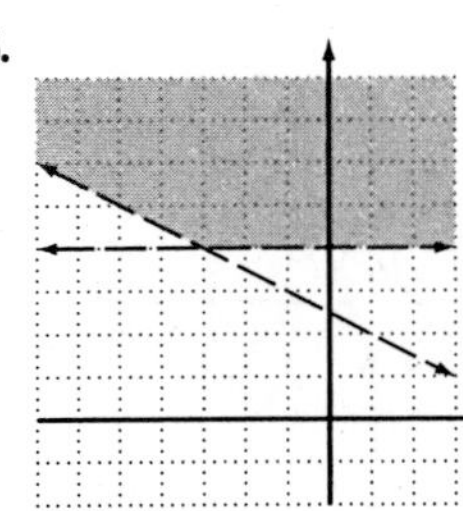

7.

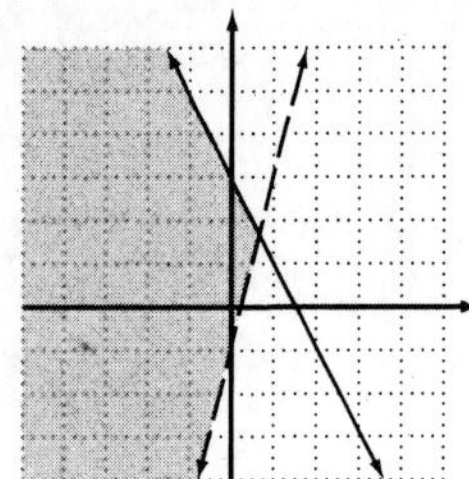

8.

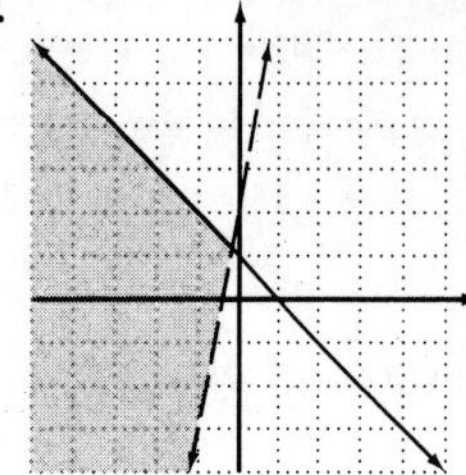

9.

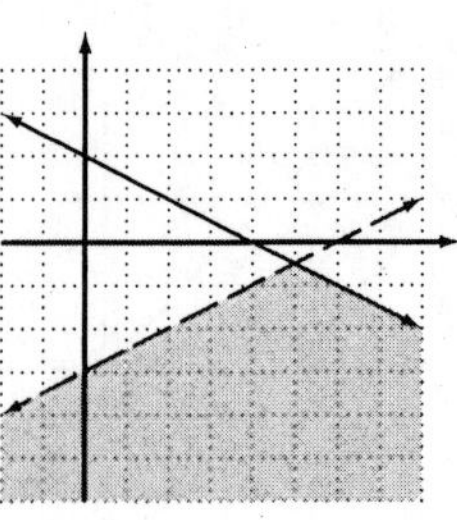

10.

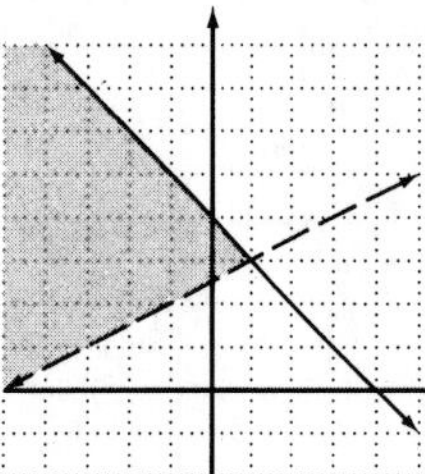

11.

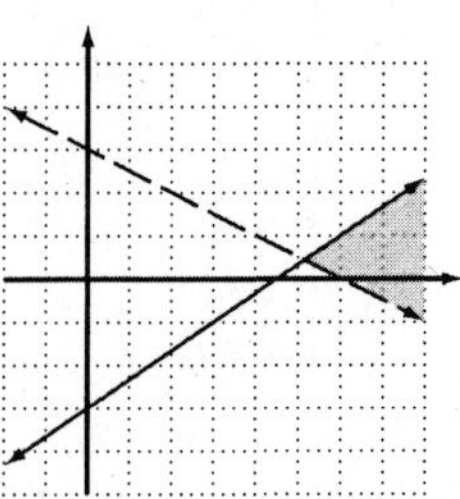

12.

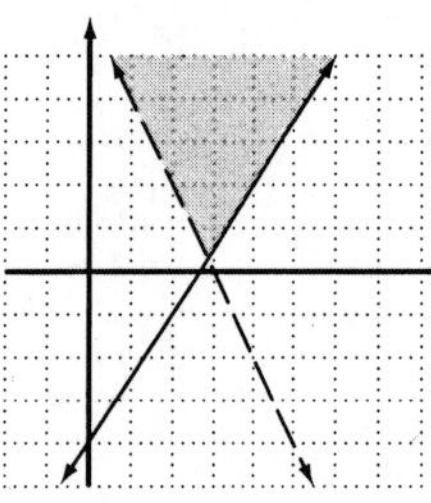

13.

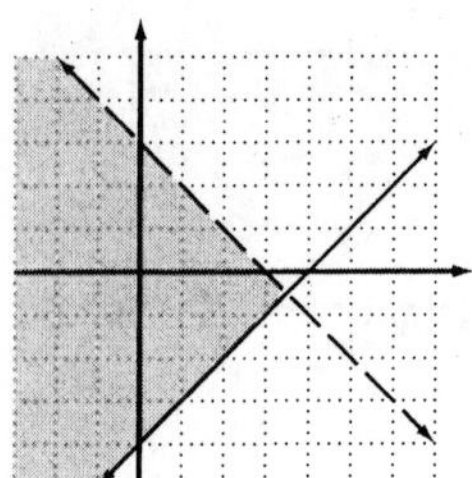

14.

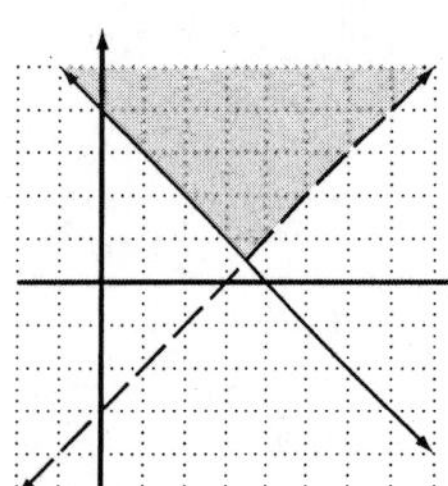

15.

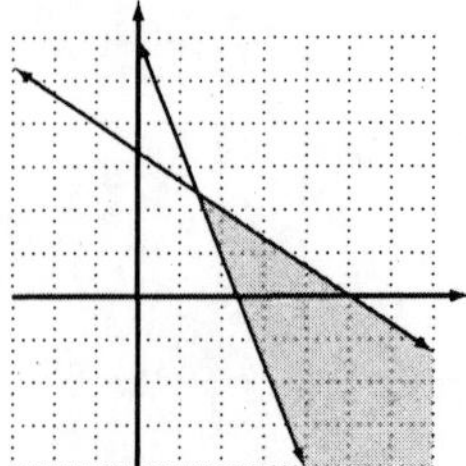

16.

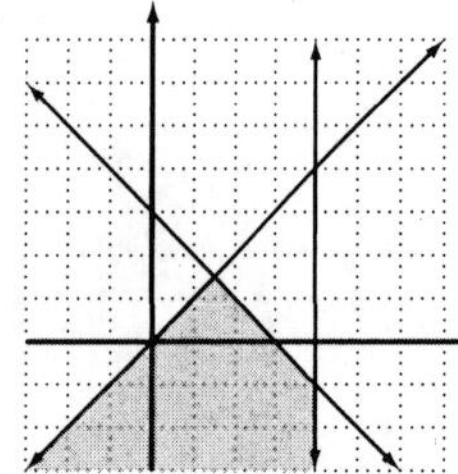

17.

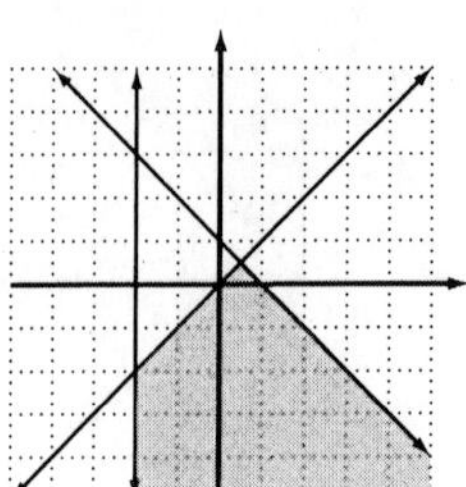

18.

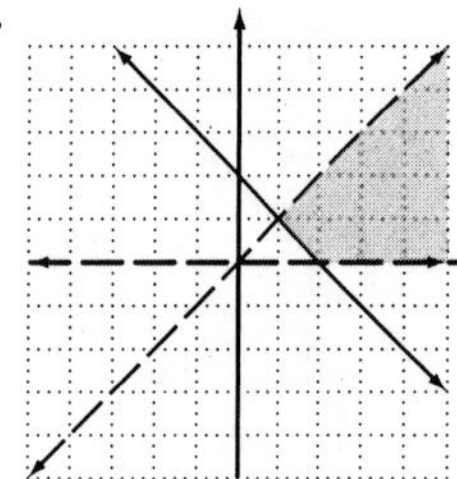

19.

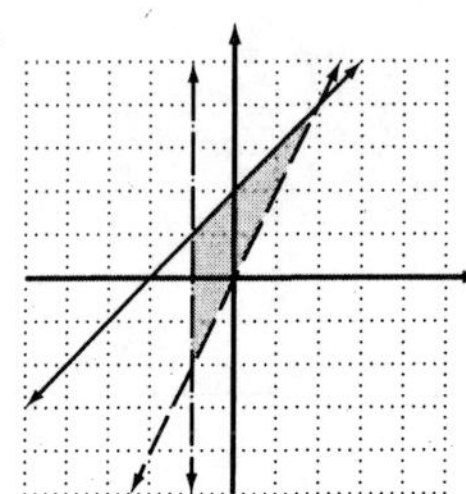

20.

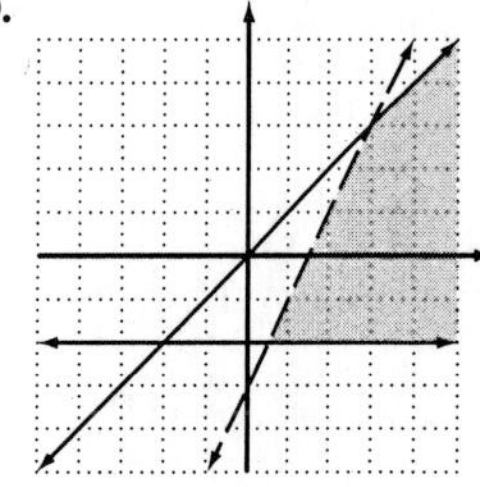

21.

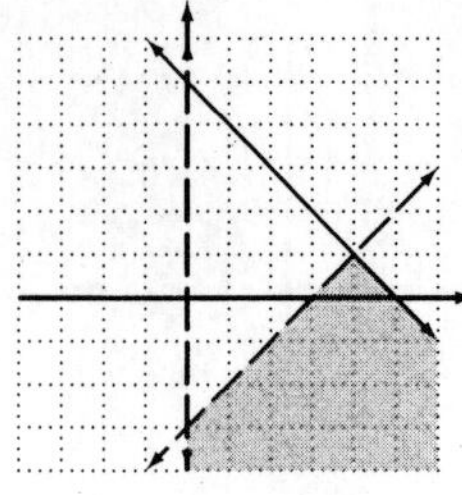

22. a. Let x = number of teachers and y = the number of aides.

$x + y \geq 20$
$x \geq 12$
$y \leq 2x$
$x + y \leq 50$
$x \geq 0, y \geq 0$

b.

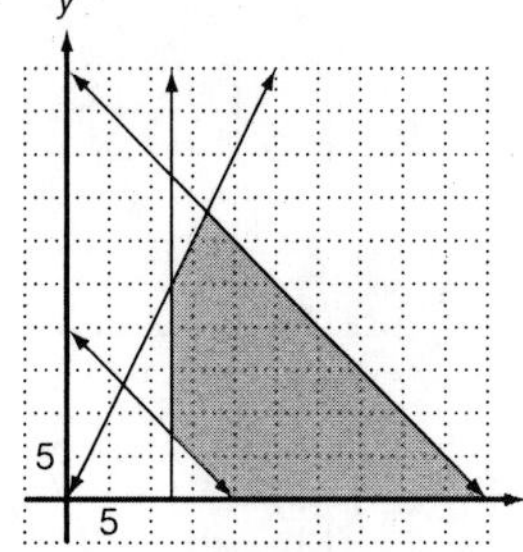

c. No ($x + y = 12 + 5 = 17$, and 17 is not greater than or equal to 20.)

23. a. Let p = the number of rolls of wrapping paper and r = the number of rolls of ribbon.

$2p + 3r < 600$
$p + r \leq 300$
$p \geq r$

b.

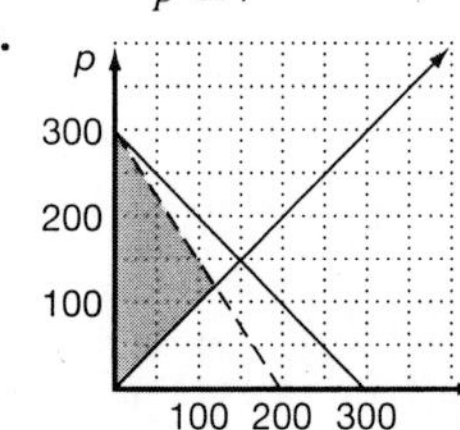

c. No, the total amount spent is not less than $600.

24. $x \geq -2, y \leq -2$ **25.** $y \geq 0, x > y$

26. $y \geq 1, y > x + 2$ **27.** $x < 3, y \leq 2, y \geq \frac{1}{2}x$

28. Answers may vary.
Ex. $0 \leq x \leq 5, 0 \leq y \leq 5$

29.

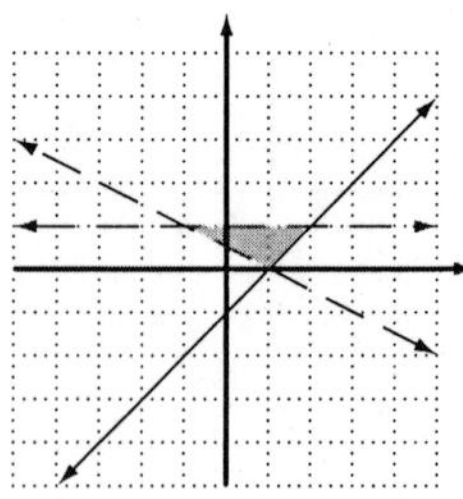

Corners: $(-1, 1), (1, 0), (2, 1)$

30.

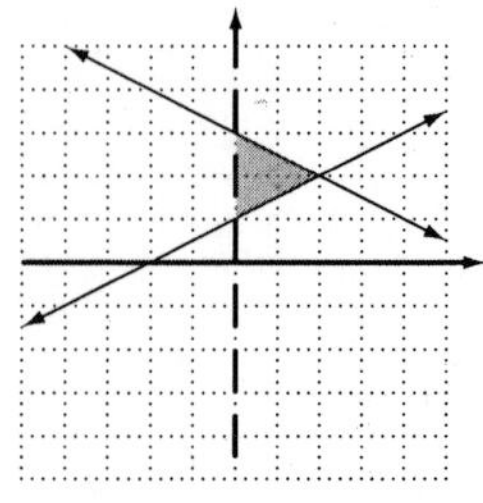

Corners: $(0, 1), (0, 3), (2, 2)$

31.

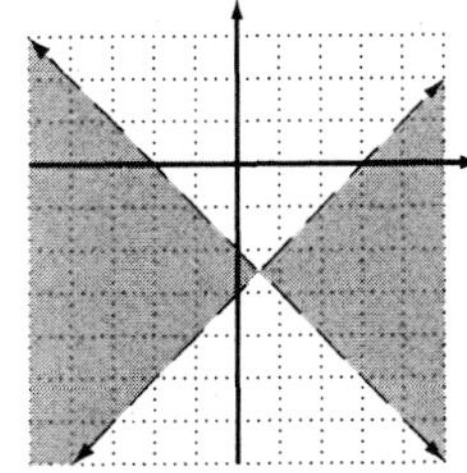

32. $x + 5 \le 16 \quad \text{or} \quad x - 3 > 5$
$x \le 11 \quad \text{or} \quad x > 8$

33. $-7 \le -3x + 2 < -1$
$-9 \le -3x < -3$
$3 \ge x > 1$

34. $|4x| > 8$
$4x > 8 \quad \text{or} \quad 4x < -8$
$x > 2 \quad \text{or} \quad x < -2$

35. $|4x| < 8$
$4x < 8 \quad \text{and} \quad 4x > -8$
$x < 2 \quad \text{and} \quad x > -2$

36. $|2y + 1| > 9$
$2y + 1 > 9 \quad \text{or} \quad 2y + 1 < -9$
$2y > 8 \quad \text{or} \quad 2y < -10$
$y > 4 \quad \text{or} \quad y < -5$

37. $|2y + 1| < 9$
$2y + 1 < 9 \quad \text{and} \quad 2y + 1 > -9$
$2y < 8 \quad \text{and} \quad 2y > -10$
$y < 4 \quad \text{and} \quad y > -5$
or $-5 < y < 4$

38. $x^2 + 3yx + 2y^2 = (x + 2y)(x + y)$

39. $b^2 + 4b + 4 = b^2 + 2 \cdot b \cdot 2 + 4 = (b + 2)^2$

40. $9x^4 - 25y^2 = (3x^2 + 5y)(3x^2 - 5y)$

41. $d + q = 81$ ①
$10d + 25q = 1620$ ②
$d = 81 - q$ Solving ① for d
$10(81 - q) + 25q = 1620$
$810 - 10q + 25q = 1620$
$15q = 810$
$q = 54$
$d = 81 - 54 = 27$
27 dimes and 54 quarters

PREPARING FOR STANDARDIZED TESTS p. 426

1. $(-1 + 1)(-1 + 4) = 0$ $\quad (-1 + 1)^2 = 0$ $\quad$ equal
$(-2 + 1)(-2 + 4) = -2$ $\quad (-2 + 1)^2 = 1$ $\quad$ B > A
(D)

2. $1 = 1$ $\quad 1 \cdot 2 = 2$ $\quad$ B > A
$-2 = -2$ $\quad -2(-1) = 2$ $\quad$ B > A
(B)

3. $1 \cdot 2 = 2$ $\quad 2 \cdot 3 = 6$ $\quad$ B > A
$-3 \cdot -2 = 6$ $\quad -2 \cdot 2 = -4$ $\quad$ A > B
(D)

4. $-3 + (-2) = -5$ $\quad -3 - (-2) = -1$ $\quad$ B > A
$4 + 5 = 9$ $\quad 4 - 5 = -1$ $\quad$ A > B
(D)

5. $5.0 < 5.1$ $\quad$ B > A
(B)

6. $2 = 2$ $\quad -4 \cdot 3 = -12$ $\quad$ A > B
(A)

7. $\frac{-1}{2} = -\frac{1}{2}$ $\quad 2(-1) = -2$ $\quad$ A > B
$\frac{-8}{8} = -1$ $\quad -8(8) = -64$ $\quad$ A > B
(A)

8. $(2 - 2)(2 + 5) = 0$ $\quad (2 - 2) = 0$ $\quad$ equal
$(4 - 2)(4 + 5) = 18$ $\quad (4 - 2) = 2$ $\quad$ A > B
(D)

9. $\frac{1}{-1} = -1$ $\quad -1 = -1$ $\quad$ equal
$\frac{1}{2} = \frac{1}{2}$ $\quad 2 = 2$ $\quad$ B > A
(D)

10. $(a + b) - c = a$
$a + b - c = a$
$b - c = 0$
$b = c$ $\quad$ equal
(C)

CHAPTER 9 WRAP UP pp. 427–428

1. a) $A = \{0, 1, 2, 3, 4, 5, 6, 7, 8\}$
b) $A = \{x \mid x \text{ is a whole number and } x < 9\}$

2. a) $B = \{1, 3, 5, \ldots\}$
b) $B = \{x \mid x \text{ is a whole number and } x \text{ is an odd number}\}$

3. a) $C = \{7, 14, 21, 28\}$
b) $C = \{x \mid x \text{ is a positive multiple of 7 and } x < 30\}$

4. a) $D = \{-4, -3, -2, -1\}$
b) $D = \{x \mid x \text{ is a negative integer and } x > -5\}$

5. $\{2, 4, 8, 12, 16, 20, 32\}$

6. $\{2, 3, 4, 6, 8, 9, 12, 15, 16, 18, 32\}$

7. $\{4, 8, 16\}$ **8.** $\{12\}$ **9.** $W \cap P = P$ **10.** $Z \cup W = Z$

11. −2 0 1

12. −1 0 12

13. −2 0 4

14. $-2 \le x + 3 \quad \text{and} \quad x + 3 < 7$
$-5 \le x \quad \text{and} \quad x < 4$
$-5 \le x < 4$
−5 0 4

15. $-1 \le x + 4 \quad \text{and} \quad x + 4 < 4$
$-5 \le x \quad \text{and} \quad x < 0$
$-5 \le x < 0$
−5 0

16. $12 + 2x < 0 \quad \text{or} \quad -2 - x \le 3$
$2x < -12 \quad -x \le 5$
$x < -6 \quad \text{or} \quad x \ge -5$
−6 −5 0

17. $x + 3 < 4 \quad \text{or} \quad x - 2 > -5$
$x < 1 \quad \text{or} \quad x > -3$
All numbers on the number line
0

18. $|x + 4| = 8$
$x + 4 = 8 \quad \text{or} \quad x + 4 = -8$
$x = 4 \quad \text{or} \quad x = -12$

19. $|3x - 6| = 18$
$3x - 6 = 18 \quad \text{or} \quad 3x - 6 = -18$
$3x = 24 \quad \text{or} \quad 3x = -12$
$x = 8 \quad \text{or} \quad x = -4$

20. $|5x + 3| = 21$
$5x + 3 = 21 \quad \text{or} \quad 5x + 3 = -21$
$5x = 18 \quad 5x = -24$
$x = \frac{18}{5} \quad \text{or} \quad x = \frac{-24}{5}$

21. $|3x - 5| = -7$
Absolute value is positive or zero.
$\varnothing$

22. $|5y| < 15$
$5y < 15$ and $5y > -15$
$y < 3$ and $y > -3$
$-3 < y < 3$

−3 0 3

23. $|y - 3| < 5$
$y - 3 < 5$ and $y - 3 > -5$
$y < 8$ and $y > -2$
$-2 < y < 8$

−2 0 8

24. $|2x - 9| \le 1$
$2x - 9 \le 1$ and $2x - 9 \ge -1$
$2x \le 10$ $2x \ge 8$
$x \le 5$ and $x \ge 4$
$4 \le x \le 5$

0 4 5

25. $|3x| \ge 15$
$3x \ge 15$ or $3x \le -15$
$x \ge 5$ or $x \le -5$

−5 0 5

26. $|5 + a| > 0$
$5 + a > 0$ or $5 + a < 0$
$a > -5$ or $a < -5$
All numbers except -5

−5 0

27. $|-2y + 5| > 3$
$-2y + 5 > 3$ or $-2y + 5 < -3$
$-2y > -2$ $-2y < -8$
$y < 1$ or $y > 4$

0 1 4

28. $x - 2y > 1$
$(0) - 2(0) > 1$
$0 - 0 > 1$
$0 > 1$
No

29. $x - 2y > 1$
$(1) - 2(3) > 1$
$1 - 6 > 1$
$-5 > 1$
No

30. $x - 2y > 1$
$(4) - 2(-1) > 1$
$4 + 2 > 1$
$6 > 1$
Yes

31. $x - 2y > 1$
$(-2) - 2(-2) > 1$
$-2 + 4 > 1$
$2 > 1$
Yes

32.
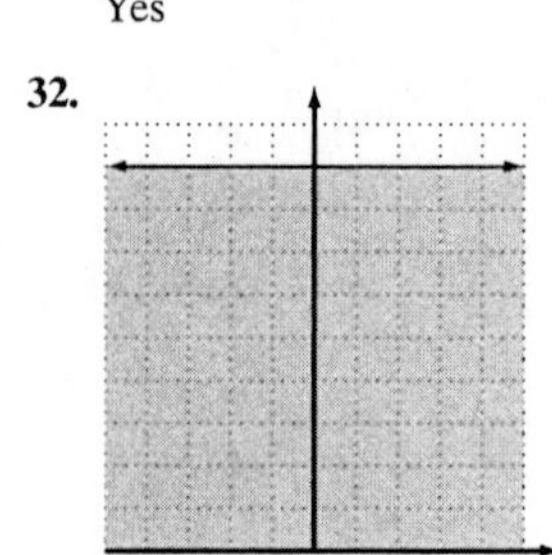

33.
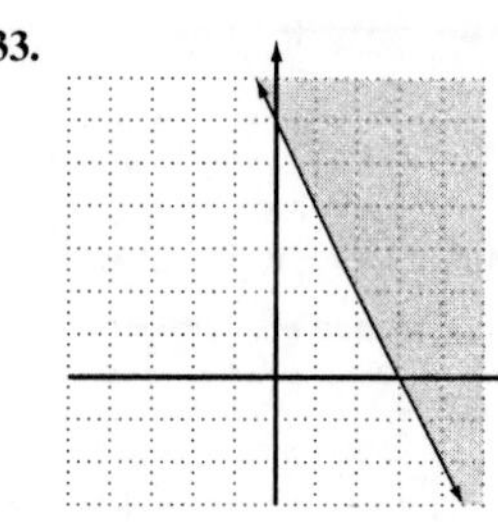

34.
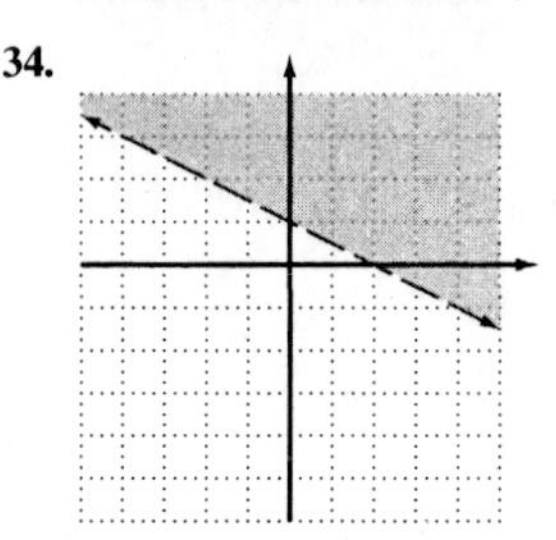

35.
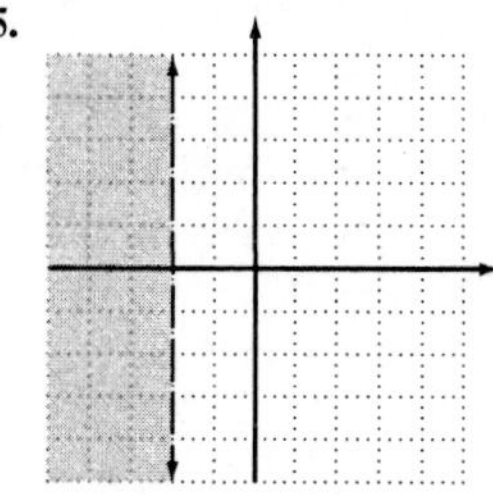

36.
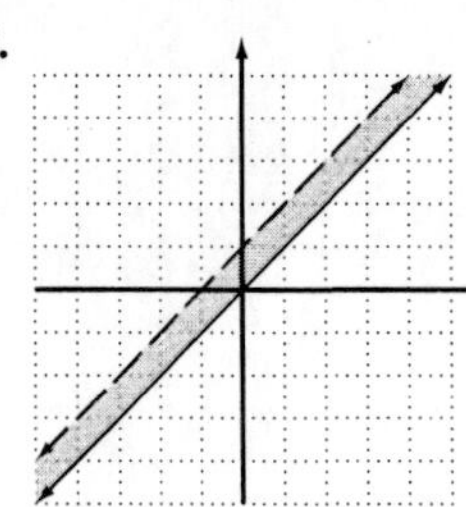

37.
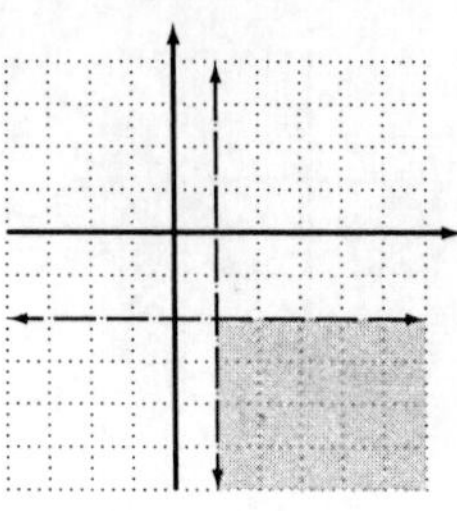

38.
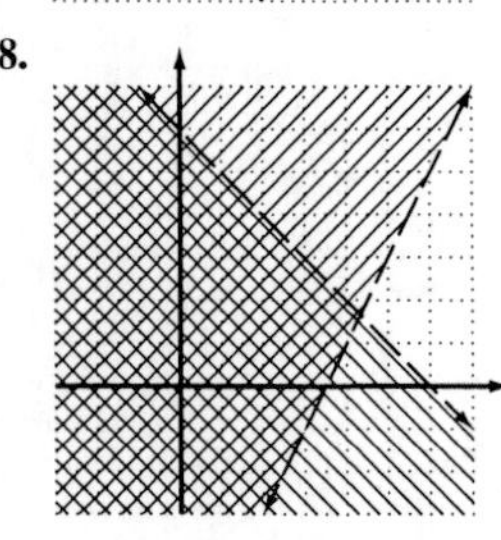

CHAPTER 9 ASSESSMENT

p. 429

1. (a) $A = \{5, 6, 7, \ldots\}$
(b) $A = \{x | x \text{ is a whole number and } x > 4\}$

2. (a) $B = \{-2, -1\}$
(b) $B = \{x | x \text{ is a negative integer and } x > -3\}$ or $\{x | x \text{ is an integer and } -3 < x < 0\}$

3. (a) $C = \varnothing$
(b) $C = \{x | x \text{ is a positive multiple of 3 and } x < -3\}$

4. $\{2\}$ 5. $\{10\}$ 6. $\{5\}$ 7. $\{2, 4, 5, 6, 8, 10, 12, 15\}$

8. $\{2, 3, 5, 7, 10, 11, 15\}$

9. $0 < x - 4$ and $x - 4 < 3$
$4 < x$ and $x < 7$
$\{x | 4 < x < 7\}$

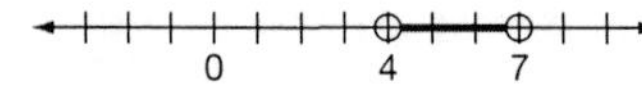

10. $-10 \le x - 5$ and $x - 5 < -8$
$-5 \le x$ and $x < -3$
$\{x | -5 \le x < -3\}$

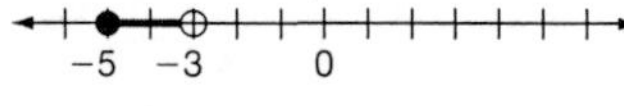

11. $x + 2 < 1$ or $x + 3 \ge 5$
$x < -1$ or $x \ge 2$
$\{x | x < -1 \text{ or } x \ge 2\}$

−1 0 2

12. $2x < -2$ or $3x - 1 > 2$
$x < -1$ or $3x > 3$
$x < -1$ or $x > 1$
$\{x | x < -1 \text{ or } x > 1\}$

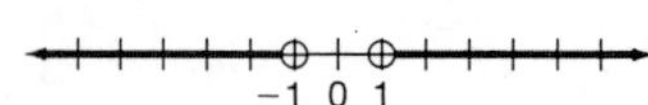

13. $|x - 2| = 4$
$x - 2 = 4$ or $x - 2 = -4$
$x = 6$ or $x = -2$

14. $|3x - 6| = 21$
$3x - 6 = 21$ or $3x - 6 = -21$
$3x = 27$ $3x = -15$
$x = 9$ or $x = -5$

15. $|3p| < 21$
$3p < 21$ and $3p > -21$
$p < 7$ and $p > -7$
$\{p | -7 < p < 7\}$

−7 0 7

16. $|x + 4| < 2$

$x + 4 < 2$ and $x + 4 > -2$

$x < -2$ and $x > -6$

$\{x | -6 < x < -2\}$

−6 −2 0

17. $|9 - r| \leq 9$

$9 - r \leq 9$ and $9 - r \geq -9$

$-r \leq 0$ $\quad$ $-r \geq -18$

$r \geq 0$ and $r \leq 18$

$\{r | 0 \leq r \leq 18\}$

0 18

18. $|4x| \geq 12$

$4x \geq 12$ or $4x \leq -12$

$x \geq 3$ or $x \leq -3$

$\{x | x \leq -3$ or $x \geq 3\}$

−3 0 3

19. $|2a - 1| > 5$

$2a - 1 > 5$ or $2a - 1 < -5$

$2a > 6$ $\quad$ $2a < -4$

$a > 3$ or $a < -2$

$\{a | a < -2$ or $a > 3\}$

−2 0 3

20. $|-3y + 6| > 12$

$-3y + 6 > 12$ or $-3y + 6 < -12$

$-3y > 6$ $\quad$ $-3y < -18$

$y < -2$ or $y > 6$

$\{y | y < -2$ or $y > 6\}$

−2 0 6

21.

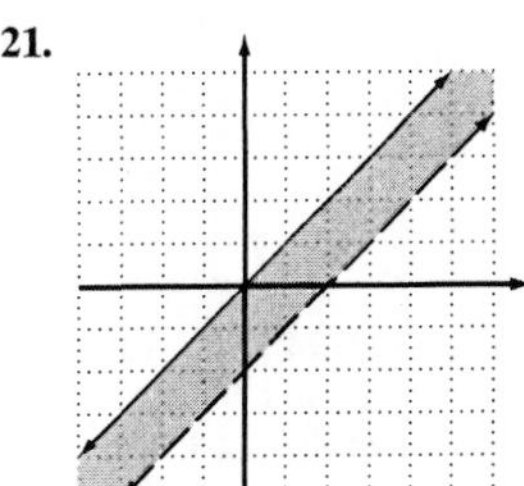

22.

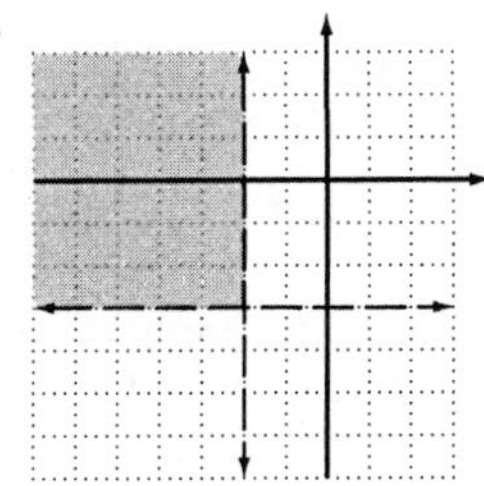

23.

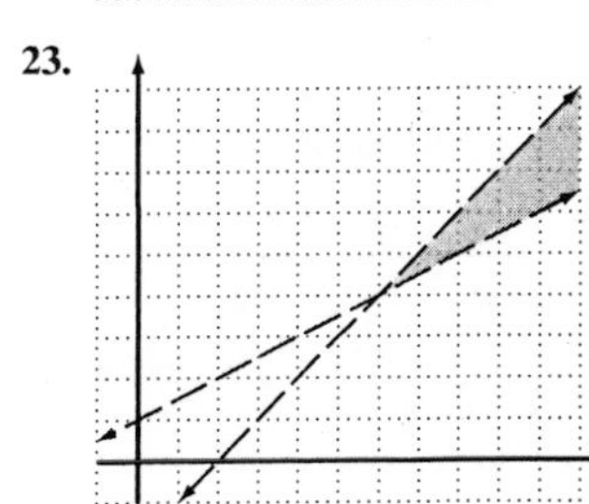

24.

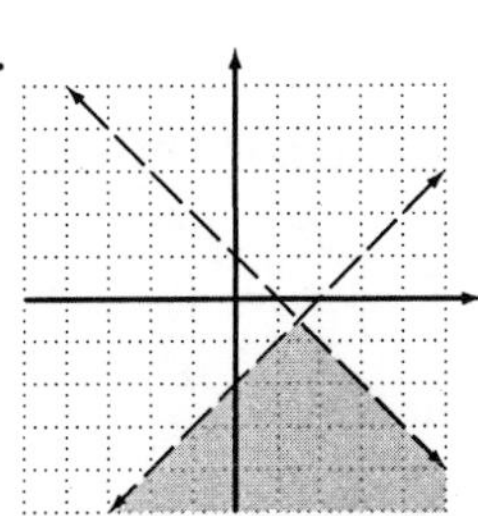

CHAPTER 10

SKILLS & CONCEPTS p. 430

1. $\frac{5}{3}$ $\quad$ 2. $\frac{y}{3x}$

3. $9 = 6(5x - 1)$

$9 = 30x - 6$

$15 = 30x$

$\frac{15}{30} = x$

$x = \frac{1}{2}$

4. $11 - 2(y + 1) = 21$

$11 - 2y - 2 = 21$

$-2y + 9 = 21$

$-2y = 12$

$y = -6$

5. $5(d + 4) = 7(d - 1)$

$5d + 20 = 7d - 7$

$20 = 2d - 7$

$27 = 2d$

$\frac{27}{2} = d$

6. $5(t + 3) + 4 = 3(t - 2) + 1$

$5t + 15 + 4 = 3t - 6 + 1$

$5t + 19 = 3t - 5$

$2t + 19 = -5$

$2t = -24$

$t = -12$

7. $(2x^2 + 3x - 7) + (x^2 + x - 8) = 3x^2 + 4x - 15$

8. $(x^2 + 6x + 8) - (x^2 - 3x - 4)$

$= x^2 + 6x + 8 - x^2 + 3x + 4$

$= 9x + 12$

9. $2x(3x + 2) = 6x^2 + 4x$

10. $(x + 1)(x^2 - 2x - 1) = x^3 - 2x^2 - x + x^2 - 2x - 1$

$= x^3 - x^2 - 3x - 1$

11. $x^2 - 4$ $\quad$ 12. $(x + 3)(x + 3) = x^2 + 6x + 9$

13. $x^2 - 9 = (x - 3)(x + 3)$

14. $x^2 - 6x + 9 = (x - 3)(x - 3)$ or $(x - 3)^2$

15. $x^2 + 3x + 2 = (x + 2)(x + 1)$

16. $16x^6 - 32x^5 = 16x^5(x - 2)$

17. $6a^2 + 5a - 6 = (3a - 2)(2a + 3)$

18. $x^2 - 5x + 6 = 0$

$(x - 2)(x - 3) = 0$

$x - 2 = 0$ or $x - 3 = 0$

$x = 2$ or $x = 3$

19. $9x^2 - 4 = 0$

$(3x + 2)(3x - 2) = 0$

$3x + 2 = 0$ or $3x - 2 = 0$

$3x = -2$ $\quad$ $3x = 2$

$x = -\frac{2}{3}$ or $x = \frac{2}{3}$

20. Let n = the number.

$(n + 1)(n - 1) = 24$

$n^2 - 1 = 24$

$n^2 - 25 = 0$

$(n + 5)(n - 5) = 0$

$n + 5 = 0$ or $n - 5 = 0$

$n = -5$ or $n = 5$

LESSON 10-1 TRY THIS pp. 433–434

a. $\frac{12y + 24}{48y} = \frac{12(y + 2)}{12 \cdot 4y}$ Factoring

$= \frac{y + 2}{4y}$ Simplifying

b. $\frac{2x^2 + x}{3x^2 + 2x} = \frac{x(2x + 1)}{x(3x + 2)}$ Factoring

$= \frac{2x + 1}{3x + 2}$ Simplifying

c. $\frac{a^2 - 1}{2a^2 - a - 1} = \frac{(a + 1)(a - 1)}{(2a + 1)(a - 1)}$ Factoring

$= \frac{a + 1}{2a + 1}$ Simplifying

d. $\frac{b - 7}{7 - b} = \frac{b - 7}{-(b - 7)} = -1$

e. $\frac{5 - 2a}{3(2a - 5)} = \frac{-(2a - 5)}{3(2a - 5)} = -\frac{1}{3}$

f. $\frac{4x - 12}{6 - 2x} = \frac{-2(6 - 2x)}{6 - 2x} = -2$

LESSON 10-1 EXERCISES pp. 434–435

1. $\frac{4x^2y}{2xy^3} = \frac{2x}{y^2}$ $\quad$ 2. $\frac{a^3b^2}{-2a^5b} = -\frac{b}{2a^2}$

3. $\frac{4x - 12}{4x} = \frac{4(x - 3)}{4x} = \frac{x - 3}{x}$

4. $\frac{-2y+6}{-4y} = \frac{-2(y-3)}{-4y} = \frac{y-3}{2y}$

5. $\frac{3m^2+3m}{6m^2+9m} = \frac{3m(m+1)}{3m(2m+3)} = \frac{m+1}{2m+3}$

6. $\frac{4y^2-2y}{5y^2-5y} = \frac{2y(2y-1)}{5y(y-1)} = \frac{2(2y-1)}{5(y-1)}$

7. $\frac{6x^5-x^4}{x^2-x} = \frac{x^4(6x-1)}{x(x-1)} = \frac{x^3(6x-1)}{x-1}$

8. $\frac{a^6-a^5}{a^8-a^7} = \frac{a^5(a-1)}{a^7(a-1)} = \frac{1}{a^2}$

9. $\frac{d+7}{d^2-49} = \frac{d+7}{(d+7)(d-7)} = \frac{1}{d-7}$

10. $\frac{a^2-9}{a^2+5a+6} = \frac{(a+3)(a-3)}{(a+3)(a+2)} = \frac{a-3}{a+2}$

11. $\frac{t^2-25}{t^2+t-20} = \frac{(t+5)(t-5)}{(t+5)(t-4)} = \frac{t-5}{t-4}$

12. $\frac{2t^2+6t+4}{4t^2-12t-16} = \frac{2(t^2+3t+2)}{4(t^2-3t-4)}$
$= \frac{2(t+2)(t+1)}{4(t-4)(t+1)}$
$= \frac{t+2}{2(t-4)}$

13. $\frac{a^2-1}{a-1} = \frac{(a+1)(a-1)}{a-1} = a+1$

14. $\frac{t^2-1}{t+1} = \frac{(t+1)(t-1)}{t+1} = t-1$

15. Already simplified

16. Already simplified

17. $\frac{6x^2-54}{4x^2-36} = \frac{6(x^2-9)}{4(x^2-9)} = \frac{3}{2}$

18. $\frac{8y^2-32}{4y^2-16} = \frac{8(y^2-4)}{4(y^2-4)} = 2$

19. $\frac{6x+12}{x^2-x-6} = \frac{6(x+2)}{(x+2)(x-3)} = \frac{6}{x-3}$

20. $\frac{5a+5}{a^2+7a+6} = \frac{5(a+1)}{(a+6)(a+1)} = \frac{5}{a+6}$

21. $\frac{b^2-10b+21}{b^2-11b+28} = \frac{(b-7)(b-3)}{(b-7)(b-4)} = \frac{b-3}{b-4}$

22. $\frac{2t-8}{12-3t} = \frac{2(t-4)}{3(4-t)} = \frac{-2(4-t)}{3(4-t)} = -\frac{2}{3}$

23. $\frac{y^2-3y-18}{y^2-2y-15} = \frac{(y-6)(y+3)}{(y-5)(y+3)} = \frac{y-6}{y-5}$

24. $\frac{t^2-4}{(t+2)^2} = \frac{(t+2)(t-2)}{(t+2)(t+2)} = \frac{t-2}{t+2}$

25. $\frac{(a-3)^2}{a^2-9} = \frac{(a-3)(a-3)}{(a-3)(a+3)} = \frac{a-3}{a+3}$

26. $\frac{5x-15}{3-x} = \frac{5(x-3)}{-1(x-3)} = -5$

27. $\frac{6-y}{y^2-2y-24} = \frac{-1(y-6)}{(y-6)(y+4)} = -\frac{1}{y+4}$

28. $\frac{4-2y}{2y^2+10y-28} = \frac{2(2-y)}{2(y^2+5y-14)} = \frac{-1(y-2)}{(y-2)(y+7)}$
$= -\frac{1}{y+7}$

29. Already simplified

30. $\frac{(a-b)^2}{b^2-a^2} = \frac{(a-b)(a-b)}{(b+a)(b-a)} = \frac{-1(b-a)(a-b)}{(b+a)(b-a)}$
$= \frac{-1(a-b)}{b+a} = \frac{b-a}{b+a}$

31. $\frac{a^4-b^4}{b^2-a^2} = \frac{(a^2+b^2)(a^2-b^2)}{-(a^2-b^2)} = -(a^2+b^2)$ or $-a^2-b^2$

32. $\frac{x^4-16y^4}{(x^2+4y^2)(x-2y)} = \frac{(x^2+4y^2)(x^2-4y^2)}{(x^2+4y^2)(x-2y)}$
$= \frac{(x+2y)(x-2y)}{x-2y} = x+2y$

33. $\frac{m^4-n^4}{4m^2+4n^2} = \frac{(m^2+n^2)(m^2-n^2)}{4(m^2+n^2)} = \frac{m^2-n^2}{4}$

34. $\frac{2y^4-2z^4}{2y^2-2z^2} = \frac{2(y^4-z^4)}{2(y^2-z^2)} = \frac{(y^2+z^2)(y^2-z^2)}{y^2-z^2} = y^2+z^2$

35. $\frac{(t-3)^3(t^2-2t+1)}{(t-1)^3(t^2-4t+4)} = \frac{(t-3)^3(t-1)^2}{(t-1)^3(t-2)^2} = \frac{(t-3)^3}{(t-1)(t-2)^2}$

36. $\frac{(x^2-y^2)(x^2-2xy+y^2)}{(x-y)^2(x^2-4xy-5y^2)} = \frac{(x+y)(x-y)(x-y)^2}{(x-y)^2(x-5y)(x+y)}$
$= \frac{x-y}{x-5y}$

37. Before: $\frac{(x+3)^2}{x^2-9} = \frac{(4+3)^2}{4^2-9} = \frac{7^2}{16-9} = \frac{49}{7} = 7$
After: $\frac{(x+3)^2}{x^2-9} = \frac{(x+3)^2}{(x+3)(x-3)} = \frac{x+3}{x-3} = \frac{4+3}{4-3}$
$= \frac{7}{1} = 7$

38. Before: $\frac{3a-6}{2-a} = \frac{3(2)-6}{2-2} = \frac{6-6}{2-2} = \frac{0}{0}$ Not defined
After: $\frac{3a-6}{2-a} = \frac{3(a-2)}{-(a-2)} = -3$

39. The expressions are equal for all values of a except 3. 3 is not an acceptable value for a in the rational expression because it would make the denominator 0. So the expressions are sometimes equal.

40. Correct

41. Incorrect; only factors can be simplified, not individual terms.

42. Incorrect; $\frac{(m-2)^2}{m^2-4} = \frac{(m-2)(m-2)}{(m-2)(m+2)} = \frac{m-2}{m+2}$

43. Incorrect; $\frac{8y^2-32}{4y^2-16} = \frac{8(y^2-4)}{4(y^2-4)} = 2$

44. Find values of x for which the denominator is 0.
$x^2+4x+4=0$
$(x+2)(x+2)=0$
$x+2=0$
$x=-2$

45. Find values of x for which the denominator is 0.
$x^2+2x-3=0$
$(x+3)(x-1)=0$
$x+3=0$ or $x-1=0$
$x=-3$ or $x=1$

46. Find values of x for which the denominator is 0.
$x^3-9x^2+14x=0$
$x(x^2-9x+14)=0$
$x(x-7)(x-2)=0$
$x=0$ or $x-7=0$ or $x-2=0$
$x=0$ or $x=7$ or $x=2$

47. $x^2-12x+35=0$
$(x-7)(x-5)=0$
$x-7=0$ or $x-5=0$
$x=7$ or $x=5$

48.
$$\begin{aligned} 25x^2 - 9 &= 0 \\ (5x+3)(5x-3) &= 0 \\ 5x+3 = 0 \quad &\text{or} \quad 5x - 3 = 0 \\ 5x = -3 \quad &\text{or} \quad 5x = 3 \\ x = -\tfrac{3}{5} \quad &\text{or} \quad x = \tfrac{3}{5} \end{aligned}$$

49.
$$\begin{aligned} 6x^2 - x - 1 &= 0 \\ (3x+1)(2x-1) &= 0 \\ 3x+1 = 0 \quad &\text{or} \quad 2x - 1 = 0 \\ 3x = -1 \quad &\text{or} \quad 2x = 1 \\ x = -\tfrac{1}{3} \quad &\text{or} \quad x = \tfrac{1}{2} \end{aligned}$$

50.
$$\begin{aligned} 3x^2 + 2x - 8 &= 0 \\ (3x-4)(x+2) &= 0 \\ 3x-4 = 0 \quad &\text{or} \quad x + 2 = 0 \\ 3x = 4 \quad &\text{or} \quad x = -2 \\ x = \tfrac{4}{3} \quad &\text{or} \quad x = -2 \end{aligned}$$

51.
$$3x - 4y = 6 \qquad x + 4y = -14$$
$$x = -14 - 4y$$
$$\begin{aligned} 3(-14-4y) - 4y &= 6 \\ -42 - 12y - 4y &= 6 \\ -42 - 16y &= 6 \\ -16y &= 48 \\ y &= -3 \end{aligned} \qquad x = -14 - 4(-3) = -2$$
$(-2, -3)$ is the solution.

52. $x - y = -6$, $x = y - 6$
$$\begin{aligned} 3x + 4y &= -4 \\ 3(y-6) + 4y &= -4 \\ 3y - 18 + 4y &= -4 \\ 7y - 18 &= -4 \\ 7y &= 14 \\ y &= 2 \end{aligned}$$
$x = (2) - 6 = -4$

The solution is $(-4, 2)$.

53.
$$2y + 7x = -4 \qquad x = y - 7$$
$$\begin{aligned} 2y + 7(y-7) &= -4 \\ 2y + 7y - 49 &= -4 \\ 9y - 49 &= -4 \\ 9y &= 45 \\ y &= 5 \end{aligned} \qquad x = (5) - 7 = -2$$
The solution is $(-2, 5)$.

LESSON 10-2 TRY THIS p. 436

a. $\frac{4a^4}{3} \cdot \frac{6}{5a^2} = \frac{24a^4}{15a^2}$ Multiplying

$= \frac{8a^2}{5}$ Simplifying

b. $\frac{(x+3)}{5} \cdot \frac{5(x+2)}{x+4} = \frac{5(x+3)(x+2)}{5(x+4)} = \frac{(x+3)(x+2)}{x+4}$

c. $\frac{-3}{4m+2} \cdot \frac{4}{2m-1} = \frac{-12}{(4m+2)(2m-1)} = \frac{-12}{2(2m+1)(2m-1)} = \frac{-6}{(2m+1)(2m-1)}$

LESSON 10-2 EXERCISES pp. 437–438

1. $\frac{4x^3}{3x} \cdot \frac{14}{x} = \frac{56x^3}{3x^2} = \frac{56x}{3}$

2. $\frac{32}{b^4} \cdot \frac{3b^2}{8} = \frac{96b^2}{8b^4} = \frac{12}{b^2}$

3. $\frac{3c}{d^2} \cdot \frac{4d}{6c^3} = \frac{12cd}{6c^3d^2} = \frac{2}{c^2d}$

4. $\frac{8}{3x} \cdot \frac{x+7}{6x^2} = \frac{8(x+7)}{18x^3} = \frac{4(x+7)}{9x^3}$

5. $\frac{y+6}{2y} \cdot \frac{4y^2}{y+6} = \frac{4y^2(y+6)}{2y(y+6)} = 2y$

6. $\frac{-5}{m} \cdot \frac{m^6}{m+2} = \frac{-5m^6}{m(m+2)} = -\frac{5m^5}{m+2}$

7. $\frac{-2n}{7(n+2)} \cdot \frac{7n+7}{n+1} = \frac{-2n(7)(n+1)}{7(n+2)(n+1)} = -\frac{2n}{n+2}$

8. $\frac{-3y}{6(y-1)} \cdot \frac{2y-2}{y^2} = \frac{-3y(2)(y-1)}{6y^2(y-1)} = \frac{-6y}{6y^2} = -\frac{1}{y}$

9. $\frac{a-6}{a^2} \cdot \frac{a+2}{a+1} = \frac{(a-6)(a+2)}{a^2(a+1)}$

10. $\frac{3x}{2} \cdot \frac{x+4}{x-1} = \frac{3x(x+4)}{2(x-1)}$

11. $\frac{4y}{5} \cdot \frac{y-3}{2y} = \frac{4y(y-3)}{10y} = \frac{2(y-3)}{5}$

12. $\frac{a-1}{a+2} \cdot \frac{a+1}{a-1} = \frac{(a-1)(a+1)}{(a+2)(a-1)} = \frac{a+1}{a+2}$

13. $\frac{m-2}{m-5} \cdot \frac{m+5}{m-2} = \frac{(m-2)(m+5)}{(m-5)(m-2)} = \frac{m+5}{m-5}$

14. $\frac{2x+3}{4} \cdot \frac{4}{x-5} = \frac{4(2x+3)}{4(x-5)} = \frac{2x+3}{x-5}$

15. $\frac{-5}{6y-4} \cdot \frac{-6}{5y+6} = \frac{30}{2(3y-2)(5y+6)} = \frac{15}{(3y-2)(5y+6)}$

16. $\frac{a-5}{a^2+1} \cdot \frac{a+1}{a^2-1} = \frac{(a-5)(a+1)}{(a^2+1)(a+1)(a-1)} = \frac{a-5}{(a^2+1)(a-1)}$

17. $\frac{t+3}{t^2-2} \cdot \frac{t+3}{t^2-9} = \frac{(t+3)(t+3)}{(t^2-2)(t+3)(t-3)} = \frac{t+3}{(t^2-2)(t-3)}$

18. $\frac{x+1}{2+x} \cdot \frac{x-1}{x+1} = \frac{(x+1)(x-1)}{(2+x)(x+1)} = \frac{x-1}{2+x}$

19. $\frac{2x}{2x} \cdot \frac{x-1}{x+4} = \frac{x-1}{x+4}$

20. $\frac{3y-1}{2y+1} \cdot \frac{y}{y} = \frac{3y-1}{2y+1}$

21. $\frac{-1}{-1} \cdot \frac{3-x}{4-x} = \frac{3-x}{4-x}$ or $\frac{x-3}{x-4}$

22. $\frac{-1}{-1} \cdot \frac{4-a}{5-a} = \frac{4-a}{5-a}$ or $\frac{a-4}{a-5}$

23. $\frac{4(x+2)}{5x} \cdot \frac{6x^2}{2x} = \frac{24x^2(x+2)}{10x^2} = \frac{12(x+2)}{5}$

24. $\frac{6(m-3)}{5m} \cdot \frac{4m^2}{2(m-3)} = \frac{24m^2(m-3)}{10m(m-3)} = \frac{12m}{5}$

25. $\frac{(y-4)^2}{3y} \cdot \frac{y-2}{(y+4)(y-4)} = \frac{(y-4)(y-4)(y-2)}{3y(y+4)(y-4)} = \frac{(y-4)(y-2)}{3y(y+4)}$

26. $\frac{(x+1)^2}{x+3} \cdot \frac{(x+3)^3}{x+1} = \frac{(x+1)^2(x+3)^3}{(x+1)(x+3)} = (x+1)(x+3)^2$

27. $\frac{5(m-1)}{(m+3)^2} \cdot \frac{m+3}{(m-1)^2} = \frac{5(m-1)(m+3)}{(m-1)^2(m+3)^2} = \frac{5}{(m-1)(m+3)}$

28. $\frac{6a + 12}{5} \cdot \frac{15a}{7a + 14} = \frac{6(a + 2)(15)a}{5(7)(a + 2)}$
$= \frac{90a}{35} = \frac{18a}{7}$

29. $\frac{25 - x^2}{12} \cdot \frac{6}{5 - x} = \frac{(5 + x)(5 - x)(6)}{12(5 - x)}$
$= \frac{5 + x}{2}$

30. $\frac{3}{x^2 - 1} \cdot \frac{x + 1}{3} = \frac{3(x + 1)}{3(x + 1)(x - 1)} = \frac{1}{x - 1}$

31. $\frac{4 - 3a}{6} \cdot \frac{3}{3a - 4} = \frac{-1(3a - 4)(3)}{6(3a - 4)}$
$= -\frac{3}{6} = -\frac{1}{2}$

32. $\frac{1 - x}{7} \cdot \frac{14}{x - 1} = \frac{-1(x - 1)(14)}{7(x - 1)} = \frac{-14}{7} = -2$

33. $\frac{7x}{4x + 3} \cdot \frac{8x + 6}{1} = \frac{7x(2)(4x + 3)}{(4x + 3)} = 14x$

34. $\frac{4c}{2c - 1} \cdot \frac{8c - 4}{1} = \frac{4c(4)(2c - 1)}{(2c - 1)}$
$= 16c$

35. $\frac{x^2 - 3x - 10}{(x - 2)^2} \cdot \frac{x - 2}{x - 5} = \frac{(x - 5)(x + 2)(x - 2)}{(x - 2)^2(x - 5)}$
$= \frac{x + 2}{x - 2}$

36. $\frac{t^2}{t^2 - 4} \cdot \frac{t^2 - 5t + 6}{t^2 - 3t} = \frac{t^2(t - 2)(t - 3)}{(t + 2)(t - 2)t(t - 3)} = \frac{t}{t + 2}$

37. $\frac{a^2 - 9}{a^2} \cdot \frac{a^2 - 3a}{a^2 + a - 12} = \frac{(a + 3)(a - 3)a(a - 3)}{a^2(a + 4)(a - 3)}$
$= \frac{(a + 3)(a - 3)}{a(a + 4)}$

38. $\frac{m^2 + 10m - 11}{m^2 - 1} \cdot \frac{m + 1}{m + 11} = \frac{(m + 11)(m - 1)(m + 1)}{(m + 1)(m - 1)(m + 11)} = 1$

39. $\frac{4a^2}{3a^2 - 12a + 12} \cdot \frac{3a - 6}{2a} = \frac{4a^2(3)(a - 2)}{3(a^2 - 4a + 4)2a}$
$= \frac{2a(a - 2)}{(a - 2)^2}$
$= \frac{2a}{a - 2}$

40. $\frac{5v + 5}{v - 2} \cdot \frac{v^2 - 4v + 4}{v^2 - 1} = \frac{5(v + 1)(v - 2)^2}{(v - 2)(v + 1)(v - 1)} = \frac{5(v - 2)}{v - 1}$

41. $\frac{x^4 - 16}{x^4 - 1} \cdot \frac{x^2 + 1}{x^2 + 4} = \frac{(x^2 + 4)(x^2 - 4)(x^2 + 1)}{(x^2 + 1)(x^2 - 1)(x^2 + 4)}$
$= \frac{(x + 2)(x - 2)}{(x + 1)(x - 1)}$

42. $\frac{t^4 - 1}{t^4 - 81} \cdot \frac{t^2 + 9}{t^2 + 1} = \frac{(t^2 + 1)(t^2 - 1)(t^2 + 9)}{(t^2 + 9)(t^2 - 9)(t^2 + 1)} = \frac{(t + 1)(t - 1)}{(t + 3)(t - 3)}$

43. $\frac{(t - 2)^3}{(t - 1)^3} \cdot \frac{t^2 - 2t + 1}{t^2 - 4t + 4} = \frac{(t - 2)^3(t - 1)^2}{(t - 1)^3(t - 2)^2} = \frac{t - 2}{t - 1}$

44. $\frac{(y + 4)^3}{(y + 2)^3} \cdot \frac{y^2 + 4y + 4}{y^2 + 8y + 16} = \frac{(y + 4)^3(y + 2)^2}{(y + 2)^3(y + 4)^2} = \frac{y + 4}{y + 2}$

45. $\frac{m^2 - n^2}{2m + 1} \cdot \frac{2m^2 - 5m - 3}{m + n}$
$= \frac{(m + n)(m - n)(2m + 1)(m - 3)}{(2m + 1)(m + n)}$
$= (m - n)(m - 3)$

46. $\frac{a^4 - b^4}{2ab} \cdot \frac{2a^2 - ab - 3b^2}{a^2 + b^2}$
$= \frac{(a^2 + b^2)(a^2 - b^2)(2a - 3b)(a + b)}{(2ab)(a^2 + b^2)}$
$= \frac{(a + b)(a - b)(2a - 3b)(a + b)}{2ab}$
$= \frac{(a + b)^2(a - b)(2a - 3b)}{2ab}$

47. $\frac{-4x^2 - 9xy - 2y^2}{x + 2y} \cdot \frac{-1}{4x^2 - 3xy - y^2}$
$= \frac{(4x + y)(x + 2y)}{(x + 2y)(4x + y)(x - y)}$
$= \frac{1}{x - y}$

48. Answers may vary. Since $8a^2 + 16a - 24 = 2 \cdot 2 \cdot 2\,(a + 3) \cdot (a - 1)$, the two numerators should consist of these factors. Since $a^2 + 13a + 40 = (a + 8)(a + 5)$, the two denominators should consist of these factors.

Ex: $\frac{2(a + 3)}{(a + 5)} \cdot \frac{4(a - 1)}{(a + 8)}$ or $\frac{8a + 24}{a + 5} \cdot \frac{a - 1}{a + 8}$

49. Find values of x for which the denominator is 0.
$x^2 + 4x + 4 = 0$
$(x + 2)^2 = 0$
$x + 2 = 0$
$x = -2$

50. Find values of x for which the denominator is 0.
$x^2 + 2x - 3 = 0$
$(x + 3)(x - 1) = 0$
$x + 3 = 0$ or $x - 1 = 0$
$x = -3$ or $x = 1$

51. Find values of x for which the denominator is 0.
$x^3 - 9x^2 + 14x = 0$
$x(x^2 - 9x + 14) = 0$
$x(x - 2)(x - 7) = 0$
$x = 0$ or $x - 2 = 0$ or $x - 7 = 0$
$x = 0$ or $x = 2$ or $x = 7$

52. Find values of x for which the denominator is 0.
$x^3 + x^2 - 6x = 0$
$x(x^2 + x - 6) = 0$
$x(x + 3)(x - 2) = 0$
$x = 0$ or $x + 3 = 0$ or $x - 2 = 0$
$x = 0$ or $x = -3$ or $x = 2$

53. $A \cup B = \{-2, 0, 1, 2, 3, 4, 5\}$

54. $A \cap C = \{-2, 0\}$

55. $B \cap C = \{0, 1\}$

56. $A \cup \varnothing = \{-2, 0, 3, 5\}$

57. $x^2 - 4 = 3x$
$x^2 - 3x - 4 = 0$
$(x - 4)(x + 1) = 0$
$x - 4 = 0$ or $x + 1 = 0$
$x = 4$ or $x = -1$

58. $2y^2 - 6y = -4$
$2y^2 - 6y + 4 = 0$
$2(y^2 - 3y + 2) = 0$
$2(y - 2)(y - 1) = 0$
$y - 2 = 0$ or $y - 1 = 0$
$y = 2$ or $y = 1$

59. $3a^2 - 5 = 2a$
$3a^2 - 2a - 5 = 0$
$(3a - 5)(a + 1) = 0$
$3a - 5 = 0$ or $a + 1 = 0$
$3a = 5$ or $a = -1$
$a = \frac{5}{3}$ or $a = -1$

60. $x - \frac{2}{5}y = -2$ ①

$3x + 2y = 10$ ②

$x = \frac{2}{5}y - 2$ Solving ① for x

$3\left(\frac{2}{5}y - 2\right) + 2y = 10$ Substituting in ②

$\frac{6}{5}y - 6 + 2y = 10$

$\frac{16}{5}y - 6 = 10$

$\frac{16}{5}y = 16$

$y = 5$

$x = \frac{2}{5}(5) - 2 = 0$ (0, 5)

61. $2x - y = 4$

$\frac{3}{4}x + y = 7$

$\frac{11}{4}x = 11$ Adding

$x = 4$

$2(4) - y = 4$

$y = 4$ (4, 4)

62. $|y + 2| = 5$

$y + 2 = 5$ or $y + 2 = -5$

$y = 3$ or $y = -7$

63. $|2y - 6| = 16$

$2y - 6 = 16$ or $2y - 6 = -16$

$2y = 22$ or $2y = -10$

$y = 11$ or $y = -5$

64. $|3x + 4| = 13$

$3x + 4 = 13$ or $3x + 4 = -13$

$3x = 9$ or $3x = -17$

$x = 3$ or $x = -\frac{17}{3}$

65. a. Two points are $\left(\frac{1}{2}, 65\right)$ and (1, 110).

$m = \frac{110 - 65}{1 - \frac{1}{2}} = 90$

$y - 110 = 90(x - 1)$

$y - 110 = 90x - 90$

$y = 90x + 20$

b. $y = 90(5) + 20$

$= \$470$

LESSON 10-3 TRY THIS p. 439

a. $\frac{9a^4}{7} \div \frac{9a^2}{14} = \frac{9a^4}{7} \cdot \frac{14}{9a^2} = \frac{9 \cdot 14a^4}{9 \cdot 7a^2} = 2a^2$

b. $\frac{4m - 8}{5} \div \frac{m - 2}{10} = \frac{4m - 8}{5} \cdot \frac{10}{m - 2} = \frac{4(m - 2)(10)}{5(m - 2)} = 8$

c. $\frac{3}{x^2 - 4} \div \frac{2}{x - 1} = \frac{3}{x^2 - 4} \cdot \frac{x - 1}{2} = \frac{3(x - 1)}{2(x + 2)(x - 2)}$

LESSON 10-3 EXERCISES pp. 440–441

1. $\frac{5x^4}{3} \div \frac{5x^2}{6} = \frac{5x^4}{3} \cdot \frac{6}{5x^2} = \frac{30x^4}{15x^2} = 2x^2$

2. $\frac{-2x^6}{7} \div \frac{4x}{5} = \frac{-2x^6}{7} \cdot \frac{5}{4x} = \frac{-10x^6}{28x} = -\frac{5x^5}{14}$

3. $\frac{3}{a^5} \div \frac{3}{a^2} = \frac{3}{a^5} \cdot \frac{a^2}{3} = \frac{3a^2}{3a^5} = \frac{1}{a^3}$

4. $\frac{2}{t^5} \cdot \frac{8}{t^2} = \frac{2}{t^5} \cdot \frac{t^2}{8} = \frac{2t^2}{8t^5} = \frac{1}{4t^3}$

5. $\frac{6m^4}{5} \div \frac{2m}{1} = \frac{6m^4}{5} \cdot \frac{1}{2m} = \frac{6m^4}{10m} = \frac{3m^3}{5}$

6. $\frac{4a^7}{3} \div \frac{5a^2}{1} = \frac{4a^7}{3} \cdot \frac{1}{5a^2} = \frac{4a^7}{15a^2} = \frac{4a^5}{15}$

7. $\frac{5x - 5}{16} \div \frac{x - 1}{6} = \frac{5x - 5}{16} \cdot \frac{6}{x - 1}$

$= \frac{5(x - 1)(6)}{16(x - 1)} = \frac{30}{16} = \frac{15}{8}$

8. $\frac{-4 + 2x}{8} \div \frac{x - 2}{2} = \frac{-4 + 2x}{8} \cdot \frac{2}{x - 2}$

$= \frac{2(x - 2)(2)}{8(x - 2)} = \frac{4}{8} = \frac{1}{2}$

9. $\frac{-6 + 3x}{5} \div \frac{4x - 8}{25} = \frac{3x - 6}{5} \cdot \frac{25}{4x - 8}$

$= \frac{3(x - 2)(25)}{5 \cdot 4(x - 2)} = \frac{75}{20} = \frac{15}{4}$

10. $\frac{-12 + 4x}{4} \div \frac{-6 + 2x}{6} = \frac{4x - 12}{4} \cdot \frac{6}{2x - 6}$

$= \frac{4(x - 3)}{4} \cdot \frac{6}{2(x - 3)}$

$= \frac{24}{8} = 3$

11. $\frac{a + 2}{a - 1} \div \frac{3a + 6}{a - 5} = \frac{a + 2}{a - 1} \cdot \frac{a - 5}{3(a + 2)}$

$= \frac{(a + 2)(a - 5)}{3(a - 1)(a + 2)} = \frac{a - 5}{3(a - 1)}$

12. $\frac{t - 3}{t + 2} \div \frac{4t - 12}{t + 1} = \frac{t - 3}{t + 2} \cdot \frac{t + 1}{4t - 12}$

$= \frac{t - 3}{t + 2} \cdot \frac{t + 1}{4(t - 3)} = \frac{t + 1}{4(t + 2)}$

13. $\frac{x^2 - 4}{x} \div \frac{x - 2}{x + 2} = \frac{x^2 - 4}{x} \cdot \frac{x + 2}{x - 2}$

$= \frac{(x + 2)(x - 2)(x + 2)}{x(x - 2)} = \frac{(x + 2)^2}{x}$

14. $\frac{x^2 - 1}{x} \div \frac{x + 1}{x - 1} = \frac{x^2 - 1}{x} \cdot \frac{x - 1}{x + 1}$

$= \frac{(x + 1)(x - 1)(x - 1)}{x(x + 1)} = \frac{(x - 1)^2}{x}$

15. $\frac{x^2 - 9}{4x + 12} \div \frac{x - 3}{6} = \frac{x^2 - 9}{4x + 12} \cdot \frac{6}{x - 3}$

$= \frac{(x + 3)(x - 3)(6)}{4(x + 3)(x - 3)} = \frac{6}{4} = \frac{3}{2}$

16. $\frac{4y - 8}{y + 2} \div \frac{y - 2}{y^2 - 4} = \frac{4y - 8}{y + 2} \cdot \frac{y^2 - 4}{y - 2}$

$= \frac{4(y - 2)(y + 2)(y - 2)}{(y + 2)(y - 2)}$

$= 4(y - 2)$

17. $\frac{c^2 + 3c}{c^2 + 2c - 3} \div \frac{c}{c + 1} = \frac{c^2 + 3c}{c^2 + 2c - 3} \cdot \frac{c + 1}{c}$

$= \frac{c(c + 3)(c + 1)}{(c + 3)(c - 1)(c)} = \frac{c + 1}{c - 1}$

18. $\frac{x - 5}{2x} \div \frac{x^2 - 25}{4x^2} = \frac{x - 5}{2x} \cdot \frac{4x^2}{x^2 - 25}$

$= \frac{4x^2(x - 5)}{2x(x + 5)(x - 5)} = \frac{2x}{x + 5}$

19. $\frac{8a-32}{a+1} \div \frac{16}{3a+3} = \frac{8a-32}{a+1} \cdot \frac{3a+3}{16}$
$= \frac{8(a-4)(3)(a+1)}{16(a+1)}$
$= \frac{24(a-4)}{16} = \frac{3(a-4)}{2}$

20. $\frac{17}{5x-10} \div \frac{34x+51}{3x-6} = \frac{17}{5x-10} \cdot \frac{3x-6}{34x+51}$
$= \frac{17(3)(x-2)}{5(x-2)(17)(2x+3)}$
$= \frac{3}{5(2x+3)}$

21. $\frac{2y^2-7y+3}{2y^2+3y-2} \div \frac{6y^2-5y+1}{3y^2+5y-2}$
$= \frac{2y^2-7y+3}{2y^2+3y-2} \cdot \frac{3y^2+5y-2}{6y^2-5y+1}$
$= \frac{(2y-1)(y-3)(3y-1)(y+2)}{(2y-1)(y+2)(3y-1)(2y-1)}$
$= \frac{y-3}{2y-1}$

22. $\frac{x^2-x-20}{x^2+7x+12} \div \frac{x^2-10x+25}{x^2+6x+9}$
$= \frac{x^2-x-20}{x^2+7x+12} \cdot \frac{x^2+6x+9}{x^2-10x+25}$
$= \frac{(x-5)(x+4)(x+3)^2}{(x+4)(x+3)(x-5)^2} = \frac{x+3}{x-5}$

23. $\frac{x^2+13x+12}{x+2} \div \frac{x+1}{1} = \frac{x^2+13x+12}{x+2} \cdot \frac{1}{x+1}$
$= \frac{(x+12)(x+1)}{(x+2)(x+1)} = \frac{x+12}{x+2}$

24. $\frac{a^2-5a+6}{a-3} \div \frac{a-2}{1} = \frac{a^2-5a+6}{a-3} \cdot \frac{1}{a-2}$
$= \frac{(a-3)(a-2)}{(a-3)(a-2)} = 1$

25. $\frac{c^2+10c+21}{c^2-2c-15} \div \frac{c^2+2c-35}{1}$
$= \frac{c^2+10c+21}{c^2-2c-15} \cdot \frac{1}{c^2+2c-35}$
$= \frac{(c+7)(c+3)}{(c-5)(c+3)(c+7)(c-5)} = \frac{1}{(c-5)^2}$

26. $\frac{1-z}{1+2z-z^2} \div \frac{1-z}{1} = \frac{1-z}{1+2z-z^2} \cdot \frac{1}{1-z}$
$= \frac{(1-z)}{(1+2z-z^2)(1-z)}$
$= \frac{1}{1+2z-z^2}$

27. $\frac{c+3}{1} \div \frac{c^2+c-6}{c+2} = \frac{c+3}{1} \cdot \frac{c+2}{c^2+c-6}$
$= \frac{(c+3)(c+2)}{(c+3)(c-2)} = \frac{c+2}{c-2}$

28. $\frac{2-x}{1} \div \frac{x^2-4}{x-7} = \frac{2-x}{1} \cdot \frac{x-7}{x^2-4}$
$= \frac{-(x-2)(x-7)}{(x+2)(x-2)} = \frac{-(x-7)}{x+2}$

29. $\frac{(t+5)^3}{(t-5)^3} \div \frac{(t+5)^2}{(t-5)^2} = \frac{(t+5)^3}{(t-5)^3} \cdot \frac{(t-5)^2}{(t+5)^2}$
$= \frac{(t+5)^3(t-5)^2}{(t-5)^3(t+5)^2}$
$= \frac{t+5}{t-5}$

30. $\frac{(y-3)^3}{(y+3)^3} \div \frac{(y-3)^2}{(y+3)^2} = \frac{(y-3)^3}{(y+3)^3} \cdot \frac{(y+3)^2}{(y-3)^2}$
$= \frac{(y-3)^3(y+3)^2}{(y+3)^3(y-3)^2}$
$= \frac{y-3}{y+3}$

31. $\left(\frac{a+7}{3}\right)^3 \div \left(\frac{a+7}{2}\right)^2 = \frac{(a+7)^3}{27} \div \frac{(a+7)^2}{4}$
$= \frac{(a+7)^3}{27} \cdot \frac{4}{(a+7)^2}$
$= \frac{4(a+7)^3}{27(a+7)^2} = \frac{4(a+7)}{27}$

32. $\left(\frac{2x-3}{2}\right)^4 \div \left(\frac{2x-3}{2}\right)^3 = \frac{(2x-3)^4}{2^4} \div \frac{(2x-3)^3}{2^3}$
$= \frac{(2x-3)^4}{2^4} \cdot \frac{2^3}{(2x-3)^3}$
$= \frac{2x-3}{2}$

33. $\left(\frac{4}{b-3}\right)^4 \div \left(\frac{3}{b-3}\right)^5$
$= \frac{4^4}{(b-3)^4} \div \frac{3^5}{(b-3)^5}$
$= \frac{256}{(b-3)^4} \cdot \frac{(b-3)^5}{243}$
$= \frac{256(b-3)^5}{243(b-3)^4}$
$= \frac{256(b-3)}{243}$ or $\frac{4^4(b-3)}{3^5}$

34. $\left(\frac{5}{y+9}\right) \div \left(\frac{5}{y+9}\right)^5$
$= \frac{5}{y+9} \div \frac{5^5}{(y+9)^5}$
$= \frac{5}{y+9} \cdot \frac{(y+9)^5}{5^5}$
$= \frac{5(y+9)^5}{5^5(y+9)}$
$= \frac{(y+9)^4}{5^4}$
$= \frac{(y+9)^4}{625}$

35. $\frac{2a^2-5ab}{c-3d} \div \frac{(4a^2-25b^2)}{1}$
$= \frac{2a^2-5ab}{c-3d} \cdot \frac{1}{(4a^2-25b^2)}$
$= \frac{2a^2-5ab}{c-3d} \cdot \frac{1}{(2a+5b)(2a-5b)}$
$= \frac{a(2a-5b)}{c-3d} \cdot \frac{1}{(2a+5b)(2a-5b)}$
$= \frac{a}{(c-3d)(2a+5b)}$

36. $\frac{3a^2-5ab-12b^2}{3ab+4b^2} \div \frac{(3b^2-ab)}{1}$
$= \frac{3a^2-5ab-12b^2}{3ab+4b^2} \cdot \frac{1}{3b^2-ab}$
$= \frac{(3a+4b)(a-3b)}{b(3a+4b)} \cdot \frac{1}{b(3b-a)}$
$= \frac{a-3b}{b^2(3b-a)} = \frac{-1}{b^2}$

37. $(x - 2a) \div \frac{a^2x^2 - 4a^4}{a^2x + 2a^3} = (x - 2a) \cdot \frac{a^2x + 2a^3}{a^2x^2 - 4a^4}$

$= (x - 2a) \cdot \frac{a^2(x + 2a)}{a^2(x^2 - 4a^2)}$

$= (x - 2a) \cdot \frac{(x + 2a)}{(x + 2a)(x - 2a)}$

$= 1$

38. $\frac{3x^2 - 2xy - y^2}{x^2 - y^2} \div \frac{3x^2 + 4xy + y^2}{1}$

$= \frac{3x^2 - 2xy - y^2}{x^2 - y^2} \cdot \frac{1}{3x^2 + 4xy + y^2}$

$= \frac{(3x + y)(x - y)}{(x + y)(x - y)} \cdot \frac{1}{(3x + y)(x + y)}$

$= \frac{1}{(x + y)^2}$

39. $\frac{z^2 - 8z + 16}{z^2 + 8z + 16} \div \frac{(z - 4)^5}{(z + 4)^5}$

$= \frac{z^2 - 8z + 16}{z^2 + 8z + 16} \cdot \frac{(z + 4)^5}{(z - 4)^5} = \frac{(z - 4)^2}{(z + 4)^2} \cdot \frac{(z + 4)^5}{(z - 4)^5}$

$= \frac{(z + 4)^3}{(z - 4)^3}$

40. $xy \cdot \frac{y^2 - 4xy}{y - x} \div \frac{16x^2y^2 - y^4}{4x^2 - 3xy - y^2}$

$= xy \cdot \frac{y^2 - 4xy}{y - x} \cdot \frac{4x^2 - 3xy - y^2}{16x^2y^2 - y^4}$

$= xy \cdot \frac{y(y - 4x)}{y - x} \cdot \frac{(4x + y)(x - y)}{y^2(16x^2 - y^2)}$

$= \frac{xy^2}{y^2} \cdot \frac{(y - 4x)}{y - x} \cdot \frac{(4x + y)(x - y)}{(4x + y)(4x - y)}$

$= x \cdot \frac{(y - 4x)}{(4x - y)} \cdot \frac{(4x + y)}{(4x + y)} \cdot \frac{(x - y)}{(y - x)}$

$= x \cdot -1 \cdot 1 \cdot -1 = x$

41. $V = lwh$

$a - 3 = \left(\frac{a + b}{a - 7}\right) w \left(\frac{a - 3}{a - 7}\right)$

$a - 3 = \frac{(a + b)(a - 3)}{(a - 7)^2} \cdot w$

$\frac{(a - 7)^2(a - 3)}{(a + b)(a - 3)} = w$

$\frac{(a - 7)^2}{a + b} = w$

42. $\frac{x^2 - x + xy - y}{x^2 + 6x - 7} \div \frac{x^2 + 2xy + y^2}{4x + 4y}$

$= \frac{x^2 - x + xy - y}{x^2 + 6x - 7} \cdot \frac{4x + 4y}{x^2 + 2xy + y^2}$

$= \frac{x(x - 1) + y(x - 1)}{(x + 7)(x - 1)} \cdot \frac{4(x + y)}{(x + y)^2}$

$= \frac{(x + y)(x - 1)}{(x + 7)(x - 1)} \cdot \frac{4(x + y)}{(x + y)^2}$

$= \frac{4}{x + 7}$

43. $\frac{3x + 3y + 3}{9x} \div \frac{x^2 + 2xy + y^2 - 1}{x^4 + x^2}$

$= \frac{3x + 3y + 3}{9x} \cdot \frac{x^4 + x^2}{x^2 + 2xy + y^2 - 1}$

$= \frac{3(x + y + 1)}{9x} \cdot \frac{x^2(x^2 + 1)}{(x + y)^2 - 1}$

$= \frac{(x + y + 1)}{3} \cdot \frac{x(x^2 + 1)}{(x + y + 1)(x + y - 1)}$

$= \frac{x(x^2 + 1)}{3(x + y - 1)}$

44. $\frac{y^2 + 5y + 6}{y^2} \cdot \frac{3y^3 + 6y^2}{y^2 - y - 12} \div \frac{y^2 - y}{y^2 - 2y - 8}$

$= \left(\frac{y^2 + 5y + 6}{y^2} \cdot \frac{3y^3 + 6y^2}{y^2 - y - 12}\right) \cdot \frac{y^2 - 2y - 8}{y^2 - y}$

$= \left(\frac{(y + 3)(y + 2)}{y^2} \cdot \frac{3y^2(y + 2)}{(y - 4)(y + 3)}\right) \cdot \frac{(y - 4)(y + 2)}{y(y - 1)}$

$= \frac{3(y + 2)^3}{y(y - 1)}$

45. $\frac{a^4 - 81b^4}{a^2c - 6abc + 9b^2c} \cdot \frac{a + 3b}{a^2 + 9b^2} \div \frac{a^2 + 6ab + 9b^2}{(a - 3b)^2}$

$= \frac{a^4 - 81b^4}{a^2c - 6abc + 9b^2c} \cdot \frac{a + 3b}{a^2 + 9b^2} \cdot \frac{(a - 3b)^2}{a^2 + 6ab + 9b^2}$

$= \frac{(a^2 + 9b^2)(a^2 - 9b^2)}{c(a - 3b)^2} \cdot \frac{a + 3b}{a^2 + 9b^2} \cdot \frac{(a - 3b)^2}{(a + 3b)^2}$

$= \frac{a^2 - 9b^2}{c} \cdot \frac{a + 3b}{1} \cdot \frac{1}{(a + 3b)^2}$

$= \frac{(a + 3b)(a - 3b)(a + 3b)}{c(a + 3b)^2} = \frac{a - 3b}{c}$

46. $2x - 3y = 9$ $\quad$ $8x + 4 = -6y$

$-3y = -2x + 9$ $\quad$ $6y = -8x - 4$

$y = \frac{2}{3}x - 3$ $\quad$ $y = -\frac{4}{3}x - \frac{2}{3}$

No, the slopes are not equal.

47. $4y + 9 = x$ $\quad$ $5 + 2y = 8x$

$4y = x - 9$ $\quad$ $2y = 8x - 5$

$y = \frac{1}{4}x - \frac{9}{4}$ $\quad$ $y = 4x - \frac{5}{2}$

No, the slopes are not equal.

48. $6y - 21x = 5$ $\quad$ $8y - 5 = 28x$

$6y = 21x + 5$ $\quad$ $8y = 28x + 5$

$y = \frac{7}{2}x + \frac{5}{6}$ $\quad$ $y = \frac{7}{2}x + \frac{5}{8}$

Yes, the slopes are equal.

49. $5y = 2x - 10$ $\quad$ $2y + 5x = 2$

$y = \frac{2}{5}x - 2$ $\quad$ $2y = -5x + 2$

$y = -\frac{5}{2}x + 1$

$\frac{2}{5} \cdot \left(-\frac{5}{2}\right) = -1$

Yes, the product of the slopes is -1.

50. $4y + 1 = 3x$ $\quad$ $3y - 4x = 3$

$4y = 3x - 1$ $\quad$ $3y = 4x + 3$

$y = \frac{3}{4}x - \frac{1}{4}$ $\quad$ $y = \frac{4}{3}x + 1$

$\frac{3}{4} \cdot \frac{4}{3} = 1$

No, the product of the slopes is not -1.

51. $y = x + 3$ $\quad$ $y + x = -3$

$y = -x - 3$

$1(-1) = -1$

Yes, the product of the slopes is -1.

52. $Q = \frac{5mv}{s}$

$sQ = 5mv$

$\frac{sQ}{5m} = v$

53. $\frac{a}{b} = \frac{c}{d}$

$\frac{ad}{b} = c$

54. $2x + y = -1$

$5 - y = 4x$

$2x + 5 = 4x - 1$ Adding

$6 = 2x$

$3 = x$

$5 - y = 4(3)$

$5 - 12 = y$

$-7 = y$ $(3, -7)$

55. $2x + 3y = 8$ ①

$5y - x = 22$ ②

$x = 5y - 22$ Solving ② for x

$2(5y - 22) + 3y = 8$ Substituting in ①

$10y - 44 + 3y = 8$

$13y = 52$

$y = 4$

$x = 5(4) - 22 = -2$ $(-2, 4)$

56. $9y - 16 = 11x \rightarrow 11x - 9y = -16$ ①

$5x + 1 = 2y \rightarrow -5x + 2y = 1$ ②

$22x - 18y = -32$ Multiplying ① by 2 and rewriting

$-45x + 18y = 9$ Multiplying ② by 9 and rewriting

$-23x = -23$ Adding

$x = 1$

$5(1) + 1 = 2y$

$y = 3$ $(1, 3)$

57. $9a^2 - 81 = 0$

$(3a + 9)(3a - 9) = 0$

$3a + 9 = 0$ or $3a - 9 = 0$

$3a = -9$ or $3a = 9$

$a = -3$ or $a = 3$

58. $c^2 - 2c = 35$

$c^2 - 2c - 35 = 0$

$(c - 7)(c + 5) = 0$

$c - 7 = 0$ or $c + 5 = 0$

$c = 7$ or $c = -5$

59. $|2x + 3| > 5$

$2x + 3 > 5$ or $2x + 3 < -5$

$2x > 2$ or $2x < -8$

$x > 1$ or $x < -4$

60. Let x = Steve's age and $2x$ = Stacey's age.

$(x - 5) + (2x - 5) = 8$

$3x - 10 = 8$

$3x = 18$

$x = 6$

Steve is 6 and Stacey is 12.

LESSON 10-4 TRY THIS pp. 442–443

a. $\frac{3a}{4} + \frac{7a}{4} = \frac{3a + 7a}{4} = \frac{10a}{4} = \frac{5a}{2}$

b. $\frac{8x^2}{x + 4} + \frac{2x^2}{x + 4} = \frac{8x^2 + 2x^2}{x + 4} = \frac{10x^2}{x + 4}$

c. $\frac{x^2 - 4x - 10}{x - 7} + \frac{x - 18}{x - 7} = \frac{x^2 - 4x - 10 + x - 18}{x - 7}$

$= \frac{x^2 - 3x - 28}{x - 7} = \frac{(x - 7)(x + 4)}{x - 7}$

$= x + 4$

d. $\frac{4m + 5}{m - 1} - \frac{2m - 1}{m - 1} = \frac{4m + 5 - (2m - 1)}{m - 1}$

$= \frac{4m + 5 - 2m + 1}{m - 1}$

$= \frac{2m + 6}{m - 1}$

$= \frac{2(m + 3)}{m - 1}$

e. $\frac{2y^2 + 4y - 3}{y + 3} - \frac{y^2 - 2y - 12}{y + 3}$

$= \frac{2y^2 + 4y - 3 - (y^2 - 2y - 12)}{y + 3}$

$= \frac{2y^2 + 4y - 3 - y^2 + 2y + 12}{y + 3}$

$= \frac{y^2 + 6y + 9}{y + 3}$

$= \frac{(y + 3)^2}{y + 3}$

$= y + 3$

LESSON 10-4 EXERCISES pp. 443–444

1. $\frac{3a}{5} + \frac{2a}{5} = \frac{3a + 2a}{5} = \frac{5a}{5} = a$

2. $\frac{6m}{11} + \frac{8m}{11} = \frac{6m + 8m}{11} = \frac{14m}{11}$

3. $\frac{7s}{10} - \frac{2s}{10} = \frac{7s - 2s}{10} = \frac{5s}{10} = \frac{s}{2}$

4. $\frac{18xy}{7} - \frac{11xy}{7} = \frac{18xy - 11xy}{7} = \frac{7xy}{7} = xy$

5. $\frac{6b^2}{c} + \frac{7b^2}{c} = \frac{6b^2 + 7b^2}{c} = \frac{13b^2}{c}$

6. $\frac{10x}{y} - \frac{7x}{y} = \frac{10x - 7x}{y} = \frac{3x}{y}$

7. $\frac{4x + 3}{x + 2} + \frac{3x + 4}{x + 2} = \frac{4x + 3 + 3x + 4}{x + 2} = \frac{7x + 7}{x + 2} = \frac{7(x + 1)}{x + 2}$

8. $\frac{-6m}{m - 5} + \frac{m - 10}{m - 5} = \frac{-6m + m - 10}{m - 5} = \frac{-5m - 10}{m - 5}$

$= \frac{-5(m + 2)}{m + 5}$

9. $\frac{a - 6}{a + 1} - \frac{3a - 4}{a + 1} = \frac{a - 6 - (3a - 4)}{a + 1}$

$= \frac{a - 6 - 3a + 4}{a + 1}$

$= \frac{-2a - 2}{a + 1}$

$= \frac{-2(a + 1)}{a + 1}$

$= -2$

10. $\frac{b + 4}{b + 2} - \frac{3b - 8}{b + 2} = \frac{b + 4 - (3b - 8)}{b + 2}$

$= \frac{b + 4 - 3b + 8}{b + 2}$

$= \frac{-2b + 12}{b + 2} = \frac{-2(b - 6)}{b + 2}$

11. $\frac{y^2 + 5}{y + 2} - \frac{4y + 17}{y + 2} = \frac{y^2 + 5 - (4y + 17)}{y + 2}$

$= \frac{y^2 + 5 - 4y - 17}{y + 2}$

$= \frac{y^2 - 4y - 12}{y + 2} = \frac{(y - 6)(y + 2)}{y + 2}$

$= y - 6$

12. $\frac{x^2+3}{x-2} - \frac{10x-7}{x-2} = \frac{x^2+3-(10x-7)}{x-2}$
$= \frac{x^2+3-10x+7}{x-2}$
$= \frac{x^2-10x+10}{x-2}$

13. $\frac{3a+5}{a-1} + \frac{2a-6}{a-1} = \frac{3a+5+2a-6}{a-1}$
$= \frac{5a-1}{a-1}$

14. $\frac{4p-3}{p+2} + \frac{5-3p}{p+2} = \frac{4p-3+5-3p}{p+2} = \frac{p+2}{p+2} = 1$

15. $\frac{z-6}{2z+3} - \frac{5z}{2z+3} = \frac{z-6-5z}{2z+3}$
$= \frac{-4z-6}{2z+3} = \frac{-2(2z+3)}{2z+3} = -2$

16. $\frac{x-9}{3x+2} - \frac{7x-5}{3x+2} = \frac{x-9-(7x-5)}{3x+2}$
$= \frac{x-9-7x+5}{3x+2}$
$= \frac{-6x-4}{3x+2} = \frac{-2(3x+2)}{3x+2} = -2$

17. $\frac{y-3}{y+5} - \frac{2y-7}{y+5} = \frac{y-3-(2y-7)}{y+5}$
$= \frac{y-3-2y+7}{y+5}$
$= \frac{-y+4}{y+5}$

18. $\frac{m+9}{m+3} - \frac{-4m-6}{m+3} = \frac{m+9-(-4m-6)}{m+3}$
$= \frac{m+9+4m+6}{m+3}$
$= \frac{5m+15}{m+3}$
$= \frac{5(m+3)}{m+3}$
$= 5$

19. $\frac{n^2+3n}{n+4} + \frac{2n^2-13n-8}{n+4} = \frac{3n^2-10n-8}{n+4}$
$= \frac{(3n+2)(n-4)}{n+4}$

20. $\frac{z+6}{z+5} + \frac{3z^2+19z+19}{z+5} = \frac{3z^2+20z+25}{z+5}$
$= \frac{(3z+5)(z+5)}{z+5}$
$= 3z+5$

21. $\frac{5x^2-3x+2}{2x-1} - \frac{3x^2+3x-2}{2x-1}$
$= \frac{5x^2-3x+2-(3x^2+3x-2)}{2x-1}$
$= \frac{5x^2-3x+2-3x^2-3x+2}{2x-1}$
$= \frac{2x^2-6x+4}{2x-1} = \frac{2(x^2-3x+2)}{2x-1}$
$= \frac{2(x-2)(x-1)}{2x-1}$

22. $\frac{4y^2+2y-3}{5y+1} - \frac{3y^2-2y-4}{5y+1}$
$= \frac{4y^2+2y-3-(3y^2-2y-4)}{5y+1}$
$= \frac{4y^2+2y-3-3y^2+2y+4}{5y+1}$
$= \frac{y^2+4y+1}{5y+1}$

23. $\frac{a-1}{a^2-2a+1} + \frac{5-3a}{a^2-2a+1} = \frac{a-1+5-3a}{a^2-2a+1}$
$= \frac{-2a+4}{a^2-2a+1}$
$= \frac{-2(a-2)}{(a-1)(a-1)}$

24. $\frac{3m-3}{m^2+3m-4} + \frac{m-7}{m^2+3m-4} = \frac{3m-3+m-7}{m^2+3m-4}$
$= \frac{4m-10}{m^2+3m-4}$
$= \frac{2(2m-5)}{(m+4)(m-1)}$

25. $\frac{4a+5}{a-2} + \frac{6a-4}{a-2} + \frac{5}{a-2} = \frac{4a+5+6a-4+5}{a-2}$
$= \frac{10a+6}{a-2}$
$= \frac{2(5a+3)}{a-2}$

26. $\frac{5x-3}{x+1} + \frac{2x}{x+1} + \frac{4}{x+1} = \frac{5x-3+2x+4}{x+1} = \frac{7x+1}{x+1}$

27. $\frac{3a+3}{a+2} + \frac{a^2-2a}{a+2} + \frac{6}{a+2} = \frac{3a+3+a^2-2a+6}{a+2}$
$= \frac{a^2+a+9}{a+2}$

28. $\frac{2b}{b+4} - \frac{4b}{b+4} - \frac{-2b^2-3b+5}{b+4}$
$= \frac{2b-4b-(-2b^2-3b+5)}{b+4}$
$= \frac{2b-4b+2b^2+3b-5}{b+4}$
$= \frac{2b^2+b-5}{b+4}$

29. $\frac{x^2+3x-2}{x-1} + \frac{2x+4}{x-1} + \frac{x^2-x+1}{x-1}$
$= \frac{x^2+3x-2+2x+4+x^2-x+1}{x-1}$
$= \frac{2x^2+4x+3}{x-1}$

30. $\frac{4a^2+2a-3}{3a+4} + \frac{a^2+2a-15}{3a+4} + \frac{a^2+6a-6}{3a+4}$
$= \frac{4a^2+2a-3+a^2+2a-15+a^2+6a-6}{3a+4}$
$= \frac{6a^2+10a-24}{3a+4} = \frac{2(3a^2+5a-12)}{3a+4} = \frac{2(3a-4)(a+3)}{3a+4}$

31. $\frac{y^2-3y}{2y+1} - \frac{3y^2+4y}{2y+1} - \frac{y^2+3y}{2y+1}$
$= \frac{y^2-3y-(3y^2+4y)-(y^2+3y)}{2y+1}$
$= \frac{y^2-3y-3y^2-4y-y^2-3y}{2y+1}$
$= \frac{-3y^2-10y}{2y+1} = \frac{y(-3y-10)}{2y+1} = \frac{-y(3y+10)}{2y+1}$

32. $\frac{p^2-6}{3p+8} + \frac{2p^2+5p-3}{3p+8} - \frac{3p^2+p-4}{3p+8}$
$= \frac{p^2-6+2p^2+5p-3-(3p^2+p-4)}{3p+8}$
$= \frac{3p^2+5p-9-3p^2-p+4}{3p+8} = \frac{4p-5}{3p+8}$

33. $\frac{3x^2+4x-12}{(3x+4)(x-1)} - \frac{5x^2-2x-6}{(3x+4)(x-1)} - \frac{-14x^2-4x+2}{(3x+4)(x-1)}$

$= \frac{3x^2+4x-12-(5x^2-2x-6)-(-14x^2-4x+2)}{(3x+4)(x-1)}$

$= \frac{3x^2+4x-12-5x^2+2x+6+14x^2+4x-2}{(3x+4)(x-1)}$

$= \frac{12x^2+10x-8}{(3x+4)(x-1)} = \frac{(3x+4)(4x-2)}{(3x+4)(x-1)}$

$= \frac{4x-2}{x-1} = \frac{2(2x-1)}{x-1}$

34. $\frac{10b^2+b-2}{(5b+2)(2b+1)} + \frac{12b^2-5b}{(5b+2)(2b+1)} - \frac{-8b^2-7b+4}{(5b+2)(2b+1)}$

$= \frac{10b^2+b-2+12b^2-5b-(-8b^2-7b+4)}{(5b+2)(2b+1)}$

$= \frac{22b^2-4b-2+8b^2+7b-4}{(5b+2)(2b+1)}$

$= \frac{30b^2+3b-6}{(5b+2)(2b+1)} = \frac{3(10b^2+b-2)}{(5b+2)(2b+1)}$

$= \frac{3(2b+1)(5b-2)}{(5b+2)(2b+1)} = \frac{3(5b-2)}{5b+2}$

35. Let length $= l$.

$l + \frac{x^2-5x-9}{x-6} + \frac{x^2-6}{x-6} = 2x+5$

$l = \frac{2x+5}{1} - \frac{x^2-5x-9}{x-6} - \frac{x^2-6}{x-6}$

$= \frac{(x-6)(2x+5)}{(x-6)} - \frac{x^2-5x-9}{x-6} - \frac{x^2-6}{x-6}$

$= \frac{2x^2-7x-30-(x^2-5x-9)-(x^2-6)}{x-6}$

$= \frac{2x^2-7x-30-x^2+5x+9-x^2+6}{x-6}$

$l = \frac{-2x-15}{x-6}$

36. $\frac{x^2}{(3x+1)(x-2)} - \frac{2x\cdot 1}{(3x+1)(x-2)} = \frac{x^2-2x}{(3x+1)(x-2)}$

$= \frac{x(x-2)}{(3x+1)(x-2)}$

$= \frac{x}{3x+1}$

37. $\frac{3}{x+4}\cdot\frac{2x+11}{x-3} - \frac{-1}{4+x}\cdot\frac{(6x+3)(-1)}{(3-x)(-1)}$

$= \frac{3(2x+11)}{(x+4)(x-3)} - \frac{(-1)(-1)(6x+3)}{(x+4)(x-3)}$

$= \frac{6x+33-6x-3}{(x+4)(x-3)} = \frac{30}{(x+4)(x-3)}$

38. $\frac{6x^2y}{3y^2} = \frac{2x^2}{y}$

39. $\frac{m^2-36}{4m+24} = \frac{(m+6)(m-6)}{4(m+6)} = \frac{m-6}{4}$

40. $\frac{4-a}{a^2-16} = \frac{-(a-4)}{(a+4)(a-4)} = \frac{-1}{a+4}$

41. $(-3t^2)^4 = (-3)^4t^{2\cdot 4} = 81t^8$

42. $\left(\frac{y^4}{6}\right)^2 = \frac{y^{4\cdot 2}}{6^2} = \frac{y^8}{36}$

43. $\left(\frac{m^4n^2}{2}\right)^6 = \frac{m^{4\cdot 6}n^{2\cdot 6}}{2^6} = \frac{m^{24}n^{12}}{64}$

44. $(-3ab)^2 = (-3)^2a^2b^2 = 9a^2b^2$

45. $\left(\frac{-2x}{y}\right)^2 = \frac{(-2)^2x^2}{y^2} = \frac{4x^2}{y^2}$

46. $x + y = -2$ ①

$xy = -24$ ②

$y = -x - 2$ Solving ① for y

$x(-x-2) = -24$ Substituting in ②

$-x^2 - 2x = -24$

$x^2 + 2x - 24 = 0$

$(x+6)(x-4) = 0$

$x + 6 = 0 \quad x - 4 = 0$

$x = -6$ or $x = 4$

If $x = -6, y = 6 - 2 = 4$.

If $x = 4, y = -4 - 2 = -6$.

The numbers are 4 and -6.

47. $x - y = 2$ ①

$x^2 - y^2 = 40$ ②

$x = y + 2$ Solving ① for x

$(y+2)^2 - y^2 = 40$ Substituting in ②

$y^2 + 4y + 4 - y^2 = 40$

$4y = 36$

$y = 9$

$x = 9 + 2 = 11$

The numbers are 9 and 11.

LESSON 10-5 TRY THIS pp. 445–448

a. $\frac{2x}{3} + \frac{6}{x} = \frac{2x(x)+6(3)}{3x} = \frac{2x^2+18}{3x} = \frac{2(x^2+9)}{3x}$

b. $\frac{7x^2}{6} + \frac{3x}{16} = \frac{7x^2(16)+3x(6)}{6(16)} = \frac{2x(56x+9)}{6(16)} = \frac{x(56x+9)}{48}$

c. $\frac{x}{x-2} + \frac{x}{x+2} = \frac{x(x+2)+4(x-2)}{(x-2)(x+2)}$

$= \frac{x^2+2x+4x-8}{(x-2)(x+2)} = \frac{x^2+6x-8}{(x-2)(x+2)}$

d. $\frac{4}{5x} - \frac{1}{x^2} = \frac{4x^2-1(5x)}{5x(x^2)} = \frac{x(4x-5)}{5x(x^2)} = \frac{4x-5}{5x^2}$

e. $\frac{3}{2x+1} - \frac{2}{2x-1} = \frac{3(2x-1)-2(2x+1)}{(2x+1)(2x-1)}$

$= \frac{6x-3-4x-2}{(2x+1)(2x-1)} = \frac{2x-5}{(2x+1)(2x-1)}$

f. $6 - \frac{1}{t-2} = \frac{6}{1} - \frac{1}{t-2} = \frac{6(t-2)-1(1)}{1(t-2)}$

$= \frac{6t-12-1}{t-2} = \frac{6t-13}{t-2}$

g. $12xy^2 = 2\cdot 2\cdot 3\cdot x\cdot y\cdot y$

$15x^3y = 5\cdot 3\cdot x\cdot x\cdot x\cdot y$

$\text{LCM} = 2\cdot 2\cdot 3\cdot 5\cdot x\cdot x\cdot x\cdot y\cdot y = 60x^3y^2$

h. $y^2 + 5y + 4 = (y+4)(y+1)$

$y^2 + 2y + 1 = (y+1)(y+1)$

$\text{LCM} = (y+1)(y+1)(y+4) = (y+1)^2(y+4)$

i. $t^2 - 16 = (t+4)(t-4)$

$4 - t = -1(t-4)$

$\text{LCM} = (t+4)(t-4)$

j. $\frac{3x}{25} + \frac{x^2}{10} = \frac{3x}{25}\cdot\frac{2}{2} + \frac{x^2}{10}\cdot\frac{5}{5} = \frac{6x}{50} + \frac{5x^2}{50}$

$= \frac{6x+5x^2}{50} = \frac{x(6+5x)}{50}$

k. $\frac{3}{xy^2} - \frac{x+y}{x^2y} = \frac{3}{xy^2}\cdot\frac{x}{x} - \frac{x+y}{x^2y}\cdot\frac{y}{y}$

$= \frac{3x}{x^2y^2} - \frac{y(x+y)}{x^2y^2} = \frac{3x-xy-y^2}{x^2y^2}$

l. $\frac{4}{3-b} + \frac{b}{2b-6} = \frac{4}{3-b}\cdot\frac{-2}{-2} + \frac{b}{2b-6} = \frac{-8}{2b-6} + \frac{b}{2b-6}$

$= \frac{b-8}{2b-6} = \frac{b-8}{2(b-3)}$

LESSON 10-5 EXERCISES pp. 448–450

1. $\frac{a^2}{2} + \frac{3a^2}{8} = \frac{a^2(8) + 3a^2(2)}{2(8)} = \frac{14a^2}{16} = \frac{7a^2}{8}$

2. $\frac{8y}{10} + \frac{2y}{5} = \frac{8y(5) + 2y(10)}{10(5)} = \frac{60y}{50y} = \frac{6y}{5}$

3. $\frac{4c}{15} + \frac{8c}{25} = \frac{4c(25) + 8c(15)}{15(25)} = \frac{220c}{375} = \frac{44c}{75}$

4. $\frac{2}{x} + \frac{5}{x^2} = \frac{2x^2 + 5x}{x(x^2)} = \frac{x(2x + 5)}{x(x^2)} = \frac{2x + 5}{x^2}$

5. $\frac{4}{x} + \frac{8}{x^2} = \frac{4x^2 + 8x}{x(x^2)} = \frac{4x(x + 2)}{x(x^2)} = \frac{4(x + 2)}{x^2}$

6. $\frac{5}{6r} + \frac{7}{8r} = \frac{5(8r) + 7(6r)}{6r(8r)} = \frac{2r(20 + 21)}{6r(8r)} = \frac{41}{24r}$

7. $\frac{3}{x - 2} + \frac{3}{x + 2} = \frac{3(x + 2) + 3(x - 2)}{(x - 2)(x + 2)} = \frac{3x + 6 + 3x - 6}{(x - 2)(x + 2)}$
$= \frac{6x}{(x - 2)(x + 2)}$

8. $\frac{2}{x - 1} + \frac{2}{x + 1} = \frac{2(x + 1) + 2(x - 1)}{(x - 1)(x + 1)} = \frac{2x + 2 + 2x - 2}{(x - 1)(x + 1)}$
$= \frac{4x}{(x - 1)(x + 1)}$

9. $\frac{3}{x + 1} + \frac{2}{3x} = \frac{3(3x) + 2(x + 1)}{(x + 1)(3x)} = \frac{9x + 2x + 2}{3x(x + 1)}$
$= \frac{11x + 2}{3x(x + 1)}$

10. $\frac{x - 2}{6} - \frac{x + 1}{3} = \frac{(x - 2)3 - (x + 1)6}{6(3)} = \frac{3x - 6 - 6x - 6}{18}$
$= \frac{-3x - 12}{18} = \frac{3(-x - 4)}{18} = \frac{-x - 4}{6}$

11. $\frac{a + 2}{2} - \frac{a - 4}{4} = \frac{(a + 2)4 - (a - 4)2}{2(4)} = \frac{4a + 8 - 2a + 8}{8}$
$= \frac{2a + 16}{8} = \frac{2(a + 8)}{8} = \frac{a + 8}{4}$

12. $\frac{y - 5}{y} - \frac{3y - 1}{4y} = \frac{(y - 5)4y - (3y - 1)y}{y(4y)}$
$= \frac{4y^2 - 20y - 3y^2 + y}{4y^2} = \frac{y^2 - 19y}{4y^2}$
$= \frac{y(y - 19)}{4y^2} = \frac{y - 19}{4y}$

13. $\frac{x - 1}{4x} - \frac{2x + 3}{x} = \frac{(x - 1)x - (2x + 3)4x}{4x(x)}$
$= \frac{x^2 - x - 8x^2 - 12x}{4x^2} = \frac{-7x^2 - 13x}{4x^2}$
$= \frac{x(-7x - 13)}{4x^2} = \frac{-7x - 13}{4x}$

14. $2 - \frac{2x + 1}{5} = \frac{2}{1} - \frac{2x + 1}{5} = \frac{2(5) - (2x + 1)1}{1(5)}$
$= \frac{10 - 2x - 1}{5} = \frac{9 - 2x}{5}$

15. $3x - \frac{x}{x - 2} = \frac{3x}{1} - \frac{x}{x - 2} = \frac{3x(x - 2) - x(1)}{1(x - 2)}$
$= \frac{3x^2 - 6x - x}{x - 2} = \frac{3x^2 - 7x}{x - 2} = \frac{x(3x - 7)}{x - 2}$

16. $\frac{2}{x + 5} - \frac{3}{4x} = \frac{2(4x) - 3(x + 5)}{(x + 5)4x} = \frac{8x - 3x - 15}{4x(x + 5)}$
$= \frac{5x - 15}{4x(x + 5)} = \frac{5(x - 3)}{4x(x + 5)}$

17. $\frac{x + 4}{x} - \frac{x}{x + 4} = \frac{(x + 4)(x + 4) - x(x)}{x(x + 4)}$
$= \frac{x^2 + 8x + 16 - x^2}{x(x + 4)} = \frac{8(x + 2)}{x(x + 4)}$

18. $\frac{x}{x - 5} - \frac{x - 5}{x} = \frac{x(x) - (x - 5)(x - 5)}{(x - 5)x}$
$= \frac{x^2 - (x^2 - 10x + 25)}{x(x - 5)}$
$= \frac{x^2 - x^2 + 10x - 25}{x(x - 5)} = \frac{5(2x - 5)}{x(x - 5)}$

19. $c^2d = c \cdot c \cdot d$
$cd^2 = c \cdot d \cdot d$
LCM $= c \cdot c \cdot d \cdot d = c^2d^2$

20. $2x^2 = 2 \cdot x \cdot x$
$6xy = 2 \cdot 3 \cdot x \cdot y$
LCM $= 2 \cdot 3 \cdot x \cdot x \cdot y = 6x^2y$

21. $(x - y)(x + y)$ 22. $(a - 5)(a + 5)$

23. $2(y - 3) = 2 \cdot (y - 3)$
$6(3 - y) = 2 \cdot 3 \cdot (3 - y)$
LCM $= 2 \cdot 3 \cdot (y - 3)$ or $2 \cdot 3 \cdot (3 - y)$
$= 6(y - 3)$ or $6(3 - y)$

24. $4(x - 1) = 2 \cdot 2 \cdot (x - 1)$
$8(1 - x) = 2 \cdot 2 \cdot 2 \cdot (1 - x)$
LCM $= 2 \cdot 2 \cdot 2 \cdot (x - 1)$ or $2 \cdot 2 \cdot 2(1 - x)$
$= 8(x - 1)$ or $8(1 - x)$

25. $(t + 2)(t - 2)$ 26. $(x + 3)(x - 3)$

27. $x^2 - 4 = (x + 2)(x - 2)$
$x^2 + 5x + 6 = (x + 2)(x + 3)$
LCM $= (x + 2)(x - 2)(x + 3)$

28. $x^2 + 3x + 2 = (x + 2)(x + 1)$
$x^2 - 4 = (x + 2)(x - 2)$
LCM $= (x + 1)(x + 2)(x - 2)$

29. $t^3 + 4t^2 + 4t = t(t^2 + 4t + 4) = t(t + 2)^2$
$t^2 - 4t = t(t - 4)$
LCM $= t(t - 4)(t + 2)^2$

30. $y^3 - y^2 = y^2(y - 1) = y \cdot y \cdot (y - 1)$
$y^4 - y^2 = y^2(y^2 - 1) = y \cdot y \cdot (y + 1)(y - 1)$
LCM $= y \cdot y \cdot (y + 1)(y - 1) = y^2(y + 1)(y - 1)$

31. $a^2 - 1 = (a + 1)(a - 1)$
$a + 1 = a + 1$
LCM $= (a + 1)(a - 1)$

32. $x^2 - y^2 = (x + y)(x - y)$
$x^2 + 2xy + y^2 = (x + y)(x + y)$
LCM $= (x + y)^2(x - y)$

33. $m^2 - 5m + 6 = (m - 2)(m - 3)$
$m^2 - 4m + 4 = (m - 2)(m - 2)$
LCM $= (m - 2)^2(m - 3)$

34. $2x^2 + 5x + 2 = (2x + 1)(x + 2)$
$2x^2 - x - 1 = (2x + 1)(x - 1)$
LCM $= (2x + 1)(x + 2)(x - 1)$

35. $\frac{2}{9t} + \frac{11}{6t} = \frac{2}{3 \cdot 3 \cdot t} + \frac{11}{2 \cdot 3 \cdot t}$ LCM $= 2 \cdot 3 \cdot 3 \cdot t = 18t$
$= \frac{2}{9t} \cdot \frac{2}{2} + \frac{11}{6t} \cdot \frac{3}{3}$
$= \frac{4}{18t} + \frac{33}{18t} = \frac{37}{18t}$

36. $\frac{x + y}{xy^2} + \frac{3x + y}{x^2y} = \frac{x + y}{x \cdot y \cdot y} + \frac{3x + y}{x \cdot x \cdot y}$
LCM $= x \cdot x \cdot y \cdot y = x^2y^2$
$= \frac{x}{x} \cdot \frac{x + y}{xy^2} + \frac{y}{y} \cdot \frac{3x + y}{x^2y}$
$= \frac{x(x + y)}{x^2y^2} + \frac{y(3x + y)}{x^2y^2}$
$= \frac{x^2 + xy}{x^2y^2} + \frac{3xy + y^2}{x^2y^2}$
$= \frac{x^2 + 4xy + y^2}{x^2y^2}$

37. $\frac{2c-d}{c^2d} + \frac{c+d}{cd^2} = \frac{2c-d}{c \cdot c \cdot d} + \frac{c+d}{c \cdot d \cdot d}$

$\text{LCM} = c \cdot c \cdot d \cdot d = c^2d^2$

$= \frac{d}{d} \cdot \frac{2c-d}{c^2d} + \frac{c}{c} \cdot \frac{c+d}{cd^2}$

$= \frac{d(2c-d)}{c^2d^2} + \frac{c(c+d)}{c^2d^2}$

$= \frac{2cd - d^2 + c^2 + cd}{c^2d^2}$

$= \frac{c^2 + 3cd - d^2}{c^2d^2}$

38. $\frac{t}{t-3} + \frac{5}{4t-12} = \frac{t}{t-3} + \frac{5}{4(t-3)}$ $\quad \text{LCM} = 4(t-3)$

$= \frac{4}{4} \cdot \frac{t}{t-3} + \frac{5}{4(t-3)}$

$= \frac{4t+5}{4(t-3)}$

39. $\frac{3}{x-1} + \frac{2}{(x-1)^2}$ $\quad \text{LCM} = (x-1)(x-1)$

$= \frac{x-1}{x-1} \cdot \frac{3}{x-1} + \frac{2}{(x-1)(x-1)}$

$= \frac{3(x-1)+2}{(x-1)(x-1)}$

$= \frac{3x-3+2}{(x-1)^2}$

$= \frac{3x-1}{(x-1)^2}$

40. $\frac{2}{x+3} + \frac{4}{(x+3)^2}$ $\quad \text{LCM} = (x+3)(x+3)$

$= \frac{x+3}{x+3} \cdot \frac{2}{x+3} + \frac{4}{(x+3)(x+3)}$

$= \frac{2(x+3)+4}{(x+3)(x+3)} = \frac{2x+6+4}{(x+3)(x+3)}$

$= \frac{2x+10}{(x+3)^2} = \frac{2(x+5)}{(x+3)^2}$

41. $\frac{4a}{5a-10} + \frac{3a}{10a-20} = \frac{4a}{5(a-2)} + \frac{3a}{10(a-2)}$

$\text{LCM} = 10(a-2)$

$= \frac{2}{2} \cdot \frac{4a}{5(a-2)} + \frac{3a}{10(a-2)}$

$= \frac{8a+3a}{10(a-2)} = \frac{11a}{10(a-2)}$

42. $\frac{3a}{4a-20} + \frac{9a}{6a-30} = \frac{3a}{4(a-5)} + \frac{9a}{6(a-5)}$

$= \frac{3a}{2 \cdot 2(a-5)} + \frac{9a}{2 \cdot 3(a-5)}$

$\text{LCM} = 2 \cdot 2 \cdot 3(a-5) = 12(a-5)$

$= \frac{3}{3} \cdot \frac{3a}{2 \cdot 2(a-5)} + \frac{2}{2} \cdot \frac{9a}{2 \cdot 3(a-5)}$

$= \frac{9a}{12(a-5)} + \frac{18a}{12(a-5)}$

$= \frac{27a}{12(a-5)} = \frac{9a}{4(a-5)}$

43. $\frac{x}{x^2+2x+1} + \frac{1}{x^2+5x+4}$

$= \frac{x}{(x+1)(x+1)} + \frac{1}{(x+4)(x+1)}$

$\text{LCM} = (x+1)(x+1)(x+4)$

$= \frac{x+4}{x+4} \cdot \frac{x}{(x+1)^2} + \frac{x+1}{x+1} \cdot \frac{1}{(x+4)(x+1)}$

$= \frac{x(x+4)}{(x+1)^2(x+4)} + \frac{x+1}{(x+1)^2(x+4)}$

$= \frac{x^2+4x+x+1}{(x+1)^2(x+4)}$

$= \frac{x^2+5x+1}{(x+1)^2(x+4)}$

44. $\frac{7}{a^2+a-2} + \frac{5}{a^2-4a+3}$

$= \frac{7}{(a+2)(a-1)} + \frac{5}{(a-3)(a-1)}$

$\text{LCM} = (a+2)(a-3)(a-1)$

$= \frac{a-3}{a-3} \cdot \frac{7}{(a+2)(a-1)} + \frac{a+2}{a+2} \cdot \frac{5}{(a-3)(a-1)}$

$= \frac{7(a-3)+5(a+2)}{(a+2)(a-3)(a-1)}$

$= \frac{7a-21+5a+10}{(a+2)(a-3)(a-1)}$

$= \frac{12a-11}{(a+2)(a-3)(a-1)}$

45. $\frac{3-b}{b-7} + \frac{2b-5}{7-b}$ $\quad \text{LCM} = (b-7)$ or $(7-b)$

Using $(b-7)$: $\quad \frac{3-b}{b-7} + \frac{(-1)(2b-5)}{b-7}$

$= \frac{3-b-2b+5}{b-7} = \frac{-3b+8}{b-7}$ or $\frac{3b-8}{7-b}$

46. $\frac{x}{x-1} + \frac{1}{1-x}$ $\quad \text{LCM} = (x-1)$ or $(1-x)$

Using $(x-1)$: $\quad \frac{x}{x-1} + \frac{(-1)}{x-1} = \frac{x-1}{x-1} = 1$

47. $\frac{t^2}{t-2} - \frac{4}{2-t}$ $\quad \text{LCM} = (t-2)$ or $(2-t)$

Using $(t-2)$: $\quad \frac{t^2}{t-2} - \frac{(-1)4}{t-2} = \frac{t^2+4}{t-2}$

48. $\frac{y^2}{y-3} - \frac{9}{3-y}$ $\quad \text{LCM} = (y-3)$ or $(3-y)$

Using $(y-3)$: $\quad \frac{y^2}{y-3} - \frac{(-1)9}{y-3} = \frac{y^2+9}{y-3}$

49. $\frac{2z}{z-1} - \frac{3z}{z+1}$ $\quad \text{LCM} = (z-1)(z+1)$

$= \frac{z+1}{z+1} \cdot \frac{2z}{z-1} - \frac{z-1}{z-1} \cdot \frac{3z}{z+1}$

$= \frac{2z(z+1) - 3z(z-1)}{(z+1)(z-1)}$

$= \frac{2z^2+2z-3z^2+3z}{(z+1)(z-1)}$

$= \frac{-z^2+5z}{(z+1)(z-1)}$

$= \frac{z(5-z)}{(z+1)(z-1)}$

50. $\frac{5x}{x^2-9} - \frac{4}{x+3} = \frac{5x}{(x+3)(x-3)} - \frac{4}{x+3}$

$\text{LCM} = (x+3)(x-3)$

$= \frac{5x}{(x+3)(x-3)} - \frac{x-3}{x-3} \cdot \frac{4}{x+3}$

$= \frac{5x-4(x-3)}{(x+3)(x-3)}$

$= \frac{5x-4x+12}{(x+3)(x-3)} = \frac{x+12}{(x+3)(x-3)}$

51. $\frac{8x}{x^2-16} - \frac{5}{x+4} = \frac{8x}{(x+4)(x-4)} - \frac{5}{x+4}$

$\text{LCM} = (x+4)(x-4)$

$= \frac{8x}{(x+4)(x-4)} - \frac{x-4}{x-4} \cdot \frac{5}{x+4}$

$= \frac{8x-5(x-4)}{(x+4)(x-4)}$

$= \frac{8x-5x+20}{(x+4)(x-4)} = \frac{3x+20}{(x+4)(x-4)}$

52. $\dfrac{3}{2t^2 - 2t} - \dfrac{5}{2t - 2} = \dfrac{3}{2t(t-1)} - \dfrac{5}{2(t-1)}$

LCM $= 2t(t-1)$

$= \dfrac{3}{2t(t-1)} - \dfrac{t}{t} \cdot \dfrac{5}{2(t-1)}$

$= \dfrac{3 - 5t}{2t(t-1)}$

53. $\dfrac{4}{5b^2 - 5b} - \dfrac{3}{5b - 5} = \dfrac{4}{5b(b-1)} - \dfrac{3}{5(b-1)}$

LCM $= 5b(b-1)$

$= \dfrac{4}{5b(b-1)} - \dfrac{b}{b} \cdot \dfrac{3}{5(b-1)}$

$= \dfrac{4 - 3b}{5b(b-1)}$

54. $\dfrac{2s}{t^2 - s^2} - \dfrac{s}{t - s} = \dfrac{2s}{(t+s)(t-s)} - \dfrac{s}{(t-s)}$

LCM $= (t+s)(t-s)$

$= \dfrac{2s}{(t+s)(t-s)} - \dfrac{t+s}{t+s} \cdot \dfrac{s}{(t-s)}$

$= \dfrac{2s - s(t+s)}{(t+s)(t-s)}$

$= \dfrac{2s - st - s^2}{(t+s)(t-s)}$

$= \dfrac{s(2 - t - s)}{(t+s)(t-s)}$

55. $\dfrac{2x}{x^2 - 16} + \dfrac{x}{x - 4} = \dfrac{2x}{(x+4)(x-4)} + \dfrac{x}{x-4}$

LCM $= (x+4)(x-4)$

$= \dfrac{2x}{(x+4)(x-4)} + \dfrac{x+4}{x+4} \cdot \dfrac{x}{x-4}$

$= \dfrac{2x + x(x+4)}{(x+4)(x-4)} = \dfrac{2x + x^2 + 4x}{(x+4)(x-4)}$

$= \dfrac{x^2 + 6x}{(x+4)(x-4)} = \dfrac{x(x+6)}{(x+4)(x-4)}$

56. $\dfrac{4x}{x^2 - 25} + \dfrac{x}{x + 5} = \dfrac{4x}{(x+5)(x-5)} + \dfrac{x}{x+5}$

LCM $= (x+5)(x-5)$

$= \dfrac{4x}{(x+5)(x-5)} + \dfrac{x-5}{x-5} \cdot \dfrac{x}{x+5}$

$= \dfrac{4x + x(x-5)}{(x+5)(x-5)}$

$= \dfrac{4x + x^2 - 5x}{(x+5)(x-5)}$

$= \dfrac{x^2 - x}{(x+5)(x-5)}$

$= \dfrac{x(x-1)}{(x+5)(x-5)}$

57. $\dfrac{5}{z + 4} + \dfrac{3}{3z + 12} = \dfrac{5}{z+4} + \dfrac{3}{3(z+4)}$ LCM $= 3(z+4)$

$= \dfrac{3}{3} \cdot \dfrac{5}{z+4} + \dfrac{3}{3(z+4)}$

$= \dfrac{3 \cdot 5 + 3}{3(z+4)}$

$= \dfrac{15 + 3}{3(z+4)} = \dfrac{18}{3(z+4)} = \dfrac{6}{z+4}$

58. $\dfrac{5x + 3y}{2x^2y} - \dfrac{3x - 4y}{xy^2} = \dfrac{5x + 3y}{2 \cdot x \cdot x \cdot y} - \dfrac{3x - 4y}{x \cdot y \cdot y}$

LCM $= 2 \cdot x \cdot x \cdot y \cdot y = 2x^2y^2$

$= \dfrac{y}{y} \cdot \dfrac{5x + 3y}{2 \cdot x \cdot x \cdot y} - \dfrac{2x}{2x} \cdot \dfrac{3x - 4y}{x \cdot y \cdot y}$

$= \dfrac{y(5x + 3y) - 2x(3x - 4y)}{2x^2y^2}$

$= \dfrac{5xy + 3y^2 - 6x^2 + 8xy}{2x^2y^2}$

$= \dfrac{-6x^2 + 13xy + 3y^2}{2x^2y^2}$

59. $\dfrac{4x + 2t}{3xt^2} - \dfrac{5x - 3t}{x^2t}$ LCM $= 3x^2t^2$

$= \dfrac{x}{x} \cdot \dfrac{4x + 2t}{3xt^2} - \dfrac{3t}{3t} \cdot \dfrac{5x - 3t}{x^2t}$

$= \dfrac{x(4x + 2t) - 3t(5x - 3t)}{3x^2t^2}$

$= \dfrac{4x^2 + 2xt - 15xt + 9t^2}{3x^2t^2}$

$= \dfrac{4x^2 - 13xt + 9t^2}{3x^2t^2}$

60. $\dfrac{5}{x + 5} - \dfrac{3}{x - 5}$ LCM $= (x+5)(x-5)$

$= \dfrac{x-5}{x-5} \cdot \dfrac{5}{x+5} - \dfrac{x+5}{x+5} \cdot \dfrac{3}{x-5}$

$= \dfrac{5(x-5) - 3(x+5)}{(x+5)(x-5)} = \dfrac{5x - 25 - 3x - 15}{(x+5)(x-5)}$

$= \dfrac{2x - 40}{(x+5)(x-5)} = \dfrac{2(x - 20)}{(x+5)(x-5)}$

61. $\dfrac{y - 8}{y^2 - 16} + \dfrac{y - 8}{16 - y^2}$ LCM $= (y^2 - 16)$ or $(16 - y^2)$

Using $y^2 - 16$: $\dfrac{y - 8}{y^2 - 16} + \dfrac{(-1)(y - 8)}{y^2 - 16}$

$= \dfrac{y - 8 - y + 8}{y^2 - 16} = \dfrac{0}{y^2 - 16} = 0$

62. $\dfrac{a + 3}{a - 5} - \dfrac{2a - 1}{5 - a}$ LCM $= (a - 5)$ or $(5 - a)$

Using $(a - 5)$: $\dfrac{a + 3}{a - 5} - \dfrac{(-1)(2a - 1)}{a - 5}$

$= \dfrac{a + 3 + 2a - 1}{a - 5} = \dfrac{3a + 2}{a - 5}$

63. $\dfrac{3(x - 2)}{2x - 3} - \dfrac{3(x - 1)}{3 - 2x}$ LCM $= (2x - 3)$ or $(3 - 2x)$

Using $(2x - 3)$: $\dfrac{3(x - 2)}{2x - 3} - \dfrac{(-1)(3)(x - 1)}{2x - 3}$

$= \dfrac{3(x - 2) + 3(x - 1)}{2x - 3} = \dfrac{3x - 6 + 3x - 3}{2x - 3}$

$= \dfrac{6x - 9}{2x - 3} = \dfrac{3(2x - 3)}{(2x - 3)} = 3$

64. $\dfrac{m - 2}{m^2 - 25} + \dfrac{m - 2}{25 - m^2}$ LCM $= (m^2 - 25)$ or $(25 - m^2)$

Using $(m^2 - 25)$: $\dfrac{m - 2}{m^2 - 25} + \dfrac{(-1)(m - 2)}{m^2 - 25}$

$= \dfrac{m - 2 - m + 2}{m^2 - 25} = \dfrac{0}{m^2 - 25} = 0$

65. $\frac{x}{(x+3)(x+2)} - \frac{2}{(x+1)(x+2)}$

$= \frac{x \cdot (x+1)}{(x+3)(x+2)(x+1)} - \frac{2 \cdot (x+3)}{(x+1)(x+2)(x+3)}$

$= \frac{x^2 + x - (2x+6)}{(x+1)(x+2)(x+3)} = \frac{x^2 + x - 2x - 6}{(x+1)(x+2)(x+3)}$

$= \frac{x^2 - x - 6}{(x+1)(x+2)(x+3)} = \frac{(x-3)(x+2)}{(x+1)(x+2)(x+3)}$

$= \frac{x-3}{(x+1)(x+3)}$

66. $\frac{x}{(x+5)(x+6)} - \frac{5}{(x+4)(x+5)}$

$= \frac{x \cdot (x+4)}{(x+5)(x+6)(x+4)} - \frac{5 \cdot (x+6)}{(x+4)(x+5)(x+6)}$

$= \frac{x^2 + 4x - 5x - 30}{(x+5)(x+6)(x+4)}$

$= \frac{x^2 - x - 30}{(x+5)(x+6)(x+4)}$

$= \frac{(x+5)(x-6)}{(x+5)(x+6)(x+4)} = \frac{x-6}{(x+6)(x+4)}$

67. $8x^2 - 8 = 8(x^2 - 1) = 2^3(x+1)(x-1)$
$6x^2 - 12x + 6 = 6(x^2 - 2x + 1) = 2 \cdot 3(x-1)(x-1)$
$10 - 10x = 10(1 - x) = -10(x - 1)$
$= -2 \cdot 5(x-1)$
$\text{LCM} = 2^3 \cdot 3 \cdot 5(x+1)(x-1)^2$
$= 120(x+1)(x-1)^2$

68. $9x^3 - 9x^2 - 18x = 9x(x^2 - x - 2)$
$= 3 \cdot 3 \cdot x(x-2)(x+1)$
$6x^5 - 24x^4 + 24x^3 = 6x^3(x^2 - 4x + 4)$
$= 3 \cdot 2 \cdot x^3(x-2)(x-2)$
$\text{LCM} = 3 \cdot 3 \cdot 2 \cdot x^3(x+1)(x-2)^2 = 18x^3(x+1)(x-2)^2$

69. $x^5 + 2x^4 + x^3 = x^3(x^2 + 2x + 1) = x^3(x+1)(x+1)$
$2x^3 - 2x = 2x(x^2 - 1) = 2x(x+1)(x-1)$
$5x - 5 = 5(x-1)$
$\text{LCM} = 2 \cdot 5 \cdot x^3(x+1)^2(x-1) = 10x^3(x+1)^2(x-1)$

70. $x^5 + 4x^4 + 4x^3 = x^3(x^2 + 4x + 4) = x^3(x+2)(x+2)$
$3x^2 - 12 = 3(x^2 - 4) = 3(x+2)(x-2)$
$2x + 4 = 2(x+2)$
$\text{LCM} = 2 \cdot 3 \cdot x^3(x+2)^2(x-2) = 6x^3(x+2)^2(x-2)$

71. $\frac{5}{z+2} + \frac{4z}{(z+2)(z-2)} + 2$

$= \frac{5(z-2)}{(z+2)(z-2)} + \frac{4z}{(z+2)(z-2)} + \frac{2(z+2)(z-2)}{(z+2)(z-2)}$

$= \frac{5z - 10 + 4z + 2z^2 - 8}{(z+2)(z-2)} = \frac{2z^2 + 9z - 18}{(z+2)(z-2)}$

$= \frac{(2z-3)(z+6)}{(z+2)(z-2)}$ or $\frac{(2z-3)(z+6)}{z^2 - 4}$

72. $\frac{-2}{(y+3)(y-3)} + \frac{4y}{(y-3)(y-3)} + \frac{6(-1)}{(3-y)(-1)}$

$= \frac{-2(y-3) + 4y(y+3) - 6(y-3)(y+3)}{(y+3)(y-3)(y-3)}$

$= \frac{-2y + 6 + 4y^2 + 12y - 6(y^2 - 9)}{(y+3)(y-3)^2}$

$= \frac{10y + 4y^2 + 6 - 6y^2 + 54}{(y+3)(y-3)^2}$

$= \frac{-2y^2 + 10y + 60}{(y+3)(y-3)^2} = \frac{-2(y^2 - 5y - 30)}{(y+3)(y-3)^2}$

73. $\frac{3z^2}{(z^2-2)(z^2+2)} + \frac{5z^2 - 3}{(2z^2-3)(z^2+2)}$

$= \frac{3z^2 \cdot (2z^2 - 3)}{(z^2-2)(z^2+2)(2z^2-3)} + \frac{(5z^2-3)(z^2-2)}{(2z^2-3)(z^2+2)(z^2-2)}$

$= \frac{6z^4 - 9z^2 + 5z^4 - 13z^2 + 6}{(z^2-2)(z^2+2)(2z^2-3)}$

$= \frac{11z^4 - 22z^2 + 6}{(z^2-2)(z^2+2)(2z^2-3)}$

74. $\frac{a+b}{a-b} = \frac{a}{a-b} + \frac{b}{a-b}$

75. Answers may vary.

Ex: $\frac{5x^2 + y}{x^2 + y^2} - \frac{2xy + y}{x^2 + y^2}$

76. In 1 minute, Jogger A will have gone $\frac{1}{6}$ of the way around the track and Jogger B will have gone $\frac{1}{8}$ of the way. In 6 minutes, they will have gone $\frac{6}{6}$ and $\frac{6}{8}$ of the way around the track respectively. In order for both to have finished complete laps, find the LCM of 6 and 8, which is 24. In 24 minutes Jogger A will have gone $\frac{24}{6} = 4$ laps and Jogger B $\frac{24}{8} = 3$ laps.

77. By the same reasoning as in problem 76, find the LCM of 12, 30, and 1.
$1 = 1$
$12 = 2 \cdot 2 \cdot 3$
$30 = 2 \cdot 3 \cdot 5$
LCM $= 2 \cdot 2 \cdot 3 \cdot 5 = 60$
Every 60 years

78. By the same reasoning as in problem 76, find the LCM of 1, 12, 30, and 84.
$1 = 1$
$12 = 2 \cdot 2 \cdot 3$
$30 = 2 \cdot 3 \cdot 5$
$84 = 2 \cdot 2 \cdot 3 \cdot 7$
LCM $= 2^2 \cdot 3 \cdot 5 \cdot 7 = 420$
Every 420 years

79. $4y = 5x + 2$ $\quad 8x = 3 - 10y$

$y = \frac{5}{4}x + \frac{1}{2}$ $\quad y = -\frac{4}{5}x + \frac{3}{10}$ $\quad \left(\frac{5}{4}\right)\left(-\frac{4}{5}\right) = -1$

Yes, the product of the slopes is -1.

80. $y + 3x = 4$ $\quad 2x = 5 - 6y$

$y = -3x + 4$ $\quad y = -\frac{1}{3}x + \frac{5}{6}$ $\quad (-3)\left(-\frac{1}{3}\right) = 1$

No, the product of the slopes is not -1.

81. $6y + 4x = 11$ $\quad 21 - 15y = 10x$

$y = -\frac{2}{3}x + \frac{11}{6}$ $\quad y = -\frac{2}{3}x + \frac{7}{5}$

$\left(-\frac{2}{3}\right)\left(-\frac{2}{3}\right) = \frac{4}{9}$

No, the product of the slopes is not -1.

82. $|11x| > 121$
$11x > 121$ or $11x < -121$
$x > 11$ or $x < -11$
$\{x | x > 11$ or $x < -11\}$

−11 0 11

83. $|3x - 5| \geq 4$
$3x - 5 \geq 4$ or $3x - 5 \leq -4$
$3x \geq 9$ or $3x \leq 1$
$x \geq 3$ or $x \leq \frac{1}{3}$
$\left\{x | x \geq 3 \text{ or } x \leq \frac{1}{3}\right\}$

0 $\frac{1}{3}$ 3

84. $|9x| \le 108$

$9x \le 108$ and $9x \ge -108$

$x \le 12$ and $x \ge -12$

$\{x \mid -12 \le x \le 12\}$

−12 0 12

85. $|2x - x| > 0$

$|x| > 0$

$x > 0$ or $x < 0$

All x except 0

$\{x \mid x \neq 0\}$

0

86. $|x - 1| \le 5$

$x - 1 \le 5$ and $x - 1 \ge -5$

$x \le 6$ and $x \ge -4$

$\{x \mid -4 \le x \le 6\}$

−4 0 6

87. $\dfrac{a^2 + 7a + 12}{a^2 - 9} = \dfrac{(a + 3)(a + 4)}{(a + 3)(a - 3)} = \dfrac{a + 4}{a - 3}$

88. $\dfrac{9x^2 - 25}{3x + 5} = \dfrac{(3x + 5)(3x - 5)}{3x + 5} = 3x - 5$

89. $\dfrac{3x - 6}{2 - x} = \dfrac{3(x - 2)}{-(x - 2)} = -3$

LESSON 10-6 TRY THIS pp. 451–452

a. $\dfrac{3}{4} + \dfrac{5}{8} = \dfrac{x}{12}$ LCM = 24

$24 \cdot \left(\dfrac{3}{4} + \dfrac{5}{8}\right) = \dfrac{x}{12} \cdot 24$

$18 + 15 = 2x$

$33 = 2x$

$x = \dfrac{33}{2}$

Check:

$$\begin{array}{c|c} \frac{3}{4} + \frac{5}{8} & \frac{x}{12} \\ \hline \frac{6}{8} + \frac{5}{8} & \frac{\frac{33}{2}}{12} \\ \frac{11}{8} & \frac{33}{2} \cdot \frac{1}{12} \\ & \frac{33}{24} \\ & \frac{11}{8} \end{array}$$

b. $\dfrac{1}{x} = \dfrac{1}{6 - x}$ LCM = $x(6 - x)$

$x(6 - x) \cdot \dfrac{1}{x} = \dfrac{1}{6 - x} \cdot x(6 - x)$

$6 - x = x$

$6 = 2x$

$x = 3$

Check:

$$\begin{array}{c|c} \frac{1}{x} & \frac{1}{6 - x} \\ \hline \frac{1}{3} & \frac{1}{6 - 3} \\ & \frac{1}{3} \end{array}$$

c. $x + \dfrac{1}{x} = 2$ LCM is x

$x\left(x + \dfrac{1}{x}\right) = 2x$

$x^2 + 1 = 2x$

$x^2 - 2x + 1 = 0$

$(x - 1)(x - 1) = 0$

$x = 1$

Check:

$$\begin{array}{c|c} x + \frac{1}{x} & 2 \\ \hline 1 + \frac{1}{1} & 2 \\ 2 & \end{array}$$

d. $\dfrac{x^2}{x + 2} = \dfrac{4}{x + 2}$ LCM = $x + 2$

$(x + 2) \cdot \dfrac{x^2}{x + 2} = \dfrac{4}{x + 2} \cdot (x + 2)$

$x^2 = 4$

$x = \pm 2$

Check:

$$\begin{array}{c|c} \frac{x^2}{x + 2} & \frac{4}{x + 2} \\ \hline \frac{2^2}{2 + 2} & \frac{4}{2 + 2} \\ \frac{4}{4} & \frac{4}{4} \\ 1 & 1 \end{array}$$

Check:

$$\begin{array}{c|c} \frac{x^2}{x + 2} & \frac{4}{x + 2} \\ \hline \frac{(-2)^2}{-2 + 2} & \frac{4}{-2 + 2} \\ \frac{4}{0} & \frac{4}{0} \end{array}$$

The number 2 is a solution, but -2 is not because it makes a denominator zero.

e. $\dfrac{1}{2x} + \dfrac{1}{x} = -12$

$2x\left(\dfrac{1}{2x} + \dfrac{1}{x}\right) = -12 \cdot 2x$

$1 + 2 = -24x$

$3 = -24x$

$-\dfrac{3}{24} = x$

$x = -\dfrac{1}{8}$

Check:

$$\begin{array}{c|c} \frac{1}{2x} + \frac{1}{x} & -12 \\ \hline \frac{1}{2\left(-\frac{1}{8}\right)} + \frac{1}{-\frac{1}{8}} & -12 \\ \frac{1}{-\frac{1}{4}} + \frac{1}{-\frac{1}{8}} & \\ -4 + -8 & \\ -12 & \end{array}$$

LESSON 10-6 EXERCISES pp. 453–454

1. $\dfrac{3}{8} + \dfrac{4}{5} = \dfrac{x}{20}$ LCM = 40

$40\left(\dfrac{3}{8} + \dfrac{4}{5}\right) = 40\left(\dfrac{x}{20}\right)$

$15 + 32 = 2x$

$47 = 2x$

$\dfrac{47}{2} = x$

2. $\dfrac{3}{5} + \dfrac{2}{3} = \dfrac{x}{9}$ LCM = 45

$45\left(\dfrac{3}{5} + \dfrac{2}{3}\right) = 45\left(\dfrac{x}{9}\right)$

$27 + 30 = 5x$

$57 = 5x$

$\dfrac{57}{5} = x$

3. $\dfrac{2}{3} - \dfrac{5}{6} = \dfrac{1}{x}$ LCM = $6x$

$6x\left(\dfrac{2}{3} - \dfrac{5}{6}\right) = 6x\left(\dfrac{1}{x}\right)$

$4x - 5x = 6$

$-x = 6$

$x = -6$

4. $\dfrac{1}{8} - \dfrac{3}{5} = \dfrac{1}{x}$ LCM = $40x$

$40x\left(\dfrac{1}{8} - \dfrac{3}{5}\right) = 40x\left(\dfrac{1}{x}\right)$

$5x - 24x = 40$

$-19x = 40$

$x = -\dfrac{40}{19}$

5. $\frac{1}{6} + \frac{1}{8} = \frac{1}{t}$ LCM = $24t$

$$24t\left(\frac{1}{6} + \frac{1}{8}\right) = 24t\left(\frac{1}{t}\right)$$
$$4t + 3t = 24$$
$$7t = 24$$
$$t = \frac{24}{7}$$

6. $\frac{1}{8} + \frac{1}{10} = \frac{1}{t}$ LCM = $40t$

$$40t\left(\frac{1}{8} + \frac{1}{10}\right) = 40t\left(\frac{1}{t}\right)$$
$$5t + 4t = 40$$
$$9t = 40$$
$$t = \frac{40}{9}$$

7. $x + \frac{4}{x} = -5$ LCM = x

$$x\left(x + \frac{4}{x}\right) = x(-5)$$
$$x^2 + 4 = -5x$$
$$x^2 + 5x + 4 = 0$$
$$(x + 4)(x + 1) = 0$$
$$x + 4 = 0 \quad \text{or} \quad x + 1 = 0$$
$$x = -4 \quad \text{or} \quad x = -1$$

8. $x + \frac{3}{x} = -4$ LCM = x

$$x\left(x + \frac{3}{x}\right) = x(-4)$$
$$x^2 + 3 = -4x$$
$$x^2 + 4x + 3 = 0$$
$$(x + 3)(x + 1) = 0$$
$$x + 3 = 0 \quad \text{or} \quad x + 1 = 0$$
$$x = -3 \quad \text{or} \quad x = -1$$

9. $\frac{x}{4} - \frac{4}{x} = 0$ LCM = $4x$

$$4x\left(\frac{x}{4} - \frac{4}{x}\right) = 4x(0)$$
$$x^2 - 16 = 0$$
$$(x + 4)(x - 4) = 0$$
$$x + 4 = 0 \quad \text{or} \quad x - 4 = 0$$
$$x = -4 \quad \text{or} \quad x = 4$$

10. $\frac{x}{5} - \frac{5}{x} = 0$ LCM = $5x$

$$5x\left(\frac{x}{5} - \frac{5}{x}\right) = 0(5x)$$
$$x^2 - 25 = 0$$
$$(x + 5)(x - 5) = 0$$
$$x + 5 = 0 \quad \text{or} \quad x - 5 = 0$$
$$x = -5 \quad \text{or} \quad x = 5$$

11. $\frac{5}{x} = \frac{6}{x} - \frac{1}{3}$ LCM = $3x$

$$3x\left(\frac{5}{x}\right) = 3x\left(\frac{6}{x} - \frac{1}{3}\right)$$
$$15 = 18 - x$$
$$-3 = -x$$
$$3 = x$$

12. $\frac{4}{x} = \frac{5}{x} - \frac{1}{2}$ LCM = $2x$

$$2x\left(\frac{4}{x}\right) = 2x\left(\frac{5}{x} - \frac{1}{2}\right)$$
$$8 = 10 - x$$
$$-2 = -x$$
$$2 = x$$

13. $\frac{5}{3x} + \frac{3}{x} = 1$ LCM = $3x$

$$3x\left(\frac{5}{3x} + \frac{3}{x}\right) = 3x(1)$$
$$5 + 9 = 3x$$
$$14 = 3x$$
$$\frac{14}{3} = x$$

14. $\frac{3}{4x} + \frac{5}{x} = 1$ LCM = $4x$

$$4x\left(\frac{3}{4x} + \frac{5}{x}\right) = 4x(1)$$
$$3 + 20 = 4x$$
$$23 = 4x$$
$$\frac{23}{4} = x$$

15. $\frac{x - 7}{x + 2} = \frac{1}{4}$ LCM = $4(x + 2)$

$$4(x + 2)\left(\frac{x - 7}{x + 2}\right) = 4(x + 2)\left(\frac{1}{4}\right)$$
$$4(x - 7) = x + 2$$
$$4x - 28 = x + 2$$
$$3x = 30$$
$$x = 10$$

16. $\frac{a - 2}{a + 3} = \frac{3}{8}$ LCM = $8(a + 3)$

$$8(a + 3)\left(\frac{a - 2}{a + 3}\right) = 8(a + 3)\left(\frac{3}{8}\right)$$
$$8(a - 2) = 3(a + 3)$$
$$8a - 16 = 3a + 9$$
$$5a = 25$$
$$a = 5$$

17. $\frac{2}{x + 1} = \frac{1}{x - 2}$ LCM = $(x + 1)(x - 2)$

$$(x + 1)(x - 2)\left(\frac{2}{x + 1}\right) = (x + 1)(x - 2)\left(\frac{1}{x - 2}\right)$$
$$2(x - 2) = x + 1$$
$$2x - 4 = x + 1$$
$$x = 5$$

18. $\frac{5}{x - 1} = \frac{3}{x + 2}$ LCM = $(x - 1)(x + 2)$

$$(x - 1)(x + 2)\left(\frac{5}{x - 1}\right) = (x - 1)(x + 2)\left(\frac{3}{x + 2}\right)$$
$$5(x + 2) = 3(x - 1)$$
$$5x + 10 = 3x - 3$$
$$2x = -13$$
$$x = -\frac{13}{2}$$

19. $\frac{x}{6} - \frac{x}{10} = \frac{1}{6}$ LCM = 30

$$30\left(\frac{x}{6} - \frac{x}{10}\right) = 30\left(\frac{1}{6}\right)$$
$$5x - 3x = 5$$
$$2x = 5$$
$$x = \frac{5}{2}$$

20. $\frac{x}{8} - \frac{x}{12} = \frac{1}{8}$ LCM = 24

$$24\left(\frac{x}{8} - \frac{x}{12}\right) = 24\left(\frac{1}{8}\right)$$
$$3x - 2x = 3$$
$$x = 3$$

21. $\frac{x+1}{3} - \frac{x-1}{2} = 1$ LCM = 6

$$6\left(\frac{x+1}{3} - \frac{x-1}{2}\right) = 6(1)$$
$$2(x+1) - 3(x-1) = 6$$
$$2x + 2 - 3x + 3 = 6$$
$$-x + 5 = 6$$
$$-x = 1$$
$$x = -1$$

22. $\frac{x+2}{5} - \frac{x-2}{4} = 1$ LCM = 20

$$20\left(\frac{x+2}{5} - \frac{x-2}{4}\right) = 20(1)$$
$$4(x+2) - 5(x-2) = 20$$
$$4x + 8 - 5x + 10 = 20$$
$$-x + 18 = 20$$
$$-x = 2$$
$$x = -2$$

23. $\frac{a-3}{3a+2} = \frac{1}{5}$ LCM = $5(3a + 2)$

$$5(3a+2)\left(\frac{a-3}{3a+2}\right) = 5(3a+2)\left(\frac{1}{5}\right)$$
$$5(a-3) = 3a + 2$$
$$5a - 15 = 3a + 2$$
$$2a = 17$$
$$a = \frac{17}{2}$$

24. $\frac{x-1}{2x+5} = \frac{1}{4}$ LCM = $4(2x + 5)$

$$4(2x+5)\left(\frac{x-1}{2x+5}\right) = 4(2x+5)\left(\frac{1}{4}\right)$$
$$4(x-1) = 2x + 5$$
$$4x - 4 = 2x + 5$$
$$2x = 9$$
$$x = \frac{9}{2}$$

25. $\frac{x-1}{x-5} = \frac{4}{x-5}$ LCM = $x - 5$

$$(x-5)\left(\frac{x-1}{x-5}\right) = (x-5)\left(\frac{4}{x-5}\right)$$
$$x - 1 = 4$$
$$x = 5$$

5 does not check; no solution

26. $\frac{x-7}{x-9} = \frac{2}{x-9}$ LCM = $x - 9$

$$(x-9)\left(\frac{x-7}{x-9}\right) = (x-9)\left(\frac{2}{x-9}\right)$$
$$x - 7 = 2$$
$$x = 9$$

9 does not check; no solution

27. $\frac{2}{x+3} = \frac{5}{x}$ LCM = $x(x + 3)$

$$x(x+3)\left(\frac{2}{x+3}\right) = x(x+3)\left(\frac{5}{x}\right)$$
$$2x = 5(x+3)$$
$$2x = 5x + 15$$
$$-3x = 15$$
$$x = -5$$

28. $\frac{3}{x+4} = \frac{4}{x}$ LCM = $x(x + 4)$

$$x(x+4)\left(\frac{3}{x+4}\right) = x(x+4)\left(\frac{4}{x}\right)$$
$$3x = 4(x+4)$$
$$3x = 4x + 16$$
$$-x = 16$$
$$x = -16$$

29. $\frac{x-2}{x-3} = \frac{x-1}{x+1}$ LCM = $(x - 3)(x + 1)$

$$(x-3)(x+1)\left(\frac{x-2}{x-3}\right) = (x-3)(x+1)\left(\frac{x-1}{x+1}\right)$$
$$(x+1)(x-2) = (x-3)(x-1)$$
$$x^2 - x - 2 = x^2 - 4x + 3$$
$$-x - 2 = -4x + 3$$
$$3x = 5$$
$$x = \frac{5}{3}$$

30. $\frac{2b-3}{3b+2} = \frac{2b+1}{3b-2}$ LCM = $(3b + 2)(3b - 2)$

$$(3b+2)(3b-2)\left(\frac{2b-3}{3b+2}\right) = (3b+2)(3b-2)\left(\frac{2b+1}{3b-2}\right)$$
$$(3b-2)(2b-3) = (3b+2)(2b+1)$$
$$6b^2 - 13b + 6 = 6b^2 + 7b + 2$$
$$-13b + 6 = 7b + 2$$
$$4 = 20b$$
$$\frac{4}{20} = b; b = \frac{1}{5}$$

31. $\frac{1}{x+3} + \frac{1}{x-3} = \frac{1}{x^2-9}$ LCM = $(x + 3)(x - 3)$

$$(x+3)(x-3)\left(\frac{1}{x+3} + \frac{1}{x-3}\right) = (x+3)(x-3)\left(\frac{1}{x^2-9}\right)$$
$$(x-3) + (x+3) = 1$$
$$2x = 1$$
$$x = \frac{1}{2}$$

32. $\frac{4}{x-3} + \frac{2x}{x^2-9} = \frac{1}{x+3}$ LCM = $(x + 3)(x - 3)$

$$(x+3)(x-3)\left(\frac{4}{x-3} + \frac{2x}{x^2-9}\right) = (x+3)(x-3)\left(\frac{1}{x+3}\right)$$
$$4(x+3) + 2x = x - 3$$
$$4x + 12 + 2x = x - 3$$
$$6x + 12 = x - 3$$
$$5x = -15$$
$$x = -3$$

-3 does not check; no solution

33. $\frac{x}{x+4} - \frac{4}{x-4} = \frac{x^2+16}{x^2-16}$ LCM = $(x + 4)(x - 4)$

$$(x+4)(x-4)\left(\frac{x}{x+4} - \frac{4}{x-4}\right) = (x+4)(x-4)\left(\frac{x^2+16}{x^2-16}\right)$$
$$x(x-4) - 4(x+4) = x^2 + 16$$
$$x^2 - 4x - 4x - 16 = x^2 + 16$$
$$-8x - 16 = 16$$
$$-8x = 32$$
$$x = -4$$

-4 does not check; no solution

34. $\frac{5}{y-3} - \frac{30}{y^2-9} = 1$

LCM = $(y - 3)(y + 3)$

$$(y-3)(y+3)\left(\frac{5}{y-3} - \frac{30}{y^2-9}\right) = (y-3)(y+3)(1)$$
$$5(y+3) - 30 = y^2 - 9$$
$$5y + 15 - 30 = y^2 - 9$$
$$0 = y^2 - 5y + 6$$
$$0 = (y-2)(y-3)$$
$$y - 2 = 0 \text{ or } y - 3 = 0$$
$$y = 2 \text{ or } y = 3$$

3 does not check; $y = 2$ is the solution.

35. $\frac{4}{y-2} - \frac{2y-3}{(y+2)(y-2)} = \frac{5}{y+2}$

$$(y-2)(y+2)\left(\frac{4}{y-2} - \frac{2y-3}{(y+2)(y-2)}\right)$$
$$= \left(\frac{5}{y+2}\right)(y-2)(y+2)$$
$$4(y+2) - (2y-3) = 5(y-2)$$
$$4y + 8 - 2y + 3 = 5y - 10$$
$$2y + 11 = 5y - 10$$
$$-3y = -21$$
$$y = 7$$ It checks.

36. $\frac{x}{(x+4)(x-1)} + \frac{x+1}{(x+4)(x+2)} = \frac{2x}{(x+2)(x-1)}$

$$(x+4)(x-1)(x+2)\left(\frac{x}{(x+4)(x-1)} + \frac{x+1}{(x+4)(x+2)}\right)$$
$$= \frac{2x}{(x+2)(x-1)} \cdot (x+4)(x-1)(x+2)$$
$$x(x+2) + (x-1)(x+1) = 2x(x+4)$$
$$x^2 + 2x + x^2 - 1 = 2x^2 + 8x$$
$$2x - 1 = 8x$$
$$-1 = 6x$$
$$-\frac{1}{6} = x$$ It checks.

37. $\frac{2a+7}{8a^2 - 2a - 1} + \frac{a-4}{2a^2 + 5a - 3} = \frac{4a-1}{4a^2 + 13a + 3}$

$$(4a+1)(2a-1)(a+3)$$
$$\times\left[\frac{2a+7}{(4a+1)(2a-1)} + \frac{a-4}{(2a-1)(a+3)}\right]$$
$$= \frac{4a-1}{(4a+1)(a+3)} \cdot (4a+1)(2a-1)(a+3)$$
$$(a+3)(2a+7) + (4a+1)(a-4) = (4a-1)(2a-1)$$
$$2a^2 + 13a + 21 + 4a^2 - 15a - 4 = 8a^2 - 6a + 1$$
$$6a^2 - 2a + 17 = 8a^2 - 6a + 1$$
$$2a^2 - 4a - 16 = 0$$
$$2(a^2 - 2a - 8) = 0$$
$$2(a-4)(a+2) = 0$$
$$a = 4 \quad \text{or} \quad a = -2$$

They both check.

38. $\frac{y}{y+0.2} - 1.2 = \frac{y-0.2}{y+0.2}$

$$(y+0.2)\left(\frac{y}{y+0.2} - 1.2\right) = \frac{y-0.2}{y+0.2}(y+0.2)$$
$$y - 1.2(y+0.2) = y - 0.2$$
$$y - 1.2y - 0.24 = y - 0.2$$
$$-1.2y = 0.04$$
$$y = -0.0\overline{3} \quad \text{or} \quad \frac{0.04}{-1.2} = \frac{4}{-120}$$
$$= -\frac{1}{30}$$

39. $\frac{x^2}{(x-2)(x+2)} = \frac{x}{x+2} - \frac{2x}{2-x}$

$$(x-2)(x+2)\left(\frac{x^2}{(x-2)(x+2)}\right)$$
$$= \left(\frac{x}{x+2} + \frac{2x}{x-2}\right)(x-2)(x+2)$$
$$x^2 = x(x-2) + 2x(x+2)$$
$$x^2 = x^2 - 2x + 2x^2 + 4x$$
$$0 = 2x^2 + 2x$$
$$0 = 2x(x+1)$$
$$2x = 0 \quad \text{or} \quad x + 1 = 0$$
$$x = 0 \quad \text{or} \quad x = -1$$ They both check.

40. $4a - 3 = \frac{a+13}{a+1}$

$$(a+1)(4a-3) = \frac{a+13}{a+1}(a+1)$$
$$4a^2 + a - 3 = a + 13$$
$$4a^2 - 16 = 0$$
$$4(a^2 - 4) = 0$$
$$4(a+2)(a-2) = 0$$
$$a = -2 \quad \text{or} \quad a = 2$$ They both check.

41. $\frac{14x-2}{x-3} = \frac{9x+8}{-2}$

$$-2(x-3)\left[\frac{14x-2}{x-3}\right] = \left[\frac{9x+8}{-2}\right](-2)(x-3)$$
$$-2(14x-2) = (9x+8)(x-3)$$
$$-28x + 4 = 9x^2 - 19x - 24$$
$$0 = 9x^2 + 9x - 28$$
$$0 = (3x-4)(3x+7)$$
$$3x - 4 = 0 \quad \text{or} \quad 3x + 7 = 0$$
$$3x = 4 \quad \text{or} \quad 3x = -7$$
$$x = \frac{4}{3} \quad \text{or} \quad x = -\frac{7}{3}$$

They both check.

42. $(y+3)\left[\frac{y^2-4}{y+3}\right] = (y+3)\left[2 - \frac{y-2}{y+3}\right]$

$$y^2 - 4 = 2(y+3) - (y-2)$$
$$y^2 - 4 = 2y + 6 - y + 2$$
$$y^2 - 4 = y + 8$$
$$y^2 - y - 12 = 0$$
$$(y-4)(y+3) = 0$$

$y = 4$ or $y = -3$; -3 does not check. It results in division by 0. The only solution is $y = 4$.

43. $\frac{8}{x} - 4 = \frac{2}{x}$ LCM $= x$

$$x\left(\frac{8}{x} - 4\right) = x\left(\frac{2}{x}\right)$$
$$8 - 4x = 2$$
$$-4x = -6$$
$$x = \frac{6}{4} = \frac{3}{2}$$

44. $\frac{9 \cdot n}{9\left(n - \frac{4}{9}\right)} - \frac{9 \cdot n}{9\left(n + \frac{4}{9}\right)} = \frac{1}{n}$

$$\frac{9n}{9n-4} - \frac{9n}{9n+4} = \frac{1}{n}$$
$$n(9n-4)(9n+4)\left[\frac{9n}{9n-4} - \frac{9n}{9n+4}\right]$$
$$= \frac{1}{n} \cdot n(9n-4)(9n+4)$$
$$n(9n+4)(9n) - n(9n-4)(9n) = (9n-4)(9n+4)$$
$$81n^3 + 36n^2 - 81n^3 + 36n^2 = 81n^2 - 16$$
$$72n^2 = 81n^2 - 16$$
$$9n^2 - 16 = 0$$
$$(3n-4)(3n+4) = 0$$
$$3n - 4 = 0 \quad \text{or} \quad 3n + 4 = 0$$
$$3n = 4 \quad \quad 3n = -4$$
$$n = \frac{4}{3} \quad \text{or} \quad n = \frac{-4}{3}$$

They both check.

45. $t = \frac{x}{y}$ and $r = \frac{w}{z}$

Then $t + r = \frac{x}{y} + \frac{w}{z}$
$$= \frac{xz + wy}{yz}$$

and $\frac{t+r}{1-tr} = (t+r)\left(\frac{1}{1-tr}\right) = \frac{xz+wy}{yz}\left(\frac{1}{1 - \frac{x}{y} \cdot \frac{w}{z}}\right)$
$$= \frac{xz + wy}{yz - xw}$$

46. $\dfrac{\left(\dfrac{ab}{a-b}\right)^2 - \left(\dfrac{ab}{a+b}\right)^2}{\left(\dfrac{ab}{a-b}\right)^2 + \left(\dfrac{ab}{a+b}\right)^2}$

$= \left[\dfrac{\dfrac{a^2b^2}{(a-b)^2} - \dfrac{a^2b^2}{(a+b)^2}}{\dfrac{a^2b^2}{(a-b)^2} + \dfrac{a^2b^2}{(a+b)^2}}\right] \dfrac{(a+b)^2(a-b)^2}{(a+b)^2(a-b)^2}$

$= \dfrac{a^2b^2(a+b)^2 - a^2b^2(a-b)^2}{a^2b^2(a+b)^2 + a^2b^2(a-b)^2}$

$= \dfrac{a^2b^2[a^2 + 2ab + b^2 - (a^2 - 2ab + b^2)]}{a^2b^2(a^2 + 2ab + b^2 + a^2 - 2ab + b^2)}$

$= \dfrac{a^2 + 2ab + b^2 - a^2 + 2ab - b^2}{2a^2 + 2b^2}$

$= \dfrac{4ab}{2(a^2 + b^2)} = \dfrac{2ab}{a^2 + b^2}$

47. $\dfrac{(x+1)^2}{(x-5)} \cdot \dfrac{(x-3)}{(x+1)} = \dfrac{(x+1)(x-3)}{x-5}$

48. $\dfrac{3x+3}{2} \div \dfrac{4}{9x+9} = \dfrac{3(x+1)}{2} \cdot \dfrac{9(x+1)}{4} = \dfrac{27(x+1)^2}{8}$

49. $\dfrac{4a}{3a-3} \cdot \dfrac{3(a-1)}{16a} = \dfrac{12a(a-1)}{48a(a-1)} = \dfrac{1}{4}$

50. $\dfrac{x+2}{x-1} \div \dfrac{5x+10}{x-2} = \dfrac{x+2}{x-1} \cdot \dfrac{x-2}{5(x+2)} = \dfrac{x-2}{5(x-1)}$

51. $|2x - 1| = 5$
$2x - 1 = 5$ or $2x - 1 = -5$
$2x = 6$ or $2x = -4$
$x = 3$ or $x = -2$

52. $|x - 3| \le 8$
$x - 3 \le 8$ and $x - 3 \ge -8$
$x \le 11$ and $x \ge -5$
$-5 \le x \le 11$

53. $x - 3 < -7$ or $x + 1 > 1$
$x < -4$ or $x > 0$

54. $x - 2 < 3$ or $x + 4 > 11$
$x < 5$ or $x > 7$

55. $11 - 8y < 6y + 39$
$-14y < 28$
$y > -2$

56. $3 - 7x < 9x + 67$
$-64 < 16x$
$-4 < x$

57. $x - y = 4$ ①
$5x = 15y$ ②
$x = y + 4$ Solving ① for x
$5(y + 4) = 15y$ Substituting in ②
$5y + 20 = 15y$
$20 = 10y$
$y = 2$
$x = y + 4 = 6$
The numbers are 2 and 6.

LESSON 10-7 TRY THIS pp. 456–457

a. $\dfrac{1}{6} + \dfrac{1}{8} = \dfrac{1}{t}$

$24t\left(\dfrac{1}{6} + \dfrac{1}{8}\right) = 24t \cdot \dfrac{1}{t}$

$4t + 3t = 24$
$7t = 24$

$t = \dfrac{24}{7} = 3\dfrac{3}{7}$ hours

b. $t = \dfrac{120}{r}$

$t = \dfrac{155}{r + 10}$

$\dfrac{120}{r} = \dfrac{155}{r + 10}$

$\dfrac{120 \cdot r(r+10)}{r} = \dfrac{155 \cdot r(r+10)}{r + 10}$

$120(r + 10) = 155r$
$120r + 1200 = 155r$
$1200 = 35r$

$\dfrac{1200}{35} = r$

$r = 34\dfrac{2}{7}$ km per hour

$r + 10 = 44\dfrac{2}{7}$ km per hour

c. $\dfrac{1}{x+2} = 3 \cdot \dfrac{1}{x}$

$\dfrac{x(x+2)}{x+2} = \dfrac{3 \cdot x(x+2)}{x}$

$x = 3x + 6$
$-2x = 6$
$x = -3$

LESSON 10-7 EXERCISES pp. 458–459

1. $\dfrac{1}{3} + \dfrac{1}{5} = \dfrac{1}{n}$

$15n\left(\dfrac{1}{3} + \dfrac{1}{5}\right) = 15n\left(\dfrac{1}{n}\right)$

$5n + 3n = 15$
$8n = 15$

$n = \dfrac{15}{8}$ or $1\dfrac{7}{8}$ hours

2. $\dfrac{1}{12} + \dfrac{1}{9} = \dfrac{1}{n}$

$36n\left(\dfrac{1}{12} + \dfrac{1}{9}\right) = 36n\left(\dfrac{1}{n}\right)$

$3n + 4n = 36$
$7n = 36$

$n = \dfrac{36}{7}$ or $5\dfrac{1}{7}$ hours

3. $\dfrac{1}{18} + \dfrac{1}{24} = \dfrac{1}{n}$

$72n\left(\dfrac{1}{18} + \dfrac{1}{24}\right) = 72n\left(\dfrac{1}{n}\right)$

$4n + 3n = 72$
$7n = 72$

$n = \dfrac{72}{7}$ or $10\dfrac{2}{7}$ hours

4. $\dfrac{1}{15} + \dfrac{1}{20} = \dfrac{1}{n}$

$60n\left(\dfrac{1}{15} + \dfrac{1}{20}\right) = 60n\left(\dfrac{1}{n}\right)$

$4n + 3n = 60$
$7n = 60$

$n = \dfrac{60}{7}$ or $8\dfrac{4}{7}$ minutes

5. Let r = slower rate.

$\dfrac{150}{r} = \dfrac{350}{r + 40}$

$r(r + 40)\left(\dfrac{150}{r}\right) = r(r + 40)\left(\dfrac{350}{r + 40}\right)$

$150(r + 40) = r(350)$
$150r + 6000 = 350r$
$6000 = 200r$
$30 = r$

30 km/h and 70 km/h

6. Let r = speed going.

$$\frac{120}{r} - \frac{120}{2r} = 3$$
$$2r\left(\frac{120}{r} - \frac{120}{2r}\right) = 2r(3)$$
$$240 - 120 = 6r$$
$$120 = 6r$$
$$20 = r$$
$$r = 20 \text{ mi/h}$$

7. $$\frac{330}{r} = \frac{400}{r + 14}$$
$$r(r + 14)\left(\frac{330}{r}\right) = r(r + 4)\left(\frac{400}{r + 14}\right)$$
$$330(r + 14) = 400r$$
$$330r + 4620 = 400r$$
$$4620 = 70r$$
$$66 = r$$

The speeds are 66 km/h and 80 km/h.

8. $$\frac{1}{4} + \frac{1}{5} = \frac{1}{x}$$
$$20x\left(\frac{1}{4} + \frac{1}{5}\right) = 20x\left(\frac{1}{x}\right)$$
$$5x + 4x = 20$$
$$9x = 20$$
$$x = \frac{20}{9} \text{ or } 2\frac{2}{9}$$

9. $$\frac{1}{2}x + \frac{1}{x} = \frac{51}{x}$$
$$2x\left(\frac{1}{2}x + \frac{1}{x}\right) = 2x\left(\frac{51}{x}\right)$$
$$x^2 + 2 = 102$$
$$x^2 = 100$$
$$x^2 - 100 = 0$$
$$(x + 10)(x - 10) = 0$$
$$x + 10 = 0 \quad \text{or} \quad x - 10 = 0$$
$$x = -10 \quad \text{or} \quad x = 10$$

10. $$\frac{-x}{12} = 3\left(\frac{1}{x}\right) - 1$$
$$12x\left(\frac{-x}{12}\right) = 12x\left(\frac{3}{x} - 1\right)$$
$$-x^2 = 36 - 12x$$
$$0 = x^2 - 12x + 36$$
$$0 = (x - 6)(x - 6)$$
$$x - 6 = 0$$
$$x = 6$$

11. $$\frac{1}{8} + \frac{1}{C} = \frac{1}{6}$$
$$48C\left[\frac{1}{8} + \frac{1}{C}\right] = \frac{1}{6} \cdot 48C$$
$$6C + 48 = 8C$$
$$48 = 2C$$
$$C = 24 \text{ hours}$$

12. $$\frac{1}{6} + \frac{1}{t} = \frac{1}{4}$$
$$12t\left[\frac{1}{6} + \frac{1}{t}\right] = \frac{1}{4} \cdot 12t$$
$$2t + 12 = 3t$$
$$t = 12 \text{ hours}$$

13. $$\frac{1}{t} + \frac{1}{2t} = \frac{1}{8}$$
$$8t\left(\frac{1}{t} + \frac{1}{2t}\right) = \frac{1}{8} \cdot 8t$$
$$8 + 4 = t$$
$$t = 12 \text{ min}$$
$$2t = 24 \text{ min}$$

14. $$\frac{1}{t} + \frac{1}{3t} = \frac{1}{9}$$
$$9t\left(\frac{1}{t} + \frac{1}{3t}\right) = \frac{1}{9} \cdot 9t$$
$$9 + 3 = t$$
$$t = 12 \text{ min}$$
$$3t = 36 \text{ min}$$

15. $$\frac{1}{10} - \frac{1}{20} = \frac{1}{t}$$
$$20t\left(\frac{1}{10} - \frac{1}{20}\right) = \frac{1}{t} \cdot 20t$$
$$2t - t = 20$$
$$t = 20 \text{ hours}$$

16. $$\frac{1}{8} - \frac{1}{12} = \frac{1}{t}$$
$$24t\left(\frac{1}{8} - \frac{1}{12}\right) = \frac{1}{t} \cdot 24t$$
$$3t - 2t = 24$$
$$t = 24 \text{ hours}$$

17. $$\frac{1}{9} - \frac{1}{12} = \frac{1}{n}$$
$$36n\left(\frac{1}{9} - \frac{1}{12}\right) = 36n\left(\frac{1}{n}\right)$$
$$4n - 3n = 36$$
$$n = 36 \text{ hours}$$

18. After 2 hours, $\frac{3}{5}$ of job remains to be done in 1 hour.

$$\frac{1}{5} + \frac{1}{t} = \frac{3}{5}$$
$$5t\left(\frac{1}{5} + \frac{1}{t}\right) = \frac{3}{5}(5t)$$
$$t + 5 = 3t$$
$$2t = 5$$
$$t = \frac{5}{2} = 2\frac{1}{2} \text{ hours}$$

19. $$\frac{30}{r} + \frac{20}{r + 15} = 1$$
$$r(r + 15)\left(\frac{30}{r} + \frac{20}{r + 15}\right) = r(r + 15)$$
$$30(r + 15) + 20r = r^2 + 15r$$
$$30r + 450 + 20r = r^2 + 15r$$
$$r^2 - 35r - 450 = 0$$
$$(r - 45)(r + 10) = 0$$
$$r = 45 \quad \text{or} \quad r = -10$$

Since rate cannot be negative, $r = 45$ mi/h.

20. $$\frac{1}{K} + \frac{1}{B} + \frac{1}{M} = \frac{1}{1\frac{1}{3}}$$
$$\frac{1}{2B - 2} + \frac{1}{B} + \frac{1}{2B} = \frac{1}{\frac{4}{3}} = \frac{3}{4}$$
$$4B(B - 1)\left(\frac{1}{2(B - 1)} + \frac{1}{B} + \frac{1}{2B}\right) = 4B(B - 1)\left(\frac{3}{4}\right)$$
$$2B + 4(B - 1) + 2(B - 1) = 3B(B - 1)$$
$$2B + 4B - 4 + 2B - 2 = 3B^2 - 3B$$
$$0 = 3B^2 - 11B + 6$$
$$0 = (3B - 2)(B - 3)$$
$$3B - 2 = 0 \quad \text{or} \quad B - 3 = 0$$
$$B = \frac{2}{3} \quad \text{or} \quad B = 3$$

If $B = \frac{2}{3}$, $K = 2\left(\frac{2}{3}\right) - 2$ = a negative number, so $B = \frac{2}{3}$ can't be a solution. If $B = 3$, $K = 2(3) - 2 = 4$, $M = 2(3) = 6$ or $4 + 2 = 6$.
Solution: Bernie, 3 h; Kurt, 4 h; Michelle, 6 h

21. $$\frac{5x - 2}{x - 1} + \frac{3x - 1}{x - 1} = \frac{5x - 2 + 3x - 1}{x - 1} = \frac{8x - 3}{x - 1}$$

22. $$\frac{x^2 + 7}{x - 3} + \frac{7x + 3}{x - 3} = \frac{x^2 + 7 + 7x + 3}{x - 3} = \frac{x^2 + 7x + 10}{x - 3}$$
$$= \frac{(x + 5)(x + 2)}{x - 3}$$

23. $$\frac{x^2 + 6x}{x + 4} - \frac{3x + 5}{x + 4} + \frac{1}{x + 4} = \frac{x^2 + 6x - (3x + 5) + 1}{x + 4}$$
$$= \frac{x^2 + 6x - 3x - 5 + 1}{x + 4}$$
$$= \frac{x^2 + 3x - 4}{x + 4}$$
$$= \frac{(x + 4)(x - 1)}{x + 4} = x - 1$$

24. $$\frac{3}{x + 1} + \frac{3}{x - 1} = \frac{(x - 1)}{(x - 1)} \cdot \frac{3}{x + 1} + \frac{(x + 1)}{(x + 1)} \cdot \frac{3}{x - 1}$$
$$= \frac{3x - 3}{(x + 1)(x - 1)} + \frac{3x + 3}{(x + 1)(x - 1)}$$
$$= \frac{6x}{(x + 1)(x - 1)}$$

25.
$$\begin{aligned} m^2 - 5m &= 14 \\ m^2 - 5m - 14 &= 0 \\ (m-7)(m+2) &= 0 \\ m = 7 \quad &\text{or} \quad m = -2 \end{aligned}$$

26.
$$\begin{aligned} 9n^2 &= 16 \\ 9n^2 - 16 &= 0 \\ (3n+4)(3n-4) &= 0 \\ 3n + 4 = 0 \quad &\text{or} \quad 3n - 4 = 0 \\ 3n = -4 \quad &\text{or} \quad 3n = 4 \\ n = -\tfrac{4}{3} \quad &\text{or} \quad n = \tfrac{4}{3} \end{aligned}$$

27.
$$\begin{aligned} x^3 + 3x^2 + 2x &= 0 \\ x(x^2 + 3x + 2) &= 0 \qquad \text{Multiplying (1) by 40} \\ x(x+1)(x+2) &= 0 \\ x = 0 \quad \text{or} \quad x + 1 = 0 \quad &\text{or} \quad x + 2 = 0 \\ x = 0 \quad \text{or} \quad x = -1 \quad &\text{or} \quad x = -2 \end{aligned}$$

28. $n \cdot 88 = 82$
$n \approx 0.93$
about 93%

29. $x = 88(0.875)$
$x = 77$

30. $72 = 0.8x$
$x = 90$

LESSON 10-8 TRY THIS p. 462

a.
$$\begin{aligned} 0.20(280) &= 0.14(280 + x) \\ 56 &= 39.2 + 0.14x \\ 5600 &= 3920 + 14x \\ 1680 &= 14x \\ 120 &= x \end{aligned}$$
120 mL of water

b.
$$\begin{aligned} 90x + 160y &= 130(175) \quad (1) \\ x + y &= 175 \quad (2) \\ x &= 175 - y \qquad \text{Solving (2) for } x \\ 90(175 - y) + 160y &= 22{,}750 \qquad \text{Substituting in (1)} \\ 15{,}750 - 90y + 160y &= 22{,}750 \\ 70y &= 7000 \\ y &= 100 \\ x &= 175 - 100 = 75 \end{aligned}$$
75 pounds at 90¢, 100 pounds at $1.60

LESSON 10-8 EXERCISES pp. 462–464

1. 2nd solution: Amount of solution = $100 - x$
Percent chlorine = 40%
Amount of chlorine = $0.40(100 - x)$
Final solution: Percent chlorine = 50%
Amount of chlorine = $0.50(100)$
$$\begin{aligned} 0.60x + 0.40(100 - x) &= 0.50(100) \\ 0.60x + 40 - 0.40x &= 50 \\ 0.20x + 40 &= 50 \\ 0.20x &= 10 \\ x &= 50 \end{aligned}$$
50 L of each solution is needed.

2. Original solution: Percent butterfat = 6%
Amount butterfat = $0.06(50)$
Skim milk: Percent butterfat = 0%
Amount butterfat = 0
Final solution: Amount = $50 + x$
Percent butterfat = 3%
Amount butterfat = $0.03(50 + x)$
$$\begin{aligned} 0.06(50) &= 0.03(50 + x) \\ 6(50) &= 3(50 + x) \\ 300 &= 150 + 3x \\ 150 &= 3x \\ 50 &= x \end{aligned}$$
50 gal of skim milk should be added.

3.

	Amount of solution	Percent acid	Amount of acid
Solution A	x	50%	$0.50x$
Solution B	$100 - x$	80%	$0.80(100 - x)$
Final solution	100	68%	$0.68(100)$

c. (Percent acid)(Amount solution)
e.
$$\begin{aligned} 0.50x + 0.80(100 - x) &= 0.68(100) \\ 50x + 80(100 - x) &= 68(100) \\ 50x + 8000 - 80x &= 6800 \\ 1200 &= 30x \\ 40 &= x \end{aligned}$$
40 mL of A and 60 mL of B should be used.

4.

	Amount (gallons)	Percent butterfat	Amount butterfat (gallons)
Original solution	100	4.6%	$0.046(100)$
Skim milk	x	0%	0
Final solution	$100 + x$	3.2%	$0.032(100 + x)$

c. (Percent butterfat)(Amount)
e.
$$\begin{aligned} 0.046(100) &= 0.032(100 + x) \\ 46(100) &= 32(100 + x) \\ 4600 &= 3200 + 32x \\ 1400 &= 32x \\ 43.75 &= x \end{aligned}$$
43.75 gallons of skim milk should be added.

5.
$$\begin{aligned} 0.30x + 0.50(200 - x) &= 0.42(200) \\ 0.30x + 100 - 0.50x &= 84 \\ 100 - 0.20x &= 84 \\ -0.20x &= -16 \\ x &= 80 \end{aligned}$$
80 L of 30%, 120 L of 50%

6.
$$\begin{aligned} 0.28x + 0.40(300 - x) &= 0.36(300) \\ 0.28x + 120 - 0.40x &= 108 \\ 120 - 0.12x &= 108 \\ -0.12x &= -12 \\ x &= 100 \end{aligned}$$
100 L of 28%, 200 L of 40%

7.
$$\begin{aligned} 8x + 9(10 - x) &= 10(8.40) \\ 8x + 90 - 9x &= 84 \\ 90 - x &= 84 \\ -x &= -6 \\ x &= 6 \end{aligned}$$
6 kg of cashews, 4 kg of pecans

8.
$$\begin{aligned} 5x + 8(300 - x) &= 7(300) \\ 5x + 2400 - 8x &= 2100 \\ 2400 - 3x &= 2100 \\ -3x &= -300 \\ x &= 100 \end{aligned}$$
100 kg of Brazilian, 200 kg of Turkish

9.
$$\begin{aligned} 0.10(x) + 0.60(5900 - x) &= 0.55(5900) \\ 10x + 60(5900 - x) &= 55(5900) \\ 10x + 354{,}000 - 60x &= 324{,}500 \\ -50x &= -29{,}500 \\ x &= 590 \text{ from Southern Maywood} \end{aligned}$$

10.
$$\begin{aligned} 120x + 150y &= 1950 \\ 120(1.5x) + 150\left(\tfrac{4}{5}y\right) &= 2400 \\ 180x + 120y = 2400 &\rightarrow -12x - 8y = -160 \\ 120x + 150y = 1950 &\rightarrow \underline{12x + 15y = 195} \\ &\qquad 7y = 35 \\ &\qquad y = 5 \\ 120x + 150(5) &= 1950 \\ x &= 10 \end{aligned}$$
10 people at $120, 5 people at $150

11. $0.10(x) + 0.60(5900 - x) = 0.45(5900)$
$$10x + 60(5900 - x) = 45(5900)$$
$$10x + 354{,}000 - 60x = 265{,}500$$
$$354{,}000 - 50x = 265{,}500$$
$$-50x = -88{,}500$$
$x = 1770$ from Southern Maywood

12. Acid in $A + B$: $0.15(12) + 0.25(3) = 2.55$ L

Percent acid in $A + B = \frac{2.55}{15} = 17\%$

$$0.17x + 0.26y = 0.20(24)$$
$$x + y = 24$$
$$17x + 26y = 480$$
$$-17x - 17y = -408$$
$$9y = 72$$
$$y = 8$$
$$x + 8 = 24$$
$$x = 16$$
16 L of combined A and B and 8 L of C are needed. However, there are only 15 L of $A - B$, so it can't be done.

13. $|x + 3| = 7$
$x + 3 = 7$ or $x + 3 = -7$
$x = 4$ or $x = -10$

14. $|2x - 4| = 16$
$2x - 4 = 16$ or $2x - 4 = -16$
$2x = 20$ or $2x = -12$
$x = 10$ or $x = -6$

15. $|4x| - 5 = 19$
$|4x| = 24$
$4x = 24$ or $4x = -24$
$x = 6$ or $x = -6$

16. $8 - |x| > 4$
$4 > |x|$
$x < 4$ and $x > -4$
$-4 < x < 4$

17. $|3x - 4| \leq 13$
$3x - 4 \leq 13$ and $3x - 4 \geq -13$
$3x \leq 17$ and $3x \geq -9$
$x \leq \frac{17}{3}$ and $x \geq -3$
$-3 \leq x \leq \frac{17}{3}$

18. $|5x - 4| + 3 < -19$
$|5x - 4| < -22$
Absolute value always ≥ 0, so no solution.

19. $d + q = 83$
$$10d + 25q = 1385$$
$$-10d - 10q = -830$$
$$15q = 555$$
$$q = 37$$
$$d + 37 = 83$$
$$d = 46$$
46 dimes, 37 quarters

CONNECTIONS: REASONING p. 464

Solution A:

	Amount of solution	Percent alcohol	Amount of alcohol
1st antifreeze	x	0.60	$0.60x$
2nd antifreeze	$10 - x$	0.40	$0.40(10 - x)$
Final solution	10	0.50	0.50(10)

$$0.60x + 0.40(10 - x) = 0.50(10)$$
$$60x + 40(10 - x) = 50(10)$$
$$60x + 400 - 40x = 500$$
$$20x = 100$$
$$x = 5$$
5 liters of each

Solution B:

	Amount of solution	Percent alcohol	Amount of alcohol
1st antifreeze	x	0.60	$0.60x$
2nd antifreeze	y	0.40	$0.40y$
Final solution	10	0.50	0.50(10)

Solution B involves systems of equations.

(1) $x + y = 10$

(2) $0.60x + 0.40y = 0.50(10)$
$$60x + 40y = 500$$
$$40x + 40y = 400$$
$$20x = 100$$
$$x = 5$$
$$5 + y = 10$$
$$y = 5$$
5 liters of each

LESSON 10-9 TRY THIS pp. 465–466

a. $\frac{4x^3 + 6x - 5}{2} = \frac{4x^3}{2} + \frac{6x}{2} - \frac{5}{2} = 2x^3 + 3x - \frac{5}{2}$

b. $\frac{2x^3 + 6x^2 + 4x}{2x} = \frac{2x^3}{2x} + \frac{6x^2}{2x} + \frac{4x}{2x} = x^2 + 3x + 2$

c.
$$\begin{array}{r} x + 4 + \frac{-1}{x-2} \\ x - 2\overline{)x^2 + 2x - 9} \\ \underline{x^2 - 2x} \\ 4x - 9 \\ \underline{4x - 8} \\ -1 \end{array}$$

d.
$$\begin{array}{r} x^2 + x + 1 \\ x - 1\overline{)x^3 + 0x^2 + 0x - 1} \\ \underline{x^3 - 1x^2} \\ x^2 + 0x \\ \underline{x^2 - x} \\ x - 1 \\ \underline{x - 1} \end{array}$$

LESSON 10-9 EXERCISES pp. 467–468

1. $\frac{24x^4}{8} - \frac{4x^3}{8} + \frac{x^2}{8} - \frac{16}{8} = 3x^4 - \frac{x^3}{2} + \frac{x^2}{8} - 2$

2. $\frac{12a^4}{6} - \frac{3a^2}{6} + \frac{a}{6} - \frac{6}{6} = 2a^4 - \frac{a^2}{2} + \frac{a}{6} - 1$

3. $\frac{u}{u} - \frac{2u^2}{u} - \frac{u^5}{u} = 1 - 2u - u^4$

4. $\frac{50x^5}{x} - \frac{7x^4}{x} + \frac{x^2}{x} = 50x^4 - 7x^3 + x$

5. $\frac{15t^3}{3t} + \frac{24t^2}{3t} - \frac{6t}{3t} = 5t^2 + 8t - 2$

6. $\frac{25t^3}{5t} + \frac{15t^2}{5t} - \frac{30t}{5t} = 5t^2 + 3t - 6$

7. $\frac{20x^6}{-5x^2} - \frac{20x^4}{-5x^2} - \frac{5x^2}{-5x^2} = -4x^4 + 4x^2 + 1$

8. $\frac{24x^6}{-8x^2} + \frac{32x^5}{-8x^2} - \frac{8x^2}{-8x^2} = -3x^4 - 4x^3 + 1$

9. $\frac{9r^2s^2}{-3rs} + \frac{3r^2s}{-3rs} - \frac{6rs^2}{-3rs} = -3rs - r + 2s$

10. $\dfrac{4x^4y}{4x^4y} - \dfrac{8x^6y^2}{4x^4y} + \dfrac{12x^8y^6}{4x^4y} = 1 - 2x^2y + 3x^4y^5$

11.
$$\begin{array}{r} x+2 \\ x+2\overline{)x^2+4x+4} \\ \underline{x^2+2x} \\ 2x+4 \\ \underline{2x+4} \end{array}$$

12.
$$\begin{array}{r} x-3 \\ x-3\overline{)x^2-6x+9} \\ \underline{x^2-3x} \\ -3x+9 \\ \underline{-3x+9} \end{array}$$

13.
$$\begin{array}{r} x-5+\dfrac{-50}{x-5} \\ x-5\overline{)x^2-10x-25} \\ \underline{x^2-5x} \\ -5x-25 \\ \underline{-5x+25} \\ -50 \end{array}$$

14.
$$\begin{array}{r} x+4+\dfrac{-32}{x+4} \\ x+4\overline{)x^2+8x-16} \\ \underline{x^2+4x} \\ 4x-16 \\ \underline{4x+16} \\ -32 \end{array}$$

15.
$$\begin{array}{r} x-3 \\ x+3\overline{)x^2+0x-9} \\ \underline{x^2+3x} \\ -3x-9 \\ \underline{-3x-9} \end{array}$$

16.
$$\begin{array}{r} x-5 \\ x+5\overline{)x^2+0x-25} \\ \underline{x^2+5x} \\ -5x-25 \\ \underline{-5x-25} \end{array}$$

17.
$$\begin{array}{r} x^4-x^3+x^2-x+1 \\ x+1\overline{)x^5+0x^4+0x^3+0x^2+0x+1} \\ \underline{x^5+x^4} \\ -x^4+0x^3 \\ \underline{-x^4-x^3} \\ x^3+0x^2 \\ \underline{x^3+x^2} \\ -x^2+0x \\ \underline{-x^2-x} \\ x+1 \\ \underline{x+1} \end{array}$$

18.
$$\begin{array}{r} x^4+x^3+x^2+x+1 \\ x-1\overline{)x^5+0x^4+0x^3+0x^2+0x-1} \\ \underline{x^5-x^4} \\ x^4+0x^3 \\ \underline{x^4-x^3} \\ x^3+0x^2 \\ \underline{x^3-x^2} \\ x^2+0x \\ \underline{x^2-x} \\ x-1 \\ \underline{x-1} \end{array}$$

19.
$$\begin{array}{r} a^2+4a+4 \\ a+2\overline{)a^3+6a^2+12a+8} \\ \underline{a^3+2a^2} \\ 4a^2+12a \\ \underline{4a^2+8a} \\ 4a+8 \\ \underline{4a+8} \end{array}$$

20.
$$\begin{array}{r} x^2-2x-3 \\ x-2\overline{)x^3-4x^2+x+6} \\ \underline{x^3-2x^2} \\ -2x^2+x \\ \underline{-2x^2+4x} \\ -3x+6 \\ \underline{-3x-6} \end{array}$$

21.
$$\begin{array}{r} 2x^2-7x+4 \\ 4x+3\overline{)8x^3+22x^2-5x+12} \\ \underline{8x^3+6x^2} \\ -28x^2-5x \\ \underline{-28x^2-21x} \\ 16x+12 \\ \underline{16x+12} \end{array}$$

22.
$$\begin{array}{r} x^2-3x+1 \\ 2x-3\overline{)2x^3-9x^2+11x-3} \\ \underline{2x^3-3x^2} \\ -6x^2+11x \\ \underline{-6x^2+9x} \\ 2x-3 \\ \underline{2x-3} \end{array}$$

23.
$$\begin{array}{r} x^3-6 \\ x^3-7\overline{)x^6-13x^3+42} \\ \underline{x^6-7x^3} \\ -6x^3+42 \\ \underline{-6x^3+42} \end{array}$$

24.
$$\begin{array}{r} x^3+8 \\ x^3-3\overline{)x^6+5x^3-24} \\ \underline{x^6-3x^3} \\ 8x^3-24 \\ \underline{8x^3-24} \end{array}$$

25.
$$\begin{array}{r} x^3+2x^2+4x+8 \\ x-2\overline{)x^4+0x^3+0x^2+0x-16} \\ \underline{x^4-2x^3} \\ 2x^3+0x^2 \\ \underline{2x^3-4x^2} \\ 4x^2+0x \\ \underline{4x^2-8x} \\ 8x-16 \\ \underline{8x-16} \end{array}$$

26.
$$\begin{array}{r} x^3+3x^2+9x+27 \\ x-3\overline{)x^4+0x^3+0x^2+0x-81} \\ \underline{x^4-3x^3} \\ 3x^3+0x^2 \\ \underline{3x^3-9x^2} \\ 9x^2+0x \\ \underline{9x^2-27x} \\ 27x-81 \\ \underline{27x-81} \end{array}$$

27.
$$\begin{array}{r} t^2+1 \\ t-1\overline{)t^3-t^2+t-1} \\ \underline{t^3-t^2} \\ t-1 \\ \underline{t-1} \end{array}$$

28.
$$\begin{array}{r} t^2-2t+3+\dfrac{-4}{t+1} \\ t+1\overline{)t^3-t^2+t-1} \\ \underline{t^3+t^2} \\ -2t^2+t \\ \underline{-2t^2-2t} \\ 3t-1 \\ \underline{3t+3} \\ -4 \end{array}$$

29.
$$\begin{array}{r} x^2+5 \\ x^2+4\overline{)x^4+9x^2+20} \\ \underline{x^4+4x^2} \\ 5x^2+20 \\ \underline{5x^2+20} \end{array}$$

30.
$$\begin{array}{r} y^3-ay^2+a^2y-a^3+\dfrac{a^2+a^4}{y+a} \\ y+a\overline{)y^4 \qquad\qquad\qquad\qquad +a^2} \\ \underline{y^4+ay^3} \\ -ay^3 \\ \underline{-ay^3-a^2y^2} \\ a^2y^2 \\ \underline{a^2y^2+a^3y} \\ -a^3y+a^2 \\ \underline{-a^3y-a^4} \\ a^2+a^4 \end{array}$$

31.
$$\begin{array}{rl} & a + 3 + \dfrac{5}{5a^2 - 7a - 2} \\ 5a^2 - 7a - 2 & \overline{)\,5a^3 + 8a^2 - 23a - 1} \\ & \underline{5a^3 - 7a^2 - 2a} \\ & 15a^2 - 21a - 1 \\ & \underline{15a^2 - 21a - 6} \\ & 5 \end{array}$$

32.
$$\begin{array}{rl} & 5y + 2 + \dfrac{-10y + 11}{3y^2 - 5y - 2} \\ 3y^2 - 5y - 2 & \overline{)\,15y^3 - 19y^2 - 30y + 7} \\ & \underline{15y^3 - 25y^2 - 10y} \\ & 6y^2 - 20y + 7 \\ & \underline{6y^2 - 10y - 4} \\ & -10y + 11 \end{array}$$

33.
$$\begin{array}{rl} & 2x^2 + x - 3 \\ 3x^3 - 2x - 1 & \overline{)\,6x^5 + 3x^4 - 13x^3 - 4x^2 + 5x + 3} \\ & \underline{6x^5 \qquad - 4x^3 - 2x^2} \\ & 3x^4 - 9x^3 - 2x^2 + 5x \\ & \underline{3x^4 \qquad - 2x^2 - x} \\ & -9x^3 + 0 \quad + 6x + 3 \\ & \underline{-9x^3 \qquad + 6x + 3} \end{array}$$

34.
$$\begin{array}{rl} & 5x^5 + 5x^4 - 8x^2 - 8x + 2 \\ x^2 - x + 1 & \overline{)\,5x^7 - 0x^6 + 0x^5 + 3x^4 + 0x^3 + 2x^2 - 10x + 2} \\ & \underline{5x^7 - 5x^6 + 5x^5} \\ & 5x^6 - 5x^5 - 3x^4 \\ & \underline{5x^6 - 5x^5 + 5x^4} \\ & -8x^4 \qquad + 2x^2 \\ & \underline{-8x^4 + 8x^3 - 8x^2} \\ & -8x^3 + 10x^2 - 10x \\ & \underline{-8x^3 + 8x^2 - 8x} \\ & 2x^2 - 2x + 2 \\ & \underline{2x^2 - 2x + 2} \end{array}$$

35.
$$\begin{array}{rl} & a^5 + a^4b + a^3b^2 + a^2b^3 + ab^4 + b^5 \\ a - b & \overline{)\,a^6 + 0a^5b + 0a^4b^2 + 0a^3b^3 + 0a^2b^4 + 0ab^5 - b^6} \\ & \underline{a^6 - a^5b} \\ & a^5b \\ & \underline{a^5b - a^4b^2} \\ & a^4b^2 \\ & \underline{a^4b^2 - a^3b^3} \\ & a^3b^3 \\ & \underline{a^3b^3 - a^2b^4} \\ & a^2b^4 \\ & \underline{a^2b^4 - ab^5} \\ & ab^5 - b^6 \\ & \underline{ab^5 - b^6} \end{array}$$

36.
$$\begin{array}{rl} & x^4 - x^3y + x^2y^2 - xy^3 + y^4 \\ x + y & \overline{)\,x^5 + 0x^4y + 0x^3y^2 + 0x^2y^3 + 0xy^4 + y^5} \\ & \underline{x^5 + x^4y} \\ & -x^4y \\ & \underline{-x^4y - x^3y^2} \\ & x^3y^2 \\ & \underline{x^3y^2 + x^2y^3} \\ & -x^2y^3 \\ & \underline{-x^2y^3 - xy^4} \\ & xy^4 + y^5 \\ & \underline{xy^4 + y^5} \end{array}$$

37. The polynomial equals the product of the quotient and the divisor.

$$\left(3a^2 + ab - b + \frac{a}{2a^2 - b}\right)(2a^2 - b)$$
$$= 6a^4 + 2a^3b - 2a^2b - 3a^2b - ab^2 + b^2 + a$$
$$= 6a^4 + 2a^3b - 5a^2b - ab^2 + b^2 + a$$

38.
$$\begin{array}{rl} & 3a^{2h} + 2a^h - 5 \\ 2a^h + 3 & \overline{)\,6a^{3h} + 13a^{2h} - 4a^h - 15} \\ & \underline{6a^{3h} + 9a^{2h}} \\ & 4a^{2h} - 4a^h \\ & \underline{4a^{2h} + 6a^h} \\ & -10a^h - 15 \\ & \underline{-10a^h - 15} \end{array}$$

39.
$$\begin{array}{rl} & x + 5 \\ x - 1 & \overline{)\,x^2 + 4x + c} \\ & \underline{x^2 - x} \\ & 5x + c \\ & \underline{5x - 5} \end{array} \qquad c \text{ must be } -5$$

40.
$$\begin{array}{rl} & 2x + 8 \\ x - 1 & \overline{)\,2x^2 + 3cx - 8} \\ & \underline{2x^2 - 2x} \\ & (3c + 2)x - 8 \\ & \underline{8x - 8} \end{array} \qquad \begin{array}{l} 3c + 2 \text{ must be } 8 \\ 3c + 2 = 8 \\ \quad 3c = 6, c = 2 \end{array}$$

41.
$$\begin{array}{rl} & c^2x - 1 \\ x - 1 & \overline{)\,c^2x^2 - 2cx + 1} \\ & \underline{c^2x^2 - c^2x} \\ & (c^2 - 2c)x + 1 \\ & \underline{-1x + 1} \\ & (c^2 - 2c + 1)x \end{array} \qquad \begin{array}{r} c^2 - 2c + 1 = 0 \\ (c - 1)^2 = 0 \\ c = 1 \end{array}$$

42.
$$\begin{array}{rl} & x^2 - 1 \\ x + 2 & \overline{)\,x^3 + 2x^2 - x - 2} \\ & \underline{x^3 + 2x^2} \\ & -x - 2 \\ & \underline{-x - 2} \end{array}$$

The quotient, $x^2 - 1$, equals $(x + 1)(x - 1)$.

43. $6(y - 1) = 2 \cdot 3 \cdot (y - 1)$
$9 - 9y = 9(1 - y) = -3 \cdot 3 \cdot (y - 1)$
$\text{LCM} = 2 \cdot 3 \cdot 3(y - 1) = 18(y - 1)$ or $-18(y - 1)$

44.
$$\frac{x + y}{x^2y} + \frac{x + y}{xy^2} = \frac{y}{y} \cdot \frac{x + y}{x^2y} + \frac{x}{x} \cdot \frac{x + y}{xy^2}$$
$$= \frac{y(x + y)}{x^2y^2} + \frac{x(x + y)}{x^2y^2}$$
$$= \frac{yx + y^2 + x^2 + xy}{x^2y^2}$$
$$= \frac{x^2 + 2xy + y^2}{x^2y^2}$$
$$= \frac{(x + y)^2}{x^2y^2}$$

45.
$$\frac{4}{7m} + \frac{1}{14m} = \frac{2}{2} \cdot \frac{4}{7m} + \frac{1}{14m}$$
$$= \frac{8}{14m} + \frac{1}{14m}$$
$$= \frac{9}{14m}$$

46.
$$\frac{2}{x + 2} - \frac{3}{x - 2} = \frac{x - 2}{x - 2} \cdot \frac{2}{x + 2} - \frac{x + 2}{x + 2} \cdot \frac{3}{x - 2}$$
$$= \frac{2(x - 2)}{(x - 2)(x + 2)} - \frac{3(x + 2)}{(x + 2)(x - 2)}$$
$$= \frac{2x - 4 - 3x - 6}{(x + 2)(x - 2)}$$
$$= \frac{-x - 10}{(x + 2)(x - 2)} \quad \text{or} \quad \frac{-1(x + 10)}{(x + 2)(x - 2)}$$

47.
$$\frac{7}{x^2 - 9} - \frac{4}{2x - 6} = \frac{7}{(x + 3)(x - 3)} - \frac{4}{2(x - 3)}$$
$$= \frac{2}{2} \cdot \frac{7}{(x + 3)(x - 3)} - \frac{x + 3}{x + 3} \cdot \frac{4}{2(x - 3)}$$
$$= \frac{14}{2(x + 3)(x - 3)} - \frac{4(x + 3)}{2(x + 3)(x - 3)}$$
$$= \frac{14 - 4x - 12}{2(x + 3)(x - 3)}$$
$$= \frac{-4x + 2}{2(x + 3)(x - 3)}$$
$$= \frac{-2x + 1}{(x + 3)(x - 3)} \quad \text{or} \quad \frac{-1(2x - 1)}{(x + 3)(x - 3)}$$

48. $\dfrac{x-3}{2x-1} - \dfrac{4(x+1)}{1-2x} = \dfrac{x-3}{2x-1} + \dfrac{4(x+1)}{2x-1}$

$= \dfrac{x-3+4x+4}{2x-1}$

$= \dfrac{5x+1}{2x-1}$

49. $x - \dfrac{3}{x} = 2$

$x\left(x - \dfrac{3}{x}\right) = 2x$

$x^2 - 3 = 2x$

$x^2 - 2x - 3 = 0$

$(x-3)(x+1) = 0$

$x = 3$ or $x = -1$

50. $\dfrac{x-3}{x+2} = \dfrac{1}{2}$

$2(x+2)\left(\dfrac{x-3}{x+2}\right) = \dfrac{1}{2}[2(x+2)]$

$2(x-3) = x+2$

$2x - 6 = x + 2$

$x = 8$

51. $\dfrac{x+2}{4} - \dfrac{x-3}{3} = 1$

$12\left(\dfrac{x+2}{4} - \dfrac{x-3}{3}\right) = 1 \cdot 12$

$3(x+2) - 4(x-3) = 12$

$3x + 6 - 4x + 12 = 12$

$-x + 18 = 12$

$-x = -6$

$x = 6$

THE FACTOR THEOREM p. 468

1. $x^2 - 9x + 8 = 0$
$(x-8)(x-1) = 0$
$x = 8$ or $x = 1$

2. $x^2 + 11x + 28 = 0$
$(x+4)(x+7) = 0$
$x = -4$ or $x = -7$

3. $x^2 - 2x - 15 = 0$
$(x-5)(x+3) = 0$
$x = 5$ or $x = -3$

4. $x^2 - x - 2$
$2^2 - 2 - 2 = 0$
$(-1)^2 - (-1) - 2 = 0$
$(-2)^2 - (-2) - 2 = 4$
The roots are 2 and -1.
The factors are $x - 2$ and $x + 1$.

5. $4x^2 - 20x + 21$
$4\left(\dfrac{7}{2}\right)^2 - 20\left(\dfrac{7}{2}\right) + 21 = 49 - 70 + 21 = 0$
$4\left(\dfrac{5}{2}\right)^2 - 20\left(\dfrac{5}{2}\right) + 21 = 25 - 50 + 21 = -4$
$4\left(\dfrac{3}{2}\right)^2 - 20\left(\dfrac{3}{2}\right) + 21 = 9 - 30 + 21 = 0$
The roots are $\dfrac{7}{2}$ and $\dfrac{3}{2}$.
The factors are $x - \dfrac{7}{2}$ and $x - \dfrac{3}{2}$.

LESSON 10-10 TRY THIS p. 470

a. $\dfrac{\frac{x}{2} + \frac{x}{3}}{\frac{1}{2}} \cdot \dfrac{6}{6} = \dfrac{6 \cdot \frac{x}{2} + 6 \cdot \frac{x}{3}}{6 \cdot \frac{1}{2}}$

$= \dfrac{3x + 2x}{3}$

$= \dfrac{5x}{3}$

b. $\dfrac{1 + \frac{1}{x}}{1 - \frac{1}{x^2}} \cdot \dfrac{x^2}{x^2} = \dfrac{x^2 + x^2 \cdot \frac{1}{x}}{x^2 - x^2 \cdot \frac{1}{x^2}}$

$= \dfrac{x^2 + x}{x^2 - 1}$

$= \dfrac{x(x+1)}{(x+1)(x-1)}$

$= \dfrac{x}{x-1}$

c. $\dfrac{\frac{3}{(t+2)(2t-1)}}{\frac{t}{t+2}} = \dfrac{3}{(t+2)(2t-1)} \div \dfrac{t}{t+2}$

$= \dfrac{3}{(t+2)(2t-1)} \cdot \dfrac{t+2}{t}$

$= \dfrac{3(t+2)}{(t+2)(2t-1)t} = \dfrac{3}{t(2t-1)}$

LESSON 10-10 EXERCISES pp. 470–471

1. $\dfrac{\frac{2}{7} + \frac{3}{7}}{\frac{3}{4}} \cdot \dfrac{28}{28} = \dfrac{8 + 12}{21} = \dfrac{20}{21}$

2. $\dfrac{3 + \frac{5}{2}}{\frac{5}{4}} \cdot \dfrac{4}{4} = \dfrac{12 + 10}{5} = \dfrac{22}{5}$

3. $\dfrac{1 + \frac{2}{x}}{\frac{3}{4}} \cdot \dfrac{4x}{4x} = \dfrac{4x + 8}{3x} = \dfrac{4(x+2)}{3x}$

4. $\dfrac{3 + \frac{x}{2}}{\frac{5}{4}} \cdot \dfrac{4}{4} = \dfrac{12 + 2x}{5} = \dfrac{2(6+x)}{5}$

5. $\dfrac{1 + \frac{9}{16}}{1 - \frac{3}{4}} \cdot \dfrac{16}{16} = \dfrac{16 + 9}{16 - 12} = \dfrac{25}{4}$

6. $\dfrac{\frac{5}{27} - 5}{\frac{1}{3} + 1} \cdot \dfrac{27}{27} = \dfrac{5 - 135}{9 + 27} = \dfrac{-130}{36} = \dfrac{-65}{18}$

7. $\dfrac{\frac{1}{x} + 3}{\frac{1}{x} - 5} \cdot \dfrac{x}{x} = \dfrac{1 + 3x}{1 - 5x}$

8. $\dfrac{\frac{3}{a}}{\frac{1}{a} - \frac{1}{3a}} \cdot \dfrac{3a}{3a} = \dfrac{9}{3 - 1} = \dfrac{9}{2}$

9. $\dfrac{\frac{7}{y}}{\frac{1}{4} + \frac{2}{y}} \cdot \dfrac{4y}{4y} = \dfrac{28}{y + 8}$

10. $\dfrac{\frac{c}{d} + 3}{4 + \frac{c}{d}} \cdot \dfrac{d}{d} = \dfrac{c + 3d}{4d + c}$

11. $\dfrac{\frac{3}{s} + s}{\frac{s}{3} + s} \cdot \dfrac{3s}{3s} = \dfrac{9 + 3s^2}{s^2 + 3s^2} = \dfrac{9 + 3s^2}{4s^2}$

12. $\dfrac{\frac{2}{y} + \frac{1}{2y}}{y + \frac{y}{2}} \cdot \dfrac{2y}{2y} = \dfrac{4 + 1}{2y^2 + y^2} = \dfrac{5}{3y^2}$

13. $\dfrac{4 - \frac{1}{x^2}}{2 - \frac{1}{x}} \cdot \dfrac{x^2}{x^2} = \dfrac{4x^2 - 1}{2x^2 - x} = \dfrac{(2x+1)(2x-1)}{x(2x-1)}$

$= \dfrac{2x + 1}{x}$

14. $\dfrac{\frac{1}{xy}}{\frac{1}{x} + \frac{1}{y}} \cdot \dfrac{xy}{xy} = \dfrac{1}{y + x}$

15. $\dfrac{\frac{2}{a+b}}{\frac{4}{a^2-b^2}} = \dfrac{\frac{2}{a+b}}{\frac{4}{(a+b)(a-b)}} \cdot \dfrac{(a+b)(a-b)}{(a+b)(a-b)}$

$= \dfrac{2(a-b)}{4}$

$= \dfrac{a-b}{2}$

16. $\dfrac{\frac{p}{q}+\frac{q}{r}}{\frac{r}{s}+\frac{s}{t}} \cdot \dfrac{qrst}{qrst} = \dfrac{prst + q^2st}{qr^2t + qrs^2}$

$= \dfrac{st(pr + q^2)}{qr(rt + s^2)}$

17. $\dfrac{\frac{x}{y}-\frac{y}{x}}{\frac{1}{y}+\frac{1}{x}} \cdot \dfrac{xy}{xy} = \dfrac{x^2 - y^2}{x + y}$

$= \dfrac{(x+y)(x-y)}{x+y}$

$= x - y$

18. $\dfrac{\frac{1}{a}-\frac{1}{2}}{a-2} \cdot \dfrac{2a}{2a} = \dfrac{2-a}{2a^2 - 4a} = \dfrac{2-a}{2a(a-2)}$

$= \dfrac{-(a-2)}{2a(a-2)}$

$= -\dfrac{1}{2a}$

19. $\dfrac{\frac{a}{(a+b)(2a+1)}}{\frac{b}{a+b}} \cdot \dfrac{(a+b)(2a+1)}{(a+b)(2a+1)} = \dfrac{a}{b(2a+1)}$

20. $\dfrac{\frac{m}{(m-n)(m+n)}}{\frac{n+1}{(m+n)^2}} \cdot \dfrac{(m-n)(m+n)^2}{(m-n)(m+n)^2} = \dfrac{m(m+n)}{(n+1)(m-n)}$

21. $\dfrac{\frac{x}{x-y}}{\frac{x^2}{x^2-y^2}} = \dfrac{\frac{x}{x-y}}{\frac{x^2}{(x+y)(x-y)}} \cdot \dfrac{(x+y)(x-y)}{(x+y)(x-y)}$

$= \dfrac{x(x+y)}{x^2}$

$= \dfrac{x+y}{x}$

22. $\dfrac{\frac{a}{b}+\frac{b}{c}}{\frac{c}{d}+\frac{d}{e}} \cdot \dfrac{bcde}{bcde} = \dfrac{acde + b^2de}{bc^2e + bcd^2}$

$= \dfrac{de(ac + b^2)}{bc(ce + d^2)}$

23. $\dfrac{\frac{g}{2f}+\frac{g+2}{f+1}}{\frac{g^2}{f+1}+\frac{2g+3}{f}} \cdot \dfrac{2f(f+1)}{2f(f+1)}$

$= \dfrac{g(f+1) + 2f(g+2)}{2fg^2 + 2(f+1)(2g+3)}$

$= \dfrac{fg + g + 2fg + 4f}{2fg^2 + 2(2fg + 3f + 2g + 3)}$

$= \dfrac{3fg + g + 4f}{2fg^2 + 4fg + 6f + 4g + 6}$

$= \dfrac{4f + 3fg + g}{2(fg^2 + 2fg + 3f + 2g + 3)}$

24. $\dfrac{\frac{x+1}{x+2}+\frac{1}{x}}{\frac{x}{x+2}+\frac{1}{x^2}} \cdot \dfrac{x^2(x+2)}{x^2(x+2)} = \dfrac{x^2(x+1) + x(x+2)}{x^3 + x + 2}$

$= \dfrac{x^3 + x^2 + x^2 + 2x}{x^3 + x + 2}$

$= \dfrac{x^3 + 2x^2 + 2x}{x^3 + x + 2}$

$= \dfrac{x(x^2 + 2x + 2)}{x^3 + x + 2}$

25. $\dfrac{\left(1 + \frac{a}{b-a}\right)(b+a)(b-a)}{\left(\frac{a}{a+b} - 1\right)(b+a)(b-a)}$

$= \dfrac{b^2 - a^2 + a(b+a)}{a(b-a) - (b^2 - a^2)} = \dfrac{b^2 - a^2 + ab + a^2}{ab - a^2 - b^2 + a^2}$

$= \dfrac{b^2 + ab}{ab - b^2} = \dfrac{b(b+a)}{b(a-b)} = \dfrac{a+b}{a-b}$

26. $\dfrac{\left(\frac{a}{b}+\frac{c}{d}\right)(abcd)}{\left(\frac{b}{d}+\frac{d}{c}\right)(abcd)} = \dfrac{a^2cd + c^2ab}{b^2cd + d^2ab}$

$= \dfrac{ac(ad + cb)}{bd(bc + da)} = \dfrac{ac}{bd}$

27. $\dfrac{\left(\frac{a}{b}-\frac{c}{d}\right)(abcd)}{\left(\frac{b}{a}-\frac{d}{c}\right)(abcd)} = \dfrac{a^2cd - c^2ab}{b^2cd - d^2ab} = \dfrac{ac(ad - cb)}{bd(cb - ad)}$

$= \dfrac{-ac(cb - ad)}{bd(cb - ad)} = -\dfrac{ac}{bd}$

28. $a + 1 \neq 0 \rightarrow a \neq -1$
$a + 2 \neq 0 \rightarrow a \neq -2$
$a - 2 \neq 0 \rightarrow a \neq 2$

29. $\dfrac{\frac{2a+3}{a+1}}{\frac{a-2}{a+1}} \cdot \dfrac{a+1}{a+1} = 12$

$\dfrac{2a+3}{a-2} = 12$

$(a-2)\left(\dfrac{2a+3}{a-2}\right) = 12(a-2)$

$2a + 3 = 12a - 24$

$27 = 10a$

$a = \dfrac{27}{10}$

30. $\dfrac{(x-1)}{(x-1)} \cdot \dfrac{\frac{x+1}{x-1}+1}{\frac{x+1}{x-1}-1} = 10$

$\dfrac{x + 1 + x - 1}{x + 1 - (x - 1)} = 10$

$\dfrac{2x}{x + 1 - x + 1} = 10$

$\dfrac{2x}{2} = 10$

$x = 10$

31. $\dfrac{4x+5}{x+5} - \dfrac{x+11}{x+5} = \dfrac{4x + 5 - (x + 11)}{x + 5}$

$= \dfrac{4x + 5 - x - 11}{x + 5}$

$= \dfrac{3x - 6}{x + 5}$

$= \dfrac{3(x-2)}{x+5}$

32. $\frac{5}{y+2} + \frac{5}{y-2} = \frac{y-2}{y-2}\cdot\frac{5}{y+2} + \frac{y+2}{y+2}\cdot\frac{5}{y-2}$
$= \frac{5y-10}{(y+2)(y-2)} + \frac{5y+10}{(y+2)(y-2)}$
$= \frac{10y}{(y+2)(y-2)}$

33. $\frac{m^2}{m-5} + \frac{25}{5-m} = \frac{m^2}{m-5} - \frac{25}{m-5}$
$= \frac{m^2-25}{m-5}$
$= \frac{(m+5)(m-5)}{m-5}$
$= m + 5$

34. $\frac{2}{x+1} + \frac{5}{2x} = \frac{2x}{2x}\cdot\frac{2}{x+1} + \frac{x+1}{x+1}\cdot\frac{5}{2x}$
$= \frac{4x}{2x(x+1)} + \frac{5x+5}{2x(x+1)}$
$= \frac{9x+5}{2x(x+1)}$

35. $\frac{x-1}{x} - \frac{3x+5}{2x} = \frac{2}{2}\cdot\frac{x-1}{x} - \frac{3x+5}{2x}$
$= \frac{2x-2-(3x+5)}{2x}$
$= \frac{2x-2-3x-5}{2x}$
$= \frac{-x-7}{2x}$ or $\frac{-1(x+7)}{2x}$

36. $\frac{5}{x+1} = \frac{4}{x-1}$
$(x+1)(x-1)\left(\frac{5}{x+1}\right) = (x+1)(x-1)\left(\frac{4}{x-1}\right)$
$5(x-1) = 4(x+1)$
$5x - 5 = 4x + 4$
$x = 9$

37. $\frac{x}{4} - \frac{x}{6} = \frac{1}{4}$
$12\left(\frac{x}{4} - \frac{x}{6}\right) = 12\cdot\frac{1}{4}$
$3x - 2x = 3$
$x = 3$

38. $\frac{x-2}{3x} = \frac{1}{4}$
$12x\left(\frac{x-2}{3x}\right) = 12x\cdot\frac{1}{4}$
$4(x-2) = 3x$
$4x - 8 = 3x$
$x = 8$

39. $x + y = -13$
$\underline{x - y = \ \ 21}$
$2x \quad = \ \ 8$
$x = 4$
$4 - y = 21$
$y = -17$
The numbers are 4 and -17.

LESSON 10-11 TRY THIS p. 473

a. 3. Associative and commutative properties
4. Reciprocal theorem
5. Division theorem
6. Transitive property of equality

b.

1. $[a + (-b)] + b$ $= a + [(-b) + b]$	Associative property of addition
2. $= a + 0$	Property of additive inverses
3. $= a$	Identity property
4. $[a + (-b)] + b = a$	Transitive property of equality

Thus, by the definition of subtraction, $a + (-b) = a - b$.

LESSON 10-11 EXERCISES p. 474

1. (c) Distributive property
(d) Division theorem
(e) Transitive property of equality

2.

1. $\frac{a}{c} = a\cdot\frac{1}{c}$ and $\frac{b}{c} = b\cdot\frac{1}{c}$	Division theorem
2. $\frac{a}{c} - \frac{b}{c} = a\cdot\frac{1}{c} - b\cdot\frac{1}{c}$	Substituting $a\cdot\frac{1}{c}$ for $\frac{a}{c}$ and $b\cdot\frac{1}{c}$ for $\frac{b}{c}$
3. $= (a-b)\frac{1}{c}$	Distributive property
4. $= \frac{a-b}{c}$	Division theorem
5. $\frac{a}{c} - \frac{b}{c} = \frac{a-b}{c}$	Transitive property of equality

3. Show $\frac{1}{\frac{a}{b}} = \frac{b}{a}$

1. $\frac{1}{\frac{a}{b}} = \frac{1\cdot b}{\frac{a}{b}\cdot b}$	Multiplicative identity
2. $= \frac{b}{\frac{a}{b}\cdot b}$	Multiplicative identity
3. $= \frac{b}{\left(a\cdot\frac{1}{b}\right)\cdot b}$	Division theorem
4. $= \frac{b}{a\left(\frac{1}{b}\cdot b\right)}$	Associative property
5. $= \frac{b}{a(1)}$	Definition of reciprocal
6. $= \frac{b}{a}$	Multiplicative identity
7. $\frac{1}{\frac{a}{b}} = \frac{b}{a}$	Transitive property of equality

4. If $\frac{a}{b} = \frac{c}{d}$, show $ad = bc$.

1. $\frac{a}{b}(bd) = \frac{c}{d}(bd)$	Multiplication property of equality
2. $\left(a\cdot\frac{1}{b}\right)(bd) = \left(c\cdot\frac{1}{d}\right)(bd)$	Division theorem
3. $\left(a\cdot\frac{1}{b}\right)(bd) = \left(c\cdot\frac{1}{d}\right)(db)$	Commutative property
4. $a\left(\frac{1}{b}\cdot b\right)d = c\left(\frac{1}{d}\cdot d\right)b$	Associative property
5. $a\cdot 1\cdot d = c\cdot 1\cdot b$	Definition of reciprocal
6. $ad = cb$	Multiplicative identity

5. $(2w)^5 = 2^5w^5 = 32w^5$ 6. $\frac{a^2b^3}{ab^2c} = \frac{a^{2-1}b^{3-2}}{c} = \frac{ab}{c}$

7. $(y^9)^9 = y^{9\cdot 9} = y^{81}$ 8. $(-3m^5)^4 = (-3)^4m^{5\cdot 4} = 81m^{20}$

9. $81c^2 - 16 = (9c + 4)(9c - 4)$

10. $5x^2 + 5x - 30 = 5(x^2 + x - 6) = 5(x + 3)(x - 2)$

11. $2x^2 + 3x - 5 = (2x + 5)(x - 1)$

12. $6x^2 + 25x + 4 = (x + 4)(6x + 1)$

13. $6x^2 + 11x + 3 = (3x + 1)(2x + 3)$

14. $10x^2 + 23x + 12 = (2x + 3)(5x + 4)$

15. $\frac{x}{7} - \frac{7}{x} = 0$
$7x\left(\frac{x}{7} - \frac{7}{x}\right) = 7x\cdot 0$
$x^2 - 49 = 0$
$(x + 7)(x - 7) = 0$
$x = -7$ or $x = 7$

16. $$x - \frac{4}{x} = 0$$
$$x\left(x - \frac{4}{x}\right) = 0 \cdot x$$
$$x^2 - 4 = 0$$
$$(x + 2)(x - 2) = 0$$
$$x = -2 \quad \text{or} \quad x = 2$$

17. $$\frac{a + 3}{2a + 2} = \frac{2}{3}$$
$$3(2a + 2)\left(\frac{a + 3}{2a + 2}\right) = \frac{2}{3}(3)(2a + 2)$$
$$3(a + 3) = 2(2a + 2)$$
$$3a + 9 = 4a + 4$$
$$5 = a$$

18. $$\begin{aligned} 3x + y &= 8 \\ 5x - y &= 8 \\ \hline 8x \quad &= 16 \\ x &= 2 \\ 3 \cdot 2 + y &= 8 \\ y &= 2 \end{aligned}$$

19. $$\begin{aligned} 2x + 5y &= 3 \\ 5x - 2y &= -7 \\ 10x + 25y &= 15 \\ -10x + 4y &= 14 \\ \hline 29y &= 29 \\ y &= 1 \\ 2x + 5(1) &= 3 \\ x &= -1 \end{aligned}$$

LESSON 10-12 PROBLEMS

p. 476

1. Strategies: Work backward
   Choose the operations

   Bonnie found 8
   Salvatore found 8 + 4 = 12
   Gus found 12 − 4 = 8
   Neil found 2 × 8 = 16
   8 + 12 + 8 + 16 = 44

   Together they found 44 new stores. They did not get the bonus.

2. Strategies: Draw a diagram
   Choose the operations

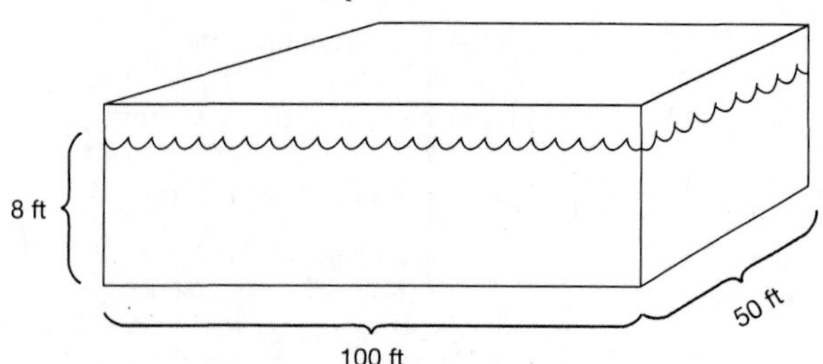

$V = l \times w \times h$
$V = 100 \times 50 \times 8$
$V = 40{,}000$ cubic ft
$\$2.25 \div 2/1000 \text{ ft}^3$
$2.25 \times 40 = \$90.00$

It will cost $90 to fill the swimming pool to a line 2 feet from the top.

3. Strategies: Work backward
   Draw a diagram

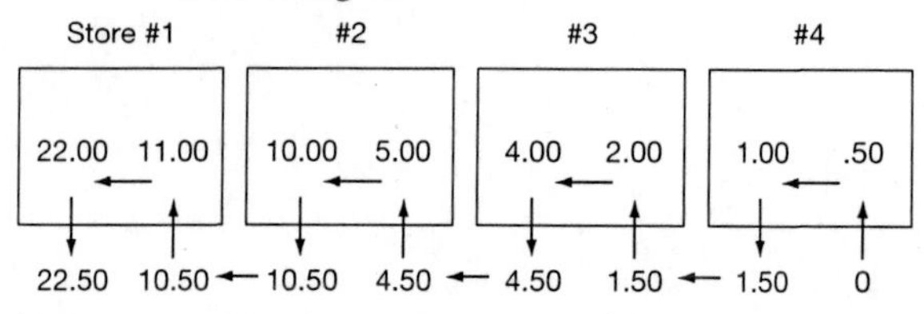

Before entering the first turnpike, Ramon had $22.50.

4. Strategies: Guess, check, revise
   Work backward

   Fill the 9-qt pail; pour into 4-qt pail, leaving 5 qt. Empty 4-qt pail and fill from large pail, leaving 1 qt in large pail.
   Empty 4-qt pail and transfer 1 qt to small pail. Fill the 9-qt pail and pour into small pail.
   It will take 3 qt to fill the small pail, leaving 6 qt in the large pail.

5. Strategy: Write an equation
$$x + \frac{2}{3}x + \frac{1}{2}x + \frac{1}{7}x = 97$$
$$42\left[x + \frac{2}{3}x + \frac{1}{2}x + \frac{1}{7}x = 97\right]$$
$$42x + 28x + 21x + 6x = 4074$$
$$97x = 4074$$
$$x = 42$$

   The number is 42.

6. Strategy: Make a table

Size of Square	Number of Cannonballs
10 × 10	100
9 × 9	81
8 × 8	64
7 × 7	49
6 × 6	36
5 × 5	25
4 × 4	16
3 × 3	9
2 × 2	4
1	1
	Total 385

385 cannonballs were used to build the monument.

CHAPTER 10 WRAP UP

pp. 477–478

1. $$\frac{3x + 9}{3x} = \frac{3(x + 3)}{3x} = \frac{x + 3}{x}$$

2. $$\frac{6y^2 + 3y}{3y^2 + 6y} = \frac{3y(2y + 1)}{3y(y + 2)} = \frac{2y + 1}{y + 2}$$

3. $$\frac{3x - 3}{3x + 6} = \frac{3(x - 1)}{3(x + 2)} = \frac{x - 1}{x + 2}$$

4. $$\frac{3c + 5d}{25d^2 - 9c^2} = \frac{3c + 5d}{(5d + 3c)(5d - 3c)} = \frac{1}{5d - 3c}$$

5. $$\frac{9y^2}{5y^2} \cdot \frac{(y - 3)}{3} = \frac{9y^2(y - 3)}{15y^2} = \frac{3(y - 3)}{5}$$

6. $$\frac{2x}{x + 1} \cdot \frac{x + 1}{4x} = \frac{2x(x + 1)}{4x(x + 1)} = \frac{1}{2}$$

7. $$\frac{7(m - 2)}{5m} \cdot \frac{4m^2}{(m - 2)} = \frac{28m^2(m - 2)}{5m(m - 2)} = \frac{28m}{5}$$

8. $$\frac{3x + 3}{3} \div \frac{x + 1}{6} = \frac{3(x + 1)}{3} \cdot \frac{6}{x + 1} = \frac{18(x + 1)}{3(x + 1)} = 6$$

9. $$\frac{y + 2}{y - 3} \div \frac{y + 2}{y + 1} = \frac{y + 2}{y - 3} \cdot \frac{y + 1}{y + 2} = \frac{(y + 2)(y + 1)}{(y + 2)(y - 3)} = \frac{y + 1}{y - 3}$$

10. $\frac{y+3}{y^2-9} \div \frac{y-3}{y^2-5y+6} = \frac{y+3}{(y+3)(y-3)} \cdot \frac{(y-2)(y-3)}{(y-3)}$
$= \frac{(y-2)(y+3)(y-3)}{(y-3)(y+3)(y-3)}$
$= \frac{y-2}{y-3}$

11. $\frac{b-2}{b^2+b} \div \frac{b^2-4}{b+1} = \frac{b-2}{b(b+1)} \cdot \frac{b+1}{(b+2)(b-2)}$
$= \frac{(b-2)(b+1)}{(b-2)(b+1)(b)(b+2)}$
$= \frac{1}{b(b+2)}$

12. $\frac{4x-6}{5} \div \frac{6x-9}{25} = \frac{2(2x-3)}{5} \cdot \frac{25}{3(2x-3)}$
$= \frac{50(2x-3)}{15(2x-3)}$
$= \frac{10}{3}$

13. $\frac{x^2-y^2}{xy^2} \div \frac{xy+y^2}{x} = \frac{(x+y)(x-y)}{xy^2} \cdot \frac{x}{y(x+y)}$
$= \frac{x(x+y)(x-y)}{x(x+y)y^3}$
$= \frac{x-y}{y^3}$

14. $\frac{3x^2+2x-5}{5x+1} + \frac{2x^2-x+6}{5x+1}$
$= \frac{3x^2+2x-5+2x^2-x+6}{5x+1} = \frac{5x^2+x+1}{5x+1}$

15. $\frac{5b}{2+b} - \frac{b-3}{2+b} = \frac{5b-(b-3)}{2+b}$
$= \frac{5b-b+3}{2+b}$
$= \frac{4b+3}{2+b}$

16. $\frac{3a}{3a} + \frac{-1}{a} = \frac{a}{a} - \frac{1}{a}$
$= \frac{a-1}{a}$

17. $\frac{2a}{a+1} + \frac{4a}{a^2-1} = \frac{2a}{a+1} + \frac{4a}{(a+1)(a-1)}$
$= \frac{2a}{a+1} \cdot \frac{a-1}{a-1} + \frac{4a}{(a+1)(a-1)}$
$= \frac{2a(a-1)}{(a+1)(a-1)} + \frac{4a}{(a+1)(a-1)}$
$= \frac{2a^2-2a+4a}{(a+1)(a-1)}$
$= \frac{2a^2+2a}{(a+1)(a-1)}$
$= \frac{2a(a+1)}{(a+1)(a-1)}$
$= \frac{2a}{a-1}$

18. $\frac{3}{3x-9} + \frac{x-2}{3-x} = \frac{3}{3(x-3)} + \frac{-1(x-2)}{(x-3)}$
$= \frac{1}{x-3} - \frac{(x-2)}{x-3}$
$= \frac{1-(x-2)}{x-3}$
$= \frac{1-x+2}{x-3}$
$= \frac{3-x}{x-3}$
$= \frac{-(x-3)}{(x-3)}$
$= -1$

19. $\frac{3x-1}{2x} - \frac{x-1}{x} = \frac{3x-1}{2x} - \frac{2(x-1)}{2x}$
$= \frac{3x-1-2(x-1)}{2x}$
$= \frac{3x-1-2x+2}{2x}$
$= \frac{x+1}{2x}$

20. $\frac{15}{b^2-4} - \frac{7}{b-2} = \frac{15}{(b+2)(b-2)} - \frac{7}{b-2}$
$= \frac{15}{(b+2)(b-2)} - \frac{7(b+2)}{(b+2)(b-2)}$
$= \frac{15-7(b+2)}{(b+2)(b-2)}$
$= \frac{15-7b-14}{(b+2)(b-2)}$
$= \frac{-7b+1}{(b+2)(b-2)}$

21. $\frac{1}{x^2-25} - \frac{x-5}{x^2-4x-5}$
$= \frac{1}{(x+5)(x-5)} - \frac{x-5}{(x-5)(x+1)}$
$= \frac{(x+1)}{(x+5)(x-5)(x+1)} - \frac{(x-5)(x+5)}{(x+5)(x-5)(x+1)}$
$= \frac{(x+1)-(x^2-25)}{(x+5)(x-5)(x+1)}$
$= \frac{x+1-x^2+25}{(x+5)(x-5)(x+1)}$
$= \frac{-x^2+x+26}{(x+5)(x-5)(x+1)}$

22. $\frac{3}{y} - \frac{1}{4} = \frac{1}{y}$
$4y\left(\frac{3}{y} - \frac{1}{4}\right) = 4y\left(\frac{1}{y}\right)$
$12 - y = 4$
$-y = -8$
$y = 8$

23. $\frac{15}{x} - \frac{15}{x+2} = 2$
$x(x+2)\left(\frac{15}{x} - \frac{15}{x+2}\right) = 2(x)(x+2)$
$15(x+2) - 15x = 2x^2 + 4x$
$15x + 30 - 15x = 2x^2 + 4x$
$0 = 2x^2 + 4x - 30$
$0 = 2(x^2 + 2x - 15)$
$0 = 2(x+5)(x-3)$
$x + 5 = 0$ or $x - 3 = 0$
$x = -5$ or $x = 3$

24. $\frac{4x}{3} - \frac{2x-1}{5} = \frac{x+3}{2}$
$30\left(\frac{4x}{3} - \frac{2x-1}{5}\right) = 30\left(\frac{x+3}{2}\right)$
$40x - 6(2x-1) = 15(x+3)$
$40x - 12x + 6 = 15x + 45$
$28x + 6 = 15x + 45$
$13x = 39$
$x = 3$

25. $\frac{5}{x} + x = -6$
$x\left(\frac{5}{x} + x\right) = -6x$
$5 + x^2 = -6x$
$x^2 + 6x + 5 = 0$
$(x+1)(x+5) = 0$
$x + 1 = 0$ or $x + 5 = 0$
$x = -1$ or $x = -5$

26. $\frac{x}{x-1} - \frac{2}{1-x^2} = \frac{8}{x+1}$

$\frac{x}{x-1} + \frac{2}{x^2-1} = \frac{8}{x+1}$

$(x^2-1)\left(\frac{x}{x-1} + \frac{2}{x^2-1}\right) = (x^2-1)\left(\frac{8}{x+1}\right)$

$x(x+1) + 2 = 8(x-1)$

$x^2 + x + 2 = 8x - 8$

$x^2 - 7x + 10 = 0$

$(x-5)(x-2) = 0$

$x - 5 = 0$ or $x - 2 = 0$

$x = 5$ or $x = 2$

27. $\frac{1}{9} + \frac{1}{12} = \frac{1}{n}$

$36n\left(\frac{1}{9} + \frac{1}{12}\right) = 36n\left(\frac{1}{n}\right)$

$4n + 3n = 36$

$7n = 36$

$n = \frac{36}{7}$ or $5\frac{1}{7}$ hours

28. $\frac{70}{r} = \frac{60}{r-40}$

$r(r-40)\left(\frac{70}{r}\right) = r(r-40)\left(\frac{60}{r-40}\right)$

$70(r-40) = 60r$

$70r - 2800 = 60r$

$10r = 2800$

$r = 280$

The rates are 280 km/h and 240 km/h.

29. $0.30x + 0.60(80-x) = 0.45(80)$

$30x + 60(80-x) = 45(80)$

$30x + 4800 - 60x = 3600$

$4800 - 30x = 3600$

$-30x = -1200$

$x = 40$

40 liters of each

30. $\frac{12y^3 + 8y - 3}{3} = \frac{12y^3}{3} + \frac{8y}{3} - \frac{3}{3}$

$= 4y^3 + \frac{8}{3}y - 1$

31.
$$\begin{array}{r} 2x - 5 \\ x + 4\overline{)2x^2 + 3x - 20} \\ \underline{2x^2 + 8x} \\ -5x - 20 \\ \underline{-5x - 20} \end{array}$$

32. $\frac{\frac{1}{x} + 1}{\frac{1}{x^2} - 1} \cdot \frac{x^2}{x^2} = \frac{x + x^2}{1 - x^2}$

$= \frac{x(1+x)}{(1+x)(1-x)}$

$= \frac{x}{1-x}$

33. $\frac{x + \frac{3}{y}}{x - \frac{2}{y^2}} \cdot \frac{y^2}{y^2} = \frac{xy^2 + 3y}{xy^2 - 2}$

$= \frac{y(xy+3)}{xy^2 - 2}$

CHAPTER 10 ASSESSMENT

p. 479

1. $\frac{5y+15}{10} = \frac{5(y+3)}{5 \cdot 2} = \frac{y+3}{2}$

2. $\frac{14y^2 + 7y}{49y^2 + 14y} = \frac{7y(2y+1)}{7y(7y+2)} = \frac{2y+1}{7y+2}$

3. $\frac{4x^2 - 8xy + 4y^2}{3x - 3y} = \frac{4(x^2 - 2xy + y^2)}{3(x-y)}$

$= \frac{4(x-y)(x-y)}{3(x-y)}$

$= \frac{4(x-y)}{3}$

4. $\frac{2x+3y}{5} \cdot \frac{10}{4x+6y} = \frac{(2x+3y)(10)}{5(2)(2x+3y)}$

$= \frac{10(2x+3y)}{10(2x+3y)}$

$= 1$

5. $\frac{25-x^2}{12} \cdot \frac{6}{5-x} = \frac{(5+x)(5-x)(6)}{12(5-x)}$

$= \frac{5+x}{2}$

6. $\frac{x^2+x}{x^2} \cdot \frac{3x-3}{x^2-1} = \frac{x(x+1)(3)(x-1)}{x^2(x+1)(x-1)}$

$= \frac{3}{x}$

7. $\frac{4x-6}{5} \div \frac{6x-9}{25} = \frac{2(2x-3)}{5} \cdot \frac{25}{3(2x-3)}$

$= \frac{50(2x-3)}{15(2x-3)}$

$= \frac{10}{3}$

8. $\frac{2x+x^2}{4x-5} \div \frac{4x^2+2x^3}{16x-20} = \frac{x(2+x)}{(4x-5)} \cdot \frac{4(4x-5)}{2x^2(2+x)}$

$= \frac{4x(2+x)(4x-5)}{2x^2(2+x)(4x-5)}$

$= \frac{2}{x}$

9. $\frac{16+x}{x^3} + \frac{7-4x}{x^3} = \frac{16+x+7-4x}{x^3}$

$= \frac{23-3x}{x^3}$

10. $\frac{5-t}{t^2+1} - \frac{t-3}{t^2+1} = \frac{5-t-(t-3)}{t^2+1}$

$= \frac{5-t-t+3}{t^2+1}$

$= \frac{8-2t}{t^2+1}$

$= \frac{2(4-t)}{t^2+1}$

11. $\frac{x-5}{x^2-1} + \frac{5}{x^2-1} = \frac{x-5+5}{x^2-1} = \frac{x}{x^2-1}$

12. $\frac{x-4}{x-3} + \frac{x-1}{3-x} = \frac{x-4}{x-3} + \frac{1-x}{x-3}$

$= \frac{x-4+1-x}{x-3}$

$= \frac{-3}{x-3}$

13. $\frac{5}{t-1} + \frac{3}{t} = \frac{5t+3(t-1)}{t(t-1)}$

$= \frac{5t+3t-3}{t(t-1)}$

$= \frac{8t-3}{t(t-1)}$

14. $\frac{1}{x^2-16} - \frac{x+4}{x^2-3x-4} = \frac{1}{(x+4)(x-4)} - \frac{(x+4)}{(x-4)(x+1)}$

$= \frac{(x+1)}{(x+1)(x+4)(x-4)} - \frac{(x+4)(x+4)}{(x+1)(x+4)(x-4)}$

$= \frac{x+1-(x+4)(x+4)}{(x+1)(x+4)(x-4)}$

$= \frac{x+1-(x^2+8x+16)}{(x+1)(x+4)(x-4)}$

$= \frac{x+1-x^2-8x-16}{(x+1)(x+4)(x-4)}$

$= \frac{-x^2-7x-15}{(x+1)(x+4)(x-4)}$

15. $\frac{6}{9-a^2} - \frac{3}{12+4a} = \frac{6}{(3+a)(3-a)} - \frac{3}{4(3+a)}$

$= \frac{4 \cdot 6}{4(3+a)(3-a)} - \frac{3(3-a)}{4(3+a)(3-a)}$

$= \frac{24-3(3-a)}{4(3+a)(3-a)}$

$= \frac{24-9+3a}{4(3+a)(3-a)}$

$= \frac{15+3a}{4(3+a)(3-a)}$

$= \frac{3(5+a)}{4(3+a)(3-a)}$

16. $\frac{4}{x^2-1} - \frac{2}{x^2-2x+1}$

$= \frac{4}{(x+1)(x-1)} - \frac{2}{(x-1)(x-1)}$

$= \frac{4(x-1)}{(x+1)(x-1)(x-1)} - \frac{2(x+1)}{(x+1)(x-1)(x-1)}$

$= \frac{4x-4-2(x+1)}{(x+1)(x-1)(x-1)}$

$= \frac{4x-4-2x-2}{(x+1)(x-1)(x-1)}$

$= \frac{2x-6}{(x+1)(x-1)(x-1)}$

$= \frac{2(x-3)}{(x+1)(x-1)^2}$

17. $\frac{3}{2a+18} + \frac{27}{a^2-81} = \frac{3}{2(a+9)} + \frac{27}{(a+9)(a-9)}$

$= \frac{3(a-9)}{2(a+9)(a-9)} + \frac{2 \cdot 27}{2(a+9)(a-9)}$

$= \frac{3a-27+54}{2(a+9)(a-9)}$

$= \frac{3a+27}{2(a+9)(a-9)}$

$= \frac{3(a+9)}{2(a+9)(a-9)}$

$= \frac{3}{2(a-9)}$

18. $\frac{7}{y} - \frac{1}{3} = \frac{1}{4}$

$12y\left(\frac{7}{y} - \frac{1}{3}\right) = 12y\left(\frac{1}{4}\right)$

$84 - 4y = 3y$

$84 = 7y$

$12 = y$

19. $\frac{15}{x} - \frac{15}{x-2} = -2$

$x(x-2)\left(\frac{15}{x} - \frac{15}{x-2}\right) = -2x(x-2)$

$15(x-2) - 15x = -2x^2 + 4x$

$15x - 30 - 15x = -2x^2 + 4x$

$0 = -2x^2 + 4x + 30$

$0 = -2(x^2 - 2x - 15)$

$0 = -2(x-5)(x+3)$

$(x-5) = 0$ or $(x+3) = 0$

$x = 5$ or $x = -3$

20. $0.25x + 0.40(60-x) = 0.30(60)$

$25x + 40(60-x) = 30(60)$

$25x + 2400 - 40x = 1800$

$-15x = -600$

$x = 40$

40 liters of A, 20 liters of B

21. $\frac{1}{6} + \frac{1}{9} = \frac{1}{n}$

$18n\left(\frac{1}{6} + \frac{1}{9}\right) = 18n\left(\frac{1}{n}\right)$

$3n + 2n = 18$

$5n = 18$

$n = \frac{18}{5}$ or $3\frac{3}{5}$ hours

22. $\frac{12x^4 + 9x^3 - 15x^2}{3x^2} = \frac{12x^4}{3x^2} + \frac{9x^3}{3x^2} - \frac{15x^2}{3x^2}$

$= 4x^2 + 3x - 5$

23.
$$
\begin{array}{r}
2x^2 - 4x - 2 + \frac{17}{3x+2} \\
3x+2\,\overline{)\,6x^3 - 8x^2 - 14x + 13} \\
\underline{6x^3 + 4x^2} \qquad\qquad\quad \\
-12x^2 - 14x \qquad\;\; \\
\underline{-12x^2 - \;\;8x} \qquad\;\; \\
-6x + 13 \\
\underline{-6x - \;\;4} \\
17
\end{array}
$$

24. $\frac{\frac{1}{14y} - \frac{1}{2y^2}}{\frac{1}{7} - \frac{6}{7y} - \frac{1}{y^2}} \cdot \frac{14y^2}{14y^2} = \frac{y-7}{2y^2-12y-14}$

$= \frac{y-7}{2(y^2-6y-7)}$

$= \frac{y-7}{2(y-7)(y+1)}$

$= \frac{1}{2(y+1)}$

25. $\frac{25 - \frac{9}{x^2}}{5 + \frac{3}{x}} \cdot \frac{x^2}{x^2} = \frac{25x^2-9}{5x^2+3x}$

$= \frac{(5x+3)(5x-3)}{x(5x+3)}$

$= \frac{5x-3}{x}$

CHAPTER 11

SKILLS & CONCEPTS

p. 480

1. $\frac{18}{50} = \frac{9}{25}$ 2. $\frac{18}{66} = \frac{3}{11}$ 3. $\frac{81}{27} = 3$ 4. $\frac{100}{50} = 2$

5. $5^2 = 5 \times 5$ 6. $4^3 = 4 \times 4 \times 4$

7. $x^5 = x \times x \times x \times x \times x$ 8. $7^6 = 7 \times 7 \times 7 \times 7 \times 7 \times 7$

9. 8 10. 15 11. 0 12. $\frac{5 \cdot 5}{3 \cdot 3} = \frac{25}{9}$

13. $\frac{-2 \cdot 2}{9 \cdot 9} = -\frac{4}{81}$ **14.** $\frac{-3 \cdot -3}{16 \cdot 16} = \frac{9}{256}$

15. $\frac{11 \cdot -11}{4 \cdot 4} = -\frac{121}{16}$ **16.** 25 **17.** -216

18. $\frac{-3 \cdot -3}{4 \cdot 4} = \frac{9}{16}$ **19.** $-\frac{1}{125}$

20. $x^3 \cdot x^3 = x^{3+3} = x^6$ **21.** $(a^2b^3)(ab^2) = a^{2+1}b^{3+2} = a^3b^5$

22. $\frac{x^9}{x^4} = x^{9-4} = x^5$ **23.** $\frac{ab^3}{ab} = a^{1-1}b^{3-1} = b^2$

24. $x^3 - x^2 = x^2(x - 1)$ **25.** $5x - 30x^2 = 5x(1 - 6x)$

26. $x^2 + 2x + 1 = (x + 1)^2$ **27.** $x^2 - 14x + 49 = (x - 7)^2$

LESSON 11-1 TRY THIS pp. 483–484

a. 13, -13 **b.** $-\sqrt{100} = -10$ **c.** $\sqrt{256} = 16$
d. Irrational **e.** Rational **f.** Irrational **g.** Irrational
h. 2.646 **i.** 8.485 **j.** 4.243 **k.** 6.708

LESSON 11-1 EXERCISES pp. 485–486

1. 1, -1 **2.** 2, -2 **3.** 4, -4 **4.** 11, -11

5. 13, -13 **6.** 18, -18 **7.** 2 **8.** -3 **9.** -5

10. -8 **11.** -9 **12.** -15 **13.** 20 **14.** 19

15. 14 **16.** 17 **17.** -6 **18.** 25

19. Irrational **20.** Rational **21.** Rational **22.** Irrational

23. Rational **24.** Irrational **25.** Irrational **26.** Rational

27. 2.236 **28.** 4.123 **29.** 9.644 **30.** 6.325 **31.** 7.348

32. 10.536 **33.** Irrational

34. $\sqrt{0.49} = 0.7$ Rational, rational

35. $\sqrt{196} = 14$ Rational, whole number **36.** Irrational

37. $\sqrt{\sqrt{16}} = \sqrt{4} = 2$

38. $\sqrt{3^2 + 4^2} = \sqrt{9 + 16} = \sqrt{25} = 5$

39. $\sqrt{(3 + 4)^2} = \sqrt{7^2} = \sqrt{49} = 7$

40. $(\sqrt{5 + 13})^2 = (\sqrt{18})^2 = 18$

41. The value of options A, C, and D are $5 + 6 = 11$. The value of option B is $\sqrt{25 + 36} = \sqrt{61}$, which is less than 11. The answer is B.

42. $-5, -6$ **43.** $-8, -7$

44. The expression $\sqrt{a^2 + b^2}$ is rational when $a = 3$ and $b = 4$, but irrational when $a = 5$ and $b = 7$. The statement "The expression $\sqrt{a^2 + b^2}$ is irrational." is sometimes true.

45. The expression $\sqrt{(a + b)^2}$ is rational when a and b are rational, but irrational when a or b is irrational. The statement "The expression $\sqrt{(a + b)^2}$ is rational." is sometimes true.

46. If $\sqrt{a}$ is an integer, then $-\sqrt{a}$ is also an integer, since the opposite of an integer is also an integer. The statement "If $\sqrt{a}$ is an integer, then $-\sqrt{a}$ is also an integer." is always true.

47. 113 **48.** $\frac{x + y}{2}$

49. 1 is $(-1)^2$ and 1^3, 64 is 8^2 and 4^3.

50.
$$E = \frac{1}{2}mv^2$$
$$20 = \frac{1}{2}(8)v^2$$
$$20 = 4v^2$$
$$5 = v^2$$
$$v = \sqrt{5}$$
$v \approx 2.2$ meters per second

51. **a.** $\sqrt{y + 6} = 3$; $y + 6 = 9$; $y = 3$ **b.** $\sqrt{y + 6} = 7$; $y + 6 = 49$; $y = 43$
c. $\sqrt{y + 6} = 0$; $y + 6 = 0$; $y = -6$ **d.** $\sqrt{y + 6} = 10$; $y + 6 = 100$; $y = 94$

52. $\frac{x^5y^2}{-3xy} = \frac{x^{5-1}y^{2-1}}{-3} = \frac{x^4y}{-3}$

53.
$$\frac{5(x + 1)}{8x} \cdot \frac{4x}{10} = \frac{5(x + 1)}{8x} \cdot \frac{2x}{5}$$
$$= \frac{x + 1}{4}$$

54. $\frac{3(x + 1)}{5x^2} \cdot \frac{x^4}{9} = \frac{(x + 1)}{5} \cdot \frac{x^2}{3} = \frac{x^2(x + 1)}{15}$

55.
$$\frac{x^2 + 8x}{x + 3} - \frac{3x + 2}{x + 3} + \frac{8}{x + 3} = \frac{x^2 + 8x - 3x - 2 + 8}{x + 3}$$
$$= \frac{x^2 + 5x + 6}{x + 3}$$
$$= \frac{(x + 2)(x + 3)}{x + 3}$$
$$= x + 2$$

56.
$$\frac{3x - 10}{x^2 - 4} - \frac{5}{x + 2} = \frac{3x - 10}{(x + 2)(x - 2)} - \frac{5(x - 2)}{(x + 2)(x - 2)}$$
$$= \frac{3x - 10 - 5x + 10}{(x + 2)(x - 2)}$$
$$= \frac{-2x}{(x + 2)(x - 2)}$$

57. $25x - 10 = 5(5x - 2)$
LCM is $5(5x - 2)(5x + 2)$.

58. LCM is $(a + c)(a - c)$.

59.
$$\frac{2}{3} + \frac{1}{4} = \frac{x}{6}$$
$$12\left(\frac{2}{3} + \frac{1}{4}\right) = \frac{x}{6}(12)$$
$$8 + 3 = 2x$$
$$11 = 2x$$
$$\frac{11}{2} = x$$

60.
$$\frac{5}{8} + \frac{1}{2} = \frac{y}{24}$$
$$24\left(\frac{5}{8} + \frac{1}{2}\right) = \frac{y}{24}(24)$$
$$15 + 12 = y$$
$$27 = y$$

61.
$$\frac{4}{9} - \frac{1}{3} = \frac{x}{36}$$
$$36\left(\frac{4}{9} - \frac{1}{3}\right) = \frac{x}{36}(36)$$
$$16 - 12 = x$$
$$4 = x$$

62.
$$\frac{2}{3} - \frac{1}{5} = \frac{1}{a}$$
$$15a\left(\frac{2}{3} - \frac{1}{5}\right) = \frac{1}{a}(15a)$$
$$10a - 3a = 15$$
$$7a = 15$$
$$a = \frac{15}{7}$$

63.
$$\frac{1}{6} + \frac{4}{9} = \frac{1}{a}$$
$$18a\left(\frac{1}{6} + \frac{4}{9}\right) = \frac{1}{a}(18a)$$
$$3a + 8a = 18$$
$$11a = 18$$
$$a = \frac{18}{11}$$

64.
$$\frac{1}{4} - \frac{5}{6} = \frac{1}{b}$$
$$12b\left(\frac{1}{4} - \frac{5}{6}\right) = \frac{1}{b}(12b)$$
$$3b - 10b = 12$$
$$-7b = 12$$
$$b = -\frac{12}{7}$$

65. $\frac{x^2 - 9x + 20}{x - 4} = \frac{(x - 5)(x - 4)}{x - 4} = x - 5$

66.
$$\begin{array}{r} y^3 + 3y^2 + 9y + 27 \\ y - 3\overline{)\,y^4 + 0y^3 + 0y^2 + 0y - 81} \\ \underline{y^4 - 3y^3} \\ 3y^3 + 0y^2 \\ \underline{3y^3 - 9y^2} \\ 9y^2 + 0y \\ \underline{9y^2 - 27y} \\ 27y - 81 \\ \underline{27y - 81} \end{array}$$

67. $y - 6x = 1$
$5x + y = 12$
Solving the first equation for y, $y = 6x + 1$.
Substituting in the second equation,
$5x + (6x + 1) = 12$
$11x + 1 = 12$
$11x = 11$
$x = 1$
Substituting for x in the first equation,
$y - 6(1) = 1$
$y - 6 = 1$
$y = 7$
The solution is (1, 7).

68. $4x + y = -4$
$10x + 3y = -9$
Solving the first equation for y, $y = -4 - 4x$.
Substituting in the second equation,
$10x + 3(-4 - 4x) = -9$
$10x - 12 - 12x = -9$
$-12 - 2x = -9$
$-2x = 3$
$x = -\frac{3}{2}$
Substituting for x in the first equation,
$4\left(-\frac{3}{2}\right) + y = -4$
$-6 + y = -4$
$y = 2$
The solution is $\left(-\frac{3}{2}, 2\right)$.

IS $\sqrt{7}$ AN IRRATIONAL NUMBER? EXERCISE p. 486

Assume that $\sqrt{5}$ is a rational number, written $\frac{a}{b}$ in simplest form.

$\sqrt{5} = \frac{a}{b}$

$5 = \frac{a^2}{b^2}$

$5b^2 = a^2$
This shows that 5 is a factor of a^2. Since 5 is a prime number, 5 must also be a factor of a.
$5b^2 = (5k)^2$
$5b^2 = 25k^2$
$b^2 = 5k^2$
This shows that 5 is a factor of b^2, and hence of b. Thus a and b have 5 as a common factor. But a and b have no common factor greater than 1. Therefore the assumption is false and $\sqrt{5}$ is an irrational number.

LESSON 11-2 TRY THIS p. 488

a. $\sqrt{15 - 2x} = \sqrt{15 - 2(8)} = \sqrt{15 - 16} = \sqrt{-1}$; No
b. $x + 1 \ge 0$
$x \ge -1$
c. $x - 3 \ge 0$
$x \ge 3$
d. $2x - 5 \ge 0$
$2x \ge 5$
$x \ge \frac{5}{2}$
e. $x^2 + 3 \ge 0$
$x^2 \ge -3$
True for all values of x
f. $\sqrt{(xy)^2} = |xy|$
g. $\sqrt{x^2y^2} = \sqrt{(xy)^2} = |xy|$
h. $\sqrt{(x - 1)^2} = |x - 1|$
i. $\sqrt{x^2 + 8x + 16} = \sqrt{(x + 4)^2} = |x + 4|$
j. $\sqrt{25y^2} = |5y| = 5|y|$
k. $\sqrt{\frac{1}{4}t^2} = \frac{1}{2}\sqrt{t^2} = \frac{1}{2}|t|$

LESSON 11-2 EXERCISES pp. 489–490

1. $\sqrt{3x - 12} = \sqrt{3(4) - 12} = \sqrt{12 - 12}$
$= \sqrt{0}$
$= 0$; Yes

2. $\sqrt{8 - 4y} = \sqrt{8 - 4(10)} = \sqrt{8 - 40}$
$= \sqrt{-32}$; No

3. $\sqrt{x + 12} = \sqrt{-6 + 12} = \sqrt{6}$; Yes

4. $\sqrt{3y + 12} = \sqrt{3(-5) + 12} = \sqrt{-15 + 12}$
$= \sqrt{-3}$; No

5. $5x \ge 0$
$x \ge 0$
6. $3y \ge 0$
$y \ge 0$
7. $t - 5 \ge 0$
$t \ge 5$
8. $y - 8 \ge 0$
$y \ge 8$

9. $y + 8 \ge 0$
$y \ge -8$
10. $x + 6 \ge 0$
$x \ge -6$
11. $x + 20 \ge 0$
$x \ge -20$

12. $m - 18 \ge 0$
$m \ge 18$
13. $2y - 7 \ge 0$
$2y \ge 7$
$y \ge \frac{7}{2}$
14. $3x + 8 \ge 0$
$3x \ge -8$
$x \ge -\frac{8}{3}$

15. $t^2 + 5 \ge 0$
$t^2 \ge -5$
Any value
16. $y^2 + 1 \ge 0$
$y^2 \ge -1$
Any value

17. $|t|$ 18. $|x|$ 19. $3|x|$ 20. $2|a|$

21. $\sqrt{(-7)^2} = \sqrt{49} = 7$ 22. $\sqrt{(-5)^2} = \sqrt{25} = 5$

23. $\sqrt{(-4d)^2} = \sqrt{16d} = 4|d|$ 24. $\sqrt{(-3b)^2} = \sqrt{9b^2} = 3|b|$

25. $|x + 3|$ 26. $|x - 7|$

27. $\sqrt{a^2 - 10a + 25} = \sqrt{(a - 5)^2} = |a - 5|$

28. $\sqrt{x^2 + 2x + 1} = \sqrt{(x + 1)^2} = |x + 1|$

29. $\sqrt{4a^2 - 4a + 1} = \sqrt{(2a - 1)^2} = |2a - 1|$

30. $\sqrt{9a^2 - 12a + 4} = \sqrt{(3a - 2)^2} = |3a - 2|$

31. $\sqrt{x^2} = 6$
$|x| = 6$
$x = 6$ or -6

32. $\sqrt{y^2} = -7$
$|y| = -7$
No solution

33. $-\sqrt{x^2} = -3$
$-|x| = -3$
$|x| = 3$
$x = 3$ or -3

34. $t^2 = 49$
$t = \pm\sqrt{49}$
$t = 7$ or -7

35. $\sqrt{(x - 3)^2} = 5$
$|x - 3| = 5$
$x - 3 = 5$ or $x - 3 = -5$
$x = 8$ or $x = -2$

36. $\sqrt{4a^2 - 12a + 9} = 3$
$\sqrt{(2a - 3)^2} = 3$
$|2a - 3| = 3$
$2a - 3 = 3$ or $2a - 3 = -3$
$2a = 6$ or $2a = 0$
$a = 3$ or $a = 0$

37. $\sqrt{(3a)^2} = |3a| = 3|a|$

38. $\sqrt{(4a)^2(4a)^2} = \sqrt{(16a^2)(16a^2)}$
$= \sqrt{(16a^2)^2}$
$= |16a^2|$
$= 16a^2$

39. $\sqrt{\frac{144x^8}{36y^6}} = \sqrt{\left(\frac{12x^4}{6y^3}\right)^2} = \sqrt{\left(\frac{2x^4}{y^3}\right)^2} = \frac{2x^4}{|y^3|}$

40. $\sqrt{\frac{y^{12}}{8100}} = \sqrt{\left(\frac{y^6}{90}\right)^2} = \frac{y^6}{90}$

41. $\sqrt{\frac{169}{m^{16}}} = \sqrt{\left(\frac{13}{m^8}\right)^2} = \frac{13}{m^8}$

42. $\sqrt{\frac{p^2}{3600}} = \sqrt{\left(\frac{p}{60}\right)^2} = \frac{|p|}{60}$

43. a. $m(m + 3) \ge 0$ will give acceptable replacement.
Both multipliers must be ≥ 0, or both must be ≤ 0.
$m \ge 0$ and $m + 3 \ge 0$ or $m \le 0$ and $m + 3 \le 0$
$m \ge 0$ and $m \ge -3$ $m \le 0$ and $m \le -3$
$m \ge 0$ or $m \le -3$

b. $x^2(x-3) \ge 0$ will give acceptable replacements.

$$\begin{array}{llllll} x^2 \ge 0 & \text{and} & x-3 \ge 0 & \text{or} & x^2 \le 0 & \text{and} \quad x-3 \le 0 \\ x^2 \ge 0 & \text{and} & x \ge 3 & & x^2 \le 0 & \text{and} \quad x \le 3 \\ x \ge 3 & & & \text{or} & & x = 0 \end{array}$$

44. a. $\sqrt{b^2-4ac} = \sqrt{b^2-4(-3)(2)}$
$= \sqrt{b^2-4(-6)}$
$= \sqrt{b^2+24}$

To be a real number, $b^2 + 24 \ge 0$
$b^2 \ge -24$

b may be any real number.

b. $\sqrt{b^2-4ac} = \sqrt{b^2-4(2)(8)}$
$= \sqrt{b^2-4(16)}$
$= \sqrt{b^2-64}$

To be a real number, $b^2 - 64 \ge 0$
$(b+8)(b-8) \ge 0$

Either both multipliers ≥ 0 or both ≤ 0.

$$\begin{array}{llll} b+8 \ge 0 & \text{and } b-8 \ge 0 & \text{or } b+8 \le 0 & \text{and } b-8 \le 0 \\ b \ge -8 \text{ and} & b \ge 8 \text{ or} & b \le -8 \text{ and} & b \le 8 \\ & b \ge 8 \text{ or} & b \le -8 & \end{array}$$

45. $\sqrt{a^2+b^2}$ is a real number since the square root of a positive number is real, and the sum of the squares of two numbers is always positive. The statement "$\sqrt{a^2+b^2}$ is a real number" is always true.

46. $\sqrt{3-t}$ is a real number for $t = 3$, but not a real number for $t > 3$. The statement "$\sqrt{3-t}$ is a real number for $t \ge 3$" is sometimes true.

47. $\sqrt{a^2-b^2}$ is a real number only when $a^2 \ge b^2$. The statement "$\sqrt{a^2-b^2}$ is a real number" is sometimes true.

48. $\sqrt{a^2+2ab+b^2} = \sqrt{(a+b)^2} = a+b$. The statement "$\sqrt{a^2+2ab+b^2}$ is a real number" is always true.

49. $(x+3)(x-2) \ge 0$

$$\begin{array}{llll} x+3 \ge 0 & \text{and } x-2 \ge 0 & \text{or } x+3 \le 0 & \text{and } x-2 \le 0 \\ x \ge -3 \text{ and} & x \ge 2 & x \le -3 \text{ and} & x \le 2 \\ x \ge 2 & & \text{or} & x \le -3 \end{array}$$

Replacements can be $x \ge 2$ or $x \le -3$.

50. $x^2 + 7x + 12 \ge 0$
$(x+4)(x+3) \ge 0$

$$\begin{array}{llll} x+4 \ge 0 & \text{and } x+3 \ge 0 & \text{or } x+4 \le 0 & \text{and } x+3 \le 0 \\ x \ge -4 \text{ and} & x \ge -3 & x \le -4 \text{ and} & x \le -3 \\ x \ge -3 & & x \le -4 & \end{array}$$

Replacements can be $x \ge -3$ or $x \le -4$.

51. $x^2 - 4 \ge 0$
$(x-2)(x+2) \ge 0$

$$\begin{array}{llll} x-2 \ge 0 \text{ and} & x+2 \ge 0 & \text{or } x-2 \le 0 \text{ and} & x+2 \le 0 \\ x \ge 2 \text{ and} & x \ge -2 & x \le 2 \text{ and} & x \le -2 \\ x \ge 2 & \text{or} & x \le -2 & \end{array}$$

Replacements can be $x \ge 2$ or $x \le -2$.

52. $4x^2 - 1 \ge 0$; $(2x+1)(2x-1) \ge 0$

$$\begin{array}{llll} 2x+1 \ge 0 & \text{and } 2x-1 \ge 0 & \text{or } 2x+1 \le 0 & \text{and } 2x-1 \le 0 \\ 2x \ge -1 & 2x \ge 1 & 2x \le -1 & 2x \le 1 \\ x \ge -\frac{1}{2} \text{ and} & x \ge \frac{1}{2} & x \le -\frac{1}{2} \text{ and} & x \le \frac{1}{2} \\ x \ge \frac{1}{2} & \text{or} & & x \le -\frac{1}{2} \end{array}$$

Replacements can be $x \ge \frac{1}{2}$ or $x \le -\frac{1}{2}$.

53. $b^2 - 4ac \ge 0$

a) $b^2 - 4ac = (-12)^2 - 4(1)(3) = 132$; Real
b) $b^2 - 4ac = 2^2 - 4(1)(-50) = 204$; Real
c) $b^2 - 4ac = 5^2 - 4(1)(7) = -3$; Not real
d) $b^2 - 4ac = 2^2 - 4(5)(1) = -16$; Not real
e) $b^2 - 4ac = 1^2 - 4(-1)(1) = 5$; Real
f) $b^2 - 4ac = 1^2 - 4(-1)(-1) = -3$; Not real

54. $|x+3| < 1$
$x+3 < 1$ and $x+3 > -1$
$x < -2$ and $x > -4$
$-4 < x < -2$

55. $|x-9| = -3$
No solution

56. $|y+3| \ge 5$
$y+3 \ge 5$ or $y+3 \le -5$
$y \ge 2$ or $y \le -8$

57. $\dfrac{x-3}{x+2} - \dfrac{3x+1}{x+2} = \dfrac{x-3-3x-1}{x+2}$
$= \dfrac{-2x-4}{x+2}$
$= \dfrac{-2(x+2)}{x+2}$
$= -2$

58. $\dfrac{6x+7}{x-3} - \dfrac{2x+3}{x-3} = \dfrac{6x+7-2x-3}{x-3} = \dfrac{4x+4}{x-3} = \dfrac{4(x+1)}{x-3}$

59. $\dfrac{5}{y+5} + \dfrac{2}{(y+5)^2} = \dfrac{5(y+5)}{(y+5)^2} + \dfrac{2}{(y+5)^2}$
$= \dfrac{5(y+5)+2}{(y+5)^2}$
$= \dfrac{5y+25+2}{(y+5)^2}$
$= \dfrac{5y+27}{(y+5)^2}$

60. $\dfrac{5}{y+4} - \dfrac{3}{y+3} = \dfrac{5(y+3)}{(y+3)(y+4)} - \dfrac{3(y+4)}{(y+3)(y+4)}$
$= \dfrac{5y+15-3y-12}{(y+3)(y+4)}$
$= \dfrac{2y+3}{(y+3)(y+4)}$

61. $x - \frac{6}{x} = 5$
$x^2 - 6 = 5x$
$x^2 - 5x - 6 = 0$
$(x-6)(x+1) = 0$
$x - 6 = 0$ or $x + 1 = 0$
$x = 6$ or $x = -1$

62. $\dfrac{6}{x} = \dfrac{5}{x} + \dfrac{1}{2}$
$2x\left(\frac{6}{x}\right) = \left(\frac{5}{x} + \frac{1}{2}\right)2x$
$12 = 10 + x$
$2 = x$

63. $\dfrac{y+1}{y-3} = 2$
$y + 1 = 2(y-3)$
$y + 1 = 2y - 6$
$7 = y$

CONNECTIONS: GEOMETRY

p. 490

$V = \pi r^2 h$
$\dfrac{V}{\pi h} = r^2$
$\sqrt{\dfrac{V}{\pi h}} = r$

1. $r = \sqrt{\dfrac{2826}{(3.14)(25)}} = \sqrt{\dfrac{2826}{78.5}} = \sqrt{36} = 6$ in.

2. $r = \sqrt{\dfrac{175}{(3.14)(6.2)}} = \sqrt{\dfrac{175}{19.468}} \approx \sqrt{9} = 3$ cm

3. Use the formula $r = \sqrt{\dfrac{V}{\pi h}}$ to find each radius.

$r = \sqrt{\dfrac{3208}{\pi(17)}} \approx \sqrt{60.06695} \approx 7.75$

$r = \sqrt{\dfrac{486}{\pi(11)}} \approx \sqrt{14.06351} \approx 3.75$

The radius of the larger can is 7.75 cm. The radius of the smaller can is 3.75 cm.

LESSON 11-3 TRY THIS

p. 492

a. $\sqrt{32} = \sqrt{16 \cdot 2} = 4\sqrt{2}$ **b.** $\sqrt{25x^2} = 5x$

c. $\sqrt{60x} = \sqrt{4 \cdot 15x} = 2\sqrt{15x}$

d. $\sqrt{45x^2} = \sqrt{9 \cdot 5x^2} = 3x\sqrt{5}$

e. $\sqrt{7x^2 - 14x + 7} = \sqrt{7(x^2 - 2x + 1)}$
$= \sqrt{7(x-1)^2}$
$= (x-1)\sqrt{7}$

f. y^4 **g.** $(x+y)^7$

h. $\sqrt{t^{15}} = \sqrt{(t^{14})t} = t^7\sqrt{t}$ **i.** $\sqrt{a^{25}} = \sqrt{(a^{24})a} = a^{12}\sqrt{a}$

LESSON 11-3 EXERCISES pp. 493–494

1. $\sqrt{12} = \sqrt{4 \cdot 3} = \sqrt{4}\sqrt{3} = 2\sqrt{3}$
2. $\sqrt{8} = \sqrt{4 \cdot 2} = \sqrt{4}\sqrt{2} = 2\sqrt{2}$
3. $\sqrt{20} = \sqrt{4 \cdot 5} = \sqrt{4}\sqrt{5} = 2\sqrt{5}$
4. $\sqrt{45} = \sqrt{9 \cdot 5} = \sqrt{9}\sqrt{5} = 3\sqrt{5}$
5. $\sqrt{75} = \sqrt{25 \cdot 3} = \sqrt{25}\sqrt{3} = 5\sqrt{3}$
6. $\sqrt{50} = \sqrt{25 \cdot 2} = \sqrt{25}\sqrt{2} = 5\sqrt{2}$
7. $\sqrt{200} = \sqrt{100 \cdot 2} = \sqrt{100}\sqrt{2} = 10\sqrt{2}$
8. $\sqrt{300} = \sqrt{100 \cdot 3} = \sqrt{100}\sqrt{3} = 10\sqrt{3}$
9. $\sqrt{3x^2} = \sqrt{3}\sqrt{x^2} = x\sqrt{3}$
10. $\sqrt{5y^2} = \sqrt{5}\sqrt{y^2} = y\sqrt{5}$
11. $\sqrt{16a} = \sqrt{16}\sqrt{a} = 4\sqrt{a}$
12. $\sqrt{49b} = \sqrt{49}\sqrt{b} = 7\sqrt{b}$
13. $\sqrt{13x^2} = \sqrt{13}\sqrt{x^2} = x\sqrt{13}$
14. $\sqrt{29t^2} = \sqrt{29}\sqrt{t^2} = t\sqrt{29}$
15. $\sqrt{9x} = \sqrt{9}\sqrt{x} = 3\sqrt{x}$
16. $\sqrt{4y} = \sqrt{4}\sqrt{y} = 2\sqrt{y}$
17. $\sqrt{64y^2} = \sqrt{64}\sqrt{y^2} = 8y$
18. $\sqrt{9x^2} = \sqrt{9}\sqrt{x^2} = 3x$
19. $\sqrt{8t^2} = \sqrt{4 \cdot 2t^2} = \sqrt{4}\sqrt{2}\sqrt{t^2} = 2t\sqrt{2}$
20. $\sqrt{125a^2} = \sqrt{25 \cdot 5a^2} = \sqrt{25}\sqrt{5}\sqrt{a^2} = 5a\sqrt{5}$
21. $\sqrt{4x^2 + 8x + 4} = \sqrt{4(x^2 + 2x + 1)}$
$= \sqrt{4(x+1)^2} = 2(x+1)$
22. $\sqrt{3x^2 + 12x + 12} = \sqrt{3(x^2 + 4x + 4)}$
$= \sqrt{3(x+2)^2}$
$= (x+2)\sqrt{3}$
23. $\sqrt{2x^2 + 12x + 18} = \sqrt{2(x^2 + 6x + 9)}$
$= \sqrt{2(x+3)^2} = (x+3)\sqrt{2}$
24. $\sqrt{5x^2 + 30x + 45} = \sqrt{5(x^2 + 6x + 9)}$
$= \sqrt{5(x+3)^2} = (x+3)\sqrt{5}$
25. $\sqrt{4x^2 + 12xy + 9y^2} = \sqrt{(2x+3y)^2} = 2x + 3y$
26. $\sqrt{3x^2 + 30xy + 75y^2} = \sqrt{3(x^2 + 10xy + 25y^2)}$
$= \sqrt{3(x+5y)^2} = (x+5y)\sqrt{3}$
27. $\sqrt{x^6} = \sqrt{(x^3)^2} = x^3$
28. $\sqrt{x^{10}} = \sqrt{(x^5)^2} = x^5$
29. $\sqrt{x^{12}} = \sqrt{(x^6)^2} = x^6$
30. $\sqrt{x^{16}} = \sqrt{(x^8)^2} = x^8$
31. $\sqrt{x^5} = \sqrt{x^4 \cdot x} = \sqrt{(x^2)^2 x} = x^2\sqrt{x}$
32. $\sqrt{x^3} = \sqrt{x^2 \cdot x} = x\sqrt{x}$
33. $\sqrt{t^{19}} = \sqrt{t^{18} \cdot t} = \sqrt{(t^9)^2 t} = t^9\sqrt{t}$
34. $\sqrt{p^{17}} = \sqrt{p^{16} \cdot p} = \sqrt{(p^8)^2 p} = p^8\sqrt{p}$
35. $\sqrt{(y-2)^8} = \sqrt{[(y-2)^4]^2} = (y-2)^4$
36. $\sqrt{(x+3)^6} = \sqrt{[(x+3)^3]^2} = (x+3)^3$
37. $\sqrt{4(x+5)^{10}} = \sqrt{[2(x+5)^5]^2} = 2(x+5)^5$
38. $\sqrt{16(a-7)^4} = \sqrt{[4(a-7)^2]^2} = 4(a-7)^2$
39. $\sqrt{36m^3} = \sqrt{6^2 \cdot m^2 \cdot m} = 6m\sqrt{m}$
40. $250y^3 = \sqrt{25 \cdot 10 \cdot y^2 \cdot y} = 5y\sqrt{10y}$
41. $8a^5 = \sqrt{4 \cdot 2 \cdot a^4 \cdot a} = 2a^2\sqrt{2a}$
42. $\sqrt{12b^7} = \sqrt{4 \cdot 3 \cdot b^6 \cdot b} = 2b^3\sqrt{3b}$
43. $\sqrt{448x^6y^3} = \sqrt{64 \cdot 7 \cdot x^6 \cdot y^2 \cdot y}$
$= 8x^3y\sqrt{7y}$
44. $\sqrt{243x^5y^4} = \sqrt{81 \cdot 3 \cdot x^4 \cdot x \cdot y^4} = 9x^2y^2\sqrt{3x}$
45. The student did not take the square root of 9:
$\sqrt{9x^2y^2}\sqrt{y} = 3xy\sqrt{y}$, not $9xy\sqrt{y}$
46. $3\sqrt{200} = 3\sqrt{100 \cdot 2} = 3 \cdot 10\sqrt{2} = 30\sqrt{2}$
47. $2\sqrt{75} = 2\sqrt{25 \cdot 3} = 2 \cdot 5\sqrt{3} = 10\sqrt{3}$
48. $4\sqrt{12} = 4\sqrt{4 \cdot 3} = 4 \cdot 2\sqrt{3} = 8\sqrt{3}$
49. $-3\sqrt{72} = -3\sqrt{36 \cdot 2} = -3 \cdot 6\sqrt{2} = -18\sqrt{2}$
50. $-2\sqrt{1000} = -2\sqrt{100 \cdot 10} = -2 \cdot 10\sqrt{10} = -20\sqrt{10}$
51. $6\sqrt{36x} = 6 \cdot 6\sqrt{x} = 36\sqrt{x}$
52. $4m\sqrt{20m^2} = 4m\sqrt{4 \cdot 5m^2} = 4m \cdot 2m\sqrt{5}$
$= 8m^2\sqrt{5}$
53. $2x\sqrt{50x^4} = 2x\sqrt{25 \cdot 2x^4} = 2x \cdot 5x^2\sqrt{2}$
$= 10x^3\sqrt{2}$
54. $5r^2\sqrt{32r^4s^3} = 5r^2\sqrt{16 \cdot 2r^4s^2 \cdot s}$
$= 5r^2 \cdot 4r^2s\sqrt{2s}$
$= 20r^4s\sqrt{2s}$
55. $3a^3\sqrt{28a^3b^5} = 3a^3\sqrt{4 \cdot 7a^2 \cdot ab^4 \cdot b}$
$= 3a^3 \cdot 2ab^2\sqrt{7ab}$
$= 6a^4b^2\sqrt{7ab}$
56. $\sqrt{3 + r^2} = \sqrt{3 + 5^2} = \sqrt{3 + 25} = \sqrt{28} = \sqrt{4 \cdot 7} = 2\sqrt{7}$
57. $\sqrt{r^2 - 1} = \sqrt{5^2 - 1} = \sqrt{25 - 1} = \sqrt{24} = \sqrt{4 \cdot 6} = 2\sqrt{6}$
58. $\sqrt{r + s^2} = \sqrt{5 + (\sqrt{5})^2} = \sqrt{5 + 5} = \sqrt{10}$
59. $\sqrt{50 - s^2} = \sqrt{50 - (\sqrt{5})^2} = \sqrt{50 - 5} = \sqrt{45}$
$= \sqrt{9 \cdot 5} = 3\sqrt{5}$
60. $\sqrt{49} = 7$
$\sqrt{490} = \sqrt{49 \cdot 10} = 7\sqrt{10}$
$\sqrt{4900} = \sqrt{490 \cdot 10} = (7\sqrt{10})\sqrt{10} = 7 \cdot 10 = 70$
$\sqrt{49{,}000} = \sqrt{4900 \cdot 10} = 70\sqrt{10}$
$\sqrt{490{,}000} = \sqrt{49{,}000 \cdot 10} = (70\sqrt{10})\sqrt{10} = 70 \cdot 10 = 700$
Each is $\sqrt{10}$ times the last.
61. $15 = \sqrt{15^2} = \sqrt{225}$, $\sqrt{225} > \sqrt{14}$,
so $15 > \sqrt{14}$
62. $15\sqrt{2} = \sqrt{2 \cdot 15^2} = \sqrt{450}$, so $15\sqrt{2} = \sqrt{450}$
63. $16 = \sqrt{256}$, $\sqrt{15} \cdot \sqrt{17} = \sqrt{15 \cdot 17} = \sqrt{255}$,
so $16 > \sqrt{15}\sqrt{17}$
64. $3\sqrt{11} = \sqrt{11 \cdot 3^2} = \sqrt{99}$, $7\sqrt{2} = \sqrt{2 \cdot 7^2} = \sqrt{98}$,
so $3\sqrt{11} > 7\sqrt{2}$
65. $5\sqrt{7} = \sqrt{7 \cdot 5^2} = \sqrt{175}$, $4\sqrt{11} = \sqrt{11 \cdot 4^2} = \sqrt{176}$,
so $5\sqrt{7} < 4\sqrt{11}$

66. $\sqrt{15}\sqrt{17} \approx 3.873 \cdot 4.123 \approx 15.968$, so $8 < \sqrt{15}\sqrt{17}$

67. $3\sqrt{x} = \sqrt{x \cdot 3^2} = \sqrt{9x}, 2\sqrt{2.5x} = \sqrt{2.5x \cdot 2^2} = \sqrt{10x}$
Since x is positive, $\sqrt{9x} < \sqrt{10x}$, so $3\sqrt{x} < 2\sqrt{2.5x}$

68. $4\sqrt{x} = \sqrt{x \cdot 4^2} = \sqrt{16x}, 5\sqrt{0.64x} = \sqrt{0.64x \cdot 5^2}$
$= \sqrt{16x}$, so $4\sqrt{x} = 5\sqrt{0.64x}$

69. $90\sqrt{100x} = \sqrt{100x \cdot 90^2} = \sqrt{810{,}000x}$,
$100\sqrt{90x} = \sqrt{90x \cdot 100^2} = \sqrt{900{,}000x}$,
so $90\sqrt{100x} < 100\sqrt{90x}$

70. $4\sqrt{5x} = \sqrt{16(5x)} = \sqrt{80x} = \sqrt{80}\sqrt{x} \approx 8.94\sqrt{x}$
$\sqrt{12x} + 4\sqrt{2x} = \sqrt{12x} + \sqrt{16(2x)} = \sqrt{12x} + \sqrt{32x}$
$= (\sqrt{12} + \sqrt{32})\sqrt{x} \approx (3.46 + 5.66)\sqrt{x} = 9.12\sqrt{x}$
Since $8.94 < 9.12$, $4\sqrt{5x} < \sqrt{12x} + 4\sqrt{2x}$

71.
$$\begin{aligned} 5x + y &= -9 \\ 2x - y &= 2 \\ \hline 7x &= -7 \\ x &= -1 \\ 5(-1) + y &= -9 \\ -5 + y &= -9 \\ y &= -4 \end{aligned}$$
$(-1, -4)$

72.
$$\begin{aligned} 2x + 3y &= 11 \\ -x + 5y &= 1 \\ 2x + 3y &= 11 \\ -2x + 10y &= 2 \\ \hline 13y &= 13 \\ y &= 1 \\ -x + 5(1) &= 1 \\ -x &= -4 \\ x &= 4 \end{aligned}$$
$(4, 1)$

73.
$$\begin{aligned} 5y + 3x &= -1 \\ -2y + 2x &= 10 \\ 10y + 6x &= -2 \\ -10y + 10x &= 50 \\ \hline 16x &= 48 \\ x &= 3 \\ 5y + 3(3) &= -1 \\ 5y + 9 &= -1 \\ 5y &= -10 \\ y &= -2 \end{aligned}$$
$(3, -2)$

74. $\dfrac{6a^2 + 24}{12a^2 + 18a + 42} = \dfrac{6(a^2 + 4)}{6(2a^2 + 3a + 7)} = \dfrac{a^2 + 4}{2a^2 + 3a + 7}$

75. $\dfrac{(x + 3)}{x^2} \cdot \dfrac{(x + 2)}{(x + 3)} = \dfrac{x + 2}{x^2}$

76.
$$\begin{aligned} x + y &= 51 \\ x - y &= 19 \\ \hline 2x &= 70 \\ x &= 35 \\ 35 + y &= 51 \\ y &= 16 \end{aligned}$$
35 and 16

CUBE ROOTS p. 494

1. $\sqrt[3]{8} = \sqrt[3]{2^3} = 2$ 2. $\sqrt[3]{27} = \sqrt[3]{3^3} = 3$

3. $\sqrt[3]{125} = \sqrt[3]{5^3} = 5$ 4. $\sqrt[3]{1000} = \sqrt[3]{10^3} = 10$

5. $\sqrt[3]{-8} = \sqrt[3]{(-2)^3} = -2$ 6. $\sqrt[3]{-64} = \sqrt[3]{(-4)^3} = -4$

7. $\sqrt[3]{-1} = \sqrt[3]{(-1)^3} = -1$ 8. $\sqrt[3]{-8000} = \sqrt[3]{(-20)^3} = -20$

9. $\sqrt[3]{x^3} = x$ 10. $\sqrt[3]{y^3} = y$ 11. $\sqrt[3]{a^3b^3} = ab$

12. $\sqrt[3]{mn^3} = n\sqrt[3]{m}$ 13. $\sqrt[3]{27x^6y^3} = \sqrt[3]{3^3(x^2)^3y^3} = 3x^2y$

14. $\sqrt[3]{125m^9n^{12}} = \sqrt[3]{5^3(m^3)^3(n^4)^3} = 5m^3n^4$

15. $\sqrt[3]{-8a^6b^9} = \sqrt[3]{(-2)^3(a^2)^3(b^3)^3} = -2a^2b^3$

16. $\sqrt[3]{-125p^{12}} = \sqrt[3]{(-5)^3(p^4)^3} = -5p^4$

LESSON 11-4 TRY THIS p. 495

a. $\sqrt{3}\sqrt{7} = \sqrt{21}$ b. $\sqrt{5}\sqrt{5} = \sqrt{25}$ or 5

c. $\sqrt{x}\sqrt{x + 1} = \sqrt{x(x + 1)} = \sqrt{x^2 + x}$

d. $\sqrt{x + 1}\sqrt{x - 1} = \sqrt{(x + 1)(x - 1)} = \sqrt{x^2 - 1}$

e. $\sqrt{3y}\sqrt{6} = \sqrt{3y \cdot 6} = \sqrt{18y} = \sqrt{9 \cdot 2 \cdot y}$
$= \sqrt{9} \cdot \sqrt{2} \cdot \sqrt{y} = 3\sqrt{2y}$

f. $\sqrt{2x}\sqrt{50x} = \sqrt{2x \cdot 50x} = \sqrt{100x^2}$
$= \sqrt{100} \cdot \sqrt{x^2} = 10x$

g. $\sqrt{2x^3}\sqrt{8x^3y^4} = \sqrt{2x^3 \cdot 8x^3y^4} = \sqrt{16x^6y^4}$
$= \sqrt{16} \cdot \sqrt{x^6} \cdot \sqrt{y^4} = 4x^3y^2$

h. $\sqrt{10xy^2}\sqrt{5x^2y^3} = \sqrt{10xy^2 \cdot 5x^2y^3}$
$= \sqrt{50x^3y^5}$
$= \sqrt{25 \cdot 2 \cdot x^2 \cdot x \cdot y^4 \cdot y}$
$= 5 \cdot \sqrt{2} \cdot x\sqrt{x} \cdot y^2\sqrt{y}$
$= 5xy^2\sqrt{2xy}$

i. $\sqrt{12x^3y^2} \cdot \sqrt{3x^2y^6} = \sqrt{36x^5y^8} = \sqrt{6^2x^4y^8 \cdot x}$
$= 6x^2y^4\sqrt{x}$

LESSON 11-4 EXERCISES pp. 496–497

1. $\sqrt{6}$ 2. $\sqrt{15}$ 3. $\sqrt{17^2} = 17$ 4. $5\sqrt{3}$ 5. $\sqrt{2x}$

6. $\sqrt{x(x - 3)}$ or $\sqrt{x^2 - 3x}$

7. $\sqrt{5(2x - 1)}$ or $\sqrt{10x - 5}$

8. $\sqrt{(x + 2)(x + 1)}$ or $\sqrt{x^2 + 3x + 2}$

9. $\sqrt{(x + 4)(x - 4)}$ or $\sqrt{x^2 - 16}$

10. $\sqrt{(x - 3)(2x + 4)}$ or $\sqrt{2x^2 - 2x - 12}$

11. $\sqrt{(2x + 5)(x - 4)}$ or $\sqrt{2x^2 - 3x - 20}$

12. $\sqrt{3a(3a + 2b)}$ or $\sqrt{9a^2 + 6ab}$

13. $\sqrt{x(3x + 4y)}$ or $\sqrt{3x^2 + 4xy}$

14. $\sqrt{(a - b)(a + b)}$ or $\sqrt{a^2 - b^2}$

15. $\sqrt{(x - 3)(x + 4)}$ or $\sqrt{x^2 + x - 12}$

16. $\sqrt{3} \cdot \sqrt{18} = \sqrt{54} = \sqrt{9 \cdot 6} = 3\sqrt{6}$

17. $\sqrt{15} \cdot \sqrt{6} = \sqrt{90} = \sqrt{9 \cdot 10} = 3\sqrt{10}$

18. $\sqrt{3} \cdot \sqrt{27} = \sqrt{81} = 9$

19. $\sqrt{18} \cdot \sqrt{14x} = \sqrt{252x} = \sqrt{36 \cdot 7x} = 6\sqrt{7x}$

20. $\sqrt{7x} \cdot \sqrt{21y} = \sqrt{147xy} = \sqrt{49 \cdot 3xy} = 7\sqrt{3xy}$

21. $\sqrt{11} \cdot \sqrt{11x} = \sqrt{121x} = 11\sqrt{x}$

22. $\sqrt{5b} \cdot \sqrt{15b} = \sqrt{75b^2} = \sqrt{25 \cdot 3b^2} = 5b\sqrt{3}$

23. $\sqrt{6a} \cdot \sqrt{18a} = \sqrt{108a^2} = \sqrt{36 \cdot 3a^2} = 6a\sqrt{3}$

24. $\sqrt{2t} \cdot \sqrt{2t} = \sqrt{4t^2} = 2t$

25. $\sqrt{ab} \cdot \sqrt{ac} = \sqrt{a^2bc} = a\sqrt{bc}$

26. $\sqrt{xy} \cdot \sqrt{xz} = \sqrt{x^2yz} = x\sqrt{yz}$

27. $\sqrt{2x^2y} \cdot \sqrt{4xy^2} = \sqrt{8x^3y^3} = \sqrt{4 \cdot 2x^2 \cdot xy^2 \cdot y} = 2xy\sqrt{2xy}$

28. $\sqrt{15mn^2} \cdot \sqrt{5m^2n} = \sqrt{75m^3n^3} = \sqrt{25 \cdot 3m^2 \cdot mn^2 \cdot n}$
$= 5mn\sqrt{3mn}$

29. $\sqrt{18x^2y^3} \cdot \sqrt{6xy^4} = \sqrt{108x^3y^7} = \sqrt{36 \cdot 3x^2 \cdot xy^6 \cdot y}$
$= 6xy^3\sqrt{3xy}$

30. $\sqrt{12x^3y^2} \cdot \sqrt{8xy} = \sqrt{96x^4y^3} = \sqrt{16 \cdot 6x^4y^2 \cdot y} = 4x^2y\sqrt{6y}$

31. $\sqrt{50ab} \cdot \sqrt{10a^2b^4} = \sqrt{500a^3b^5} = \sqrt{100 \cdot 5a^2 \cdot ab^4 \cdot b}$
$= 10ab^2\sqrt{5ab}$

32. $\sqrt{5a} \cdot \sqrt{20ab} = \sqrt{100a^2b} = 10a\sqrt{b}$

33. $\sqrt{7a^2b} \cdot \sqrt{42a^3b^2} = \sqrt{294a^5b^3} = \sqrt{49 \cdot 6a^4 \cdot ab^2 \cdot b}$
$= 7a^2b\sqrt{6ab}$

34. $\sqrt{56x^2y^7} \cdot \sqrt{8xy} = \sqrt{448x^3y^8} = \sqrt{64 \cdot 7x^2 \cdot xy^8} = 8xy^4\sqrt{7x}$

35. $\sqrt{10x^6y^3} \cdot \sqrt{2x^5y} = \sqrt{20x^{11}y^4} = \sqrt{4 \cdot 5x^{10} \cdot xy^4}$
$= 2x^5y^2\sqrt{5x}$

36. $\sqrt{15xy^{12}} \cdot \sqrt{3x^3y^5} = \sqrt{45x^4y^{17}} = \sqrt{9 \cdot 5x^4y^{16} \cdot y}$
$= 3x^2y^8\sqrt{5y}$

37. $\sqrt{8xyz^3} \cdot \sqrt{10x^3y^2z} = \sqrt{80x^4y^3z^4} = \sqrt{16 \cdot 5x^4y^2 \cdot yz^4}$
$= 4x^2yz^2\sqrt{5y}$

38. $\sqrt{12x^3y^5z} \cdot \sqrt{5xy^2z} = \sqrt{60x^4y^7z^2} = \sqrt{4 \cdot 15x^4y^6 \cdot yz^2}$
$= 2x^2y^3z\sqrt{15y}$

39. $\sqrt{12x^3} \cdot \sqrt{5x} \cdot \sqrt{45} = \sqrt{2700x^4} = \sqrt{900 \cdot 3x^4} = 30x^2\sqrt{3}$

40. $\sqrt{12x^6} \cdot \sqrt{7x^3} \cdot \sqrt{42x} = \sqrt{3528x^{10}} = \sqrt{1764 \cdot 2x^{10}}$
$= 42x^5\sqrt{2}$

41. $\sqrt{6x^3} \cdot \sqrt{5x^5} \cdot \sqrt{10x^6} = \sqrt{300x^{14}} = \sqrt{100 \cdot 3x^{14}} = 10x^7\sqrt{3}$

42. $(\sqrt{2y})(\sqrt{3})(\sqrt{8y}) = \sqrt{48y^2} = \sqrt{16y^2}\sqrt{3} = 4y\sqrt{3}$

43. $\sqrt{a}(\sqrt{a^3} - 5) = \sqrt{a^4} - 5\sqrt{a} = a^2 - 5\sqrt{a}$

44. $\sqrt{27(x+1)} \cdot \sqrt{12y(x+1)^2}$
$= \sqrt{(3 \cdot 9)(3 \cdot 4y)(x+1)^2(x+1)}$
$= \sqrt{9^2 \cdot 2^2y(x+1)^2(x+1)}$
$= 9 \cdot 2(x+1)\sqrt{y(x+1)} = 18(x+1)\sqrt{y(x+1)}$

45. $\sqrt{9 \cdot 2(x-2)} \cdot \sqrt{4 \cdot (x-2)^2 \cdot 5(x+2)}$
$= 3\sqrt{2(x-2)} \cdot 2(x-2)\sqrt{5(x-2)}$
$= 6(x-2)\sqrt{10(x-2)^2}$
$= 6(x-2)(x-2)\sqrt{10}$ or $6(x-2)^2\sqrt{10}$

46. $\sqrt{x}\sqrt{2x}\sqrt{10x^5} = \sqrt{20x^7} = \sqrt{4x^6}\sqrt{5x} = 2x^3\sqrt{5x}$

47. $\sqrt{0.04x^{4n}} = 0.2x^{2n}$

48. $\sqrt{2^{109}}\sqrt{x^{306}}\sqrt{x^{11}} = \sqrt{2^{108} \cdot 2} \cdot \sqrt{x^{317}} = 2^{54}\sqrt{2}\sqrt{x^{316} \cdot x}$
$= 2^{54}x^{158}\sqrt{2x}$

49. $\sqrt{147}\sqrt{y^{27}}\sqrt{x^{315}} = \sqrt{49 \cdot 3}\sqrt{y^{26} \cdot y}\sqrt{x^{314} \cdot x}$
$= 7\sqrt{3}y^{13}\sqrt{y}x^{157}\sqrt{x}$
$= 7y^{13}x^{157}\sqrt{3xy}$

50. $\sqrt{(x+9)^4}\sqrt{(x+9)^{99}} = \sqrt{(x+9)^{103}} = (x+9)^{51}\sqrt{x+9}$

51. $\sqrt{a^2 + 4ab + 4b^2}\sqrt{(a+2b)^{32}} = \sqrt{(a+2b)^2(a+2b)^{16}}$
$= (a+2b)(a+2b)^{16}$
$= (a+2b)^{17}$

52. $\sqrt{x^{2n}} \cdot \sqrt{y^{2n+1}} = \sqrt{(x^n)^2}\sqrt{(y^n)^2(y)}$
$= x^ny^n\sqrt{y}$

53. $\sqrt{x^{2n}} \cdot \sqrt{x^3y^{3n}} \cdot \sqrt{y^{n+1}} = \sqrt{x^{2n+3}y^{4n+1}}$
$= \sqrt{(x^{n+1})^2(x)(y^{2n})^2(y)}$
$= x^{n+1}y^{2n}\sqrt{xy}$

54. It's true only if a or b is 0.

55. $\sqrt{y^n}$; since n is even, $\sqrt{y^n} = y^{(\frac{n}{2})}$

56. Since n is odd, $n - 1$ is even.
$\sqrt{y^n} = \sqrt{y^{n-1}}\sqrt{y} = y^{[\frac{(n-1)}{2}]}\sqrt{y}$

57. $(x^2 + \sqrt{2}xy + y^2)(x^2 - \sqrt{2}xy + y^2)$
$= x^4 - \sqrt{2}x^3y + x^2y^2 + \sqrt{2}x^3y - 2x^2y^2 + \sqrt{2}xy^3$
$+ x^2y^2 - \sqrt{2}xy^3 + y^4 = x^4 + y^4$
So $(x^8 + y^8) = (x^4 + \sqrt{2}x^2y^2 + y^4)(x^4 - \sqrt{2}x^2y^2 + y^4)$

58. $m^6 \cdot m^2 = m^{6+2} = m^8$

59. $(3y^2)^3 = 3^3y^{2 \cdot 3} = 27y^6$

60. $(4x^3)(x^2) = 4x^{3+2} = 4x^5$

61. $(4c^2)(-2c^3) = -8c^{2+3} = -8c^5$

62. $a^2 - b^2 = (a+b)(a-b)$

63. $144y^2 - 1 = (12y+1)(12y-1)$

64. $4m^2 - 9n^2 = (2m+3n)(2m-3n)$

65. $\frac{-7x}{x+3} - \frac{2x+9}{x+3} = \frac{-7x-2x-9}{x+3} = \frac{-9x-9}{x+3}$
$= \frac{-9(x+1)}{x+3}$

66. $\frac{4}{x} + \frac{3}{x^2} = \frac{4x}{x^2} + \frac{3}{x^2} = \frac{4x+3}{x^2}$

67. $\frac{x+1}{2} - \frac{x-3}{4} = \frac{2(x+1)}{4} - \frac{x-3}{4} = \frac{2x+2-x+3}{4}$
$= \frac{x+5}{4}$

68. ± 6 69. ± 11 70. ± 25

71. 4 72. -6 73. -15 74. 9

RATIONAL EXPONENTS p. 497

1. $16^{\frac{1}{2}} = \sqrt{16} = 4$ 2. $81^{\frac{1}{2}} = \sqrt{81} = 9$

3. $27^{\frac{1}{3}} = \sqrt[3]{27} = 3$ 4. $125^{\frac{1}{3}} = \sqrt[3]{125} = 5$

5. $343^{\frac{1}{3}} = \sqrt[3]{343} = 7$ 6. $(9^{\frac{1}{2}})^3 = (\sqrt{9})^3 = 3^3 = 27$

7. $(4^{\frac{1}{2}})^3 = (\sqrt{4})^3 = 2^3 = 8$

8. $(64^{\frac{1}{3}})^2 = (\sqrt[3]{64})^2 = 4^2 = 16$

9. $(27^{\frac{1}{3}})^2 = (\sqrt[3]{27})^2 = 3^2 = 9$

10. $(125^{\frac{1}{3}})^2 = (\sqrt[3]{125})^2 = 5^2 = 25$

LESSON 11-5 TRY THIS pp. 498–500

a. $\frac{4}{3}$ b. $\frac{1}{5}$ c. $\frac{1}{3}$ d. $\sqrt{\frac{18}{32}} = \sqrt{\frac{9}{16}} = \frac{3}{4}$

e. $\sqrt{\frac{2250}{2560}} = \sqrt{\frac{225}{256}} = \frac{15}{16}$ f. $\frac{\sqrt{50}}{\sqrt{2}} = \sqrt{\frac{50}{2}} = \sqrt{25} = 5$

g. $\frac{\sqrt{42x^4}}{\sqrt{7x^2}} = \sqrt{6x^2} = x\sqrt{6}$ h. $\frac{\sqrt{5}}{\sqrt{7}} \cdot \frac{\sqrt{7}}{\sqrt{7}} = \frac{\sqrt{35}}{7}$

i. $\frac{8}{\sqrt{6}} \cdot \frac{\sqrt{6}}{\sqrt{6}} = \frac{8\sqrt{6}}{6} = \frac{4\sqrt{6}}{3}$ j. $\frac{\sqrt{x}}{\sqrt{y}} \cdot \frac{\sqrt{y}}{\sqrt{y}} = \frac{\sqrt{xy}}{y}$

k. $\sqrt{\frac{3}{7}} = \frac{\sqrt{3}}{\sqrt{7}} \cdot \frac{\sqrt{7}}{\sqrt{7}} = \frac{\sqrt{21}}{7}$

l. $\sqrt{\frac{5}{8}} = \frac{\sqrt{5}}{\sqrt{8}} \cdot \frac{\sqrt{8}}{\sqrt{8}} = \frac{\sqrt{40}}{8} = \frac{\sqrt{4 \cdot 10}}{8} = \frac{2\sqrt{10}}{8} = \frac{\sqrt{10}}{4}$

m. $\sqrt{\frac{2}{27}} = \frac{\sqrt{2}}{\sqrt{27}} \cdot \frac{\sqrt{27}}{\sqrt{27}} = \frac{\sqrt{54}}{27} = \frac{\sqrt{9 \cdot 6}}{27} = \frac{3\sqrt{6}}{27} = \frac{\sqrt{6}}{9}$

n. $\sqrt{\frac{5}{2a}} = \frac{\sqrt{5}}{\sqrt{2a}} \cdot \frac{\sqrt{2a}}{\sqrt{2a}} = \frac{\sqrt{10a}}{2a}$

o. $\sqrt{\frac{7}{3b^5}} = \frac{\sqrt{7}}{\sqrt{3b^5}} \cdot \frac{\sqrt{3b^5}}{\sqrt{3b^5}} = \frac{\sqrt{21b^5}}{3b^5} = \frac{b^2\sqrt{21b}}{3b^5} = \frac{\sqrt{21b}}{3b^3}$

p. $\sqrt{\frac{x}{18y^3}} = \frac{\sqrt{x}}{\sqrt{18y^3}} \cdot \frac{\sqrt{18y^3}}{\sqrt{18y^3}} = \frac{\sqrt{18xy^3}}{18y^3} = \frac{3y\sqrt{2xy}}{18y^3} = \frac{\sqrt{2xy}}{6y^2}$

LESSON 11-5 EXERCISES pp. 501–502

1. $\frac{3}{7}$ **2.** $\frac{4}{5}$ **3.** $\frac{1}{6}$ **4.** $\frac{1}{2}$ **5.** $-\frac{4}{9}$ **6.** $-\frac{5}{7}$ **7.** $\frac{8}{17}$

8. $\frac{9}{19}$ **9.** $-\frac{3}{10}$ **10.** $-\frac{7}{10}$

11. $\sqrt{\frac{27}{75}} = \sqrt{\frac{9}{25}} = \frac{3}{5}$ **12.** $\sqrt{\frac{50}{18}} = \sqrt{\frac{25}{9}} = \frac{5}{3}$

13. $\sqrt{9} = 3$ **14.** $\sqrt{4} = 2$ **15.** $\sqrt{4} = 2$ **16.** $\sqrt{36} = 6$

17. $\sqrt{5}$ **18.** $\sqrt{6}$ **19.** $\sqrt{\frac{1}{25}} = \frac{1}{5}$ **20.** $\sqrt{\frac{1}{16}} = \frac{1}{4}$

21. $\sqrt{\frac{4}{25}} = \frac{2}{5}$ **22.** $\sqrt{\frac{9}{16}} = \frac{3}{4}$ **23.** $\sqrt{4} = 2$ **24.** $\sqrt{9} = 3$

25. $\sqrt{9y^2} = 3y$ **26.** $\sqrt{16x^2} = 4x$ **27.** $\sqrt{5x^4} = x^2\sqrt{5}$

28. $\sqrt{6a^4} = a^2\sqrt{6}$ **29.** $\frac{\sqrt{7}}{\sqrt{3}} \cdot \frac{\sqrt{3}}{\sqrt{3}} = \frac{\sqrt{21}}{3}$ or $\frac{1}{3}\sqrt{21}$

30. $\frac{\sqrt{2}}{\sqrt{5}} \cdot \frac{\sqrt{5}}{\sqrt{5}} = \frac{\sqrt{10}}{5}$ or $\frac{1}{5}\sqrt{10}$

31. $\frac{\sqrt{9}}{\sqrt{8}} \cdot \frac{\sqrt{8}}{\sqrt{8}} = \frac{\sqrt{72}}{8} = \frac{\sqrt{36 \cdot 2}}{8} = \frac{6\sqrt{2}}{8} = \frac{3\sqrt{2}}{4}$ or $\frac{3}{4}\sqrt{2}$

32. $\frac{\sqrt{4}}{\sqrt{27}} \cdot \frac{\sqrt{27}}{\sqrt{27}} = \frac{\sqrt{108}}{27} = \frac{\sqrt{36 \cdot 3}}{27} = \frac{6\sqrt{3}}{27} = \frac{2\sqrt{3}}{9}$ or $\frac{2}{9}\sqrt{3}$

33. $\sqrt{\frac{2}{5}} = \frac{\sqrt{2}}{\sqrt{5}} \cdot \frac{\sqrt{5}}{\sqrt{5}} = \frac{\sqrt{10}}{5}$ or $\frac{1}{5}\sqrt{10}$

34. $\sqrt{\frac{2}{7}} = \frac{\sqrt{2}}{\sqrt{7}} \cdot \frac{\sqrt{7}}{\sqrt{7}} = \frac{\sqrt{14}}{7}$ or $\frac{1}{7}\sqrt{14}$

35. $\sqrt{\frac{3}{8}} = \frac{\sqrt{3}}{\sqrt{8}} \cdot \frac{\sqrt{8}}{\sqrt{8}} = \frac{\sqrt{24}}{8} = \frac{\sqrt{4 \cdot 6}}{8} = \frac{2\sqrt{6}}{8} = \frac{\sqrt{6}}{4}$ or $\frac{1}{4}\sqrt{6}$

36. $\sqrt{\frac{7}{8}} = \frac{\sqrt{7}}{\sqrt{8}} \cdot \frac{\sqrt{8}}{\sqrt{8}} = \frac{\sqrt{56}}{8} = \frac{\sqrt{4 \cdot 14}}{8} = \frac{2\sqrt{14}}{8} = \frac{\sqrt{14}}{4}$ or $\frac{1}{4}\sqrt{14}$

37. $\sqrt{\frac{7}{12}} = \frac{\sqrt{7}}{\sqrt{12}} \cdot \frac{\sqrt{12}}{\sqrt{12}} = \frac{\sqrt{84}}{12} = \frac{\sqrt{4 \cdot 21}}{12} = \frac{2\sqrt{21}}{12} = \frac{\sqrt{21}}{6}$ or $\frac{1}{6}\sqrt{21}$

38. $\sqrt{\frac{1}{12}} = \frac{\sqrt{1}}{\sqrt{12}} \cdot \frac{\sqrt{12}}{\sqrt{12}} = \frac{\sqrt{12}}{12} = \frac{\sqrt{4 \cdot 3}}{12} = \frac{2\sqrt{3}}{12} = \frac{\sqrt{3}}{6}$ or $\frac{1}{6}\sqrt{3}$

39. $\sqrt{\frac{1}{18}} = \frac{\sqrt{1}}{\sqrt{18}} \cdot \frac{\sqrt{18}}{\sqrt{18}} = \frac{\sqrt{18}}{18} = \frac{\sqrt{9 \cdot 2}}{18} = \frac{3\sqrt{2}}{18} = \frac{\sqrt{2}}{6}$ or $\frac{1}{6}\sqrt{2}$

40. $\sqrt{\frac{5}{18}} = \frac{\sqrt{5}}{\sqrt{18}} \cdot \frac{\sqrt{18}}{\sqrt{18}} = \frac{\sqrt{90}}{18} = \frac{\sqrt{9 \cdot 10}}{18} = \frac{3\sqrt{10}}{18} = \frac{\sqrt{10}}{6}$ or $\frac{1}{6}\sqrt{10}$

41. $\sqrt{\frac{1}{2}} = \frac{\sqrt{1}}{\sqrt{2}} \cdot \frac{\sqrt{2}}{\sqrt{2}} = \frac{\sqrt{2}}{2}$ or $\frac{1}{2}\sqrt{2}$

42. $\sqrt{\frac{1}{3}} = \frac{\sqrt{1}}{\sqrt{3}} \cdot \frac{\sqrt{3}}{\sqrt{3}} = \frac{\sqrt{3}}{3}$ or $\frac{1}{3}\sqrt{3}$

43. $\sqrt{\frac{8}{3}} = \frac{\sqrt{8}}{\sqrt{3}} \cdot \frac{\sqrt{3}}{\sqrt{3}} = \frac{\sqrt{24}}{3} = \frac{\sqrt{4 \cdot 6}}{3} = \frac{2\sqrt{6}}{3}$ or $\frac{2}{3}\sqrt{3}$

44. $\sqrt{\frac{12}{5}} = \frac{\sqrt{12}}{\sqrt{5}} \cdot \frac{\sqrt{5}}{\sqrt{5}} = \frac{\sqrt{60}}{5} = \frac{\sqrt{4 \cdot 15}}{5} = \frac{2\sqrt{15}}{5}$ or $\frac{2}{5}\sqrt{15}$

45. $\sqrt{\frac{3}{x}} = \frac{\sqrt{3}}{\sqrt{x}} \cdot \frac{\sqrt{x}}{\sqrt{x}} = \frac{\sqrt{3x}}{x}$ or $\frac{1}{x}\sqrt{3x}$

46. $\sqrt{\frac{2}{x}} = \frac{\sqrt{2}}{\sqrt{x}} \cdot \frac{\sqrt{x}}{\sqrt{x}} = \frac{\sqrt{2x}}{x}$ or $\frac{1}{x}\sqrt{2x}$

47. $\sqrt{\frac{x}{y}} = \frac{\sqrt{x}}{\sqrt{y}} \cdot \frac{\sqrt{y}}{\sqrt{y}} = \frac{\sqrt{xy}}{y}$ or $\frac{1}{y}\sqrt{xy}$

48. $\sqrt{\frac{a}{b}} = \frac{\sqrt{a}}{\sqrt{b}} \cdot \frac{\sqrt{b}}{\sqrt{b}} = \frac{\sqrt{ab}}{b}$ or $\frac{1}{b}\sqrt{ab}$

49. $\sqrt{\frac{x^2}{18}} = \frac{\sqrt{x^2}}{\sqrt{18}} \cdot \frac{\sqrt{18}}{\sqrt{18}} = \frac{x\sqrt{9 \cdot 2}}{18} = \frac{3x\sqrt{2}}{18} = \frac{x\sqrt{2}}{6}$

50. $\sqrt{\frac{x^2}{20}} = \frac{\sqrt{x^2}}{\sqrt{20}} \cdot \frac{\sqrt{20}}{\sqrt{20}} = \frac{x\sqrt{4 \cdot 5}}{20} = \frac{2x\sqrt{5}}{20} = \frac{x\sqrt{5}}{10}$

51. $\sqrt{\frac{6c}{2d^3}} = \frac{\sqrt{6c}}{\sqrt{2d^3}} \cdot \frac{\sqrt{2d^3}}{\sqrt{2d^3}} = \frac{\sqrt{12cd^3}}{2d^3} = \frac{2d\sqrt{3cd}}{2d^3} = \frac{\sqrt{3cd}}{d^2}$

52. $\sqrt{\frac{x}{8y^7}} = \frac{x}{\sqrt{8y^7}} \cdot \frac{\sqrt{8y^7}}{\sqrt{8y^7}} = \frac{\sqrt{8xy^7}}{8y^7} = \frac{2y^3\sqrt{2xy}}{8y^7} = \frac{\sqrt{2xy}}{4y^4}$

53. $\frac{\sqrt{2}}{\sqrt{5}} \cdot \frac{\sqrt{5}}{\sqrt{5}} = \frac{\sqrt{10}}{5}$ **54.** $\frac{\sqrt{3}}{\sqrt{2}} \cdot \frac{\sqrt{2}}{\sqrt{2}} = \frac{\sqrt{6}}{2}$

55. $\frac{2}{\sqrt{2}} \cdot \frac{\sqrt{2}}{\sqrt{2}} = \frac{2\sqrt{2}}{2} = \sqrt{2}$ **56.** $\frac{3}{\sqrt{3}} \cdot \frac{\sqrt{3}}{\sqrt{3}} = \frac{3\sqrt{3}}{3} = \sqrt{3}$

57. $\frac{\sqrt{48}}{\sqrt{32}} = \frac{\sqrt{16 \cdot 3}}{\sqrt{16 \cdot 2}} = \frac{4\sqrt{3}}{4\sqrt{2}} \cdot \frac{\sqrt{2}}{\sqrt{2}} = \frac{\sqrt{6}}{2}$

58. $\frac{\sqrt{56}}{\sqrt{40}} = \sqrt{\frac{56}{40}} = \sqrt{\frac{7}{5}} = \frac{\sqrt{7}}{\sqrt{5}} \cdot \frac{\sqrt{5}}{\sqrt{5}} = \frac{\sqrt{35}}{5}$

59. $\frac{\sqrt{450}}{\sqrt{18}} = \sqrt{\frac{450}{18}} = \sqrt{25} = 5$

60. $\frac{\sqrt{224}}{\sqrt{14}} = \sqrt{\frac{224}{14}} = \sqrt{16} = 4$

61. $\frac{\sqrt{3}}{\sqrt{x}} \cdot \frac{\sqrt{x}}{\sqrt{x}} = \frac{\sqrt{3x}}{x}$ **62.** $\frac{\sqrt{2}}{\sqrt{y}} \cdot \frac{\sqrt{y}}{\sqrt{y}} = \frac{\sqrt{2y}}{y}$

63. $\frac{4y}{\sqrt{3}} \cdot \frac{\sqrt{3}}{\sqrt{3}} = \frac{4y\sqrt{3}}{3}$

64. $\frac{8x}{\sqrt{5}} \cdot \frac{\sqrt{5}}{\sqrt{5}} = \frac{8x\sqrt{5}}{5}$

65. $\frac{\sqrt{a^3}}{\sqrt{8}} \cdot \frac{\sqrt{8}}{\sqrt{8}} = \frac{\sqrt{8a^3}}{8} = \frac{2a\sqrt{2a}}{8} = \frac{a\sqrt{2a}}{4}$

66. $\frac{\sqrt{x^3}}{\sqrt{27}} \cdot \frac{\sqrt{27}}{\sqrt{27}} = \frac{\sqrt{27x^3}}{27} = \frac{3x\sqrt{3x}}{27} = \frac{x\sqrt{3x}}{9}$

67. $\frac{\sqrt{56}}{\sqrt{12x}} = \sqrt{\frac{56}{12x}} = \sqrt{\frac{14}{3x}} = \frac{\sqrt{14}}{\sqrt{3x}} \cdot \frac{\sqrt{3x}}{\sqrt{3x}} = \frac{\sqrt{42x}}{3x}$

68. $\frac{\sqrt{45}}{\sqrt{8a}} = \frac{3\sqrt{5}}{2\sqrt{2a}} \cdot \frac{\sqrt{2a}}{\sqrt{2a}} = \frac{3\sqrt{10a}}{4a}$

69. $\frac{\sqrt{27c}}{\sqrt{32c^3}} = \frac{3\sqrt{3c}}{4c\sqrt{2c}} \cdot \frac{\sqrt{2c}}{\sqrt{2c}} = \frac{3\sqrt{6c^2}}{8c^2} = \frac{3c\sqrt{6}}{8c^2} = \frac{3\sqrt{6}}{8c}$

70. $\frac{\sqrt{7x^3}}{\sqrt{12x}} = \sqrt{\frac{7x^3}{12x}} = \sqrt{\frac{7x^2}{12}} = \frac{\sqrt{7x^2}}{\sqrt{12}} \cdot \frac{\sqrt{12}}{\sqrt{12}} = \frac{x\sqrt{84}}{12}$
$= \frac{2x\sqrt{21}}{12} = \frac{x\sqrt{21}}{6}$

71. $\frac{\sqrt{y^5}}{\sqrt{xy^2}} \cdot \frac{\sqrt{xy^2}}{\sqrt{xy^2}} = \frac{\sqrt{xy^7}}{xy^2} = \frac{y^3\sqrt{xy}}{xy^2} = \frac{y\sqrt{xy}}{x}$

72. $\frac{\sqrt{x^3}}{\sqrt{xy}} \cdot \frac{\sqrt{xy}}{\sqrt{xy}} = \frac{\sqrt{x^4y}}{xy} = \frac{x^2\sqrt{y}}{xy} = \frac{x\sqrt{y}}{y}$

73. $\frac{\sqrt{2}}{3\sqrt{3}} \cdot \frac{\sqrt{3}}{\sqrt{3}} = \frac{\sqrt{6}}{3 \cdot 3} = \frac{\sqrt{6}}{9}$

74. $\frac{3\sqrt{6}}{6\sqrt{2}} \cdot \frac{\sqrt{2}}{\sqrt{2}} = \frac{3\sqrt{12}}{6\sqrt{4}} = \frac{3\sqrt{4 \cdot 3}}{6 \cdot 2} = \frac{6\sqrt{3}}{12} = \frac{\sqrt{3}}{2}$

75. $\frac{5\sqrt{2}}{3\sqrt{5}} \cdot \frac{\sqrt{5}}{\sqrt{5}} = \frac{5\sqrt{10}}{3 \cdot 5} = \frac{\sqrt{10}}{3}$

76. $\frac{3\sqrt{15}}{5\sqrt{32}} \cdot \frac{\sqrt{2}}{\sqrt{2}} = \frac{3\sqrt{30}}{5\sqrt{64}} = \frac{3\sqrt{30}}{40}$

77. $\frac{4\sqrt{\frac{6}{7}}}{\sqrt{\frac{12}{63}}} \cdot \frac{\sqrt{\frac{63}{12}}}{\sqrt{\frac{63}{12}}} = \frac{4\sqrt{\frac{63}{14}}}{1} = 4\sqrt{\frac{63}{14} \cdot \frac{14}{14}} = \frac{4\sqrt{882}}{14}$

$= \frac{4\sqrt{441 \cdot 2}}{14} = \frac{4 \cdot 21\sqrt{2}}{14} = 6\sqrt{2}$

78. $\frac{\sqrt{\frac{2}{3}}}{\sqrt{\frac{3}{2}}} \cdot \frac{\sqrt{\frac{3}{2}}}{\sqrt{\frac{3}{2}}} = \frac{\sqrt{1}}{\frac{3}{2}} = 1 \cdot \frac{2}{3} = \frac{2}{3}$

79. $\frac{a\sqrt{b}}{b\sqrt{a}} \cdot \frac{\sqrt{a}}{\sqrt{a}} = \frac{a\sqrt{ab}}{ba} = \frac{\sqrt{ab}}{b}$

80. $(\sqrt{5} + 7)(\sqrt{5} - 7) = (\sqrt{5})^2 - 7^2 = 5 - 49 = -44$

81. $(1 + \sqrt{5})(1 - \sqrt{5}) = 1^2 - (\sqrt{5})^2 = 1 - 5 = -4$

82. $(\sqrt{6} - \sqrt{3})(\sqrt{6} + \sqrt{3}) = (\sqrt{6})^2 - (\sqrt{3})^2 = 6 - 3 = 3$

83. $(\sqrt{3} + \sqrt{2})(\sqrt{3} + \sqrt{2}) = 3 + \sqrt{6} + \sqrt{6} + 2 = 5 + 2\sqrt{6}$

84. a. $T = 2\pi\sqrt{\frac{L}{32}}$

For $L = 2$, $T = 2(3.14)\sqrt{\frac{2}{32}} = 6.28\sqrt{\frac{1}{16}}$

$= (6.28)\frac{1}{4} = 1.57$ sec

For $L = 8$, $T = 2(3.14)\sqrt{\frac{8}{32}} = 6.28\sqrt{\frac{1}{4}}$

$= (6.28)\frac{1}{2} = 3.14$ sec

For $L = 64$, $T = 2(3.14)\sqrt{\frac{64}{32}} = 6.28\sqrt{2}$

$= (6.28)\sqrt{2} \approx 8.88$ sec

For $L = 100$, $T = 2(3.14)\sqrt{\frac{100}{32}} = 6.28\sqrt{\frac{50}{16}}$

$= (6.28)\frac{5}{4}\sqrt{2} \approx 11.10$ sec

b. $T = 2\pi\sqrt{\frac{L}{32}}$

$L = \frac{2}{3}\text{in.} = \frac{2}{3} \cdot \frac{1}{12} = \frac{1}{18}\text{ft}$

$T = 2(3.14)\sqrt{\frac{\left(\frac{1}{18}\right)}{32}} = 6.28\sqrt{\frac{1}{18 \cdot 32}} = 6.28\sqrt{\frac{1}{576}}$

$= \frac{6.28}{24} \approx 0.262$ sec

c. $T = 2\pi\sqrt{\frac{L}{32}}$ For $L = \frac{32}{\pi^2}$,

$T = 2\pi\sqrt{\frac{\left(\frac{32}{\pi^2}\right)}{32}} = 2\pi\sqrt{\frac{1}{\pi^2}} = 2\pi\left(\frac{1}{\pi}\right) = 2$

$T = 2$ seconds, thus one swing requires $\frac{1}{2} \cdot 2 = 1$ second

85. Irrational 86. Rational 87. Irrational

88. Rational 89. Rational 90. Irrational

91. Rational 92. $16a^2 - 25c^4 = (4a + 5c^2)(4a - 5c^2)$

93. $x^2 - 2x - 15 = (x - 5)(x + 3)$

94. $5m^2 - 30m + 45 = 5(m^2 - 6m + 9) = 5(m - 3)^2$

95. $2am + bm - 6an - 3bn = m(2a + b) - 3n(2a + b)$
$= (2a + b)(m - 3n)$

96. $\frac{7}{2x} + \frac{2}{x} = 1$

$2x\left(\frac{7}{2x} + \frac{2}{x}\right) = 2x$

$7 + 4 = 2x$

$11 = 2x$

$\frac{11}{2} = x$

97. $\frac{12}{x + 4} = \frac{3}{x - 2}$

$12(x - 2) = 3(x + 4)$

$12x - 24 = 3x + 12$

$9x = 36$

$x = 4$

98. $\frac{a + 1}{4a - 4} = \frac{1}{2}$

$2(a + 1) = 4a - 4$

$2a + 2 = 4a - 4$

$6 = 2a$

$3 = a$

99. $3x \geq 0$
$x \geq 0$

100. $2x^2 \geq 0$
$x^2 \geq 0$
Any real number

101. $x - 2 \geq 0$
$x \geq 2$

102. $2x + 5 \geq 0$
$2x \geq -5$
$x \geq -\frac{5}{2}$

OPERATIONS WITH RATIONAL EXPONENTS p. 503

1. $8^{\frac{4}{6}} = 8^{\frac{2}{3}} = (2^3)^{\frac{2}{3}} = 2^2 = 4$

2. $(7^{\frac{1}{3}})^{\frac{2}{5}} = 7^{\frac{2}{15}} = \sqrt[15]{7^2}$ or $\sqrt[15]{49}$

3. $(10^{\frac{1}{4}})(10^{\frac{5}{8}}) = (10^{\frac{2}{8}})(10^{\frac{5}{8}}) = 10^{\frac{7}{8}} = \sqrt[8]{10^7}$ or $\sqrt[8]{10{,}000{,}000}$

4. $\frac{2^{\frac{7}{4}}}{2^{\frac{3}{8}}} = 2^{\frac{14}{8} - \frac{3}{8}} = 2^{\frac{11}{8}} = \sqrt[8]{2^{11}}$ or $2\sqrt[8]{2^3}$ or $2\sqrt[8]{8}$

5. $t^{\frac{-2}{3}} \cdot t^{\frac{5}{9}} = t^{\frac{-1}{9}} = \frac{1}{t^{\frac{1}{9}}} = \frac{1}{t^{\frac{1}{9}}} \cdot \frac{t^{\frac{8}{9}}}{t^{\frac{8}{9}}} = \frac{\sqrt[9]{t^8}}{t}$

6. $\left(\frac{a^{\frac{1}{3}}}{a^{\frac{4}{6}}}\right)^{\frac{1}{2}} = \left(\frac{1}{a^{\frac{1}{3}}}\right)^{\frac{1}{2}} = \frac{1}{a^{\frac{1}{6}}} = \frac{1}{a^{\frac{1}{6}}} \cdot \frac{a^{\frac{5}{6}}}{a^{\frac{5}{6}}} = \frac{\sqrt[6]{a^5}}{a}$

7. $(m^{\frac{5}{8}}n^{\frac{2}{3}})^{\frac{3}{4}} = m^{\frac{15}{32}}n^{\frac{1}{2}} = m^{\frac{15}{32}}n^{\frac{16}{32}} = \sqrt[32]{m^{15}n^{16}}$ or
$\sqrt[32]{m^{15}}\sqrt{n}$

8. $((b^{\frac{2}{3}})^{\frac{6}{10}})^{\frac{1}{4}} = (b^{\frac{12}{30}})^{\frac{1}{4}} = b^{\frac{12}{120}} = b^{\frac{1}{10}} = \sqrt[10]{b}$

9. $(x^{\frac{5}{3}}y^{\frac{1}{5}})^{\frac{3}{6}} \cdot y^{\frac{3}{10}} = x^{\frac{5}{6}}y^{\frac{1}{10}} \cdot y^{\frac{3}{10}} = x^{\frac{5}{6}}y^{\frac{4}{10}} = x^{\frac{5}{6}}y^{\frac{2}{5}}$

$= \sqrt[6]{x^5}\sqrt[5]{y^2}$ or $\sqrt[30]{x^{25}y^{12}}$

10. $x^{\frac{2}{3}}y^{\frac{1}{3}} \cdot \sqrt[3]{xy^5} = x^{\frac{2}{3}}y^{\frac{1}{3}} \cdot x^{\frac{1}{3}}y^{\frac{5}{3}} = x^{\frac{3}{3}}y^{\frac{6}{3}} = xy^2$

11. $\frac{\sqrt[3]{m^4n^5}}{m^{\frac{2}{3}}n^{\frac{7}{3}}} = \frac{m^{\frac{4}{3}}n^{\frac{5}{3}}}{m^{\frac{2}{3}}n^{\frac{7}{3}}} = \frac{m^{\frac{2}{3}}}{n^{\frac{2}{3}}} = \sqrt[3]{\frac{m^2}{n^2}}$

12. $\sqrt[5]{6a^4b^4} \cdot (5a^3b^7)^{\frac{1}{5}} = 6^{\frac{1}{5}}a^{\frac{4}{5}}b^{\frac{4}{5}} \cdot 5^{\frac{1}{5}}a^{\frac{3}{5}}b^{\frac{7}{5}} =$
$30^{\frac{1}{5}}a^{\frac{7}{5}}b^{\frac{11}{5}} = \sqrt[5]{30a^7b^{11}}$ or $ab^2\sqrt[5]{30a^2b}$

LESSON 11-6 TRY THIS pp. 504–505

a. $3\sqrt{2} + 9\sqrt{2} = (3 + 9)\sqrt{2} = 12\sqrt{2}$

b. $8\sqrt{5} - 3\sqrt{5} = (8 - 3)\sqrt{5} = 5\sqrt{5}$

c. $2\sqrt{10} - 7\sqrt{40} = 2\sqrt{10} - 7\sqrt{4 \cdot 10}$
$= 2\sqrt{10} - 7 \cdot 2\sqrt{10}$
$= 2\sqrt{10} - 14\sqrt{10}$
$= (2 - 14)\sqrt{10} = -12\sqrt{10}$

d. $\sqrt{24y} + \sqrt{54y} = \sqrt{4 \cdot 6y} + \sqrt{9 \cdot 6y}$
$= 2\sqrt{6y} + 3\sqrt{6y} = 5\sqrt{6y}$

e. $\sqrt{9x+9} - \sqrt{4x+4} = \sqrt{9(x+1)} - \sqrt{4(x+1)}$
$= 3\sqrt{x+1} - 2\sqrt{x+1}$
$= \sqrt{x+1}$

f. $\sqrt{2} + \sqrt{\frac{1}{2}} = \sqrt{2} + \sqrt{\frac{1}{2}\cdot\frac{2}{2}}$
$= \sqrt{2} + \sqrt{\frac{2}{4}}$
$= \sqrt{2} + \frac{1}{2}\sqrt{2}$
$= \left(1 + \frac{1}{2}\right)\sqrt{2} = \frac{3}{2}\sqrt{2}$

g. $\sqrt{\frac{5}{3}} - \sqrt{\frac{3}{5}} = \sqrt{\frac{5}{3}\cdot\frac{3}{3}} - \sqrt{\frac{3}{5}\cdot\frac{5}{5}}$
$= \sqrt{\frac{15}{9}} - \sqrt{\frac{15}{25}}$
$= \frac{1}{3}\sqrt{15} - \frac{1}{5}\sqrt{15}$
$= \frac{5}{5}\cdot\frac{1}{3}\sqrt{15} - \frac{3}{3}\cdot\frac{1}{5}\sqrt{15}$
$= \frac{5}{15}\sqrt{15} - \frac{3}{15}\sqrt{15} = \frac{2}{15}\sqrt{15}$

h. $\frac{x}{\sqrt{x}} + \sqrt{x} = \frac{x}{\sqrt{x}}\cdot\frac{\sqrt{x}}{\sqrt{x}} + \sqrt{x}$
$= \frac{x\sqrt{x}}{x} + \sqrt{x}$
$= \sqrt{x} + \sqrt{x} = 2\sqrt{x}$

LESSON 11-6 EXERCISES pp. 505–506

1. $7\sqrt{2}$ **2.** $11\sqrt{3}$ **3.** $4\sqrt{5}$ **4.** $3\sqrt{2}$

5. $13\sqrt{x}$ **6.** $12\sqrt{y}$ **7.** $-2\sqrt{x}$ **8.** $-8\sqrt{a}$

9. $5\sqrt{8} + 15\sqrt{2} = 5\sqrt{4\cdot2} + 15\sqrt{2}$
$= 5\cdot2\sqrt{2} + 15\sqrt{2}$
$= 10\sqrt{2} + 15\sqrt{2}$
$= 25\sqrt{2}$

10. $3\sqrt{12} + 2\sqrt{3} = 3\sqrt{4\cdot3} + 2\sqrt{3}$
$= 3\cdot2\sqrt{3} + 2\sqrt{3}$
$= 6\sqrt{3} + 2\sqrt{3}$
$= 8\sqrt{3}$

11. $\sqrt{27} - 2\sqrt{3} = \sqrt{9\cdot3} - 2\sqrt{3}$
$= 3\sqrt{3} - 2\sqrt{3}$
$= \sqrt{3}$

12. $7\sqrt{50} - 3\sqrt{2} = 7\sqrt{25\cdot2} - 3\sqrt{2}$
$= 7\cdot5\sqrt{2} - 3\sqrt{2}$
$= 35\sqrt{2} - 3\sqrt{2}$
$= 32\sqrt{2}$

13. $\sqrt{45} - \sqrt{20} = \sqrt{9\cdot5} - \sqrt{4\cdot5}$
$= 3\sqrt{5} - 2\sqrt{5}$
$= \sqrt{5}$

14. $\sqrt{27} - \sqrt{12} = \sqrt{9\cdot3} - \sqrt{4\cdot3}$
$= 3\sqrt{3} - 2\sqrt{3}$
$= \sqrt{3}$

15. $\sqrt{72} + \sqrt{98} = \sqrt{36\cdot2} + \sqrt{49\cdot2}$
$= 6\sqrt{2} + 7\sqrt{2}$
$= 13\sqrt{2}$

16. $\sqrt{45} + \sqrt{80} = \sqrt{9\cdot5} + \sqrt{16\cdot5}$
$= 3\sqrt{5} + 4\sqrt{5}$
$= 7\sqrt{5}$

17. $2\sqrt{12} + \sqrt{27} - \sqrt{48} = 2\sqrt{4\cdot3} + \sqrt{9\cdot3} - \sqrt{16\cdot3}$
$= 2\cdot2\sqrt{3} + 3\sqrt{3} - 4\sqrt{3}$
$= 4\sqrt{3} - \sqrt{3}$
$= 3\sqrt{3}$

18. $9\sqrt{8} - \sqrt{72} + \sqrt{98} = 9\sqrt{4\cdot2} - \sqrt{36\cdot2} + \sqrt{49\cdot2}$
$= 9\cdot2\sqrt{2} - 6\sqrt{2} + 7\sqrt{2}$
$= 18\sqrt{2} + \sqrt{2}$
$= 19\sqrt{2}$

19. $3\sqrt{18} - 2\sqrt{32} - 5\sqrt{50}$
$= 3\sqrt{9\cdot2} - 2\sqrt{16\cdot2} - 5\sqrt{25\cdot2}$
$= 3\cdot3\sqrt{2} - 2\cdot4\sqrt{2} - 5\cdot5\sqrt{2}$
$= 9\sqrt{2} - 8\sqrt{2} - 25\sqrt{2}$
$= -24\sqrt{2}$

20. $\sqrt{18} - 3\sqrt{8} + \sqrt{50} = \sqrt{9\cdot2} - 3\sqrt{4\cdot2} + \sqrt{25\cdot2}$
$= 3\sqrt{2} - 3\cdot2\sqrt{2} + 5\sqrt{2}$
$= 8\sqrt{2} - 6\sqrt{2}$
$= 2\sqrt{2}$

21. $2\sqrt{27} - 3\sqrt{48} + 2\sqrt{18}$
$= 2\sqrt{9\cdot3} - 3\sqrt{16\cdot3} + 2\sqrt{9\cdot2}$
$= 2\cdot3\sqrt{3} - 3\cdot4\sqrt{3} + 2\cdot3\sqrt{2}$
$= 6\sqrt{3} - 12\sqrt{3} + 6\sqrt{2}$
$= -6\sqrt{3} + 6\sqrt{2}$ or $6(\sqrt{2} - \sqrt{3})$

22. $3\sqrt{48} - 2\sqrt{27} - 2\sqrt{18} = 3\sqrt{16\cdot3} - 2\sqrt{9\cdot3} - 2\sqrt{9\cdot2}$
$= 3\cdot4\sqrt{3} - 2\cdot3\sqrt{3} - 2\cdot3\sqrt{2}$
$= 12\sqrt{3} - 6\sqrt{3} - 6\sqrt{2}$
$= 6\sqrt{3} - 6\sqrt{2}$ or $6(\sqrt{3} - \sqrt{2})$

23. $\sqrt{4x} + \sqrt{81x^3} = 2\sqrt{x} + 9x\sqrt{x}$
$= (2 + 9x)\sqrt{x}$

24. $\sqrt{12x^2} + \sqrt{27} = \sqrt{4\cdot3x^2} + \sqrt{9\cdot3}$
$= 2x\sqrt{3} + 3\sqrt{3}$
$= (2x + 3)\sqrt{3}$

25. $\sqrt{27} - \sqrt{12x^2} = \sqrt{9\cdot3} - \sqrt{4\cdot3x^2}$
$= 3\sqrt{3} - 2x\sqrt{3}$
$= (3 - 2x)\sqrt{3}$

26. $\sqrt{81x^3} - \sqrt{4x} = 9x\sqrt{x} - 2\sqrt{x}$
$= (9x - 2)\sqrt{x}$

27. $\sqrt{8x+8} + \sqrt{2x+2} = \sqrt{8(x+1)} + \sqrt{2(x+1)}$
$= \sqrt{4\cdot2(x+1)} + \sqrt{2(x+1)}$
$= 2\sqrt{2(x+1)} + \sqrt{2(x+1)}$
$= 3\sqrt{2(x+1)}$ or $3\sqrt{2x+2}$

28. $\sqrt{12x+12} + \sqrt{3x+3} = \sqrt{12(x+1)} + \sqrt{3(x+1)}$
$= \sqrt{4\cdot3(x+1)} + \sqrt{3(x+1)}$
$= 2\sqrt{3(x+1)} + \sqrt{3(x+1)}$
$= 3\sqrt{3(x+1)}$ or $3\sqrt{3x+3}$

29. $\sqrt{x^5 - x^2} + \sqrt{9x^3 - 9} = \sqrt{x^2(x^3-1)} + \sqrt{9(x^3-1)}$
$= x\sqrt{x^3-1} + 3\sqrt{x^3-1}$
$= (x + 3)\sqrt{x^3-1}$

30. $\sqrt{16x-16} + \sqrt{25x^3 - 25x^2}$
$= \sqrt{16(x-1)} + \sqrt{25x^2(x-1)}$
$= 4\sqrt{x-1} + 5x\sqrt{x-1}$
$= (4 + 5x)\sqrt{x-1}$

31. $3x\sqrt{y^3x} - x\sqrt{yx^3} + y\sqrt{y^3x} = 3xy\sqrt{yx} - x^2\sqrt{yx} + y^2\sqrt{yx}$
$= (-x^2 + 3xy + y^2)\sqrt{xy}$

32. $4a\sqrt{a^2b} + a\sqrt{a^2b^3} - 5\sqrt{b^3} = 4a^2\sqrt{b} + a^2b\sqrt{b} - 5b\sqrt{b}$
$= (4a^2 + a^2b - 5b)\sqrt{b}$

33. $\sqrt{4(a+b)} - \sqrt{(a+b)^3} = 2\sqrt{a+b} - (a+b)\sqrt{a+b}$
$= (2 - a - b)\sqrt{a+b}$

34. $\sqrt{x^2y} + \sqrt{4x^2y} + \sqrt{9y} - \sqrt{y^3}$
$= x\sqrt{y} + 2x\sqrt{y} + 3\sqrt{y} - y\sqrt{y}$
$= (x + 2x + 3 - y)\sqrt{y} = (3x + 3 - y)\sqrt{y}$

35. $\sqrt{3} - \sqrt{\frac{1}{3}} = \sqrt{3} - \frac{\sqrt{1}}{\sqrt{3}} \cdot \frac{\sqrt{3}}{\sqrt{3}}$
$= \sqrt{3} - \frac{\sqrt{3}}{3}$
$= \frac{3\sqrt{3}}{3} - \frac{\sqrt{3}}{3} = \frac{2\sqrt{3}}{3}$

36. $\sqrt{2} - \sqrt{\frac{1}{2}} = \sqrt{2} - \frac{\sqrt{1}}{\sqrt{2}} \cdot \frac{\sqrt{2}}{\sqrt{2}}$
$= \sqrt{2} - \frac{\sqrt{2}}{2}$
$= \frac{2\sqrt{2}}{2} - \frac{\sqrt{2}}{2} = \frac{\sqrt{2}}{2}$

37. $5\sqrt{2} + 3\sqrt{\frac{1}{2}} = 5\sqrt{2} + 3\left(\frac{\sqrt{1}}{\sqrt{2}} \cdot \frac{\sqrt{2}}{\sqrt{2}}\right)$
$= 5\sqrt{2} + \frac{3\sqrt{2}}{2}$
$= \frac{10\sqrt{2}}{2} + \frac{3\sqrt{2}}{2} = \frac{13\sqrt{2}}{2}$

38. $4\sqrt{3} + 2\sqrt{\frac{1}{3}} = 4\sqrt{3} + 2\left(\frac{\sqrt{1}}{\sqrt{3}} \cdot \frac{\sqrt{3}}{\sqrt{3}}\right)$
$= 4\sqrt{3} + \frac{2\sqrt{3}}{3}$
$= \frac{12\sqrt{3}}{3} + \frac{2\sqrt{3}}{3} = \frac{14\sqrt{3}}{3}$

39. $\sqrt{\frac{2}{3}} - \sqrt{\frac{1}{6}} = \frac{\sqrt{2}}{\sqrt{3}} \cdot \frac{\sqrt{3}}{\sqrt{3}} - \frac{\sqrt{1}}{\sqrt{6}} \cdot \frac{\sqrt{6}}{\sqrt{6}}$
$= \frac{\sqrt{6}}{3} - \frac{\sqrt{6}}{6}$
$= \frac{2\sqrt{6}}{6} - \frac{\sqrt{6}}{6} = \frac{\sqrt{6}}{6}$

40. $\sqrt{\frac{1}{2}} - \sqrt{\frac{1}{8}} = \frac{\sqrt{1}}{\sqrt{2}} \cdot \frac{\sqrt{2}}{\sqrt{2}} - \frac{\sqrt{1}}{\sqrt{8}} \cdot \frac{\sqrt{8}}{\sqrt{8}}$
$= \frac{\sqrt{2}}{2} - \frac{\sqrt{8}}{8}$
$= \frac{\sqrt{2}}{2} - \frac{\sqrt{4 \cdot 2}}{8}$
$= \frac{\sqrt{2}}{2} - \frac{2\sqrt{2}}{8} = \frac{4\sqrt{2}}{8} - \frac{2\sqrt{2}}{8} = \frac{2\sqrt{2}}{8} = \frac{\sqrt{2}}{4}$

41. $\sqrt{\frac{1}{12}} - \sqrt{\frac{1}{27}} = \frac{\sqrt{1}}{\sqrt{12}} \cdot \frac{\sqrt{12}}{\sqrt{12}} - \frac{\sqrt{1}}{\sqrt{27}} \cdot \frac{\sqrt{27}}{\sqrt{27}}$
$= \frac{\sqrt{12}}{12} - \frac{\sqrt{27}}{27}$
$= \frac{\sqrt{4 \cdot 3}}{12} - \frac{\sqrt{9 \cdot 3}}{27}$
$= \frac{2\sqrt{3}}{12} - \frac{3\sqrt{3}}{27}$
$= \frac{\sqrt{3}}{6} - \frac{\sqrt{3}}{9}$
$= \frac{3\sqrt{3}}{18} - \frac{2\sqrt{3}}{18} = \frac{\sqrt{3}}{18}$

42. $\sqrt{\frac{5}{6}} - \sqrt{\frac{6}{5}} = \frac{\sqrt{5}}{\sqrt{6}} \cdot \frac{\sqrt{6}}{\sqrt{6}} - \frac{\sqrt{6}}{\sqrt{5}} \cdot \frac{\sqrt{5}}{\sqrt{5}}$
$= \frac{\sqrt{30}}{6} - \frac{\sqrt{30}}{5}$
$= \frac{5\sqrt{30}}{30} - \frac{6\sqrt{30}}{30}$
$= -\frac{\sqrt{30}}{30}$

43. a. None,
$\sqrt{10} + \sqrt{50} = \sqrt{10} + \sqrt{10}\sqrt{5} = \sqrt{10}(1 + \sqrt{5})$
$\sqrt{10} + \sqrt{50} = \sqrt{10} + \sqrt{2 \cdot 25} = \sqrt{10} + 5\sqrt{2}$
$\sqrt{10} + \sqrt{50} = \sqrt{5}\sqrt{2} + \sqrt{2 \cdot 25}$
$= \sqrt{5}\sqrt{2} + 5\sqrt{2} = \sqrt{2}(5 + \sqrt{5})$

b. $\sqrt{10} + 5\sqrt{2}$ is in simplest form since both terms are in the form $a\sqrt{b}$.

44. $\sqrt{125} - \sqrt{45} + 2\sqrt{5} = \sqrt{25 \cdot 5} - \sqrt{9 \cdot 5} + 2\sqrt{5}$
$= 5\sqrt{5} - 3\sqrt{5} + 2\sqrt{5}$
$= 4\sqrt{5}$

45. $3\sqrt{\frac{1}{2}} + \frac{5}{2}\sqrt{18} + \sqrt{98} = 3\sqrt{\frac{1}{2} \cdot \frac{2}{2}} + \frac{5}{2}\sqrt{9 \cdot 2} + \sqrt{49 \cdot 2}$
$= 3\sqrt{\frac{2}{4}} + \frac{5}{2} \cdot 3\sqrt{2} + 7\sqrt{2}$
$= 3 \cdot \frac{1}{2}\sqrt{2} + \frac{15}{2}\sqrt{2} + 7\sqrt{2}$
$= \frac{3}{2}\sqrt{2} + \frac{15}{2}\sqrt{2} + 7\sqrt{2}$
$= \frac{18}{2}\sqrt{2} + 7\sqrt{2}$
$= 9\sqrt{2} + 7\sqrt{2} = 16\sqrt{2}$

46. $\frac{3}{5}\sqrt{24} + \frac{2}{5}\sqrt{150} - \sqrt{96}$
$= \frac{3}{5}\sqrt{4 \cdot 6} + \frac{2}{5}\sqrt{25 \cdot 6} - \sqrt{16 \cdot 6}$
$= \frac{3 \cdot 2}{5}\sqrt{6} + \frac{2 \cdot 5}{5}\sqrt{6} - 4\sqrt{6}$
$= \frac{6}{5}\sqrt{6} + \frac{10}{5}\sqrt{6} - 4\sqrt{6}$
$= \frac{16}{5}\sqrt{6} - \frac{20}{5}\sqrt{6}$
$= -\frac{4}{5}\sqrt{6}$

47. $\sqrt{ab^6} + b\sqrt{a^3} + a\sqrt{a} = b^3\sqrt{a} + ab\sqrt{a} + a\sqrt{a}$
$= (b^3 + ab + a)\sqrt{a}$

48. $\frac{1}{3}\sqrt{27} + \sqrt{8} + \sqrt{300} - \sqrt{18} - \sqrt{162}$
$= \frac{1}{3}\sqrt{9 \cdot 3} + \sqrt{4 \cdot 2} + \sqrt{100 \cdot 3} - \sqrt{9 \cdot 2} - \sqrt{81 \cdot 2}$
$= \frac{3}{3}\sqrt{3} + 2\sqrt{2} + 10\sqrt{3} - 3\sqrt{2} - 9\sqrt{2}$
$= 11\sqrt{3} - 10\sqrt{2}$

49. $x\sqrt{2y} - \sqrt{8x^2y} + \frac{x}{3}\sqrt{18y}$
$= x\sqrt{2y} - \sqrt{4 \cdot 2 \cdot x^2 \cdot y} + \frac{x}{3}\sqrt{9 \cdot 2y}$
$= x\sqrt{2y} - 2x\sqrt{2y} + \frac{x \cdot 3}{3}\sqrt{2y}$
$= -x\sqrt{2y} + x\sqrt{2y}$
$= 0$

50. $7x\sqrt{12xy^2} - 9y\sqrt{27x^3} + 5\sqrt{300x^3y^2}$
$= 7x\sqrt{4 \cdot 3 \cdot x \cdot y^2} - 9y\sqrt{9 \cdot 3 \cdot x^2 \cdot x} + 5\sqrt{100 \cdot 3 \cdot x^2 \cdot x \cdot y^2}$
$= 7x \cdot 2y\sqrt{3x} - 9y \cdot 3x\sqrt{3x} + 5 \cdot 10xy\sqrt{3x}$
$= (14xy - 27xy + 50xy)\sqrt{3x}$
$= 37xy\sqrt{3x}$

51. $\sqrt{x} + \sqrt{\frac{1}{x}} = \sqrt{x} + \sqrt{\frac{1}{x} \cdot \frac{x}{x}}$
$= \sqrt{x} + \sqrt{\frac{x}{x^2}}$
$= \sqrt{x} + \frac{1}{x}\sqrt{x}$
$= \sqrt{x}\left(1 + \frac{1}{x}\right) = \frac{x+1}{x}\sqrt{x}$

52. $\sqrt{x^2 + y^2} = \sqrt{x^2} + \sqrt{y^2}$
$= x + y$
$x^2 + y^2 = (x + y)^2$
$x^2 + y^2 = x^2 + 2xy + y^2$
$0 = 2xy$
If either x or $y = 0$, the other can be any number.

53. $5\sqrt{\frac{3}{10}} + 2\sqrt{\frac{5}{6}} - 6\sqrt{\frac{15}{32}}$
$= 5\sqrt{\frac{3}{10} \cdot \frac{10}{10}} + 2\sqrt{\frac{5}{6} \cdot \frac{6}{6}} - 6\sqrt{\frac{15}{32} \cdot \frac{2}{2}}$
$= 5\sqrt{\frac{30}{100}} + 2\sqrt{\frac{30}{36}} - 6\sqrt{\frac{30}{64}}$
$= \frac{5}{10}\sqrt{30} + \frac{2}{6}\sqrt{30} - \frac{6}{8}\sqrt{30}$
$= \frac{12}{12} \cdot \frac{1}{2}\sqrt{30} + \frac{4}{4} \cdot \frac{2}{6}\sqrt{30} - \frac{3}{3} \cdot \frac{6}{8}\sqrt{30}$
$= \frac{12}{24}\sqrt{30} + \frac{8}{24}\sqrt{30} - \frac{18}{24}\sqrt{30}$
$= \frac{2}{24}\sqrt{30} = \frac{\sqrt{30}}{12}$

54. $2\sqrt{\frac{2a}{b}} - 4\sqrt{\frac{b}{2a^3}} + 5\sqrt{\frac{1}{8}a^3b}$
$= 2\sqrt{\frac{2a}{b} \cdot \frac{b}{b}} - 4\sqrt{\frac{b}{2a^3} \cdot \frac{2a}{2a}} + 5\sqrt{\frac{a^3b}{8} \cdot \frac{8}{8}}$
$= 2\sqrt{\frac{2ab}{b^2}} - 4\sqrt{\frac{2ab}{4a^4}} + 5\sqrt{\frac{8a^3b}{64}}$
$= \frac{2}{b}\sqrt{2ab} - \frac{4}{2a^2}\sqrt{2ab} + \frac{5}{8}\sqrt{4 \cdot 2 \cdot a^2 \cdot ab}$
$= \frac{2}{b}\sqrt{2ab} - \frac{2}{a^2}\sqrt{2ab} + \frac{10a}{8}\sqrt{2ab}$
$= \left(\frac{2}{b} - \frac{2}{a^2} + \frac{5}{4}a\right)\sqrt{2ab}$

55. For $a = 1, b = 3, c = 2, d = 4$
a. $\sqrt{a^2 + c^2} = \sqrt{1^2 + 2^2} = \sqrt{1 + 4} = \sqrt{5}$
$\sqrt{a^2} + \sqrt{c^2} = \sqrt{1^2} + \sqrt{2^2} = 1 + 2 = 3$
b. $\sqrt{b^2 + c^2} = \sqrt{3^2 + 2^2} = \sqrt{9 + 4} = \sqrt{13}$
$\sqrt{b^2} + \sqrt{c^2} = \sqrt{3^2} + \sqrt{2^2} = 3 + 2 = 5$
c. $\sqrt{a^2 + d^2} = \sqrt{1^2 + 4^2} = \sqrt{1 + 16} = \sqrt{17}$
$\sqrt{a^2} + \sqrt{d^2} = \sqrt{1^2} + \sqrt{4^2} = 1 + 4 = 5$
d. $\sqrt{b^2 + d^2} = \sqrt{3^2 + 4^2} = \sqrt{9 + 16} = \sqrt{25} = 5$
$\sqrt{b^2} + \sqrt{d^2} = \sqrt{3^2} + \sqrt{4^2} = 3 + 4 = 7$
e. $\sqrt{a^2 + b^2} = \sqrt{1^2 + 3^2} = \sqrt{1 + 9} = \sqrt{10}$
$\sqrt{a^2} + \sqrt{b^2} = \sqrt{1^2} + \sqrt{3^2} = 1 + 3 = 4$
f. $\sqrt{c^2 + d^2} = \sqrt{2^2 + 4^2} = \sqrt{4 + 16} = \sqrt{20} = \sqrt{4 \cdot 5}$
$= 2\sqrt{5}; \sqrt{c^2} + \sqrt{d^2} = \sqrt{2^2} + \sqrt{4^2} = 2 + 4 = 6$

56. $\frac{5}{1 - \sqrt{2}} = \frac{5}{1 - \sqrt{2}} \cdot \frac{1 + \sqrt{2}}{1 + \sqrt{2}}$
$= \frac{5(1 + \sqrt{2})}{1 - 2} = -\frac{5(1 + \sqrt{2})}{1}$
$= -5 - 5\sqrt{2}$

57. $\frac{8 + \sqrt{3}}{3 - \sqrt{2}} = \frac{8 + \sqrt{3}}{3 - \sqrt{2}} \cdot \frac{3 + \sqrt{2}}{3 + \sqrt{2}} = \frac{(8 + \sqrt{3})(3 + \sqrt{2})}{9 - 2}$
$= \frac{(8 + \sqrt{3})(3 + \sqrt{2})}{7} = \frac{24 + 8\sqrt{2} + 3\sqrt{3} + \sqrt{6}}{7}$

58. $\sqrt{25y^2} = 5|y|$ 59. $\sqrt{(-6)^2} = 6$

60. $\sqrt{(x + 2)^2} = |x + 2|$

61. $\sqrt{y^2 + 10y + 25} = \sqrt{(y + 5)^2}$
$= |y + 5|$

62. $\sqrt{5}\sqrt{15} = \sqrt{75} = \sqrt{25 \cdot 3} = 5\sqrt{3}$

63. $\sqrt{6}\sqrt{8} = \sqrt{48} = \sqrt{16 \cdot 3} = 4\sqrt{3}$

64. $\sqrt{11}\sqrt{11} = 11$ 65. $\sqrt{a + c}\sqrt{a - c} = \sqrt{a^2 - c^2}$

66. $\sqrt{20} = \sqrt{4 \cdot 5} = 2\sqrt{5}$ 67. $\sqrt{16x^2y} = 4x\sqrt{y}$

68. $\sqrt{x^3 - 4x^2 + 4x} = \sqrt{x(x^2 - 4x + 4)}$
$= \sqrt{x(x - 2)^2}$
$= (x - 2)\sqrt{x}$

69.
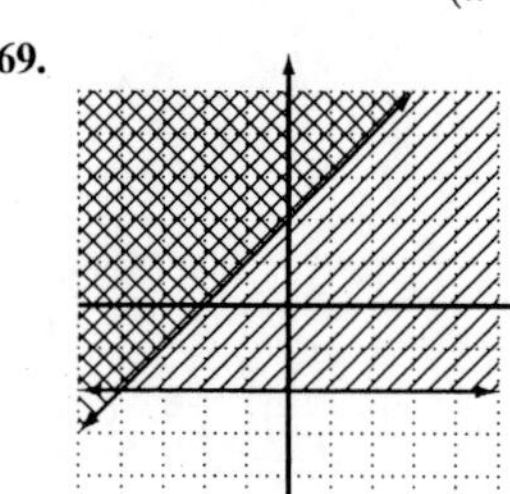

70.
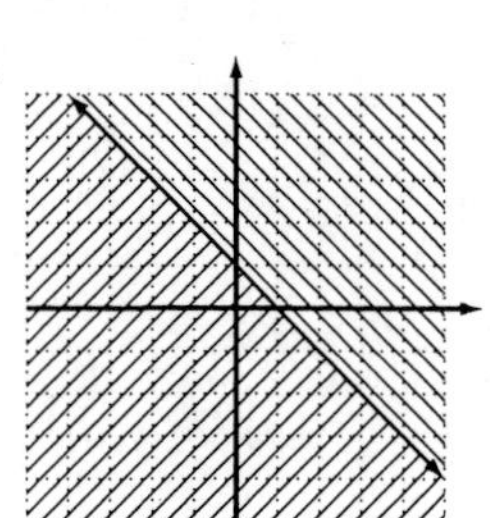

71.
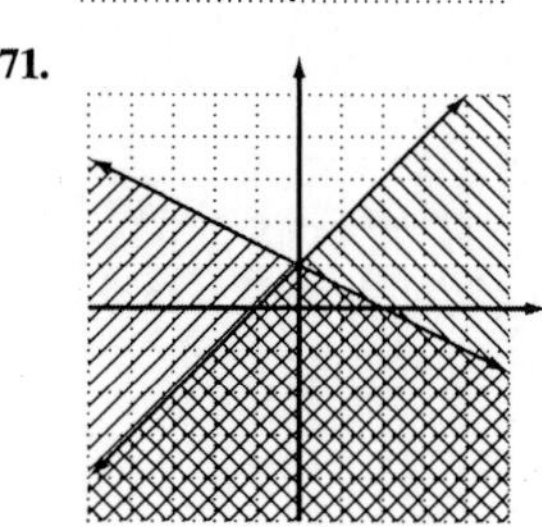

PROBLEMS

p. 508

1. $3^2 + 5^2 + 1^2$
$9 + 25 + 1 = 35$

2. $4^2 + 5^2 + 3^2$
$16 + 25 + 9 = 50$

3. For any code 6 injury, the ISS is 75.

4. $1^2 + 2^2 + 5^2$
$1 + 4 + 25 = 30$

5. $5^2 + 3^2 + 2^2$
$25 + 9 + 4 = 38$

6. $4^2 + 5^2 + 3^2$
$16 + 25 + 9 = 50$

7. $3^2 + 5^2 + 3^2$
$9 + 25 + 9 = 43$

8. $5^2 + 4^2 + 4^2$
$25 + 16 + 16 = 57$

9. $5^2 + 4^2 + 3^2$
$25 + 16 + 9 = 50$

10. $5^2 + 2^2 + 1^2$
$25 + 4 + 1 = 30$

11. From highest score to lowest: 8, 6, 9, 7, 5, 10 or 8, 9, 6, 7, 5, 10

12. (5) $P = 1 - \left(\frac{38}{80}\right)^2$
$\approx 77\%$
(6) $P = 1 - \left(\frac{50}{80}\right)^2$
$\approx 61\%$

(7) $P = 1 - \left(\frac{43}{80}\right)^2$

$\approx 71\%$

(8) $P = 1 - \left(\frac{57}{80}\right)^2$

$\approx 49\%$

(9) $P = 1 - \left(\frac{50}{80}\right)^2$

$\approx 61\%$

(10) $P = 1 - \left(\frac{30}{80}\right)^2$

$\approx 86\%$

LESSON 11-7 TRY THIS p. 510

a. $c^2 = 4^2 + 7^2$
$= 16 + 49$
$c^2 = 65$
$c = \sqrt{65} \approx 8.062$

b. $a^2 + 11^2 = 14^2$
$a^2 = 14^2 - 11^2$
$= 196 - 121$
$= 75$
$a = \sqrt{75} \approx 8.660$

c. $b^2 + 1^2 = (\sqrt{11})^2$
$b^2 = 11 - 1$
$= 10$
$b = \sqrt{10} \approx 3.162$

d. $a^2 + 15^2 = 20^2$
$a^2 = 20^2 - 15^2$
$= 400 - 225$
$a = \sqrt{175} = 5\sqrt{7}$
≈ 13.229

LESSON 11-7 EXERCISES pp. 510–512

1. $c^2 = 8^2 + 15^2$
$= 64 + 225$
$= 289$
$c = \sqrt{289} = 17$

2. $c^2 = 3^2 + 5^2$
$= 9 + 25$
$= 34$
$c = \sqrt{34}$ or 5.831

3. $c^2 = 4^2 + 4^2$
$= 16 + 16$
$= 32$
$c = \sqrt{32} = 4\sqrt{2}$ or 5.657

4. $c^2 = 7^2 + 7^2$
$= 49 + 49$
$= 98$
$c = \sqrt{98} = 7\sqrt{2}$ or 9.899

5. $b^2 + 5^2 = 13^2$
$b^2 + 25 = 169$
$b^2 = 144$
$b = \sqrt{144} = 12$

6. $a^2 + 12^2 = 13^2$
$a^2 + 144 = 169$
$a^2 = 25$
$a = \sqrt{25} = 5$

7. $b^2 + (4\sqrt{3})^2 = 8^2$
$b^2 + 16(3) = 64$
$b^2 + 48 = 64$
$b^2 = 16$
$b = \sqrt{16} = 4$

8. $b^2 + (\sqrt{5})^2 = 6^2$
$b^2 + 5 = 36$
$b^2 = 31$
$b = \sqrt{31}$ or 5.568

9. $c^2 = 10^2 + 24^2$
$= 100 + 576$
$= 676$
$c = \sqrt{676} = 26$

10. $c^2 = 5^2 + 12^2$
$= 25 + 144$
$= 169$
$c = \sqrt{169} = 13$

11. $9^2 + b^2 = 15^2$
$81 + b^2 = 225$
$b^2 = 144$
$b = \sqrt{144} = 12$

12. $18^2 + b^2 = 30^2$
$324 + b^2 = 900$
$b^2 = 576$
$b = \sqrt{576} = 24$

13. $a^2 + 1^2 = (\sqrt{5})^2$
$a^2 + 1 = 5$
$a^2 = 4$
$a = \sqrt{4} = 2$

14. $a^2 + 1^2 = (\sqrt{2})^2$
$a^2 + 1 = 2$
$a^2 = 1$
$a = \sqrt{1} = 1$

15. $1^2 + b^2 = (\sqrt{3})^2$
$1 + b^2 = 3$
$b^2 = 2$
$b = \sqrt{2}$ or 1.414

16. $(\sqrt{3})^2 + (\sqrt{5})^2 = c^2$
$3 + 5 = c^2$
$8 = c^2$
$c = \sqrt{8} = 2\sqrt{2}$ or 2.828

17. $a^2 + (5\sqrt{3})^2 = 10^2$
$a^2 + 25(3) = 100$
$a^2 + 75 = 100$
$a^2 = 25$
$a = \sqrt{25} = 5$

18. $(3\sqrt{3})^2 + b^2 = (5\sqrt{3})^2$
$9(3) + b^2 = 25(3)$
$27 + b^2 = 75$
$b^2 = 48$
$b = \sqrt{48} = 4\sqrt{3}$ or 6.928

19. In the third step of the solution, the student took the square root of each monomial before simplifying it.
$\sqrt{5^2 + 8^2} = \sqrt{25 + 64} = \sqrt{89}$, not $5 + 8 = 13$.

20. $a^2 = h^2 + \left(\frac{a}{2}\right)^2$
$= h^2 + \frac{a^2}{4}$
$h^2 = a^2 - \frac{a^2}{4}$
$= \frac{4a^2}{4} - \frac{a^2}{4} = \frac{3a^2}{4}$
$h = \sqrt{\frac{3a^2}{4}} = \frac{a}{2}\sqrt{3}$

21. $A = \frac{1}{2}ah$; from problem 19, $h = \frac{a}{2}\sqrt{3}$.
$A = \frac{1}{2}a\left(\frac{a}{2}\sqrt{3}\right) = \frac{a^2}{4}\sqrt{3}$

22. $A = \frac{a^2}{4}\sqrt{3}$

$h = \frac{a}{2}\sqrt{3}$

$\frac{2h}{\sqrt{3}} = a$ Solving for a

$A = \frac{1}{4}\left(\frac{2h}{\sqrt{3}}\right)^2\sqrt{3}$ Substituting

$= \frac{1}{4}\left(\frac{4h^2}{3}\right)\sqrt{3}$

$A = \frac{h^2}{3}\sqrt{3}$

23. A. The diagonal of a square with 6 cm sides is $\sqrt{36 + 36} = \sqrt{72}$ cm long.
B. The diagonal of a rectangle with length 7 cm and width 5 cm is $\sqrt{49 + 25} = \sqrt{74}$ cm long.
C. The hypotenuse of a right triangle with legs 4 cm and 9 cm long is $\sqrt{16 + 81} = \sqrt{97}$ cm long.
D. The leg of a right triangle with the other leg 10 cm and the hypotenuse 15 cm long is $\sqrt{225 - 100} = \sqrt{125}$ cm long.
Answer D is the longest, so the answer is D.

24. $AC^2 = \left(\frac{\sqrt{2}}{3}\right)^2 + \left(\frac{\sqrt{2}}{3}\right)^2$

$= \frac{2}{9} + \frac{2}{9}$

$= \frac{4}{9}$

$AC = \sqrt{\frac{4}{9}} = \frac{2}{3}$

25. Let a be the length of the shortest side of the triangle. Then the other two sides are of length $a + 1$ and $a + 2$, and

$(a + 2)^2 = (a + 1)^2 + a^2$
$a^2 + 4a + 4 = a^2 + 2a + 1 + a^2$
$a^2 - 2a - 3 = 0$
$(a + 1)(a - 3) = 0$
$a = -1$ or $a = 3$
Since length cannot be negative, $a = 3, a + 1 = 4, a + 2 = 5$

26. Answers may vary, but the sum of the squares of the lengths of the legs should equal 18. Samples: $\sqrt{12}$ and $\sqrt{6}$, 2 and $\sqrt{14}$.

27. First find the length of the diagonal of any side, for example the bottom.
$c^2 = 10^2 + 10^2$
$c^2 = 200$, so $c = \sqrt{200} = 10\sqrt{2}$
The diagonal of the cube is the hypotenuse of a right triangle formed by the diagonal of the bottom and a side.
$d^2 = (10\sqrt{2})^2 + 10^2$
$= 200 + 100 = 300$
So $d = \sqrt{300} = 10\sqrt{3}$

28. First find the entire bottom length.
$l^2 + 5^2 = 13^2$
$l^2 = 13^2 - 5^2 = 169 - 25 = 144$
$l = \sqrt{144} = 12$
Then find the length of the unlabeled section of the bottom.
$5^2 + u^2 = 7^2$
$u^2 = 7^2 - 5^2 = 49 - 25 = 24$, so $u = \sqrt{24}$
Then $x = 12 - \sqrt{24} \approx 12 - 4.90 \approx 7.1$

29. Let d = the length of the entire upper hypotenuse.
$d^2 = \sqrt{3}^2 + 1^2$
$= 3 + 1$
$= 4$
$d = 2$
Let y = the length of the section of d above the right angle.
$(\sqrt{3})^2 = x^2 + (d - y)^2$ and $1^2 = x^2 + y^2$
$3 = x^2 + (2 - y)^2$ $\quad 1 - x^2 = y^2$
$3 = x^2 + 4 - 4y + y^2$ $\quad \sqrt{1 - x^2} = y$
$0 = x^2 - 4y + y^2 + 1$
Substituting: $0 = x^2 - 4\sqrt{1 - x^2} + 1 - x^2 + 1$
$0 = 2 - 4\sqrt{1 - x^2}$
$(-2)^2 = (-4\sqrt{1 - x^2})^2$
$4 = 16(1 - x^2)$
$\frac{1}{4} = 1 - x^2$
$x^2 = \frac{3}{4}$
$x = \frac{\sqrt{3}}{2} \approx 0.87$

30. Let a = the upper left hypotenuse and b = the upper right.
We have a system of equations.
$x^2 + 4^2 = a^2$
$x^2 + 9^2 = b^2$
$a^2 + b^2 = (4 + 9)^2$
Substituting in the last equation
$(x^2 + 4^2) + (x^2 + 9^2) = (4 + 9)^2$
$x^2 + 16 + x^2 + 81 = 169$
$2x^2 = 72$
$x^2 = 36$
$x = 6$

31. **a-d.** Answers may vary. Samples given.

a. $\frac{1}{2}$

b. -0.237

c. $\sqrt{2.4}$

d. $\sqrt{10.79}$

e. Yes. The average of two numbers will always be another real number between the two given numbers.

32. -13 33. $|x + 3|$ 34. $5\sqrt{y}$

35. $\sqrt{16 \cdot 2a^2} = 4|a|\sqrt{2}$ 36. $x^3\sqrt{x}$ 37. a^{10}

38. $(x + 5)^2$ 39. $|x - 3|\sqrt{x - 3}$

40. $\sqrt{4 \cdot 3a^4 \cdot a} = 2a^2\sqrt{3a}$ 41. $\sqrt{36 \cdot 6x^4} = 6x^2\sqrt{6}$

42. $\sqrt{4 \cdot 3x^2 \cdot xy} = 2x\sqrt{3xy}$ 43. $\sqrt{9 \cdot 2a^2 \cdot ab^4} = 3ab^2\sqrt{2a}$

44. $\frac{3}{2x} + \frac{1}{2} = \frac{10}{4x}$
$4x\left(\frac{3}{2x} + \frac{1}{2}\right) = \frac{10}{4x}(4x)$
$6 + 2x = 10$
$2x = 4$
$x = 2$

45. $\frac{x}{4} - \frac{x}{12} = \frac{1}{2}$
$12\left(\frac{x}{4} - \frac{x}{12}\right) = \frac{1}{2}(12)$
$3x - x = 6$
$2x = 6$
$x = 3$

46. $x + \frac{12}{x} = 7$
$x^2 + 12 = 7x$
$x^2 - 7x + 12 = 0$
$(x - 3)(x - 4) = 0$
$x - 3 = 0$ or $x - 4 = 0$
$x = 3$ or $x = 4$

47. $x(x+1) = 210$
$x^2 + x - 210 = 0$
$(x+15)(x-14) = 0$
$x + 15 = 0$ or $x - 14 = 0$
$x = -15$ or $x = 14$
The numbers are positive, so $x = 14$ and $x + 1 = 15$.

48. $x + y = 7$
$x - y = -17$
$2x = -10$
$x = -5$
$-5 + y = 7$
$y = 12$

THE DISTANCE FORMULA p. 513

1. $d = \sqrt{(8-3)^2 + (-5-7)^2}$
$= \sqrt{5^2 + (-12)^2}$
$= \sqrt{25 + 144}$
$= \sqrt{169}$
$= 13$

2. $d = \sqrt{(-4-0)^2 + (6-4)^2}$
$= \sqrt{(-4)^2 + 2^2}$
$= \sqrt{16 + 4}$
$= \sqrt{20}$
$= 2\sqrt{5}$

3. $d = \sqrt{(-3-[-6])^2 + (-5-[-8])^2}$
$= \sqrt{3^2 + 3^2}$
$= \sqrt{9 + 9}$
$= \sqrt{18}$
$= 3\sqrt{2}$

4. $d = \sqrt{(5-[-2])^2 + (6-6)^2}$
$= \sqrt{7^2 + 0^2}$
$= \sqrt{49}$
$= 7$

5. $d = \sqrt{(4-[-4])^2 + (4-[-4])^2}$
$= \sqrt{8^2 + 8^2}$
$= \sqrt{64 + 64}$
$= \sqrt{128}$
$= 8\sqrt{2}$

6. $d = \sqrt{(7-[-6])^2 + (0-4)^2}$
$= \sqrt{13^2 + (-4)^2}$
$= \sqrt{169 + 16}$
$= \sqrt{185}$

LESSON 11-8 TRY THIS p. 514

a. $15^2 + 10^2 = w^2$
$225 + 100 = w^2$
$325 = w^2$
$18.0 \approx w$ About 18.0 feet

b. $7^2 + l^2 = 12^2$
$49 + l^2 = 144$
$l^2 = 95$
$l \approx 9.7$ About 9.7 feet

LESSON 11-8 EXERCISES pp. 515–518

1. $h^2 + 5^2 = 10^2$
$h^2 + 25 = 100$
$h^2 = 75$
$h = \sqrt{75} \approx 8.7$ m

2. $9^2 + 13^2 = l^2$
$81 + 169 = l^2$
$250 = l^2$
$l = \sqrt{250} \approx 15.8$ m

3. $w^2 = 15^2 + 75^2$
$= 225 + 5625$
$= 5850$
$w = \sqrt{5850} \approx 76.5$ ft

4. $d^2 = 90^2 + 90^2$
$= 8100 + 8100$
$= 16{,}200$
$d = \sqrt{16{,}200} \approx 127.3$ ft

5. $d^2 = 20^2 + 65^2$
$= 400 + 4225$
$= 4625$
$d = \sqrt{4625} \approx 68.0$ m

6. $d^2 = 25^2 + 35^2$
$= 625 + 1225$
$= 1850$
$d = \sqrt{1850} \approx 43.0$ m

7. $d^2 = 20^2 + 75^2$
$= 400 + 5625$
$= 6025$
$d = \sqrt{6025} \approx 77.6$ mi

8. $w^2 = 15^2 + 60^2$
$= 225 + 3600$
$= 3825$
$w = \sqrt{3825} \approx 61.8$ ft

9. $d^2 + (4.1)^2 = (15.1)^2$
$d^2 + 16.81 = 228.01$
$d^2 = 211.2$
$d = \sqrt{211.2} \approx 14.5$ km

10. $d^2 = (90 + 40)^2 + 90^2$
$= 130^2 + 90^2$
$= 16{,}900 + 8100$
$= 25{,}000$
$d = \sqrt{25{,}000} \approx 158.1$ ft

11. The height of the tent is one leg of a right triangle with hypotenuse 6 ft and other leg 3.5 ft.
$a^2 + 3.5^2 = 6^2$
$a^2 + 12.25 = 36$
$a^2 = 23.75$
$a = \sqrt{23.75} \approx 4.9$
The height of the tent is about 4.9 ft.

12. $d^2 + 200^2 = 800^2$
$d^2 + 40{,}000 = 640{,}000$
$d^2 = 600{,}000$
$d = \sqrt{600{,}000} \approx 774.6$ ft

13. Drop altitude from apex of roof perpendicular to and bisecting base.

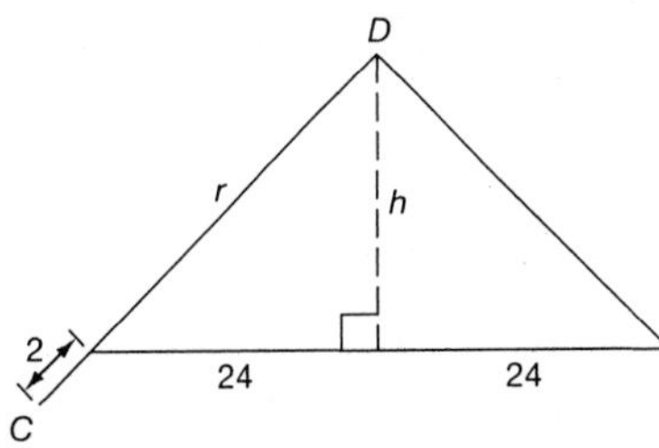

Since roof raises 4 ft for each 12-ft horizontal change, $h = 8$ ft because of 24-ft horizontal change.
$r^2 = h^2 + 24^2$
$= 8^2 + 24^2$
$= 64 + 576$
$= 640$
$r = \sqrt{640} \approx 25.3$ ft
$CD = r + 2 \approx 25.3 + 2 = 27.3$ ft

14. Let a = length of side.
$a^2 + a^2 = (8\sqrt{2})^2$
$2a^2 = 64 \cdot 2$
$a^2 = 64$
$a = \sqrt{64}$
$a = 8$ ft

15. $l^2 + w^2 = d^2$
$12^2 + 7^2 = d^2$
$144 + 49 = d^2$
$193 = d^2$
$\sqrt{193} = d$
$d \approx 13.9$ in.

16. Let l = length of long leg.
$l^2 + \left(\frac{1}{5}\right)^2 = 60^2$
$l^2 + \frac{1}{25}l^2 = 3600$
$\frac{26}{25}l^2 = 3600$
$26l^2 = 90{,}000$
$l^2 \approx 3461.54$
$l \approx 58.8$ About 58.8 ft

17. 24-ft horizontal change means $h = 9$ ft.

$$\begin{aligned} r^2 &= 9^2 + 24^2 \\ &= 81 + 576 \\ &= 657 \\ r &= \sqrt{657} \approx 25.6 \text{ ft} \\ CD &= r + 2 \approx 25.6 + 2 = 27.6 \text{ ft} \end{aligned}$$

18. Answers may vary, but students should recognize that the square of the hypotenuse equals the sum of the squares of the legs, regardless of what variables are used to name them.

19.
$$\begin{aligned} 45^2 + 60^2 &= d^2 \\ 2025 + 3600 &= d^2 \\ 5625 &= d^2 \\ 75 &= d \end{aligned}$$

$$\text{time (old road)} = \frac{75}{30} = 2.5 \text{ h}$$

$$\text{time (major highway)} = \frac{60 + 45}{50} = \frac{105}{50} = 2.1 \text{ h}$$

The time is shorter on the major highway.

20. After $\frac{1}{2}$ h, lengths of legs of hypotenuse are 25 and 30.

$$\begin{aligned} 25^2 + 30^2 &= d^2 \\ 625 + 900 &= d^2 \\ 1525 &= d^2 \\ \sqrt{1525} &= d \end{aligned}$$

$$d \approx 39.05 \text{ mi after } \frac{1}{2} \text{ h}$$

Distance traveled by faster car $= \frac{6}{5}$ distance of slower

$$\begin{aligned} s^2 + \left(\frac{6}{5}s\right)^2 &= 100^2 \\ s^2 + \frac{36}{25}s^2 &= 10{,}000 \\ \frac{61}{25}s^2 &= 10{,}000 \\ s &\approx 64 \end{aligned}$$

Time $= \frac{d}{r} = \frac{64}{50} = 1.28$ After about 1.28 hours

21. $\sqrt{\frac{3}{5}} = \frac{\sqrt{3}}{\sqrt{5}} \cdot \frac{\sqrt{5}}{\sqrt{5}} = \frac{\sqrt{15}}{5}$

22. $\frac{\sqrt{20}}{\sqrt{5y}} \cdot \frac{\sqrt{5y}}{\sqrt{5y}} = \frac{\sqrt{100y}}{5y} = \frac{10\sqrt{y}}{5y} = \frac{2\sqrt{y}}{y}$

23. $\frac{\sqrt{y}}{\sqrt{xy}} \cdot \frac{\sqrt{xy}}{\sqrt{xy}} = \frac{\sqrt{xy^2}}{xy} = \frac{y\sqrt{x}}{xy} = \frac{\sqrt{x}}{x}$

24. $\sqrt{15}\sqrt{10} = \sqrt{150} = \sqrt{25 \cdot 6} = 5\sqrt{6}$

25. $\sqrt{xy}\sqrt{xyz} = \sqrt{x^2y^2z} = xy\sqrt{z}$

26. $\sqrt{2} + 4\sqrt{2} = 5\sqrt{2}$

27. $4\sqrt{12} - 2\sqrt{3} = 4\sqrt{4 \cdot 3} - 2\sqrt{3} = 8\sqrt{3} - 2\sqrt{3} = 6\sqrt{3}$

28. $6\sqrt{12} - 4\sqrt{3} = 6\sqrt{4 \cdot 3} - 4\sqrt{3} = 12\sqrt{3} - 4\sqrt{3} = 8\sqrt{3}$

29. $\sqrt{45} + \sqrt{20} = \sqrt{9 \cdot 5} + \sqrt{4 \cdot 5} = 3\sqrt{5} + 2\sqrt{5} = 5\sqrt{5}$

30. $2\sqrt{8} + 6\sqrt{18} = 2\sqrt{4 \cdot 2} + 6\sqrt{9 \cdot 2}$
$= 4\sqrt{2} + 18\sqrt{2} = 22\sqrt{2}$

31. $\sqrt{24} - \sqrt{6} = \sqrt{4 \cdot 6} - \sqrt{6} = 2\sqrt{6} - \sqrt{6} = \sqrt{6}$

32. $\sqrt{18} - 5\sqrt{8} + \sqrt{72} = \sqrt{9 \cdot 2} - 5\sqrt{4 \cdot 2} + \sqrt{36 \cdot 2}$
$= 3\sqrt{2} - 10\sqrt{2} + 6\sqrt{2}$
$= -\sqrt{2}$

LESSON 11-9 TRY THIS pp. 520–521

a.
$$\begin{aligned} \sqrt{3x} - 5 &= 3 \\ \sqrt{3x} &= 8 \\ (\sqrt{3x})^2 &= 8^2 \\ 3x &= 64 \\ x &= \frac{64}{3} \end{aligned}$$

Check:

$\sqrt{3x} - 5$	$= 3$
$\sqrt{3\left(\frac{64}{3}\right)} - 5$	3
$\sqrt{64} - 5$	
$8 - 5$	
3	

b.
$$\begin{aligned} \sqrt{3x + 1} &= \sqrt{2x + 3} \\ (\sqrt{3x + 1})^2 &= (\sqrt{2x + 3})^2 \\ 3x + 1 &= 2x + 3 \\ x &= 2 \quad \text{It checks.} \end{aligned}$$

c.
$$\begin{aligned} \sqrt{x - 2} - 5 &= 3 \\ \sqrt{x - 2} &= 8 \\ (\sqrt{x - 2})^2 &= 8^2 \\ x - 2 &= 64 \\ x &= 66 \quad \text{It checks.} \end{aligned}$$

d. $V = 3.5\sqrt{h} = 3.5\sqrt{8000} \approx 3.5(89.4) \approx 313$ km

e. $V = 3.5\sqrt{h} = 3.5\sqrt{20} \approx 3.5(4.5) \approx 16$ km

f. $V = 3.5\sqrt{h}, 3.5\sqrt{h} = 61$

$$\begin{aligned} \sqrt{h} &= \frac{61}{3.5} \\ (\sqrt{h})^2 &= \left(\frac{61}{3.5}\right)^2 \\ h &= 303.76 \text{ m} \quad \text{or} \quad \approx 300 \text{ m} \end{aligned}$$

LESSON 11-9 EXERCISES pp. 521–522

1.
$$\begin{aligned} \sqrt{x} &= 5 \\ (\sqrt{x})^2 &= 5^2 \\ x &= 25 \end{aligned}$$

2.
$$\begin{aligned} \sqrt{x} &= 7 \\ (\sqrt{x})^2 &= 7^2 \\ x &= 49 \end{aligned}$$

3.
$$\begin{aligned} \sqrt{x} &= 6.2 \\ (\sqrt{x})^2 &= (6.2)^2 \\ x &= 38.44 \end{aligned}$$

4.
$$\begin{aligned} \sqrt{x} &= 4.3 \\ (\sqrt{x})^2 &= (4.3)^2 \\ x &= 18.49 \end{aligned}$$

5.
$$\begin{aligned} \sqrt{x + 3} &= 20 \\ (\sqrt{x + 3})^2 &= 20^2 \\ x + 3 &= 400 \\ x &= 397 \end{aligned}$$

6.
$$\begin{aligned} \sqrt{x + 4} &= 11 \\ (\sqrt{x + 4})^2 &= 11^2 \\ x + 4 &= 121 \\ x &= 117 \end{aligned}$$

7.
$$\begin{aligned} \sqrt{2x + 4} &= 25 \\ (\sqrt{2x + 4})^2 &= 25^2 \\ 2x + 4 &= 625 \\ 2x &= 621 \\ x &= 310.5 \end{aligned}$$

8.
$$\begin{aligned} \sqrt{2x + 1} &= 13 \\ (\sqrt{2x + 1})^2 &= 13^2 \\ 2x + 1 &= 169 \\ 2x &= 168 \\ x &= 84 \end{aligned}$$

9.
$$\begin{aligned} 3 + \sqrt{x - 1} &= 5 \\ \sqrt{x - 1} &= 2 \\ (\sqrt{x - 1})^2 &= 2^2 \\ x - 1 &= 4 \\ x &= 5 \end{aligned}$$

10.
$$\begin{aligned} 4 + \sqrt{y - 3} &= 11 \\ \sqrt{y - 3} &= 7 \\ (\sqrt{y - 3})^2 &= 7^2 \\ y - 3 &= 49 \\ y &= 52 \end{aligned}$$

11.
$$\begin{aligned} 6 - 2\sqrt{3n} &= 0 \\ 6 &= 2\sqrt{3n} \\ 6^2 &= (2\sqrt{3n})^2 \\ 36 &= 4(3n) \\ 36 &= 12n \\ 3 &= n \end{aligned}$$

12.
$$\begin{aligned} 8 - 4\sqrt{5n} &= 0 \\ 8 &= 4\sqrt{5n} \\ 8^2 &= (4\sqrt{5n})^2 \\ 64 &= 16(5n) \\ 64 &= 80n \\ n &= \frac{64}{80} = \frac{4}{5} \end{aligned}$$

13.
$$\begin{aligned} \sqrt{5x - 7} &= \sqrt{x + 10} \\ (\sqrt{5x - 7})^2 &= (\sqrt{x + 10})^2 \\ 5x - 7 &= x + 10 \\ 4x &= 17 \\ x &= \frac{17}{4} \end{aligned}$$

14.
$$\begin{aligned} \sqrt{4x - 5} &= \sqrt{x + 9} \\ (\sqrt{4x - 5})^2 &= (\sqrt{x + 9})^2 \\ 4x - 5 &= x + 9 \\ 3x &= 14 \\ x &= \frac{14}{3} \end{aligned}$$

15. $\sqrt{x} = -7$

$\sqrt{x}$ is positive; no value

16. $-\sqrt{x} = 5$

$\sqrt{x} = -5$

$\sqrt{x}$ is positive; no value

17.
$$\begin{aligned} \sqrt{2y + 6} &= \sqrt{2y - 5} \\ (\sqrt{2y + 6})^2 &= (\sqrt{2y - 5})^2 \\ 2y + 6 &= 2y - 5 \\ 6 &= -5 \end{aligned}$$

No value

18.
$$\begin{aligned} 2\sqrt{x - 2} &= \sqrt{7 - x} \\ (2\sqrt{x - 2})^2 &= (\sqrt{7 - x})^2 \\ 4(x - 2) &= 7 - x \\ 4x - 8 &= 7 - x \\ 5x &= 15 \\ x &= 3 \end{aligned}$$

19. $V = 3.5\sqrt{9800}$
$\approx 3.5(98.99)$
≈ 346 km

20. $V = 3.5\sqrt{24}$
$\approx 3.5(4.9)$
≈ 17 km

21. $350 = 3.5\sqrt{h}$
$100 = \sqrt{h}$
$(100)^2 = (\sqrt{h})^2$
$10{,}000 \text{ m} = h$

22. $100 = 3.5\sqrt{h}$
$28.57 \approx \sqrt{h}$
$(28.57)^2 \approx (\sqrt{h})^2$
$816 \text{ m} \approx h$

23. $50 = 2\sqrt{5L}$
$25 = \sqrt{5L}$
$(25)^2 = (\sqrt{5L})^2$
$625 = 5L$
$125 \text{ ft} = L$

$70 = 2\sqrt{5L}$
$35 = \sqrt{5L}$
$(35)^2 = (\sqrt{5L})^2$
$1225 = 5L$
$245 \text{ ft} = L$

24. $60 = 2\sqrt{5L}$
$30 = \sqrt{5L}$
$(30)^2 = (\sqrt{5L})^2$
$900 = 5L$
$180 \text{ ft} = L$

$100 = 2\sqrt{5L}$
$50 = \sqrt{5L}$
$(50)^2 = (\sqrt{5L})^2$
$2500 = 5L$
$500 \text{ ft} = L$

25. $\sqrt{5x^2 + 5} = 5$
$(\sqrt{5x^2 + 5})^2 = 5^2$
$5x^2 + 5 = 25$
$5x^2 = 20$
$x^2 = 4$
$x = \pm\sqrt{4} = 2$ or -2. They both check.

26. $\sqrt{x} = -x$
$(\sqrt{x})^2 = (-x)^2$
$x = x^2$
$0 = x^2 - x$
$0 = x(x - 1)$
$x = 0$ or $x = 1$
$x = 1$ doesn't check, but $x = 0$ does. The solution is $x = 0$.

27. $2\sqrt{x} = 14$
$\sqrt{x} = \frac{14}{2}$
$(\sqrt{x})^2 = 7^2$
$x = 49$; It checks.

28. $-3\sqrt{x} = -33$
$3\sqrt{x} = 33$
$\sqrt{x} = \frac{33}{3}$
$(\sqrt{x})^2 = 11^2$
$x = 121$; It checks.

29. $T = 2\pi\sqrt{\frac{L}{32}}$
$1.6 = 2(3.14)\sqrt{\frac{L}{32}}$
$\frac{1.6}{6.28} = \sqrt{\frac{L}{32}}$
$\left(\frac{1.6}{6.28}\right)^2 = \frac{L}{32}$
$L = 32\left(\frac{1.6}{6.28}\right)^2 = \frac{32 \cdot 2.56}{39.4384} = \frac{81.92}{39.4384} \approx 2.08 \text{ ft}$

30. (An alternate method to that used in 29)
Solve $T = 2\pi\sqrt{\frac{L}{32}}$ for L.
$\frac{T}{2\pi} = \sqrt{\frac{L}{32}}$
$\left(\frac{T}{2\pi}\right)^2 = \frac{L}{32}$
$L = 32\left(\frac{T^2}{4\pi^2}\right) = \frac{8T^2}{\pi^2}$
For $T = 3$, $L = \frac{8(3)^2}{(3.14)^2} = \frac{72}{9.8596} \approx 7.30 \text{ ft}$

31. $\sqrt{5x + 4} = 8$
$(\sqrt{5x + 4})^2 = 8^2$
$5x + 4 = 64$
$5x = 64 - 4$
$x = \frac{60}{5} = 12$; It checks.

32. **a.** Given
b. Multiplication Property of Equality
c. Multiplication Property of Equality
d. Transitive Property
e. Definition of a square number

33. $x - 1 = \sqrt{x + 5}$
$(x - 1)^2 = (\sqrt{x + 5})^2$
$x^2 - 2x + 1 = x + 5$
$x^2 - 3x - 4 = 0$
$(x - 4)(x + 1) = 0$
$x = 4$ or $x = -1$
Check:
$4 - 1 = \sqrt{4 + 5}$
$3 = 3$
$-1 - 1 = \sqrt{-1 + 5}$
$-2 \neq 2$ So only 4 checks.

34. $\sqrt{y^2 + 6} + y - 3 = 0$
$\sqrt{y^2 + 6} = 3 - y$
$(\sqrt{y^2 + 6})^2 = (3 - y)^2$
$y^2 + 6 = 9 - 6y + y^2$
$6y = 3$
$y = \frac{3}{6} = \frac{1}{2}$; It checks.

35. $\sqrt{x - 5} + \sqrt{x} = 5$
$\sqrt{x - 5} = 5 - \sqrt{x}$
$(\sqrt{x - 5})^2 = (5 - \sqrt{x})^2$
$x - 5 = 25 - 10\sqrt{x} + x$
$10\sqrt{x} = 30$
$\sqrt{x} = \frac{30}{10}$
$(\sqrt{x})^2 = 3^2$
$x = 9$; It checks.

36. $\sqrt{3x + 1} = 1 + \sqrt{x + 4}$
$(\sqrt{3x + 1})^2 = (1 + \sqrt{x + 4})^2$
$3x + 1 = 1 + 2\sqrt{x + 4} + x + 4$
$2x - 4 = 2\sqrt{x + 4}$
$(x - 2)^2 = (\sqrt{x + 4})^2$
$x^2 - 4x + 4 = x + 4$
$x^2 - 5x = 0$
$x(x - 5) = 0$
$x = 0$ or $x = 5$
0 does not check, so $x = 5$.

37. $4 + \sqrt{10 - x} = 6 + \sqrt{4 - x}$
$\sqrt{10 - x} - \sqrt{4 - x} = 6 - 4$
$(\sqrt{10 - x} - \sqrt{4 - x})^2 = 2^2$
$10 - x - 2\sqrt{(10 - x)(4 - x)} + 4 - x = 4$
$2\sqrt{40 - 14x + x^2} = 2x - 10$
$(\sqrt{x^2 - 14x + 40})^2 = (x - 5)^2$
$x^2 - 14x + 40 = x^2 - 10x + 25$
$4x = 15$
$x = \frac{15}{4}$; It checks.

38. $x = (x - 2)\sqrt{x}$
$x^2 = [(x - 2)\sqrt{x}]^2$
$x^2 = (x - 2)^2(\sqrt{x})^2$
$x^2 = (x^2 - 4x + 4)x$
$x^2 = x^3 - 4x^2 + 4x$
$0 = x^3 - 5x^2 + 4x$
$0 = x(x^2 - 5x + 4)$
$0 = x(x - 4)(x - 1)$
$x = 0, x = 4$, or $x = 1$
$x = 1$ doesn't check; $x = 0, x = 4$ check.

39. $A = \sqrt{1 + \frac{a^2}{b^2}}$
$A^2 = 1 + \frac{a^2}{b^2}$
$A^2 - 1 = \frac{a^2}{b^2}$
$b^2(A^2 - 1) = a^2$
$b^2 = \frac{a^2}{A^2 - 1}$
$b = \pm\sqrt{\frac{a^2}{A^2 - 1}}$

40. $t = \sqrt{\frac{2s}{g}}$
$t^2 = \left(\sqrt{\frac{2s}{g}}\right)^2$
$t^2 = \frac{2s}{g}$
$t^2 g = 2s$
$s = \frac{t^2 g}{2}$

41. $s = \frac{t^2 g}{2}$, $g = 32.2$ and $t = 5$
$s = \frac{(5)^2(32.2)}{2} = 402.5$ feet

42. $s = \frac{t^2 g}{2}$, $g = 32.2$ and $t = 10$
$s = \frac{(10)^2(32.2)}{2} = 1610$ feet

43. $x + 1 \geq 0$
$x \geq -1$

44. $x - 1 \geq 0$
$x \geq 1$

45. $5x + 1 \geq 0$
$5x \geq -1$
$x \geq -\frac{1}{5}$

46. $x^2 + 4 \geq 0$
$x^2 \geq -4$
Any real number

47. $\sqrt{225} = 15$

48. $\sqrt{m^2} = |m|$

49. $\sqrt{x^2 - 2x + 1} = \sqrt{(x - 1)^2} = |x - 1|$

50. $\sqrt{(-9a)^2} = \sqrt{81a^2} = 9|a|$

51. $\sqrt{y^{13}} = \sqrt{y^{12} \cdot y} = y^6\sqrt{y}$

52. $\sqrt{9(y + 7)^4} = 3(y + 7)^2$

53. $\sqrt{144m^5} = 12m^2\sqrt{m}$

54. $y^2 - \frac{8}{15}y + \frac{15}{225} = 0$
$225\left(y^2 - \frac{8}{15}y + \frac{15}{225}\right) = 0 \cdot 225$
$225y^2 - 120y + 15 = 0$
$15y^2 - 8y + 1 = 0$
$(3y - 1)(5y - 1) = 0$
$3y - 1 = 0$ or $5y - 1 = 0$
$3y = 1$ or $5y = 1$
$y = \frac{1}{3}$ or $y = \frac{1}{5}$

55. $x^2 + \frac{1}{12}x - \frac{12}{144} = 0$
$12\left(x^2 + \frac{1}{12}x - \frac{12}{144}\right) = 12 \cdot 0$
$12x^2 + x - 1 = 0$
$(3x + 1)(4x - 1) = 0$
$3x + 1 = 0$ or $4x - 1 = 0$
$3x = -1$ or $4x = 1$
$x = -\frac{1}{3}$ or $x = \frac{1}{4}$

PREPARING FOR STANDARDIZED TESTS — p. 524

1. O + O = E
E ÷ 2 = E or O
II and III
(D)

2. (A) $n, n + 1, n + 2$
$3, 3 + 1, 3 + 2$
$3, 4, 5$
(B) $n + 1, n + 3, n + 5$
$3 + 1, 3 + 3, 3 + 5$
$4, 6, 8$
(C) $3n, 5n, 7n$
$3(4), 5(4), 7(4)$
$12, 20, 28$
(D) $2n + 1, 2n + 3, 2n + 5$
$2(3) + 1, 2(3) + 3, 2(3) + 5$
$7, 9, 11$
(E) $2n, 2n + 2, 2n + 4$
$2(3), 2(3) + 2, 2(3) + 4$
$6, 8, 10$
(D)

3. $w + w + 1 + w + 2$
$3w + 3$
$3(2) + 3$ $\quad 3(3) + 3$
9 $\quad$ 12
(B)

4. (A) O + E = O
(B) O − E = O
(C) $\frac{O}{2} + E \neq$ integer
(D) (O × O) + O = O + O = E
(E) $\frac{O}{2} + \frac{E}{2} \neq$ integer
(D)

5. E·O + E = E + E = E
(C)

6. $a^2 + ab^2 + 2b^3 = c$
O + O·E + 2·E
O + E + E = O $\quad c =$ O
$b^2 + ba^2 + 2a^3$
E + E·O + 2·O
E + E + E = E $\quad d =$ E
I $\quad c^2 + cd^2 + 2d^2$
O + O·E + 2·E
O + E + E = O
II $\quad 3c^2 + 3d^2 + 2c^2$
3·O + 3·E + 2·O
O + E + E = O
III $\quad c^2 + dc^2 + 2d^3$
O + E·O + 2·E
O + E + E = O
(E)

CHAPTER 11 WRAP UP — pp. 525–527

1. 6 $\quad$ 2. −9 $\quad$ 3. 7 $\quad$ 4. −13

5. Irrational $\quad$ 6. Rational $\quad$ 7. Irrational $\quad$ 8. Rational

9. $x + 7 \geq 0$
$x \geq -7$

10. $x - 10 \geq 0$
$x \geq 10$

11. $\sqrt{m^2} = |m|$

12. $\sqrt{49t^2} = 7|t|$

13. $\sqrt{p^2} = |p|$

14. $\sqrt{(x - 4)^2} = |x - 4|$

15. $-\sqrt{48} = -\sqrt{16 \cdot 3} = -4\sqrt{3}$

16. $\sqrt{x^2 - 14x + 49} = \sqrt{(x - 7)^2} = x - 7$

17. $\sqrt{64x^2} = \sqrt{64}\sqrt{x^2} = 8x$

18. $\sqrt{36x} = \sqrt{36}\sqrt{x} = 6\sqrt{x}$

19. $\sqrt{x^{12}} = x^6$

20. $\sqrt{y^5} = \sqrt{y^4 \cdot y} = \sqrt{y^4}\sqrt{y} = y^2\sqrt{y}$

21. $\sqrt{(x - 2)^4} = (x - 2)^2$

22. $\sqrt{75y^{15}} = \sqrt{25 \cdot 3 \cdot y^{14} \cdot y}$
$= \sqrt{25y^{14}}\sqrt{3y} = 5y^7\sqrt{3y}$

23. $\sqrt{25x^9} = \sqrt{25x^8 \cdot x} = \sqrt{25x^8}\sqrt{x} = 5x^4\sqrt{x}$

24. $\sqrt{(y+7)^{10}} = (y+7)^5$ 25. $\sqrt{3}\sqrt{7} = \sqrt{3\cdot 7} = \sqrt{21}$

26. $\sqrt{a}\sqrt{t} = \sqrt{at}$

27. $\sqrt{x-3}\sqrt{x+3} = \sqrt{(x-3)(x+3)}$ or $\sqrt{x^2-9}$

28. $\sqrt{2x}\sqrt{3y} = \sqrt{6xy}$ 29. $\sqrt{\frac{3}{4}}\sqrt{\frac{5}{7}} = \sqrt{\frac{3}{4}\cdot\frac{5}{7}} = \sqrt{\frac{15}{28}}$

30. $\sqrt{3x}\sqrt{2x+1} = \sqrt{3x(2x+1)}$ or $\sqrt{6x^2+3x}$

31. $\sqrt{3}\sqrt{6} = \sqrt{3\cdot 6} = \sqrt{18} = \sqrt{9\cdot 2} = 3\sqrt{2}$

32. $\sqrt{2x^2}\sqrt{5x^5} = \sqrt{10x^7} = \sqrt{10x^6\cdot x} = x^3\sqrt{10x}$

33. $\sqrt{ab}\sqrt{bc} = \sqrt{ab^2c} = b\sqrt{ac}$

34. $\sqrt{5b}\sqrt{15b^3} = \sqrt{75b^4} = \sqrt{25b^4\cdot 3} = 5b^2\sqrt{3}$

35. $\sqrt{\frac{9}{16}} = \frac{\sqrt{9}}{\sqrt{16}} = \frac{3}{4}$ 36. $\sqrt{\frac{1}{25}} = \frac{\sqrt{1}}{\sqrt{25}} = \frac{1}{5}$

37. $\sqrt{\frac{20}{45}} = \sqrt{\frac{4}{9}} = \frac{\sqrt{4}}{\sqrt{9}} = \frac{2}{3}$

38. $\sqrt{\frac{9}{32}} = \frac{\sqrt{9}}{\sqrt{32}} = \frac{3}{4\sqrt{2}}\cdot\frac{\sqrt{2}}{\sqrt{2}} = \frac{3\sqrt{2}}{4(2)} = \frac{3\sqrt{2}}{8}$

39. $\frac{\sqrt{48}}{\sqrt{3}} = \sqrt{\frac{48}{3}} = \sqrt{16} = 4$

40. $\frac{\sqrt{45x^4}}{\sqrt{9}} = \sqrt{\frac{45x^4}{9}} = \sqrt{5x^4} = x^2\sqrt{5}$

41. $\frac{\sqrt{100x^3}}{\sqrt{25x^3}} = \sqrt{\frac{100x^3}{25x^3}} = \sqrt{4} = 2$

42. $\frac{\sqrt{80y^4}}{\sqrt{5y^4}} = \sqrt{\frac{80y^4}{5y^4}} = \sqrt{16} = 4$ 43. $\frac{\sqrt{3}}{\sqrt{5}}\cdot\frac{\sqrt{5}}{\sqrt{5}} = \frac{\sqrt{15}}{5}$

44. $\frac{5}{\sqrt{3}}\cdot\frac{\sqrt{3}}{\sqrt{3}} = \frac{5\sqrt{3}}{3}$

45. $\frac{\sqrt{8}}{\sqrt{x}}\cdot\frac{\sqrt{x}}{\sqrt{x}} = \frac{\sqrt{8x}}{x} = \frac{\sqrt{4\cdot 2x}}{x} = \frac{2\sqrt{2x}}{x}$

46. $\frac{\sqrt{64a^3}}{\sqrt{6}} = \frac{8a\sqrt{a}}{\sqrt{6}}\cdot\frac{\sqrt{6}}{\sqrt{6}} = \frac{8a\sqrt{6a}}{6} = \frac{4a\sqrt{6a}}{3}$

47. $\sqrt{\frac{1}{8}} = \frac{\sqrt{1}}{\sqrt{8}}\cdot\frac{\sqrt{8}}{\sqrt{8}} = \frac{\sqrt{8}}{8} = \frac{\sqrt{4\cdot 2}}{8} = \frac{2\sqrt{2}}{8} = \frac{\sqrt{2}}{4}$

48. $\sqrt{\frac{5}{y}} = \frac{\sqrt{5}}{\sqrt{y}}\cdot\frac{\sqrt{y}}{\sqrt{y}} = \frac{\sqrt{5y}}{y}$ 49. $13\sqrt{5}$

50. $\sqrt{80} - \sqrt{45} = \sqrt{16\cdot 5} - \sqrt{9\cdot 5} = 4\sqrt{5} - 3\sqrt{5} = \sqrt{5}$

51. $\sqrt{x} + \sqrt{9x} = \sqrt{x} + 3\sqrt{x} = 4\sqrt{x}$

52. $3\sqrt{2} - 5\sqrt{\frac{1}{2}} = 3\sqrt{2} - 5\left(\frac{\sqrt{1}}{\sqrt{2}}\cdot\frac{\sqrt{2}}{\sqrt{2}}\right)$
$= 3\sqrt{2} - 5\left(\frac{\sqrt{2}}{2}\right) = 3\sqrt{2} - \frac{5}{2}\sqrt{2}$
$= \frac{6}{2}\sqrt{2} - \frac{5}{2}\sqrt{2} = \frac{\sqrt{2}}{2}$

53. $\sqrt{9x+9} + \sqrt{x+1} = \sqrt{9(x+1)} + \sqrt{x+1}$
$= 3\sqrt{x+1} + \sqrt{x+1}$
$= 4\sqrt{x+1}$

54. $\sqrt{12x^2} + \sqrt{3x^2} = \sqrt{4x^2\cdot 3} + \sqrt{3x^2}$
$= 2x\sqrt{3} + x\sqrt{3}$
$= 3x\sqrt{3}$

55. $15^2 + 20^2 = c^2$
$225 + 400 = c^2$
$625 = c^2$
$\sqrt{625} = c$
$25 = c$

56. $a^2 + 5^2 = (5\sqrt{2})^2$
$a^2 + 25 = 25(2)$
$a^2 + 25 = 50$
$a^2 = 25$
$a = \sqrt{25} = 5$

57. $6^2 + b^2 = 10^2$
$36 + b^2 = 100$
$b^2 = 64$
$b = \sqrt{64} = 8$

58. $c^2 = (\sqrt{2})^2 + (\sqrt{5})^2$
$= 2 + 5$
$= 7$
$c = \sqrt{7}$

59. $a^2 + 14^2 = 18^2$
$a^2 + 196 = 324$
$a^2 = 128$
$a = \sqrt{128}$
$= \sqrt{64\cdot 2}$
$= 8\sqrt{2}$

60. $c^2 = (6\sqrt{3})^2 + 6^2$
$= 36(3) + 36$
$= 108 + 36$
$= 144$
$c = \sqrt{144} = 12$

61. $x^2 + 14^2 = 18^2$
$x^2 + 196 = 324$
$x^2 = 128$
$x = \sqrt{128} \approx 11.3$ ft

62. $x^2 = 8^2 + 12^2$
$= 64 + 144$
$= 208$
$x = \sqrt{208} \approx 14.4$ ft

63. $\sqrt{x-3} = 7$
$(\sqrt{x-3})^2 = 7^2$
$x - 3 = 49$
$x = 52$

64. $\sqrt{3x} - 8 = 13$
$\sqrt{3x} = 21$
$(\sqrt{3x})^2 = 21^2$
$3x = 441$
$x = 147$

65. $V = 3.5\sqrt{h}$
$75.6 = 3.5\sqrt{h}$
$21.6 = \sqrt{h}$
$(21.6)^2 = (\sqrt{h})^2$
$466.56 = h$
The mountain is 466.56 m high.

CHAPTER 11 ASSESSMENT p. 528

1. 8 2. -5 3. Rational 4. Irrational

5. $\sqrt{a^2} = |a|$ 6. $\sqrt{36y^2} = 6|y|$

7. $\sqrt{(y+2)^2} = |y+2|$

8. $-\sqrt{40} = -\sqrt{4\cdot 10} = -2\sqrt{10}$

9. $\sqrt{27} = \sqrt{9\cdot 3} = 3\sqrt{3}$

10. $\sqrt{25x-25} = \sqrt{25(x-1)} = 5\sqrt{x-1}$

11. x^3 12. $\sqrt{y^9} = \sqrt{y^8\cdot y} = y^4\sqrt{y}$

13. $(y+2)^2$ 14. $\sqrt{33}$ 15. $\sqrt{3xy}$

16. $\sqrt{\frac{2}{3}}\cdot\sqrt{\frac{5}{7}} = \sqrt{\frac{2}{3}\cdot\frac{5}{7}} = \sqrt{\frac{10}{21}}$

17. $\sqrt{5}\sqrt{10} = \sqrt{50} = \sqrt{25\cdot 2} = 5\sqrt{2}$

18. $\sqrt{3ab}\sqrt{6ab^3} = \sqrt{18a^2b^4} = \sqrt{9a^2b^4\cdot 2} = 3ab^2\sqrt{2}$

19. $\sqrt{xy}\cdot\sqrt{y^2} = y\sqrt{xy}$

20. $\sqrt{\frac{27}{12}} = \sqrt{\frac{9}{4}} = \frac{\sqrt{9}}{\sqrt{4}} = \frac{3}{2}$

21. $\sqrt{\frac{144}{a^2}} = \frac{\sqrt{144}}{\sqrt{a^2}} = \frac{12}{a}$ 22. $\sqrt{\frac{1}{36}} = \frac{\sqrt{1}}{\sqrt{36}} = \frac{1}{6}$

23. $\frac{\sqrt{36}}{\sqrt{12}} = \sqrt{\frac{36}{12}} = \sqrt{3}$

24. $\frac{\sqrt{75x^4}}{\sqrt{3}} = \sqrt{\frac{75x^4}{3}} = \sqrt{25x^4} = 5x^2$

25. $\frac{\sqrt{96y^3}}{\sqrt{16y}} = \sqrt{\frac{96y^3}{16y}} = \sqrt{6y^2} = y\sqrt{6}$

26. $\frac{\sqrt{2x}}{\sqrt{y}}\cdot\frac{\sqrt{y}}{\sqrt{y}} = \frac{\sqrt{2xy}}{y}$ 27. $\frac{7}{\sqrt{2}}\cdot\frac{\sqrt{2}}{\sqrt{2}} = \frac{7\sqrt{2}}{2}$

28. $\sqrt{\frac{2}{5}} = \frac{\sqrt{2}}{\sqrt{5}} \cdot \frac{\sqrt{5}}{\sqrt{5}} = \frac{\sqrt{10}}{5}$

29. $3\sqrt{18} - 5\sqrt{18} = -2\sqrt{18} = -2\sqrt{9 \cdot 2}$
$= -2(3)\sqrt{2}$
$= -6\sqrt{2}$

30. $\sqrt{5} + \sqrt{\frac{1}{5}} = \sqrt{5} + \frac{\sqrt{1}}{\sqrt{5}} \cdot \frac{\sqrt{5}}{\sqrt{5}}$
$= \sqrt{5} + \frac{\sqrt{5}}{5}$
$= \frac{5\sqrt{5}}{5} + \frac{\sqrt{5}}{5} = \frac{6\sqrt{5}}{5}$ or $\frac{6}{5}\sqrt{5}$

31. $\sqrt{20x^2} + \sqrt{45x^2} = \sqrt{4 \cdot 5x^2} + \sqrt{9 \cdot 5x^2}$
$= 2x\sqrt{5} + 3x\sqrt{5}$
$= 5x\sqrt{5}$

32. $a^2 + 84^2 = 91^2$
$a^2 + 7056 = 8281$
$a^2 = 1225$
$a = \sqrt{1225} = 35$

33. $c^2 = 65^2 + 65^2$
$= 4225 + 4225$
$= 8450$
$c = \sqrt{8450} \approx 92$ ft

34. $\sqrt{3x} + 2 = 14$
$\sqrt{3x} = 12$
$(\sqrt{3x})^2 = 12^2$
$3x = 144$
$x = 48$

35. $\sqrt{y - 2} + 3 = 9$
$\sqrt{y - 2} = 6$
$(\sqrt{y - 2})^2 = 6^2$
$y - 2 = 36$
$y = 38$

36. $r = 2\sqrt{5d}$
$55 = 2\sqrt{5d}$
$(55)^2 = (2\sqrt{5d})^2$
$3025 = 4(5d)$
$3025 = 20d$
$151.25 \text{ ft} = d$

CHAPTERS 1-11 CUMULATIVE REVIEW pp. 529–533

1. $x - (x - 1) + (x^2 + 1) = (10) - (10 - 1) + (10^2 + 1)$
$= 10 - 9 + (100 + 1)$
$= 10 - 9 + 101$
$= 102$

2. $xy + (xy)^2 + x + y = (5)(2) + (5 \cdot 2)^2 + 5 + 2$
$= 10 + 10^2 + 7$
$= 17 + 100$
$= 117$

3. $121a + 88b = 11(11a + 8b)$

4. $36x + 24y + 12z = 12(3x + 2y + z)$

5. $\frac{x(y - 4)}{x - 8y}$ 6. $a^5 + 19$ 7. 70

8. $\frac{22}{18} - \frac{4}{18} + \frac{3}{18} - \frac{12}{18} + \frac{9}{18} = \frac{18}{18} = 1$

9. -72 10. 10.12 11. 8 12. -3

13. $-21x - 28w = -7(3x + 4w)$

14. $144a^2 - 60b^2 = 12(12a^2 - 5b^2)$

15. $-7(x - 1) + 2x = -7x + 7 + 2x = -5x + 7$

16. $8[4 - (6x - 5)] = 8[4 - 6x + 5]$
$= 8[9 - 6x]$
$= 72 - 48x$

17. $R + 2R + 2(2R) = 21$
$3R + 4R = 21$
$7R = 21$
$R = 3$
He read 3 books.

18. $5(a + 3) = 8a + 18$
$5a + 15 = 8a + 18$
$-3 = 3a$
$-1 = a$

19. $-3(m + 2) - 4 = -12 - (-2 + m)$
$-3m - 6 - 4 = -12 + 2 - m$
$-3m - 10 = -10 - m$
$0 = 2m$
$0 = m$

20. $n \cdot 1 = \frac{1}{2} = 0.5 = 50\%$

21. $50 = 0.2n$
$\frac{50}{0.2} = n$
$250 = n$

22. $2.5n = 6.25$
$n = \frac{6.25}{2.5}$
$n = 2.5$

23. $\frac{7}{12} = \frac{n}{1320}$
$1320\left(\frac{7}{12}\right) = n$
$770 = n$
770 oranges were sold.

24. $8x - 2 \geq 7x + 5$
$x \geq 7$

25. $-4x \geq 24$
$x \leq -6$

26. $-3x < 30 + 2x$
$-5x < 30$
$x > -6$

27. $x + 3 > 6(x - 4) + 7$
$x + 3 > 6x - 24 + 7$
$x + 3 > 6x - 17$
$20 > 5x$
$4 > x$

28. $\frac{85 + 87 + 88 + 92 + x}{5} \geq 90$
$\frac{352 + x}{5} \geq 90$
$352 + x \geq 450$
$x \geq 98$
She must score at least 98.

29. $(a^2b^4)(ab^5) = a^{2+1}b^{4+5} = a^3b^9$

30. $x^4 \cdot x^6 \cdot x = x^{4+6+1} = x^{11}$

31. $\frac{a^8b^4}{a^5b^3} = a^{8-5}b^{4-3} = a^3b$ 32. $a^0 = 1$

33. $7^{-4} = \frac{1}{7^4}$ 34. $(3^3)^2 = 3^{3 \cdot 2} = 3^6$

35. $(-3x^5y^2)^3 = (-3)^3x^{5 \cdot 3}y^{2 \cdot 3}$
$= -27x^{15}y^6$

36. $\left(\frac{y^4}{2}\right)^3 = \frac{y^{4 \cdot 3}}{2^3} = \frac{y^{12}}{8}$

37. $346{,}000 = 3.46 \times 10^5$

38. $.0000628 = 6.28 \times 10^{-5}$

39. $10a^2 + 6a - 8a^2 + 3a - 2a^2 - 8a$
$= a^2(10 - 8 - 2) + a(6 + 3 - 8)$
$= a^2(0) + a(1)$
$= a$

40. $(8m + 6n) - (12n + 7m) + 2(4m - 11n)$
$= 8m + 6n - 12n - 7m + 8m - 22n$
$= m(8 - 7 + 8) + n(6 - 12 - 22)$
$= m(9) + n(-28)$
$= 9m - 28n$

41. $(4 + 2b + c)(c - 1) = 4c - 4 + 2bc - 2b + c^2 - c$
$= 3c + 2bc + c^2 - 4 - 2b$

42. $(2.5x - 0.3y)^2$
$= (2.5x)^2 - 2(2.5x)(0.3y) + (0.3y)^2$
$= 6.25x^2 - 1.5xy + 0.09y^2$

43. $(5x - 6y)(x + 2y)$
$= 5x^2 + 10xy - 6xy - 12y^2$
$= 5x^2 + 4xy - 12y^2$

44. $(a + 2c + 1)(a + 2c - 1)$
$= ([a + 2c] + 1)([a + 2c] - 1)$
$= [a + 2c]^2 - 1^2$
$= a^2 + 4ac + 4c^2 - 1$

45. $(h - 4k)^2 = h^2 - 2h(4k) + (4k)^2$
$= h^2 - 8hk + 16k^2$

46. $(2x + 7y)^2 = (2x)^2 + 2(2x)(7y) + (7y)^2$
$= 4x^2 + 28xy + 49y^2$

47. $(x^2 + 3)(x^2 - 3) = (x^2)^2 - (3)^2$
$= x^4 - 9$

48. $(4x + 2)(3x - 1) = 12x^2 - 4x + 6x - 2$
$= 12x^2 + 2x - 2$

49. $x^3y^3 + x^2y^2 - 4xy = xy(x^2y^2 + xy - 4)$

50. $a^8 + a^7 - a^6 = a^6(a^2 + a - 1)$

51. $4 - 9m^4 = (2 + 3m^2)(2 - 3m^2)$

52. $9x^2 - 9b^2 = 9(x^2 - b^2) = 9(x + b)(x - b)$

53. $x^2 - 4x - 12 = (x - 6)(x + 2)$

54. $s^2 - 16s + 15 = (s - 15)(s - 1)$

55. $t^3 - 5t^2 + 6t = t(t^2 - 5t + 6)$
$= t(t - 2)(t - 3)$

56. $7x^2 - 6x - 1 = (7x + 1)(x - 1)$

57. $20y^2 + 19y + 3 = (4y + 3)(5y + 1)$

58. $6y^2 + 9y - 15 = 3(2y^2 + 3y - 5)$
$= 3(2y + 5)(y - 1)$

59. $x^2 - 3x - 10 = 0$
$(x - 5)(x + 2) = 0$
$x - 5 = 0$ or $x + 2 = 0$
$x = 5$ or $x = -2$

60. $y(3y - 2) = 0$
$y = 0$ or $3y - 2 = 0$
$y = 0$ or $3y = 2$
$y = 0$ or $y = \frac{2}{3}$

61. $y = 5x$

62. $y = mx + b$
y-intercept is 3, so $y = mx + 3$.
x-intercept is 6, or $(6, 0)$.
$0 = m(6) + 3$
$-3 = 6m$
$-\frac{1}{2} = m$
$y = -\frac{1}{2}x + 3$

63. slope is -1, so $y = -x + b$.
y-intercept is (-12), so $b = -12$.
$y = -x - 12$

64. y-intercept is -6, so $y = mx - 6$.
x-intercept is 7, or $(7, 0)$.
$0 = m(7) - 6$
$6 = 7m$
$\frac{6}{7} = m$
$y = \frac{6}{7}x - 6$

65. $m = \frac{11 - 2}{2 - (-1)} = \frac{9}{3} = 3$
$y = 3x + b$
$(2) = 3(-1) + b$
$5 = b$
$y = 3x + 5$

66. $6x + 3y = -6$ $-2x + 5y = 14$
$-6x + 15y = 42 \leftarrow -6x + 15y = 42$
$18y = 36$
$y = 2$
$6x + 3(2) = -6$
$6x + 6 = -6$
$6x = -12$
$x = -2$
The solution is $(-2, 2)$.

67. $2x + 3y = -3$ $y = 2x - 9$
$2x - y = 9 \leftarrow 9 = 2x - y$
$4y = -12$
$y = -3$
$2x - (-3) = 9$
$2x + 3 = 9$
$2x = 6$
$x = 3$
The solution is $(3, -3)$.

68. $x + y = 337$
$x - y = 43$
$2x = 380$
$x = 190$
$190 - y = 43$
$147 = y$
The numbers are 147 and 190.

69. Let $10x + y =$ the number.
$y = 2x + 1$
$y - 2x = 1$
$10y + x - (10x + y) = 36$
$10y + x - 10x - y = 36$
$9y - 9x = 36$
$y - x = 4$
$y - 2x = 1$
$x = 3$
$y = 2(3) + 1$
$y = 7$
The number is 37.

70. $A \cup B = \{-12, -10, -8, -6, -4, -2, 0, 2, 4, 6, 8, 10, 12\}$

71. $A \cap B = \{0\}$

72. $|2x + 4| = 12$
$2x + 4 = 12$ or $2x + 4 = -12$
$2x = 8$ $2x = -16$
$x = 4$ or $x = -8$

73. $|2x - 5| = 7$
$2x - 5 = 7$ or $2x - 5 = -7$
$2x = 12$ $2x = -2$
$x = 6$ or $x = -1$

74. $|3y| < 12$
$3y < 12$ and $3y > -12$
$y < 4$ and $y > -4$
$-4 < y < 4$

−4 0 4

75. $|4x| \geq 20$
$4x \geq 20$ or $4x \leq -20$
$x \geq 5$ or $x \leq -5$

−5 0 5

76. $\frac{3y}{y + 1} \cdot \frac{y + 1}{2} = \frac{(y + 1)(3y)}{(y + 1)(2)} = \frac{3y}{2}$

77. $\frac{-4}{3y + 3} \cdot \frac{y + 1}{2} = \frac{(y + 1)(-4)}{(y + 1)(3)(2)} = \frac{-4}{6} = -\frac{2}{3}$

78. $\frac{2x - 6}{5} \div \frac{x^2 - 9}{15} = \frac{2(x - 3)}{5} \cdot \frac{15}{(x + 3)(x - 3)}$
$= \frac{(x - 3)(2)(15)}{(x - 3)(x + 3)(5)}$
$= \frac{6}{x + 3}$

79. $\frac{x^2y + x^3y}{x} \div \frac{1 + x}{x^2y} = \frac{x^2y(1 + x)}{x} \cdot \frac{x^2y}{(1 + x)}$
$= \frac{x^4y^2(1 + x)}{x(1 + x)}$
$= x^3y^2$

80. $\frac{4}{2x+8}+\frac{6}{x+4}=\frac{4}{2(x+4)}+\frac{6}{x+4}$
$=\frac{4}{2(x+4)}+\frac{2\cdot 6}{2(x+4)}$
$=\frac{4+12}{2(x+4)}$
$=\frac{16}{2(x+4)}$
$=\frac{8}{x+4}$

81. $\frac{3y}{y+1}-\frac{2y+6}{y^2-1}=\frac{3y}{y+1}-\frac{2y+6}{(y+1)(y-1)}$
$=\frac{(y-1)3y}{(y-1)(y+1)}-\frac{2y+6}{(y+1)(y-1)}$
$=\frac{3y^2-3y-(2y+6)}{(y+1)(y-1)}$
$=\frac{3y^2-3y-2y-6}{(y+1)(y-1)}$
$=\frac{3y^2-5y-6}{(y+1)(y-1)}$

82. $\frac{y^2}{x-2}+\frac{5}{x-2}-\frac{3x}{x-2}=\frac{y^2+5-3x}{x-2}$

83. $\frac{3}{x-3}-\frac{2}{x+3}=\frac{5}{x^2-9}$
$(x^2-9)\left(\frac{3}{x-3}-\frac{2}{x+3}\right)=(x^2-9)\left(\frac{5}{x^2-9}\right)$
$3(x+3)-2(x-3)=5$
$3x+9-2x+6=5$
$x+15=5$
$x=-10$

84. $\frac{12}{y}-\frac{12}{y+1}=1$
$y(y+1)\left(\frac{12}{y}-\frac{12}{y+1}\right)=y(y+1)(1)$
$12(y+1)-12(y)=y^2+y$
$12y+12-12y=y^2+y$
$0=y^2+y-12$
$0=(y+4)(y-3)$
$y+4=0$ or $y-3=0$
$y=-4$ or $y=3$

85. $\frac{1}{16}+\frac{1}{x}=\frac{1}{10}$
$80x\left(\frac{1}{16}+\frac{1}{x}\right)=80x\left(\frac{1}{10}\right)$
$5x+80=8x$
$80=3x$
$\frac{80}{3}=x$

It takes $\frac{80}{3}$ h or $26\frac{2}{3}$ h or 26 h 40 min.

86. $x+8\,\overline{)\,x^2+5x-28}$ with quotient $x-3-\frac{4}{x+8}$
x^2+8x
$-3x-28$
$-3x-24$
-4

87. $\frac{\frac{1}{x}+3}{\frac{1}{x}-2}\cdot\frac{x}{x}=\frac{1+3x}{1-2x}$

88. $\sqrt{49}=7$ 89. $-\sqrt{121}=-11$

90. $\sqrt{64p^2}=8|p|$ 91. $\sqrt{(-7c)^2}=\sqrt{49c^2}=7|c|$

92. $\sqrt{(x-2)^2}=|x-2|$

93. $\sqrt{x^2-6x+9}=\sqrt{(x-3)^2}=|x-3|$

94. $-\sqrt{56}=-\sqrt{4\cdot 14}=-2\sqrt{14}$

95. $\sqrt{x^8}=x^4$

96. $\sqrt{36b^5}=\sqrt{36b^4\cdot b}=6b^2\sqrt{b}$

97. $\sqrt{20x^4y^5}=\sqrt{4x^4y^4\cdot 5y}=2x^2y^2\sqrt{5y}$

98. $\sqrt{6}\cdot\sqrt{8}=\sqrt{48}=\sqrt{16\cdot 3}=4\sqrt{3}$

99. $\sqrt{6a}\cdot\sqrt{3a^2b^2}=\sqrt{18a^3b^2}$
$=\sqrt{9a^2b^2\cdot 2a}$
$=3|ab|\sqrt{2a}$

100. $\sqrt{2b}\cdot\sqrt{5a+3b}=\sqrt{2b(5a+3b)}$
or $\sqrt{10ab+6b^2}$

101. $\sqrt{x+4y}\cdot\sqrt{2x-5y}=\sqrt{(x+4y)(2x-5y)}$
or $\sqrt{2x^2+3xy-20y^2}$

102. $\sqrt{\frac{1}{81}}=\frac{1}{9}$

103. $\frac{\sqrt{200x^3}}{\sqrt{25x}}=\sqrt{\frac{200x^3}{25x}}=\sqrt{8x^2}=\sqrt{4x^2\cdot 2}=2|x|\sqrt{2}$

104. $\frac{6}{\sqrt{2}}\cdot\frac{\sqrt{2}}{\sqrt{2}}=\frac{6\sqrt{2}}{2}=3\sqrt{2}$ 105. $\sqrt{\frac{1}{9}}=\frac{1}{3}$

106. $6\sqrt{2}-8\sqrt{2}=(6-8)\sqrt{2}=-2\sqrt{2}$

107. $\sqrt{200}-\sqrt{8}=\sqrt{100\cdot 2}-\sqrt{4\cdot 2}$
$=10\sqrt{2}-2\sqrt{2}$
$=8\sqrt{2}$

108. $\sqrt{7}+\sqrt{\frac{1}{7}}=\sqrt{7}+\frac{\sqrt{1}}{\sqrt{7}}\cdot\frac{\sqrt{7}}{\sqrt{7}}$
$=\sqrt{7}+\frac{\sqrt{7}}{7}$
$=\frac{7\sqrt{7}}{7}+\frac{\sqrt{7}}{7}$
$=\frac{8\sqrt{7}}{7}$

109. $\sqrt{\frac{3}{4}}-\sqrt{\frac{4}{3}}=\frac{\sqrt{3}}{\sqrt{4}}-\frac{\sqrt{4}}{\sqrt{3}}\cdot\frac{\sqrt{3}}{\sqrt{3}}$
$=\frac{\sqrt{3}}{2}-\frac{2\sqrt{3}}{3}$
$=\frac{3\sqrt{3}}{6}-\frac{4\sqrt{3}}{6}$
$=\frac{-\sqrt{3}}{6}$

110. $a^2+b^2=c^2$
$9^2+b^2=15^2$
$81+b^2=225$
$b^2=144$
$b=12$

111. $c^2=a^2+b^2$
$c^2=16^2+30^2$
$=256+900$
$=1156$
$c=34$

112. $30^2+80^2=d^2$
$900+6400=d^2$
$7300=d^2$
$\sqrt{7300}=d$
$85.4\approx d$
No; the maximum diameter is about 85 in.

113. $\sqrt{x-5}=3$
$(\sqrt{x-5})^2=3^2$
$x-5=9$
$x=14$

114. $\sqrt{2y-3}=\sqrt{y+6}$
$(\sqrt{2y-3})^2=(\sqrt{y+6})^2$
$2y-3=y+6$
$y=9$

CHAPTER 12

SKILLS & CONCEPTS YOU NEED FOR CHAPTER 12 p. 534

1. $-\frac{2x}{y} = -\frac{2(5)}{(-3)} = -\left(-\frac{10}{3}\right) = \frac{10}{3}$

2. $x^2 + 1 = (5)^2 + 1 = 25 + 1 = 26$

3. $y^3 - 4 = (-3)^3 - 4 = -27 - 4 = -31$

4. $A = \frac{1}{2}bh = \frac{1}{2}(7)(6) = \frac{1}{2}(42) = 21$

5. $I = Prt = 1500(0.12)(2) = 360$

6. $A = \frac{1}{2}h(b_1 + b_2)$
$2A = h(b_1 + b_2)$
$\frac{2A}{b_1 + b_2} = h$

7. $C = 2\pi r$
$\frac{C}{2\pi} = r$

8. $\frac{5}{3} = \frac{1750}{x}$
$3x\left(\frac{5}{3}\right) = 3x\left(\frac{1750}{x}\right)$
$5x = 5250$
$x = 1050$ votes

9.

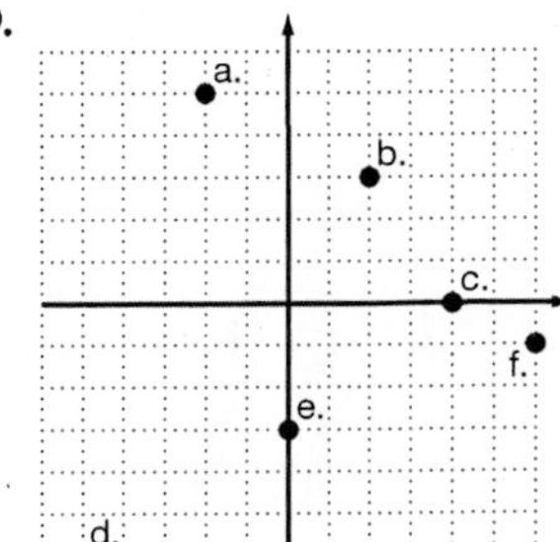

10.

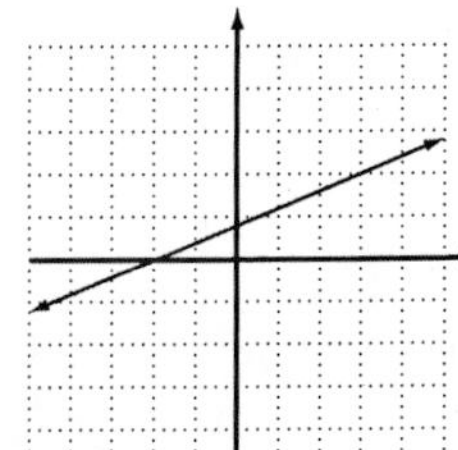

11.

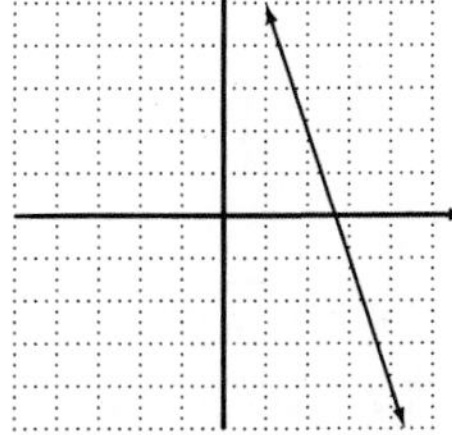

LESSON 12-1 TRY THIS pp. 538–539

a. Domain: {Tom, Sue}, Range: {12, 18, 28} The relation is not a function because the domain element *Sue* is assigned to more than one range value.

b. Domain: {3, 6, 7}, Range: {35, 36} The relation is a function because each element of the domain is assigned to exactly one element of the range.

c. $f(5) = 5 + 3 = 8$
$f(-8) = -8 + 3 = -5$
$f(-2) = -2 + 3 = 1$

d. $G(0) = 3(0) - (0)^2 = 0$
$G(-2) = 3(-2) - (-2)^2 = -10$
$G(1) = 3(1) - (1)^2 = 2$

e. $f(-1) = 8(-1)^2 + 3 = 11$
$f(2) = 8(2)^2 + 3 = 35$
$f\left(\frac{1}{2}\right) = 8\left(\frac{1}{2}\right)^2 + 3 = 5$

f. $p(0) = 2(0)^2 + (0) - 1 = -1$
$p(-2) = 2(-2)^2 + (-2) - 1 = 5$
$p(3) = 2(3)^2 + (3) - 1 = 20$

LESSON 12-1 EXERCISES pp. 539–541

1. Yes
2. No; the domain value 5 is assigned to two range values.
3. Yes
4. Domain: {3, 4, 6, 7}, Range: {− 7, − 6, − 4, − 3}; yes
5. Domain: {a, d}, Range: {b, c, e} The relation is not a function because the domain element a is assigned to more than one range element.
6. Domain: {− 2, 1, 4, 7}, Range: {1, 4}; yes

7. $f(x) = x + 5$
$f(3) = 3 + 5 = 8$
$f(7) = 7 + 5 = 12$
$f(-9) = -9 + 5 = -4$

8. $g(t) = t - 6$
$g(0) = 0 - 6 = -6$
$g(6) = 6 - 6 = 0$
$g(18) = 18 - 6 = 12$

9. $h(p) = 3p$
$h(-2) = 3(-2) = -6$
$h(5) = 3(5) = 15$
$h(24) = 3(24) = 72$

10. $f(x) = -4x$
$f(6) = -4(6) = -24$
$f\left(-\frac{1}{2}\right) = -4\left(-\frac{1}{2}\right) = 2$
$f(20) = -4(20) = -80$

11. $g(s) = 2s + 4$
$g(1) = 2(1) + 4 = 2 + 4 = 6$
$g(-7) = 2(-7) + 4 = -14 + 4 = -10$
$g(6) = 2(6) + 4 = 12 + 4 = 16$

12. $h(x) = 19$
$h(4) = 19$
$h(-6) = 19$
$h(12) = 19$

13. $F(x) = 2x^2 - 3x + 2$
$F(0) = 2(0)^2 - 3(0) + 2 = 2(0) - 0 + 2 = 2$
$F(-1) = 2(-1)^2 - 3(-1) + 2 = 2(1) + 3 + 2 = 7$
$F(2) = 2(2)^2 - 3(2) + 2 = 2(4) - 6 + 2 = 4$

14. $P(x) = 3x^2 - 2x + 5$
$P(0) = 3(0)^2 - 2(0) + 5 = 0 - 0 + 5 = 5$
$P(-2) = 3(-2)^2 - 2(-2) + 5 = 3(4) + 4 + 5 = 21$
$P(3) = 3(3)^2 - 2(3) + 5 = 3(9) - 6 + 5 = 26$

15. $h(x) = |x|$
$h(-4) = |-4| = 4$
$h(4) = |4| = 4$
$h(-3) = |-3| = 3$

16. $f(t) = |t| + 1$
$f(-5) = |-5| + 1 = 5 + 1 = 6$
$f(0) = |0| + 1 = 0 + 1 = 1$
$f(-9) = |-9| + 1 = 9 + 1 = 10$

17. $f(x) = |x| - 2$
$f(3) = |3| - 2 = 3 - 2 = 1$
$f(93) = |93| - 2 = 93 - 2 = 91$
$f(-100) = |-100| - 2 = 100 - 2 = 98$

18. $g(t) = t^3 + 3$
$g(1) = 1^3 + 3 = 1 + 3 = 4$
$g(-5) = (-5)^3 + 3 = -125 + 3 = -122$
$g(0) = 0^3 + 3 = 0 + 3 = 3$

19. $h(x) = x^4 - 3$
$h(0) = 0^4 - 3 = 0 - 3 = -3$
$h(-1) = (-1)^4 - 3 = 1 - 3 = -2$
$h(3) = 3^4 - 3 = 81 - 3 = 78$

20. $f(m) = 3m^2 - 5$
$f(4) = 3(4)^2 - 5 = 3(16) - 5 = 48 - 5 = 43$
$f(-3) = 3(-3)^2 - 5 = 3(9) - 5 = 27 - 5 = 22$
$f(6) = 3(6)^2 - 5 = 3(36) - 5 = 108 - 5 = 103$

21. $\$64.50 \times 0.70 = \$45.15$ **22.** $\$78.50 \times 0.30 = \$23.55$

23. $\$67.80 \times 0.80 = \$54.24$ **24.** $\$72.40 \times 0.55 = \$39.82$

25.
$$P(20) = 1 + \frac{20}{33} = 1\frac{20}{33}$$
$$P(30) = 1 + \frac{30}{33} = 1\frac{30}{33}$$
$$P(100) = 1 + \frac{100}{33} = 4\frac{1}{33}$$

26.
$$R(5) = 33\tfrac{1}{3}(5) = 166\tfrac{2}{3}$$
$$R(20) = 33\tfrac{1}{3}(20) = 666\tfrac{2}{3}$$
$$R(25) = 33\tfrac{1}{3}(25) = 833\tfrac{1}{3}$$

27.
$$\begin{aligned} T(5) &= 10(5) + 20 = 70°\text{C} \\ T(2) &= 10(20) + 20 = 220°\text{C} \\ T(1000) &= 10(1000) + 20 = 10{,}020°\text{C} \end{aligned}$$

28.
$$\begin{aligned} W(16) &= 0.112(16) = 1.792 \text{ cm} \\ W(25) &= 0.112(25) = 2.8 \text{ cm} \\ W(100) &= 0.112(100) = 11.2 \text{ cm} \end{aligned}$$

29.
$$\begin{aligned} f(0) &= 3(0) + 5 = 5 \\ f(1) &= 3(1) + 5 = 8 \\ f(2) &= 3(2) + 5 = 11 \\ f(3) &= 3(3) + 5 = 14 \end{aligned}$$
The range is $\{5, 8, 11, 14\}$.

30.
$$\begin{aligned} g(-3) &= (-3)^2 - 5 = 4 \\ g(-2) &= (-2)^2 - 5 = -1 \\ g(-1) &= (-1)^2 - 5 = -4 \\ g(0) &= (0)^2 - 5 = -5 \\ g(1) &= (1)^2 - 5 = -4 \end{aligned}$$
The range is $\{-5, -4, -1, 4\}$.

31.
$$\begin{aligned} h(-1) &= |-1| - (-1) = 1 + 1 = 2 \\ h(0) &= |0| - 0 = 0 \\ h(1) &= |1| - 1 = 0 \end{aligned}$$
For any positive number x, $|x| = x$, so $|x| - x = 0$ for all other values in the domain. The range is $\{0, 2\}$.

32. There are five possible relations.

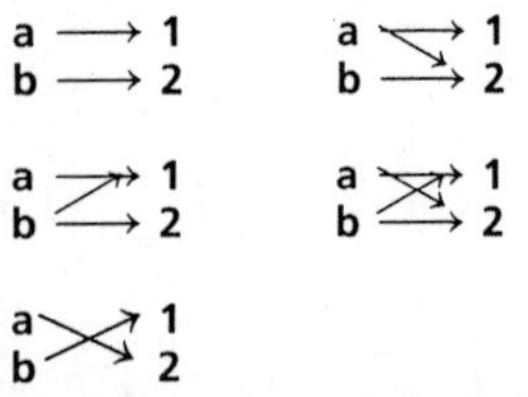

a → 1, b → 2

a → 2, b → 2

a → 1, b → 1

a → 1, a → 2, b → 2

a → 1, a → 2

33. a. Always; every domain element is assigned to exactly one range element.

b. Sometimes; a domain element could be assigned to more than one range element.

c. Never; at least one domain element must be assigned to two range elements.

34. $3(8) - [-4(2)^2] = 24 - (-16) = 40$

35. $3(0) - [-4(-5)^2] = 0 - (-100) = 100$

36. $2[3(1)] + 3[-4(4)^2] = 6 + 3(-64) = 6 - 192 = -186$

37. $-4(-3)^2 \cdot 3(-8) + 16 = -36 \cdot (-24) + 16 = 880$

38. $f[-4(-2)^2] = f[-4(4)] = f(-16) = 3(-16) = -48$

39. $g[-4(-1)^2] = g[-4(1)] = g(-4) = -4(-4)^2 = -64$

40. $f(-1) = -7$ and $f(3) = 8$. Two ordered pairs are $(-1, -7)$ and $(3, 8)$.
$$\text{slope} = \frac{(8) - (-7)}{3 - (-1)} = \frac{15}{4}$$
$$y - 8 = \frac{15}{4}(x - 3)$$
$$y - 8 = \frac{15}{4}x - \frac{45}{4}$$
$$y = \frac{15}{4}x - \frac{45}{4} + 8$$
$$y = \frac{15}{4}x - \frac{13}{4}$$
$$f(x) = \frac{15}{4}x - \frac{13}{4}$$

41.
$$\begin{aligned} x - y &= -7 \\ x + y &= 5 \\ \hline 2x &= -2 \\ x &= -1 \\ -1 + y &= 5 \\ y &= 6 \qquad (-1, 6) \end{aligned}$$

42.
$$\begin{aligned} 2x + 3y &= 11 \\ -2x + 10y &= 2 \\ \hline 13y &= 13 \\ y &= 1 \\ 5 - x &= 1 \\ x &= 4 \qquad (4, 1) \end{aligned}$$

43.
$$\begin{aligned} 5x + 2y &= 4 \\ 4x + 3y &= 13 \\ 15x + 6y &= 12 \\ -8x - 6y &= -26 \\ \hline 7x &= -14 \\ x &= -2 \\ -8 + 3y &= 13 \\ y &= 7 \qquad (-2, 7) \end{aligned}$$

44. $\sqrt{x}\sqrt{y} = \sqrt{xy}$ **45.** $\sqrt{y}\sqrt{y - 2} = \sqrt{y^2 - 2y}$

46. $\sqrt{a}\sqrt{a + 3} = \sqrt{a^2 + 3a}$

47. $\sqrt{m + n}\sqrt{m - n} = \sqrt{m^2 - n^2}$

48. $\sqrt{a + 3}\sqrt{2a + 1} = \sqrt{2a^2 + 7a + 3}$

49. $\sqrt{x - 4}\sqrt{3x + 2} = \sqrt{3x^2 - 10x - 8}$

50. $y = mx + b$
$$m = \frac{7 - 2}{3 - (-2)} = \frac{5}{5} = 1$$
So
$$\begin{aligned} y &= x + b \\ 7 &= 3 + b \\ 4 &= b \\ y &= x + 4 \end{aligned}$$

51. $y = 1$

52.
$$m = \frac{-1 - (-5)}{6 - (-2)} = \frac{-1 + 5}{6 + 2} = \frac{4}{8} = \frac{1}{2}$$
$$y = \frac{1}{2}x + b$$
$$-1 = \frac{1}{2}(6) + b$$
$$-1 = 3 + b$$
$$-4 = b$$
$$y = \frac{1}{2}x - 4$$

53. $x = 3$

54. $\sqrt{18} = \sqrt{9 \cdot 2} = 3\sqrt{2}$ **55.** $\sqrt{144m^2} = 12|m|$

56. $\sqrt{20c^2} = \sqrt{4 \cdot 5c^2} = 2|c|\sqrt{5}$

57. $\sqrt{32a^3} = \sqrt{16 \cdot 2a^3} = 4|a|\sqrt{2a}$

OPERATIONS WITH FUNCTIONS p. 541

1. $f(x) - g(x) = 5x - \frac{1}{x} = \frac{5x^2}{x} - \frac{1}{x} = \frac{5x^2 - 1}{x}$

2. $f(x) \cdot g(x) = 5x \cdot \frac{1}{x} = 5$ for $x \neq 0$

3.
$$\begin{aligned} g(x) + h(x) &= \frac{1}{x} + \frac{2}{x - 3} = \frac{x - 3}{x(x - 3)} + \frac{2x}{x(x - 3)} \\ &= \frac{x - 3 + 2x}{x(x - 3)} = \frac{3x - 3}{x(x - 3)} \end{aligned}$$

4. $g(x) \cdot h(x) = \frac{1}{x} \cdot \frac{2}{x - 3} = \frac{2}{x(x - 3)}$

5. $g(x) \div h(x) = \frac{1}{x} \div \frac{2}{x - 3} = \frac{1}{x} \cdot \frac{x - 3}{2} = \frac{x - 3}{2x}$

6. $f(x) \cdot h(x) = 5x \cdot \frac{2}{x - 3} = \frac{10x}{x - 3}$

INTRODUCING THE CONCEPT: GRAPHS OF RELATIONS AND FUNCTIONS p. 542

$y = x - 1$

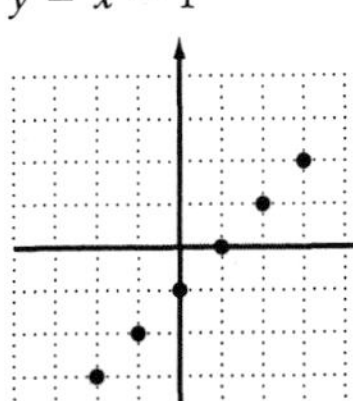

A function; explanations may vary.

$y^2 = x + 1$

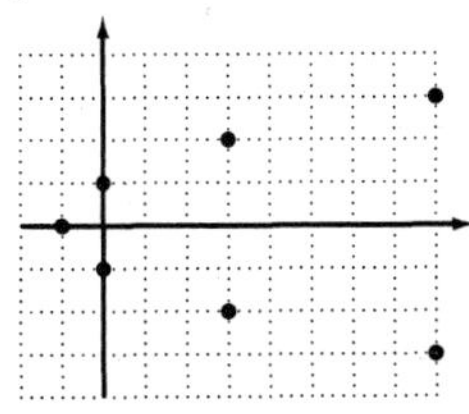

Not a function; explanations may vary.

LESSON 12-2 TRY THIS p. 543

a. Yes **b.** No **c.** No
d. Yes **e.** No **f.** Yes
g. All real numbers
h. $\{x \mid x \neq 5\}$
i. $\{x \mid x \geq 1\}$
j.

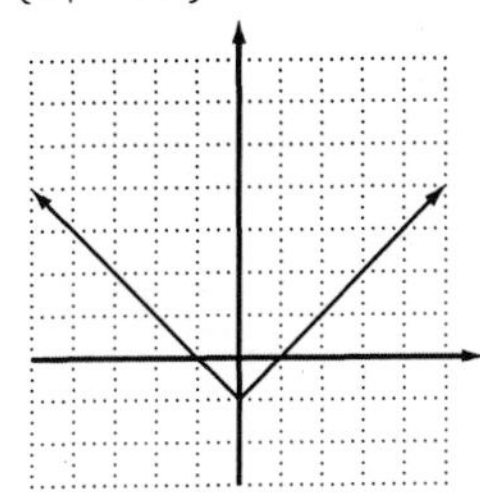

$\{y \mid y \geq -1\}$

k.

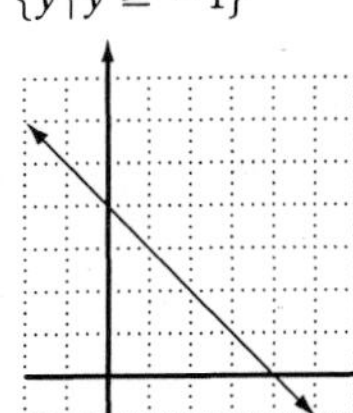

All real numbers

l.

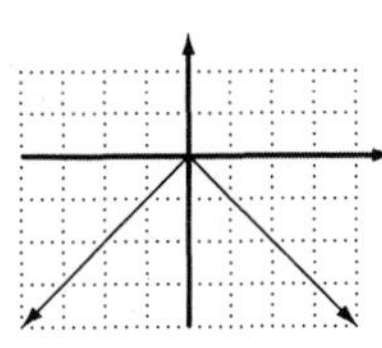

$\{y \mid y \leq 0\}$

LESSON 12-2 EXERCISES pp. 544–545

1.

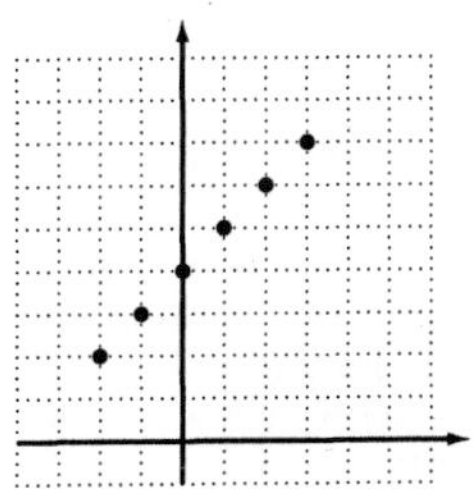

2.

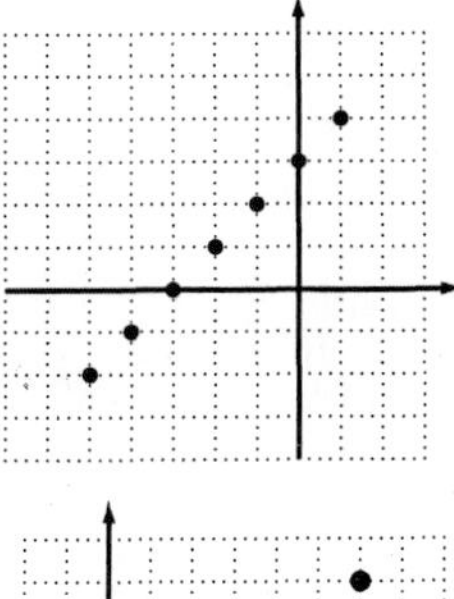

3.

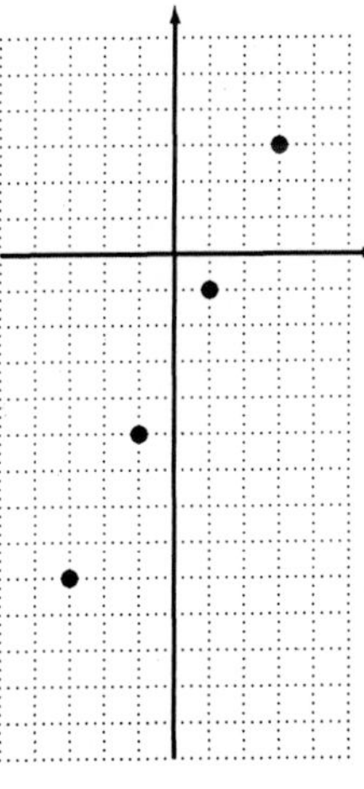

4.

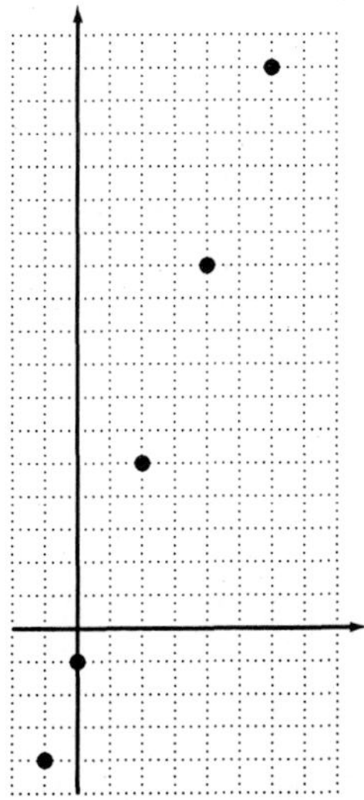

5. Yes **6.** Yes
7. No; both (0, 1) and (0, − 1) satisfy the equation.
8. No; both (6, 2) and (6, − 2) satisfy the equation.
9. Yes **10.** Yes **11.** No **12.** Yes **13.** Yes
14. No
15. $\{x \mid x \neq 0\}$
16. All real numbers
17. $\{x \mid x \geq 0\}$
18. $\{x \mid x \neq 7\}$
19. $\{x \mid x \geq -2\}$
20. All real numbers
21. $\{x \mid x \neq -3\}$
22. All real numbers
23. $\{x \mid x \leq 4\}$
24.

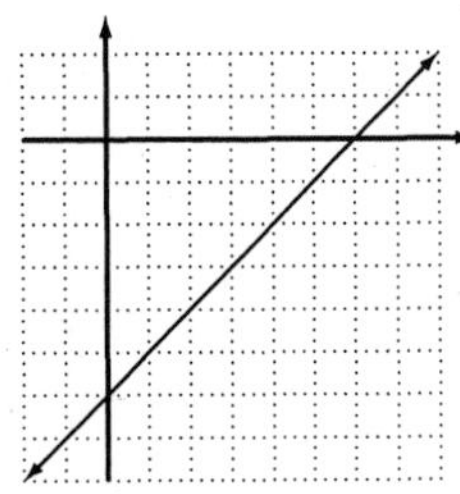

Domain: all real numbers
Range: all real numbers

25.

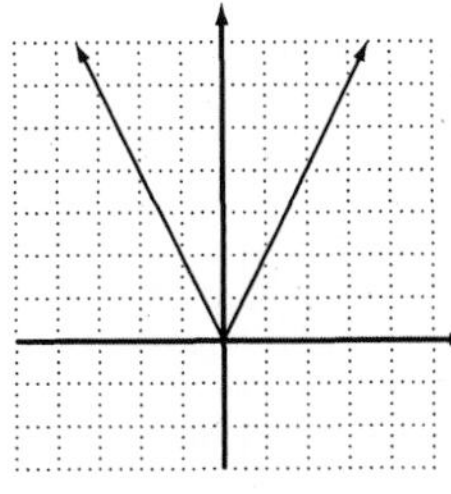

Domain: all real numbers
Range: $\{y \mid y \geq 0\}$

26.

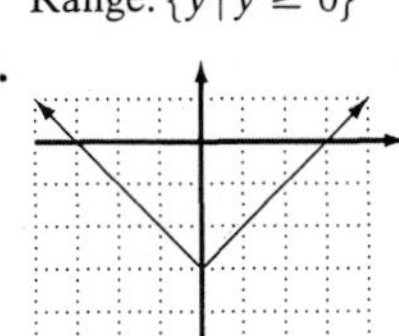

Domain: all real numbers
Range: all real numbers

27.

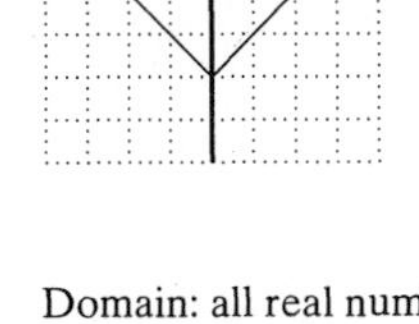

Domain: all real numbers
Range: $\{y \mid y \geq -3\}$

28.

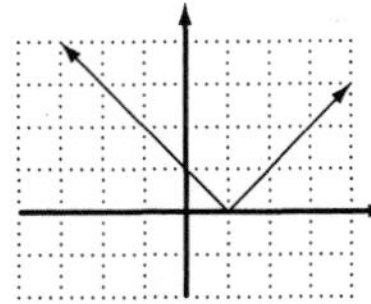

Domain: all real numbers
Range: $\{y \mid y \geq 0\}$

29.

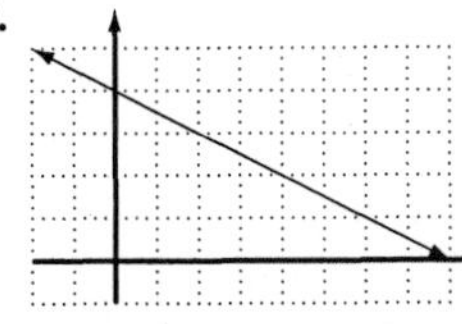

Domain: all real numbers
Range: all real numbers

30. Domain: {0, 1, 2, 3}, Range: {0, 2, 4, 6}
$f(0) = 0, f(1) = 2, f(2) = 4, f(3) = 6; f(x) = 2x$

31.

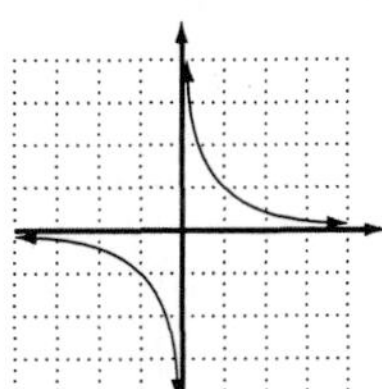

Domain: $\{x \mid x \neq 0\}$
Range: $\{y \mid y \neq 0\}$; yes

32. Answers may vary. Sample:

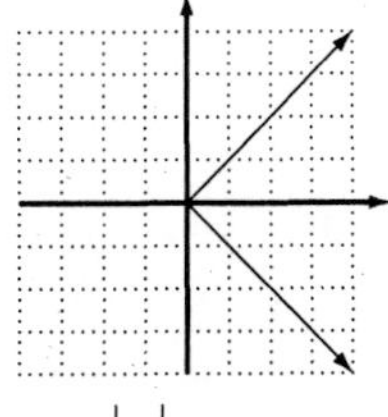

$x = |y|$

33. $f(x) = \frac{1}{x+4}; f(0) = \frac{1}{0+4} = \frac{1}{4}$.

Since $f(0)$ is defined, 0 is in the domain of $f(x) = \frac{1}{x+4}$. The correct answer is A.

34. Answers may vary. Sample: $f(x) = \frac{1}{x}$ (See Exercise 31.)

35. V shaped, Λ if a is negative, with "point" on the y-axis b units up or down from the origin.

36. If $|a|$ increases, the graph gets thinner; if b increases, the graph is moved upward.

37. $\frac{\sqrt{3}}{\sqrt{147}} = \sqrt{\frac{3}{147}} = \sqrt{\frac{1}{49}} = \frac{1}{7}$

38. $\sqrt{\frac{20}{45}} = \sqrt{\frac{4}{9}} = \frac{2}{3}$

39. $\sqrt{\frac{30}{18}} = \sqrt{\frac{15}{9}} = \frac{\sqrt{15}}{3}$

40. $\frac{\sqrt{7}}{\sqrt{xy}} = \frac{\sqrt{7}}{\sqrt{xy}} \cdot \frac{\sqrt{xy}}{\sqrt{xy}} = \frac{\sqrt{7xy}}{xy}$

41. $\frac{x^2 - 9x + 20}{x - 4} = \frac{(x-4)(x-5)}{x-4} = x - 5$

42.
$$\begin{array}{r} y^3 + 3y^2 + 9y + 27 + \frac{72}{y-3} \\ y - 3\overline{)y^4 - 0y^3 + 0y^2 + 0y - 9} \\ \underline{y^4 - 3y^3} \qquad\qquad\qquad \\ 3y^3 + 0y^2 \qquad\qquad \\ \underline{3y^3 - 9y^2} \qquad\qquad \\ 9y^2 + 0y \qquad \\ \underline{9y^2 - 27y} \qquad \\ 27y - 9 \\ \underline{27y - 81} \\ 72 \end{array}$$

43.
$$\begin{aligned} \frac{x^2 + 4x}{x + 3} - \frac{3x + 1}{x + 3} - \frac{5}{x + 3} &= \frac{x^2 + 4x - 3x - 1 - 5}{x + 3} \\ &= \frac{x^2 + x - 6}{x + 3} \\ &= \frac{(x + 3)(x - 2)}{x + 3} \\ &= x - 2 \end{aligned}$$

44.
$$\begin{aligned} \frac{3y}{y^2 - 25} - \frac{2(y - 5)}{(y + 5)(y - 5)} &= \frac{3y - 2(y - 5)}{y^2 - 25} \\ &= \frac{3y - 2y + 10}{y^2 - 25} \\ &= \frac{y + 10}{y^2 - 25} \end{aligned}$$

LESSON 12-3 TRY THIS p. 548

a.
$$\begin{aligned} c(h) &= 3.50 + 3.65h \\ c(9) &= 3.50 + 3.65(9) \\ &= 3.50 + 32.85 \\ &= \$36.35 \end{aligned}$$

LESSON 12-3 EXERCISES pp. 548–549

1.
$$\begin{aligned} c(k) &= 35 + 0.21k \\ c(340) &= 35 + 0.21(340) = 35 + 71.40 = \$106.40 \end{aligned}$$

2.
$$\begin{aligned} c(m) &= 27.00 + 3.95m \\ c(3) &= 27.00 + 3.95(3) = 27.00 + 11.85 = \$38.85 \end{aligned}$$

3.
$$\begin{aligned} c(h) &= 6.50 + 5.90h \\ c(7.5) &= 6.50 + 5.90(7.5) \\ &= 6.50 + 44.25 \\ &= \$50.75 \end{aligned}$$

4.
$$\begin{aligned} c(h) &= 0.70(h - 1) + 1.25 \\ c(18) &= 0.70(18 - 1) + 1.25 \\ &= 0.70(17) + 1.25 \\ &= 11.9 + 1.25 \\ &= \$13.15 \end{aligned}$$

5.
$$\begin{aligned} c(h) &= 5.50 + 4.25h \\ c(4.5) &= 5.50 + 4.25(4.5) \\ &= 5.50 + 19.125 \\ &= 24.625 \\ &\approx \$24.63 \end{aligned}$$

6.
$$\begin{aligned} c(m) &= 29 + 0.19m \\ c(280) &= 29 + 0.19(280) \\ &= 29 + 53.2 \\ &= \$82.20 \end{aligned}$$

7. $L(w) = \frac{1}{3}w + 40$

$L(15) = \frac{1}{3}(15) + 40 = 5 + 40 = 45$ cm

8. $L(w) = \frac{1}{5}w + 60$

$L(20) = \frac{1}{5}(20) + 60 = 4 + 60 = 64$ cm

9.
$$\begin{aligned} c &= 0.15m + b \\ 18 &= 0.15(62) + b \\ 18 &= 9.30 + b \end{aligned}$$
(a) $b = \$8.70$
(b) $c = 0.15(76) + 8.70 = \$20.10$

10.
$$\begin{aligned} c &= 0.23k + f \\ 26.60 &= 0.23(70) + f \\ 26.60 &= 16.10 + f \end{aligned}$$
(a) $f = \$10.50$
(b) $c = 0.23(85) + 10.50 = \$30.05$

11.
$$\begin{aligned} c &= 2.00 + 1.50h_1 + 0.75h_2 \\ &= 2.00 + 1.50(6) + 0.75(2) \\ &= 2.00 + 9.00 + 1.50 \\ &= \$12.50 \end{aligned}$$

12. $c = 41d + 0.24m$
(a) $c = 41(3) + 0.24(50) = 123 + 12 = \$135$
(b) $150 = 41(3) + 0.24m$
$150 = 123 + 0.24m$
$27 = 0.24m$
$112 \approx m$ Add this to 100, giving 212 miles.

13. A horizontal line

14. Answers may vary.
If you make a yearly salary, you are paid a constant amount each month regardless of the number of hours you work. Say you make \$600 a month, then $f(h) = 600$ no matter what h (hours worked) is. This of course differs from a job where you are paid by the hour, which is not a constant function.

15.

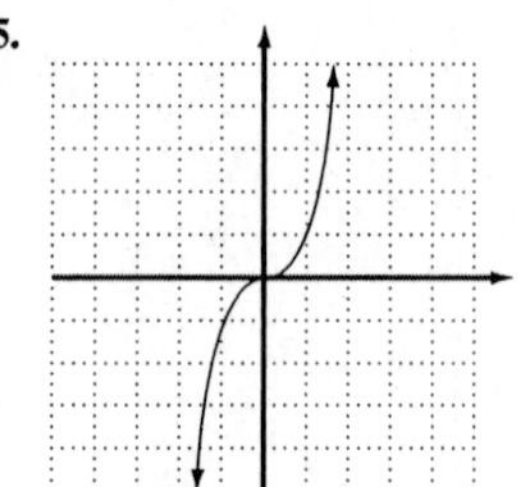

16. (4000, \$1300) and (2800, \$970)
$$\begin{aligned} m &= 0.275 \\ c(p) &= 200 + 0.275p \\ c(1500) &= \$612.50 \end{aligned}$$

17.
$$\begin{aligned} 3\sqrt{8} + 2\sqrt{2} &= 3\sqrt{4 \cdot 2} + 2\sqrt{2} = 3 \cdot 2\sqrt{2} + 2\sqrt{2} \\ &= 6\sqrt{2} + 2\sqrt{2} = 8\sqrt{2} \end{aligned}$$

18. $\sqrt{24} - \sqrt{6} = \sqrt{4 \cdot 6} - \sqrt{6} = 2\sqrt{6} - \sqrt{6} = \sqrt{6}$

19. 5.47×10^6 20. 3.4709×10^{-3}

21. $\dfrac{6(x+1)}{5x} \cdot \dfrac{35x}{21(x+1)} = \dfrac{210x(x+1)}{105x(x+1)} = 2$

22. $\dfrac{(y+2)^3}{(y-2)^2} \cdot \dfrac{(y-2)^2}{(y+2)^3} = 1$

23. $3x > 12$ or $3x < -12$
$x > 4$ or $x < -4$

24. $2x \geq 6$ or $2x \leq -6$
$x \geq 3$ or $x \leq -3$

25. $x - 1 > 3$ or $x - 1 \leq -3$
$x > 4$ or $x < -2$

CONNECTIONS: DISCRETE MATH p. 551

1. Filipe could also visit the library just after Becca leaves, while Abdul is still at the library. This would not change the number of students that Becca sees because she does not see Filipe in either case.

2. a.

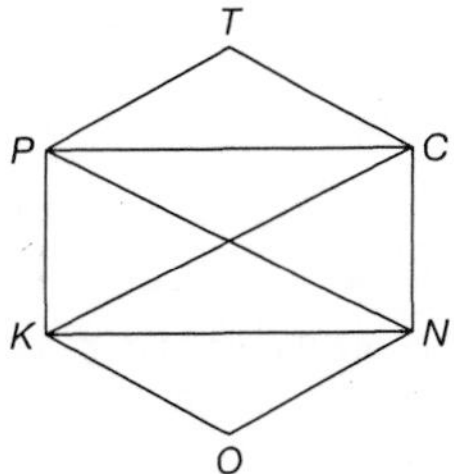

b.

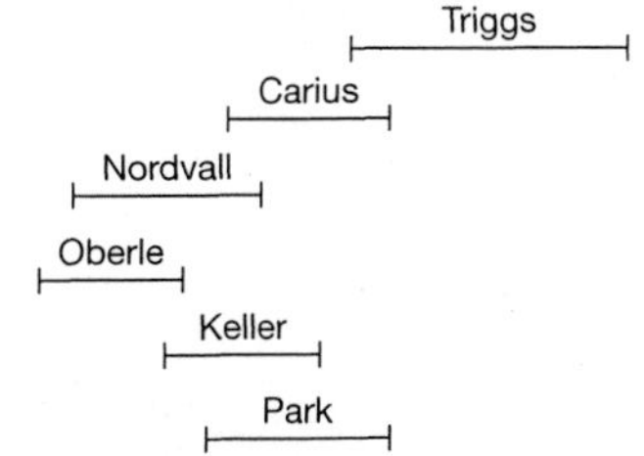

c. Yes d. No e. No f. Yes

INTRODUCING THE CONCEPT: GRAPHS OF QUADRATIC FUNCTIONS p. 552

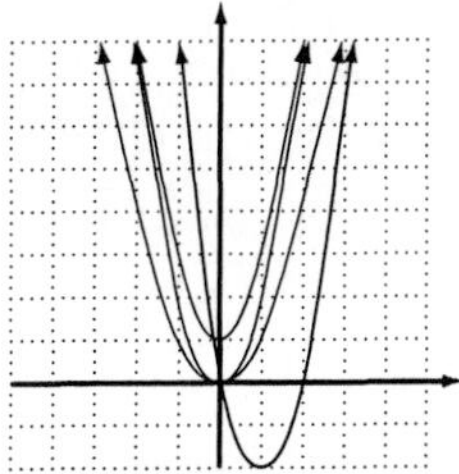

Lowest point: (0, 0)
The y-axis divides the graph in half.
It is narrower.
It is the same but moved up one.
It is the same but moved 1 to the right and down 2.
It is the same but moved 1 to the right and down 3.

LESSON 12-4 TRY THIS pp. 553–554

a.

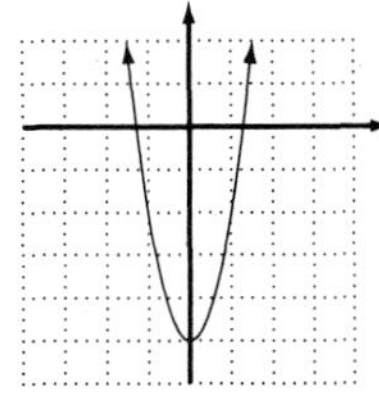

b.

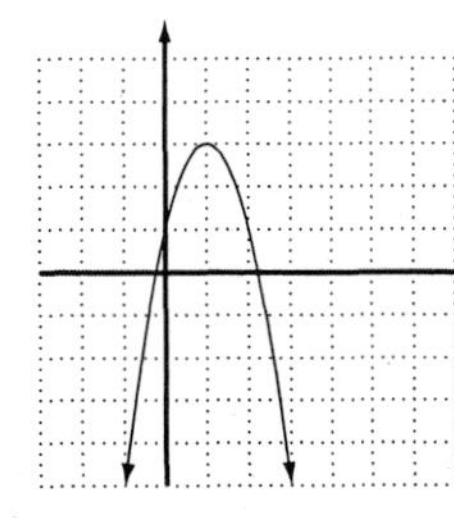

c.

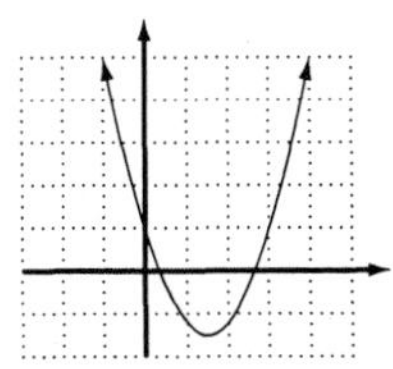

d. 2, 3 e. $-1, 4$

LESSON 12-4 EXERCISES p. 554–556

1.

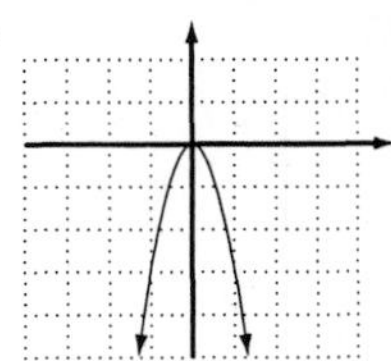

Domain: all real numbers
Range: $\{y \mid y \leq 0\}$

2.

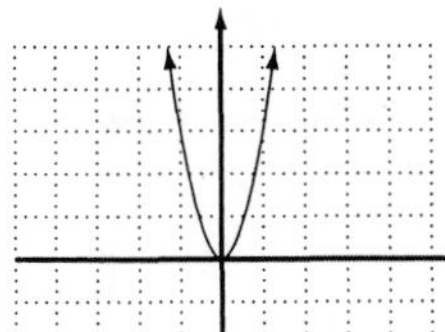

Domain: all real numbers
Range: $\{y \mid y \geq 0\}$

3.

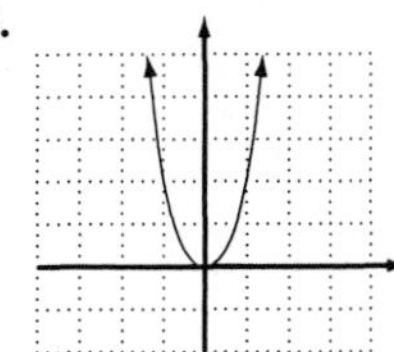

Domain: all real numbers
Range: $\{y \mid y \leq 0\}$

4.

Domain: all real numbers
Range: $\{y \mid y \geq 0\}$

5.

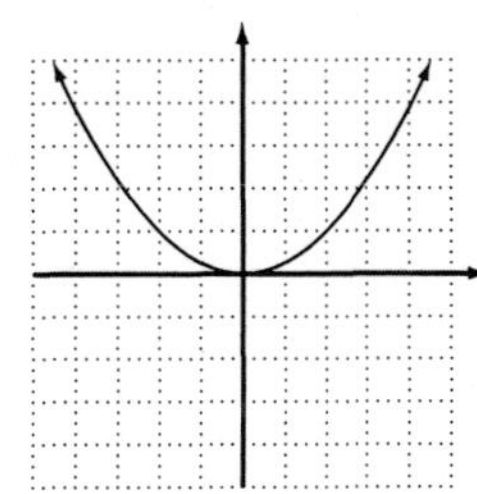

Domain: all real numbers
Range: $\{y \mid y \geq 0\}$

6.

Domain: all real numbers
Range: $\{y \mid y \geq 0\}$

7.

Domain: all real numbers
Range: $\{y \mid y \geq -3\}$

8.

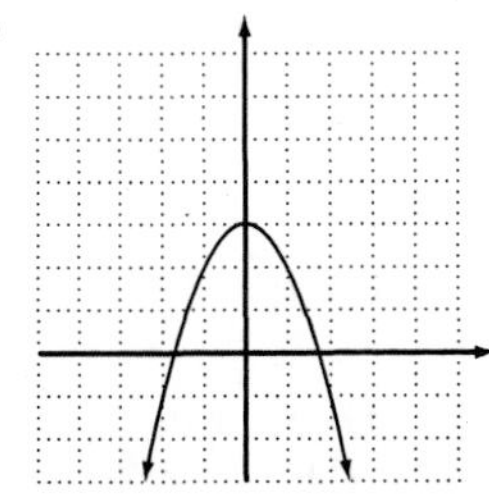

Domain: all real numbers
Range: $\{y \mid y \leq 3\}$

9.

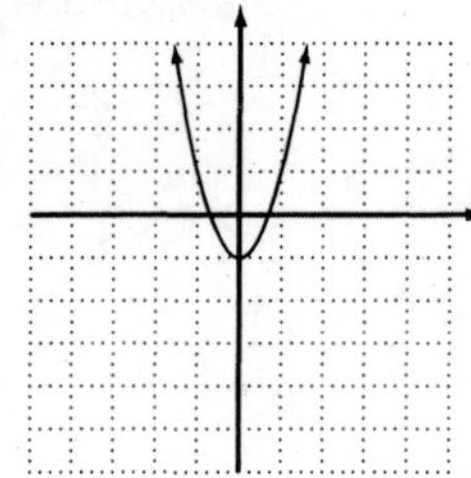

Domain: all real numbers
Range: $\{y \mid y \geq -1\}$

10.

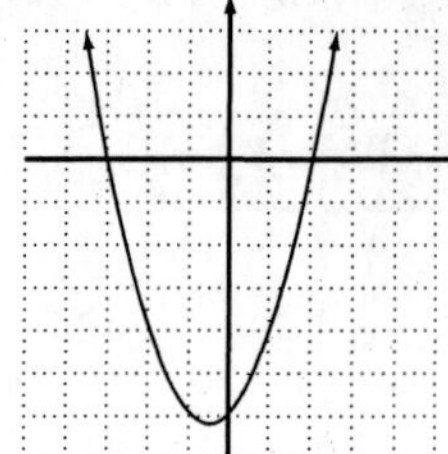

11.

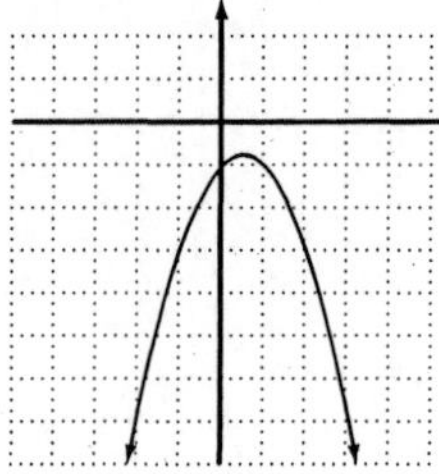

12.

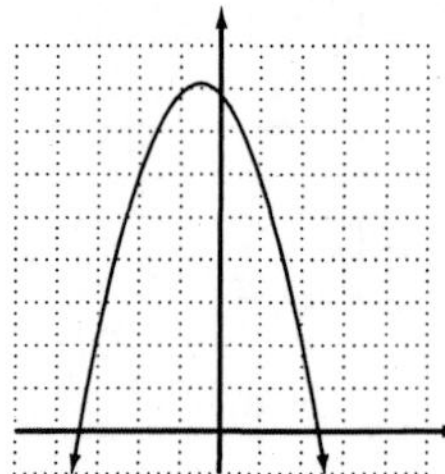

13.

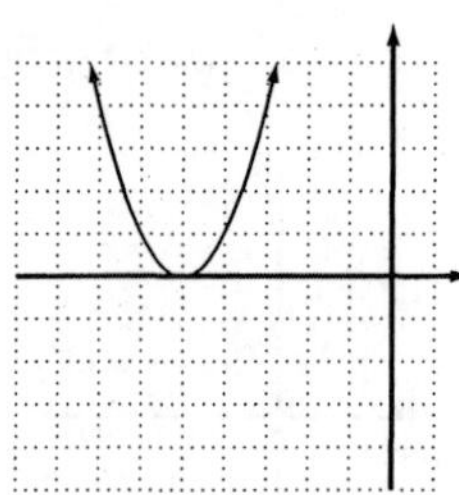

14.

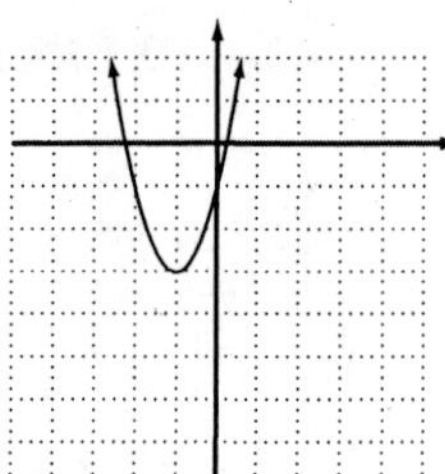

15.

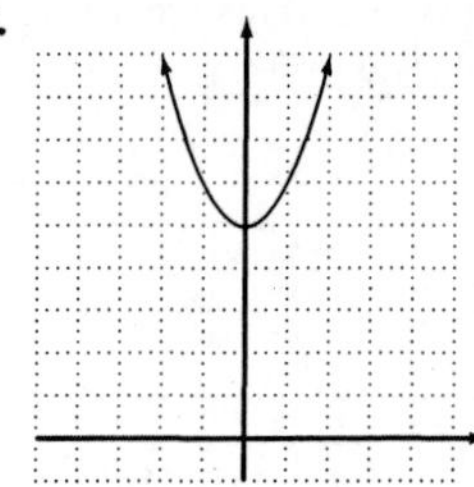

16. $x^2 - 3x - 10 = 0;$
$(x - 5)(x + 2) = 0;$
$x = 5, x = -2.$
The x-intercepts are -2 and 5.

17. $x^2 + 2x = 0;$
$x(x + 2) = 0;$
$x = 0, x = -2.$
The x-intercepts are -2 and 0.

18. $-x^2 + 10x - 21 = 0;$
$(-x + 3)(x - 7) = 0;$
$x = 3, x = 7.$
The x-intercepts are 3 and 7.

19. $x^2 - 8x + 16 = 0;$
$(x - 4)^2 = 0; x = 4.$
The x-intercept is 4.

20. $2x^2 - 9x + 10 = 0;$
$(2x - 5)(x - 2) = 0;$

$x = \frac{5}{2}, x = 2.$

The x-intercepts are 2 and $\frac{5}{2}$.

21. $-x^2 - 11x - 18 = 0;$
$(-x - 9)(x + 2) = 0;$
$x = -9, -2.$
The x-intercepts are -9 and -2.

22.

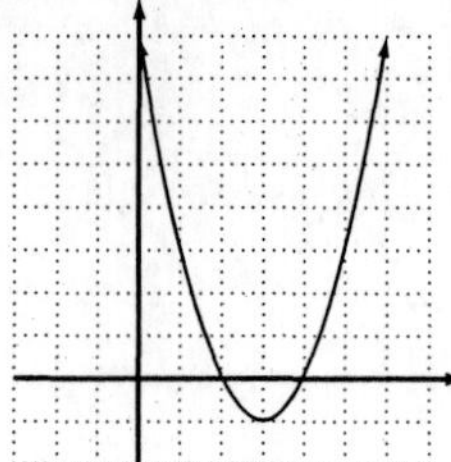

The x-intercepts of the graph are 2 and 4. The roots of the polynomial are 2 and 4.

23.

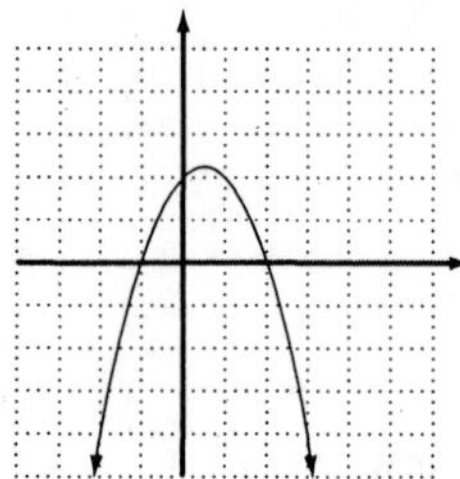

The x-intercepts of the graph are -1 and 2. The roots of the polynomial are -1 and 2.

24. When the function is in standard form, the y-intercept is the constant term.

25. $a > 0; a < 0$
a. upward
b. downward
c. downward

26. Graphs that open upward have a minimum point. Graphs that open downward have a maximum point.

27. **a.** $(0, -4)$ min. pt.
b. $(0, 7)$ max. pt.
c. $\left(\frac{1}{4}, \frac{19}{8}\right)$ max. pt.

28. $x = 0, x = 0, x = 0, x = -\frac{1}{2}, x = \frac{1}{2},$

$x = -\frac{1}{2}, x = -5, x = -1, x = 0;$

Each axis is parallel to the y-axis and contains a maximum or minimum point.

29. 2 sec, 4 sec

30. 3 sec; 144 ft

31. 6 sec

32. **a.** $d = 80t - 16t^2$
b.

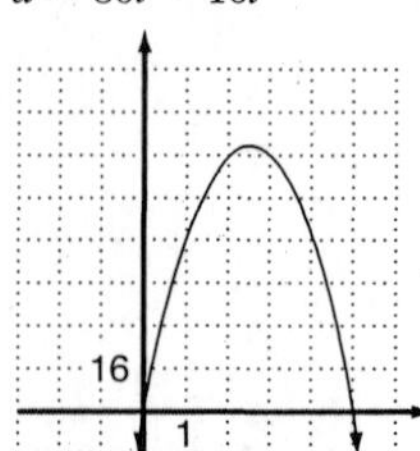

c. $d = 80t - 16t^2$
1 sec: $d = 80(1) - 16(1)^2 = 80 - 16 = 64$ ft
2 sec: $d = 80(2) - 16(2)^2 = 160 - 64 = 96$ ft
d. 2.5 sec
e. $d = 80(2.5) - 16(2.5)^2$
$= 200 - 16(6.25)$
$= 200 - 100$
$= 100$ ft

33. As $|a|$ increases, the graph narrows.

34.

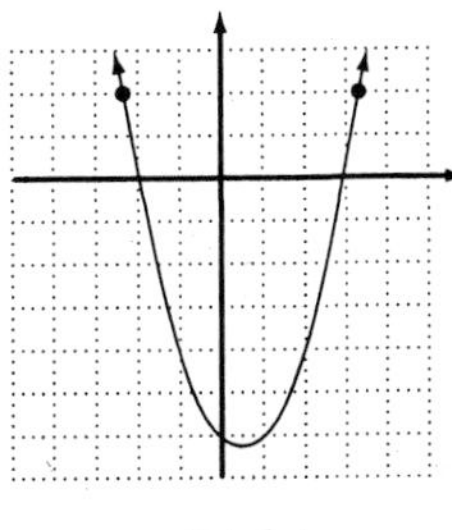

$-2.4, 3.4$

35.

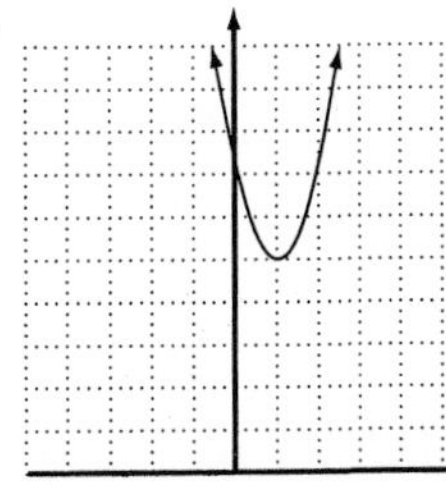

The graph of the function does not cross the x-axis, so the equation has no real-number solution.

36. $A = l(18 - l)$
$A = 18l - l^2$

The maximum occurs when $l = \frac{-18}{-2} = 9$. The maximum is at $(9, 81)$. The largest area is 81 ft^2.

37. 0.0000005115 **38.** 479,330 **39.** $x = 17^2 = 289$

40.
$$\begin{aligned} 2y - 1 &= 81 \\ 2y &= 82 \\ y &= 41 \end{aligned}$$

41.
$$\begin{aligned} 11 - \sqrt{x+1} &= 2 \\ 9 &= \sqrt{x+1} \\ 81 &= x + 1 \\ 80 &= x \end{aligned}$$

42.
$$\begin{aligned} 2\sqrt{2x} &= 20 \\ \sqrt{2x} &= 10 \\ 2x &= 100 \\ x &= 50 \end{aligned}$$

43.
$$\begin{aligned} \sqrt{3x+4} &= 5 \\ 3x + 4 &= 25 \\ 3x &= 21 \\ x &= 7 \end{aligned}$$

44.
$$\begin{aligned} 5 + \sqrt{2x-1} &= 8 \\ \sqrt{2x-1} &= 3 \\ 2x - 1 &= 9 \\ 2x &= 10 \\ x &= 5 \end{aligned}$$

45.
$$\begin{aligned} \sqrt{\frac{5}{7}} - \sqrt{\frac{7}{5}} &= \frac{\sqrt{5}}{\sqrt{7}} - \frac{\sqrt{7}}{\sqrt{5}} \\ &= \frac{\sqrt{5}}{\sqrt{7}} \cdot \frac{\sqrt{5}}{\sqrt{5}} - \frac{\sqrt{7}}{\sqrt{5}} \cdot \frac{\sqrt{7}}{\sqrt{7}} \\ &= \frac{5-7}{\sqrt{35}} = \frac{-2}{\sqrt{35}} \cdot \frac{\sqrt{35}}{\sqrt{35}} = \frac{-2\sqrt{35}}{35} \end{aligned}$$

46.
$$\begin{aligned} x - \frac{x}{\sqrt{x}} &= x - \frac{x}{\sqrt{x}} \cdot \frac{\sqrt{x}}{\sqrt{x}} = x - \frac{x\sqrt{x}}{x} \\ &= x - \sqrt{x} \end{aligned}$$

47.
$$\begin{aligned} \sqrt{\frac{2}{5}} + \sqrt{\frac{1}{15}} &= \frac{\sqrt{2}}{\sqrt{5}} + \frac{1}{\sqrt{15}} \\ &= \frac{\sqrt{2}}{\sqrt{5}} \cdot \frac{\sqrt{3}}{\sqrt{3}} + \frac{1}{\sqrt{15}} \\ &= \frac{\sqrt{6}+1}{\sqrt{15}} \cdot \frac{\sqrt{15}}{\sqrt{15}} \\ &= \frac{\sqrt{90} + \sqrt{15}}{15} \\ &= \frac{\sqrt{9 \cdot 10} + \sqrt{15}}{15} \\ &= \frac{3\sqrt{10} + \sqrt{15}}{15} \end{aligned}$$

48.
$$\begin{aligned} f(-1) &= 2(-1) - 1 = -2 - 1 = -3 \\ f(4) &= 2(4) - 1 = 8 - 1 = 7 \\ f(2) &= 2(2) - 1 = 4 - 1 = 3 \\ f(-11) &= 2(-11) - 1 = -22 - 1 = -23 \end{aligned}$$

49.
$$\begin{aligned} g(2) &= -3(2) + 5 = -6 + 5 = -1 \\ g(-2) &= -3(-2) + 5 = 6 + 5 = 11 \\ g(0) &= -3(0) + 5 = 5 \\ g(5) &= -3(5) + 5 = -15 + 5 = -10 \end{aligned}$$

50. $\sqrt{36} = 6$ **51.** $\sqrt{(x-5)^2} = |x - 5|$

52. $\sqrt{(-5y)^2} = 5|y|$ **53.** $\sqrt{243m^3} = \sqrt{81 \cdot 3m^3} = 9|m|\sqrt{3m}$

CONNECTIONS: GEOMETRY p. 556

$A = l(8 - l)$
$A = 8l - l^2$

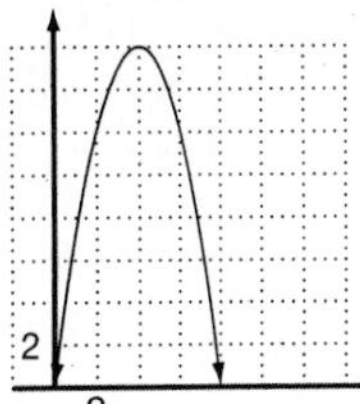

The maximum is at $(4, 16)$, so the largest area that can be enclosed is 16 ft^2.

LESSON 12-5 TRY THIS p. 558

a. $y = kx$; $84 = k(12)$, $k = \frac{84}{12} = 7$

$y = 7x$

b. $y = kx$; $50 = k(80)$, $k = \frac{50}{80} = \frac{5}{8}$ or 0.625

$y = \frac{5}{8}x$ or $y = 0.625x$

c. $c = kn$; $14 = k(30)$, $k = \frac{14}{30} = \frac{7}{15}$; $c = \frac{7}{15}n$

For 1 day, $c = \frac{7}{15}(1) = \frac{7}{15} = 0.46\frac{2}{3}$ or about 47¢

For 1 hour, $c = \frac{7}{15}\left(\frac{1}{24}\right) = \frac{7}{360} = 1\frac{17}{18}$ or about 2¢

d.
$$\begin{aligned} V &= kE \\ 106 &= k(120) \\ \frac{106}{120} &= k \\ k &= \frac{53}{60} \\ V &= \frac{53}{60}E \\ &= \frac{53}{60}(150) \\ V &= 132.5 \text{ lb} \end{aligned}$$

LESSON 12-5 EXERCISES pp. 559–560

1. $y = kx$
$28 = k(7)$
$4 = k$
$y = 4x$

2. $y = kx$
$30 = k(8)$
$3.75 = k$
$y = 3.75x$

3. $y = kx$
$0.7 = k(0.4)$
$1.75 = k$
$y = 1.75x$

4. $y = kx$
$0.8 = k(0.5)$
$1.6 = k$
$y = 1.6x$

5. $y = kx$
$400 = k(125)$
$3.2 = k$
$y = 3.2x$

6. $y = kx$
$630 = k(175)$
$3.6 = k$
$y = 3.6x$

7. $y = kx$
$200 = k(300)$
$\frac{2}{3} = k$
$y = \frac{2}{3}x$

8. $y = kx$
$500 = k(60)$
$\frac{25}{3} = k$
$y = \frac{25}{3}x$

9. $p = kh$
$236.25 = k(15)$
$15.75 = k$
$p = 15.75h$
$= 15.75(35)$
$p = \$551.25$

10. $b = kt$
$6578 = k(2)$
$3289 = k$
$b = 3289t$
$= 3289(5)$
$b = 16{,}445$ bolts

11. $n = kw$
$40 = k(22)$
$1.82 \approx k$
$n = 1.82w$
$= 1.82(14)$
$= 25.48$
$n \approx 25$ servings

12. $n = kw$
$70 = k(9)$
$7.78 \approx k$
$n = 7.78w$
$= 7.78(12)$
$= 93.36$
$n \approx 93$ servings

13. $M = kE$
$19 = k(115)$
$0.165 \approx k$
$m = 0.165E$
$= 0.165(150)$
$= 24.75$
$m \approx 25$ lb

14. $M = kE$
$44 = k(115)$
$0.383 \approx k$
$M = 0.383E$
$= 0.383(150)$
$= 57.45$
$m \approx 57$ lb

15. $W = kB$
$54 = k(75)$
$0.72 = k$
$W = 0.72B$
$= 0.72(95)$
$W = 68.4$ kg

16. $A = kI$
$2560 = k(32{,}000)$
$0.08 = k$
$A = 0.08$
$= 0.08(42{,}000)$
$A \approx \$3360$

17. $d = kg$
$1500 = k(6)$
$250 = k$
$d = 250g$
$= 250(10)$
$d = 2500$ miles

18. $v = kt$
$3 = k(300)$
$0.01 = k$
$v = 0.01t$
$= 0.01(350)$
$v = 3.5$ L

19. Yes 20. No 21. No 22. Yes 23. No

24. $P = kS$ (k = number of sides) 25. $C = kr (k = 2\pi)$

26. $B = kN$ 27. $C = kA$

28. The graph is a line through the origin. k is the slope of the line.

29. $S = kV^6$ 30. $P^2 = kt$ 31. $A = kr^2$

32. $5t \ge 0$
$t \ge 0$

33. $3x^2 \ge 0$
$x^2 \ge 0$
Any real number

34. $a - 7 \ge 0$
$a \ge 7$

35. $3m - 1 \ge 0$
$3m \ge 1$
$m \ge \frac{1}{3}$

36. $y^2 + 3 \ge 0$
$y^2 \ge -3$
Any real number

37. $\sqrt{(x-2)^2} \ge 0$
$|x - 2| \ge 0$
Any real number

38. $\sqrt{(a+3)^2} \ge 0$
$|a + 3| \ge 0$
Any real number

39. $\frac{\sqrt{y}}{\sqrt{xy}} \cdot \frac{\sqrt{xy}}{\sqrt{xy}} = \frac{y\sqrt{x}}{xy} = \frac{\sqrt{x}}{x}$

40. $\sqrt{\frac{15x^3y^2}{5x^2y}} = \sqrt{3xy}$

41. $\sqrt{\frac{18m^2n}{16n}} = \frac{\sqrt{9 \cdot 2m^2}}{4} = \frac{3|m|\sqrt{2}}{4}$

42. $b = \sqrt{c^2 - a^2}$
$= \sqrt{196 - 49}$
$= \sqrt{147}$
$= \sqrt{49 \cdot 3}$
$= 7\sqrt{3}$

43. $c = \sqrt{a^2 + b^2}$
$= \sqrt{100 + 100}$
$= \sqrt{200}$
$= \sqrt{100 \cdot 2}$
$= 10\sqrt{2}$

44. $a = \sqrt{c^2 - b^2} = \sqrt{225 - 144}$
$= \sqrt{81}$
$= 9$

45. $f(1) = 2(1)^2 - 10 = 2(1) - 10 = 2 - 10 = -8$
$f(-2) = 2(-2)^2 - 10 = 2(4) - 10 = 8 - 10 = -2$
$f(5) = 2(5)^2 - 10 = 2(25) - 10 = 50 - 10 = 40$
$f(-4) = 2(-4)^2 - 10 = 2(16) - 10 = 32 - 10 = 22$

46. $g(1) = |1| - 3 = 1 - 3 = -2$
$g(5) = |5| - 3 = 5 - 3 = 2$
$g(-3) = |-3| - 3 = 3 - 3 = 0$
$g(-7) = |-7| - 3 = 7 - 3 = 4$

LESSON 12-6 TRY THIS p. 562

a. $y = 105$ when $x = 0.6$
$y = \frac{k}{x}$, so $105 = \frac{k}{0.6}$
$105(0.6) = k$, or $k = 63$
So $y = \frac{63}{x}$ is the equation of inverse variation.

b. $y = 45$ when $x = 20$
$y = \frac{k}{x}$, so $45 = \frac{k}{20}$
$45(20) = k$, or $k = 900$
So $y = \frac{900}{x}$ is the equation of inverse variation.

c. $t = \frac{k}{r}$, so $5 = \frac{k}{60}$
$5(60) = k$, or $k = 300$
$t = \frac{300}{r}$ is an equation of inverse variation.
$t = \frac{300}{40} = \frac{15}{2} = 7\frac{1}{2}$ h

d. $t = \frac{k}{n}$, so $4 = \frac{k}{20}$
$4(20) = k$, or $k = 80$
$t = \frac{80}{n}$ is an equation of inverse variation.
$t = \frac{80}{25} = \frac{16}{5} = 3\frac{1}{5}$ h

LESSON 12-6 EXERCISES pp. 563–564

1. $y = \frac{k}{x}$
$25 = \frac{k}{3}$
$75 = k$
$y = \frac{75}{x}$

2. $y = \frac{k}{x}$
$45 = \frac{k}{2}$
$90 = k$
$y = \frac{90}{x}$

3. $y = \frac{k}{x}$
$8 = \frac{k}{10}$
$80 = k$
$y = \frac{80}{x}$

4. $y = \frac{k}{x}$
$7 = \frac{k}{10}$
$70 = k$
$y = \frac{70}{x}$

5. $y = \frac{k}{x}$
$0.125 = \frac{k}{8}$
$1 = k$
$y = \frac{1}{x}$

6. $y = \frac{k}{x}$
$6.25 = \frac{k}{0.16}$
$1 = k$
$y = \frac{1}{x}$

7. $y = \frac{k}{x}$

$42 = \frac{k}{25}$

$1050 = k$

$y = \frac{1050}{x}$

8. $y = \frac{k}{x}$

$42 = \frac{k}{50}$

$2100 = k$

$y = \frac{2100}{x}$

9. $y = \frac{k}{x}$

$0.2 = \frac{k}{0.3}$

$0.06 = k$

$y = \frac{0.06}{x}$

10. $y = \frac{k}{x}$

$0.4 = \frac{k}{0.6}$

$0.24 = k$

$y = \frac{0.24}{x}$

11. $y = \frac{k}{x}$

$0.8 = \frac{k}{4}$

$3.2 = k$

$y = \frac{3.2}{x}$

12. $y = \frac{k}{x}$

$80 = \frac{k}{0.7}$

$56 = k$

$y = \frac{56}{x}$

13. $y = \frac{k}{x}$

$\frac{2}{5} = \frac{k}{\frac{5}{2}}$

$\frac{2}{5} \cdot \frac{5}{2} = k$

$1 = k$

$y = \frac{1}{x}$

14. $y = \frac{k}{x}$

$\frac{4}{3} = \frac{k}{\frac{3}{2}}$

$\frac{4}{3} \cdot \frac{3}{2} = k$

$2 = k$

$y = \frac{2}{x}$

15. $t = \frac{k}{n}$

$16 = \frac{k}{2}$

$32 = k$

$t = \frac{32}{n}$

$t = \frac{32}{6} = 5\frac{1}{3}$ hr

16. $t = \frac{k}{n}$

$4 = \frac{k}{9}$

$36 = k$

$t = \frac{36}{n}$

$t = \frac{36}{8} = 4\frac{1}{2}$ hr

17. $V = \frac{k}{P}$

$200 = \frac{k}{32}$

$6400 = k$

$V = \frac{6400}{P}$

$V = \frac{6400}{20} = 320 \text{ cm}^3$

18. $I = \frac{k}{r}$

$2 = \frac{k}{960}$

$1920 = k$

$I = \frac{1920}{r}$

$= \frac{1920}{540} = 3\frac{5}{9}$ amp

19. $t = \frac{k}{r}$

$90 = \frac{k}{1200}$

$108{,}000 = k$

$t = \frac{108{,}000}{r}$

$= \frac{108{,}000}{2000}$

$= 54$ min

20. $H = \frac{k}{B}$

$50 = \frac{k}{40}$

$2000 = k$

$H = \frac{2000}{B}$

$= \frac{2000}{8}$

$= 250$ cm

The area is $\frac{1}{2}(50)(40) = \frac{1}{2}(2000) = 1000 \text{ cm}^2$.

21. $C = \frac{k}{N}$ 22. $N = \frac{k}{C}$ 23. $I = \frac{k}{R}$ 24. $I = \frac{k}{d^2}$

25. Since a runner's speed equals distance divided by time, the time it takes a runner to run a race varies inversely with the runner's speed. The correct answer is B.

26. $y = \frac{k}{x}$

Double x: $\frac{k}{2x} = \frac{1}{2}\left(\frac{k}{x}\right) = \frac{1}{2}y$

y is halved.

Double y: $2y = 2\left(\frac{k}{x}\right) = \frac{1}{\frac{1}{2}}\left(\frac{k}{x}\right) = \frac{k}{\frac{1}{2}x}$

x is halved.

27. $F = \frac{kS^2m}{r}$ 28. $L = \frac{kwt^2}{d}$

29. $\sqrt{2x^2 - 20x + 50} = \sqrt{2(x-5)^2} = |x-5|\sqrt{2}$

30. $\sqrt{ac^3}\sqrt{a^2c} = \sqrt{a^3c^4} = |a|c^2\sqrt{a}$

31. $\sqrt{x-2} = 4$

$x - 2 = 16$

$x = 18$

32. $7 - \sqrt{x+3} = 1$

$6 = \sqrt{x+3}$

$36 = x + 3$

$33 = x$

33. $3(-3) + 4(1) = -9 + 4 = -5$, No

34. $3(2) + 4(0) = 6$, Yes 35. $3(0) + 4(1) = 4$, Yes

36. $3(-1) + 4(1) = -3 + 4 = 1$, No

37.

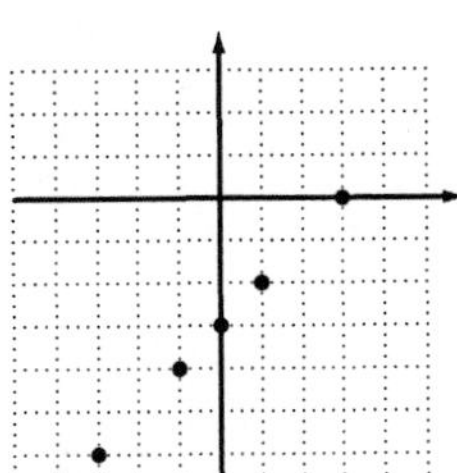

38.

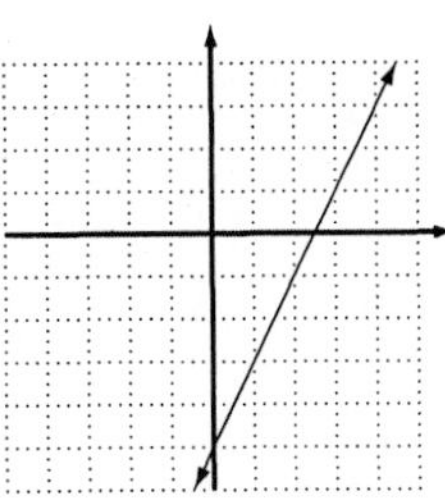

39.

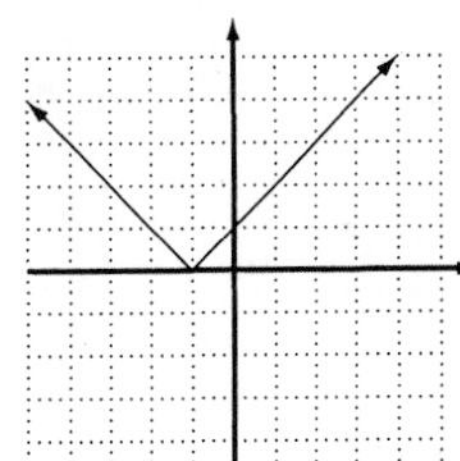

CONNECTIONS: REASONING p. 564

1. d 2. d 3. a

LESSON 12-7 TRY THIS pp. 565–567

a. $w = kxyz$

$36 = k(3 \cdot 5 \cdot 6)$

$36 = 90k$

$\frac{36}{90} = k$

$k = \frac{2}{5} = 0.4$, so $w = 0.4xyz$

$w = 0.4(2 \cdot 8 \cdot 5)$

$w = 0.4(80)$

$w = 32$

b. $P = \frac{kq}{r}$

$0.064 = \frac{k(16)}{5}$

$0.32 = 16k$

$0.02 = k$, so $P = \frac{0.02q}{r}$

$P = \frac{0.02(12)}{10}$

$P = 0.024$

c.
$$\begin{aligned} t &= kpv \\ 300 &= k(200)(100) \\ &= k(20{,}000) \\ 0.015 &= k \\ t &= 0.015pv \\ &= 0.015(70)(400) \\ t &= 420 \text{ K} \end{aligned}$$

LESSON 12-7 EXERCISES pp. 568–569

1.
$$\begin{aligned} r &= kst \\ 28 &= k(7)(8) \\ &= k(56) \\ \tfrac{1}{2} &= k \\ r &= \tfrac{1}{2}st \\ &= \tfrac{1}{2}(12)(9) \\ r &= 54 \end{aligned}$$

2.
$$\begin{aligned} m &= knp \\ 86.4 &= k(9)(12) \\ &= k(108) \\ 0.8 &= k \\ m &= 0.8np \\ &= 0.8(20)(6.5) \\ m &= 104 \end{aligned}$$

3.
$$\begin{aligned} q &= krs \\ 2.4 &= k(0.6)(0.8) \\ &= k(0.48) \\ 5 &= k \\ q &= 5rs \\ &= 5(1.6)(0.1) \\ q &= 0.8 \end{aligned}$$

4.
$$\begin{aligned} a &= kbc \\ 1 &= k(5)(0.2) \\ &= k(1) \\ 1 &= k \\ a &= bc \\ &= (2.4)(0.01) \\ a &= 0.024 \end{aligned}$$

5.
$$\begin{aligned} x &= kwyz \\ 18 &= k(2)(6)(5) \\ &= k(60) \\ \tfrac{3}{10} &= k \\ x &= \tfrac{3}{10}wyz \\ &= \tfrac{3}{10}(5)(12)(3) \\ x &= 54 \end{aligned}$$

6.
$$\begin{aligned} a &= \frac{kb}{c} \\ 14 &= \frac{k(7)}{3} \\ 6 &= k \\ a &= \frac{6b}{c} \\ &= \frac{6(4)}{8} \\ a &= 3 \end{aligned}$$

7.
$$\begin{aligned} m &= \frac{kn}{p} \\ 5 &= \frac{k(2)}{4} \\ 10 &= k \\ m &= \frac{10n}{p} \\ &= \frac{10(10)}{50} \\ m &= 2 \end{aligned}$$

8.
$$\begin{aligned} w &= \frac{kx}{y} \\ 3 &= \frac{k(9)}{2} \\ \tfrac{2}{3} &= k \\ w &= \frac{2x}{3y} \\ w &= \frac{2(15)}{3(5)} \\ w &= 2 \end{aligned}$$

9.
$$\begin{aligned} p &= \frac{kq}{r} \\ 0.8 &= \frac{k(8)}{7} \\ 0.7 &= k \\ p &= \frac{0.7q}{r} \\ &= \frac{0.7(12)}{3} \\ p &= 2.8 \end{aligned}$$

10.
$$\begin{aligned} u &= \frac{kv}{w} \\ 5.75 &= \frac{k(2.3)}{0.6} \\ 1.5 &= k \\ u &= \frac{1.5v}{w} \\ &= \frac{1.5(0.5)}{0.8} \\ u &= 0.9375 \end{aligned}$$

11.
$$\begin{aligned} A &= \frac{kbc}{d} \\ 0.525 &= \frac{k(6)(7)}{8} \\ 0.1 &= k \\ A &= \frac{0.1bc}{d} \\ &= \frac{0.1(12)(7)}{3} \\ A &= 2.8 \end{aligned}$$

12.
$$\begin{aligned} W &= \frac{kxy}{z} \\ 112 &= \frac{k(4)(8)}{0.2} \\ 0.7 &= k \\ W &= \frac{0.7xy}{z} \\ &= \frac{0.7(8)(10)}{4} \\ W &= 14 \end{aligned}$$

13.
$$\begin{aligned} V &= khA \\ 140 &= k(15)(28) \\ &= k(420) \\ \tfrac{1}{3} &= k \\ V &= \tfrac{1}{3}hA \\ &= \tfrac{1}{3}(7)(12) \\ V &= 28 \text{ cm}^3 \end{aligned}$$

14.
$$\begin{aligned} a &= \frac{kr}{i} \\ 2.55 &= \frac{k(85)}{300} \\ 9 &= k \\ a &= \frac{9r}{i} \\ 2.55 &= \frac{9(r)}{353} \\ r &\approx 100 \text{ earned runs} \end{aligned}$$

15.
$$\begin{aligned} A &= krh \\ 29.76 &= k(0.8)(6) \\ &= k(4.8) \\ 6.2 &= k \\ A &= 6.2rh \\ 74.4 &= 6.2(1.5)h \\ &= 9.3h \\ h &= 8 \text{ in.} \end{aligned}$$

16.
$$\begin{aligned} A &= 6.2rh \\ 111.6 &= 6.2(r)(6) \\ &= 37.2r \\ r &= 3 \text{ cm} \end{aligned}$$

17. $A = kd^2$
The area of a circle equals πr^2.
So $kd^2 = \pi r^2$.
Substitute $d = 2r$:
$$\begin{aligned} k(2r)^2 &= \pi r^2 \\ k(4r^2) &= \pi r^2 \\ k &= \frac{\pi r^2}{4r^2} \\ k &= \frac{\pi}{4} \end{aligned}$$

18. a. Answers may vary. Sample: A pyramid with sides 1 and height 3 has volume $= \frac{1}{3}(1)^2(3) = 1$. A pyramid with sides 2 and height 6 has volume $= \frac{1}{3}(2)^2(6) = 8$. The volume of the larger pyramid is not 4 times the volume of the smaller pyramid.

b. Answers may vary. Sample: If a pyramid has a square base and you double the length of the sides of the base and double the height, the volume of the new pyramid will be eight times the volume of the original pyramid.

19. $y = kx$
Doubling x: $y_2 = k(2x) = 2(kx) = 2y$
y is doubled.

20. $y = kx^2$
Doubling x: $y_2 = k(2x)^2 = k(4x^2) = 4(kx^2) = 4y$
y is quadrupled.

21.
$$\begin{aligned} d &= kr^2 \\ 106 &= k(35)^2 \\ 0.087 &\approx k \\ d &= 0.087\,r^2 \\ 228 &= 0.087\,r^2 \\ r &\approx 51 \text{ mi/h} \end{aligned}$$

22.
$$\begin{aligned} F &= \frac{km}{d^2} \\ 7.8 &= \frac{10k}{(20)^2} \\ 7.8 &= \frac{10k}{400} \\ 312 &= k \\ F &= \frac{312m}{d^2} \\ 31.2 &= \frac{312(10)}{d^2} \\ d^2 &= \frac{3120}{31.2} \\ d^2 &= 100 \\ d &= 10 \text{ m} \end{aligned}$$

23. $\dfrac{\sqrt{16}}{\sqrt{3}} \cdot \dfrac{\sqrt{3}}{\sqrt{3}} = \dfrac{4\sqrt{3}}{3}$

24. $\dfrac{\sqrt{5}}{\sqrt{x}} \cdot \dfrac{\sqrt{x}}{\sqrt{x}} = \dfrac{\sqrt{5x}}{x}$

25. $\frac{\sqrt{x}}{\sqrt{xy}} \cdot \frac{\sqrt{xy}}{\sqrt{xy}} = \frac{\sqrt{x^2y}}{xy} = \frac{x\sqrt{y}}{xy} = \frac{\sqrt{y}}{y}$

26. $\frac{\sqrt{18}}{2y} \cdot \frac{\sqrt{2y}}{\sqrt{2y}} = \frac{\sqrt{36y}}{2y} = \frac{6\sqrt{y}}{2y} = \frac{3\sqrt{y}}{y}$

27. $\frac{\sqrt{3x}}{\sqrt{12y}} \cdot \frac{\sqrt{12y}}{\sqrt{12y}} = \frac{\sqrt{36xy}}{12y} = \frac{6\sqrt{xy}}{12y} = \frac{\sqrt{xy}}{2y}$

28. $\frac{\sqrt{x^4y}}{\sqrt{xy^2}} \cdot \frac{\sqrt{xy^2}}{\sqrt{xy^2}} = \frac{\sqrt{x^5y^3}}{xy^2} = \frac{x^2y\sqrt{xy}}{xy^2} = \frac{x\sqrt{xy}}{y}$

29. $\frac{\sqrt{6c}}{\sqrt{8c^3}} \cdot \frac{\sqrt{8c^3}}{\sqrt{8c^3}} = \frac{\sqrt{48c^4}}{8c^3} = \frac{\sqrt{16 \cdot 3c^4}}{8c^3} = \frac{4c^2\sqrt{3}}{8c^3} = \frac{\sqrt{3}}{2c}$

30. $\frac{\sqrt{12cd}}{\sqrt{3c^4d^4}} \cdot \frac{\sqrt{3}}{\sqrt{3}} = \frac{\sqrt{36cd}}{c^2d^2(3)} = \frac{6\sqrt{cd}}{3c^2d^2} = \frac{2\sqrt{cd}}{c^2d^2}$

31. $c = \sqrt{a^2 + b^2}$
$= \sqrt{10^2 + 24^2}$
$= \sqrt{100 + 576}$
$= \sqrt{676}$
$= 26$

32. $c = \sqrt{a^2 + b^2}$
$= \sqrt{6^2 + 12^2}$
$= \sqrt{36 + 144}$
$= \sqrt{180}$
$= 6\sqrt{5}$

33. $c^2 = \sqrt{a^2 + b^2}$
$= \sqrt{24^2 + 32^2}$
$= \sqrt{576 + 1024}$
$= \sqrt{1600}$
$= 40$

34. $\sqrt{2x + 3} = \sqrt{5x - 6}$
$2x + 3 = 5x - 6$
$9 = 3x$
$3 = x$

35. $-\sqrt{x} = 7$
$\sqrt{x} = -7$
No real number solution

36. $\sqrt{x + 7} = 2\sqrt{x - 5}$
$x + 7 = 4(x - 5)$
$x + 7 = 4x - 20$
$27 = 3x$
$9 = x$

37. $\sqrt{x + 30} = 3\sqrt{x - 2}$
$x + 30 = 9(x - 2)$
$x + 30 = 9x - 18$
$48 = 8x$
$6 = x$

38.

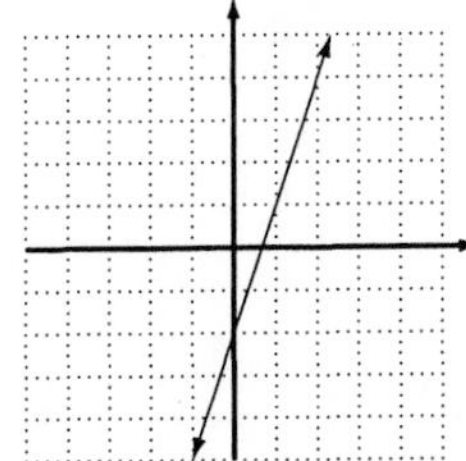

39.

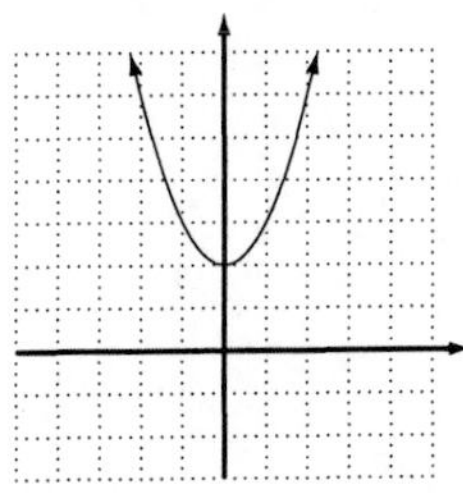

CHAPTER 12 WRAP UP pp. 571–573

1. No 2. Yes

3. $f(x) = 3x - 4$
$f(2) = 3(2) - 4 = 6 - 4 = 2$
$f(0) = 3(0) - 4 = 0 - 4 = -4$
$f(-1) = 3(-1) - 4 = -3 - 4 = -7$

4. $g(t) = |t| - 3$
$g(3) = |3| - 3 = 3 - 3 = 0$
$g(-5) = |-5| - 3 = 5 - 3 = 2$
$g(0) = |0| - 3 = 0 - 3 = -3$

5. $h(x) = x^3 + 1$
$h(-2) = (-2)^3 + 1 = -8 + 1 = -7$
$h(0) = (0)^3 + 1 = 0 + 1 = 1$
$h(-1) = (-1)^3 + 1 = -1 + 1 = 0$

6.

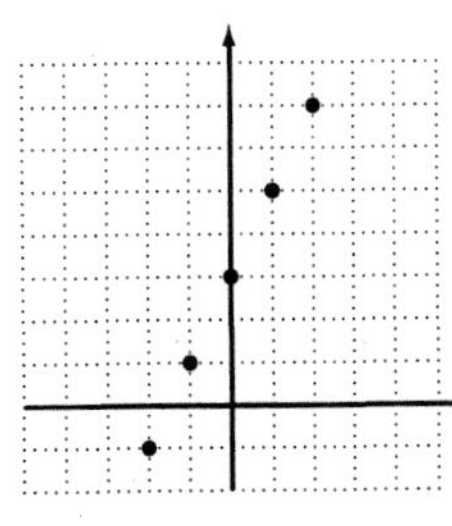

7.

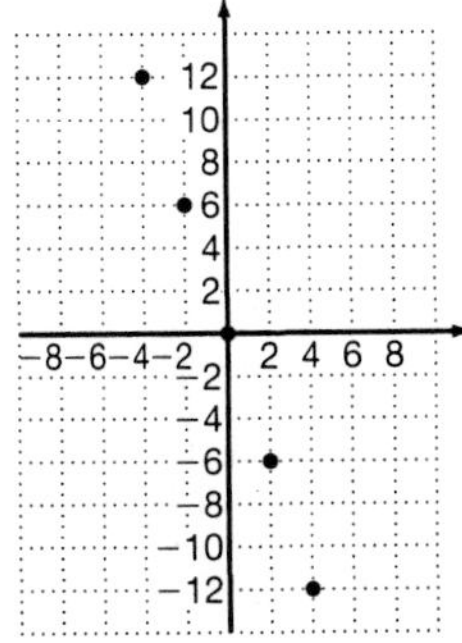

8.

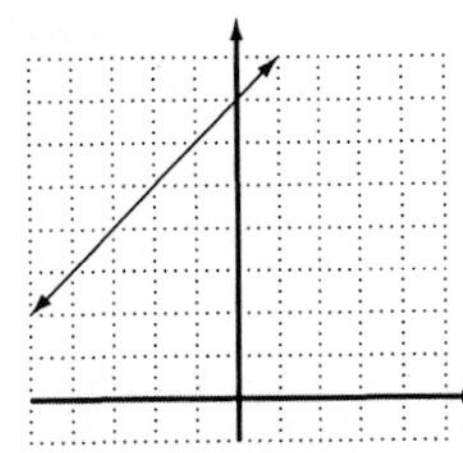

9.

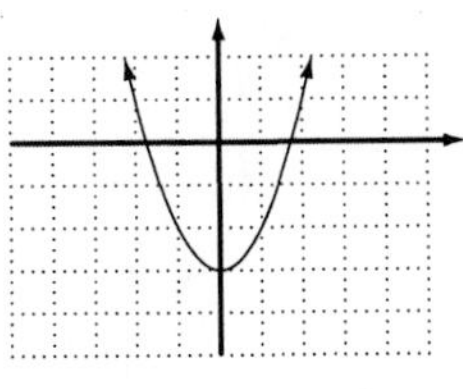

10.

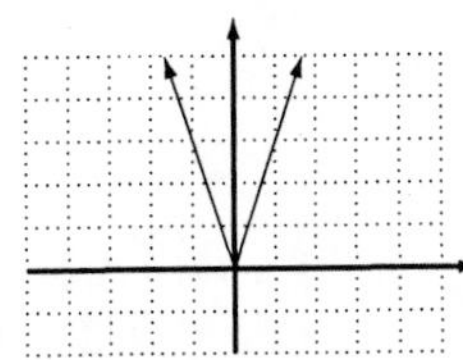

11. No 12. Yes

13. $y = 1.50x + 30$
$y = 1.5(5) + 30$
$= 37.5$
The total cost is \$37.50.

14.

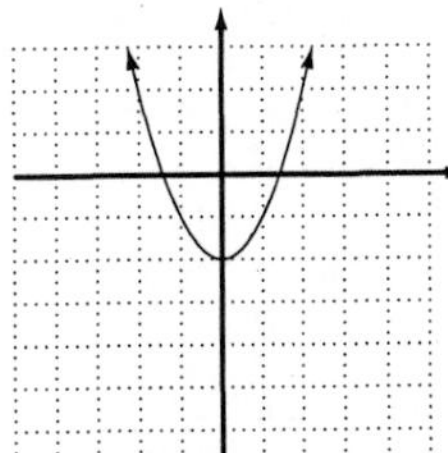

15.

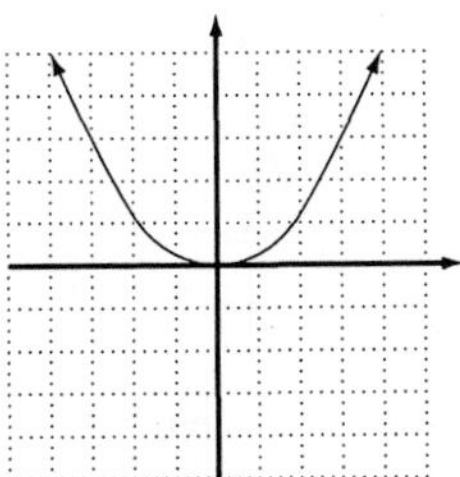

16. $y = kx$
$12 = k(4)$
$3 = k$
$y = 3x$

17. $y = kx$
$4 = k(8)$
$\frac{1}{2} = k$
$y = \frac{1}{2}x$

18. $P = kh$
$165 = k(20)$
$8.25 = k$
$P = 8.25h$
$= 8.25(30)$
$P = \$247.50$

19. $y = \frac{k}{x}$
$5 = \frac{k}{6}$
$30 = k$
$y = \frac{30}{x}$

20. $y = \frac{k}{x}$
$0.5 = \frac{k}{2}$
$1 = k$
$y = \frac{1}{x}$

21. $t = \frac{k}{n}$
$5 = \frac{k}{2}$
$10 = k$
$t = \frac{10}{n}$
$t = \frac{10}{10} = 1$ hr

22. a. $A = ka(b_1 + b_2)$
$120 = k(8)(12 + 18)$
$= k(8)(30)$
$= k(240)$
$\frac{1}{2} = k$

b. $A = \frac{1}{2}a(b_1 + b_2)$
$= \frac{1}{2}(6)(8 + 12)$
$= 3(20)$
$A = 60$

23. a. $W = \frac{kxy}{z^2}$
$189 = \frac{k(28)(16)}{(8)^2}$
$189 = \frac{k(448)}{64}$
$27 = k$

b. $W = \frac{27xy}{z^2}$
$= \frac{27(24)(4)}{(6)^2}$
$= \frac{27(96)}{36}$
$W = 72$

CHAPTER 12 ASSESSMENT p. 573

1. $f(x) = \frac{1}{2}x + 1$

$f(0) = \frac{1}{2}(0) + 1 = 0 + 1 = 1$

$f(1) = \frac{1}{2}(1) + 1 = \frac{1}{2} + 1 = 1\frac{1}{2}$ or $\frac{3}{2}$

$f(2) = \frac{1}{2}(2) + 1 = 1 + 1 = 2$

2. $g(t) = -2|t| + 3$
$g(-1) = -2|-1| + 3 = -2(1) + 3 = -2 + 3 = 1$
$g(0) = -2|0| + 3 = -2(0) + 3 = 0 + 3 = 3$
$g(3) = -2|3| + 3 = -2(3) + 3 = -6 + 3 = -3$

3. Yes **4.** No

5. $c = 19d + 0.2m$
$= 19(2) + 0.2(310)$
$= 38 + 62$
$c = \$100$

6.

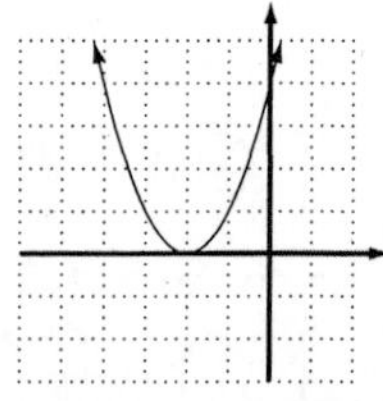

domain: all real numbers
range: $y \geq 0$

7.

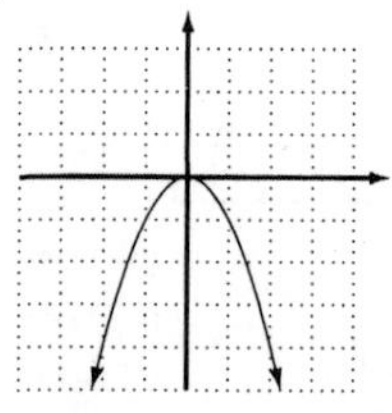

domain: all real numbers
range: $y \leq 0$

8. $y = kx$
$6 = k(3)$
$2 = k$
$y = 2x$

9. $y = \frac{k}{x}$
$6 = \frac{k}{2}$
$12 = k$
$y = \frac{12}{x}$

10. $t = \frac{k}{n}$
$3 = \frac{k}{2}$
$6 = k$
$t = \frac{6}{n}$
$t = \frac{6}{5}$ h or $1\frac{1}{5}$ h

11. $y = kxz^2$
$375 = k(3)(25)^2$
$= k(3)(625)$
$= k(1825)$
$0.2 = k$
$y = 0.2xz^2$
$= 0.2(8)(6)^2$
$= 1.6(36)$
$y = 57.6$

12. $x = \frac{kyz}{m}$
$2 = \frac{k(4)(6)}{3}$
$2 = k(8)$
$\frac{1}{4} = k$
$x = \frac{yz}{4m}$
$= \frac{(7.5)(8)}{4(3)}$
$x = 5$

CHAPTER 13

SKILLS & CONCEPTS p. 574

1. $(x - 5)^2 = (x - 5)(x - 5) = x^2 - 5x - 5x + 25$
$= x^2 - 10x + 25$

2. $(3x + 1)^2 = (3x + 1)(3x + 1) = 9x^2 + 3x + 3x + 1$
$= 9x^2 + 6x + 1$

3. $x^2 - 6x = 0$
$x(x - 6) = 0$
$x = 0$ or $x - 6 = 0$
$x = 0$ or $x = 6$

4. $x^2 - 5x + 6 = 0$
$(x - 2)(x - 3) = 0$
$x - 2 = 0$ or $x - 3 = 0$
$x = 2$ or $x = 3$

5. $2x + \frac{8}{x} = 8$
$x\left(2x + \frac{8}{x}\right) = x(8)$
$2x^2 + 8 = 8x$
$2x^2 - 8x + 8 = 0$
$2(x^2 - 4x + 4) = 0$
$2(x - 2)(x - 2) = 0$
$x - 2 = 0$
$x = 2$

6. $\frac{x - 2}{x + 2} = \frac{1}{4}$
$4(x + 2)\left(\frac{x - 2}{x + 2}\right) = 4(x + 2)\left(\frac{1}{4}\right)$
$4(x - 2) = x + 2$
$4x - 8 = x + 2$
$3x = 10$
$x = \frac{10}{3}$

7. $\sqrt{88} = \sqrt{4 \cdot 22} = \sqrt{4}\sqrt{22} = 2\sqrt{22}$

8. $\sqrt{20} = \sqrt{4 \cdot 5} = \sqrt{4}\sqrt{5} = 2\sqrt{5}$

9. $\sqrt{44} = \sqrt{4 \cdot 11} = \sqrt{4}\sqrt{11} = 2\sqrt{11}$

10. $\sqrt{32} = \sqrt{16 \cdot 2} = \sqrt{16}\sqrt{2} = 4\sqrt{2}$

11. $\sqrt{\frac{7}{3}} = \frac{\sqrt{7}}{\sqrt{3}} \cdot \frac{\sqrt{3}}{\sqrt{3}} = \frac{\sqrt{21}}{3}$

12. $\sqrt{\frac{5}{2}} = \frac{\sqrt{5}}{\sqrt{2}} \cdot \frac{\sqrt{2}}{\sqrt{2}} = \frac{\sqrt{10}}{2}$

13. $\sqrt{\frac{1}{5}} = \frac{\sqrt{1}}{\sqrt{5}} \cdot \frac{\sqrt{5}}{\sqrt{5}} = \frac{\sqrt{5}}{5}$

14. $\sqrt{\frac{7}{8}} = \frac{\sqrt{7}}{\sqrt{8}} \cdot \frac{\sqrt{8}}{\sqrt{8}} = \frac{\sqrt{56}}{8} = \frac{\sqrt{4 \cdot 14}}{8} = \frac{2\sqrt{14}}{8} = \frac{\sqrt{14}}{4}$

15.

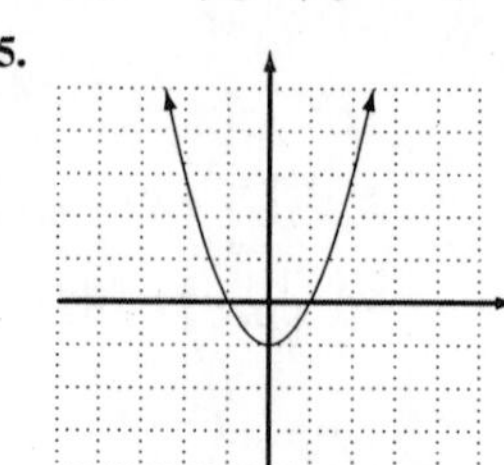

16.

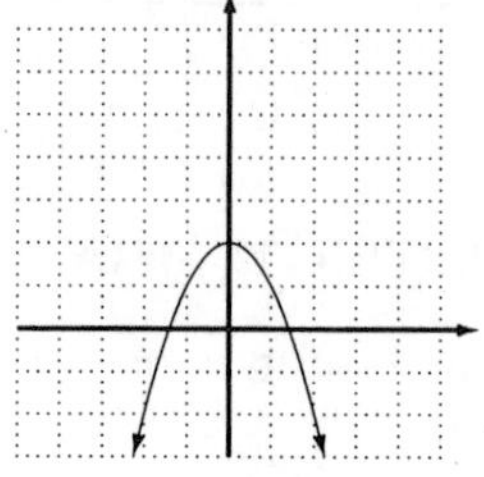

LESSON 13-1 TRY THIS pp. 577–578

a. $x^2 - 7x + 0 = 0;\quad a = 1, b = -7, c = 0$
b. $x^2 + 9x - 3 = 0;\quad a = 1, b = 9, c = -3$
c. $5x^2 + 0x + 4 = 0;\quad a = 5, b = 0, c = 4$

d. $3x^2 + 5x = 0$
$x(3x + 5) = 0$
$x = 0$ or $3x + 5 = 0$
$x = 0$ or $3x = -5$
$x = 0$ or $x = -\frac{5}{3}$

e. $10x^2 - 6x = 0$
$2x(5x - 3) = 0$
$2x = 0$ or $5x - 3 = 0$
$x = 0$ or $5x = 3$
$x = 0$ or $x = \frac{3}{5}$

f. $3x^2 + x - 2 = 0$
$(3x - 2)(x + 1) = 0$
$3x - 2 = 0$ or $x + 1 = 0$
$3x = 2$ or $x = -1$
$x = \frac{2}{3}$ or $x = -1$

g. $x^2 + 4x + 8 = 8x + 29$
$x^2 - 4x - 21 = 0$
$(x - 7)(x + 3) = 0$
$x - 7 = 0$ or $x + 3 = 0$
$x = 7$ or $x = -3$

LESSON 13-1 EXERCISES pp. 578–579

1. $x^2 - 3x + 2 = 0$;
$a = 1, b = -3, c = 2$

2. $x^2 - 8x - 5 = 0$;
$a = 1, b = -8, c = -5$

3. $2x^2 - 3 = 0$;
$a = 2, b = 0, c = -3$

4. $5x^2 - 9 = 0$;
$a = 5, b = 0, c = -9$

5. $7x^2 - 4x + 3 = 0$;
$a = 7, b = -4, c = 3$

6. $9x^2 - x - 5 = 0$;
$a = 9, b = -1, c = -5$

7. $2x^2 - 3x + 5 = 0$;
$a = 2, b = -3, c = 5$

8. $x^2 - 2x - 5 = 0$;
$a = 1, b = -2, c = -5$

9. $3x^2 - 2x + 8 = 0$;
$a = 3, b = -2, c = 8$

10. $x^2 + 7x = 0$
$x(x + 7) = 0$
$x = 0$ or $x + 7 = 0$
$x = 0$ or $x = -7$

11. $x^2 + 5x = 0$
$x(x + 5) = 0$
$x = 0$ or $x + 5 = 0$
$x = 0$ or $x = -5$

12. $3x^2 + 6x = 0$
$3x(x + 2) = 0$
$3x = 0$ or $x + 2 = 0$
$x = 0$ or $x = -2$

13. $4p^2 + 8p = 0$
$4p(p + 2) = 0$
$4p = 0$ or $p + 2 = 0$
$p = 0$ or $p = -2$

14. $5x^2 - 2x = 0$
$x(5x - 2) = 0$
$x = 0$ or $5x - 2 = 0$
$5x = 2$
$x = 0$ or $x = \frac{2}{5}$

15. $3n^2 - 7n = 0$
$n(3n - 7) = 0$
$n = 0$ or $3n - 7 = 0$
$3n = 7$
$n = 0$ or $n = \frac{7}{3}$

16. $4x^2 + 4x = 0$
$4x(x + 1) = 0$
$4x = 0$ or $x + 1 = 0$
$x = 0$ or $x = -1$

17. $2t^2 - 2t = 0$
$2t(t - 1) = 0$
$2t = 0$ or $t - 1 = 0$
$t = 0$ or $t = 1$

18. $10x^2 - 30x = 0$
$10x(x - 3) = 0$
$10x = 0$ or $x - 3 = 0$
$x = 0$ or $x = 3$

19. $10x^2 - 50x = 0$
$10x(x - 5) = 0$
$10x = 0$ or $x - 5 = 0$
$x = 0$ or $x = 5$

20. $55x^2 - 11x = 0$
$11x(5x - 1) = 0$
$11x = 0$ or $5x - 1 = 0$
$x = 0$ or $5x = 1$
$x = 0$ or $x = \frac{1}{5}$

21. $33x^2 + 11x = 0$
$11x(3x + 1) = 0$
$11x = 0$ or $3x + 1 = 0$
$x = 0$ or $3x = -1$
$x = 0$ or $x = -\frac{1}{3}$

22. $14x^2 - 3x = 0$
$x(14x - 3) = 0$
$x = 0$ or $14x - 3 = 0$
$14x = 3$
$x = 0$ or $x = \frac{3}{14}$

23. $17x^2 - 8x = 0$
$x(17x - 8) = 0$
$x = 0$ or $17x - 8 = 0$
$17x = 8$
$x = 0$ or $x = \frac{8}{17}$

24. $3x^2 - 81x = 0$
$3x(x - 27) = 0$
$3x = 0$ or $x - 27 = 0$
$x = 0$ or $x = 27$

25. $p^2 - 16p + 48 = 0$
$(p - 4)(p - 12) = 0$
$p - 4 = 0$ or $p - 12 = 0$
$p = 4$ or $p = 12$

26. $x^2 + 8x - 48 = 0$
$(x - 4)(x + 12) = 0$
$x - 4 = 0$ or $x + 12 = 0$
$x = 4$ or $x = -12$

27. $x^2 + 7x + 6 = 0$
$(x + 1)(x + 6) = 0$
$x + 1 = 0$ or $x + 6 = 0$
$x = -1$ or $x = -6$

28. $x^2 + 6x + 5 = 0$
$(x + 5)(x + 1) = 0$
$x + 5 = 0$ or $x + 1 = 0$
$x = -5$ or $x = -1$

29. $m^2 + 4m - 21 = 0$
$(m + 7)(m - 3) = 0$
$m + 7 = 0$ or $m - 3 = 0$
$m = -7$ or $m = 3$

30. $x^2 + 7x - 18 = 0$
$(x + 9)(x - 2) = 0$
$x + 9 = 0$ or $x - 2 = 0$
$x = -9$ or $x = 2$

31. $t^2 - 9t + 14 = 0$
$(t - 7)(t - 2) = 0$
$t - 7 = 0$ or $t - 2 = 0$
$t = 7$ or $t = 2$

32. $x^2 - 8x + 15 = 0$
$(x - 3)(x - 5) = 0$
$x - 3 = 0$ or $x - 5 = 0$
$x = 3$ or $x = 5$

33. $x^2 + 10x + 25 = 0$
$(x + 5)^2 = 0$
$x + 5 = 0$
$x = -5$

34. $x^2 + 6x + 9 = 0$
$(x + 3)^2 = 0$
$x + 3 = 0$
$x = -3$

35. $x^2 - 2x + 1 = 0$
$(x - 1)^2 = 0$
$x - 1 = 0$
$x = 1$

36. $x^2 - 8x + 16 = 0$
$(x - 4)^2 = 0$
$x - 4 = 0$
$x = 4$

37. $2x^2 - 13x + 15 = 0$
$(x - 5)(2x - 3) = 0$
$x - 5 = 0$ or $2x - 3 = 0$
$x = 5$ or $2x = 3$
$x = 5$ or $x = \frac{3}{2}$

38. $6x^2 + x - 2 = 0$
$(2x - 1)(3x + 2) = 0$
$2x - 1 = 0$ or $3x + 2 = 0$
$2x = 1$ or $3x = -2$
$x = \frac{1}{2}$ or $x = -\frac{2}{3}$

39. $3a^2 - 10a - 8 = 0$
$(a - 4)(3a + 2) = 0$
$a - 4 = 0$ or $3a + 2 = 0$
$a = 4$ or $3a = -2$
$a = 4$ or $a = -\frac{2}{3}$

40. $9b^2 - 15b + 4 = 0$
$(3b - 4)(3b - 1) = 0$
$3b - 4 = 0$ or $3b - 1 = 0$
$3b = 4$ or $3b = 1$
$b = \frac{4}{3}$ or $b = \frac{1}{3}$

41. $3x^2 - 7x = 20$
$3x^2 - 7x - 20 = 0$
$(x - 4)(3x + 5) = 0$
$x - 4 = 0$ or $3x + 5 = 0$
$x = 4$ or $3x = -5$
$x = 4$ or $x = -\frac{5}{3}$

42. $6x^2 - 4x = 10$
$6x^2 - 4x - 10 = 0$
$2(3x^2 - 2x - 5) = 0$
$2(x + 1)(3x - 5) = 0$
$x + 1 = 0$ or $3x - 5 = 0$
$x = -1$ or $3x = 5$
$x = -1$ or $x = \frac{5}{3}$

43. $2x^2 + 12x = -10$
$2x^2 + 12x + 10 = 0$
$2(x^2 + 6x + 5) = 0$
$2(x + 5)(x + 1) = 0$
$x + 5 = 0$ or $x + 1 = 0$
$x = -5$ or $x = -1$

44. $12x^2 - 5x = 2$
$12x^2 - 5x - 2 = 0$
$(4x + 1)(3x - 2) = 0$
$4x + 1 = 0$ or $3x - 2 = 0$
$4x = -1$ or $3x = 2$
$x = -\frac{1}{4}$ or $x = \frac{2}{3}$

45. $6x^2 + x - 1 = 0$
$(3x - 1)(2x + 1) = 0$
$3x - 1 = 0$ or $2x + 1 = 0$
$3x = 1$ or $2x = -1$
$x = \frac{1}{3}$ or $x = -\frac{1}{2}$

46. $6x^2 + 13x + 6 = 0$
$(2x + 3)(3x + 2) = 0$
$2x + 3 = 0$ or $3x + 2 = 0$
$2x = -3$ or $3x = -2$
$x = -\frac{3}{2}$ or $x = -\frac{2}{3}$

47. $2x^2 + 3x = 35$
$2x^2 + 3x - 35 = 0$
$(x + 5)(2x - 7) = 0$
$x + 5 = 0$ or $2x - 7 = 0$
$x = -5$ or $2x = 7$
$x = -5$ or $x = \frac{7}{2}$

48. $12x^2 + 7x - 12 = 0$
$(4x - 3)(3x + 4) = 0$
$4x - 3 = 0$ or $3x + 4 = 0$
$4x = 3$ or $3x = -4$
$x = \frac{3}{4}$ or $x = -\frac{4}{3}$

49. $t(t - 5) = 14$
$t^2 - 5t = 14$
$t^2 - 5t - 14 = 0$
$(t - 7)(t + 2) = 0$
$t - 7 = 0$ or $t + 2 = 0$
$t = 7$ or $t = -2$

50. $m(3m + 1) = 2$
$3m^2 + m = 2$
$3m^2 + m - 2 = 0$
$(3m - 2)(m + 1) = 0$
$3m - 2 = 0$ or $m + 1 = 0$
$m = \frac{2}{3}$ or $m = -1$

51. $3y^2 + 8y = 12y + 15$
$3y^2 - 4y - 15 = 0$
$(3y + 5)(y - 3) = 0$
$3y + 5 = 0$ or $y - 3 = 0$
$y = -\frac{5}{3}$ or $y = 3$

52. $18 + 2z = z^2 - 5z$
$0 = z^2 - 7z - 18$
$0 = (z - 9)(z + 2)$
$z - 9 = 0$ or $z + 2 = 0$
$z = 9$ or $z = -2$

53. $t(9 + t) = 4(2t + 5)$
$9t + t^2 = 8t + 20$
$t^2 + t - 20 = 0$
$(t + 5)(t - 4) = 0$
$t + 5 = 0$ or $t - 4 = 0$
$t = -5$ or $t = 4$

54. $16(p - 1) = p(p + 8)$
$16p - 16 = p^2 + 8p$
$0 = p^2 - 8p + 16$
$0 = (p - 4)(p - 4)$
$p - 4 = 0$
$p = 4$

55. $(2x - 3)(x + 1) = 4(2x - 3)$
$2x^2 - x - 3 = 8x - 12$
$2x^2 - 9x + 9 = 0$
$(2x - 3)(x - 3) = 0$
$2x - 3 = 0$ or $x - 3 = 0$
$x = \frac{3}{2}$ or $x = 3$

56. $(3x - 1)(2x + 1) = 3(2x + 1)$
$6x^2 + x - 1 = 6x + 3$
$6x^2 - 5x - 4 = 0$
$(3x - 4)(2x + 1) = 0$
$3x - 4 = 0$ or $2x + 1 = 0$
$x = \frac{4}{3}$ or $x = -\frac{1}{2}$

57. $(2m-1)(m+3)=-2(m+4)$
$2m^2+5m-3=-2m-8$
$2m^2+7m+5=0$
$(2m+5)(m+1)=0$
$2m+5=0$ or $m+1=0$
$2m=-5$ or $m=-1$
$m=-\frac{5}{2}$ or $m=-1$

58. $(m+2)(2m+3)=(m+2)^2$
$2m^2+7m+6=m^2+4m+4$
$m^2+3m+2=0$
$(m+2)(m+1)=0$
$m+2=0$ or $m+1=0$
$m=-2$ or $m=-1$

59. $1=\frac{1}{3}x^2$
$3=x^2$
$\pm\sqrt{3}=x$

60. $x^2+\sqrt{3}x=0$
$x(x+\sqrt{3})=0$
$x=0$ or $x+\sqrt{3}=0$
$x=0$ or $x=-\sqrt{3}$

61. $\sqrt{5}y^2-y=0$
$y(\sqrt{5}y-1)=0$
$y=0$ or $\sqrt{5}y-1=0$
$\sqrt{5}y=1$
$y=\frac{1}{\sqrt{5}}\cdot\frac{\sqrt{5}}{\sqrt{5}}=\frac{\sqrt{5}}{5}$
$y=0$ or $y=\frac{\sqrt{5}}{5}$

62. $\sqrt{7}x^2+\sqrt{3}x=0$
$x(\sqrt{7}x+\sqrt{3})=0$
$x=0$ or $\sqrt{7}x+\sqrt{3}=0$
$\sqrt{7}x=-\sqrt{3}$
$x=\frac{-\sqrt{3}}{\sqrt{7}}\cdot\frac{\sqrt{7}}{\sqrt{7}}$
$x=0$ or $x=\frac{-\sqrt{21}}{7}$

63. $y(\sqrt{5}y+1)=0$
$y=0$ or $\sqrt{5}y+1=0$
$\sqrt{5}y=-1$
$y=\frac{-1}{\sqrt{5}}\cdot\frac{\sqrt{5}}{\sqrt{5}}=\frac{-\sqrt{5}}{5}$
$y=0$ or $y=-\frac{\sqrt{5}}{5}$

64. $\sqrt{3}x^2-\sqrt{8}x=0$
$x(\sqrt{3}x-\sqrt{8})=0$
$x=0$ or $\sqrt{3}x-\sqrt{8}=0$
$\sqrt{3}x=\sqrt{8}$
$3x^2=8$
$x^2=\frac{8}{3}$
$x=\frac{\sqrt{8}}{\sqrt{3}}\cdot\frac{\sqrt{3}}{\sqrt{3}}$
$x=\frac{\sqrt{24}}{3}$
$x=0$ or $x=\frac{2\sqrt{6}}{3}$

65. Axis of symmetry $=-\frac{b}{2a}=-\frac{3}{8}$
$b=3$ $\quad 2a=8$ $\quad c=7$
$a=4$
Equation: $f(x)=4x^2+3x+7$
Other answers are possible.

66. Answers may vary. Ex: $x^2+6x=0$

67. Answers may vary. Ex: $4x^2-19x+12=0$

68. Answers may vary. Ex: $5x^2+23x-10=0$

69. Answers may vary. Ex: $2x^3+5x^2-3x=0$

70. Infinitely many. All equations of the form $k(x-2)(x-5)=0$, or $kx^2-7kx+10k=0$, where k is any real number, have 2 and 5 as solutions.

71. $5x^2\ge 0$
$x^2\ge 0$
Any value

72. $x-3\ge 0$
$x\ge 3$

73. $x+5\ge 0$
$x\ge -5$

74. $3x-2\ge 0$
$3x\ge 2$
$x\ge\frac{2}{3}$

75. $4m^2-10m-6=2(2m^2-5m-3)$
$=2(2m+1)(m-3)$

76. $c^2-c-90=(c-10)(c+9)$

77. $y^2-121=(y+11)(y-11)$

78. $9x^2+63x+54=9(x^2+7x+6)$
$=9(x+1)(x+6)$

79. $x^2y+4xy+4y=y(x^2+4x+4)$
$=y(x+2)^2$

80. $2ab+2bc+3ad+3dc=2b(a+c)+3d(a+c)$
$=(a+c)(2b+3d)$

81. $\{1,2,3,6\}$

82. $\{25,36,49\}$

LESSON 13-2 TRY THIS

pp. 580–583

a. $2x^2=20$
$x^2=10$
$x=\pm\sqrt{10}$

b. $3y^2=5$
$y^2=\frac{5}{3}$
$y=\pm\frac{\sqrt{5}}{\sqrt{3}}\cdot\frac{\sqrt{3}}{\sqrt{3}}$
$y=\pm\frac{\sqrt{15}}{3}$

c. $4m^2-100=0$
$4m^2=100$
$m^2=25$
$m=\pm\sqrt{25}$
$m=\pm 5$

d. $9h^2+4=4$
$9h^2=0$
$h^2=0$
$h=0$

e. $(x-3)^2=16$
$x-3=\pm\sqrt{16}$
$x-3=\pm 4$
$x=7$ or $x=-1$

f. $(x+3)^2=10$
$x+3=\pm\sqrt{10}$
$x=-3\pm\sqrt{10}$

g. $(m-1)^2=5$
$m-1=\pm\sqrt{5}$
$m=1\pm\sqrt{5}$

h. $x^2-14x+49=3$
$(x-7)^2=3$
$x-7=\pm\sqrt{3}$
$x=7\pm\sqrt{3}$

i. $z^2+22z+121=169$
$(z+11)^2=169$
$z+11=\pm\sqrt{169}$
$z=-11\pm 13$
$z=2$ or $z=-24$

j. Substitute $v_0 = 14$, $c = 3$, and $h = 0$ in

$$-5t^2 + v_0t + c = h$$
$$-5t^2 + 14t + 3 = 0$$
$$5t^2 - 14t - 3 = 0$$
$$(5t + 1)(t - 3) = 0$$
$$5t + 1 = 0 \quad \text{or} \quad t - 3 = 0$$
$$5t = -1 \quad \text{or} \quad t = 3$$
$$t = -\frac{1}{5} \quad \text{or} \quad t = 3$$

Since the time cannot be negative, the marble will hit the ground in about 3 seconds.

k.
$$A = P(1 + r)^t$$
$$529 = 400(1 + r)^2$$
$$\frac{529}{400} = (1 + r)^2$$
$$\pm\frac{23}{20} = 1 + r$$
$$r = \frac{3}{20} \quad \text{or} \quad r = -\frac{43}{20}$$

Since interest can't be negative, the solution is $\frac{3}{20}$ or 15%.

LESSON 13-2 EXERCISES pp. 583–585

1. $x^2 = 121$
$x = \pm\sqrt{121}$
$x = \pm 11$

2. $x^2 = 10$
$x = \pm\sqrt{10}$

3. $5x^2 = 35$
$x^2 = 7$
$x = \pm\sqrt{7}$

4. $3x^2 = 30$
$x^2 = 10$
$x = \pm\sqrt{10}$

5. $5a^2 = 3$
$a^2 = \frac{3}{5}$
$a = \pm\sqrt{\frac{3}{5}} = \pm\frac{\sqrt{3}}{\sqrt{5}} \cdot \frac{\sqrt{5}}{\sqrt{5}} = \pm\frac{\sqrt{15}}{5}$

6. $2x^2 = 5$
$x^2 = \frac{5}{2}$
$x = \pm\sqrt{\frac{5}{2}} = \pm\frac{\sqrt{5}}{\sqrt{2}} \cdot \frac{\sqrt{2}}{\sqrt{2}} = \pm\frac{\sqrt{10}}{2}$

7. $4t^2 - 25 = 0$
$4t^2 = 25$
$t^2 = \frac{25}{4}$
$t = \pm\sqrt{\frac{25}{4}} = \pm\frac{5}{2}$

8. $9x^2 - 4 = 0$
$9x^2 = 4$
$x^2 = \frac{4}{9}$
$x = \pm\sqrt{\frac{4}{9}} = \pm\frac{2}{3}$

9. $3x^2 - 49 = 0$
$3x^2 = 49$
$x^2 = \frac{49}{3}$
$x^2 = \pm\sqrt{\frac{49}{3}} = \pm\frac{\sqrt{49}}{\sqrt{3}} \cdot \frac{\sqrt{3}}{\sqrt{3}} = \pm\frac{7\sqrt{3}}{3}$

10. $5x^2 - 16 = 0$
$5x^2 = 16$
$x^2 = \frac{16}{5}$
$x = \pm\sqrt{\frac{16}{5}} = \pm\frac{\sqrt{16}}{\sqrt{5}} \cdot \frac{\sqrt{5}}{\sqrt{5}} = \pm\frac{4\sqrt{5}}{5}$

11. $4y^2 - 3 = 9$
$4y^2 = 12$
$y^2 = 3$
$y = \pm\sqrt{3}$

12. $49m^2 - 16 = 0$
$49m^2 = 16$
$m^2 = \frac{16}{49}$
$m = \pm\sqrt{\frac{16}{49}} = \pm\frac{4}{7}$

13. $25n^2 - 36 = 0$
$25n^2 = 36$
$n^2 = \frac{36}{25}$
$n = \pm\sqrt{\frac{36}{25}} = \pm\frac{6}{5}$

14. $d^2 - 100 = 0$
$5d^2 = 100$
$d^2 = 20$
$d = \pm\sqrt{20} = \pm\sqrt{4 \cdot 5} = \pm 2\sqrt{5}$

15. $100x^2 - 5 = 0$
$100x^2 = 5$
$x^2 = \frac{1}{20}$
$x = \pm\sqrt{\frac{1}{20}} = \pm\frac{\sqrt{1}}{\sqrt{20}} \cdot \frac{\sqrt{20}}{\sqrt{20}}$
$= \pm\frac{\sqrt{20}}{20} = \pm\frac{\sqrt{4 \cdot 5}}{20} = \pm\frac{2\sqrt{5}}{20} = \pm\frac{\sqrt{5}}{10}$

16. $(x - 2)^2 = 49$
$x - 2 = \pm 7$
$x = 9$ or $x = -5$

17. $(x + 1)^2 = 6$
$x + 1 = \pm\sqrt{6}$
$x = -1 \pm \sqrt{6}$

18. $(d + 3)^2 = 21$
$d + 3 = \pm\sqrt{21}$
$d = -3 \pm \sqrt{21}$

19. $(b - 3)^2 = 6$
$b - 3 = \pm\sqrt{6}$
$b = 3 \pm \sqrt{6}$

20. $(x + 13)^2 = 8$
$x + 13 = \pm\sqrt{8}$
$x + 13 = \pm 2\sqrt{2}$
$x = -13 \pm 2\sqrt{2}$

21. $(x - 13)^2 = 64$
$x - 13 = \pm 8$
$x = 21$ or $x = 5$

22. $(x - 7)^2 = 12$
$x - 7 = \pm\sqrt{12}$
$x - 7 = \pm 2\sqrt{3}$
$x = 7 \pm 2\sqrt{3}$

23. $(n + 1)^2 = 14$
$n + 1 = \pm\sqrt{14}$
$n = -1 \pm \sqrt{14}$

24. $(x + 9)^2 = 34$
$x + 9 = \pm\sqrt{34}$
$x = -9 \pm \sqrt{34}$

25. $(y + 4)^2 = 36$
$y + 4 = \pm 6$
$y = 2$ or $y = -10$

26. $(m + 10)^2 = 15$
$m + 10 = \pm\sqrt{15}$
$m = -10 \pm \sqrt{15}$

27. $(y - 5)^2 = 20$
$y - 5 = \pm\sqrt{20}$
$y - 5 = \pm 2\sqrt{5}$
$y = 5 \pm 2\sqrt{5}$

28. $x^2 + 2x + 1 = 81$
$(x + 1)^2 = 81$
$x + 1 = \pm 9$
$x = 8$ or $x = -10$

29. $x^2 - 2x + 1 = 16$
$(x - 1)^2 = 16$
$x - 1 = \pm 4$
$x = 5$ or $x = -3$

30. $y^2 + 10y + 25 = 121$
$(y + 5)^2 = 121$
$y + 5 = \pm 11$
$y = 6$ or $y = -16$

31. $y^2 - 12y + 36 = 49$
$(y - 6)^2 = 49$
$y - 6 = \pm 7$
$y = 13$ or $y = -1$

32. $m^2 + 4m + 4 = 29$
$(m + 2)^2 = 29$
$m + 2 = \pm\sqrt{29}$
$m = -2 \pm \sqrt{29}$

33. $c^2 + 16c + 64 = 15$
$(c + 8)^2 = 15$
$c + 8 = \pm\sqrt{15}$
$c = -8 \pm \sqrt{15}$

34. $x^2 - 6x + 9 = 91$
$(x - 3)^2 = 91$
$x - 3 = \pm\sqrt{91}$
$x = 3 \pm \sqrt{91}$

35. $x^2 - 14x + 49 = 19$
$(x - 7)^2 = 19$
$x - 7 = \pm\sqrt{19}$
$x = 7 \pm \sqrt{19}$

36. $n^2 - 8n + 16 = 15$
$(n - 4)^2 = 15$
$n - 4 = \pm\sqrt{15}$
$n = 4 \pm \sqrt{15}$

37. $d^2 + 24d + 144 = 8$
$(d + 12)^2 = 8$
$d + 12 = \pm\sqrt{8}$
$d + 12 = \pm 2\sqrt{2}$
$d = -12 \pm 2\sqrt{2}$

38. Substitute $v_0 = 15$, $c = 20$, and $h = 0$ in
$-5t^2 + v_0t + c = h$
$-5t^2 + 15t + 20 = 0$
$-5(t^2 - 3t - 4) = 0$
$-5(t + 1)(t - 4) = 0$
$t + 1 = 0$ or $t - 4 = 0$
$t = -1$ or $t = 4$
Since the time cannot be negative, the ball will hit the ground in about 4 seconds.

39. Substitute $v_0 = 19$, $c = 4$, and $h = 0$ in
$-5t^2 = v_0t + c = h$
$-5t^2 + 19t + 4 = 0$
$5t^2 - 19t - 4 = 0$
$(5t + 1)(t - 4) = 0$
$5t + 1 = 0$ or $t - 4 = 0$
$5t = -1$ or $t = 4$
$t = -\frac{1}{5}$ or $t = 4$
Since the time cannot be negative, it took the stone about 4 seconds to hit the water.

40. Substitute $v_0 = 0$, $c = 80$, and $h = 0$ in
$-5t^2 + v_0t + c = h$
$-5t^2 + 0t + 80 = 0$
$5t^2 = 80$
$t^2 = 16$
$t = \pm 4$
Since the time cannot be negative, it takes the rock about 4 seconds to fall to the ground.

41. Substitute $v_0 = -1$, $c = 4$, and $h = 0$ in
$-5t^2 + v_0t + c = h$
$-5t^2 - t + 4 = 0$
$5t^2 + t - 4 = 0$
$(5t - 4)(t + 1) = 0$
$5t - 4 = 0$ or $t + 1 = 0$
$5t = 4$ or $t = -1$
$t = \frac{4}{5}$ or $t = -1$
Since the time cannot be negative, it took the acorn about $\frac{4}{5}$ second to fall to the ground.

42. $A = P(1 + r)^2$
$121 = 100(1 + r)^2$
$\frac{121}{100} = (1 + r)^2$
$\sqrt{\frac{121}{100}} = 1 + r$
$\frac{11}{10} = 1 + r$
$\frac{11}{10} - \frac{10}{10} = r$
$\frac{1}{10} = r$
$r = 10\%$

43. $3610 = 2560(1 + r)^2$
$\frac{3610}{2560} = (1 + r)^2$
$\frac{361}{256} = (1 + r)^2$
$\frac{19}{16} = 1 + r$
$\frac{19}{16} - \frac{16}{16} = r$
$\frac{3}{16} = r$
$r = 18.75\%$

44. $7290 = 6250(1 + r)^2$
$\frac{7290}{6250} = (1 + r)^2$
$\frac{729}{625} = (1 + r)^2$
$\frac{27}{25} = 1 + r$
$\frac{27}{25} - \frac{25}{25} = r$
$\frac{2}{25} = r$
$r = 8\%$

45. $453.69 = 400(1 + r)^2$
$\frac{453.69}{400} = (1 + r)^2$
$\frac{21.3}{20} = 1 + r$
$\frac{213}{200} = 1 + r$
$\frac{213}{200} - \frac{200}{200} = r$
$\frac{13}{200} = r$
$r = 6.5\%$

46. $1267.88 = 1000(1 + r)^2$
$\frac{1267.88}{1000} = (1 + r)^2$
$1.26788 = (1 + r)^2$
$1.126 \approx 1 + r$
$0.126 \approx r$
$r \approx 12.6\%$

47. $5267.03 = 4000(1 + r)^2$
$\frac{5267.03}{4000} = (1 + r)^2$
$1.3167575 \approx (1 + r)^2$
$1.1475 \approx 1 + r$
$0.1475 \approx r$
$r \approx 14.75\%$

48. $1772.41 = 1600(1 + r)^2$
$\frac{1772.41}{1600} = (1 + r)^2$
$\frac{42.1}{40} = 1 + r$
$1.0525 = 1 + r$
$0.0525 = r$
$r = 5.25\%$

49. $1232.10 = 1000(1 + r)^2$
$\frac{1232.10}{1000} = (1 + r)^2$
$1.2321 = (1 + r)^2$
$1.11 = 1 + r$
$0.11 = r$
$r = 11\%$

50. $4x^2 - (x^2 + 2x + 1) = 0$
$4x^2 - x^2 - 2x - 1 = 0$
$3x^2 - 2x - 1 = 0$
$(3x + 1)(x - 1) = 0$
$3x + 1 = 0$ or $x - 1 = 0$
$3x = -1$ or $x = 1$
$x = -\frac{1}{3}$ or $x = 1$

51. $(x - b)^2 = 4b^2$
$x - b = 2b$ or $x - b = -2b$
$x = 3b$ or $x = -b$

52. $2(3x + 1)^2 = 8$
$(3x + 1)^2 = 4$
$3x + 1 = 2$ or $3x + 1 = -2$
$3x = 1$ $\quad 3x = -3$
$x = \frac{1}{3}$ or $x = -1$

53. $5(5x - 2)^2 - 7 = 13$
$5(5x - 2)^2 = 20$
$(5x - 2)^2 = 4$
$5x - 2 = 2$ or $5x - 2 = -2$
$5x = 4$ $\quad 5x = 0$
$x = \frac{4}{5}$ or $x = 0$

54. $9x^2 - 24x + 16 = 2$
$(3x - 4)^2 = 2$
$3x - 4 = \pm\sqrt{2}$
$3x = 4 \pm \sqrt{2}$
$x = \frac{4 \pm \sqrt{2}}{3}$

55. $64x^2 + 48x + 9 = 100$
$(8x + 3)^2 = 100$
$8x + 3 = 10$ or $8x + 3 = -10$
$8x = 7$ $\quad 8x = -13$
$x = \frac{7}{8}$ or $x = \frac{-13}{8}$

56. $\frac{x - 1}{9} = \frac{1}{x - 1}$
$(x - 1)^2 = 9$
$x - 1 = 3$ or $x - 1 = -3$
$x = 4$ or $x = -2$

57. $\frac{5}{x+4} - \frac{3}{x-2} = 4$

$$5(x-2) - 3(x+4) = 4(x+4)(x-2)$$
$$5x - 10 - 3x - 12 = 4(x^2 + 2x - 8)$$
$$2x - 22 = 4x^2 + 8x - 32$$
$$0 = 4x^2 + 6x - 10$$
$$0 = 2(2x^2 + 3x - 5)$$
$$0 = 2(2x+5)(x-1)$$
$$2x + 5 = 0 \quad \text{or} \quad x - 1 = 0$$
$$2x = -5 \quad \text{or} \quad x = 1$$
$$x = -\frac{5}{2} \quad \text{or} \quad x = 1$$

58. Substitute $v_0 = \frac{7}{4}$, $c = 10$, and $h = 0$ in

$$-5t^2 + v_0 t + c = h$$
$$-5t^2 + \frac{7}{4}t + 10 = 0$$
$$20t^2 - 7t - 40 = 0$$
$$(5t - 8)(4t + 5) = 0$$
$$5t - 8 = 0 \quad \text{or} \quad 4t + 5 = 0$$
$$5t = 8 \quad \text{or} \quad 4t = -5$$
$$t = \frac{8}{5} \quad \text{or} \quad t = -\frac{5}{4}$$

Since the time cannot be negative, the diver will enter the water in about $\frac{8}{5}$, or $1\frac{3}{5}$, seconds.

59. Substitute $v_0 = 0$ and $d = 134$ m

$$d = 5t^2 + v_0 t$$
$$134 = 5t^2 + 0t$$
$$134 = 5t^2$$
$$t^2 = \frac{134}{5} = 26.8$$
$$t = \pm\sqrt{26.8} \approx \pm 5.2$$

Since the time cannot be negative, it took the piece from the roof about 5 seconds to hit the ground.

60. Substitute $v_0 = 0$ and $t = 6.75$ in

$$d = 5t^2 + v_0 t$$
$$d = 5(6.75)^2 + 0(6.75)$$
$$d \approx 227.8$$

The chimney was about 228 m high.

61. a. For Chimney Rock, substitute $v_0 = 0$ and $d = 136$ in

$$d = 5t^2 + v_0 t$$
$$136 = 5t^2 + (0)t$$
$$136 = 5t^2$$
$$t^2 = \frac{136}{5} = 27.2$$
$$t = \pm\sqrt{27.2} \approx \pm 5.2$$

Since the time cannot be negative, it would take an object about 5.2 seconds to fall a distance equal to the height of Chimney Rock.

For Devil's Tower, substitute $v_0 = 0$ and $d = 386$ in

$$d = 5t^2 + v_0 t$$
$$386 = 5t^2 + (0)t$$
$$386 = 5t^2$$
$$t^2 = \frac{386}{5} = 77.2$$
$$t = \pm\sqrt{77.2} \approx \pm 8.8$$

Since the time cannot be negative, it would take an object about 8.8 seconds to fall a distance equal to the height of Devil's Tower.

For El Capitan, substitute $v_0 = 0$ and $d = 1095$ in

$$d = 5t^2 + v_0 t$$
$$1095 = 5t^2 + (0)t$$
$$1095 = 5t^2$$
$$t^2 = \frac{1095}{5} = 219$$
$$t = \pm\sqrt{219} \approx \pm 14.8$$

Since the time cannot be negative, it would take an object about 14.8 seconds to fall a distance equal to the height of El Capitan.

b. From part a, it takes about $\sqrt{77.2}$ seconds for a dropped object to fall 386 m. Substitute $t = \sqrt{77.2}$ and $d = 1095$ in

$$d = 5t^2 + v_0 t$$
$$1095 = 5(\sqrt{77.2})^2 + v_0(\sqrt{77.2})$$
$$v_0 = \frac{1095 - (77.2)}{\sqrt{77.2}} \approx 80.7$$

The object would have to be thrown downward with an initial velocity of about 81 m/s.

From part a, it takes about $\sqrt{27.2}$ seconds for a dropped object to fall 136 m. Substitute $t = \sqrt{27.2}$ and $d = 1095$ in

$$d = 5t^2 + v_0 t$$
$$1095 = 5(\sqrt{27.2})^2 + v_0(\sqrt{27.2})$$
$$v_0 = \frac{1095 - 5(27.2)}{\sqrt{27.2}} \approx 183.9$$

The object would have to be thrown downward with an initial velocity of about 184 m/s.

62. a. For the tallest building, substitute $v_0 = 0$ and $d = 260$ in

$$d = 5t^2 + v_0 t$$
$$260 = 5t^2 + (0)t$$
$$260 = 5t^2$$
$$t^2 = \frac{260}{5} = 52$$
$$t = \pm\sqrt{52} \approx \pm 7.2$$

Since the time cannot be negative, it would take an object dropped from the tallest building about 7.2 seconds to reach the ground.

For the second-tallest building, substitute $v_0 = 0$ and $d =$ 237 in

$$d = 5t^2 + v_0 t$$
$$237 = 5t^2 + (0)t$$
$$237 = 5t^2$$
$$t^2 = \frac{237}{5} = 47.4$$
$$t = \pm\sqrt{47.4} \approx \pm 6.9$$

Since the time cannot be negative, it would take an object dropped from the second-tallest building about 6.9 seconds to reach the ground.

The difference in times $\approx 7.2 - 6.9 = 0.3$ second.

b. From both buildings, the object falls 237 m in the same time. The time difference in part a is the time it takes the object to travel the last 23 m.

63.

$$x^2 + 4x + 4 = 9$$
$$x^2 + 4x - 5 = 0$$
$$(x-1)(x+5) = 0$$
$$x - 1 = 0 \quad \text{or} \quad x + 5 = 0$$
$$x = 1 \quad \text{or} \quad x = -5$$

Check: $x = 1$

$x^2 + 4x + 4$	$= 9$
$1^2 + 4(1) + 4$	9
$1 + 4 + 4$	9
9	9

Check: $x = -5$

$x^2 + 4x + 4$	$= 9$
$(-5)^2 + 4(-5) + 4$	9
$25 - 20 + 4$	9
9	9

$$x^2 + 4x + 4 = 8$$
$$(x+2)^2 = 8$$
$$x + 2 = \pm 2\sqrt{2}$$
$$x = -2 + 2\sqrt{2} \quad \text{or} \quad x = -2 - 2\sqrt{2}$$

Check: $x = -2 + 2\sqrt{2}$

$x^2 + 4x + 4$	$= 8$
$(-2 + 2\sqrt{2})^2 + 4(-2 + 2\sqrt{2}) + 4$	8
$4 - 8\sqrt{2} + (2\sqrt{2})^2 - 8 + 8\sqrt{2} + 4$	8
$4 - 8\sqrt{2} + 8 - 8 + 8\sqrt{2} + 4$	8
8	8

Check: $x = -2 - 2\sqrt{2}$

$x^2 + 4x + 4$	$= 8$
$(-2 - 2\sqrt{2})^2 + 4(-2 - 2\sqrt{2}) + 4$	8
$4 + 8\sqrt{2} + (2\sqrt{2})^2 - 8 - 8\sqrt{2} + 4$	8
$4 + 8\sqrt{2} + 8 - 8 - 8\sqrt{2} + 4$	8
8	8

64. $3^2 + (3 + a)^2 = 5^2$
$9 + 9 + 6a + a^2 = 25$
$a^2 + 6a + 18 = 25$
$a^2 + 6a - 7 = 0$
$(a + 7)(a - 1) = 0$
$a + 7 = 0$ or $a - 1 = 0$
$a = -7$ or $a = 1$
a must be positive, so $a = 1$.

65. $a^2 + (a - 7)^2 = 13^2$
$a^2 + a^2 - 14a + 49 = 169$
$2a^2 - 14a - 120 = 0$
$a^2 - 7a - 60 = 0$
$(a - 12)(a + 5) = 0$
$a - 12 = 0$ or $a + 5 = 0$
$a = 12$ or $a = -5$
a is positive, so $a = 12$.

66. a. $A = P(1 + r)^t$
$4000 = 2000(1 + r)^2$
$2 = (1 + r)^2$
$1 + r = \sqrt{2}$ or $1 + r = -\sqrt{2}$
$r = \sqrt{2} - 1$ $\quad r = -\sqrt{2} - 1$
$= 1.4142 - 1$ gives a negative rate
$= 0.4142$ or 41.5% (rounding up)

b. For P dollars invested at 30%, for 2 years,
$A = P(1 + r)^t$
$= P(1 + 0.30)^2$
$= P(1.3)^2$
$= 1.69P$
The amount will grow to $1.69P$, not $2P$, no matter what P is.

Alternative solution:
If P were to double, then
$2P = P(1 + r)^2$
$2 = (1 + r)^2$
$\sqrt{2} = 1 + r$
$r = \sqrt{2} - 1$
$r \approx 0.4142 \approx 41.5\%$ (rounded up).
An interest rate of about 41.5% would be needed to double *any* value of P in 2 years.

67. $3000 = P(1 + 0.0575)^2$
$\frac{3000}{(1.0575)^2} = P$
$\$2682.63 = P$

68. $y^4 - 4y^2 + 4 = 0$
Let $x = y^2$ so $x^2 = y^4$.
Then $y^4 - 4y^2 + 4 = x^2 - 4x + 4 = 0$
$(x - 2)^2 = 0$
$x - 2 = 0$
$x = 2$
$x = y^2$ so $2 = y^2$
$\pm\sqrt{2} = y$

69. $A = 1000(1.02)^8$
$A = \$1171.66$

70. $A = 2000(1.03)^8$
$A = \$2533.54$

71.

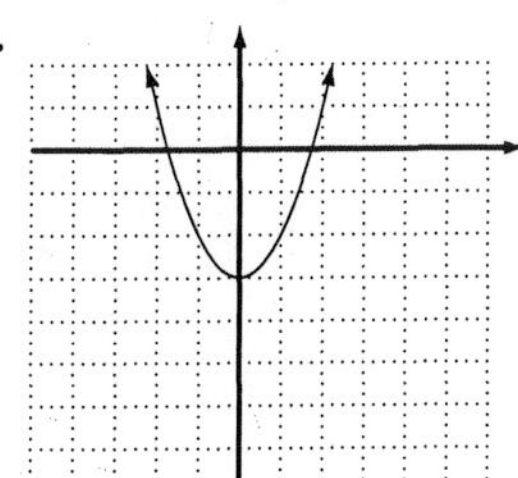

72.

73. $\frac{\sqrt{10}}{\sqrt{5}} = \sqrt{\frac{10}{5}} = \sqrt{2}$

74. $\frac{\sqrt{45y^3}}{\sqrt{5y}} = \sqrt{\frac{45y^3}{5y}} = \sqrt{9y^2} = 3y, y > 0$

75. $\frac{\sqrt{27a^2}}{\sqrt{9a^2}} = \sqrt{\frac{27a^2}{9a^2}} = \sqrt{3}$

76. $\frac{\sqrt{16}}{\sqrt{3}} = \frac{4}{\sqrt{3}} \cdot \frac{\sqrt{3}}{\sqrt{3}} = \frac{4\sqrt{3}}{3}$

77. $f(t) = 2t^2 - 4t + 1$
$f(-2) = 2(-2)^2 - 4(-2) + 1 = 8 + 8 + 1 = 17$
$f(1) = 2(1)^2 - 4(1) + 1 = 2 - 4 + 1 = -1$
$f(3) = 2(3)^2 - 4(3) + 1 = 18 - 12 + 1 = 7$

78. $g(x) = |x| - 5$
$g(-7) = |-7| - 5 = 7 - 5 = 2$
$g(-2) = |-2| - 5 = 2 - 5 = -3$
$g(1) = |1| - 5 = 1 - 5 = -4$

79. $h(s) = s^3 - 5$
$h(-3) = (-3)^3 - 5 = -27 - 5 = -32$
$h(1) = (1)^3 - 5 = 1 - 5 = -4$
$h(3) = (3)^3 - 5 = 27 - 5 = 22$

80. $f(x) = x^4 + 2$
$f(-2) = (-2)^4 + 2 = 16 + 2 = 18$
$f(0) = (0)^4 + 2 = 0 + 2 = 2$
$f(3) = (3)^4 + 2 = 81 + 2 = 83$

LESSON 13-3 TRY THIS pp. 586–587

a. $x^2 - 8x$
$(-4)^2 = 16$
$x^2 - 8x + 16 = (x - 4)^2$

b. $x^2 + 12x$
$(6)^2 = 36$
$x^2 + 12x + 36 = (x + 6)^2$

c. $y^2 + 7y$
$\left(\frac{7}{2}\right)^2 = \frac{49}{4}$
$y^2 + 7y + \frac{49}{4} = \left(y + \frac{7}{2}\right)^2$

d. $m^2 - 3m$
$\left(-\frac{3}{2}\right)^2 = \frac{9}{4}$
$m^2 - 3m + \frac{9}{4} = \left(m - \frac{3}{2}\right)^2$

e. $x^2 + 8x + 12 = 0$
$x^2 + 8x = -12$
$x^2 + 8x + 16 = -12 + 16$
$(x + 4)^2 = 4$
$x + 4 = 2$ or $x + 4 = -2$
$x = -2$ or $x = -6$

f. $2x^2 + 3x - 3 = 0$
$x^2 + \frac{3}{2}x - \frac{3}{2} = 0$
$x^2 + \frac{3}{2}x = \frac{3}{2}$
$x^2 + \frac{3}{2}x + \frac{9}{16} = \frac{3}{2} + \frac{9}{16}$
$\left(x + \frac{3}{4}\right)^2 = \frac{33}{16}$
$x + \frac{3}{4} = \pm\frac{\sqrt{33}}{4}$
$x = \frac{-3 \pm \sqrt{33}}{4}$

g. $3x^2 - 2x - 3 = 0$
$x^2 - \frac{2}{3}x - 1 = 0$
$x^2 - \frac{2}{3}x = 1$
$x^2 - \frac{2}{3}x + \frac{1}{9} = 1 + \frac{1}{9}$
$\left(x - \frac{1}{3}\right)^2 = \frac{10}{9}$
$x - \frac{1}{3} = \pm\frac{\sqrt{10}}{3}$
$x = \frac{1 \pm \sqrt{10}}{3}$

LESSON 13-3 EXERCISES

p. 588

1. $x^2 - 6x \quad (-3)^2 = 9$
$x^2 - 6x + 9 = (x - 3)^2$

2. $y^2 + 8y \quad 4^2 = 16$
$y^2 + 8y + 16 = (y + 4)^2$

3. $m^2 + 7m \quad \left(\frac{7}{2}\right)^2 = \frac{49}{4}$
$m^2 + 7m + \frac{49}{4} = \left(m + \frac{7}{2}\right)^2$

4. $t^2 - 5t \quad \left(-\frac{5}{2}\right)^2 = \frac{25}{4}$
$t^2 - 5t + \frac{25}{4} = \left(t - \frac{5}{2}\right)^2$

5. $x^2 + 4x \quad 2^2 = 4$
$x^2 + 4x + 4 = (x + 2)^2$

6. $n^2 - 12n \quad (-6)^2 = 36$
$n^2 - 12n + 36 = (n - 6)^2$

7. $z^2 - 20z \quad (-10)^2 = 100$
$z^2 - 20z + 100 = (z - 10)^2$

8. $y^2 + 9y \quad \left(\frac{9}{2}\right)^2 = \frac{81}{4}$
$y^2 + 9y + \frac{81}{4} = \left(y + \frac{9}{2}\right)^2$

9. $x^2 + 15x \quad \left(\frac{15}{2}\right)^2 = \frac{225}{4}$
$x^2 + 15x + \frac{225}{4} = \left(x + \frac{15}{2}\right)^2$

10. $x^2 - 6x - 16 = 0$
$x^2 - 6x = 16$
$x^2 - 6x + 9 = 16 + 9$
$(x - 3)^2 = 25$
$x - 3 = 5$ or $x - 3 = -5$
$x = 8$ or $x = -2$

11. $m^2 + 8m + 15 = 0$
$m^2 + 8m = -15$
$m^2 + 8m + 16 = -15 + 16$
$(m + 4)^2 = 1$
$m + 4 = 1$ or $m + 4 = -1$
$m = -3$ or $m = -5$

12. $x^2 + 22x + 21 = 0$
$x^2 + 22x = -21$
$x^2 + 22x + 121 = 121 - 21$
$(x + 11)^2 = 100$
$x + 11 = 10$ or $x + 11 = -10$
$x = -1$ or $x = -21$

13. $x^2 + 14x - 15 = 0$
$x^2 + 14x = 15$
$x^2 + 14x + 49 = 49 + 15$
$(x + 7)^2 = 64$
$x + 7 = 8$ or $x + 7 = -8$
$x = 1$ or $x = -15$

14. $x^2 - 2x - 5 = 0$
$x^2 - 2x = 5$
$x^2 - 2x + 1 = 5 + 1$
$(x - 1)^2 = 6$
$x - 1 = \pm\sqrt{6}$
$x = 1 \pm \sqrt{6}$

15. $x^2 - 4x - 11 = 0$
$x^2 - 4x = 11$
$x^2 - 4x + 4 = 11 + 4$
$(x - 2)^2 = 15$
$x - 2 = \pm\sqrt{15}$
$x = 2 \pm \sqrt{15}$

16. $n^2 - 22n + 102 = 0$
$n^2 - 22n = -102$
$n^2 - 22n + 121 = 121 - 102$
$(n - 11)^2 = 19$
$n - 11 = \pm\sqrt{19}$
$n = 11 \pm \sqrt{19}$

17. $x^2 - 18x + 74 = 0$
$x^2 - 18x = -74$
$x^2 - 18x + 81 = 81 - 74$
$(x - 9)^2 = 7$
$x - 9 = \pm\sqrt{7}$
$x = 9 \pm \sqrt{7}$

18. $x^2 + 10x - 4 = 0$
$x^2 + 10x = 4$
$x^2 + 10x + 25 = 4 + 25$
$(x + 5)^2 = 29$
$x + 5 = \pm\sqrt{29}$
$x = -5 \pm \sqrt{29}$

19. $x^2 - 10x - 4 = 0$
$x^2 - 10x = 4$
$x^2 - 10x + 25 = 25 + 4$
$(x - 5)^2 = 29$
$x - 5 = \pm\sqrt{29}$
$x = 5 \pm \sqrt{29}$

20. $n^2 - 7n - 2 = 0$
$n^2 - 7n = 2$
$n^2 - 7n + \frac{49}{4} = 2 + \frac{49}{4}$
$\left(n - \frac{7}{2}\right)^2 = \frac{57}{4}$
$n - \frac{7}{2} = \pm\sqrt{\frac{57}{4}}$
$n - \frac{7}{2} = \pm\frac{\sqrt{57}}{2}$
$n = \frac{7 \pm \sqrt{57}}{2}$

21. $t^2 + 7t - 2 = 0$
$t^2 + 7t = 2$
$t^2 + 7t + \frac{49}{4} = 2 + \frac{49}{4}$
$\left(t + \frac{7}{2}\right)^2 = \frac{57}{4}$
$t + \frac{7}{2} = \pm\sqrt{\frac{57}{4}}$
$t + \frac{7}{2} = \pm\frac{\sqrt{57}}{2}$
$t = \frac{-7 \pm \sqrt{57}}{2}$

22. $x^2 + 3x - 28 = 0$
$x^2 + 3x = 28$
$x^2 + 3x + \frac{9}{4} = 28 + \frac{9}{4}$
$\left(x + \frac{3}{2}\right)^2 = \frac{121}{4}$
$x + \frac{3}{2} = \sqrt{\frac{121}{4}}$ or $x + \frac{3}{2} = -\sqrt{\frac{121}{4}}$
$x + \frac{3}{2} = \frac{11}{2}$ or $x + \frac{3}{2} = -\frac{11}{2}$
$x = 4$ or $x = -7$

23. $x^2 - 3x - 28 = 0$
$x^2 - 3x = 28$
$x^2 - 3x + \frac{9}{4} = 28 + \frac{9}{4}$
$\left(x - \frac{3}{2}\right)^2 = \frac{121}{4}$
$x - \frac{3}{2} = \sqrt{\frac{121}{4}}$ or $x - \frac{3}{2} = -\sqrt{\frac{121}{4}}$
$x - \frac{3}{2} = \frac{11}{2}$ or $x - \frac{3}{2} = -\frac{11}{2}$
$x = 7$ or $x = -4$

24. $2x^2 + 3x - 17 = 0$
$x^2 + \frac{3}{2}x - \frac{17}{2} = 0$
$x^2 + \frac{3}{2}x = \frac{17}{2}$
$x^2 + \frac{3}{2}x + \frac{9}{16} = \frac{17}{2} + \frac{9}{16}$
$\left(x + \frac{3}{4}\right)^2 = \frac{145}{16}$
$x + \frac{3}{4} = \pm\sqrt{\frac{145}{16}}$
$x + \frac{3}{4} = \pm\frac{\sqrt{145}}{4}$
$x = \frac{-3 \pm \sqrt{145}}{4}$

25. $2r^2 - 3r - 1 = 0$

$$r^2 - \frac{3}{2}r - \frac{1}{2} = 0$$
$$r^2 - \frac{3}{2}r = \frac{1}{2}$$
$$r^2 - \frac{3}{2}r + \frac{9}{16} = \frac{1}{2} + \frac{9}{16}$$
$$\left(r - \frac{3}{4}\right)^2 = \frac{17}{16}$$
$$r - \frac{3}{4} = \pm\sqrt{\frac{17}{16}}$$
$$r - \frac{3}{4} = \pm\frac{\sqrt{17}}{4}$$
$$r = \frac{3 \pm \sqrt{17}}{4}$$

26. $3x^2 + 4x - 1 = 0$

$$x^2 + \frac{4}{3}x - \frac{1}{3} = 0$$
$$x^2 + \frac{4}{3}x = \frac{1}{3}$$
$$x^2 + \frac{4}{3}x + \frac{4}{9} = \frac{1}{3} + \frac{4}{9}$$
$$\left(x + \frac{2}{3}\right)^2 = \frac{7}{9}$$
$$x + \frac{2}{3} = \pm\sqrt{\frac{7}{9}}$$
$$x + \frac{2}{3} = \pm\frac{\sqrt{7}}{3}$$
$$x = \frac{-2 \pm \sqrt{7}}{3}$$

27. $3x^2 - 4x - 3 = 0$

$$x^2 - \frac{4}{3}x - 1 = 0$$
$$x^2 - \frac{4}{3}x = 1$$
$$x^2 - \frac{4}{3}x + \frac{4}{9} = 1 + \frac{4}{9}$$
$$\left(x - \frac{2}{3}\right)^2 = \frac{13}{9}$$
$$x - \frac{2}{3} = \pm\sqrt{\frac{13}{9}}$$
$$x - \frac{2}{3} = \pm\frac{\sqrt{13}}{3}$$
$$x = \frac{2 \pm \sqrt{13}}{3}$$

28. $2x^2 - 9x - 5 = 0$

$$x^2 - \frac{9}{2}x - \frac{5}{2} = 0$$
$$x^2 - \frac{9}{2}x = \frac{5}{2}$$
$$x^2 - \frac{9}{2}x + \frac{81}{16} = \frac{5}{2} + \frac{81}{16}$$
$$\left(x - \frac{9}{4}\right)^2 = \frac{121}{16}$$
$$x - \frac{9}{4} = \sqrt{\frac{121}{16}} \quad \text{or} \quad x - \frac{9}{4} = -\sqrt{\frac{121}{16}}$$
$$x - \frac{9}{4} = \frac{11}{4} \quad \text{or} \quad x - \frac{9}{4} = -\frac{11}{4}$$
$$x = 5 \quad \text{or} \quad x = -\frac{1}{2}$$

29. $2x^2 - 5x - 12 = 0$

$$x^2 - \frac{5}{2}x - 6 = 0$$
$$x^2 - \frac{5}{2}x = 6$$
$$x^2 - \frac{5}{2}x + \frac{25}{16} = 6 + \frac{25}{16}$$
$$\left(x - \frac{5}{4}\right)^2 = \frac{121}{16}$$
$$x - \frac{5}{4} = \sqrt{\frac{121}{16}} \quad \text{or} \quad x - \frac{5}{4} = -\sqrt{\frac{121}{16}}$$
$$x - \frac{5}{4} = \frac{11}{4} \quad \text{or} \quad x - \frac{5}{4} = -\frac{11}{4}$$
$$x = 4 \quad \text{or} \quad x = -\frac{3}{2}$$

30. Half the coefficient b of the middle term squared = last term.
So $\left(\frac{b}{2}\right)^2 = 36$, $\frac{b}{2} = \pm 6$, $b = \pm 12$; $\pm 12x$ is the middle term.

31. $\left(\frac{b}{2}\right)^2 = 55$, $\frac{b}{2} = \pm\sqrt{55}$, $b = \pm 2\sqrt{55}$;
$\pm 2\sqrt{55}x$ or $\pm 2x\sqrt{55}$

32. $4x^2 + 20x + c = 4\left(x^2 + 5x + \frac{c}{4}\right)$

$$\left(\frac{5}{2}\right)^2 = \frac{c}{4}$$
$$\frac{25}{4} = \frac{c}{4}$$
$$25 = c$$

The constant term is 25.

33. $4x^2 + bx + 16 = 4\left(x^2 + \frac{b}{4}x + 4\right)$

$$\left(\frac{\frac{b}{4}}{2}\right)^2 = 4,\ \frac{b}{8} = \pm 2,\ b = \pm 16;\ \pm 16x$$

34. $\left(\frac{b}{2}\right)^2 = c$, $\frac{b}{2} = \pm\sqrt{c}$, $b = \pm 2\sqrt{c}$; $\pm 2\sqrt{c}x$ or $\pm 2x\sqrt{c}$

35. $ax^2 + bx + c = a\left(x^2 + \frac{b}{a}x + \frac{c}{a}\right)$

$$\left(\frac{\frac{b}{a}}{2}\right)^2 = \frac{c}{a},\ \frac{b^2}{4a^2} = \frac{c}{a},\ b^2 = \frac{4a^2c}{a} = 4ac,\ b = \pm 2\sqrt{ac}$$

Middle term: $\pm 2\sqrt{ac}\,x$ or $\pm 2x\sqrt{ac}$

36. $ax^2 + bx + c = 0$

$$x^2 + \frac{b}{a}x + \frac{c}{a} = 0$$
$$x^2 + \frac{b}{a}x = -\frac{c}{a}$$
$$x^2 + \frac{b}{a}x + \frac{b^2}{4a^2} = -\frac{c}{a} + \frac{b^2}{4a^2}$$
$$\left(x + \frac{b}{2a}\right)^2 = \frac{-4ac + b^2}{4a^2}$$
$$x + \frac{b}{2a} = \pm\sqrt{\frac{b^2 - 4ac}{4a^2}}$$
$$x + \frac{b}{2a} = \frac{\pm\sqrt{b^2 - 4ac}}{2a}$$
$$x = \frac{-b \pm \sqrt{b^2 - 4ac}}{2a}$$

Restrictions: $a \neq 0$; $b^2 - 4ac \geq 0$
$b^2 \geq 4ac$

37.

$$x^2 - ax = 6a^2$$
$$x^2 - ax + \left(\frac{a}{2}\right)^2 = 6a^2 + \left(\frac{a}{2}\right)^2$$
$$\left(x - \frac{a}{2}\right)^2 = 6a^2 + \frac{a^2}{4}$$
$$\left(x - \frac{a}{2}\right)^2 = \frac{25a^2}{4}$$
$$x - \frac{a}{2} = \frac{5a}{2} \quad \text{or} \quad x - \frac{a}{2} = -\frac{5a}{2}$$
$$x = \frac{6a}{2} \quad \text{or} \quad x = \frac{-4a}{2}$$
$$x = 3a \quad \text{or} \quad x = -2a$$

38.

$$x^2 + 4bx = -2b$$
$$x^2 + 4bx + (2b)^2 = -2b + (2b)^2$$
$$(x + 2b)^2 = -2b + 4b^2$$
$$x + 2b = \pm\sqrt{4b^2 - 2b}$$
$$x = -2b \pm \sqrt{4b^2 - 2b}$$
$$= -2b \pm \sqrt{2b(2b - 1)}$$

39.

$$x^2 - x = c^2 + c$$
$$x^2 - x + \left(\frac{1}{2}\right)^2 = c^2 + c + \left(\frac{1}{2}\right)^2$$
$$\left(x - \frac{1}{2}\right)^2 = \left(c + \frac{1}{2}\right)^2$$
$$x - \frac{1}{2} = c + \frac{1}{2} \quad \text{or} \quad x - \frac{1}{2} = -c - \frac{1}{2}$$
$$x = c + 1 \quad \text{or} \quad x = -c$$

40. $3x^2 - bx = -1$

$$x^2 - \frac{b}{3}x = -\frac{1}{3}$$

$$x^2 - \frac{b}{3}x + \left(\frac{b}{6}\right)^2 = -\frac{1}{3} + \left(\frac{b}{6}\right)^2$$

$$\left(x - \frac{b}{6}\right)^2 = -\frac{12}{36} + \frac{b^2}{36}$$

$$x - \frac{b}{6} = \pm\frac{\sqrt{b^2 - 12}}{6}$$

$$x = \frac{b \pm \sqrt{b^2 - 12}}{6}$$

41. $kx^2 + mx = -n$

$$x^2 + \frac{m}{k}x = -\frac{n}{k}$$

$$x^2 + \frac{m}{k}x + \left(\frac{m}{2k}\right)^2 = \frac{-n}{k} + \frac{m^2}{4k^2}$$

$$\left(x + \frac{m}{2k}\right)^2 = \frac{-4nk + m^2}{4k^2}$$

$$x + \frac{m}{2k} = \pm\frac{\sqrt{m^2 - 4nk}}{2k}$$

$$x = \frac{-m \pm \sqrt{m^2 - 4nk}}{2k}$$

42. $b^2x^2 - 2bx = -c^2$

$$x^2 - \frac{2bx}{b^2} = -\frac{c^2}{b^2}$$

$$x^2 - \frac{2x}{b} + \left(\frac{1}{b}\right)^2 = \frac{-c^2}{b^2} + \frac{1}{b^2}$$

$$\left(x - \frac{1}{b}\right)^2 = \frac{1 - c^2}{b^2}$$

$$x - \frac{1}{b} = \frac{\pm\sqrt{1 - c^2}}{b}$$

$$x = \frac{1 \pm \sqrt{1 - c^2}}{b}$$

43. $y = kx$

$11 = k(4)$

$\frac{11}{4} = k$

$y = \frac{11}{4}x$

44. $y = kx$

$16 = k(8)$

$\frac{16}{8} = k$

$2 = k$

45. Irrational

46. Rational

47. Rational

48. $\sqrt{2x + 3} = 5$

$2x + 3 = 25$

$2x = 22$

$x = 11$

49. $-\sqrt{4x} = 4$

$\sqrt{4x} = -4$

No real-number solution

LESSON 13-4 TRY THIS pp. 590–592

a. $2x^2 = 4 - 7x$

$2x^2 + 7x - 4 = 0 \qquad a = 2, b = 7, c = -4$

$$x = \frac{-b \pm \sqrt{b^2 - 4ac}}{2a}$$

$$x = \frac{-7 \pm \sqrt{7^2 - 4 \cdot 2 \cdot (-4)}}{2 \cdot 2}$$

$$x = \frac{-7 \pm \sqrt{49 - (-32)}}{4}$$

$$x = \frac{-7 \pm \sqrt{81}}{4}$$

$$x = \frac{-7 \pm 9}{4}$$

$$x = \frac{-7 + 9}{4} \quad \text{or} \quad x = \frac{-7 - 9}{4}$$

$$x = \frac{1}{2} \quad \text{or} \quad x = -4$$

The solutions are $\frac{1}{2}$ and -4.

b. $3m^2 - 8 = 10m$

$3m^2 - 10m - 8 = 0 \qquad a = 3, b = -10, c = -8$

$$x = \frac{-b \pm \sqrt{b^2 - 4ac}}{2a}$$

$$x = \frac{-(-10) \pm \sqrt{(-10)^2 - 4 \cdot 3 - (-8)}}{2 \cdot 3}$$

$$x = \frac{10 \pm \sqrt{100 - (-96)}}{6}$$

$$x = \frac{10 \pm \sqrt{196}}{6}$$

$$x = \frac{10 \pm 14}{6}$$

$$x = \frac{10 + 14}{6} \quad \text{or} \quad x = \frac{10 - 14}{6}$$

$$x = \frac{24}{6} \quad \text{or} \quad x = -\frac{4}{6}$$

$$x = 4 \quad \text{or} \quad x = -\frac{2}{3}$$

The solutions are 4 and $-\frac{2}{3}$.

c. $2x^2 - 4x = 5$

$2x^2 - 4x - 5 = 0 \qquad a = 2, b = -4, c = -5$

$$x = \frac{-(-4) \pm \sqrt{(-4)^2 - 4 \cdot 2 \cdot (-5)}}{2 \cdot 2}$$

$$x = \frac{4 \pm \sqrt{16 - (-40)}}{4}$$

$$x = \frac{4 \pm \sqrt{56}}{4}$$

$$= \frac{4 \pm \sqrt{4 \cdot 14}}{4}$$

$$= \frac{4 \pm 2\sqrt{14}}{4}$$

$$= \frac{2 \pm \sqrt{14}}{2}$$

$$x \approx 2.9 \quad \text{or} \quad x \approx -0.9$$

d. $x^2 + 5x = -3$

$x^2 + 5x + 3 = 0 \qquad a = 1, b = 5, c = 3$

$$x = \frac{-5 \pm \sqrt{5^2 - 4 \cdot 1 \cdot 3}}{2 \cdot 1}$$

$$x = \frac{-5 \pm \sqrt{25 - 12}}{2}$$

$$x = \frac{-5 \pm \sqrt{13}}{2}$$

$$x \approx -0.7 \quad \text{or} \quad x \approx -4.3$$

e. $6x^2 - 6 - 5x = 6x^2 - 5x - 6$, so $a = 6, b = -5$, and $c = -6$.
The roots are

$$\frac{-(-5) \pm \sqrt{(-5)^2 - 4(6)(-6)}}{2(6)} = \frac{5 \pm \sqrt{25 + 144}}{12}$$

$$= \frac{5 \pm \sqrt{169}}{12}$$

$$= \frac{5 \pm 13}{12}$$

$$= \frac{18}{12} \quad \text{or} \quad -\frac{8}{12}$$

$$= \frac{3}{2} \quad \text{or} \quad -\frac{2}{3}$$

f. For $6x^2 - 6x - 5$, $a = 6, b = -6$, and $c = -5$. The roots are

$$\frac{-(-6) \pm \sqrt{(-6)^2 - 4(6)(-5)}}{2(6)} = \frac{6 \pm \sqrt{36 + 120}}{12}$$

$$= \frac{6 \pm \sqrt{156}}{12}$$

$$= \frac{6 \pm \sqrt{4 \cdot 39}}{12}$$

$$= \frac{6 \pm 2\sqrt{39}}{12}$$

$$= \frac{3 \pm \sqrt{39}}{6}$$

g. For $a = 2, b = -4$, and $c = -5$,
$b^2 - 4ac = (-4)^2 - 4(2)(-5) = 56$, two real-number solutions

h. For $a = 1, b = 5$, and $c = 8$,
$b^2 - 4ac = (5)^2 - 4(1)(8) = 25 - 32 = -7$, no real-number solutions

i. For $a = 4, b = -8$, and $c = 4$,
$b^2 - 4ac = (-8)^2 - 4(4)(4) = 64 - 64 = 0$, one real-number solution

j. 13, two points **k.** -19, no points **l.** 0, one point

LESSON 13-4 EXERCISES pp. 593–594

1. $x^2 - 4x - 21 = 0$
$x = \frac{4 \pm \sqrt{16 - 4(1)(-21)}}{2} = \frac{4 \pm \sqrt{100}}{2} = \frac{4 \pm 10}{2}$
$x = 7$ or -3

2. $x^2 + 7x - 18 = 0$
$x = \frac{-7 \pm \sqrt{49 - 4(1)(-18)}}{2} = \frac{-7 \pm \sqrt{121}}{2} = \frac{-7 \pm 11}{2}$
$x = -9$ or 2

3. $x^2 - 6x + 9 = 0$
$x = \frac{6 \pm \sqrt{36 - 4(1)(9)}}{2} = \frac{6 \pm \sqrt{0}}{2} = \frac{6 \pm 0}{2} = 3$

4. $x^2 - 8x + 16 = 0$
$x = \frac{8 \pm \sqrt{64 - 4(1)(16)}}{2} = \frac{8 \pm \sqrt{0}}{2} = \frac{8 \pm 0}{2} = 4$

5. $3y^2 - 2y - 8 = 0$
$y = \frac{2 \pm \sqrt{4 - 4(3)(-8)}}{6} = \frac{2 \pm \sqrt{100}}{6} = \frac{2 \pm 10}{6}$
$y = 2$ or $-\frac{4}{3}$

6. $3y^2 - 7y + 4 = 0$
$y = \frac{7 \pm \sqrt{49 - 4(3)(4)}}{6} = \frac{7 \pm \sqrt{1}}{6} = \frac{7 \pm 1}{6}$
$y = \frac{4}{3}$ or 1

7. $4x^2 + 12x - 7 = 0$
$x = \frac{-12 \pm \sqrt{144 - 4(4)(-7)}}{8} = \frac{-12 \pm \sqrt{256}}{8} = \frac{-12 \pm 16}{8}$
$x = -\frac{7}{2}$ or $\frac{1}{2}$

8. $4x^2 + 4x - 15 = 0$
$x = \frac{-4 \pm \sqrt{16 - 4(4)(-15)}}{8} = \frac{-4 \pm \sqrt{256}}{8} = \frac{-4 \pm 16}{8}$
$x = -\frac{5}{2}$ or $\frac{3}{2}$

9. $x^2 + 0x - 9 = 0$
$x = \frac{0 \pm \sqrt{0 - 4(1)(-9)}}{2} = \frac{0 \pm 6}{2}$
$x = 3$ or -3

10. $x^2 + 0x - 4 = 0$
$x = \frac{0 \pm \sqrt{0 - 4(1)(-4)}}{2} = \frac{0 \pm 4}{2}$
$x = 2$ or -2

11. $x^2 - 2x + 1 = 0$
$x = \frac{2 \pm \sqrt{4 - 4(1)(1)}}{2} = \frac{2 \pm \sqrt{0}}{2} = \frac{2 \pm 0}{2} = 1$

12. $x^2 - 4x - 7 = 0$
$x = \frac{4 \pm \sqrt{16 - 4(1)(-7)}}{2} = \frac{4 \pm \sqrt{44}}{2} = \frac{4 \pm 2\sqrt{11}}{2}$
$x = 2 \pm \sqrt{11}$

13. $y^2 - 10y + 22 = 0$
$y = \frac{10 \pm \sqrt{100 - 4(1)(22)}}{2} = \frac{10 \pm \sqrt{12}}{2} = \frac{10 \pm 2\sqrt{3}}{2}$
$y = 5 \pm \sqrt{3}$

14. $y^2 + 6y - 9 = 0$
$y = \frac{-6 \pm \sqrt{36 - 4(1)(-9)}}{2} = \frac{-6 \pm \sqrt{72}}{2} = \frac{-6 \pm 6\sqrt{2}}{2}$
$y = -3 \pm 3\sqrt{2}$

15. $x^2 + 4x + 4 = 7$
$x^2 + 4x - 3 = 0$
$x = \frac{-4 \pm \sqrt{16 - 4(1)(-3)}}{2} = \frac{-4 \pm \sqrt{28}}{2} = \frac{-4 \pm 2\sqrt{7}}{2}$
$x = -2 \pm \sqrt{7}$

16. $x^2 - 2x + 1 = 5$
$x^2 - 2x - 4 = 0$
$x = \frac{2 \pm \sqrt{4 - 4(1)(-4)}}{2} = \frac{2 \pm \sqrt{20}}{2} = \frac{2 \pm 2\sqrt{5}}{2}$
$x = 1 \pm \sqrt{5}$

17. $3x^2 + 8x + 2 = 0$
$x = \frac{-8 \pm \sqrt{64 - 4(3)(2)}}{6} = \frac{-8 \pm \sqrt{40}}{6} = \frac{-8 \pm 2\sqrt{10}}{6}$
$x = \frac{-4 \pm \sqrt{10}}{3}$

18. $3x^2 - 4x - 2 = 0$
$x = \frac{4 \pm \sqrt{16 - 4(3)(-2)}}{6} = \frac{4 \pm \sqrt{40}}{6} = \frac{4 \pm 2\sqrt{10}}{6}$
$x = \frac{2 \pm \sqrt{10}}{3}$

19–27. The roots of the polynomial $ax^2 + bx + c$ are the solutions of the equation $ax^2 + bx + c = 0$.

19. $4y^2 + 3y - 1 = 0$
$y = \frac{-3 \pm \sqrt{9 + 16}}{8} = \frac{-3 \pm \sqrt{25}}{8} = \frac{-3 \pm 5}{8}$
$= \frac{2}{8}$ or $\frac{-8}{8}$
$= \frac{1}{4}$ or -1

20. $4y^2 + 4y + 1 = 0$
$y = \frac{-4 \pm \sqrt{16 - 16}}{8} = \frac{-4 \pm \sqrt{0}}{8} = \frac{-4}{8} = -\frac{1}{2}$

21. $3x^2 + 5x + 0 = 0$
$x = \frac{-5 \pm \sqrt{25 - 4(3)(0)}}{6} = \frac{-5 \pm 5}{6}$
$x = \frac{-5}{3}$ or 0

22. $5x^2 - 2x + 0 = 0$
$x = \frac{2 \pm \sqrt{4 - 4(5)(0)}}{10} = \frac{2 \pm 2}{10}$
$x = \frac{2}{5}$ or 0

23. $4x^2 + 0x - 100 = 0$
$x = \frac{0 \pm \sqrt{0 - 4(4)(100)}}{8} = \frac{\pm 40}{8} = \pm 5$

24. $5t^2 - 80 = 0$
$5t^2 + 0t - 80 = 0$
$t = \frac{0 \pm \sqrt{0 - 4(5)(-80)}}{10} = \frac{\pm\sqrt{1600}}{10} = \pm 4$

25. $2t^2 + 6t + 5 = 0$
$t = \frac{-6 \pm \sqrt{36 - 4(2)(5)}}{4} = \frac{-6 \pm \sqrt{36 - 40}}{4}$
Discriminant < 0; no real-number roots

26. $4y^2 + 3y + 2 = 0$
$y = \frac{-3 \pm \sqrt{9 - 4 \cdot 4 \cdot 2}}{2 \cdot 4} = \frac{-3 \pm \sqrt{9 - 32}}{8}$
Discriminant < 0; no real-number roots

27. For $3x^2 - 8x + 4 = 0$

$$x = \frac{8 \pm \sqrt{64 - 4 \cdot 3 \cdot 4}}{6} = \frac{8 \pm \sqrt{16}}{6} = \frac{8 \pm 4}{6}$$

$$= \frac{12}{6} \text{ or } \frac{4}{6}$$

$$= 2 \text{ or } \frac{2}{3}$$

28. When the drop hits the river, $h = 0$.

$h = 20 + 76t - 16t^2$

$0 = 20 + 76t - 16t^2$

$0 = -16t^2 + 76t + 20$

$$t = \frac{-76 \pm \sqrt{76^2 - 4(-16)(20)}}{2(-16)}$$

$$= \frac{-76 \pm \sqrt{5776 + 1280}}{-32}$$

$$= \frac{-76 \pm \sqrt{7056}}{-32}$$

$$= \frac{-76 \pm 84}{-32} \qquad y = 2x$$

$$= \frac{8}{-32} \text{ or } \frac{-160}{-32}$$

$$= -\frac{1}{4} \text{ or } 5$$

Since the time cannot be negative, it will take 5 s for the drop to hit the river.

29. $x^2 - 4x - 7 = 0$

$$x = \frac{4 \pm \sqrt{16 - 4(1)(-7)}}{2} = \frac{4 \pm \sqrt{44}}{2}$$

$x \approx -1.3$ or 5.3

30. $x^2 + 2x - 2 = 0$

$$x = \frac{-2 \pm \sqrt{4 - 4(1)(-2)}}{2} = \frac{-2 \pm \sqrt{12}}{2}$$

$x \approx -2.7$ or 0.7

31. $y^2 - 6y - 1 = 0$

$$y = \frac{6 \pm \sqrt{36 - 4(1)(-1)}}{2} = \frac{6 \pm \sqrt{40}}{2}$$

$y \approx -0.2$ or 6.2

32. $4x^2 + 4x - 1 = 0$

$$x = \frac{-4 \pm \sqrt{16 - 4(4)(-1)}}{8} = \frac{-4 \pm \sqrt{32}}{8}$$

$x \approx -1.2$ or 0.2

33. $4x^2 - 4x - 1 = 0$

$$x = \frac{4 \pm \sqrt{16 - 4(4)(-1)}}{8} = \frac{4 \pm \sqrt{32}}{8}$$

$x \approx 1.2$ or -0.2

34. $3x^2 + 4x - 2 = 0$

$$x = \frac{-4 \pm \sqrt{16 - 4(3)(-2)}}{6} = \frac{-4 \pm \sqrt{40}}{6}$$

$x \approx -1.7$ or 0.4

35. $3x^2 - 8x + 2 = 0$

$$x = \frac{8 \pm \sqrt{64 - 4(3)(2)}}{6} = \frac{8 \pm \sqrt{40}}{6}$$

$x \approx 0.3$ or 2.4

36. $2y^2 + 6y - 2 = 0$

$y^2 + 3y - 1 = 0$

$$y = \frac{-3 \pm \sqrt{9 - 4(1)(-1)}}{2} = \frac{-3 \pm \sqrt{13}}{2}$$

$y \approx -3.3$ or 0.3

37. $x^2 - 3x + 1 = 3$

$x^2 - 3x - 2 = 0$

$$x = \frac{3 \pm \sqrt{9 - 4(1)(-2)}}{2} = \frac{3 \pm \sqrt{17}}{2}$$

$x \approx 3.6$ or -0.6

38. $2x^2 - 10x + 9 = 0$

$$x = \frac{10 \pm \sqrt{100 - 4(2)(9)}}{4} = \frac{10 \pm \sqrt{28}}{4}$$

$x \approx 3.8$ or 1.2

39. $5x^2 - 2x - 6 = 0$

$$x = \frac{2 \pm \sqrt{4 - 4(5)(-6)}}{10} = \frac{2 \pm \sqrt{124}}{10}$$

$x \approx 1.3$ or -0.9

40. $7x^2 + 0x - 3 = 0$

$$x = \frac{0 \pm \sqrt{0 - 4(7)(-3)}}{14} = \frac{\pm\sqrt{84}}{14}$$

$x \approx 0.7$ or -0.7

41. $b^2 - 4ac = (-5)^2 - 4(1)(7) = 25 - 28 = -3$

No real-number solutions

42. $b^2 - 4ac = (-8)^2 - 4(1)(3) = 64 - 12 = 52$

Two real-number solutions

43. $b^2 - 4ac = (12)^2 - 4(1)(36) = 144 - 144 = 0$

One real-number solution

44. $b^2 - 4ac = (-1)^2 - 4(2)(-6) = 1 + 48 = 49$

Two real-number solutions

45. $b^2 - 4ac = (-3)^2 - 4(4)(3) = 9 - 48 = -39$

Zero points

46. $b^2 - 4ac = (-4)^2 - 4(2)(-6) = 16 + 48 = 64$

Two points

47. $b^2 - 4ac = (-3)^2 - 4(3)(4) = 9 - 48 = -39$

Zero points

48. $b^2 - 4ac = (4)^2 - 4(-3)(2) = 16 + 24 = 40$

Two points

49. The x-intercepts of $y = (x - 4)(x + 3)$ are the solutions of $(x - 4)(x + 3) = 0$.

$x - 4 = 0$ or $x + 3 = 0$

$x = 4$ or $x = -3$

The x-intercepts are 4 and -3.

50. The intercepts of $y = (x - 5)^2$ are the solutions of $(x - 5)^2 = 0$.

$x - 5 = \pm\sqrt{0}$

$x - 5 = 0$

$x = 5$

The one x-intercept is 5.

51. The x-intercepts of $y = x^2 + 1$ are the solutions of $x^2 + 1 = 0$. Since $x^2 + 1 > 0$ for all values of x, $x^2 + 1 = 0$ has no real-number solutions. Thus, $y = x^2 + 1$ has no x-intercepts.

52. The x-intercepts of $y = x(x + 10)$ are the solutions of $x(x + 10) = 0$.

$x = 0$ or $x + 10 = 0$

$x = 0$ or $x = -10$

The x-intercepts are 0 and -10.

53. $5x + x(x - 7) = 0$

$5x + x^2 - 7x = 0$

$x^2 - 2x = 0$

$$x = \frac{2 \pm \sqrt{2^2 - 4(1)(0)}}{2 \cdot 1} = \frac{2 \pm \sqrt{4}}{2}$$

$$= \frac{2 + 2}{2} = 2 \text{ or } = \frac{2 - 2}{2} = 0$$

54. $x(3x + 7) - 3x = 0$

$3x^2 + 7x - 3x = 0$

$3x^2 + 4x = 0$

$$x = \frac{-4 \pm \sqrt{4^2 - 4(3)(0)}}{2 \cdot 3} = \frac{-4 \pm \sqrt{16}}{6}$$

$$= \frac{-4 + 4}{6} = 0 \text{ or } = \frac{-4 - 4}{6} = \frac{-8}{6} = -\frac{4}{3}$$

55. $3 - x(x - 3) = 4$

$3 - x^2 + 3x = 4$

$-x^2 + 3x - 1 = 0$

$$x = \frac{-3 \pm \sqrt{(-3)^2 - 4(-1)(-1)}}{2(-1)}$$

$$= \frac{-3 \pm \sqrt{9 - 4}}{-2} = \frac{-3 \pm \sqrt{5}}{-2} \text{ or } \frac{3 \pm \sqrt{5}}{2}$$

56. $x(5x - 7) = 1$
$5x^2 - 7x - 1 = 0$
$$x = \frac{7 \pm \sqrt{7^2 - 4(5)(-1)}}{2 \cdot 5}$$
$$= \frac{7 \pm \sqrt{49 + 20}}{10} = \frac{7 \pm \sqrt{69}}{10}$$

57. $(y + 4)(y + 3) = 15$
$y^2 + 7y + 12 = 15$
$y^2 + 7y - 3 = 0$
$$y = \frac{-7 \pm \sqrt{49 - 4(1)(-3)}}{2 \cdot 1}$$
$$= \frac{-7 \pm \sqrt{49 + 12}}{2} = \frac{-7 \pm \sqrt{61}}{2}$$

58. $(y + 5)(y - 1) = 27$
$y^2 + 4y - 5 = 27$
$y^2 + 4y - 32 = 0$
$$y = \frac{-4 \pm \sqrt{4^2 - 4(1)(-32)}}{2 \cdot 1}$$
$$= \frac{-4 \pm \sqrt{16 + 128}}{2} = \frac{-4 \pm \sqrt{144}}{2} = \frac{-4 \pm 12}{2}$$
$$y = \frac{-4 + 12}{2} = 4 \text{ or } y = \frac{-4 - 12}{2} = -8$$

59. $(x + 2)^2 + (x + 1)^2 = 0$
$x^2 + 4x + 4 + x^2 + 2x + 1 = 0$
$2x^2 + 6x + 5 = 0$
$$x = \frac{-6 \pm \sqrt{6^2 - 4(2)(5)}}{2 \cdot 2}$$
$$= \frac{-6 \pm \sqrt{-4}}{4}$$
No real-number solution

60. $(x + 3)^2 + (x + 1)^2 = 0$
$x^2 + 6x + 9 + x^2 + 2x + 1 = 0$
$x^2 + 8x + 10 = 0$
$$x = \frac{-8 \pm \sqrt{8^2 - 4(2)(10)}}{2 \cdot 2}$$
$$= \frac{-8 \pm \sqrt{-16}}{4}$$
No real-number solution

61. The roots of $x^2 + 2x - 8$ are the x-intercepts of $y = x^2 + 2x - 8$. The graph of $y = x^2 + 2x - 8$

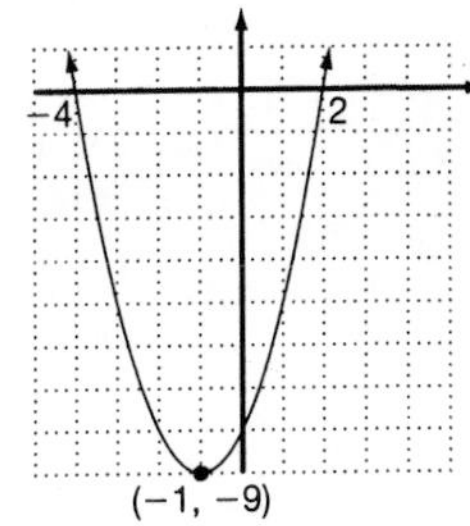

shows that the x-intercepts are -4 and 2. Thus the roots of $x^2 + 2x - 8$ are -4 and 2.

62. The roots of $x^2 - 8x + 16$ are the x-intercepts of $y = x^2 - 8x + 16$. The graph of $y = x^2 - 8x + 16$

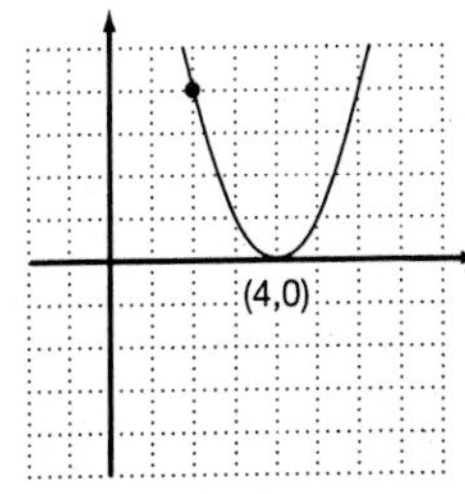

shows that the only x-intercept is 4. Thus the only root of $x^2 - 8x + 16$ is 4.

63. The roots of $x^2 + 1$ are the x-intercepts of $y = x^2 + 1$. The graph of $y = x^2 + 1$

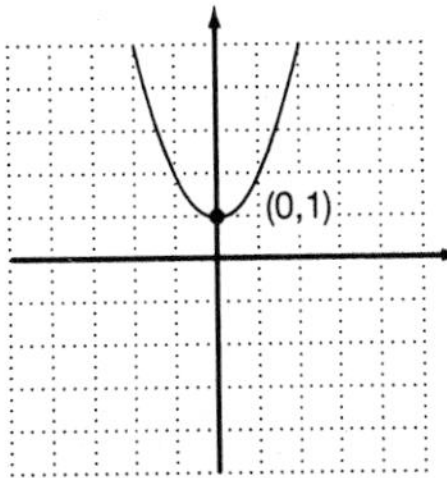

shows that there are no x-intercepts. Thus, $x^2 + 1$ has no real-number roots.

64. The x-intercepts of $y = (x + 4)(x - 2)$ are the roots of $(x + 4)(x - 2)$. The roots of $(x + 4)(x - 2)$ are the solutions of $(x + 4)(x - 2) = 0$.
$(x + 4)(x - 2) = 0$
$x + 4 = 0$ or $x - 2 = 0$
$x = -4$ or $x = 2$
The x-intercepts are -4 and 2. Since the intercepts, $(-4, 0)$ and $(2, 0)$ are the same distance from the axis of symmetry of the graph (parabola), the axis of symmetry must cross the x-axis at $(-1, 0)$, and hence must be the line $x = -1$. Since the vertex of the parabola is on the axis of symmetry, substitute -1 for x in
$y = (x + 4)(x - 2)$
$= (-1 + 4)(-1 - 2)$
$= (3)(-3)$
$= -9$
The vertex of the graph is $(-1, -9)$. Use the x-intercepts and the vertex to sketch the graph:

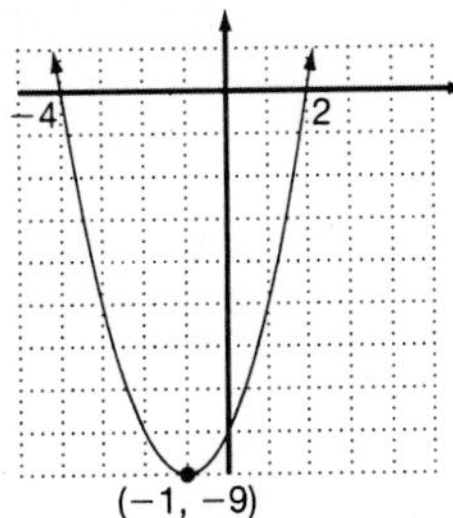

65. The x-intercepts of $y = x(x + 6)$ are the roots of $x(x + 6)$. The roots of $x(x + 6)$ are the solutions of $x(x + 6) = 0$.
$x(x + 6) = 0$
$x = 0$ or $x + 6 = 0$
$x = 0$ or $x = -6$
The x-intercepts are -6 and 0. Since the intercepts, $(-6, 0)$ and $(0, 0)$ are the same distance from the axis of symmetry of the graph (parabola), the axis of symmetry must cross the x-axis at $(-3, 0)$, and hence must be the line $x = -3$. Since the vertex of the parabola is on the axis of symmetry, substitute -3 for x in
$y = x(x + 6)$
$= -3(-3 + 6)$
$= -3(3)$
$= -9$
The vertex of the graph is $(-3, -9)$. Use the x-intercepts and the vertex to sketch the graph:

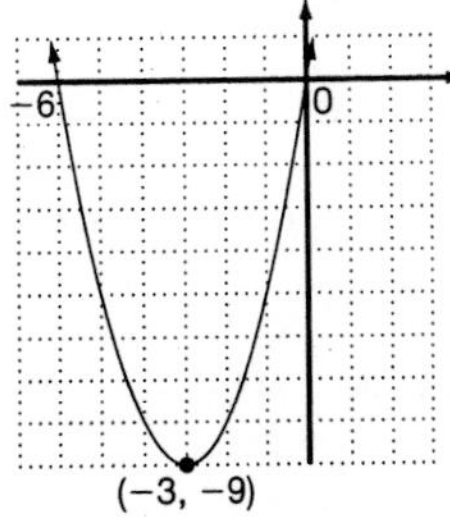

66. The x-intercepts of $y = \frac{1}{5}(2x - 3)(2x + 7)$ are the roots of $\frac{1}{5}(2x - 3)(2x + 7)$. The roots of $\frac{1}{5}(2x - 3)(2x + 7)$ are the solutions of $\frac{1}{5}(2x - 3)(2x + 7) = 0$.

$$\begin{aligned} 2x - 3 &= 0 \quad \text{or} \quad 2x + 7 = 0 \\ 2x &= 3 \quad \text{or} \quad 2x = -7 \\ x &= \frac{3}{2} \quad \text{or} \quad x = -\frac{7}{2} \end{aligned}$$

The x-intercepts are $-\frac{7}{2}$ and $\frac{3}{2}$. Since the intercepts, $\left(-\frac{7}{2}, 0\right)$ and $\left(\frac{3}{2}, 0\right)$ are the same distance from the axis of symmetry of the graph (parabola), the axis of symmetry must cross the x-axis at $(-1, 0)$, and hence must be the line $x = -1$. Since the vertex of the parabola is on the axis of symmetry, substitute -1 for x in

$$\begin{aligned} y &= \frac{1}{5}(2x - 3)(2x + 7) \\ &= \frac{1}{5}(-2 - 3)(-2 + 7) \\ &= \frac{1}{5}(-5)(5) \\ &= \frac{1}{5}(-25) \\ &= -5 \end{aligned}$$

The vertex of the graph is $(-1, -5)$. Use the x-intercepts and the vertex to sketch the graph:

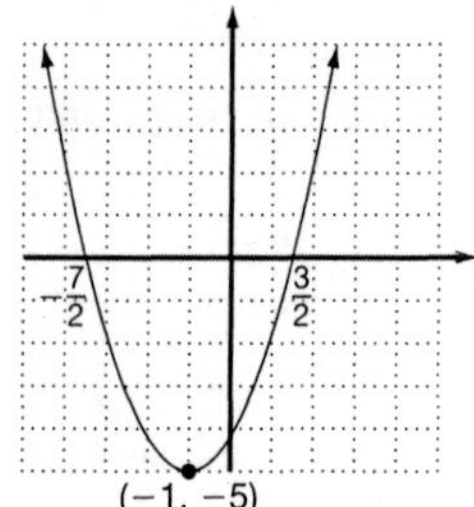

67. For parts a–c, the equation $ax^2 + bx + c = 0$ has two real-number solutions when $b^2 - 4ac > 0$.

a. When $b^2 > 4ac$, $b^2 - 4ac > 0$ no matter what the value of b is. Thus, $ax^2 + bx + c = 0$ has two real-number solutions for all values of b.

b. When $ac < 0$, $4ac < 0$, and $-4ac > 0$. For any value of b, $b^2 \geq 0$. Thus, $b^2 - 4ac > 0$, and the equation $ax^2 + bx + c = 0$ has two real-number solutions for all values of b.

c. $b^2 - 4ac > 0$ only when $b^2 > 4ac$, or $|b| > 2\sqrt{ac}$. This occurs for some values of a, b, and c (for example, $a = 1$, $b = 4$, $c = 1$), but not for all values (for example, $a = 1$, $b = 1$, $c = 1$).

68. **a.** $$\text{Sum} = \frac{-b + \sqrt{b^2 - 4ac}}{2a} + \frac{-b - \sqrt{b^2 - 4ac}}{2a} = -\frac{2b}{2a} = -\frac{b}{a}$$

b. $$\text{Product} = \left(\frac{-b + \sqrt{b^2 - 4ac}}{2a}\right)\left(\frac{-b - \sqrt{b^2 - 4ac}}{2a}\right) = \frac{b^2 - (b^2 - 4ac)}{4a^2} = \frac{b^2 - b^2 + 4ac}{4a^2} = \frac{4ac}{4a^2} = \frac{c}{a}$$

c. Sum $= -\frac{5}{2}$; product $= -\frac{3}{2}$

d. Let s = other solution.

From part b, the product of the solutions $-5s = \frac{c}{a} = \frac{-3}{2}$.

Thus, $s = \frac{3}{10}$.

69. The sum of the roots is $-\frac{b}{a}$ (see Exercise 68, part a). To find the average, divide by 2: Average $= -\frac{b}{2a}$, which is the x-coordinate of the vertex.

70. If $r_1 = \frac{-b + \sqrt{b^2 - 4ac}}{2a}$ and $r_2 = \frac{-b - \sqrt{b^2 - 4ac}}{2a}$, then (using Exercise 68, parts a and b),

$$\begin{aligned} a(x - r_1)(x - r_2) &= a(x^2 - (r_1 + r_2)x + r_1r_2) \\ &= a\left(x^2 - \left(-\frac{b}{a}\right)x + \frac{c}{a}\right) \\ &= ax^2 + bx + c \\ &= f(x) \end{aligned}$$

71. At each x-intercept, $f(x) = 0$.
For $f(x) = x^2 + x - 12$,

$$\begin{aligned} x^2 + x - 12 &= 0 \\ (x + 4)(x - 3) &= 0 \\ x + 4 = 0 \quad &\text{or} \quad x - 3 = 0 \\ x = -4 \quad &\text{or} \quad x = 3 \end{aligned}$$

$f(x) = x^2 + x - 12$ has two x-intercepts, -4 and 3.

72. At each x-intercept, $f(x) = 0$.
For $f(x) = 3x^2 - 6x + 3$,

$$\begin{aligned} 3x^2 - 6x + 3 &= 0 \\ 3(x^2 - 2x + 1) &= 0 \\ 3(x - 1)^2 &= 0 \\ x - 1 &= 0 \\ x &= 1 \end{aligned}$$

$f(x) = 3x^2 - 6x + 3$ has one x-intercept, 1.

73. At each x-intercept, $f(x) = 0$.
For $f(x) = -6x^2 + 11x - 4$,

$$\begin{aligned} -6x^2 + 11x - 4 &= 0 \\ 6x^2 - 11x + 4 &= 0 \\ (2x - 1)(3x - 4) &= 0 \\ 2x - 1 = 0 \quad &\text{or} \quad 3x - 4 = 0 \\ 2x = 1 \quad &\text{or} \quad 3x = 4 \\ x = \frac{1}{2} \quad &\text{or} \quad x = \frac{4}{3} \end{aligned}$$

$f(x) = -6x^2 + 11x - 4$ has two x-intercepts, $\frac{1}{2}$ and $\frac{4}{3}$.

74. $x^2 + 7x - 8 = 0 \qquad a = 1, b = 7, c = -8$

75. $4x^2 + 5x + 16 = 0 \qquad a = 4, b = 5, c = 16$

76.
$$\begin{aligned} 3x^2 - 12 &= 8x + 10 \\ 3x^2 - 8x - 22 &= 0 \qquad a = 3, b = -8, c = -22 \end{aligned}$$

77.
$$\begin{aligned} y &= \frac{k}{x} \\ 16 &= \frac{k}{4} \\ 64 &= k \\ y &= \frac{64}{x} \end{aligned}$$

78.
$$\begin{aligned} y &= \frac{k}{x} \\ 0.1 &= \frac{k}{1} \\ 0.1 &= k \\ y &= \frac{0.1}{x} \end{aligned}$$

79.
$$\begin{aligned} 11 - \sqrt{30 + x} &= 5 \\ 6 &= \sqrt{30 + x} \\ 36 &= 30 + x \\ 6 &= x \end{aligned}$$

80.
$$\begin{aligned} \sqrt{2x + 2} &= \sqrt{5x - 13} \\ 2x + 2 &= 5x - 13 \\ 15 &= 3x \\ 5 &= x \end{aligned}$$

81. $5m^2 - 30m + 45 = 5(m^2 - 6m + 9) = 5(m - 3)^2$

82.
$$\begin{aligned} c^3 - c^2 - c + 1 &= c^2(c - 1) - 1 \cdot (c - 1) \\ &= (c - 1)(c^2 - 1) \\ &= (c - 1)(c - 1)(c + 1) \\ &= (c - 1)^2(c + 1) \end{aligned}$$

LESSON 13-5 TRY THIS

p. 595

a.

$$x + 3 = \frac{10}{x}$$
$$x(x + 3) = x\left(\frac{10}{x}\right)$$
$$x^2 + 3x = 10$$
$$x^2 + 3x - 10 = 0$$
$$(x + 5)(x - 2) = 0$$
$$x + 5 = 0 \quad \text{or} \quad x - 2 = 0$$
$$x = -5 \quad \text{or} \quad x = 2$$

b.

$$1 = \frac{1}{a} + \frac{12}{a^2}$$
$$a^2(1) = a^2\left(\frac{1}{a} + \frac{12}{a^2}\right)$$
$$a^2 = a + 12$$
$$a^2 - a - 12 = 0$$
$$(a - 4)(a + 3) = 0$$
$$a - 4 = 0 \quad \text{or} \quad a + 3 = 0$$
$$a = 4 \quad \text{or} \quad a = -3$$

c.

$$\frac{2}{x + 2} + \frac{2}{x - 2} = 1$$
$$(x + 2)(x - 2)\left(\frac{2}{x + 2} + \frac{2}{x - 2}\right) = 1(x + 2)(x - 2)$$
$$2(x - 2) + 2(x + 2) = x^2 - 4$$
$$2x - 4 + 2x + 4 = x^2 - 4$$
$$0 = x^2 - 4x - 4$$

Using the quadratic formula,

$$x = \frac{-(-4) \pm \sqrt{(-4)^2 - 4(1)(-4)}}{2(1)}$$
$$= \frac{4 \pm \sqrt{16 + 16}}{2}$$
$$= \frac{4 \pm \sqrt{32}}{2}$$
$$= \frac{4 \pm 4\sqrt{2}}{2}$$
$$= 2 \pm 2\sqrt{2}$$

LESSON 13-5 EXERCISES

pp. 596–597

1.

$$\frac{7}{x + 3} = x - 3$$
$$(x + 3)\left(\frac{7}{x + 3}\right) = (x + 3)(x - 3)$$
$$7 = x^2 - 9$$
$$16 = x^2$$
$$\pm 4 = x$$

2.

$$\frac{5}{y - 2} = y + 2$$
$$(y - 2)\left(\frac{5}{y - 2}\right) = (y - 2)(y + 2)$$
$$5 = y^2 - 4$$
$$9 = y^2$$
$$\pm 3 = y$$

3.

$$\frac{x - 2}{3} = \frac{1}{x}$$
$$3x\left(\frac{x - 2}{3}\right) = 3x\left(\frac{1}{x}\right)$$
$$x(x - 2) = 3$$
$$x^2 - 2x = 3$$
$$x^2 - 2x - 3 = 0$$
$$(x - 3)(x + 1) = 0$$
$$x - 3 = 0 \quad \text{or} \quad x + 1 = 0$$
$$x = 3 \quad \text{or} \quad x = -1$$

4.

$$\frac{a - 1}{2} = \frac{3}{a}$$
$$2a\left(\frac{a - 1}{2}\right) = 2a\left(\frac{3}{a}\right)$$
$$a(a - 1) = 2 \cdot 3$$
$$a^2 - a = 6$$
$$a^2 - a - 6 = 0$$
$$(a - 3)(a + 2) = 0$$
$$a - 3 = 0 \quad \text{or} \quad a + 2 = 0$$
$$a = 3 \quad \text{or} \quad a = -2$$

5.

$$\frac{5}{n^2} + \frac{4}{n} = 1$$
$$n^2\left(\frac{5}{n^2} + \frac{4}{n}\right) = n^2(1)$$
$$5 + 4n = n^2$$
$$0 = n^2 - 4n - 5$$
$$0 = (n - 5)(n + 1)$$
$$n - 5 = 0 \quad \text{or} \quad n + 1 = 0$$
$$n = 5 \quad \text{or} \quad n = -1$$

6.

$$\frac{4}{a^2} - \frac{2}{a} = 2$$
$$a^2\left(\frac{4}{a^2} - \frac{2}{a}\right) = a^2 \cdot 2$$
$$4 - 2a = 2a^2$$
$$0 = 2a^2 + 2a - 4$$
$$0 = 2(a + 2)(a - 1)$$
$$a + 2 = 0 \quad \text{or} \quad a - 1 = 0$$
$$a = -2 \quad \text{or} \quad a = 1$$

7.

$$x - 3 = \frac{5}{x - 3}$$
$$(x - 3)(x - 3) = \left(\frac{5}{x - 3}\right)(x - 3)$$
$$x^2 - 6x + 9 = 5$$
$$x^2 - 6x + 4 = 0$$
$$x = \frac{6 \pm \sqrt{36 - 4 \cdot 1 \cdot 4}}{2} = \frac{6 \pm \sqrt{20}}{2}$$
$$= \frac{6 \pm 2\sqrt{5}}{2}$$
$$x = 3 \pm \sqrt{5}$$

8.

$$x + 2 = \frac{3}{x + 2}$$
$$(x + 2)(x + 2) = \left(\frac{3}{x + 2}\right)(x + 2)$$
$$x^2 + 4x + 4 = 3$$
$$x^2 + 4x + 1 = 0$$
$$x = \frac{-4 \pm \sqrt{16 - 4}}{2} = \frac{-4 \pm \sqrt{12}}{2}$$
$$= \frac{-4 \pm 2\sqrt{3}}{2}$$
$$x = -2 \pm \sqrt{3}$$

9.

$$\frac{x^2}{x - 4} - \frac{7}{x - 4} = 0$$
$$(x - 4)\left(\frac{x^2}{x - 4} - \frac{7}{x - 4}\right) = (x - 4)(0)$$
$$x^2 - 7 = 0$$
$$x^2 = 7$$
$$x = \pm\sqrt{7}$$

10.

$$\frac{x^2}{x + 3} - \frac{5}{x + 3} = 0$$
$$(x + 3)\left(\frac{x^2}{x + 3} - \frac{5}{x + 3}\right) = (x + 3)(0)$$
$$x^2 - 5 = 0$$
$$x^2 = 5$$
$$x = \pm\sqrt{5}$$

11.
$$\frac{y+2}{y} = \frac{1}{y+2}$$
$$y(y+2)\left(\frac{y+2}{y}\right) = y(y+2)\left(\frac{1}{y+2}\right)$$
$$(y+2)(y+2) = y$$
$$y^2 + 4y + 4 = y$$
$$y^2 + 3y + 4 = 0$$
Discriminant < 0; no real-number solutions

12.
$$\frac{8}{x-2} + \frac{8}{x+2} = 3$$
$$(x-2)(x+2)\left(\frac{8}{x-2} + \frac{8}{x+2}\right) = (x-2)(x+2)(3)$$
$$8(x+2) + 8(x-2) = (x^2-4)(3)$$
$$8x + 16 + 8x - 16 = 3x^2 - 12$$
$$16x = 3x^2 - 12$$
$$0 = 3x^2 - 16x - 12$$
$$0 = (x-6)(3x+2)$$
$$x - 6 = 0 \quad \text{or} \quad 3x + 2 = 0$$
$$x = 6 \quad \text{or} \quad 3x = -2$$
$$x = 6 \quad \text{or} \quad x = -\frac{2}{3}$$

13.
$$\frac{24}{x-2} + \frac{24}{x+2} = 5$$
$$(x-2)(x+2)\left(\frac{24}{x-2} + \frac{24}{x+2}\right) = (x-2)(x+2)(5)$$
$$24(x+2) + 24(x-2) = (x^2-4)(5)$$
$$24x + 48 + 24x - 48 = 5x^2 - 20$$
$$48x = 5x^2 - 20$$
$$0 = 5x^2 - 48x - 20$$
$$0 = (x-10)(5x+2)$$
$$x - 10 = 0 \quad \text{or} \quad 5x + 2 = 0$$
$$x = 10 \quad \text{or} \quad 5x = -2$$
$$x = 10 \quad \text{or} \quad x = -\frac{2}{5}$$

14.
$$1 + \frac{12}{x^2-4} = \frac{3}{x-2}$$
$$(x^2-4)\left(1 + \frac{12}{x^2-4}\right) = (x^2-4)\left(\frac{3}{x-2}\right)$$
$$x^2 - 4 + 12 = 3(x+2)$$
$$x^2 + 8 = 3x + 6$$
$$x^2 - 3x + 2 = 0$$
$$(x-2)(x-1) = 0$$
$$x - 2 = 0 \quad \text{or} \quad x - 1 = 0$$
$$x = 2 \quad \text{or} \quad x = 1$$
$x = 2$ does not check, so $x = 1$.

15.
$$\frac{5}{t-3} - \frac{30}{t^2-9} = 1$$
$$(t^2-9)\left(\frac{5}{t-3} - \frac{30}{t^2-9}\right) = (t^2-9)(1)$$
$$5(t+3) - 30 = t^2 - 9$$
$$5t + 15 - 30 = t^2 - 9$$
$$0 = t^2 - 5t + 6$$
$$0 = (t-2)(t-3)$$
$$t - 2 = 0 \quad \text{or} \quad t - 3 = 0$$
$$t = 2 \quad \text{or} \quad t = 3$$
$t = 3$ does not check, so $t = 2$.

16.
$$\frac{4}{x+2} - \frac{5}{x-3} = 2$$
$$(x+2)(x-3)\left(\frac{4}{x+2} - \frac{5}{x-3}\right) = (x+2)(x-3)(2)$$
$$4(x-3) - 5(x+2) = (x^2 - x - 6)(2)$$
$$4x - 12 - 5x - 10 = 2x^2 - 2x - 12$$
$$0 = 2x^2 - x + 10$$
Discriminant < 0; no real-number solutions

17.
$$\frac{2}{y-1} + \frac{3}{y+1} = 1$$
$$(y-1)(y+1)\left(\frac{2}{y-1} + \frac{3}{y+1}\right) = (y-1)(y+1)(1)$$
$$2(y+1) + 3(y-1) = y^2 - 1$$
$$2y + 2 + 3y - 3 = y^2 - 1$$
$$0 = y^2 - 5y$$
$$0 = y(y-5)$$
$$y = 0 \quad \text{or} \quad y - 5 = 0$$
$$y = 0 \quad \text{or} \quad y = 5$$

18.
$$\frac{1}{t+2} + \frac{5}{t} = 1$$
$$t(t+2)\left(\frac{1}{t+2} + \frac{5}{t}\right) = t(t+2)(1)$$
$$t + 5(t+2) = t^2 + 2t$$
$$t + 5t + 10 = t^2 + 2t$$
$$0 = t^2 - 4t - 10$$
$$t = \frac{4 \pm \sqrt{16 - 4(1)(-10)}}{2} = \frac{4 \pm \sqrt{56}}{2}$$
$$= \frac{4 \pm 2\sqrt{14}}{2}$$
$$t = 2 \pm \sqrt{14}$$

19.
$$\frac{2}{a+1} - \frac{3}{a} = 2$$
$$a(a+1)\left(\frac{2}{a+1} - \frac{3}{a}\right) = a(a+1)(2)$$
$$2a - 3(a+1) = (a^2 + a)(2)$$
$$2a - 3a - 3 = 2a^2 + 2a$$
$$0 = 2a^2 + 3a + 3$$
Discriminant < 0; no real-number solutions

20.
$$\frac{x}{x+1} - \frac{x}{x-2} = 1$$
$$(x+1)(x-2)\left(\frac{x}{x+1} - \frac{x}{x-2}\right) = (x+1)(x-2)(1)$$
$$x(x-2) - x(x+1) = x^2 - x - 2$$
$$x^2 - 2x - x^2 - x = x^2 - x - 2$$
$$0 = x^2 + 2x - 2$$
$$x = \frac{-2 \pm \sqrt{4 - 4(1)(-2)}}{2}$$
$$= \frac{-2 \pm \sqrt{12}}{2}$$
$$= \frac{-2 \pm 2\sqrt{3}}{2}$$
$$x = -1 \pm \sqrt{3}$$

21.
$$\frac{y}{y+3} - \frac{y}{y-1} = 1$$
$$(y+3)(y-1)\left(\frac{y}{y+3} - \frac{y}{y-1}\right) = (y+3)(y-1)(1)$$
$$y(y-1) - y(y+3) = y^2 + 2y - 3$$
$$y^2 - y - y^2 - 3y = y^2 + 2y - 3$$
$$0 = y^2 + 6y - 3$$
$$y = \frac{-6 \pm \sqrt{36 - 4(1)(-3)}}{2}$$
$$= \frac{-6 \pm \sqrt{48}}{2}$$
$$= \frac{-6 \pm 4\sqrt{3}}{2}$$
$$y = -3 \pm 2\sqrt{3}$$

22.
$$\frac{2x-1}{5} - \frac{2}{x} = \frac{x}{2}$$
$2x(2x-1) - 10(2) = 5x(x)$ Multiplying by $10x$
$$4x^2 - 2x - 20 = 5x^2$$
$$0 = x^2 + 2x + 20$$
Discriminant < 0; no real-number solutions

23. $\frac{n-1}{2} - \frac{1}{n} = \frac{n}{3}$

$3n(n-1) - 6(1) = 2n(n)$ Multiplying by $6n$

$3n^2 - 3n - 6 = 2n^2$

$n^2 - 3n - 6 = 0$

$n = \frac{3 \pm \sqrt{9 - 4(1)(-6)}}{2} = \frac{3 \pm \sqrt{33}}{2}$

24. $\frac{6}{a+1} - \frac{1}{a} = \frac{1}{2}$

$2a(6) - 2(a+1) = a(a+1)$ Multiplying by $2a(a+1)$

$12a - 2a - 2 = a^2 + a$

$0 = a^2 - 9a + 2$

$a = \frac{9 + \sqrt{81 - 4(1)(2)}}{2} = \frac{9 \pm \sqrt{73}}{2}$

25. $\frac{2}{x-2} - \frac{1}{x} = \frac{1}{3}$

$3x(2) - 3(x-2) = x(x-2)$ Multiplying by $3x(x-2)$

$6x - 3x + 6 = x^2 - 2x$

$0 = x^2 - 5x - 6$

$0 = (x-6)(x+1)$

$x - 6 = 0$ or $x + 1 = 0$

$x = 6$ or $x = -1$

26. $\frac{x}{x+1} - \frac{x}{x-1} = \frac{1}{3}$

Multiplying by $3(x+1)(x-1)$

$3x(x-1) - 3x(x+1) = (x+1)(x-1)$

$3x^2 - 3x - 3x^2 - 3x = x^2 - 1$

$0 = x^2 + 6x - 1$

$x = \frac{-6 \pm \sqrt{36 - 4(1)(-1)}}{2}$

$= \frac{-6 \pm \sqrt{40}}{2}$

$= \frac{-6 \pm 2\sqrt{10}}{2} = -3 \pm \sqrt{10}$

27. $\frac{y}{y-2} - \frac{y}{y+2} = \frac{1}{2}$

Multiplying by $2(y-2)(y+2)$

$2y(y+2) - 2y(y-2) = (y-2)(y+2)$

$2y^2 + 4y - 2y^2 + 4y = y^2 - 4$

$0 = y^2 - 8y - 4$

$y = \frac{8 \pm \sqrt{64 - 4(1)(-4)}}{2}$

$= \frac{8 \pm \sqrt{80}}{2}$

$= \frac{8 \pm 4\sqrt{5}}{2}$

$= 4 \pm 2\sqrt{5}$

28. $\frac{1}{a-1} + \frac{2}{1-a} = 3a$

$\frac{1}{a-1} - \frac{2}{a-1} = 3a$

$1 - 2 = 3a(a-1)$ Multiplying by $(a-1)$

$0 = 3a^2 - 3a + 1$

$a = \frac{3 \pm \sqrt{9 - 4 \cdot 3 \cdot 1}}{6}$

No real-number solutions

29. $\frac{1}{2x-1} + \frac{1}{1-2x} = x$

$\frac{1}{2x-1} - \frac{1}{2x-1} = x$

$1 - 1 = x(2x-1)$ Multiplying by $(2x-1)$

$0 = 2x^2 - x$

$0 = x(2x-1)$

$x = 0$ or $2x - 1 = 0$

$2x = 1$

$x = \frac{1}{2}$

$x = 0$ but $x = \frac{1}{2}$ doesn't check

30. $\frac{1}{x-2} - \frac{2}{x^2-4} = 0$

$\frac{1}{x-2} - \frac{2}{(x+2)(x-2)} = 0$

$x + 2 - 2 = 0$ Multiplying by $(x+2)(x-2)$

$x = 0$

31. $\frac{2}{x+3} + \frac{5}{x^2-9} = 0$

$\frac{2}{x+3} + \frac{5}{(x+3)(x-3)} = 0$

$2(x-3) + 5 = 0$ Multiplying by $(x+3)(x-3)$

$2x - 6 + 5 = 0$

$2x = 1$

$x = \frac{1}{2}$

32. $\frac{1}{x+2} - \frac{2}{x^2-4} = 0$

$\frac{1}{x+2} - \frac{2}{(x+2)(x-2)} = \frac{2}{x}$

Multiplying by $x(x+2)(x-2)$

$x(x-2) - 2x = 2(x^2 - 4)$

$x^2 - 2x - 2x = 2x^2 - 8$

$0 = x^2 + 4x - 8$

$x = \frac{-4 \pm \sqrt{16 - 4(1)(-8)}}{2}$

$= \frac{-4 \pm \sqrt{48}}{2}$

$= \frac{-4 \pm 4\sqrt{3}}{2}$

$= -2 \pm 2\sqrt{3}$

33. $\frac{2}{y+3} - \frac{1}{y^2-9} = \frac{1}{y}$

$\frac{2}{y+3} - \frac{1}{(y+3)(y-3)} = \frac{1}{y}$

Multiplying by $y(y+3)(y-3)$

$2y(y-3) - y = y^2 - 9$

$2y^2 - 6y - y = y^2 - 9$

$y^2 - 7y + 9 = 0$

$y = \frac{7 \pm \sqrt{49 - 4 \cdot 1 \cdot 9}}{2}$

$= \frac{7 \pm \sqrt{13}}{2}$

34. $x + \frac{1}{2}\left(\frac{1}{x}\right) + \left(\frac{1}{x} + 1\right) = \frac{9}{2}$

$$2x\left(x + \frac{1}{2x} + \frac{1}{x} + 1\right) = 2x\left(\frac{9}{2}\right)$$
$$2x^2 + 1 + 2 + 2x = 9x$$
$$2x^2 - 7x + 3 = 0$$
$$(2x - 1)(x - 3) = 0$$
$$2x - 1 = 0 \quad \text{or} \quad x - 3 = 0$$
$$2x = 1 \quad \text{or} \quad x = 3$$
$$x = \frac{1}{2} \quad \text{or} \quad x = 3$$

$\frac{1}{2}$ is not an integer, so $x = 3$.

35. Leah computed the discriminant (-15) of $x^2 - 3x + 6$ instead of the discriminant (1) of $x^2 - 3x + 2$.

36. The only possible values of x that could be extraneous solutions are those that result in denominators of 0.
$2x - 2 = 0$ if $x = 1$.
$x^2 - 1 = 0$ if $x = -1$ or 1.
The answer is C.

37. Answers may vary. Sample:

$$\frac{x+2}{x} = \frac{2}{x}$$
$$x\left(\frac{x+2}{x}\right) = x\left(\frac{2}{x}\right)$$
$$x + 2 = 2$$
$x = 0$, which is extraneous.

38. $\frac{1}{x} - \frac{3}{1 - x} = \frac{2}{x(x-1)}$

$$\frac{1}{x} + \frac{3}{x - 1} = \frac{2}{x(x-1)}$$
$x - 1 + 3x = 2$ Multiplying by $x(x - 1)$
$$4x = 3$$
$$x = \frac{3}{4}$$

39. $\frac{2}{y} + \frac{1}{1 - y} = \frac{5}{y^2 - y}$

$$\frac{2}{y} + \frac{1}{1-y} = \frac{5}{y(y-1)} \rightarrow \frac{2}{y} - \frac{1}{y-1} = \frac{5}{y(y-1)}$$
$2(y - 1) - y = 5$ Multiplying by $y(y - 1)$
$$2y - 2 - y = 5$$
$$y = 7$$

40. $\frac{2}{x^2 - x - 6} + \frac{3}{x^2 - 7x + 12} = \frac{1}{x - 4}$

$$\frac{2}{(x-3)(x+2)} + \frac{3}{(x-3)(x-4)} = \frac{1}{x-4}$$
$$2(x - 4) + 3(x + 2) = (x - 3)(x + 2)$$
$$2x - 8 + 3x + 6 = x^2 - x - 6$$
$$0 = x^2 - 6x - 4$$
$$x = \frac{6 \pm \sqrt{36 - 4(1)(-4)}}{2}$$
$$= \frac{6 \pm \sqrt{52}}{2}$$
$$= \frac{6 \pm 2\sqrt{13}}{2}$$
$$= 3 \pm \sqrt{13}$$

41. $\frac{-1}{x^2 + 4x - 5} + \frac{2}{x^2 + x - 20} = \frac{2}{x - 4}$

$$\frac{-1}{(x+5)(x-1)} + \frac{2}{(x+5)(x-4)} = \frac{2}{x-4}$$
$$-(x - 4) + 2(x - 1) = 2(x + 5)(x - 1)$$
$$-x + 4 + 2x - 2 = 2x^2 + 8x - 10$$
$$0 = 2x^2 + 7x - 12$$
$$x = \frac{-7 \pm \sqrt{49 - 4(2)(-12)}}{4}$$
$$= \frac{-7 \pm \sqrt{145}}{4}$$

42. $\frac{1}{x^2 + 3x - 4} + \frac{1}{x^2 + 2x - 8} = \frac{1}{x^2 - 8x + 12}$

$$\frac{1}{(x+4)(x-1)} + \frac{1}{(x+4)(x-2)} = \frac{1}{(x-6)(x-2)}$$
$$(x - 2)(x - 6) + (x - 1)(x - 6) = (x + 4)(x - 1)$$
$$x^2 - 8x + 12 + x^2 - 7x + 6 = x^2 + 3x - 4$$
$$x^2 - 18x + 22 = 0$$
$$x = \frac{18 \pm \sqrt{324 - 4 \cdot 1 \cdot 22}}{2}$$
$$x = \frac{18 \pm \sqrt{236}}{2}$$
$$x = \frac{18 \pm 2\sqrt{59}}{2}$$
$$x = 9 \pm \sqrt{59}$$

43. $\frac{1}{x^2 - 2x - 15} + \frac{1}{x^2 + x - 6} = \frac{1}{x^2 + 2x - 8}$

$$\frac{1}{(x-5)(x+3)} + \frac{1}{(x+3)(x-2)} = \frac{1}{(x+4)(x-2)}$$
$$(x + 4)(x - 2) + (x + 4)(x - 5) = (x + 3)(x - 5)$$
$$x^2 + 2x - 8 + x^2 - x - 20 = x^2 - 2x - 15$$
$$x^2 + 3x - 13 = 0$$
$$x = \frac{-3 \pm \sqrt{9 - 4(1)(-13)}}{2}$$
$$x = \frac{-3 \pm \sqrt{61}}{2}$$

44. $x^2 + 3x = 0$

$$x(x + 3) = 0$$
$$x = 0 \quad \text{or} \quad x = -3$$

45. $a^2 = 15$

$$a = \pm\sqrt{15}$$

46. $y^2 - 5y - 14 = 0$

$$(y - 7)(y + 2) = 0$$
$$y = 7 \quad \text{or} \quad y = -2$$

47. $7x^2 + 4x = 0$

$$x(7x + 4) = 0$$
$$x = 0 \quad \text{or} \quad 7x + 4 = 0$$
$$x = 0 \quad \text{or} \quad x = -\frac{4}{7}$$

48. $9x^2 - 20 = 0$

$$9x^2 = 20$$
$$x^2 = \frac{20}{9}$$
$$x = \pm\sqrt{\frac{20}{9}}$$
$$= \pm\frac{2\sqrt{5}}{3}$$

49. $2x^2 - 7x - 15 = 0$

$$(2x + 3)(x - 5) = 0$$
$$2x + 3 = 0 \quad \text{or} \quad x - 5 = 0$$
$$2x = -3 \quad \text{or} \quad x = 5$$
$$x = -\frac{3}{2} \quad \text{or} \quad x = 5$$

50.

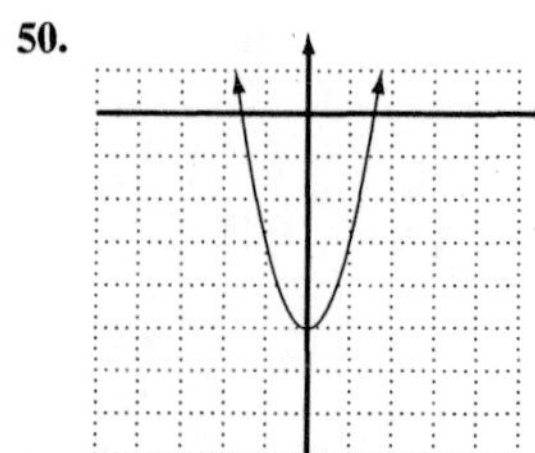

51.

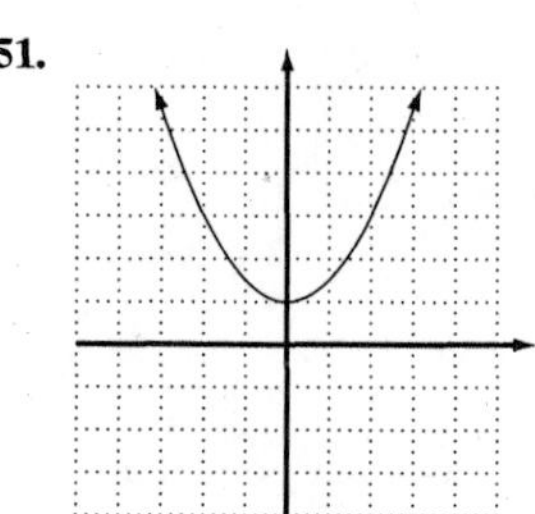

52. 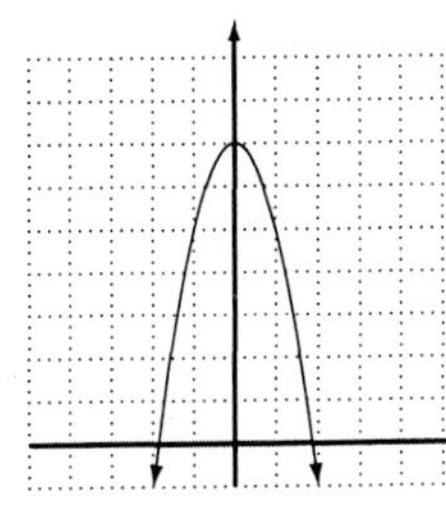

53. 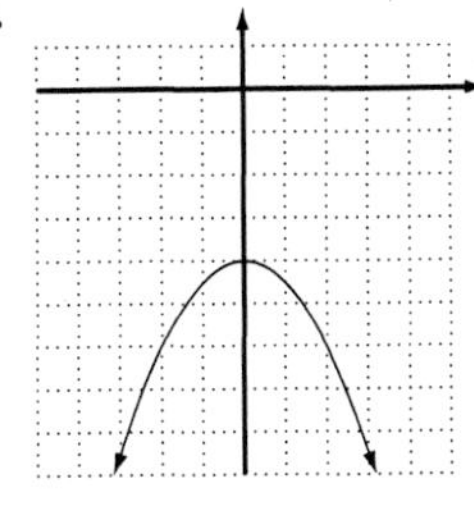

54. $y = kx$
$0.6 = 0.4k$
$\frac{0.6}{0.4} = k$
$k = 1.5$
$y = 1.5x$

55. $y = \frac{k}{x}$
$2 = \frac{k}{3}$
$k = 6$
$y = \frac{6}{x}$

56. $y = \frac{k}{x}$
$5 = \frac{k}{2}$
$10 = k$
$y = \frac{10}{x}$

57. $y = \frac{kx}{z}$
$y = \frac{k(8)}{6}$
$24 = 8k$
$3 = k$
$y = \frac{3x}{z}$

58. 3.485117×10^6

59. 7.0023×10^{-3}

60. $m = \frac{1 - (-9)}{1 - (-5)} = \frac{10}{6} = \frac{5}{3}$

LESSON 13-6 TRY THIS pp. 598–599

a.
$$\sqrt{x + 2} = 4 - x$$
$$(\sqrt{x + 2})^2 = (4 - x)^2$$
$$x + 2 = 16 - 8x + x^2$$
$$x^2 + 9x - 14 = 0$$
$$(x - 7)(x - 2) = 0$$
$$x - 7 = 0 \text{ or } x - 2 = 0$$
$$x = 7 \text{ or } x = 2$$

Check:

$\sqrt{x + 2}$	$4 - x$
$\sqrt{7 + 2}$	$4 - 7$
$\sqrt{9}$	-3
3	-3

$\sqrt{x + 2}$	$4 - x$
$\sqrt{2 + 2}$	$4 - 2$
$\sqrt{4}$	2
2	2

Only 2 checks; therefore the solution is 2.

b.
$$\sqrt{30 - 3x} + 4 = x$$
$$\sqrt{30 - 3x} = x - 4$$
$$(\sqrt{30 - 3x})^2 = (x - 4)^2$$
$$30 - 3x = x^2 - 8x + 16$$
$$x^2 - 5x - 14 = 0$$
$$(x - 7)(x + 2) = 0$$
$$x - 7 = 0 \text{ or } x + 2 = 0$$
$$x = 7 \text{ or } x = -2$$

Check:

$\sqrt{30 - 3x} + 4$	x
$\sqrt{30 - 21} + 4$	7
$\sqrt{9} + 4$	7
$3 + 4$	7
7	7

or

$\sqrt{30 - 3x} + 4$	x
$\sqrt{30 - (-6)} + 4$	-2
$\sqrt{36} + 4$	-2
$6 + 4$	-2
10	-2

The only solution is 7.

c.
$$r = 2\sqrt{5L}$$
$$(r)^2 = (2)^2(\sqrt{5L})^2$$
$$r^2 = 4 \cdot 5L$$
$$r^2 = 20L$$
$$L = \frac{r^2}{20}$$

d.
$$T = 2\pi\sqrt{\frac{L}{g}}$$
$$(T)^2 = (2)^2(\pi)^2\left(\sqrt{\frac{L}{g}}\right)^2$$
$$T^2 = 4\pi^2\frac{L}{g}$$
$$T^2g = 4\pi^2L$$
$$L = \frac{T^2g}{4\pi^2}$$

e.
$$c = \sqrt{\frac{E}{m}}$$
$$(c)^2 = \left(\sqrt{\frac{E}{m}}\right)^2$$
$$c^2 = \frac{E}{m}$$
$$mc^2 = E$$
$$m = \frac{E}{c^2}$$

f.
$$A = \pi r^2$$
$$\frac{A}{\pi} = r^2$$
$$\sqrt{\frac{A}{\pi}} = r$$

g.
$$C = P(d - 1)^2$$
$$\frac{C}{P} = (d - 1)^2$$
$$\pm\sqrt{\frac{C}{P}} = d - 1$$
$$1 \pm \sqrt{\frac{C}{P}} = d$$

LESSON 13-6 EXERCISES pp. 600–601

1.
$$\sqrt{a} = 6$$
$$(\sqrt{a})^2 = 6^2$$
$$a = 36$$

2.
$$\sqrt{x} = 9$$
$$(\sqrt{x})^2 = 9^2$$
$$x = 81$$

3.
$$\sqrt{x + 2} = 3$$
$$(\sqrt{x + 2})^2 = 3^2$$
$$x + 2 = 9$$
$$x = 7$$

4.
$$\sqrt{m - 4} = 5$$
$$(\sqrt{m - 4})^2 = 5^2$$
$$m - 4 = 25$$
$$m = 29$$

5.
$$\sqrt{\frac{x}{3}} = 2$$
$$\left(\sqrt{\frac{x}{3}}\right)^2 = 2^2$$
$$\frac{x}{3} = 4$$
$$x = 12$$

6.
$$\sqrt{\frac{m}{2}} = 5$$
$$\left(\sqrt{\frac{m}{2}}\right)^2 = 5^2$$
$$\frac{m}{2} = 25$$
$$m = 50$$

7.
$$\sqrt{2x} + 3 = 7$$
$$\sqrt{2x} = 4$$
$$(\sqrt{2x})^2 = 4^2$$
$$2x = 16$$
$$x = 8$$

8.
$$\sqrt{5t} - 2 = 1$$
$$\sqrt{5t} = 3$$
$$(\sqrt{5t})^2 = 3^2$$
$$5t = 9$$
$$t = \frac{9}{5}$$

9.
$$\sqrt{2x + 3} = 3$$
$$(\sqrt{2x + 3})^2 = 3^2$$
$$2x + 3 = 9$$
$$2x = 6$$
$$x = 3$$

10.
$$\sqrt{4m - 1} = 5$$
$$(\sqrt{4m - 1})^2 = 5^2$$
$$4m - 1 = 25$$
$$4m = 26$$
$$m = \frac{26}{4} = \frac{13}{2}$$

11.
$$\sqrt{\frac{x + 2}{3}} = 6$$
$$\left(\sqrt{\frac{x + 2}{3}}\right)^2 = 6^2$$
$$\frac{x + 2}{3} = 36$$
$$x + 2 = 108$$
$$x = 106$$

12.
$$\sqrt{\frac{a - 3}{4}} = 2$$
$$\left(\sqrt{\frac{a - 3}{4}}\right)^2 = 2^2$$
$$\frac{a - 3}{4} = 4$$
$$a - 3 = 16$$
$$a = 19$$

13.
$$x - 7 = \sqrt{x - 5}$$
$$(x - 7)^2 = (\sqrt{x - 5})^2$$
$$x^2 - 14x + 49 = x - 5$$
$$x^2 - 15x + 54 = 0$$
$$(x - 9)(x - 6) = 0$$
$$x - 9 = 0 \text{ or } x - 6 = 0$$
$$x = 9 \text{ or } x = 6$$

Only $x = 9$ checks.

14.
$$\sqrt{x + 7} = x - 5$$
$$(\sqrt{x + 7})^2 = (x - 5)^2$$
$$x + 7 = x^2 - 10x + 25$$
$$0 = x^2 - 11x + 18$$
$$0 = (x - 2)(x - 9)$$
$$x - 2 = 0 \text{ or } x - 9 = 0$$
$$x = 2 \text{ or } x = 9$$

Only $x = 9$ checks.

15.
$$\sqrt{x + 18} = x - 2$$
$$(\sqrt{x + 18})^2 = (x - 2)^2$$
$$x + 18 = x^2 - 4x + 4$$
$$0 = x^2 - 5x - 14$$
$$0 = (x - 7)(x + 2)$$
$$x - 7 = 0 \text{ or } x + 2 = 0$$
$$x = 7 \text{ or } x = -2$$

Only $x = 7$ checks.

16.
$$x - 9 = \sqrt{x - 3}$$
$$(x - 9)^2 = (\sqrt{x - 3})^2$$
$$x^2 - 18x + 81 = x - 3$$
$$x^2 - 19x + 84 = 0$$
$$(x - 12)(x - 7) = 0$$
$$x - 12 = 0 \quad \text{or} \quad x - 7 = 0$$
$$x = 12 \quad \text{or} \quad x = 7$$
Only $x = 12$ checks.

17.
$$\sqrt{5x + 21} = x + 3$$
$$(\sqrt{5x + 21})^2 = (x + 3)^2$$
$$5x + 21 = x^2 + 6x + 9$$
$$0 = x^2 + x - 12$$
$$0 = (x + 4)(x - 3)$$
$$x + 4 = 0 \quad \text{or} \quad x - 3 = 0$$
$$x = -4 \quad \text{or} \quad x = 3$$
Only $x = 3$ checks.

18.
$$\sqrt{2x + 3} = 6 - x$$
$$(\sqrt{2x + 3})^2 = (6 - x)^2$$
$$2x + 3 = 36 - 12x + x^2$$
$$0 = x^2 - 14x + 33$$
$$0 = (x - 11)(x - 3)$$
$$x - 11 = 0 \quad \text{or} \quad x - 3 = 0$$
$$x = 11 \quad \text{or} \quad x = 3$$
Only $x = 3$ checks.

19.
$$x = 1 + 6\sqrt{x - 9}$$
$$x - 1 = 6\sqrt{x - 9}$$
$$(x - 1)^2 = (6\sqrt{x - 9})^2$$
$$x^2 - 2x + 1 = 36(x - 9)$$
$$x^2 - 2x + 1 = 36x - 324$$
$$x^2 - 38x + 325 = 0$$
$$(x - 13)(x - 25) = 0$$
$$x - 13 = 0 \quad \text{or} \quad x - 25 = 0$$
$$x = 13 \quad \text{or} \quad x = 25$$

20.
$$\sqrt{2x - 1} + 2 = x$$
$$\sqrt{2x - 1} = x - 2$$
$$(\sqrt{2x - 1})^2 = (x - 2)^2$$
$$2x - 1 = x^2 - 4x + 4$$
$$0 = x^2 - 6x + 5$$
$$0 = (x - 1)(x - 5)$$
$$x - 1 = 0 \quad \text{or} \quad x - 5 = 0$$
$$x = 1 \quad \text{or} \quad x = 5$$
Only $x = 5$ checks.

21.
$$x + 4 = 4\sqrt{x + 1}$$
$$(x + 4)^2 = (4\sqrt{x + 1})^2$$
$$x^2 + 8x + 16 = 16(x + 1)$$
$$x^2 + 8x + 16 = 16x + 16$$
$$x^2 - 8x = 0$$
$$x(x - 8) = 0$$
$$x = 0 \quad \text{or} \quad x - 8 = 0$$
$$x = 0 \quad \text{or} \quad x = 8$$

22.
$$x + 1 = 3\sqrt{x + 5}$$
$$(x + 1)^2 = (3\sqrt{x + 5})^2$$
$$x^2 + 2x + 1 = 9(x + 5)$$
$$x^2 + 2x + 1 = 9x + 45$$
$$x^2 - 7x - 44 = 0$$
$$(x - 11)(x + 4) = 0$$
$$x - 11 = 0 \quad \text{or} \quad x + 4 = 0$$
$$x = 11 \quad \text{or} \quad x = -4$$
Only $x = 11$ checks.

23.
$$c^2 = a^2 + b^2$$
$$c^2 - b^2 = a^2$$
$$\sqrt{c^2 - b^2} = a$$

24.
$$E = mc^2$$
$$\frac{E}{m} = c^2$$
$$\sqrt{\frac{E}{m}} = c$$

25.
$$c = \sqrt{a^2 + b^2}$$
$$(c)^2 = (\sqrt{a^2 + b^2})^2$$
$$c^2 = a^2 + b^2$$
$$c^2 - a^2 = b^2$$
$$\sqrt{c^2 - a^2} = b$$

26.
$$N = 2.5\sqrt{A}$$
$$(N)^2 = (2.5\sqrt{A})^2$$
$$N^2 = 6.25A$$
$$\frac{N^2}{6.25} = A$$

27.
$$V = \pi r^2 h$$
$$\frac{V}{\pi h} = r^2$$
$$\sqrt{\frac{V}{\pi h}} = r$$
$$\text{or} \quad r = \frac{\sqrt{V\pi h}}{\pi h}$$

28.
$$s = \frac{gt^2}{2}$$
$$\frac{2s}{g} = t^2$$
$$\sqrt{\frac{2s}{g}} = t$$
$$\text{or} \quad t = \frac{\sqrt{2sg}}{g}$$

29.
$$x^2 + y^2 + z^2 = r^2$$
$$x^2 = r^2 - y^2 - z^2$$
$$x = \pm\sqrt{r^2 - y^2 - z^2}$$

30.
$$P = \frac{V^2}{R}$$
$$PR = V^2$$
$$\sqrt{PR} = V$$

31.

$F = \frac{GmM}{r^2}$	
$Fr^2 = GmM$	Multiply by r^2.
$r^2 = \frac{GmM}{F}$	Multiply by $\frac{1}{F}$.
$r = \sqrt{\frac{GmM}{F}}$	Take square roots.

32.

$\sqrt{\frac{2s}{a}} = t$	
$\left(\sqrt{\frac{2s}{a}}\right)^2 = (t)^2$	Square both sides.
$\frac{2s}{a} = t^2$	Simplify.
$2s = at^2$	Multiply by a.
$s = \frac{at^2}{2}$	Multiply by $\frac{1}{2}$.

33.

$\sqrt{\frac{P}{R}} = I$	
$\left(\sqrt{\frac{P}{R}}\right)^2 = (I)^2$	Square both sides.
$\frac{P}{R} = I^2$	Simplify.
$P = RI^2$	Multiply by R.
$\frac{P}{I^2} = R$	Multiply by $\frac{1}{I^2}$.

34.

$x = 2V + at^2$	
$x - 2V = at^2$	Add $-2V$.
$\frac{x - 2V}{a} = t^2$	Multiply by $\frac{1}{a}$.
$\sqrt{\frac{x - 2V}{a}} = t$	Take square roots.

35.

$P = R(4 + I)^2$	
$\frac{P}{R} = (4 + I)^2$	Multiply by $\frac{1}{R}$.
$\sqrt{\frac{P}{R}} = 4 + I$	Take square roots.
$\sqrt{\frac{P}{R}} - 4 = I$	Add -4.

36.

$T = 2\pi\sqrt{\frac{l}{g}}$	
$T^2 = 4\pi^2\left(\frac{l}{g}\right)$	Square both sides.
$gT^2 = 4\pi^2 l$	Multiply by g.
$g = \frac{4\pi^2 l}{T^2}$	Multiply by $\frac{1}{T^2}$.

37. $$(\sqrt{x+3})^2 = \left(\frac{8}{\sqrt{x-9}}\right)^2$$
$$x + 3 = \frac{64}{x-9}$$
$$(x+3)(x-9) = 64$$
$$x^2 - 6x - 27 = 64$$
$$x^2 - 6x - 91 = 0$$
$$(x+7)(x-13) = 0$$
$$x = -7 \quad \text{or} \quad x = 13$$
Only $x = 13$ checks.

38. $$\left(\frac{12}{\sqrt{5x+6}}\right)^2 = (\sqrt{2x+5})^2$$
$$\frac{144}{5x+6} = 2x + 5$$
$$144 = (2x+5)(5x+6)$$
$$144 = 10x^2 + 37x + 30$$
$$0 = 10x^2 + 37x - 114$$
$$x = \frac{-37 \pm \sqrt{37^2 - 4(10)(-114)}}{2(10)}$$
$$= \frac{-37 \pm \sqrt{5929}}{20}$$
$$x = \frac{-37+77}{20} = 2 \quad \text{or} \quad x = \frac{-37-77}{20} = -5.7$$
Only $x = 2$ checks.

39. $$\sqrt{4x^2+3} = 3x$$
$$4x^2 + 3 = 9x^2$$
$$3 = 5x^2$$
$$\frac{3}{5} = x^2$$
$$x = \sqrt{\frac{3}{5}} = \frac{\sqrt{15}}{5}$$

40. $$\sqrt{2y^2 - 4} = y$$
$$2y^2 - 4 = y^2$$

41. $$6\sqrt{a} = 18\sqrt{7}$$
$$36a = 324 \cdot 7$$
$$36a = 2268$$
$$a = 63$$

42. $$2\sqrt{x} = 5\sqrt{10}$$
$$4x = 25(10)$$
$$4x = 250$$
$$x = \frac{125}{2}$$

43. $$\sqrt{t^2+1} = 1 - t$$
$$t^2 + 1 = 1 - 2t + t^2$$
$$0 = -2t$$
$$0 = t$$

44. $$\sqrt{a^2 - 1} = 1 + a$$
$$a^2 - 1 = 1 + 2a + a^2$$
$$-2 = 2a$$
$$-1 = a$$

45. (a) $A = s^2$ and $P = 4s$
$$A = \left(\frac{P}{4}\right)^2 \leftarrow \frac{P}{4} = s$$
$$A = \frac{P^2}{16}$$

(b) $$A = \frac{P^2}{16}$$
$$16A = P^2$$
$$\sqrt{16A} = P$$
$$4\sqrt{A} = P$$

46. (a) $C = 2\pi r$ and $A = \pi r^2$
$$\frac{A}{\pi} = r^2$$
$$C = 2\pi\sqrt{\frac{A}{\pi}} \leftarrow \sqrt{\frac{A}{\pi}} = r$$
$$C = \frac{2\pi\sqrt{A}}{\sqrt{\pi}} \cdot \frac{\sqrt{\pi}}{\sqrt{\pi}}$$
$$C = \frac{2\pi\sqrt{A\pi}}{\pi}$$
$$C = 2\sqrt{A\pi}$$

(b) $$C = 2\sqrt{A\pi}$$
$$C^2 = 4(A\pi)$$
$$\frac{C^2}{4\pi} = A$$

47. The student squared $x + 3$ incorrectly.
$(x+3)^2 = x^2 + 6x + 9$. The correct solutions are -2 and -1.

48. The student forgot to check. The correct solution is just 8.

49. $\sqrt{x^2} = x$
$x^2 = x^2$,
which is true for all real numbers x. However, if $x < 0$, then $\sqrt{x^2} \neq x$, since $\sqrt{x^2} > 0$.
Thus, all real numbers $x < 0$ are extraneous solutions.

50. $\sqrt{x^2} = -x$
$x^2 = (-x)^2$
$x^2 = x^2$,
which is true for all real numbers x. However, if $x > 0$, then $-x < 0$, and $\sqrt{x^2} \neq -x$, since $\sqrt{x^2} > 0$.
Thus, all real numbers $x > 0$ are extraneous solutions.

51. $$\sqrt{x^2} = \begin{cases} x \text{ if } x \geq 0 \\ -x \text{ if } x < 0 \end{cases}$$
$$|x| = \begin{cases} x \text{ if } x \geq 0 \\ -x \text{ if } x < 0 \end{cases}$$
Thus, $\sqrt{x^2} = |x|$ for all real numbers. There are no extraneous solutions.

52. $$\frac{1}{\sqrt{x}} = \sqrt{x}$$
$$\left(\frac{1}{\sqrt{x}}\right)^2 = (\sqrt{x})^2$$
$$\frac{1}{x} = x$$
$$x\left(\frac{1}{x}\right) = x^2$$
$$1 = x^2$$
$$\pm\sqrt{1} = x$$
$$x = 1 \quad \text{or} \quad x = -1$$
Of these results, $x = -1$ is extraneous because $\sqrt{-1}$ is not a real number.

53. $$(2\sqrt{x-1} - \sqrt{3x-5})^2 = (\sqrt{x-9})^2$$
$$4(x-1) - 4\sqrt{(x-1)(3x-5)} + 3x - 5 = x - 9$$
$$4x - 4 - 4\sqrt{3x^2 - 8x + 5} = -2x - 4$$
$$(-4\sqrt{3x^2 - 8x + 5})^2 = (-6x)^2$$
$$16(3x^2 - 8x + 5) = 36x^2$$
$$4(3x^2 - 8x + 5) = 9x^2$$
$$12x^2 - 32x + 20 = 9x^2$$
$$3x^2 - 32x + 20 = 0$$
$$(3x-2)(x-10) = 0$$
$$3x - 2 = 0 \quad \text{or} \quad x - 10 = 0$$
$$x = \frac{2}{3} \quad \text{or} \quad x = 10$$
For $x = \frac{2}{3}$, $\sqrt{x-1}$ is not real; only $x = 10$ checks.

54. $$\sqrt{y+1} - \sqrt{2y-5} = \sqrt{y-2}$$
$$(\sqrt{y+1} - \sqrt{y-2})^2 = (\sqrt{2y-5})^2$$
$$y + 1 - 2\sqrt{(y+1)(y-2)} + y - 2 = 2y - 5$$
$$(-2\sqrt{y^2 - y - 2})^2 = (-4)^2$$
$$4(y^2 - y - 2) = 16$$
$$4y^2 - 4y - 8 = 16$$
$$4y^2 - 4y - 24 = 0$$
$$4(y^2 - y - 6) = 0$$
$$4(y-3)(y+2) = 0$$
$$y = 3 \quad \text{or} \quad y = -2$$
Only $y = 3$ checks.

55. Method 1:

$$\begin{aligned} 3\sqrt{x+1} &= 28 - 1 - x \\ (3\sqrt{x+1})^2 &= (27 - x)^2 \\ 9(x+1) &= 729 - 54x + x^2 \\ 9x + 9 &= 729 - 54x + x^2 \\ 0 &= x^2 - 63x + 720 \\ 0 &= (x - 15)(x - 48) \\ x = 15 \quad &\text{or} \quad x = 48 \end{aligned}$$

Only $x = 15$ checks.

Method 2:

Let $y = \sqrt{x+1}$; $y^2 = x + 1$.

$$\begin{aligned} y^2 + 3y - 28 &= 0 \\ (y - 4)(y + 7) &= 0 \\ y = 4 \quad &\text{or} \quad y = -7 \\ \sqrt{x+1} = 4 \quad &\text{or} \quad \sqrt{x+1} = -7 \\ x + 1 = 16 \quad &\text{or} \quad x + 1 = 49 \\ x = 15 \quad &\text{or} \quad x = 48 \end{aligned}$$

Only $x = 15$ checks.

56. $h = vt + 8t^2$

$0 = 8t^2 + vt - h$

$$t = \frac{-v \pm \sqrt{v^2 - 4(8)(-h)}}{2(8)} = \frac{-v \pm \sqrt{v^2 + 32h}}{16}$$

57.

$$\begin{aligned} 2\sqrt{a} + 3\sqrt{b} &= 21 \\ -2\sqrt{a} + 2\sqrt{b} &= 4 \\ \hline 5\sqrt{b} &= 25 \\ \sqrt{b} &= 5 \\ b &= 25 \\ \sqrt{a} - \sqrt{25} &= -2 \\ \sqrt{a} - 5 &= -2 \\ \sqrt{a} &= 3 \\ a &= 9 \end{aligned}$$

58.

$$\begin{aligned} 5\sqrt{m} + 2\sqrt{n} &= 39 \\ 6\sqrt{m} - 2\sqrt{n} &= 38 \\ \hline 11\sqrt{m} &= 77 \\ \sqrt{m} &= 7 \\ m &= 49 \\ 3\sqrt{49} - \sqrt{n} &= 19 \\ 3(7) - \sqrt{n} &= 19 \\ 21 - \sqrt{n} &= 19 \\ 2 &= \sqrt{n} \\ 4 &= n \end{aligned}$$

59.

$$\begin{aligned} 3r^2 + 2s^2 &= 11 \\ r^2 - 2s^2 &= -7 \\ \hline 4r^2 &= 4 \\ r^2 &= 1 \\ r &= \pm 1 \\ 1 - 2s^2 &= -7 \\ 8 &= 2s^2 \\ 4 &= s^2 \\ \pm 2 &= s \quad (-1, -2), (1, -2), (-1, 2), (1, 2) \end{aligned}$$

60.

$$\begin{aligned} 5x^2 - 3y^2 &= -7 \\ -x^2 + 3y^2 &= 23 \\ \hline 4x^2 &= 16 \\ x^2 &= 4 \\ x &= \pm 2 \\ -4 + 3y^2 &= 23 \\ 3y^2 &= 27 \\ y^2 &= 9 \\ y &= \pm 3 \quad (-2, -3), (2, -3), (-2, 3), (2, 3) \end{aligned}$$

61. $x^2 + 4x + \left(\frac{4}{2}\right)^2 = x^2 + 4x + 4$

62. $m^2 - 5m + \left(\frac{5}{2}\right)^2 = m^2 - 5m + \frac{25}{4}$

63. $a^2 - a + \left(\frac{1}{2}\right)^2 = a^2 - a + \frac{1}{4}$

64.

$$\begin{aligned} 9a^2 - 18a &= 0 \\ 9a(a - 2) &= 0 \\ 9a = 0 \quad \text{or} \quad a - 2 &= 0 \\ a = 0 \quad \text{or} \quad a &= 2 \end{aligned}$$

65.

$$\begin{aligned} 3x^2 - 13x + 4 &= 0 \\ (3x - 1)(x - 4) &= 0 \\ 3x - 1 = 0 \quad \text{or} \quad x - 4 &= 0 \\ x = \frac{1}{3} \quad \text{or} \quad x &= 4 \end{aligned}$$

66.

$$\begin{aligned} 2m^2 - 25 &= 0 \\ 2m^2 &= 25 \\ m^2 &= \frac{25}{2} \\ m &= \frac{\pm\sqrt{25}}{\sqrt{2}} \cdot \frac{\sqrt{2}}{\sqrt{2}} \\ m &= \pm\frac{5\sqrt{2}}{2} \end{aligned}$$

67.

$$\begin{aligned} (x - 3)^2 &= 36 \\ x - 3 = 6 \quad \text{or} \quad x - 3 &= -6 \\ x = 9 \quad \text{or} \quad x &= -3 \end{aligned}$$

68.

$$\begin{aligned} (c - 5)^2 &= 17 \\ c - 5 &= \pm\sqrt{17} \\ c &= 5 \pm \sqrt{17} \end{aligned}$$

69. $\sqrt{\frac{1}{81}} = \frac{1}{9}$ **70.** $-\frac{\sqrt{4}}{\sqrt{121}} = -\frac{2}{11}$

71. $\sqrt{\frac{11}{22}} = \sqrt{\frac{1}{2}} = \frac{\sqrt{1}}{\sqrt{2}} \cdot \frac{\sqrt{2}}{\sqrt{2}} = \frac{\sqrt{2}}{2}$ **72.** $\sqrt{\frac{56}{8}} = \sqrt{7}$

73. $\sqrt{\frac{64}{4}} = \sqrt{16} = 4$

74.

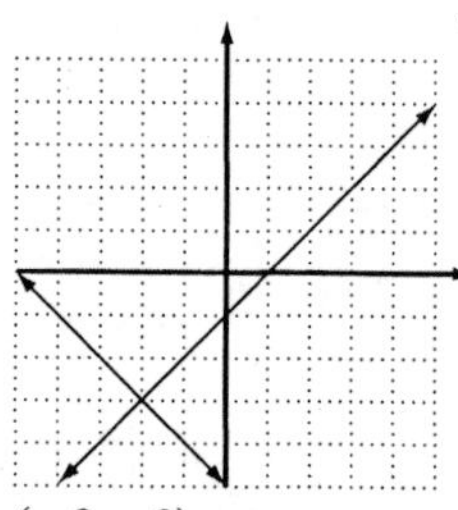

$(-2, -3)$

75.

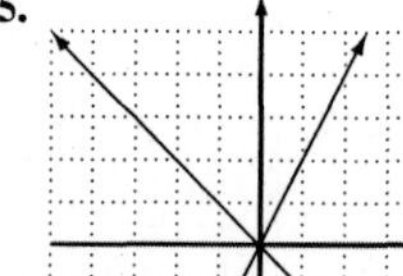

$(0, 0)$

76.

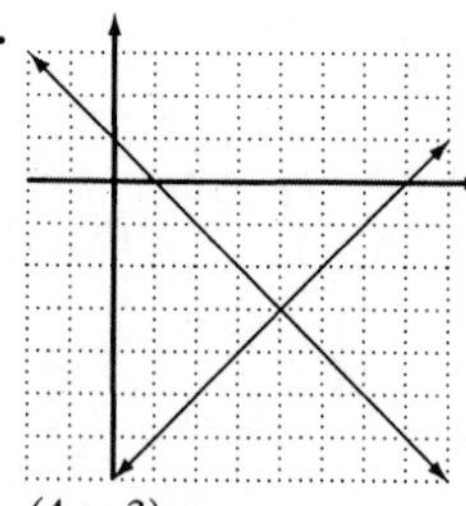

$(4, -3)$

77. Let s = length of side.

$$\begin{aligned} s^2 - 32 &= 4s \\ s^2 - 4s - 32 &= 0 \\ (s - 8)(s + 4) &= 0 \\ s = 8 \quad &\text{or} \quad s = -4 \end{aligned}$$

Since s cannot be negative, $s = 8$ units.

LESSON 13-7 TRY THIS pp. 603–605

a. Let x = width of the strip.

$$\begin{aligned} A &= lw \\ 800 &= (80 - 2x)(60 - 2x) \\ 800 &= 4x^2 - 280x + 4800 \\ 4x^2 - 280x + 4000 &= 0 \\ x^2 - 70x + 1000 &= 0 \\ (x - 20)(x - 50) &= 0 \\ x = 20 \quad &\text{or} \quad x = 50 \end{aligned}$$

When $x = 50$, $60 - 2x = -40$. The width of the garden cannot be negative, so the strip is 20 m wide.

b. $x^2 + (x+1)^2 = 4^2$

$x^2 + x^2 + 2x + 1 = 16$

$2x^2 + 2x - 15 = 0$

$a = 2, b = 2, c = -15$ so $b^2 - 4ac = 124$

$$x = \frac{-b \pm \sqrt{b^2 - 4ac}}{2a}$$

$$x = \frac{-2 \pm \sqrt{124}}{4}$$

$$x = \frac{-2 \pm \sqrt{4 \cdot 31}}{4}$$

$$x = \frac{-2 \pm 2 \cdot \sqrt{31}}{2 \cdot 2}$$

$$x = \frac{-1 \pm \sqrt{31}}{2}$$

$x \approx \frac{-1 - 5.6}{2} = -3.3$ This is not a solution.

or

$x \approx \frac{-1 + 5.6}{2} = 2.3$ This checks. $x + 1 = 2.3 + 1 = 3.3$

The sides are 2.3 cm and 3.3 cm.

c. Let s = the speed of the stream. Then $12 - s$ is speed upstream and $12 + s$ is speed downstream.

$$\frac{45}{12-s} + \frac{45}{12+s} = 8$$

$$(12-s)(12+s)\left(\frac{45}{12-s} + \frac{45}{12+s}\right) = 8(12-s)(12+s)$$

$45(12+s) + 45(12-s) = 8(144 - s^2)$

$540 + 45s + 540 - 45s = 1152 - 8s^2$

$8s^2 - 72 = 0$

$s^2 - 9 = 0$

$(s+3)(s-3) = 0$

$s = 3$ or $s = -3$

Since speed can't be negative, the stream speed is 3 km/h.

LESSON 13-7 EXERCISES pp. 605–606

1. $(20 - 2w)(12 - 2w) = 84$

$240 - 64w + 4w^2 = 84$

$4w^2 - 64w + 156 = 0$

$w^2 - 16w + 39 = 0$

$(w - 13)(w - 3) = 0$

$w - 13 = 0$ or $w - 3 = 0$

$w = 13$ or $w = 3$

$w = 13$ does not check, so width = 3 cm.

2. $(18 - 2w)(14 - 2w) = 192$

$252 - 64w + 4w^2 = 192$

$4w^2 - 64w + 60 = 0$

$w^2 - 16w + 15 = 0$

$(w - 15)(w - 1) = 0$

$w - 15 = 0$ or $w - 1 = 0$

$w = 15$ or $w = 1$

$w = 15$ does not check, so width = 1 cm.

3. $n^2 + (n + 17)^2 = 25^2$

$n^2 + n^2 + 34n + 289 = 625$

$2n^2 + 34n - 336 = 0$

$n^2 + 17n - 168 = 0$

$(n + 24)(n - 7) = 0$

$n + 24 = 0$ or $n - 7 = 0$

$n = -24$ or $n = 7$

Length is positive, so sides are 7 ft and 24 ft.

4. $n^2 + (n + 14)^2 = 26^2$

$n^2 + n^2 + 28n + 196 = 676$

$2n^2 + 28n - 480 = 0$

$n^2 + 14n - 240 = 0$

$(n + 24)(n - 10) = 0$

$n + 24 = 0$ or $n - 10 = 0$

$n = -24$ or $n = 10$

Length is positive, so sides are 10 yd and 24 yd.

5. $w(w + 2) = 80$

$w^2 + 2w = 80$

$w^2 + 2w - 80 = 0$

$(w + 10)(w - 8) = 0$

$w + 10 = 0$ or $w - 8 = 0$

$w = -8$ or $w = 8$

Width is positive, so width = 8 cm, length = 10 cm.

6. $w(w + 4) = 320$

$w^2 + 4w = 320$

$w^2 + 4w - 320 = 0$

$(w + 20)(w - 16) = 0$

$w + 20 = 0$ or $w - 16 = 0$

$w = -20$ or $w = 16$

Width is positive, so width = 16 cm, length = 20 cm.

7. $n^2 + (n + 2)^2 = 8^2$

$n^2 + n^2 + 4n + 4 = 64$

$2n^2 + 4n + 4 = 64$

$2n^2 + 4n - 60 = 0$

$n^2 + 2n - 30 = 0$

$$n = \frac{-2 \pm \sqrt{4 + 120}}{2} = \frac{-2 \pm \sqrt{124}}{2}$$

$n \approx -4.6$ or -6.6

Length is positive, so legs are 4.6 cm and 6.6 cm.

8. $n^2 + (n + 2)^2 = 5^2$

$n^2 + n^2 + 4n + 4 = 25$

$2n^2 + 4n - 21 = 0$

$$n = \frac{-4 \pm \sqrt{16 + 168}}{2} = \frac{-4 \pm \sqrt{184}}{4}$$

$n \approx 2.4$ or -4.4

Length is positive, so legs are 2.4 cm and 4.4 cm.

9. $$\frac{40}{r-3} + \frac{40}{r+3} = 14$$

$$(r-3)(r+3)\left(\frac{40}{r-3} + \frac{40}{r+3}\right) = (r-3)(r+3)(14)$$

$40(r + 3) + 40(r - 3) = (r^2 - 9)(14)$

$40r + 120 + 40r - 120 = 14r^2 - 126$

$0 = 14r^2 - 80r - 126$

$0 = 7r^2 - 40r - 63$

$0 = (7r + 9)(r - 7)$

$7r + 9 = 0$ or $r - 7 = 0$

$7r = -9$ or $r = 7$

$r = -\frac{9}{7}$ or $r = 7$

Rate is positive, so speed = 7 km/h.

10. $$\frac{4}{r-4} + \frac{12}{r+4} = 2$$

$$(r-4)(r+4)\left(\frac{4}{r-4} + \frac{12}{r+4}\right) = (r-4)(r+4)(2)$$

$4(r + 4) + 12(r - 4) = (r^2 - 16)(2)$

$4r + 16 + 12r - 48 = 2r^2 - 32$

$0 = 2r^2 - 16r$

$0 = 2r(r - 8)$

$2r = 0$ or $r - 8 = 0$

$r = 0$ or $r = 8$

Rate > 0, so speed = 8 mi/h.

11. $$\frac{12}{10-r} + \frac{28}{10+r} = 4$$

$$(10-r)(10+r)\left(\frac{12}{10-r} + \frac{28}{10+r}\right) = 4(10-r)(10+r)$$

$12(10 + r) + 28(10 - r) = 4(100 - r^2)$

$120 + 12r + 280 - 28r = 400 - 4r^2$

$4r^2 - 16r = 0$

$4r(r - 4) = 0$

$4r = 0$ or $r - 4 = 0$

$r = 0$ or $r = 4$

Rate > 0, so speed = 4 km/h.

12. $$\frac{738}{200-r}+\frac{1062}{200+r}=9$$
$$\frac{1}{9}\left(\frac{738}{200-r}+\frac{1062}{200+r}\right)=\frac{1}{9}(9)$$
$$\frac{82}{200-r}+\frac{118}{200+r}=1$$
$$(200-r)(200+r)\left(\frac{82}{200-r}+\frac{118}{200+r}\right)=(200-r)(200+r)$$
$$82(200+r)+118(200-r)=40{,}000-r^2$$
$$16{,}400+82r+23{,}600-118r=40{,}000-r^2$$
$$r^2-36r=0$$
$$r(r-36)=0$$
$$r=0 \quad \text{or} \quad r-36=0$$
$$r=0 \quad \text{or} \quad r=36$$
Rate > 0, so speed = 36 mi/h.

13. $$s^2+s^2=(s+3)^2$$
$$2s^2=s^2+6s+9$$
$$s^2-6s-9=0$$
$$s=\frac{6\pm\sqrt{36-4(1)(-9)}}{2}$$
$$=\frac{6\pm\sqrt{72}}{2}=\frac{6\pm 6\sqrt{2}}{2}=3\pm 3\sqrt{2}$$
$3-3\sqrt{2}$ would give a negative length.
So $s=3+3\sqrt{2}\approx 3+3(1.414)=7.242$ cm

14. $$r^2+r^2=(r+1)^2$$
$$2r^2=r^2+2r+1$$
$$r^2-2r-1=0$$
$$r=\frac{2\pm\sqrt{2^2-4(1)(-1)}}{2\cdot 1}$$
$$=\frac{2\pm\sqrt{8}}{2}$$
$$r\approx\frac{2+2.82}{2}\approx 2.41 \quad \text{or} \quad r\approx\frac{2-2.82}{2}=-0.41$$
In the figure, $r=2.41$ cm (length cannot be negative).

15. $2\pi r^2=\pi R^2,\ r=\frac{10}{2}=5$
$$2(3.14)(5^2)=3.14R^2$$
$$50=R^2$$
$$7.07\approx R$$
So the diameter of the big pizza = 2(7.07) = 14.14″.
Therefore a 15″ pizza has a larger area (more to eat).

16. $$\pi R^2-\pi r^2=24$$
$$3.14(6)^2-3.14r^2=24$$
$$113.04-24=3.14r^2$$
$$\frac{89.04}{3.14}=r^2$$
$$r^2\approx 28.36$$
$r\approx 5.33$ cm (Ignore the possible negative solution.)

17. Let r = rate of train A, thus $r+5$ = rate of train B.
$$(2r)^2+(2r+10)^2=50^2$$
$$4r^2+4r^2+40r+100=2500$$
$$8r^2+40r-2400=0$$
$$r^2+5r-300=0$$
$$(r-15)(r+20)=0$$
$$r=15 \quad \text{or} \quad r=-20 \text{ (not possible)}$$
Speed of train A = 15 mi/h.
Speed of train B = $x+5$ = 20 mi/h.

18. y = the vertical height of the ladder top after the ladder is pulled away.
x is the distance the ladder is pulled away from the wall.
① $10^2=y^2+(x+6)^2$
② $10^2=6^2+(x+y)^2$
$$100-36=x^2+2xy+y^2$$
$$64=(x+y)^2$$
$x+y=8, x=8-y$ or $x+y=-8, x=-8-y$
Substituting $x=8-y$ in eq. ①
$$100=y^2+(8-y+6)^2$$
$$100=y^2+(14-y)^2$$
$$100=y^2+196-28y+y^2$$
$$0=2y^2-28y+96$$
$$0=y^2-14y+48$$
$$0=(y-6)(y-8)$$
$$y=6 \quad \text{or} \quad y=8$$
$$x=8-6=2 \quad \text{or} \quad x=8-8=0$$
$x=0$ means the ladder doesn't move, so the solution is 2 ft.

19. $$d=45(5)-5(5)^2$$
$$=225-5(25)=225-125$$
$d=100$ m above its starting point

20. $$50=55t-5t^2$$
$$10=11t-t^2$$
$$t^2-11t+10=0$$
$$(t-10)(t-1)=0$$
$$t-10=0 \quad \text{or} \quad t-1=0$$
$$t=10 \quad \text{or} \quad t=1$$
1 s; it will also be 50 m above its starting point in 10 seconds.

21. $$d=20(5)-5(5)^2$$
$$=100-125$$
$$=-25$$
It will be 25 meters below the starting point.

22. $$\sqrt{m-3}=10$$
$$m-3=100$$
$$m=103$$

23. $$\sqrt{\frac{a}{3}}=1$$
$$\frac{a}{3}=1$$
$$a=3$$

24. $$x+7=2\sqrt{x+7}$$
$$x^2+14x+49=4(x+7)$$
$$x^2+14x+49=4x+28$$
$$x^2+10x+21=0$$
$$(x+3)(x+7)=0$$
$$x=-3 \quad \text{or} \quad x=-7$$

25. $$x^2+2x-15=0$$
$$(x+5)(x-3)=0$$
$$x=-5 \quad \text{or} \quad x=3$$

26. $$x^2-10x+25=0$$
$$(x-5)^2=0$$
$$(x-5)=0$$
$$x=5$$

27. $$x^2+5x+2=0$$
$$x=\frac{-5\pm\sqrt{25-8}}{2}$$
$$x=\frac{-5\pm\sqrt{17}}{2}$$

28. $$x^2-7x+12=0$$
$$(x-3)(x-4)=0$$
$$x=3 \quad \text{or} \quad x=4$$

29. $m = \frac{-2-(-4)}{-3-2} = \frac{-2+4}{-5} = -\frac{2}{5}$

$y = -\frac{2}{5}x + b$

$-4 = -\frac{2}{5}(2) + b$

$-4 = -\frac{4}{5} + b$

$-4 + \frac{4}{5} = b$

$-\frac{16}{5} = b$

So, $y = -\frac{2}{5}x - \frac{16}{5}$.

APPLICATION PROBLEMS p. 607

1. $\$2100 \times 6.2\% = \$130.20$

2. $E = \left(1 + \frac{0.062}{12}\right)^{12} - 1 = (1.005)^{12} - 1 = 6.38\%$

3. $E = \left(1 + \frac{0.041}{365}\right)^{365} - 1 = (1.0001)^{365} - 1 = 4.18\%$

4. $E = \left(1 + \frac{0.081}{12}\right)^{12} - 1 = (1.0068)^{12} - 1 = 8.41\%$

$E = \left(1 + \frac{0.08}{365}\right)^{365} = (1.0002)^{365} = 8.33\%$

8.1% compounded monthly

CHAPTER 13 WRAP UP pp. 609–610

1. $3x^2 + 6x + 4 = 0$

2. $5x^2 - 2x = 0$

3. $5x^2 - 7x = 0$
$x(5x - 7) = 0$
$x = 0$ or $5x - 7 = 0$
$5x = 7$
$x = 0$ or $x = \frac{7}{5}$

4. $3x^2 - 4x = 0$
$x(3x - 4) = 0$
$x = 0$ or $3x - 4 = 0$
$3x = 4$
$x = 0$ or $x = \frac{4}{3}$

5. $5x^2 - 8x + 3 = 0$
$(5x - 3)(x - 1) = 0$
$5x - 3 = 0$ or $x - 1 = 0$
$5x = 3$ or $x = 1$
$x = \frac{3}{5}$ or $x = 1$

6. $3y^2 + 5y - 2 = 0$
$(3y - 1)(y + 2) = 0$
$3y - 1 = 0$ or $y + 2 = 0$
$3y = 1$ or $y = -2$
$y = \frac{1}{3}$ or $y = -2$

7. $5x^2 = 40$
$x^2 = 8$
$\sqrt{x^2} = \pm\sqrt{8}$
$x = \pm\sqrt{8} = \pm 2\sqrt{2}$

8. $8x^2 = 24$
$x^2 = 3$
$\sqrt{x^2} = \pm\sqrt{3}$
$x = \pm\sqrt{3}$

9. $(x + 8)^2 = 13$
$\sqrt{(x + 8)^2} = \pm\sqrt{13}$
$x + 8 = \pm\sqrt{13}$
$x = -8 \pm \sqrt{13}$

10. $(x + 6)^2 = 49$
$\sqrt{(x + 6)^2} = \pm\sqrt{49}$
$x + 6 = \pm 7$
$x = -6 \pm 7$
$x = 1$ or -13

11. $4y^2 + 20y + 25 = 16$
$(2y + 5)^2 = 16$
$\sqrt{(2y + 5)^2} = \pm\sqrt{16}$
$2y + 5 = \pm 4$
$2y = -5 \pm 4$
$2y = -1$ or $2y = -9$
$y = -\frac{1}{2}$ or $y = -\frac{9}{2}$

12. $d = \frac{n^2 - 3n}{2}$
$35 = \frac{n^2 - 3n}{2}$
$70 = n^2 - 3n$
$0 = n^2 - 3n - 70$
$0 = (n - 10)(n + 3)$
$n - 10 = 0$ or $n + 3 = 0$
$n = 10$ or $n = -3$
n is positive, so there are 10 sides.

13. $A = P(1 + r)^2$
$1690 = 1000(1 + r)^2$
$1.69 = (1 + r)^2$
$1.3 = 1 + r$
$0.3 = r$
The rate is 30%.

14. $A = 4000(1 + 0.08)^2$
$= 4000(1.08)^2$
$= 4000(1.1664)$
$A = \$4665.60$

15. $c^2 + 22c$
$\frac{22}{2} = 11, 11^2 = 121$
$c^2 + 22c + 121 = (c + 11)^2$

16. $w^2 - 7w$
$\left(\frac{7}{2}\right)^2 = \frac{49}{4}$
$w^2 - 7w + \frac{49}{4} = \left(w - \frac{7}{2}\right)^2$

17. $x^2 - 2x - 10 = 0$
$x^2 - 2x = 10$
$x^2 - 2x + 1 = 10 + 1$
$(x - 1)^2 = 11$
$x - 1 = \pm\sqrt{11}$
$x = 1 \pm \sqrt{11}$

18. $9x^2 - 6x = 9$
$x^2 - \frac{2}{3}x = 1$
$x^2 - \frac{2}{3}x + \frac{1}{9} = 1 + \frac{1}{9}$
$\left(x - \frac{1}{3}\right)^2 = \frac{10}{9}$
$x - \frac{1}{3} = \pm\sqrt{\frac{10}{9}} = \frac{\pm\sqrt{10}}{3}$
$x = \frac{1 \pm \sqrt{10}}{3}$

19. $3x^2 - 2x - 5 = 0$
$x^2 - \frac{2}{3}x = \frac{5}{3}$
$x^2 - \frac{2}{3}x + \frac{1}{9} = \frac{5}{3} + \frac{1}{9}$
$\left(x - \frac{1}{3}\right)^2 = \frac{16}{9}$
$x - \frac{1}{3} = \pm\frac{4}{3}$
$x = \frac{1}{3} \pm \frac{4}{3}$
$x = \frac{5}{3}$ or $x = -1$

20. $2x^2 + 7x - 1 = 0$

$$x^2 + \frac{7}{2}x = \frac{1}{2}$$
$$x^2 + \frac{7}{2}x + \frac{49}{16} = \frac{1}{2} + \frac{49}{16}$$
$$\left(x + \frac{7}{4}\right)^2 = \frac{57}{16}$$
$$x + \frac{7}{4} = \frac{\pm\sqrt{57}}{4}$$
$$x = \frac{-7 \pm \sqrt{57}}{4}$$

21. $x^2 - 6x - 9 = 0$

$$x = \frac{6 \pm \sqrt{36 + 36}}{2} = \frac{6 \pm \sqrt{72}}{2} = \frac{6 \pm 6\sqrt{2}}{2}$$
$$x = 3 \pm 3\sqrt{2}$$

22. $3x^2 - x - 5 = 0$

$$x = \frac{1 \pm \sqrt{1 + 60}}{6} = \frac{1 \pm \sqrt{61}}{6}$$

23. $x^2 - 3x - 6 = 0$

$$x = \frac{3 \pm \sqrt{9 + 24}}{2} = \frac{3 \pm \sqrt{33}}{2}$$

24. $5x^2 + 3x - 4 = 0$

$$x = \frac{-3 \pm \sqrt{9 + 80}}{10} = \frac{-3 \pm \sqrt{89}}{10}$$

25. $x^2 + 6x + 7 = 0$

$$x = \frac{-6 \pm \sqrt{36 - 28}}{2} = \frac{-6 \pm \sqrt{8}}{2} = \frac{-6 \pm 2\sqrt{2}}{2}$$
$$x = -3 \pm \sqrt{2}$$

26. $x^2 - 14x + 49 = 0$

$$x = \frac{14 \pm \sqrt{196 - 196}}{2} = \frac{14 \pm 0}{2} = \frac{14}{2} = 7$$

27. $5x^2 - 8x + 2 = 0$

$$b^2 - 4ac = (-8)^2 - 4(5)(2)$$
$$= 64 - 40$$
$$= 24$$

Two real-number solutions

28. $x^2 - 18x + 83 = 0$

$$b^2 - 4ac = (-18)^2 - 4(1)(83)$$
$$= 324 - 332$$
$$= -8$$

No real-number solutions

29.
$$\frac{15}{x} - \frac{15}{x + 2} = 2$$
$$x(x + 2)\left(\frac{15}{x} - \frac{15}{x + 2}\right) = 2(x)(x + 2)$$
$$15(x + 2) - 15x = 2x^2 + 4x$$
$$15x + 30 - 15x = 2x^2 + 4x$$
$$0 = 2x^2 + 4x - 30$$
$$0 = x^2 + 2x - 15$$
$$0 = (x + 5)(x - 3)$$
$$x + 5 = 0 \quad \text{or} \quad x - 3 = 0$$
$$x = -5 \quad \text{or} \quad x = 3$$

30.
$$x + \frac{1}{x} = 2$$
$$x\left(x + \frac{1}{x}\right) = (x)2$$
$$x^2 + 1 = 2x$$
$$x^2 - 2x + 1 = 0$$
$$(x - 1)^2 = 0$$
$$x - 1 = 0$$
$$x = 1$$

31.
$$\sqrt{x - 3} = 7$$
$$(\sqrt{x - 3})^2 = 7^2$$
$$x - 3 = 49$$
$$x = 52$$

32.
$$\sqrt{3x + 4} = \sqrt{2x + 14}$$
$$(\sqrt{3x + 4})^2 = (\sqrt{2x + 14})^2$$
$$3x + 4 = 2x + 14$$
$$x = 10$$

33.
$$V = \sqrt{\frac{Fqr}{m}}$$
$$V^2 = \frac{Fqr}{m}$$
$$mV^2 = Fqr$$
$$\frac{mV^2}{qr} = F$$

34.
$$A = \frac{1}{3}\pi r^2$$
$$3A = \pi r^2$$
$$\frac{3A}{\pi} = r^2$$
$$\sqrt{\frac{3A}{\pi}} = r$$

35.
$$w(w + 3) = 70$$
$$w^2 + 3w = 70$$
$$w^2 + 3w - 70 = 0$$
$$(w + 10)(w - 7) = 0$$
$$w + 10 = 0 \quad \text{or} \quad w - 7 = 0$$
$$w = -10 \quad \text{or} \quad w = 7$$

Width is positive, so width = 7 m, length = 10 m.

36.
$$\frac{5}{r - 2} + \frac{5}{r + 2} = 3\frac{1}{3}$$
$$3(r - 2)(r + 2)\left(\frac{5}{r - 2} + \frac{5}{r + 2}\right) = \frac{10}{3}(r - 2)(r + 2)(3)$$
$$15(r + 2) + 15(r - 2) = 10(r^2 - 4)$$
$$15r + 30 + 15r - 30 = 10r^2 - 40$$
$$0 = 10r^2 - 30r - 40$$
$$0 = r^2 - 3r - 4$$
$$0 = (r - 4)(r + 3)$$
$$r - 4 = 0 \quad \text{or} \quad r + 3 = 0$$
$$r = 4 \quad \text{or} \quad r = -3$$

Rate is positive, so $r = 4$ mi/h.

37. 1 ft, 4 in. = 16 in.

$$h^2 = (h - 2)^2 + (h - 16)^2$$
$$h^2 = h^2 - 4h + 4 + h^2 - 32h + 256$$
$$0 = h^2 - 36h + 260$$
$$0 = (h - 26)(h - 10)$$
$$h - 26 = 0 \quad \text{or} \quad h - 10 = 0$$
$$h = 26 \quad \text{or} \quad h = 10$$

$h = 10$ does not check, so the legs are 24 in. and 10 in.

CHAPTER 13 ASSESSMENT p. 611

1. $6x^2 - 3x - 4 = 0$ **2.** $2y^2 - 3y = 0$

3.
$$4a^2 + 4a = 0$$
$$4a(a + 1) = 0$$
$$4a = 0 \quad \text{or} \quad a + 1 = 0$$
$$a = 0 \quad \text{or} \quad a = -1$$

4.
$$7x^2 + 8x = 0$$
$$x(7x + 8) = 0$$
$$x = 0 \quad \text{or} \quad 7x + 8 = 0$$
$$7x = -8$$
$$x = 0 \quad \text{or} \quad x = -\frac{8}{7}$$

5.
$$x^2 + 2x - 48 = 0$$
$$(x + 8)(x - 6) = 0$$
$$x + 8 = 0 \quad \text{or} \quad x - 6 = 0$$
$$x = -8 \quad \text{or} \quad x = 6$$

6.
$$3y^2 + 5y - 2 = 0$$
$$(3y - 1)(y + 2) = 0$$
$$3y - 1 = 0 \quad \text{or} \quad y + 2 = 0$$
$$3y = 1 \quad \text{or} \quad y = -2$$
$$y = \frac{1}{3} \quad \text{or} \quad y = -2$$

7.
$$16b^2 - 25b = 0$$
$$b(16b - 25) = 0$$
$$b = 0 \quad \text{or} \quad 16b - 25 = 0$$
$$16b = 25$$
$$b = 0 \quad \text{or} \quad b = \frac{25}{16}$$

8.
$$7x^2 = 35$$
$$x^2 = 5$$
$$\sqrt{x^2} = \pm\sqrt{5}$$
$$x = \pm\sqrt{5}$$

9. $(x + 8)^2 = 13$

$$\sqrt{(x+8)^2} = \pm\sqrt{13}$$
$$x + 8 = \pm\sqrt{13}$$
$$x = -8 \pm \sqrt{13}$$

10. $(x - 1)^2 = 8$

$$\sqrt{(x-1)^2} = \pm\sqrt{8}$$
$$(x - 1) = \pm\sqrt{8} = \pm 2\sqrt{2}$$
$$x = 1 \pm 2\sqrt{2}$$

11. $x^2 + 8x$

$$\frac{8}{2} = 4, 4^2 = 16$$
$$x^2 + 8x + 16 = (x + 4)^2$$

12. $y^2 + 9y$

$$\left(\frac{9}{2}\right)^2 = \frac{81}{4}$$
$$y^2 + 9y + \frac{81}{4} = \left(y + \frac{9}{2}\right)^2$$

13. $x^2 + 4x - 10 = 0$

$$x = \frac{-4 \pm \sqrt{16 + 40}}{2} = \frac{-4 \pm \sqrt{56}}{2}$$
$$= \frac{-4 \pm 2\sqrt{14}}{2}$$
$$x = -2 \pm \sqrt{14}$$

14. $x^2 - 3x - 7 = 0$

$$x = \frac{3 \pm \sqrt{9 + 28}}{2} = \frac{3 \pm \sqrt{37}}{2}$$

15. $x^2 - x - 3 = 0$

$$x = \frac{1 \pm \sqrt{1 + 12}}{2} = \frac{1 \pm \sqrt{13}}{2}$$

16. $3x^2 - 7x + 1 = 0$

$$x = \frac{7 \pm \sqrt{49 - 12}}{6} = \frac{7 \pm \sqrt{37}}{6}$$

17. $x - \frac{2}{x} = 1$

$$x\left(x - \frac{2}{x}\right) = x \cdot 1$$
$$x^2 - 2 = x$$
$$x^2 - x - 2 = 0$$
$$(x - 2)(x + 1) = 0$$
$$x - 2 = 0 \text{ or } x + 1 = 0$$
$$x = 2 \text{ or } x = -1$$

18. $\frac{4}{x} - \frac{4}{x + 2} = 1$

$$x(x + 2)\left(\frac{4}{x} - \frac{4}{x + 2}\right) = x(x + 2)(1)$$
$$4(x + 2) - 4x = x^2 + 2x$$
$$4x + 8 - 4x = x^2 + 2x$$
$$0 = x^2 + 2x - 8$$
$$0 = (x + 4)(x - 2)$$
$$x + 4 = 0 \text{ or } x - 2 = 0$$
$$x = -4 \text{ or } x = 2$$

19. $3x^2 + 12x + 13 = 0$

$b^2 - 4ac = (12)^2 - 4(3)(13) = 144 - 156 = -12$

No real-number solutions

20. $5x^2 + 17x + 14 = 0$

$b^2 - 4ac = 289 - 4(5)(14) = 289 - 280 = 9$

Two real-number solutions

21. $\sqrt{x + 1} = 6$

$$(\sqrt{x + 1})^2 = 6^2$$
$$x + 1 = 36$$
$$x = 35$$

22. $\sqrt{6x + 1} = \sqrt{5x + 13}$

$$(\sqrt{6x + 1})^2 = (\sqrt{5x + 13})^2$$
$$6x + 1 = 5x + 13$$
$$x = 12$$

23. $g = 2\sqrt{\frac{v}{kh}}$

$$g^2 = 4\left(\frac{v}{kh}\right)$$
$$khg^2 = 4v$$
$$h = \frac{4v}{kg^2}$$

24. $A = P(1 + r)^t$

$$2621.59 = 2000(1 + r)^4$$
$$1.310795 = (1 + r)^4$$
$$1.07 = 1 + r$$
$$0.07 = r$$
$$\text{rate} = 7\%$$

25. $w(w + 4) = 16.25$

$$w^2 + 4w = 16.25$$
$$4w^2 + 16w = 65$$
$$4w^2 + 16w - 65 = 0$$
$$(2w + 13)(2w - 5) = 0$$
$$2w + 13 = 0 \text{ or } 2w - 5 = 0$$
$$2w = -13 \text{ or } 2w = 5$$
$$w = -\frac{13}{2} \text{ or } w = \frac{5}{2} = 2\frac{1}{2}$$

Width is positive, so width $= 2\frac{1}{2}$ m, length $= 6\frac{1}{2}$ m.

26. $\frac{700}{r - 25} - \frac{700}{r + 25} = \frac{1}{4}$

$$4(r - 25)(r + 25)\left(\frac{700}{r - 25} - \frac{700}{r + 25}\right) = \frac{1}{4}(4)(r - 25)(r + 25)$$
$$4(700)(r + 25) - 4(700)(r - 25) = (r - 25)(r + 25)$$
$$2800r + 70{,}000 - 2800r + 70{,}000 = r^2 - 625$$
$$140{,}625 = r^2$$
$$375 = r$$

rate = 375 mi/h.

CHAPTERS 1–13 CUMULATIVE REVIEW pp. 612–617

1. $(x - 3)^2 + 5 = (10 - 3)^2 + 5 = 7^2 + 5 = 49 + 5 = 54$

2. $(y - 1)^2 + (y + 6)^2 = (4 - 1)^2 + (4 + 6)^2 = 3^2 + 10^2 = 9 + 100 = 109$

3. $(x - y)^2 + 2(x + y) = (10 - 2)^2 + 2(10 + 2) = 8^2 + 2(12) = 64 + 24 = 88$

4. $(7 + 6) + 4 = 7 + (6 + 4)$

5. $a \cdot (b \cdot c) = (a \cdot b) \cdot c$

6. $-12.8 + 2.6 + (-11.9) + 6.2 + 0.9 = -24.7 + 9.7 = -15$

7. $-\frac{1}{8} - 4 - \frac{3}{4} + 2\frac{1}{2} - 6\frac{1}{4} = -11\frac{1}{8} + 2\frac{1}{2} = -8\frac{5}{8}$

8. $2 + 6x - 14 - 5x = (6 - 5)x + 2 - 14 = x - 12$

9. $18a + 16b + 2a - 10b = (18 + 2)a + (16 - 10)b = 20a + 6b$

10. 40

11. -34.72

12. $-\frac{4}{7} \div \frac{1}{14} = -\frac{4}{7} \cdot \frac{14}{1} = -\frac{56}{7} = -8$

13. $-\frac{8}{9} \div \left(-\frac{1}{3}\right) = -\frac{8}{9} \cdot \left(-\frac{3}{1}\right) = \frac{24}{9} = \frac{8}{3}$

14. $3x - 12 = 2x$

$$x = 12$$

15. $-\frac{7}{8}x + 7 = \frac{3}{8}x - 3$

$$8\left(-\frac{7}{8}x + 7\right) = 8\left(\frac{3}{8}x - 3\right)$$
$$-7x + 56 = 3x - 24$$
$$80 = 10x$$
$$8 = x$$

16. $0.6x - 1.8 = 1.2x$

$$10(0.6x - 1.8) = 10(1.2x)$$
$$6x - 18 = 12x$$
$$-18 = 6x$$
$$-3 = x$$

17. $\frac{3}{5}n = 3654$

$$5\left(\frac{3}{5}n\right) = 5(3654)$$
$$3n = 18{,}270$$
$$n = 6090 \text{ cars}$$

18. $A = \pi r^2$

$\frac{A}{\pi} = r^2$

$r = \sqrt{\frac{A}{\pi}}$

or (rationalizing denominator), $r = \frac{\sqrt{A\pi}}{\pi}$

19. $A = 2\pi r^2 + 2\pi rh$

$A - 2\pi r^2 = 2\pi rh$

$\frac{A - 2\pi r^2}{2\pi r} = h$

or $\frac{A}{2\pi r} - \frac{2\pi r^2}{2\pi r} = \frac{A}{2\pi r} - r = h$

20. $n = \frac{5}{9}(378) = 210$ votes

21. $52n = 13$

$n = \frac{13}{52} = 0.25 = 25\%$

22. $86n = 129$

$n = \frac{129}{86} = 1.5 = 150\%$

23. $60 = 720n$

$n = \frac{60}{720} = 0.08\overline{3} = 8\frac{1}{3}\%$

24. $12 = 0.5n$

$n = \frac{12}{0.5} = 24 = 2400\%$

25. $1.1n = 11$

$n = \frac{11}{1.1} = 10$

26. $n = 0.25(16) = 4$

27. $x - 9 < 12$

$x < 21$

28. $3a + 8 \geq -5 + 2a$

$a \geq -13$

29. $6y \leq 3$

$y \leq \frac{3}{6}$ or $\frac{1}{2}$

30. $3c - 6 < 5c$

$-6 < 2c$

$-3 < c$

31. $7y + 2 > 5y - 8$

$2y > -10$

$y > -5$

32. $23 - 7x - 3x \geq -11$

$23 - 10x \geq -11$

$-10x \geq -34$

$x \leq \frac{34}{10}$

$x \leq \frac{17}{5}$

33. $15l \geq 225$

$l \geq 15$

The length must be ≥ 15 cm.

34. $a^4 \cdot a^6 = a^{4+6} = a^{10}$

35. $\frac{4m^5}{m^3} = 4m^{5-3} = 4m^2$

36. $y^{-3} = \frac{1}{y^3}$

37. $(2y^6)^3 = 2^3y^{6\cdot3} = 8y^{18}$

38. $\left(\frac{x}{y^3}\right)^2 = \frac{x^2}{y^{3\cdot2}} = \frac{x^2}{y^6}$

39. $(3x^5y^4)^3 = 3^3x^{5\cdot3}y^{4\cdot3}$

$= 27x^{15}y^{12}$

40. $(-3y)(2y^2) = -6y^3$

41. $(-3ab^2c)(-4b^2c^4) = 12ab^4c^5$

42. $\frac{-25x^4}{10x} = -\frac{5}{2}x^{4-1} = -\frac{5x^3}{2}$

43. $\frac{-18x^2y^3z}{-3xyz} = 6x^{2-1}y^{3-1}z^{1-1} = 6xy^2$

44. $(2m^3 - 9) + (5m^3 - 10m^2 + 10) = 7m^3 - 10m^2 + 1$

45. $(-6a^2 - a + 3) - (a^3 - 10a^2 + a + 3)$

$= -6a^2 - a + 3 - a^3 + 10a^2 - a - 3$

$= -a^3 + 4a^2 - 2a$

46. $(4b - 1)(4b + 3) = 16b^2 + 12b - 4b - 3$

$= 16b^2 + 8b - 3$

47. $(2m + 3)(m - 6) = 2m^2 - 12m + 3m - 18$

$= 2m^2 - 9m - 18$

48. $(7y + 6)(7y - 6) = 49y^2 - 36$

49. $(a + 2)^2 = a^2 + 2(a)(2) + 2^2$

$= a^2 + 4a + 4$

50. $(a - 3)^2 = a^2 - 2(a)(3) + 3^2$

$= a^2 - 6a + 9$

51. $(3m + 5)^2 = (3m)^2 + 2(3m)(5) + (5)^2$

$= 9m^2 + 30m + 25$

52. $m^3 - m = m(m^2 - 1) = m(m - 1)(m + 1)$

53. $49x^2 - 64 = (7x + 8)(7x - 8)$

54. $m^4 - 1 = (m^2 + 1)(m^2 - 1)$

$= (m^2 + 1)(m + 1)(m - 1)$

55. $2x^2 + 13x - 99 = (2x - 9)(x + 11)$

56. $7m^2 - 8m + 1 = (7m - 1)(m - 1)$

57. $9x^2 - 24x + 16 = (3x - 4)^2$

58. $9x^4 - 30x^2y + 25y^2 = (3x^2 - 5y)^2$

59. $100x^3 + 60x^2 + 9x = x(100x^2 + 60x + 9)$

$= x(10x + 3)^2$

60.

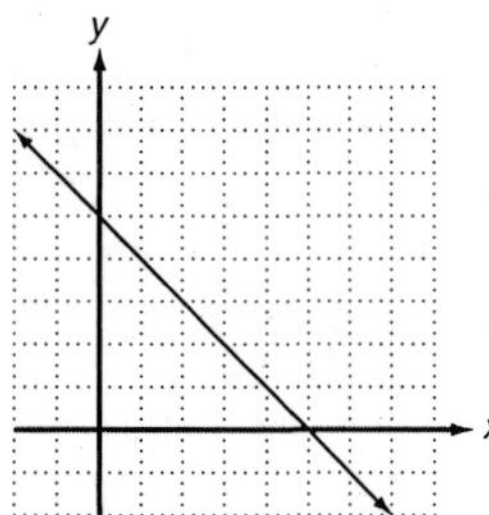

61.

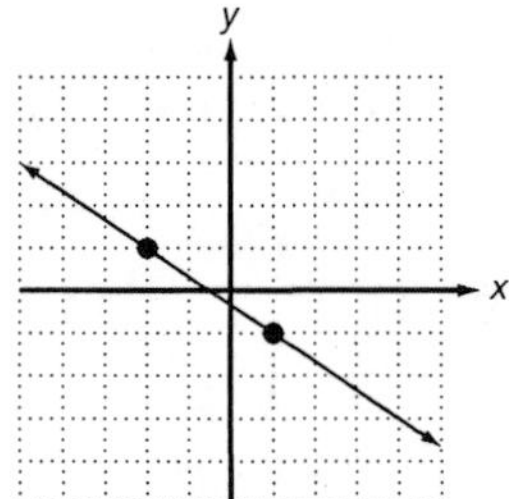

62.

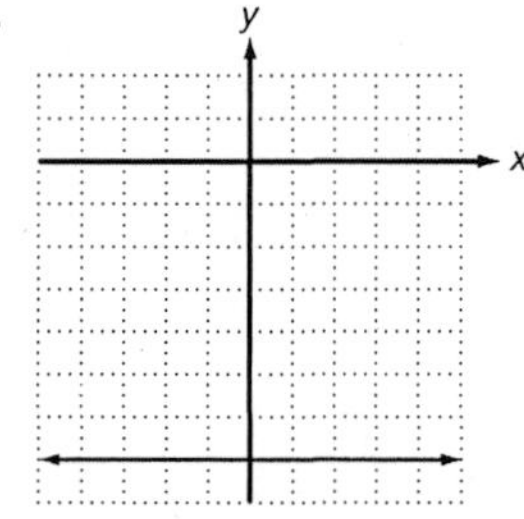

63. $10x = 125 - 20y$

$20y = -10x + 125$

$y = -\frac{1}{2}x + \frac{25}{4}$

slope $= -\frac{1}{2}$ y-intercept $= \frac{25}{4}$

64. $2y - 3x + 1 = 0$

$2y = 3x - 1$

$y = \frac{3}{2}x - \frac{1}{2}$

slope $= \frac{3}{2}$ y-intercept $= -\frac{1}{2}$

65. $y = 10$

66. y-intercept $= 0$ $m = \frac{3}{-3} = -1$

$y = -x$

67. $m = -\frac{2}{3}$ $(-7, 0)$ is on graph.

$y = -\frac{2}{3}x + b$

$0 = -\frac{2}{3}(-7) + b$

$0 = \frac{14}{3} + b$

$-\frac{14}{3} = b$

$y = -\frac{2}{3}x - \frac{14}{3}$

68. $b = -1$ so $y = mx - 1$
(6, 0) is on graph.
$0 = m(6) - 1$
$1 = 6m$
$\frac{1}{6} = m$
$y = \frac{1}{6}x - 1$

69. For (0, 0), $5x - 2y = 5 \cdot 0 - 2 \cdot 0 = 0 \neq -12$.
For (−2, 1), $5x - 2y = 5(-2) - 2(1) = -10 - 2 = -12$.
For (4, 3), $5x - 2y = 5(4) - 2(3) = 20 - 6 = 14 \neq -12$.
For (1, 1), $5x - 2y = 5(1) - 2(1) = 5 - 2 = 3 \neq -12$.
For (−2, 1), $3x + 8y = 3(-2) + 8(1) = -6 + 8 = 2$.
The solution is (−2, 1).

70. For (0, 0), $2y = 2 \cdot 0 = 0 \neq 6$.
For (−2, 1), $2y = 2(1) = 2 \neq 6$.
For (4, 3), $2y = 2(3) = 6$.
For (1, 1), $2y = 2(1) = 2 \neq 6$.
For (4, 3), $-3x = -3(4) = -12$.
The solution is (4, 3).

71. For (0, 0), $x + 8y = 0 + 8 \cdot 0 = 0 \neq 6$.
For (−2, 1), $x + 8y = -2 + 8(1) = -2 + 8 = 6$.
For (4, 3), $x + 8y = 4 + 8(3) = 4 + 24 = 28 \neq 6$.
For (1, 1), $x + 8y = 1 + 8(1) = 1 + 8 = 9 \neq 6$.
For (−2, 1), $3x + 6y = 3(-2) + 6(1) = -6 + 6 = 0$.
The solution is (−2, 1).

72. $y = x - 6$
$x + y = -2$
$x + (x - 6) = -2$
$2x - 6 = -2$
$2x = 4$
$x = 2$
$y = (2) - 6$
$= -4$
(2, −4) is the solution.

73. $\frac{1}{2}x + 2y = 9$
$-8\left(\frac{1}{2}x + 2y\right) = -8(9)$
$-4x - 16y = -72$
$4x + 3y = 7$
$-13y = -65$
$y = 5$
$4x + 3y = 7$
$4x + 3(5) = 7$
$4x + 15 = 7$
$4x = -8$
$x = -2$
(−2, 5) is the solution.

74. $x - y = 14$
$4(x - y) = 4(14)$
$4x - 4y = 56$
$-3x + 4y = 45$
$x = 101$
$4y - 3x = 45$
$4y - 3(101) = 45$
$4y - 303 = 45$
$4y = 348$
$y = 87$
The numbers are 87 and 101.

75. $D + 15 = 3(S + 15)$
$D + 15 = 3S + 45$
$D - 3S = 30$
$-D + 3S = -30$
$(D - 5) - (S - 5) = 50$
$D - 5 - S + 5 = 50$
$D - S = 50$
$-D + 3S = -30$
$2S = 20$
$S = 10$
$D - S = 50$
$D - 10 = 50$
$D = 60$
Dorothy is 60; Stan 10.

76. Rate with wind = 560 Rate against wind = 500
Let time with wind = x.
Let time against wind = y.
$x + y = 10$
$y = 10 - x$
$560x = 500y$
$560x = 500(10 - x)$
$= 5000 - 500x$
$1060x = 5000$
$x \approx 4.71698$
distance with wind $\approx 560(4.71698) \approx 2641.5$
Total distance $\approx 2 \times 2641.5 = 5283$ mi.

77. $x + y = 600$
$-160(x + y) = -160(600)$
$-160x - 160y = -96{,}000$
$160x + 225y = 112{,}250$
$65y = 16{,}250$
$y = 250$
$160x + 225y = 112{,}250$
$x + y = 600$
$x + 250 = 600$
$x = 350$
350 student tickets
250 adult tickets

78. {100, 102, 104, 105, 106, 108, 110, 112, 115, 120}

79. {99, 100, 102, 105, 108, 110, 111, 115, 120}

80. {99, 100, 102, 104, 105, 106, 108, 110, 111, 112}

81. {100, 110} **82.** {105} **83.** {102, 108}

84. $|x| < 4$
$x < 4$ and $x > -4$
$-4 < x < 4$

85. $|x| > 5$
$x > 5$ or $x < -5$

86. $|x - 6| \leq 10$
$x - 6 \leq 10$ and $x - 6 \geq -10$
$x \leq 16$ and $x \geq -4$
$-4 < x < 16$

87. $2|x| \geq 6$
$|x| \geq 3$
$x \geq 3$ or $x \leq -3$

88. $\frac{-5}{3x - 4} \cdot \frac{-6}{5x + 6} = \frac{30}{(3x - 4)(5x + 6)}$
$= \frac{30}{15x^2 - 2x - 24}$

89. $\frac{x + 3}{x^2 - 2} \cdot \frac{x + 3}{x^2 - 2} = \frac{x^2 + 6x + 9}{x^4 - 4x^2 + 4}$

90. $\frac{x^2 - 6x}{x - 6} \cdot \frac{x + 3}{x} = \frac{x(x - 6)(x + 3)}{x(x - 6)} = x + 3$

91. $\frac{5a + 5}{a + 3} \cdot \frac{2a + 6}{a^2 + 2a + 1} = \frac{5(a + 1)(2)(a + 3)}{(a + 3)(a + 1)(a + 1)}$
$= \frac{10}{a + 1}$

92. $\frac{y + 4}{y^2 - 1} \div \frac{y^2 + y - 12}{y + 1} = \frac{y + 4}{(y + 1)(y - 1)} \cdot \frac{y + 1}{(y + 4)(y - 3)}$
$= \frac{(y + 4)(y + 1)}{(y + 1)(y - 1)(y + 4)(y - 3)}$
$= \frac{1}{(y - 1)(y - 3)}$

93. $\frac{8x - 12}{5} \div \frac{6x - 9}{35} = \frac{4(2x - 3)}{5} \cdot \frac{35}{3(2x - 3)}$
$= \frac{4(2x - 3)(35)}{5(3)(2x - 3)}$
$= \frac{140}{15} = \frac{28}{3}$

94. $\frac{2x^2}{2x - 1} - \frac{1 - x}{2x - 1} = \frac{2x^2 - (1 - x)}{2x - 1}$
$= \frac{2x^2 - 1 + x}{2x - 1}$
$= \frac{(2x - 1)(x + 1)}{(2x - 1)}$
$= x + 1$

95. $\frac{x^2}{x-3} + \frac{9}{3-x} = \frac{x^2}{x-3} - \frac{9}{x-3}$

$= \frac{x^2-9}{x-3}$

$= \frac{(x+3)(x-3)}{x-3}$

$= x + 3$

96. $\frac{x-5}{x} - \frac{x}{x-5} = \frac{(x-5)(x-5)}{(x-5)(x)} - \frac{(x)(x)}{(x)(x-5)}$

$= \frac{x^2 - 10x + 25 - x^2}{x(x-5)}$

$= \frac{-10x + 25}{x(x-5)}$

97. $\frac{3}{12 + x - x^2} - \frac{2}{x^2 - 9}$

$= \frac{-3}{x^2 - x - 12} - \frac{2}{(x+3)(x-3)}$

$= \frac{-3}{(x-4)(x+3)} - \frac{2}{(x+3)(x-3)}$

$= \frac{-3(x-3)}{(x-4)(x+3)(x-3)} - \frac{2(x-4)}{(x-4)(x+3)(x-3)}$

$= \frac{-3x + 9 - 2x + 8}{(x-4)(x+3)(x-3)}$

$= \frac{-5x + 17}{(x-4)(x+3)(x-3)}$

98. $\frac{6x-2}{2x-1} = \frac{9x}{3x+1}$

$(2x-1)(3x+1)\left(\frac{6x-2}{2x-1}\right) = (2x-1)(3x+1)\left(\frac{9x}{3x+1}\right)$

$(3x+1)(6x-2) = (2x-1)(9x)$

$18x^2 - 2 = 18x^2 - 9x$

$-2 = -9x$

$\frac{2}{9} = x$

99. $\frac{2}{x+1} = \frac{5}{2x}$

$(2x)(x+1)\left(\frac{2}{x+1}\right) = (2x)(x+1)\left(\frac{5}{2x}\right)$

$2(2x) = 5(x+1)$

$4x = 5x + 5$

$-5 = x$

100. $\frac{1}{8} + \frac{1}{10} = \frac{1}{x}$

$40x\left(\frac{1}{8} + \frac{1}{10}\right) = 40x\left(\frac{1}{x}\right)$

$5x + 4x = 40$

$9x = 40$

$x = \frac{40}{9}$ h or $4\frac{4}{9}$ h

101. $\frac{85}{r} = \frac{110}{r+5}$

$r(r+5)\left(\frac{85}{r}\right) = r(r+5)\left(\frac{110}{r+5}\right)$

$85(r+5) = 110r$

$85r + 425 = 110r$

$425 = 25r$

$17 = r$

Rates are 17 km/h and 22 km/h.

102. One receives $\frac{38}{88}$, the other $\frac{50}{88}$.

$\frac{38}{88}(11{,}000) = \$4750 \quad \frac{50}{88}(11{,}000) = \$6250$

103. $\sqrt{49} = 7$ **104.** $-\sqrt{81} = -9$

105. $x + 4 \geq 0$, $x \geq -4$ **106.** $x - 6 \geq 0$, $x \geq 6$

107. $|cd|$ **108.** $|x+1|$ **109.** $8|x|$

110. $\sqrt{150} = \sqrt{25 \cdot 6} = 5\sqrt{6}$ **111.** $\sqrt{9y} = 3\sqrt{y}$

112. $\sqrt{16x - 16} = \sqrt{16(x-1)} = 4\sqrt{x-1}$

113. $\sqrt{y^7} = \sqrt{y^6 \cdot y} = y^3\sqrt{y}$

114. $\sqrt{8x^4y^4} = \sqrt{4x^4y^4 \cdot 2} = 2x^2y^2\sqrt{2}$

115. $\sqrt{9(a+4)^2} = 3(a+4)$

116. $\sqrt{4xy^2}\sqrt{8x^2y} = \sqrt{32x^3y^3}$

$= \sqrt{16x^2y^2 \cdot 2xy}$

$= 4xy\sqrt{2xy}$

117. $\sqrt{32ab}\sqrt{6a^4b^2} = \sqrt{192a^5b^3}$

$= \sqrt{64a^4b^2 \cdot 3ab}$

$= 8a^2b\sqrt{3ab}$

118. $\sqrt{\frac{1}{6}} = \frac{\sqrt{1}}{\sqrt{6}} \cdot \frac{\sqrt{6}}{\sqrt{6}} = \frac{\sqrt{6}}{6}$

119. $\frac{\sqrt{5}}{\sqrt{18}} \cdot \frac{\sqrt{18}}{\sqrt{18}} = \frac{\sqrt{90}}{18} = \frac{\sqrt{9 \cdot 10}}{18} = \frac{3\sqrt{10}}{18} = \frac{\sqrt{10}}{6}$

120. $\sqrt{\frac{x^2}{27}} = \frac{\sqrt{x^2}}{\sqrt{27}} \cdot \frac{\sqrt{27}}{\sqrt{27}} = \frac{x\sqrt{9 \cdot 3}}{27}$

$= \frac{3x\sqrt{3}}{27}$

$= \frac{x\sqrt{3}}{9}$

121. $13\sqrt{a}$ **122.** $9y\sqrt{y} - 2\sqrt{y} = (9y - 2)\sqrt{y}$

123. $3x\sqrt{x^2y} - x\sqrt{x^2y^3} - 2\sqrt{y^3}$

$= 3x^2\sqrt{y} - x^2y\sqrt{y} - 2y\sqrt{y}$

$= (3x^2 - x^2y - 2y)\sqrt{y}$

124. $a^2 + b^2 = c^2$

$9^2 + b^2 = 41^2$

$81 + b^2 = 1681$

$b^2 = 1600$

$b = \sqrt{1600}$

$b = 40$

125. $f(x) = 2x^2 + 7x - 4$

$f(0) = 2(0)^2 + 7(0) - 4$

$= 0 + 0 - 4$

$f(0) = -4$

126. $f\left(\frac{1}{2}\right) = 2\left(\frac{1}{2}\right)^2 + 7\left(\frac{1}{2}\right) - 4$

$= 2\left(\frac{1}{4}\right) + \frac{7}{2} - 4$

$= \frac{1}{2} + \frac{7}{2} - 4$

$= 0$

127. $f(-2) = 2(-2)^2 + 7(-2) - 4$

$= 2(4) - 14 - 4$

$= 8 - 14 - 4$

$= -10$

128.

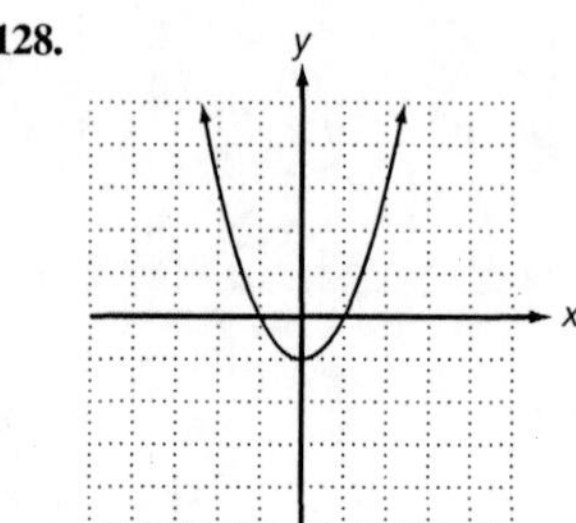

129.

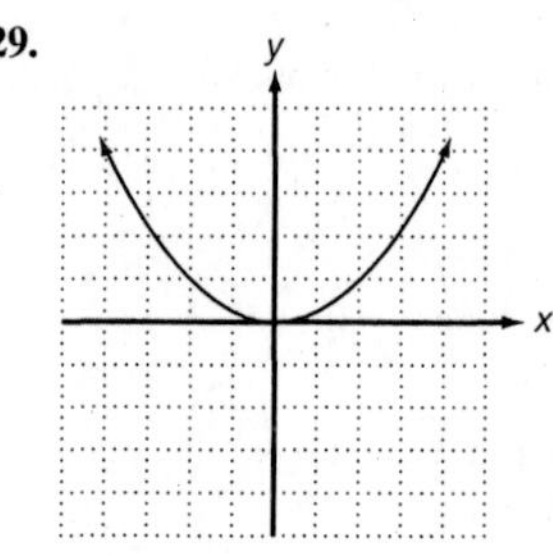

130.
$$\begin{aligned} p &= kd \\ 21.5 &= k(50) \\ 0.43 &= k \\ p &= 0.43d \\ &= 0.43(20) \\ p &= 8.6 \text{ psi} \end{aligned}$$

131.
$$\begin{aligned} v &= \frac{k}{p} \\ 3 &= \frac{k}{15} \\ 45 &= k \\ v &= \frac{45}{p} \\ 5 &= \frac{45}{p} \\ p &= 9 \text{ psi} \end{aligned}$$

132.
$$\begin{aligned} p &= \frac{kr}{s} \\ 10 &= \frac{k(8)}{4} \\ 5 &= k \\ p &= \frac{5r}{s} \\ &= \frac{5(10)}{2} \\ p &= 25 \end{aligned}$$

133.
$$\begin{aligned} 3x^2 &= 30 \\ x^2 &= 10 \\ x &= \sqrt{10}, x = -\sqrt{10} \end{aligned}$$

134.
$$\begin{aligned} 3x^2 - 7x &= 0 \\ x(3x - 7) &= 0 \\ x = 0 \quad \text{or} \quad 3x - 7 &= 0 \\ 3x &= 7 \\ x = 0 \quad \text{or} \quad x &= \frac{7}{3} \end{aligned}$$

135.
$$\begin{aligned} x^2 - 4x + 4 &= 0 \\ (x - 2)^2 &= 0 \\ x - 2 &= 0 \\ x &= 2 \end{aligned}$$

136.
$$\begin{aligned} 6x^2 + x - 2 &= 0 \\ (3x + 2)(2x - 1) &= 0 \\ 3x + 2 = 0 \quad &\text{or} \quad 2x - 1 = 0 \\ 3x = -2 \quad &\text{or} \quad 2x = 1 \\ x = -\frac{2}{3} \quad &\text{or} \quad x = \frac{1}{2} \end{aligned}$$

137.
$$\begin{aligned} (x - 3)^2 &= 6 \\ x - 3 &= \pm\sqrt{6} \\ x &= 3 \pm \sqrt{6} \end{aligned}$$

138.
$$\begin{aligned} x^2 - 10x - 4 &= 0 \\ x &= \frac{10 \pm \sqrt{100 + 16}}{2} = \frac{10 \pm \sqrt{116}}{2} = \frac{10 \pm 2\sqrt{29}}{2} \\ x &= 5 \pm \sqrt{29} \end{aligned}$$

139.
$$\begin{aligned} 9x^2 - 12x - 2 &= 0 \\ x &= \frac{12 \pm \sqrt{144 + 72}}{18} = \frac{12 \pm \sqrt{216}}{18} \\ x &= \frac{12 \pm 6\sqrt{6}}{18} = \frac{2 \pm \sqrt{6}}{3} \end{aligned}$$

140.
$$\begin{aligned} x^2 - 7x + 1 &= 0 \\ x &= \frac{7 \pm \sqrt{49 - 4}}{2} = \frac{7 \pm \sqrt{45}}{2} = \frac{7 \pm 3\sqrt{5}}{2} \end{aligned}$$

141.
$$\begin{aligned} \frac{x + 2}{x^2 - 2} &= \frac{2}{2 - x} \\ (x + 2)(2 - x) &= 2(x^2 - 2) \\ 2x + 4 - x^2 - 2x &= 2x^2 - 4 \\ 4 - x^2 &= 2x^2 - 4 \\ 8 &= 3x^2 \\ \frac{8}{3} &= x^2 \\ x = \pm\sqrt{\frac{8}{3}} &= \frac{\pm\sqrt{8}}{\sqrt{3}} \cdot \frac{\sqrt{3}}{\sqrt{3}} = \frac{\pm 2\sqrt{6}}{3} \end{aligned}$$

142.
$$\begin{aligned} 1 + \frac{1}{x} &= \frac{6}{x^2} \\ x^2\left(1 + \frac{1}{x}\right) &= x^2\left(\frac{6}{x^2}\right) \\ x^2 + x &= 6 \\ x^2 + x - 6 &= 0 \\ (x + 3)(x - 2) &= 0 \\ x + 3 = 0 \quad &\text{or} \quad x - 2 = 0 \\ x = -3 \quad &\text{or} \quad x = 2 \end{aligned}$$

143.
$$\begin{aligned} p &= \sqrt{4p - 3} \\ p^2 &= 4p - 3 \\ p^2 - 4p + 3 &= 0 \\ (p - 1)(p - 3) &= 0 \\ p - 1 = 0 \quad &\text{or} \quad p - 3 = 0 \\ p = 1 \quad &\text{or} \quad p = 3 \end{aligned}$$

144.
$$\begin{aligned} 2\sqrt{x^2 - 1} &= x - 1 \\ (2\sqrt{x^2 - 1})^2 &= (x - 1)^2 \\ 4(x^2 - 1) &= x^2 - 2x + 1 \\ 4x^2 - 4 &= x^2 - 2x + 1 \\ 3x^2 + 2x - 5 &= 0 \\ (3x + 5)(x - 1) &= 0 \\ 3x + 5 = 0 \quad &\text{or} \quad x - 1 = 0 \\ 3x = -5 \quad &\text{or} \quad x = 1 \\ x = -\frac{5}{3} \quad &\text{or} \quad x = 1 \end{aligned}$$

Only $x = 1$ checks.

145.
$$\begin{aligned} \frac{60}{8 - r} + \frac{60}{8 + r} &= 16 \\ 60(8 + r) + 60(8 - r) &= 16(8 + r)(8 - r) \\ 480 + 60r + 480 - 60r &= 16(64 - r^2) \\ 960 &= 1024 - 16r^2 \\ 60 &= 64 - r^2 \\ r^2 &= 4 \\ r &= 2 \end{aligned}$$

The speed is 2 km/h.

146.
$$\begin{aligned} w(2w) &= 32 \\ 2w^2 &= 32 \\ w^2 &= 16 \\ w &= \pm 4 \end{aligned}$$

Width is positive, so width = 4 m, length = 8 m.

MIXED PRACTICE

MIXED PRACTICE 1

p. 618

1. $\frac{a}{3} \cdot \frac{2}{2} = \frac{2a}{6}$
2. $\frac{3}{4} \cdot \frac{m}{m} = \frac{3m}{4m}$
3. $\frac{x}{7} \cdot \frac{y}{y} = \frac{xy}{7y}$

4–9. Answers may vary.

4. $m \cdot (5 \cdot n)$ or $5 \cdot (n \cdot m)$ or $(m \cdot n) \cdot 5$
5. $s + (t + 3)$ or $(3 + s) + t$ or $3 + (t + s)$
6. $a \cdot 11 \cdot b$ or $11 \cdot a \cdot b$ or $b \cdot a \cdot 11$
7. $(2 + s)rt$ or $(2 + s)t \cdot r$ or $r \cdot t(s + 2)$
8. $(2m^2 + n) + 1$ or $2m^2 + (1 + n)$ or $1 + (n + 2m^2)$
9. $x(yz) + w$ or $w + (xz)y$ or $w + x(yz)$
10. $\begin{aligned} 9 + y + y &= 9 + 2 + 2 \\ &= 13 \end{aligned}$
11. $\begin{aligned} 2a + 5b &= 2 \cdot 3 + 5 \cdot 7 \\ &= 6 + 35 \\ &= 41 \end{aligned}$
12. $\frac{3x}{5y} = \frac{3 \cdot 10}{5 \cdot 2} = \frac{30}{10} = 3$
13. $\frac{2m + n}{3} = \frac{2 \cdot 7 + 4}{3} = \frac{14 + 4}{3} = \frac{18}{3} = 6$
14. $h + 3k = 5 + 3 \cdot 1 = 5 + 3 = 8$

15. $4(r + 6) - 3 = 4(7 + 6) - 3 = 4(13) - 3 = 52 - 3 = 49$

16. $(3a)^2 = (3 \cdot 11)^2 = 33^2 = 33 \cdot 33 = 1089$

17. $5y^2 = 5 \cdot 1^2 = 5 \cdot 1 = 5$

18. $6a^3 = 6 \cdot 2^3 = 6 \cdot 2 \cdot 2 \cdot 2 = 6 \cdot 8 = 48$

19. $5r^2 + 1 = 5 \cdot 2^2 + 1 = 5 \cdot 2 \cdot 2 + 1 = 5 \cdot 4 + 1 = 20 + 1 = 21$

20. $m^3 + 4 = 0^3 + 4 = 0 + 4 = 4$

21. $x^3 - 7 = 2^3 - 7 = 2 \cdot 2 \cdot 2 - 7 = 8 - 7 = 1$

22. $(2c)^5 = (2 \cdot 1)^5 = 2^5 = 2 \cdot 2 \cdot 2 \cdot 2 \cdot 2 = 32$

23. $2c^2 = 2 \cdot 1^2 = 2 \cdot 1 \cdot 1 = 2$

24. $5y^8 = 5 \cdot 0^8 = 5 \cdot 0 = 0$

25. $(3xy)^2 = (3 \cdot 5 \cdot 1)^2 = 15^2 = 15 \cdot 15 = 225$

26. $(ab)^3 = (2 \cdot 3)^3 = 6^3 = 6 \cdot 6 \cdot 6 = 216$

27. $(2mn)^4 = (2 \cdot 0 \cdot 2)^4 = 0^4 = 0$

28. $(st)^5 = (1 \cdot 1)^5 = 1^5 = 1$

29. $(m - 4)(m + 1) = (6 - 4)(6 + 1) = (2)(7) = 14$

30. $(9 - w)^2 = (9 - 5)^2 = 4^2 = 4 \cdot 4 = 16$

31. $y(11 - y) = 5(11 - 5) = 5(6) = 30$

32. $5(a + 3) = 5(9 + 3) = 5(12) = 60$

33. $\frac{a^2 + 4}{3a} = \frac{6^2 + 4}{3 \cdot 6} = \frac{6 \cdot 6 + 4}{18} = \frac{36 + 4}{18} = \frac{40}{18} = \frac{20}{9}$

34. $\frac{m^2 + 3m}{7m} = \frac{4^2 + 3 \cdot 4}{7 \cdot 4} = \frac{4 \cdot 4 + 12}{28} = \frac{16 + 12}{28} = \frac{28}{28} = 1$

35. $3 \cdot 3 \cdot 3 \cdot 3 = 3^4$ 36. $7 \cdot n \cdot n \cdot n \cdot n = 7n^4$

37. $w = w^1$ 38. No 39. No 40. No

41. Yes 42. No 43. Yes

44. $18 - 6 \times 8 - 2 = 18 - 48 - 2 = -30 - 2 = -32$

45. $19 - 2 \times 8 + 1 = 19 - 16 + 1 = 3 + 1 = 4$

46. $3 \times 8 - 6 \times 0 = 24 - 0 = 24$

47. $\frac{3w}{15w} = \frac{1 \cdot 3w}{5 \cdot 3w} = \frac{1}{5} \cdot \frac{3w}{3w} = \frac{1}{5}$

48. $\frac{24mn}{6m} = \frac{6m \cdot 4n}{6m \cdot 1} = \frac{6m}{6m} \cdot \frac{4n}{1} = \frac{4n}{1} = 4n$

49. $\frac{11uvw}{2uw} = \frac{uw \cdot 11v}{uw \cdot 2} = \frac{uw}{uw} \cdot \frac{11v}{2} = \frac{11v}{2}$

50. $\frac{8ced}{2ec} = \frac{2ce \cdot 4d}{2ce \cdot 1} = \frac{2ce}{2ce} \cdot \frac{4d}{1} = \frac{4d}{1} = 4d$

51. $\frac{12st}{3rs} = \frac{3s \cdot 4t}{3s \cdot r} = \frac{3s}{3s} \cdot \frac{4t}{r} = \frac{4t}{r}$

52. $\frac{5xtv}{7vxy} = \frac{xv \cdot 5t}{xv \cdot 7y} = \frac{xv}{xv} \cdot \frac{5t}{7y} = \frac{5t}{7y}$

53. $(5 + 2)^2 = 7^2 = 7 \cdot 7 = 49$

54. $5 + 2^2 = 5 + 2 \cdot 2 = 5 + 4 = 9$

55. $5^2 + 2 = 5 \cdot 5 + 2 = 25 + 2 = 27$

56. $(5 - 2)^2 = 3^2 = 3 \cdot 3 = 9$

57. $5^2 - 2 = 5 \cdot 5 - 2 = 25 - 2 = 23$

58. $5 - 2^2 = 5 - 2 \cdot 2 = 5 - 4 = 1$

59. $5 \cdot 2^2 = 5 \cdot 2 \cdot 2 = 5 \cdot 4 = 20$

60. $(5 \cdot 2)^2 = 10^2 = 10 \cdot 10 = 100$

61. $5^2 \cdot 2^2 = 5 \cdot 5 \cdot 2 \cdot 2 = 25 \cdot 4 = 100$

MIXED PRACTICE 2 p. 619

1. $12a + 42b + 18 = 6 \cdot 2a + 6 \cdot 7b + 6 \cdot 3 = 6(2a + 7b + 3)$
$6(2a + 7b + 3) = 6 \cdot 2a + 6 \cdot 7b + 6 \cdot 3 = 12a + 42b + 18$

2. $25x + 60y + 40z = 5 \cdot 5x + 5 \cdot 12y + 5 \cdot 8z$
$= 5(5x + 12y + 8z)$
$5(5x + 12y + 8z) = 5 \cdot 5x + 5 \cdot 12y + 5 \cdot 8z$
$= 25x + 60y + 40z$

3. $14m + 10n + 6 = 2 \cdot 7m + 2 \cdot 5n + 2 \cdot 3 = 2(7m + 5n + 3)$
$2(7m + 5n + 3) = 2 \cdot 7m + 2 \cdot 5n + 2 \cdot 3 = 14m + 10n + 6$

4. $xy + 3x + 6xy + 4x = (3 + 4)x + (1 + 6)xy$
$= 7x + 7xy$
$= 7x \cdot 1 + 7x \cdot y$
$= 7x(1 + y)$

5. $6a^2 + 3ab + 2ab + 4a^2 = (6 + 4)a^2 + (3 + 2)ab$
$= 10a^2 + 5ab$
$= 5a \cdot 2a + 5a \cdot b$
$= 5a(2a + b)$

6. $8xy + 9xz + 4xy + 3xz = (8 + 4)xy + (9 + 3)xz$
$= 12xy + 12xz$
$= 12x \cdot y + 12x \cdot z$
$= 12x(y + z)$

7. $27c + 5 + 8c = (27 + 8)c + 5$
$= 35c + 5$
$= 5 \cdot 7c + 5 \cdot 1$
$= 5(7c + 1)$

8. $\frac{n}{5}$ 9. $y + 17$ 10. $p + 8$

11. $\frac{b}{2}$ 12. $w - 6$

13. $\frac{12m}{18n} = \frac{12 \cdot 12}{18 \cdot 8} = \frac{144}{144} = 1$

14. $\frac{x \cdot y}{6} + \frac{x + 2}{2} = \frac{8 \cdot 3}{6} + \frac{8 + 2}{2} = \frac{24}{6} + \frac{10}{2} = 4 + 5 = 9$

15. $\frac{2a + c}{5} = \frac{2 \cdot 3 + 4}{5} = \frac{6 + 4}{5} = \frac{10}{5} = 2$

16. $\frac{2a + c}{5} = \frac{2 \cdot 2 + 1}{5} = \frac{4 + 1}{5} = \frac{5}{5} = 1$

17. $\frac{2a + c}{5} = \frac{2 \cdot 15 + 30}{5} = \frac{30 + 30}{5} = \frac{60}{5} = 12$

18. $\frac{2a + c}{5} = \frac{2 \cdot \frac{25}{2} + 25}{5} = \frac{25 + 25}{5} = \frac{50}{5} = 10$

19.
$3(2)^2 - 1 = 47$	$3(4)^2 - 1 = 47$	$3(6)^2 - 1 = 47$
$3(4) - 1 = 47$	$3(16) - 1 = 47$	$3(36) - 1 = 47$
$12 - 1 = 47$	$48 - 1 = 47$	$108 - 1 = 47$
$11 = 47$	$47 = 47$	$107 = 47$
False	True	False

The solution set is {4}.

20.
$5 + 3 = 5(5) - 25$	$6 + 3 = 5(6) - 25$
$8 = 25 - 25$	$9 = 30 - 25$
$8 = 0$	$9 = 5$
False	False

$7 + 3 = 5(7) - 25$
$10 = 35 - 25$
$10 = 10$
True
The solution set is {7}.

21. $6x + 3x = 36$
$9x = 36$
$x = 4$

22. $n + 7n = 16$
$8n = 16$
$n = 2$

23. $3t + 2t = 35$
$5t = 35$
$t = 7$

24. $\frac{32m}{8} = 12$
$4m = 12$
$m = 3$

25. $5a^2 = 5$
$a = \pm 1$

26. $\frac{15k}{3} = 20$
$5k = 20$
$k = 4$

27. No 28. No 29. Yes 30. No

31. $A = lw$ $\quad l = 25 \text{ yd} \cdot 3\frac{\text{ft}}{\text{yd}} = 75 \text{ ft}$
$a = 75(50)$
$a = 3750 \text{ ft}^2$

32. $T = 0.06p$
$T = 0.06(12.50)$
$T = \$0.75$

MIXED PRACTICE 3 p. 620

1. $+3$ 2. -1073 3. 22 4. 15

5. 0.6 6. 1.295 7. $-9 < 7$

8. $3 < 4$ 9. $5 > -8$ 10. $-2 > -3$

11. $-63 < -51$ 12. $0.01 < 0.011$

13. $4.12 > -4.13$ 14. $7.52 > 7.25$

15. $\frac{2}{3} > \frac{1}{2}$ 16. $-\frac{1}{8} > -\frac{3}{16}$

17. $-\frac{2}{5} < \frac{1}{3}$ 18. $\frac{4}{5} > \frac{7}{10}$

19. -11 20. -13 21. 2

22. $\frac{1}{8}$ 23. $-\frac{2}{5}$ 24. $-\frac{13}{16}$

25. $17 + (-39) + 3.5 = -22 + 3.5 = -18.5$

26. $-21 + (-5) + 103 = -26 + 103 = 77$

27. $-\frac{2}{3} + \frac{5}{6} + \left(-\frac{1}{4}\right) + 1 = \frac{1}{6} + \left(-\frac{1}{4}\right) + 1 = -\frac{1}{12} + 1 = \frac{11}{12}$

28. $3 + \left(-\frac{1}{5}\right) + \left(-\frac{2}{3}\right) = 3 + \left(-\frac{13}{15}\right) = \frac{45}{15} + \left(-\frac{13}{15}\right) = \frac{32}{15}$

29. $-7 - (-7) = -7 + 7 = 0$ 30. $19 - (-21) = 19 + 21 = 40$

31. $-8 - 1.75 = -9.75$ 32. $23 - 35.2 = -12.2$

33. $-1.25 - (-3.4) = -1.25 + 3.4 = 2.15$

34. $-9 - (-5.1) = -9 + 5.1 = -3.9$

35. $|2| + |-9| = 2 + 9 = 11$

36. $|-4| \cdot |2| + |-7| = 4 \cdot 2 + 7 = 8 + 7 = 15$

37. $|3| + |-4| \cdot |0| = 3 + 4 \cdot 0 = 3 + 0 = 3$

38. $|a| - 17 = |-23| - 17 = 23 - 17 = 6$

39. $|n| - |m| = |-5| - |6| = 5 - 6 = -1$

40. $2|x| \cdot |y| = 2|-3| \cdot |-4| = 2(3) \cdot 4 = 6 \cdot 4 = 24$

41. $16 - 3|t| = 16 - 3|-5| = 16 - 3(5) = 16 - 15 = 1$

42. $19 + (-27) - 5 - (-13) = -8 - 5 + 13$
$= -13 + 13 = 0$

43. $-53 + (-19) - 41 - (-8) = -72 - 41 + 8$
$= -113 + 8 = -105$

44. $-7 - (16) + (-9) - (-25) = -23 + (-9) + 25$
$= -32 + 25 = -7$

45. $11 - (3a) - 26a + 8 - (-17a) = 11 + 8 - 3a - 26a + 17a$
$= 19 - 12a$

46. $21x - (17x) - (-32) + (-9x) = 4x + (-9x) + 32$
$= -5x + 32$

47. $10 - (-5y) + (-9) + (-8y) = 1 + 5y + (-8y)$
$= 1 - 3y$

48. $8 + 4 + (-10) + 3 = 12 + (-10) + 3 = 2 + 3 = 5$

49.

-102.75 -67.85

$-67.85 - (-102.75) = -67.85 + 102.75 = 34.90$
She deposited \$34.90.

50.

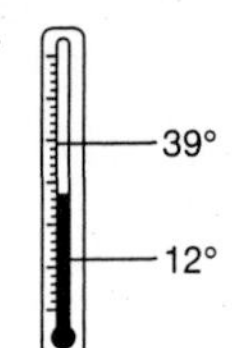

$39 - (-12) = 39 + 12 = 51$
The temperature rose 51°.

MIXED PRACTICE 4 p. 621

1. $2[5(6 - 4) + (-3)^2] = 2[5(2) + 9] = 2[10 + 9]$
$= 2[19] = 38$

2. $(-2)^3 - (-1)^8 + (-3)^2 = -8 - 1 + 9 = -9 + 9 = 0$

3. $3(-2)^3 \cdot (-1)^{21} = 3(-8) \cdot (-1) = -24 \cdot (-1) = 24$

4. $5[-3(2^3) + (-2)^2(7)] = 5[-3(8) + (4)(7)] = 5[-24 + 28]$
$= 5[4] = 20$

5. $\frac{5(-11) + (-1)}{7} = \frac{-55 + (-1)}{7} = \frac{-56}{7} = -8$

6. $3\frac{1}{8} \div 5\frac{1}{2} = \frac{25}{8} \div \frac{11}{2} = \frac{25}{8} \cdot \frac{2}{11} = \frac{50}{88} = \frac{25}{44}$

7. $\frac{4^3}{(-2)^6} = \frac{64}{64} = 1$

8. $2\frac{1}{3} \div 5\frac{1}{4} = \frac{7}{3} \div \frac{21}{4} = \frac{7}{3} \cdot \frac{4}{21} = \frac{28}{63} = \frac{4}{9}$

9. $\frac{(-6)^3}{-(3^2)} = \frac{-216}{-9} = 24$

10. $\frac{4 + (-8)5}{-9} = \frac{4 + (-40)}{-9} = \frac{-36}{-9} = 4$

11. $\frac{(-8)^2}{(-2)^2} = \frac{64}{4} = 16$

12. $\frac{10 + 2(-5)^2}{(2^2)(3)} = \frac{10 + 2(25)}{(4)(3)} = \frac{10 + 50}{12} = \frac{60}{12} = 5$

13. $-4\frac{2}{5} \div 2\frac{5}{8} = -\frac{22}{5} \div \frac{21}{8} = -\frac{22}{5} \cdot \frac{8}{21} = -\frac{176}{105} = -1\frac{71}{105}$

14. $45 - (-21) + (-7) - 9 + 3 - (-5) + (-12) - 37$
$= 45 + 21 + (-7) + (-9) + 3 + 5 + (-12) + (-37)$
$= 66 + (-16) + 8 + (-49)$
$= 50 + (-41)$
$= 9$

15. $-11 + (-36) + 27 - (-8) - 15 + (-2) + 21 - 6$
$= -11 + (-36) + 27 + 8 + (-15) + (-2) + 21 + (-6)$
$= -47 + 35 + (-17) + 15$
$= -12 + (-2)$
$= -14$

16. $[3(x + 5) - 7] + [-5(x - 2) + 11]$
$= [3x + 15 - 7] + [-5x + 10 + 11]$
$= 3x + 8 + (-5x) + 21$
$= -2x + 29$

17. $[4(x - 3) + 18] - [3(x + 1) + 2]$
$= [4x - 12 + 18] - [3x + 3 + 2]$
$= 4x + 6 - 3x - 5$
$= x + 1$

18. $[4(x + 1) + 11] - [7(x - 3) - 1]$
$= [4x + 4 + 11] - [7x - 21 - 1]$
$= 4x + 15 - 7x + 22$
$= -3x + 37$

19. $[9(3 - x) + 7] + [4(5 + x) - 2]$
$= [27 - 9x + 7] + [20 + 4x - 2]$
$= 34 - 9x + 18 + 4x$
$= 52 - 5x$

20. $(-2x)yz = (-2 \cdot -4)2 \cdot 3 = (8)2 \cdot 3 = 16 \cdot 3 = 48$

21. $5y^2 + 2xz = 5 \cdot 2^2 + 2(-4)3 = 5 \cdot 4 + (-8)3 = 20 + (-24)$
$= -4$

22. $y(x^2) - 5z = 2(-4)^2 - 5 \cdot 3 = 2(16) - 15 = 32 - 15 = 17$

23. $5(2y - x) + z = 5(2 \cdot 2 - [-4]) + 3 = 5(4 + 4) + 3$
$= 5(8) + 3 = 40 + 3 = 43$

24. $2[(x - y) + z] = 2[(-4 - 2) + 3] = 2[-6 + 3] = 2[-3]$
$= -6$

25. $z(9y + 4x) = 3(9 \cdot 2 + 4 \cdot -4) = 3(18 + [-16]) = 3(2) = 6$

26. $3|x| - yz = 3|-4| - 2 \cdot 3 = 12 - 6 = 6$

27. $5x - 2|y| = 5(-4) - 2|2| = -20 - 4 = -20 + (-4)$
$= -24$

28. $4|x| + 7|z| - 5y = 4|-4| + 7|3| - 5 \cdot 2 = 16 + 21 - 10$
$= 27$

29. $|x| \cdot |y| + |z| = |-4| \cdot |2| + |3| = 8 + 3 = 11$

30. $|x| \cdot |-y| \cdot |z| = |-4| \cdot |-2| \cdot |3| = 8 \cdot 3 = 24$

31. $|x| - |y| + |z| = |-4| - |2| + |3| = 4 - 2 + 3 = 2 + 3$
$= 5$

32. $3(-5)(1.2)(1)(-2.5)(0.08)(-10)$
$= -15(1.2)(-0.2)(-10)$
$= -18(2)$
$= -36$

33. $-2(5)(1.4)(-0.25)(20)(0.5)$
$= -10(-0.35)(10)$
$= 3.5(10)$
$= 35$

34. $-\frac{1}{3}\left(\frac{2}{5}\right)\left(\frac{5}{7}\right)\left(-\frac{7}{8}\right)\left(-\frac{3}{8}\right)$
$= -\frac{2}{15}\left(-\frac{35}{56}\right)\left(-\frac{3}{8}\right)$
$= -\frac{210}{6720}$
$= -\frac{1}{32}$

35. $\left(-\frac{2}{9}\right)\left(\frac{6}{5}\right)\left(-\frac{4}{7}\right)\left(-\frac{1}{8}\right)\left(\frac{3}{20}\right)$
$= -\frac{12}{45}\left(\frac{4}{56}\right)\left(\frac{3}{20}\right)$
$= -\frac{144}{50{,}400}$
$= -\frac{1}{350}$

36. $\frac{3}{8}\left(\frac{1}{5}x - \frac{2}{3}y + 4\right)$
$= \frac{3}{8}\cdot\frac{1}{5}x - \frac{3}{8}\cdot\frac{2}{3}y + \frac{3}{8}\cdot 4$
$= \frac{3}{40}x - \frac{6}{24}y + \frac{12}{8}$
$= \frac{3}{40}x - \frac{1}{4}y + \frac{3}{2}$

37. $-\frac{2}{5}\left(-\frac{3}{8}x + \frac{1}{2}y - \frac{2}{3}\right)$
$= -\frac{2}{5}\cdot\left(-\frac{3}{8}x\right) + \left(-\frac{2}{5}\right)\cdot\frac{1}{2}y - \left(-\frac{2}{5}\right)\cdot\frac{2}{3}$
$= \frac{6}{40}x + \frac{-2}{10}y - \frac{-4}{15}$
$= \frac{3}{20}x - \frac{1}{5}y + \frac{4}{15}$

38. $1.2(2x + 4y - 7)$
$= 1.2\cdot 2x + 1.2\cdot 4y - 1.2\cdot 7$
$= 2.4x + 4.8y - 8.4$

39. $-2.25(-5x + 2.4y)$
$= -2.25\cdot(-5x) + (-2.25)\cdot 2.4y$
$= 11.25x - 5.4y$

40. $-\frac{2}{3} \div \frac{3}{8} = -\frac{2}{3}\cdot\frac{8}{3} = -\frac{16}{9}$

41. $\frac{5}{6} \div \left(-\frac{3}{4}\right) = \frac{5}{6}\cdot\left(-\frac{4}{3}\right) = \frac{-20}{18} = \frac{-10}{9}$

42. $-\frac{3}{16} \div \left(-\frac{3}{4}\right) = -\frac{3}{16}\cdot\left(-\frac{4}{3}\right) = \frac{12}{48} = \frac{1}{4}$

43. $107.25 \div (-5.5) = -19.5$

44. $-69.3 \div (4.2) = -16.5$

45. $-48.16 \div (-8.6) = 5.6$

46. $256 - 80y = 16\cdot 16 - 16\cdot 5y = 16(16 - 5y)$

47. $21x - 56y + 14 = 7\cdot 3x - 7\cdot 8y + 7\cdot 2 = 7(3x - 8y + 2)$

48. $12x + 12y - 36z = 12\cdot x + 12\cdot y - 12\cdot 3z$
$= 12(x + y - 3z)$

49. $-\frac{2}{3}x + y - \frac{1}{3}z = -\frac{1}{3}\cdot 2x - \frac{1}{3}\cdot(-3) - \frac{1}{3}(z)$
$= -\frac{1}{3}(2x - 3 + z)$

50. $\frac{5}{24}x - \frac{5}{4}y = \frac{5}{4}\cdot\frac{1}{6}x - \frac{5}{4}\cdot y = \frac{5}{4}\left(\frac{1}{6}x - y\right)$

51. $\frac{24}{5}x - \frac{4}{5}y + \frac{8}{15} = \frac{4}{5}\cdot 6x - \frac{4}{5}\cdot y + \frac{4}{5}\cdot\frac{2}{3} = \frac{4}{5}\left(6x - y + \frac{2}{3}\right)$

MIXED PRACTICE 5 p. 622

1. $-17.4t = 87$
$\frac{1}{-17.4}\cdot(-17.4t) = \frac{1}{-17.4}\cdot 87$
$t = -5$

2. $-9y = 193.5$
$\frac{1}{-9}\cdot(-9y) = \frac{1}{-9}\cdot 193.5$
$y = -21.5$

3. $-14x = -126$
$\frac{1}{-14}\cdot(-14x) = \frac{1}{-14}\cdot(-126)$
$x = 9$

4. $-\frac{2}{3}x = 4$
$-\frac{3}{2}\cdot\left(-\frac{2}{3}x\right) = -\frac{3}{2}\cdot 4$
$x = -\frac{12}{2}$
$x = -6$

5. $\frac{5}{8}x = -\frac{3}{16}$
$\frac{8}{5}\cdot\frac{5}{8}x = \frac{8}{5}\cdot\left(-\frac{3}{16}\right)$
$x = -\frac{24}{80}$
$x = -\frac{3}{10}$

6. $-\frac{3}{4}y = \frac{1}{8}$
$-\frac{4}{3}\cdot\left(-\frac{3}{4}y\right) = -\frac{4}{3}\cdot\frac{1}{8}$
$y = -\frac{4}{24}$
$y = -\frac{1}{6}$

7. $m + \frac{2}{5} = -\frac{1}{2}$
$m + \frac{2}{5} - \frac{2}{5} = -\frac{1}{2} - \frac{2}{5}$
$m = -\frac{5}{10} - \frac{4}{10} = -\frac{9}{10}$

8. $x + \frac{5}{8} = \frac{1}{4}$
$x + \frac{5}{8} - \frac{5}{8} = \frac{1}{4} - \frac{5}{8}$
$x = \frac{2}{8} - \frac{5}{8} = -\frac{3}{8}$

9. $y - \frac{5}{6} = -\frac{3}{8}$
$y - \frac{5}{6} + \frac{5}{6} = -\frac{3}{8} + \frac{5}{6}$
$y = -\frac{9}{24} + \frac{20}{24} = \frac{11}{24}$

10. $x - 7.3 = -2.5$
$x - 7.3 + 7.3 = -2.5 + 7.3$
$x = 4.8$

11. $3.4 = r - 6.1$
$3.4 + 6.1 = r - 6.1 + 6.1$
$9.5 = r$

12. $$\begin{aligned} y + 9 &= 5.4 \\ y + 9 - 9 &= 5.4 - 9 \\ y &= -3.6 \end{aligned}$$

13. $$\begin{aligned} 10 - x - 7 &= 3x - 1 \\ 3 - x &= 3x - 1 \\ 3 - x + x &= 3x - 1 + x \\ 3 &= 4x - 1 \\ 3 + 1 &= 4x - 1 + 1 \\ 4 &= 4x \\ \frac{1}{4} \cdot 4 &= \frac{1}{4} \cdot 4x \\ 1 &= x \end{aligned}$$

14. $$\begin{aligned} 18 + 3x - 5 &= 7x - 14 - x \\ 13 + 3x &= 6x - 14 \\ 13 + 3x - 3x &= 6x - 14 - 3x \\ 13 &= 3x - 14 \\ 13 + 14 &= 3x - 14 + 14 \\ 27 &= 3x \\ \frac{1}{3} \cdot 27 &= \frac{1}{3} \cdot 3x \\ 9 &= x \end{aligned}$$

15. $$\begin{aligned} 4a - (5a + 3) &= -1 \\ -a - 3 &= -1 \\ -a - 3 + 3 &= -1 + 3 \\ -a &= 2 \\ -1 \cdot (-a) &= -1 \cdot 2 \\ a &= -2 \end{aligned}$$

16. $$\begin{aligned} 7y - 5 &= 8(5 - y) \\ 7y - 5 &= 40 - 8y \\ 7y - 5 + 5 &= 40 - 8y + 5 \\ 7y &= 45 - 8y \\ 7y + 8y &= 45 - 8y + 8y \\ 15y &= 45 \\ \frac{1}{15} \cdot 15y &= \frac{1}{15} \cdot 45 \\ y &= 3 \end{aligned}$$

17. $$\begin{aligned} 6(m + 3) &= 2(m - 1) \\ 6m + 18 &= 2m - 2 \\ 6m + 18 - 18 &= 2m - 2 - 18 \\ 6m &= 2m - 20 \\ 6m - 2m &= 2m - 2m - 20 \\ 4m &= -20 \\ \frac{1}{4} \cdot 4m &= \frac{1}{4} \cdot (-20) \\ m &= -5 \end{aligned}$$

18. $$\begin{aligned} 7(a - 7) &= -3(a + 3) \\ 7a - 49 &= -3a - 9 \\ 7a + 3a - 49 &= -3a + 3a - 9 \\ 10a - 49 &= -9 \\ 10a - 49 + 49 &= -9 + 49 \\ 10a &= 40 \\ \frac{1}{10} \cdot 10a &= \frac{1}{10} \cdot (40) \\ a &= 4 \end{aligned}$$

19. $$\begin{aligned} 2(5t - 3) &= 3(2t + 6) \\ 10t - 6 &= 6t + 18 \\ 10t - 6 + 6 &= 6t + 18 + 6 \\ 10t &= 6t + 24 \\ 10t - 6t &= 6t - 6t + 24 \\ 4t &= 24 \\ \frac{1}{4} \cdot 4t &= \frac{1}{4} \cdot 24 \\ t &= 6 \end{aligned}$$

20. $$\begin{aligned} 4(2m + 1) &= 2(3m - 1) \\ 8m + 4 &= 6m - 2 \\ 8m + 4 - 4 &= 6m - 2 - 4 \\ 8m &= 6m - 6 \\ 8m - 6m &= 6m - 6m - 6 \\ 2m &= -6 \\ \frac{1}{2} \cdot 2m &= \frac{1}{2} \cdot (-6) \\ m &= -3 \end{aligned}$$

21. $$\begin{aligned} x + 5 &= x + (9 - x) \\ x + 5 &= 9 \\ x + 5 - 5 &= 9 - 5 \\ x &= 4 \end{aligned}$$

22. $$\begin{aligned} 20 - (4 - y) &= 26 \\ 16 + y &= 26 \\ 16 - 16 + y &= 26 - 16 \\ y &= 10 \end{aligned}$$

23. $$\begin{aligned} 5x + 6 &= 7x \\ 5x - 5x + 6 &= 7x - 5x \\ 6 &= 2x \\ \frac{1}{2} \cdot 6 &= \frac{1}{2} \cdot 2x \\ 3 &= x \end{aligned}$$

24. $$\begin{aligned} 4t + 5t &= -27 \\ 9t &= -27 \\ \frac{1}{9} \cdot 9t &= \frac{1}{9} \cdot (-27) \\ t &= -3 \end{aligned}$$

25. $$\begin{aligned} 3y - 9y &= 102 \\ -6y &= 102 \\ -\frac{1}{6} \cdot (-6y) &= -\frac{1}{6} \cdot 102 \\ y &= -\frac{102}{6} = -17 \end{aligned}$$

26. $$\begin{aligned} 4.3x - 7.9x &= -18 \\ -3.6x &= -18 \\ -\frac{1}{3.6} \cdot (-3.6x) &= -\frac{1}{3.6}(-18) \\ x &= \frac{18}{3.6} = 5 \end{aligned}$$

27. $$\begin{aligned} 4(5x - 7) - 8x &= -16 \\ 20x - 28 - 8x &= -16 \\ 12x - 28 &= -16 \\ 12x - 28 + 28 &= -16 + 28 \\ 12x &= 12 \\ \frac{1}{12} \cdot 12x &= \frac{1}{12} \cdot 12 \\ x &= 1 \end{aligned}$$

28. $$\begin{aligned} 2(9 - 6x) - 49 &= 5 \\ 18 - 12x - 49 &= 5 \\ -12x - 31 &= 5 \\ -12x - 31 + 31 &= 5 + 31 \\ -12x &= 36 \\ \frac{1}{-12} \cdot (-12x) &= \frac{1}{-12} \cdot 36 \\ x &= \frac{36}{-12} = -3 \end{aligned}$$

29. $$\begin{aligned} -2(4x + 5) - 11 &= -5 \\ -8x - 10 - 11 &= -5 \\ -8x - 21 &= -5 \\ -8x - 21 + 21 &= -5 + 21 \\ -8x &= 16 \\ \frac{1}{-8} \cdot (-8x) &= \frac{1}{-8} \cdot 16 \\ x &= -2 \end{aligned}$$

30. $$\begin{aligned} 6x - 5(3 + 2x) &= 1 \\ 6x - 15 - 10x &= 1 \\ -15 - 4x &= 1 \\ -15 + 15 - 4x &= 1 + 15 \\ -4x &= 16 \\ \frac{1}{-4} \cdot (-4x) &= \frac{1}{-4} \cdot 16 \\ x &= -4 \end{aligned}$$

31. $\frac{x}{2} - 24$ **32.** $3\left(x + \frac{1}{x}\right)$

33. $4(x - 3)$ **34.** $\frac{1}{2}(x \cdot 5)$

35. $$\begin{aligned} x + 9 &= -53 \\ x + 9 - 9 &= -53 - 9 \\ x &= -62 \end{aligned}$$

36. Let b = the number of boys.
$64 - b$ = the number of girls

$$64 - b = \frac{1}{2} \cdot 64 - 11$$
$$64 - b = 32 - 11$$
$$64 - b = 21$$
$$64 - 64 - b = 21 - 64$$
$$-b = -43$$
$$-1 \cdot (-b) = -1 \cdot (-43)$$
$$b = 43$$

There are 43 boys.

37. Let n = the number of boys and girls.
$n - 19$ = number of boys

$$19 = 2(n - 19) + 3$$
$$19 = 2n - 38 + 3$$
$$19 = 2n - 35$$
$$19 + 35 = 2n - 35 + 35$$
$$54 = 2n$$
$$\frac{1}{2} \cdot 54 = \frac{1}{2} \cdot 2n$$
$$27 = n$$

There are 27 boys and girls.

38. Let t = time.

$$36 = 0.75 \cdot t$$
$$\frac{1}{0.75} \cdot 36 = \frac{1}{0.75} \cdot 0.75t$$
$$\frac{36}{0.75} = t$$
$$t = 48$$

She will read 36 pages in 48 minutes.

39. Let h = the number of additional hours

$$3.5h = 18.5 - 8$$
$$3.5h = 10.5$$
$$\frac{1}{3.5} \cdot 3.5h = \frac{1}{3.5} \cdot 10 \cdot 5$$
$$h = \frac{10.5}{3.5} = 3$$

He rented the mower for 4 hours.

40. Let n = the number

$$12 \cdot n = 132$$
$$\frac{1}{12} \cdot 12 \cdot n = \frac{1}{12} \cdot 132$$
$$n = \frac{132}{12}$$
$$n = 11$$

The number is 11.

MIXED PRACTICE 6 p. 623

1. $23\% = 0.23$ **2.** $0.04\% = 0.0004$

3. $13.5\% = 0.135$ **4.** $160\% = 1.6$

5. $6.7\% = 0.067$ **6.** $\frac{3}{5} = 0.6 = 60\%$

7. $\frac{1}{25} = 0.04 = 4\%$ **8.** $\frac{5}{8} = 0.625 = 62.5\%$

9. $\frac{2}{3} \approx 0.667 = 66.7\%$ **10.** $\frac{37}{100} = 0.37 = 37\%$

11.
$$\frac{3}{2}x + \frac{3}{4}x + \frac{3}{8}x = 21$$
$$\frac{12}{8}x + \frac{6}{8}x + \frac{3}{8}x = 21$$
$$\frac{21}{8}x = 21$$
$$\frac{8}{21} \cdot \frac{21}{8}x = \frac{8}{21} \cdot 21$$
$$x = 8$$

12.
$$\frac{3}{4}n - \frac{1}{8}n = 6 + \frac{1}{8}n$$
$$\frac{6}{8}n - \frac{1}{8}n = 6 + \frac{1}{8}n$$
$$\frac{5}{8}n = 6 + \frac{1}{8}n$$
$$\frac{5}{8}n - \frac{1}{8}n = 6 + \frac{1}{8}n - \frac{1}{8}n$$
$$\frac{4}{8}n = 6$$
$$\frac{8}{4} \cdot \frac{4}{8}n = \frac{8}{4} \cdot 6$$
$$n = 12$$

13.
$$\frac{1}{4} - x = \frac{1}{2}x + \frac{9}{4}$$
$$\frac{1}{4} - x + x = \frac{1}{2}x + x + \frac{9}{4}$$
$$\frac{1}{4} = \frac{3}{2}x + \frac{9}{4}$$
$$\frac{1}{4} - \frac{9}{4} = \frac{3}{2}x + \frac{9}{4} - \frac{9}{4}$$
$$-\frac{8}{4} = \frac{3}{2}x$$
$$\frac{2}{3} \cdot \left(-\frac{8}{4}\right) = \frac{2}{3} \cdot \frac{3}{2}x$$
$$-\frac{16}{12} = x$$
$$x = -\frac{4}{3}$$

14.
$$5|x| + 7 = 32$$
$$5|x| + 7 - 7 = 32 - 7$$
$$5|x| = 25$$
$$\frac{1}{5} \cdot 5|x| = \frac{1}{5} \cdot 25$$
$$|x| = 5$$
$$x = 5 \quad \text{or} \quad x = -5$$

15.
$$|y| + 7 = 3|y| - 9$$
$$|y| - |y| + 7 = 3|y| - |y| - 9$$
$$7 = 2|y| - 9$$
$$7 + 9 = 2|y| - 9 + 9$$
$$16 = 2|y|$$
$$\frac{1}{2} \cdot 16 = \frac{1}{2} \cdot 2|y|$$
$$8 = |y|$$
$$y = 8 \quad \text{or} \quad y = -8$$

16.
$$|-x| = 14$$
$$x = 14 \quad \text{or} \quad x = -14$$

17.
$$A = \frac{1}{2}bh$$
$$2 \cdot A = 2 \cdot \frac{1}{2} \cdot b \cdot h$$
$$2A = bh$$
$$\frac{1}{b} \cdot 2A = \frac{1}{b} \cdot bh$$
$$\frac{2A}{b} = h$$

18.
$$V = \frac{s}{t + r}$$
$$V \cdot (t + r) = \frac{s}{t + r} \cdot (t + r)$$
$$Vt + Vr = s$$
$$Vt + Vr - Vr = s - Vr$$
$$Vt = s - Vr$$
$$\frac{1}{V} \cdot Vt = \frac{1}{V} \cdot (s - Vr)$$
$$t = \frac{s - Vr}{V}$$
$$t = \frac{s}{V} - r$$

19.
$$B = 2(x + y)$$
$$B = 2x + 2y$$
$$B - 2y = 2x + 2y - 2y$$
$$B - 2y = 2x$$
$$\frac{1}{2} \cdot (B - 2y) = \frac{1}{2} \cdot 2x$$
$$\frac{B - 2y}{2} = x$$
$$x = \frac{B}{2} - y$$

20.
$$n = 0.4 \cdot 65$$
$$n = 2.6$$

21.
$$15 = 0.06 \cdot n$$
$$\frac{1}{0.06} \cdot 15 = \frac{1}{0.06} \cdot 0.06n$$
$$250 = n$$

22.
$$28 = p \cdot 35$$
$$\frac{1}{35} \cdot 28 = p \cdot 35 \cdot \frac{1}{35}$$
$$\frac{28}{35} = p$$
$$p = 0.8 \quad \text{or} \quad 80\%$$

23. The ratio of right-handed students to total students is 7:9.

$$\frac{7}{9} = \frac{x}{27}$$
$$27 \cdot \frac{7}{9} = 27 \cdot \frac{x}{27}$$
$$21 = x$$

There are 21 right-handed students.

24. $x + (x + 1) + (x + 2) = 108$
$$3x + 3 = 108$$
$$3x + 3 - 3 = 108 - 3$$
$$3x = 105$$
$$\frac{1}{3} \cdot 3x = \frac{1}{3} \cdot 105$$
$$x = 35$$

The integers are 35, 36 and 37.

25. $x - 57.34 - 19.09 - 30.77 + 42 + 15.85 = 440.28$
$$x - 49.35 = 440.28$$
$$x - 49.35 + 49.35 = 440.28 + 49.35$$
$$x = 489.63$$

She had \$489.63 in her account.

26. Let p = price of 1 pen.
$$36 \cdot p = 20.88$$
$$\frac{1}{36} \cdot 36p = \frac{1}{36} \cdot 20.88$$
$$p = 0.58$$

A single pen costs \$0.58.

27. Let n = number of rolls of film.
$$3n + 8 = 35$$
$$3n + 8 - 8 = 35 - 8$$
$$3n = 27$$
$$\frac{1}{3} \cdot 3n = \frac{1}{3} \cdot 27$$
$$n = 9$$

He bought 9 rolls of film.

28. Let w = Carl's weight.
$$32 = \frac{1}{3}w - 25$$
$$32 + 25 = \frac{1}{3}w - 25 + 25$$
$$57 = \frac{1}{3}w$$
$$3 \cdot 57 = 3 \cdot \frac{1}{3}w$$
$$171 = w$$

Carl weighs 171 pounds.

29. Let x = occupied seats.
$320 - x$ = empty seats
$$x = (320 - x) + 46$$
$$x = 366 - x$$
$$x + x = 366 - x + x$$
$$2x = 366$$
$$\frac{1}{2} \cdot 2x = \frac{1}{2} \cdot 366$$
$$x = 183$$

There are 183 occupied seats.

30.
$$\frac{5}{28.75} = \frac{x}{69}$$
$$69 \cdot \frac{5}{28.75} = 69 \cdot \frac{x}{69}$$
$$12 = x$$

It will take her 12 hours.

MIXED PRACTICE 7 p. 624

1. a. No **b.** Yes **c.** Yes **d.** No

2. a. Yes **b.** Yes **c.** No **d.** No

3. a. Yes **b.** No **c.** Yes **d.** No

4. a. Yes **b.** Yes **c.** No **d.** No

5. a. Yes **b.** No **c.** Yes **d.** Yes

6. $x \le -1$ **7.** $x > -2$ **8.** $x \ge 2$

9. $x < -3$ **10.** $x \ge -3$

11.
$$x + \frac{1}{2} < \frac{1}{8}$$
$$x + \frac{1}{2} - \frac{1}{2} < \frac{1}{8} - \frac{1}{2}$$
$$x < \frac{1}{8} - \frac{4}{8}$$
$$x < -\frac{3}{8}$$

12.
$$y - \frac{2}{3} > \frac{1}{4}$$
$$y - \frac{2}{3} + \frac{2}{3} > \frac{1}{4} + \frac{2}{3}$$
$$y > \frac{3}{12} + \frac{8}{12}$$
$$y > \frac{11}{12}$$

13.
$$x - \frac{1}{5} \le \frac{2}{3}$$
$$x - \frac{1}{5} + \frac{1}{5} \le \frac{2}{3} + \frac{1}{5}$$
$$x \le \frac{10}{15} + \frac{3}{15}$$
$$x \le \frac{13}{15}$$

14.
$$x - \frac{1}{8} > 0$$
$$x - \frac{1}{8} + \frac{1}{8} > 0 + \frac{1}{8}$$
$$x > \frac{1}{8}$$

15.
$$\frac{2}{5} + a < \frac{1}{2}$$
$$\frac{2}{5} - \frac{2}{5} + a < \frac{1}{2} - \frac{2}{5}$$
$$a < \frac{5}{10} - \frac{4}{10}$$
$$a < \frac{1}{10}$$

16.
$$x + \frac{1}{8} \ge \frac{3}{4}$$
$$x + \frac{1}{8} - \frac{1}{8} \ge \frac{3}{4} - \frac{1}{8}$$
$$x \ge \frac{6}{8} - \frac{1}{8}$$
$$x \ge \frac{5}{8}$$

17.
$$-6m < 102$$
$$-\frac{1}{6} \cdot 6m > -\frac{1}{6} \cdot 102$$
$$m > -17$$

18.
$$9y \ge 31.5$$
$$\frac{1}{9} \cdot 9y \ge \frac{1}{9} \cdot 31.5$$
$$y \ge 3.5$$

19.
$$-15x \ge 225$$
$$\frac{1}{-15} \cdot (-15x) \le \frac{1}{-15} \cdot 225$$
$$x \le -15$$

20.
$$7y \le -98$$
$$\frac{1}{7} \cdot 7y \le \frac{1}{7} \cdot (-98)$$
$$y \le -14$$

21. $9x - 7x \le 6$
$$2x \le 6$$
$$\frac{1}{2} \cdot 2x \le \frac{1}{2} \cdot 6$$
$$x \le 3$$

22.
$$66 \ge 2y - 8y$$
$$66 \ge -6y$$
$$-\frac{1}{6} \cdot 66 \le -\frac{1}{6} \cdot (-6y)$$
$$-11 \le y$$

23. $5(x + 3) - 4x < 17$
$$5x + 15 - 4x < 17$$
$$x + 15 < 17$$
$$x + 15 - 15 < 17 - 15$$
$$x < 2$$

24. $3y - 2(y + 4) > 2$
$$3y - 2y - 8 > 2$$
$$y - 8 > 2$$
$$y - 8 + 8 > 2 + 8$$
$$y > 10$$

25. $-3(x + 5) + 4(x + 8) > 24$
$$-3x - 15 + 4x + 32 > 24$$
$$x + 17 > 24$$
$$x + 17 - 17 > 24 - 17$$
$$x > 7$$

26. $-5m + 4 + 6m < 2$
$$4 + m < 2$$
$$4 - 4 + m < 2 - 4$$
$$m < -2$$

27. $5(x - 2) - 4x > 5$
$$5x - 10 - 4x > 5$$
$$x - 10 > 5$$
$$x - 10 + 10 > 5 + 10$$
$$x > 15$$

28. $-2(x - 4) + 3x \le 1$
$$-2x + 8 + 3x \le 1$$
$$8 + x \le 1$$
$$8 - 8 + x \le 1 - 8$$
$$x \le -7$$

29. False **30.** False **31.** True

32. True **33.** False **34.** True

35. True **36.** True **37.** True

38.
$$t + \frac{3}{5} \le \frac{9}{10}$$
$$t + \frac{3}{5} - \frac{3}{5} \le \frac{9}{10} - \frac{3}{5}$$
$$t \le \frac{9}{10} - \frac{6}{10}$$
$$t \le \frac{3}{10}$$

−1 0 1

39. $m + \frac{1}{3} > -2$

$m + \frac{1}{3} - \frac{1}{3} > -2 - \frac{1}{3}$

$m > -\frac{6}{3} - \frac{1}{3}$

$m > -\frac{7}{3}$

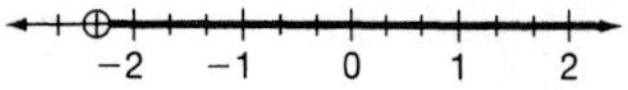

40. $\frac{1}{3}x \leq \frac{7}{6}$

$3 \cdot \frac{1}{3}x \leq 3 \cdot \frac{7}{6}$

$x \leq \frac{7}{2}$

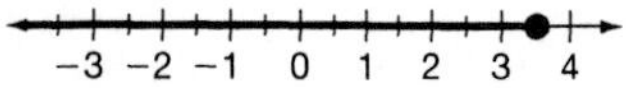

41. $-6y > 9$

$-\frac{1}{6} \cdot (-6y) < -\frac{1}{6} \cdot 9$

$y < -\frac{9}{6}$

$y < -\frac{3}{2}$

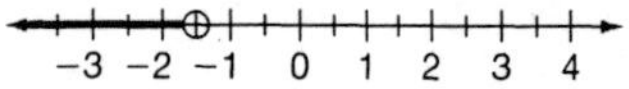

42. $8m > -4$

$\frac{1}{8} \cdot 8m > \frac{1}{8} \cdot (-4)$

$m > -\frac{4}{8}$

$m > -\frac{1}{2}$

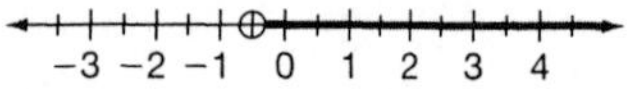

43. $5x + 4 - 7x \leq 10$

$4 - 2x \leq 10$

$4 - 4 - 2x \leq 10 - 4$

$-2x \leq 6$

$-\frac{1}{2} \cdot (-2x) \geq -\frac{1}{2} \cdot 6$

$x \geq -3$

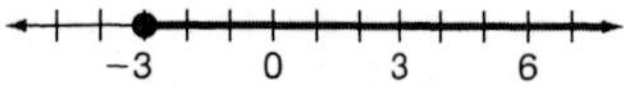

MIXED PRACTICE 8 p. 625

1. $3(5 - x) \leq 2(x - 9)$

$15 - 3x \leq 2x - 18$

$15 - 3x + 3x \leq 2x - 18 + 3x$

$15 \leq 5x - 18$

$15 + 18 \leq 5x - 18 + 18$

$33 \leq 5x$

$\frac{1}{5} \cdot 33 \leq \frac{1}{5} \cdot 5x$

$6.6 \leq x$

2. $4(x + 5) \leq 3(6 + x)$

$4x + 20 \leq 18 + 3x$

$4x - 3x + 20 \leq 18 + 3x - 3x$

$x + 20 \leq 18$

$x + 20 - 20 \leq 18 - 20$

$x \leq -2$

3. $10 + 3y - 3 \geq 5y - 7$

$7 + 3y \geq 5y - 7$

$7 + 3y - 3y \geq 5y - 7 - 3y$

$7 \geq 2y - 7$

$7 + 7 \geq 2y - 7 + 7$

$14 \geq 2y$

$\frac{1}{2} \cdot 14 \geq \frac{1}{2} \cdot 2y$

$7 \geq y$

4. $4x - 3 < 10x - 5$

$4x - 4x - 3 < 10x - 4x - 5$

$-3 < 6x - 5$

$-3 + 5 < 6x - 5 + 5$

$2 < 6x$

$\frac{1}{6} \cdot 2 < \frac{1}{6} \cdot 6x$

$\frac{1}{3} < x$

5. $12 - 9c > 38 + 4c$

$12 - 9c + 9c > 38 + 4c + 9c$

$12 > 38 + 13c$

$12 - 38 > 38 - 38 + 13c$

$-26 > 13c$

$\frac{1}{13} \cdot (-26) > \frac{1}{13} \cdot 13c$

$-2 > c$

6. $2(x - 6) + 5 \geq 9$

$2x - 12 + 5 \geq 9$

$2x - 7 \geq 9$

$2x - 7 + 7 \geq 9 + 7$

$2x \geq 16$

$\frac{1}{2} \cdot 2x \geq \frac{1}{2} \cdot 16$

$x \geq 8$

7. $\frac{3}{8}y - 5 > \frac{7}{8}y$

$\frac{3}{8}y - \frac{3}{8}y - 5 > \frac{7}{8}y - \frac{3}{8}y$

$-5 > \frac{4}{8}y$

$\frac{8}{4} \cdot (-5) > \frac{8}{4} \cdot \frac{4}{8}y$

$-\frac{40}{4} > y$

$y < -10$

8. $\frac{3}{4}x + 3 \leq x + \frac{1}{2}$

$\frac{3}{4}x + 3 - \frac{3}{4}x \leq x + \frac{1}{2} - \frac{3}{4}x$

$3 \leq \frac{1}{4}x + \frac{1}{2}$

$3 - \frac{1}{2} \leq \frac{1}{4}x + \frac{1}{2} - \frac{1}{2}$

$\frac{5}{2} \leq \frac{1}{4}x$

$4 \cdot \frac{5}{2} \leq 4 \cdot \frac{1}{4}x$

$\frac{20}{2} \leq x$

$x \geq 10$

9. $1.6x - 0.5 \leq 1.2x + 1.5$

$1.6x - 0.5 + 0.5 \leq 1.2x + 1.5 + 0.5$

$1.6x \leq 1.2x + 2$

$1.6x - 1.2x \leq 1.2x - 1.2x + 2$

$0.4x \leq 2$

$\frac{1}{0.4} \cdot 0.4x \leq \frac{1}{0.4} \cdot 2$

$x \leq \frac{2}{0.4}$

$x \leq 5$

10. $2.2y + 3.2 < 3.4y - 1.6$

$2.2y - 2.2y + 3.2 < 3.4y - 2.2y - 1.6$

$3.2 < 1.2y - 1.6$

$3.2 + 1.6 < 1.2y - 1.6 + 1.6$

$4.8 < 1.2y$

$\frac{1}{1.2} \cdot 4.8 < \frac{1}{1.2} \cdot 1.2y$

$\frac{4.8}{1.2} < y$

$y > 4$

11. $6(1.5 - x) + 3x < 4(3 - x)$
$9 - 6x + 3x < 12 - 4x$
$9 - 3x < 12 - 4x$
$9 - 3x + 4x < 12 - 4x + 4x$
$9 + x < 12$
$9 - 9 + x < 12 - 9$
$x < 3$

12. $5(x + 2) - 4 > 3x$
$5x + 10 - 4 > 3x$
$5x + 6 > 3x$
$5x - 5x + 6 > 3x - 5x$
$6 > -2x$
$-\frac{1}{2} \cdot 6 < -\frac{1}{2} \cdot (-2x)$
$-\frac{6}{2} < x$
$x > -3$

13. $\frac{n}{2} + 6 < 7$ 14. $2n - 9 < 2$

15. $15 \geq \frac{n}{2}$ 16. $5n + 7 \leq 31$

17. $4n - 6 \geq 40$ 18. $\frac{n}{2} + 3 \geq 15$

19. $n + (2n - 4) \leq 50$
$3n - 4 \leq 50$
$3n - 4 + 4 \leq 50 + 4$
$3n \leq 54$
$\frac{1}{3} \cdot 3n \leq \frac{1}{3} \cdot 54$
$n \leq 18$
The greatest pair is 18 and 32.

20. $n + 24 > 4n$
$n - n + 24 > 4n - n$
$24 > 3n$
$\frac{1}{3} \cdot 24 > \frac{1}{3} \cdot 3n$
$8 > n$
All number greater than 8

21. Let n = first integer.
$n + (n + 2) + (n + 4) + (n + 6) \leq 116$
$4n + 12 \leq 116$
$4n + 12 - 12 \leq 116 - 12$
$4n \leq 104$
$\frac{1}{4} \cdot 4n \leq \frac{1}{4} \cdot 104$
$n \leq 26$
The number are 26, 28, 30, and 32.

22. Let s = price of sweater.
$s + 33.80 \leq 56.00$
$s + 33.80 - 33.80 \leq 56.00 - 33.80$
$s \leq 22.20$
She can pay $22.20 for the sweater.

23. Let p = points scored in the fourth game.
$\frac{25 + 18 + 35 + p}{4} \geq 28$
$4\left(\frac{25 + 18 + 35 + p}{4}\right) \geq 4 \cdot 28$
$25 + 18 + 35 + p \geq 112$
$78 + p \geq 112$
$78 - 78 + p \geq 112 - 78$
$p \geq 34$
He must score at least 34 points.

24. Let w = width.
$22.5 \cdot w \geq 405$
$\frac{1}{22.5} \cdot 22.5w \geq \frac{1}{22.5} \cdot 405$
$w \geq 18$
The width should be at least 18 cm.

25. Let n = one integer.
$n + (3n - 2) < 42$
$4n - 2 < 42$
$4n - 2 + 2 < 42 + 2$
$4n < 44$
$\frac{1}{4} \cdot 4n < \frac{1}{4} \cdot 44$
$n < 11$
The greatest pair is 10 and 28.

MIXED PRACTICE 9 p. 626

1. $(-8)^0 = 1$

2. $(x^3y)(x^2y) = x^{3+2}y^{1+1}$
$= x^5y^2$

3. $(3^{-1})^4 = 3^{-1 \cdot 4} = 3^{-4}$

4. $(2w^9)^5 = 2^5w^{9 \cdot 5} = 32w^{45}$

5. $[2(-x^9)]^3 = 2^3(-x^9)^3$
$= 8(-x^{9 \cdot 3})$
$= 8(-x^{27})$
$= -8x^{27}$

6. $(-3m^4)^3 = -3^3(m^4)^3$
$= -3^3(m^{4 \cdot 3})$
$= -27m^{12}$

7. $(2y^2)(y^5)^2 = (2y^2)(y^{5 \cdot 2})$
$= (2y^2)(y^{10})$
$= 2y^{2+10}$
$= 2y^{12}$

8. $(x^2)^3(x^3)^2 = (x^{2 \cdot 3})(x^{3 \cdot 2})$
$= (x^6)(x^6)$
$= x^{6+6}$
$= x^{12}$

9. $\frac{2^5}{2^8} = 2^{5-8} = 2^{-3} = \frac{1}{8}$

10. $\frac{(-2)^2}{(-2)^9} = (-2)^{2-9} = (-2)^{-7} = -\frac{1}{128}$

11. $\frac{x^3 \cdot y^4}{x^2y} = x^{3-2}y^{4-1} = xy^3$

12. $\frac{(4 \cdot 2^3)^2}{3} = \frac{(2^2 \cdot 2^3)^2}{3}$
$= \frac{(2^{2+3})^2}{3}$
$= \frac{(2^5)^2}{3}$
$= \frac{2^{5 \cdot 2}}{3}$
$= \frac{2^{10}}{3}$ or $\frac{1024}{3}$

13. $\frac{(-y)^4}{2y} = \frac{y^4}{2y}$
$= \frac{y \cdot y^3}{y \cdot 2}$
$= \frac{y}{y} \cdot \frac{y^3}{2}$
$= \frac{y^3}{2}$

14. $\frac{(3y^4)^2}{27y^5} = \frac{3^2(y^4)^2}{27y^5}$
$= \frac{9y^8}{27y^5}$
$= \frac{9}{27} \cdot y^{8-5}$
$= \frac{1}{3}y^3 = \frac{y^3}{3}$

15. $\frac{-16m^5}{-4m^2n} = \frac{-16}{-4}m^{5-2}n^{-1}$
$= \frac{4m^3}{n}$

16. $\frac{-3ab^2}{27a^2} = -\frac{3}{27}a^{1-2}b^2$
$= -\frac{1}{9}a^{-1}b^2$
$= -\frac{b^2}{9a}$

17. $(5.1 \times 10^3)(2.4 \times 10^{-5}) = (5.1 \times 2.4)(10^3 \times 10^{-5})$
$= 12.24 \times 10^{-2}$
$= 1.224 \times 10^{-1}$
$= 0.1224$

18. $(1.1 \times 10^{-4})(3.0 \times 10^{-3}) = (1.1 \times 3.0)(10^{-4} \times 10^{-3})$
$= 3.3 \times 10^{-7}$
$= 0.00000033$

19. $\frac{1.8 \times 10^4}{2 \times 10^7} = \frac{1.8}{2} \times \frac{10^4}{10^7} = 0.9 \times 10^{-3}$
$= 9.0 \times 10^{-4}$
$= 0.0009$

20. $\dfrac{3.5 \times 10^{-3}}{7 \times 10^{-5}} = \dfrac{3.5}{7} \times \dfrac{10^{-3}}{10^{-5}} = 0.5 \times 10^{2}$
$= 5.0 \times 10^{1}$
$= 50$

21. $\dfrac{4.0 \times 10^3(9.0 \times 10^5)}{(6.0 \times 10^5)} = \dfrac{(4.0 \times 9.0)(10^3 \times 10^5)}{6.0 \times 10^5}$
$= \dfrac{36.0}{6.0} \times \dfrac{10^8}{10^5}$
$= 6.0 \times 10^3$
$= 6{,}000$

22. $\dfrac{(1.2 \times 10^4)(4.0 \times 10^{-3})}{(6.0 \times 10^7)} = \dfrac{(1.2 \times 4.0)(10^4 \times 10^{-3})}{6.0 \times 10^7}$
$= \dfrac{4.8}{6.0} \times \dfrac{10^1}{10^7}$
$= 0.8 \times 10^{-6}$
$= 8.0 \times 10^{-7}$
$= 0.0000008$

23. $x^2 \cdot x^1 = 10^2 \cdot 10^1 = 100 \cdot 10 = 1000$

24. $2^a \cdot 2^b \cdot 2^c = 2^1 \cdot 2^4 \cdot 2^0 = 2^{1+4+0} = 2^5 = 32$

25. $7^a \cdot 5^a \cdot 3^a = 7^0 \cdot 5^0 \cdot 3^0 = 1 \cdot 1 \cdot 1 = 1$

26. $10^x \cdot 10^y \cdot 10^z = 10^3 \cdot 10^2 \cdot 10^1 = 10^{3+2+1} = 10^6 = 1{,}000{,}000$

27. $4.003 \times 10^5 = 400{,}300$

28. $9.6 \times 10^{-4} = 0.00096$

29. $1.392 \times 10^3 = 1{,}392$

30. $1.4 \times 10^{-3} = 0.0014$

31. $3.8 \times 10^4 = 38{,}000$

32. $3.752 \times 10^{-5} = 0.00003752$

33. 4, 4, 0; 4

34. 8, 13, 22, 0; 22

35. 2, 0, 3, 1; 3

36. 5, 6, 3, 0; 6

37. $9{,}475{,}001 = 9.475001 \times 10^6$

38. $0.00037 = 3.7 \times 10^{-4}$

39. $65 = 6.5 \times 10^1$

40. $0.000001 = 1.0 \times 10^{-6}$

41. $0.0939 = 9.39 \times 10^{-2}$

42. $46{,}300 = 4.63 \times 10^4$

43. Terms: $-3a^3c, 11a^2c^2, 5c^3$
Coefficients: $-3, 11, 5$

44. Terms: $4x^2, -6xy, -8y^2$
Coefficients: $4, -6, -8$

45. Terms: $-3x^3yz, 4x^2y^2z, -19xy^2z^3, 15$
Coefficients: $-3, 4, -19, 15$

46. $9xy^3 - 3x^2y - 2xy^3 = (9 - 2)xy^3 - 3x^2y$
$= 7xy^3 - 3x^2y$

47. $3m^2 - m^2 + 3m + m = (3 - 1)m^2 + (3 + 1)m$
$= 2m^2 + 4m$

48. $\frac{3}{5}x^2 + 4 - 2x - x^2 = \left(\frac{3}{5} - 1\right)x^2 - 2x + 4$
$= -\frac{2}{5}x^2 - 2x + 4$

49. $\frac{1}{2}x + \frac{2}{3}x^2 - x + 3 = \frac{2}{3}x^2 + \left(\frac{1}{2} - 1\right)x + 3$
$= \frac{2}{3}x^2 - \frac{1}{2}x + 3$

50. $2 - \frac{1}{2}x^3 - 2x + \frac{2}{3}x^3 = \left(-\frac{1}{2} + \frac{2}{3}\right)x^3 - 2x + 2$
$= \left(-\frac{3}{6} + \frac{4}{6}\right)x^3 - 2x + 2$
$= \frac{1}{6}x^3 - 2x + 2$

51. $\frac{1}{2}x^4 - 2x^2 - \frac{4}{5}x^4 + \frac{4}{5}x = \left(\frac{1}{2} - \frac{4}{5}\right)x^4 - 2x^2 + \frac{4}{5}x$
$= \left(\frac{5}{10} - \frac{8}{10}\right)x^4 - 2x^2 + \frac{4}{5}x$
$= -\frac{3}{10}x^4 - 2x^2 - \frac{4}{5}x$

MIXED PRACTICE 10

p. 627

1. $5x^3 + 6x - 4x^2 - x + 4 = 5x^3 - 4x^2 + (6 - 1)x + 4$
$= 5x^3 - 4x^2 + 5x + 4$

2. $xy - 7x^2 + 5xy + 21 - 3 = -7x^2 + (1 + 5)xy + 21 - 3$
$= -7x^2 + 6xy + 18$

3. $3x - 3x^2 + 4x - x^2 = (-3 - 1)x^2 + (3 + 4)x$
$= -4x^2 + 7x$

4. $5y^2 - x^2 + 4xy + 7x^2 = (-1 + 7)x^2 + 4xy + 5y^2$
$= 6x^2 + 4xy + 5y^2$

5. $-xy + 5x^2y^3 - 5 + 7xy - x^3 + 4xy + x^2y^3 - 2$
$= -x^3 + (5 + 1)x^2y^3 + (-1 + 7 + 4)xy - 5 - 2$
$= -x^3 + 6x^2y^3 + 10xy - 7$

6. $(-3x^2y + 4x - 19) + (9x + 11 + 4x^2y - 5y)$
$= (-3 + 4)x^2y + (4 + 9)x - 5y + (-19 + 11)$
$= x^2y + 13x - 5y - 8$

7. $(3m^2n + mn - 25) - (6m^2n - 5m + 9)$
$= 3m^2n + mn - 25 - 6m^2n + 5m - 9$
$= (3 - 6)m^2n + 5m + mn + (-25 - 9)$
$= -3m^2n + 5m + mn - 34$

8. $(4x^3 + 8x^2 - x + 4) - (3x^2 - 5x^3 + 1)$
$= 4x^3 + 8x^2 - x + 4 - 3x^2 + 5x^3 - 1$
$= (4 + 5)x^3 + (8 - 3)x^2 - x + (4 - 1)$
$= 9x^3 + 5x^2 - x + 3$

9. $(2x^5y^2 - 4x^3 - 2x + 4) + (x^3 - 4x^5y^2 - 9x + 6)$
$= (2 - 4)x^5y^2 + (-4 + 1)x^3 + (-2 - 9)x + (4 + 6)$
$= -2x^5y^2 - 3x^3 - 11x + 10$

10. $(x^2 - x) + (x - 8) - (x + 5x^2) + (2x^2 - 9x + 1)$
$= x^2 - x + x - 8 - x - 5x^2 + 2x^2 - 9x + 1$
$= (1 - 5 + 2)x^2 + (-1 + 1 - 1 - 9)x + (-8 + 1)$
$= -2x^2 - 10x - 7$

11. $(5x^2 - 2x + 1) - (3x + 4) + (25 - 4x^2) - (9x + 7)$
$= 5x^2 - 2x + 1 - 3x - 4 + 25 - 4x^2 - 9x - 7$
$= (5 - 4)x^2 + (-2 - 3 - 9)x + (1 - 4 + 25 - 7)$
$= x^2 - 14x + 15$

12. $(4x^2y - 5x + 1) + (3y^2 - 4) - (7x + 4y^2 + 2x^2y)$
$= 4x^2y - 5x + 1 + 3y^2 - 4 - 7x - 4y^2 - 2x^2y$
$= (4 - 2)x^2y + (5 - 7)x + (3 - 4)y^2 + (1 - 4)$
$= 2x^2y - 12x - y^2 - 3$

13. $(-4x^4 + 2xy) - (x^2 - 5xy + x^4) + (3x^4 + 2xy)$
$= -4x^4 + 2xy - x^2 + 5xy - x^4 + 3x^4 + 2xy$
$= (-4 - 1 + 3)x^4 - x^2 + (2 + 5 + 2)xy$
$= -2x^4 - x^2 + 9xy$

14. $4x^2 - 5xy = 4(-2)^2 - 5(-2)(3)$
$= 4(4) + 10(3)$
$= 16 + 30$
$= 46$

15. $10 - 3x^2 - 5y = 10 - 3(-2)^2 - 5(3)$
$= 10 - 3(4) - 15$
$= 10 - 12 - 15$
$= -17$

16. $3x^2 + 10xy + 2y^2 = 3(-2)^2 + 10(-2)(3) + 2(3^2)$
$= 3(4) - 20(3) + 2(9)$
$= 12 - 60 + 18$
$= -30$

17. $x^3y^2 + 9x - 2y + 10 = (-2)^3(3)^2 + 9(-2) - 2(3) + 10$
$= (-8)(9) + (-18) - 6 + 10$
$= -72 - 18 - 6 + 10$
$= -86$

18. $x^2y^3 + 15x - 20 = (-2)^2(3)^3 + 15(-2) - 20$
$= (4)(27) - 30 - 20$
$= 108 - 50$
$= 58$

19. $2y^3 - 2y^2x + 4x^2 + 1 = 2(3)^3 - 2(3)^2(-2) + 4(-2)^2 + 1$
$= 2(27) - 2(9)(-2) + 4(4) + 1$
$= 54 + 36 + 16 + 1$
$= 107$

20.
$$\begin{array}{r} 7y^5 \phantom{{}- 5y^3} + 4y^2 \phantom{{}- 6y} - 9 \\ - 5y^3 + 7y^2 - 6y + 3 \\ \hline 7y^5 - 5y^3 + 11y^2 - 6y - 6 \end{array}$$

21.
$$\begin{array}{r} 3x^5 - 9x^3y - 9x \qquad + 15 \\ -11x^5 + 14x^3y + 6x - y + 4 \\ \hline -8x^5 + 5x^3y - 3x - y + 19 \end{array}$$

22.
$$\begin{array}{r} 4x^5y \qquad\qquad + 3x^3y^3 - 9xy + 4 \\ -2x^5y - 4x^4y^2 \qquad\qquad - 10xy + 3 \\ \hline 2x^5y - 4x^4y^2 + 3x^3y^3 + xy + 7 \end{array}$$

23.
$$\begin{array}{r} 3m^4 - m^3 \qquad\quad - 4mn^2 + 6n \qquad \\ + 7m^3 - m^2 + 6mn^2 + 15n - 4 \\ \hline 3m^4 + 6m^3 - m^2 + 2mn^2 + 21n - 4 \end{array}$$

24.
$$\begin{aligned} (0.5x^3)(4x^5) &= (0.5 \cdot 4)(x^3 \cdot x^5) \\ &= 2x^8 \end{aligned}$$

25.
$$\begin{aligned} 4x^2(x^3 - 5x + 16) &= 4x^2(x^3) + 4x^2(-5x) + 4x^2(16) \\ &= 4x^5 - 20x^3 + 64x^2 \end{aligned}$$

26.
$$\begin{aligned} &(5a^3 - 7)(-2a^2 + a) \\ &= 5a^3(-2a^2) + 5a^3(a) - 7(-2a^2) - 7(a) \\ &= -10a^5 + 5a^4 + 14a^2 - 7a \end{aligned}$$

27.
$$\begin{aligned} (4x + 3)(3x - 4) &= 4x(3x) + 4x(-4) + 3(3x) + 3(-4) \\ &= 12x^2 - 16x + 9x - 12 \\ &= 12x^2 - 7x - 12 \end{aligned}$$

28.
$$\begin{aligned} &(4m + 0.5)(4m - 0.5) \\ &= 4m(4m) + 4m(-0.5) + 0.5(4m) + 0.5(-0.5) \\ &= 16m^2 - 2m + 2m - 0.25 \\ &= 16m^2 - 0.25 \end{aligned}$$

29.
$$\begin{aligned} (7 - 5x)^2 &= (7 - 5x)(7 - 5x) \\ &= 7(7) + 7(-5x) - 5x(7) - 5x(-5x) \\ &= 49 - 35x - 35x + 25x^2 \\ &= 25x^2 - 70x + 49 \end{aligned}$$

30.
$$\begin{aligned} (3y + 2)^2 &= (3y + 2)(3y + 2) \\ &= 3y(3y) + 3y(2) + 2(3y) + 2(2) \\ &= 9y^2 + 6y + 6y + 4 \\ &= 9y^2 + 12y + 4 \end{aligned}$$

31.
$$\begin{aligned} &(2x^3 - 11)(2x^3 + 11) \\ &= 2x^3(2x^3) + 2x^3(11) - 11(2x^3) - 11(11) \\ &= 4x^6 + 22x^3 - 22x^3 - 121 \\ &= 4x^6 - 121 \end{aligned}$$

32.
$$\begin{aligned} &(x^2 - 5)(x^3 - 2x^2 - 2) \\ &= x^2(x^3) + x^2(-2x^2) + x^2(-2) - 5(x^3) - 5(-2x^2) - 5(-2) \\ &= x^5 - 2x^4 - 2x^2 - 5x^3 + 10x^2 + 10 \\ &= x^5 - 2x^4 - 2x^2 - 5x^3 + 10x^2 + 10 \\ &= x^5 - 2x^4 - 5x^3 + 8x^2 + 10 \end{aligned}$$

33.
$$\begin{aligned} &(-2x^3 + 5x + 1)(x + 1) \\ &= -2x^3(x) - 2x^3(1) + 5x(x) + 5x(1) + 1(x) + 1(1) \\ &= -2x^4 - 2x^3 + 5x^2 + 5x + x + 1 \\ &= -2x^4 - 2x^3 + 5x^2 + 6x + 1 \end{aligned}$$

34.
$$\begin{aligned} A &= l \times w \\ A &= (a + 5)(a - 7) \\ A &= a(a) + a(-7) + 5(a) + 5(-7) \\ A &= a^2 - 7a + 5a - 35 \\ A &= a^2 - 2a - 35 \end{aligned}$$

35.
$$\begin{aligned} A &= s^2 \\ A &= (x + y)^2 \\ A &= (x + y)(x + y) \\ A &= x(x) + x(y) + y(x) + y(y) \\ A &= x^2 + xy + xy + y^2 \\ A &= x^2 + 2xy + y^2 \end{aligned}$$

36. Let s = smallest number.
$$\begin{aligned} s^2 + (s + 1)^2 + (s + 2)^2 &= 3s^2 + 29 \\ s^2 + s^2 + 2s + 1 + s^2 + 4s + 4 &= 3s^2 + 29 \\ 3s^2 + 6s + 5 &= 3s^2 + 29 \\ 3s^2 - 3s^2 + 6s + 5 &= 3s^2 - 3s^2 + 29 \\ 6s + 5 &= 29 \\ 6s + 5 - 5 &= 29 - 5 \\ 6s &= 24 \\ \frac{1}{6} \cdot 6s &= \frac{1}{6} \cdot 24 \\ s &= 4 \end{aligned}$$

The numbers are 4, 5, and 6.

MIXED PRACTICE 11 p. 628

1. $m^4 - 25 = (m^2 + 5)(m^2 - 5)$
2. $81t^2 - 100s^4 = (9t + 10s^2)(9t - 10s^2)$
3. $-9 + 4y^2 = 4y^2 - 9 = (2y + 3)(2y - 3)$
4. $49 - w^6 = (7 + w^3)(7 - w^3)$
5. $x^4 - 5x^3 + x^2 = x^2(x^2 - 5x + 1)$
6. $x^2 - 3x - 10 = (x - 5)(x + 2)$
7. $t^2 + 4t + 3 = (t + 3)(t + 1)$
8. $c^2 - 8c + 7 = (c - 7)(c - 1)$

9. No 10. Yes 11. No

12. No 13. Yes 14. No

15. $c^2 - 4 = (c + 2)(c - 2)$
16. $81m^2 - 25 = (9m + 5)(9m - 5)$
17. $y^{10} - z^{10} = (y^5 + z^5)(y^5 - z^5)$
18. $49 - n^8 = (7 + n^4)(7 - n^4)$
19. $2a^4b + 2a^3b^2 - 2a^2b^2 = 2a^2b(a^2 + ab - b)$
20. $5x^4y + 5x^2y - 10x = 5x(x^3y + xy - 2)$
21. $2x^2 - 8x - 10 = 2(x^2 - 4x - 5) = 2(x - 5)(x + 1)$
22. $2x^2 - 9x - 5 = (2x + 1)(x - 5)$
23. $2x^2 + 3x - 5 = (2x + 5)(x - 1)$
24. $2x^2 - 3x - 5 = (2x - 5)(x + 1)$

25. No 26. Yes 27. Yes

28. Yes 29. No 30. No

31. Yes 32. No 33. No

34. No

35. $m^4 - 9 = (m^2 + 3)(m^2 - 3)$
36. $4y^2 - 1 = (2y + 1)(2y^2 - 1)$
37. $6x^2 + 3x - 9 = 3(2x^2 + x - 3) = 3(2x + 3)(x - 1)$
38. $10x^2 + x - 3 = (5x + 3)(2x - 1)$
39. $x^2 - 4x - 45 = (x + 5)(x - 9)$
40. $t^2 - 7t + 12 = (t - 4)(t - 3)$
41. $12 - x - x^2 = (3 - x)(x + 4)$
42. $2y^2 - 9y - 5 = (2y + 1)(y - 5)$
43. $4x^2y = 4x(xy)$ or $x^2(4y)$ or $y(4x^2)$, etc.
44. $-9m^3n = 3(-3m^3n)$ or $n(-9m^3)$ or $m^3(-9n)$, etc.
45. $15t^23 = 3(15t^2)$ or $15(3t^2)$ or $t(15t3)$, etc.
46. $-12pq^2 = q^2(-12p)$ or $-4(3pq^2)$ or $p(-12q^2)$, etc.
47.
$$\begin{aligned} x^5 - 4x^3 + 3x &= x(x^4 - 4x^2 + 3) \\ &= x(x^2 - 3)(x^2 - 1) \\ &= x(x^2 - 3)(x + 1)(x - 1) \end{aligned}$$
48.
$$\begin{aligned} 7x - 6 - 2x^2 &= -2x^2 + 7x - 6 \\ &= (-2x + 3)(x - 2) \\ \text{or} &\quad (3 - 2x)(x - 2) \end{aligned}$$
49. $4y^3 - 12y^2 + 4y = 4y(y^2 - 3y + 1)$
50. $6a^2 - 2a + 10 = 2(3a^2 - a + 5)$
51. $x^2 + 5x - xy - 5y = x(x + 5) - y(x + 5) = (x + 5)(x - y)$
52. $6t^2 + 5t + 1 = (3t + 1)(2t + 1)$
53. $2x^2 - 9x + 4 = (2x - 1)(x - 4)$
54. $3x^2 + 10x - 8 = (3x - 2)(x + 4)$

MIXED PRACTICE 12 p. 629

1. $2y^2 - 9y - 5 = (2y + 1)(y - 5)$
2. $2t^2 + 25t + 12 = (2t + 1)(t + 12)$

3. $4m^2 - 1 = (2m + 1)(2m - 1)$

4. $3y^2 + y - 10 = (3y - 5)(y + 2)$

5. $x^2 + 4x - 21 = (x - 7)(x - 3)$

6. $y^2 - 12y + 36 = (y - 6)(y - 6) = (y - 6)^2$

7. $10 + 3x - x^2 = (2 + x)(5 - x)$

8. $t^2 + 8t + 16 = (t + 4)(t + 4) = (t + 4)^2$

9. $3x^3 + 3x^2 - 15x = 3x(x^2 + x - 5)$

10. $x^3 + 3x^2 - x = x(x^2 + 3x - 1)$

11.
$$\begin{aligned} t^2 - 25 &= 0 \\ (t + 5)(t - 5) &= 0 \\ t + 5 = 0 \quad &\text{or} \quad t - 5 = 0 \\ t = -5 \quad &\text{or} \quad t = 5 \end{aligned}$$

12.
$$\begin{aligned} x^2 - x &= 20 \\ x^2 - x - 20 &= 0 \\ (x + 4)(x - 5) &= 0 \\ x + 4 = 0 \quad &\text{or} \quad x - 5 = 0 \\ x = -4 \quad &\text{or} \quad x = 5 \end{aligned}$$

13.
$$\begin{aligned} x^2 + 49 &= 14x \\ x^2 - 14x + 49 &= 0 \\ (x - 7)(x - 7) &= 0 \\ x - 7 &= 0 \\ x &= 7 \end{aligned}$$

14.
$$\begin{aligned} 3x^2 + x &= 0 \\ x(3x + 1) &= 0 \\ x = 0 \quad &\text{or} \quad 3x + 1 = 0 \\ x = 0 \quad &\text{or} \quad 3x = -1 \\ x = 0 \quad &\text{or} \quad x = -\tfrac{1}{3} \end{aligned}$$

15.
$$\begin{aligned} (2y - 1)(y - 5) &= 0 \\ 2y - 1 = 0 \quad &\text{or} \quad (y - 5) = 0 \\ 2y = 1 \quad &\text{or} \quad y = 5 \\ y = \tfrac{1}{2} \quad &\text{or} \quad y = 5 \end{aligned}$$

16.
$$\begin{aligned} t(t + 7) &= 4(3 + 2t) \\ t(t + 7) - 4(3 + 2t) &= 0 \\ t^2 + 7t - 12 - 8t &= 0 \\ t^2 - t - 12 &= 0 \\ (t - 4)(t + 3) &= 0 \\ t - 4 = 0 \quad &\text{or} \quad t + 3 = 0 \\ t = 4 \quad &\text{or} \quad t = -3 \end{aligned}$$

17.
$$\begin{aligned} t^2 + 3t - 4 &= 36 \\ t^2 + 3t - 40 &= 0 \\ (t + 8)(t - 5) &= 0 \\ t + 8 = 0 \quad &\text{or} \quad t - 5 = 0 \\ t = -8 \quad &\text{or} \quad t = 5 \end{aligned}$$

18.
$$\begin{aligned} 3y^2 + 17y + 10 &= 0 \\ (3y + 2)(y + 5) &= 0 \\ 3y + 2 = 0 \quad &\text{or} \quad y + 5 = 0 \\ 3y = -2 \quad &\text{or} \quad y = -5 \\ y = -\tfrac{2}{3} \quad &\text{or} \quad y = -5 \end{aligned}$$

19.
$$\begin{aligned} t^2 - \tfrac{25}{4} &= 0 \\ \left(t + \tfrac{5}{2}\right)\left(t - \tfrac{5}{2}\right) &= 0 \\ t + \tfrac{5}{2} = 0 \quad &\text{or} \quad t - \tfrac{5}{2} = 0 \\ t = -\tfrac{5}{2} \quad &\text{or} \quad t = \tfrac{5}{2} \end{aligned}$$

20.
$$\begin{aligned} \frac{3x^2}{4} &= 27 \\ 4\left(\frac{3x^2}{4}\right) &= 4 \cdot 27 \\ 3x^2 &= 108 \\ x^2 &= 36 \\ x = -6 \quad &\text{or} \quad x = 6 \end{aligned}$$

21.
$$\begin{aligned} x^3 + 3x^2 - x - 3 &= (x^3 + 3x^2) - (x + 3) \\ &= x^2(x + 3) - 1(x + 3) \\ &= (x^2 - 1)(x + 3) \\ &= (x + 1)(x - 1)(x + 3) \end{aligned}$$

22.
$$\begin{aligned} 2x^4 + 5x^3 + 2x + 5 &= (2x^4 + 5x^3) + (2x + 5) \\ &= x^3(2x + 5) + 1(2x + 5) \\ &= (x^3 + 1)(2x + 5) \\ &= (x + 1)(x^2 - x + 1)(2x + 5) \end{aligned}$$

23.
$$\begin{aligned} 6y^3 - 10y^2 + 9y - 15 &= (6y^3 - 10y^2) + (9y - 15) \\ &= 2y^2(3y - 5) + 3(3y - 5) \\ &= (2y^2 + 3)(3y - 5) \end{aligned}$$

24.
$$\begin{aligned} x^3 + 2x^2 - 7x - 14 &= (x^3 + 2x^2) - (7x + 14) \\ &= x^2(x + 2) - 7(x + 2) \\ &= (x^2 - 7)(x + 2) \end{aligned}$$

25. Let n = smaller number.
$$\begin{aligned} n(n + 2) &= 288 \\ n^2 + 2n &= 288 \\ n^2 + 2n - 288 &= 0 \\ (n - 16)(n + 18) &= 0 \\ n - 16 = 0 \quad &\text{or} \quad n + 18 = 0 \\ n = 16 \quad &\text{or} \quad n = -18 \end{aligned}$$
The numbers are 16 and 18 or -16 and -18.

26. Let n = the number.
$$\begin{aligned} n^2 + 12 &= 7n \\ n^2 - 7n + 12 &= 0 \\ (n - 4)(n - 3) &= 0 \\ n - 4 = 0 \quad &\text{or} \quad n - 3 = 0 \\ n = 4 \quad &\text{or} \quad n = 3 \end{aligned}$$
The number is 3 or 4.

27. Let l = length of rectangle.
$$\begin{aligned} l(l - 7) &= 228 \\ l^2 - 7l &= 228 \\ l^2 - 7l - 228 &= 0 \\ (l + 12)(l - 19) &= 0 \\ l + 12 = 0 \quad &\text{or} \quad l - 19 = 0 \\ l = -12 \quad &\text{or} \quad l = 19 \end{aligned}$$
Length can't be negative, so the length is 19 ft and the width is 12 ft.

28. Let s = length of original side.
$$\begin{aligned} (s + 4)^2 &= 256 \\ s^2 + 8s + 16 &= 256 \\ s^2 + 8s - 240 &= 0 \\ (s + 20)(s - 12) &= 0 \\ s + 20 = 0 \quad &\text{or} \quad s - 12 = 0 \\ s = -20 \quad &\text{or} \quad s = 12 \end{aligned}$$
Length can't be negative, so the length of a side in the original square is 12 inches.

29. Let n = smaller number.
$$\begin{aligned} n(n + 1) &= 182 \\ n^2 + n &= 182 \\ n^2 + n - 182 &= 0 \\ (n + 14)(n - 13) &= 0 \\ n + 14 = 0 \quad &\text{or} \quad n - 13 = 0 \\ n = -14 \quad &\text{or} \quad n = 13 \end{aligned}$$
The numbers are 13 and 14 or -13 and -14.

30. Let n = smaller number.
$$\begin{aligned} n^2 + (n + 2)^2 &= 202 \\ n^2 + n^2 + 4n + 4 &= 202 \\ 2n^2 + 4n - 198 &= 0 \\ 2(n^2 + 2n - 99) &= 0 \\ 2(n + 11)(n - 9) &= 0 \\ n + 11 = 0 \quad &\text{or} \quad n - 9 = 0 \\ n = -11 \quad &\text{or} \quad n = 9 \end{aligned}$$
The integers are positive, so they are 9 and 11.

31. Let b = base of triangle.

$$\frac{1}{2}b(b + 6) = 216$$
$$\frac{b^2}{2} + 3b = 216$$
$$b^2 + 6b = 432$$
$$b^2 + 6b - 432 = 0$$
$$(b + 24)(b - 18) = 0$$
$$b + 24 = 0 \quad \text{or} \quad b - 18 = 0$$
$$b = -24 \quad \text{or} \quad b = 18$$

Base can't be negative, so base is 18 m and height is 24 m.

32. Let x = the number.

$$x^2 - x = 2$$
$$x^2 - x - 2 = 0$$
$$(x - 2)(x + 1) = 0$$
$$x - 2 = 0 \quad \text{or} \quad x + 1 = 0$$
$$x = 2 \quad \text{or} \quad x = -1$$

The number is 2 or -1.

33. Let x = the number.

$$4x^2 = 9$$
$$4x^2 - 9 = 0$$
$$(2x + 3)(2x - 3) = 0$$
$$2x + 3 = 0 \quad \text{or} \quad 2x - 3 = 0$$
$$2x = -3 \quad \text{or} \quad 2x = 3$$
$$x = -\frac{3}{2} \quad \text{or} \quad x = \frac{3}{2}$$

The number is $\frac{3}{2}$ or $-\frac{3}{2}$.

MIXED PRACTICE 13 p. 630

1. (3, 4) **2.** (−4, 4) **3.** (4, −3)

4. (−3, −1) **5.** (2, 1) **6.** (3, −2)

7. *a* **8.** *e* **9.** *b* **10.** *c* **11.** *d*

12. $m = \frac{5 - 7}{6 - 3} = \frac{-2}{3}$ **13.** $m = \frac{4 - 9}{2 - 10} = \frac{-5}{-8} = \frac{5}{8}$

14. $m = \frac{2 - (-2)}{10 - 2} = \frac{4}{8} = \frac{1}{2}$ **15.** $m = \frac{16 - 13}{7 - 4} = \frac{3}{3} = 1$

16. $y = \frac{1}{2}x - 3;$ $\begin{array}{c|c} (1) & \frac{1}{2}(4) - 3 \\ \hline 1 & -1 \end{array}$, no

17. $y = -\frac{1}{4}x + 1;$ $\begin{array}{c|c} \left(\frac{9}{8}\right) & -\frac{1}{4}\left(-\frac{1}{2}\right) + 1 \\ \hline \frac{9}{8} & \frac{9}{8} \end{array}$, yes

18. $5y = 2x + 10;$ $\begin{array}{c|c} 5(2) & 2(0) + 10 \\ \hline 10 & 10 \end{array}$, yes

19. $2y + 3x = 4;$ $\begin{array}{c|c} 2(-4) + 3(4) & 4 \\ \hline 4 & 4 \end{array}$, yes

20. (1, 2), (3, 6), (−2, −4), etc. **21.** (0, 3), (−3, 0), (3, 6), etc.

22. $\left(0, \frac{5}{2}\right)$, (−5, 0), (3, 4), etc.

23. $\frac{-5 - 10}{x - (-3)} = -3$

$$-5 - 10 = -3(x + 3)$$
$$-15 = -3x - 9$$
$$-6 = -3x$$
$$2 = x$$

24. $\frac{8 - (-17)}{x - (-2)} = 5$

$$8 - (-17) = 5(x + 2)$$
$$25 = 5x + 10$$
$$15 = 5x$$
$$3 = x$$

25. $\frac{-9 - 7}{x - 2} = 2$

$$-9 - 7 = 2(x - 2)$$
$$-16 = 2x - 4$$
$$-12 = 2x$$
$$-6 = x$$

26. $AB: m = \frac{-2 - 2}{4 - 3} = \frac{-4}{1} = -4$

$BC: m = \frac{-1 - (-2)}{-1 - 4} = \frac{1}{-5}$

$CA: m = \frac{2 - (-1)}{3 - (-1)} = \frac{3}{4}$

27. $x = -3$ **28.** $y = -2.5$

29. IV **30.** III **31.** None **32.** I

MIXED PRACTICE 14 p. 631

1. $m = \frac{-5 - 5}{-4 - 1} = \frac{-10}{-5} = 2$

$$y = 2x + b$$
$$5 = 2(1) + b$$
$$5 = 2 + b$$
$$3 = b \qquad y = 2x + 3$$

2. $m = \frac{-1 - 1}{0 - (-3)} = \frac{-2}{3}$

$$y = \frac{-2}{3}x + b$$
$$-1 = -\frac{2}{3}(0) + b$$
$$-1 = b \qquad y = \frac{-2}{3}x - 1$$

3. $m = \frac{-24 - 6}{-4 - 2} = \frac{-30}{-6} = 5$

$$y = 5x + b$$
$$6 = 5(2) + b$$
$$6 = 10 + b$$
$$-4 = b \qquad y = 5x - 4$$

4. $m = \frac{-13 - 5}{3 - 0} = \frac{-18}{3} = -6$

$$y = -6x + b$$
$$5 = -6(0) + b$$
$$5 = b \qquad y = -6x + 5$$

5. $4y + 8x = -12$

$$4y = -8x - 12$$
$$y = -2x - 3$$

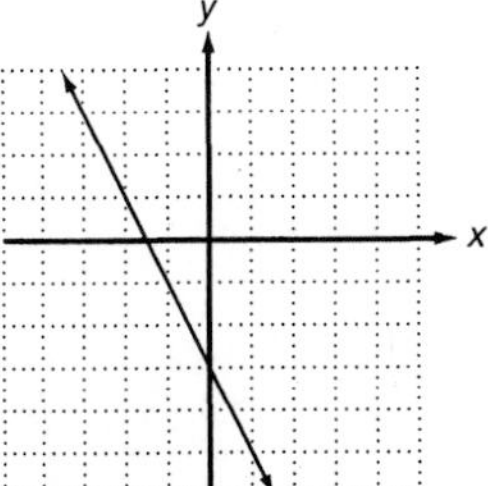

6. $2y - 10 = 6x$

$$2y = 6x + 10$$
$$y = 3x + 5$$

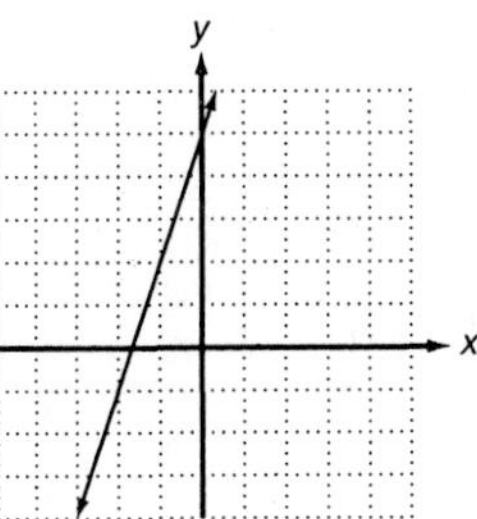

7. $5y + 20x = 5$

$$5y = -20x + 5$$
$$y = -4x + 1$$

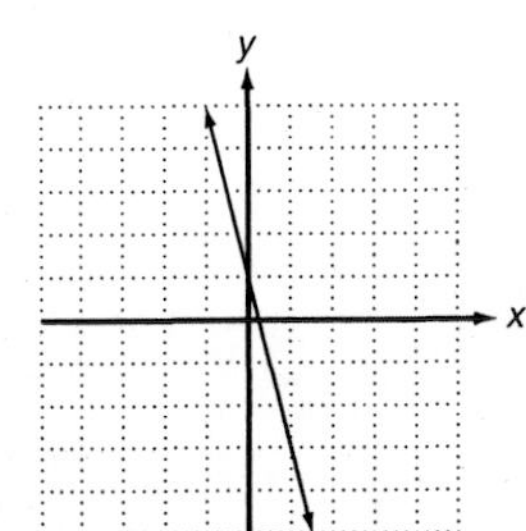

8. $x - y = 2$
$-y = -x + 2$
$y = x - 2$

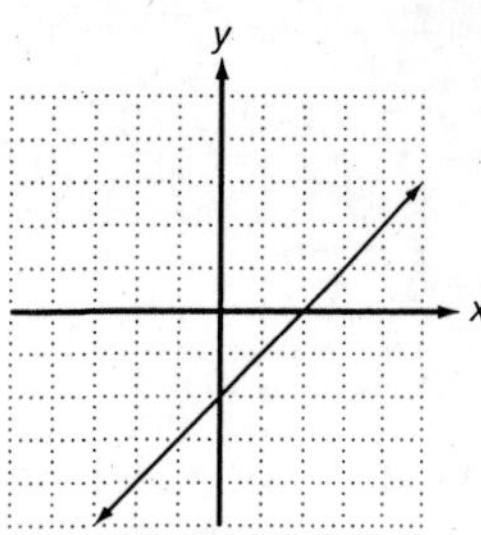

9. Slope of $y + 2x = 3$ is -2, so slope of desired line is -2.
$(-3, 1)$ is on the line, so $1 = -2(-3) + b$
$-5 = b$

Equation: $y = -2x - 5$

10. Slope of $4y = x - 4$ is $\frac{1}{4}$, so slope of desired line is -4.

$(2, 6)$ is on the line, so $(6) = -4(2) + b$.
$6 = -8 + b$
$14 = b$
Equation: $y = -4x + 14$

11. Slope of $3y = 15x - 7$ is 5, so slope of desired line is 5.
$(3, 5)$ is on the line so, $5 = 5(3) + b$.
$5 = 15 + b$
$-10 = b$
Equation: $y = 5x - 10$

12. Slope of $y = -3x + 5$ is -3, so slope of desired line is $\frac{1}{3}$.

$(2, -4)$ is on the line, so $-4 = \frac{1}{3}(2) + b$

$-4 = \frac{2}{3} + b$

$\frac{-14}{3} = b$

Equation: $y = \frac{1}{3}x - \frac{14}{3}$ or $3y = x - 14$

13. $5y = 2x - 15$

$y = \frac{2}{5}x - 3$, slope is $\frac{2}{5}$

$-1 = \frac{2}{5}(-5) = b$

$1 = b$

$y = \frac{2}{5}x + 1$

14. $2y = -4x + 6$
$y = -2x + 3$, slope is -2
$5 = -2(-6) = b$
$-7 = b$
$y = -2x - 7$

15. $y = 3$

16. $2x + 2y = 6$
$2(0) + 2y = 6$
$y = 3$
y-intercept is $(0, 3)$

$2x + 2(0) = 6$
$x = 3$
x-intercept is $(3, 0)$

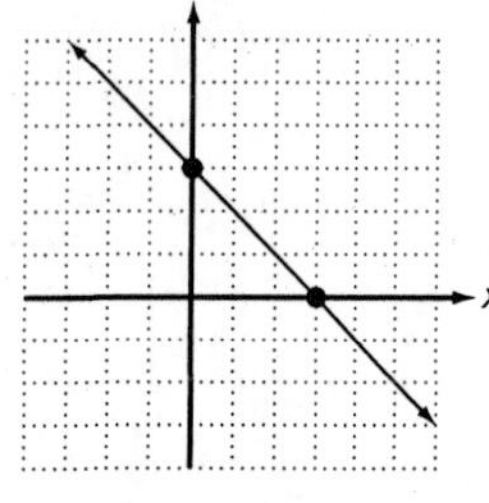

17. $2y + 1 = x$
$2(0) + 1 = x$
$1 = x$
x-intercept is $(1, 0)$

$2y + 1 = 0$

$y = -\frac{1}{2}$

y-intercept is $\left(0, -\frac{1}{2}\right)$

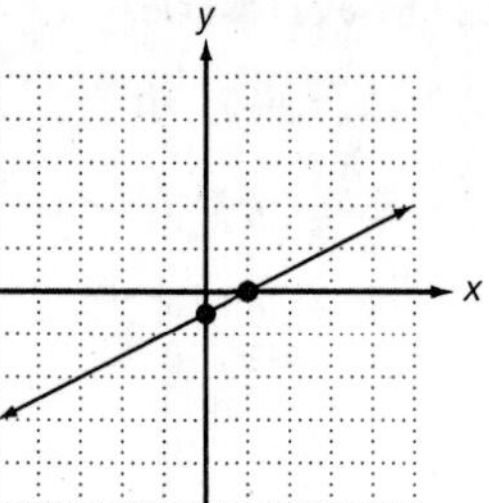

18. $3y + 6 = 15x$
$3(0) + 6 = 15x$

$\frac{6}{15} = x$

x-intercept is $\left(\frac{6}{15}, 0\right)$

$3y + 6 = 15(0)$
$y = -2$
y-intercept is $(0, -2)$

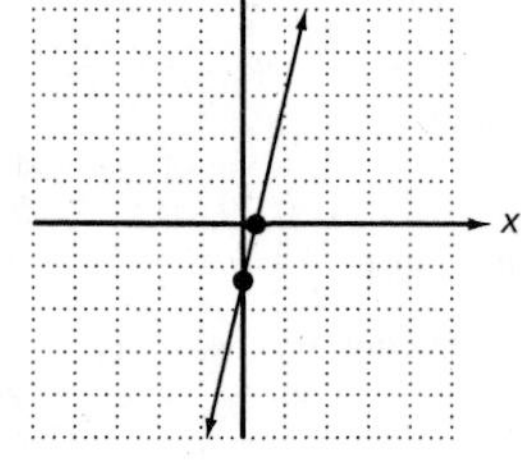

19. $3y - 2x = 12$
$3(0) - 2x = 12$
$x = -6$
x-intercept is $(-6, 0)$

$3y - 2(0) = 12$
$y = 4$
y-intercept is $(0, 4)$

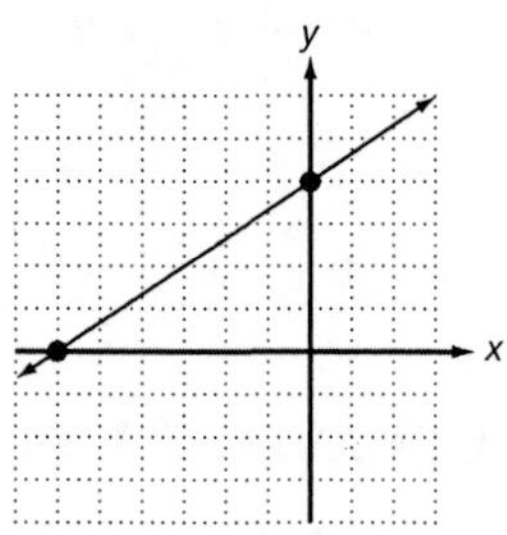

20. $8y + 3x = 16$
$8y = -3x + 16$

$y = -\frac{3}{8}x + 2$

slope is $-\frac{3}{8}$

21. $-9x = -1 - y$
$-9x + 1 = -y$
$y = 9x - 1$
slope is 9

22. $2y + 4 = x - 2$
$2y = x - 6$

$y = \frac{1}{2}x - 3$

slope is $\frac{1}{2}$

23. $2y + 8x = 14$
$2y = -8x + 14$
$y = -4x + 7$
slope is -4

24. $y = -\frac{1}{3}x + 2$ **25.** $y = \frac{4}{3}x + \frac{1}{8}$

26. $y = 2x$ **27.** $y = -1$

28. a. $m = \frac{526 - 277.5}{120 - 50} = \frac{248.5}{70} = 3.55$

$d - 526 = 3.55(p - 120)$
$d - 526 = 3.55p - 426$
$d = 3.55p + 100$

b. $d = 3.55(65) + 100$
$d = 230.75 + 100 = 330.75$
Lunch for 65 people will cost \$330.75.

MIXED PRACTICE 15

p. 632

1.

$2y - x = 6$	
$2(5) - 4$	6
$10 - 4$	6
6	6

$y + x = 7$	
$5 + 4$	7
9	7

No

2.

$8y + 40 = 3x$	
$8(-8) + 40$	$3(-8)$
$-64 + 40$	-24
-24	-24

$y - x = 0$	
$-8 - (-8)$	0
0	0

Yes

3.

$4y + 8 = 5x$	
$4(3) + 8$	$5(4)$
$12 + 8$	20
20	20

$2x - y = 5$	
$2(4) - 3$	5
$8 - 3$	5
5	5

Yes

4.

$3x + y = -1$	
$3(2) + (-7)$	-1
$6 + (-7)$	-1
-1	-1

$y + 5 = -x$	
$-7 + 5$	-2
-2	-2

Yes

5.

$2x - y = -7$	
$2(-2) - 3$	-7
$-4 - 3$	-7
-7	-7

$-y + x = -5$	
$-3 + (-2)$	-5
-5	-5

$y = 3$	
3	3

Yes

6.

$x + 2y = 3$	
$7 + 2(-2)$	3
$7 + (-4)$	3
3	3

$-y + 9 = x$	
$-(-2) + 9$	7
$2 + 9$	7
11	7

$-x - y = -5$	
$-7 - (-2)$	-5
-5	-5

No

7. $3x - 4y = 1$
$\underline{-2x + 4y = 6}$ Multiplied by 2
$x \quad = 7$
$3(7) - 4y = 1$
$21 - 4y = 1$
$-4y = -20$
$y = 5$
(7, 5) is the solution.

8. $3x - 5y = -2$
$\underline{-2x + 5y = -2}$
$x \quad = -4$
$3(-4) - 5y = -2$
$-12 - 5y = -2$
$-5y = 10$
$y = -2$
$(-4, -2)$ is the solution.

9. $-9x - 6y = -3$ Multiplied by -3
$\underline{10x + 6y = -2}$ Multiplied by 2
$x \quad = -5$
$-9(-5) - 6y = -3$
$45 - 6y = -3$
$-6y = -48$
$y = 8$
$(-5, 8)$ is the solution.

10. $12x + 27y = 18$ Multiplied by 3
$\underline{-12x - 20y = -4}$ Multiplied by -4
$7y = 14$
$y = 2$
$12x + 27(2) = 18$
$12x + 54 = 18$
$12x = -36$
$x = -3$
$(-3, 2)$ is the solution.

11. $3y = x - 2$
$y - x = -4$
Solve second equation for y.
$y = x - 4$
Substitute $x - 4$ for y in first equation.
$3(x - 4) = x - 2$
$3x - 12 = x - 2$
$2x = 10$
$x = 5$
Substitute 5 for x in $y = x - 4$.
$y = 5 - 4 = 1$
The solution is (5, 1).

12. $2y + 5x = 4$
$x + y = 5$
Solve second equation for x.
$x = 5 - y$
Substitute $5 - y$ for x in first equation.
$2y + 5(5 - y) = 4$
$2y + 25 - 5y = 4$
$-3y = -21$
$y = 7$
Substitute 7 for y in $x = 5 - y$.
$x = 5 - 7 = -2$
The solution is $(-2, 7)$.

13. $5y - x = -1$
$3y - 2x = 5$
Solve first equation for x.
$x = 5y + 1$
Substitute $5y + 1$ for x in second equation.
$3y - 2(5y + 1) = 5$
$3y - 10y - 2 = 5$
$-7y = 7$
$y = -1$
Substitute -1 for y in $x = 5y + 1$.
$x = 5(-1) + 1 = -5 + 1 = -4$
The solution is $(-4, -1)$.

14. $5x + 2y = 5$
$2x - \ y = 11$
Solve second equation for y.
$y = 2x - 11$
Substitute $2x - 11$ for y in first equation.
$5x + 2(2x - 11) = 5$
$5x + 4x - 22 = 5$
$9x = 27$
$x = 3$
Substitute 3 for x in $y = 2x - 11$.
$y = 2(3) - 11 = 6 - 11 = -5$
The solution is $(3, -5)$.

15.

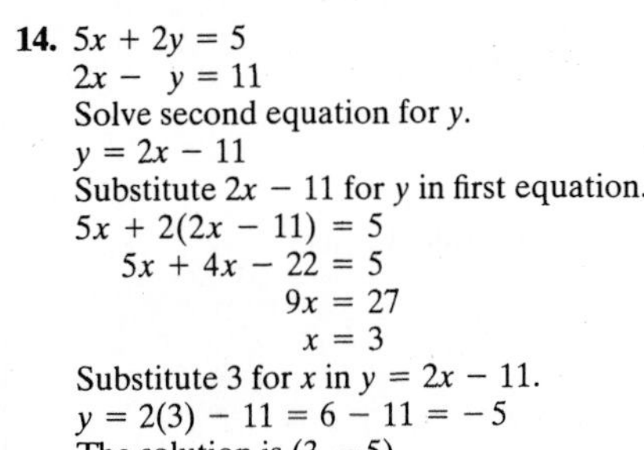

16.

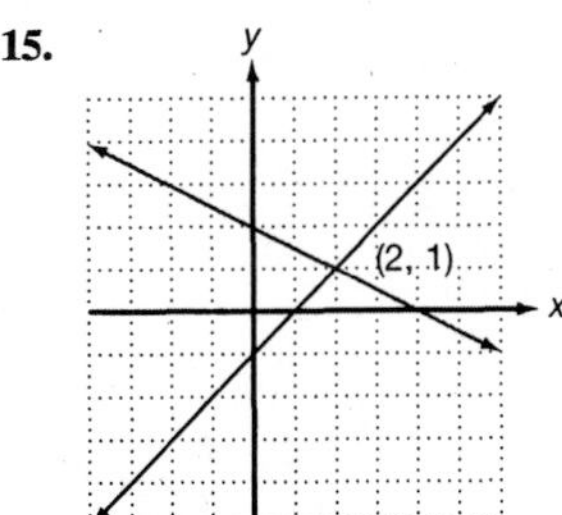

17.

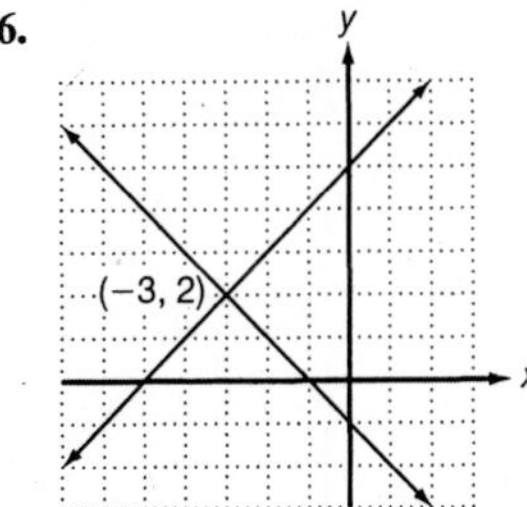

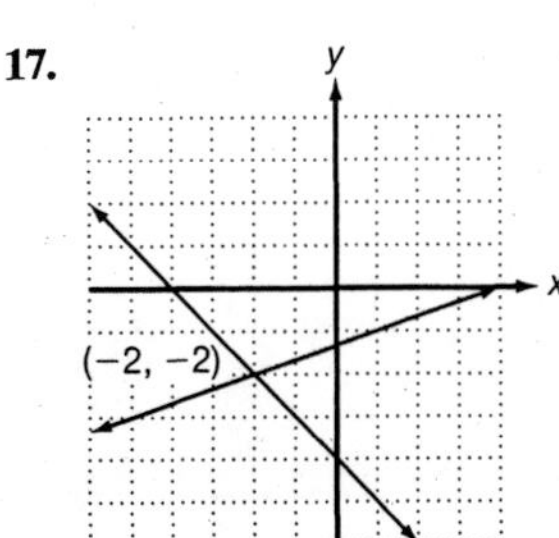

18.

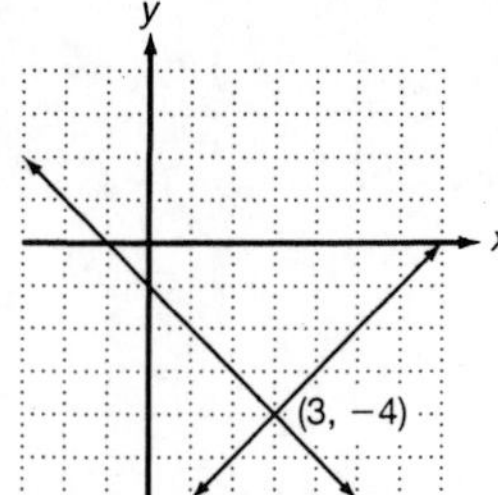

19. Let l = length and w = width.
$2l + 2w = 61$
$l = 2w - 7$
Substitute $2w - 7$ for l in first equation.
$2(2w - 7) + 2w = 61$
$4w - 14 + 2w = 61$
$6w = 75$
$w = 12.5$
Substitute 12.5 for w in $l = 2w - 7$.
$l = 2(12.5) - 7 = 25 - 7 = 18$
The length is 18 m, the width is 12.5 m.

20. Let x = first number and y = second number.
$$\begin{aligned} x + y &= 101 \\ x - y &= 45 \\ \hline 2x &= 146 \end{aligned}$$
$x = 73$
Substitute 73 for x in first equation.
$73 + y = 101$
$y = 28$
The number are 73 and 28.

21. Let x = large number and y = smaller number.
$x - y = 36$
$5x = 11y$
Solve first equation for x.
$x = 36 + y$
Substitute $36 + y$ for x in second equation.
$5(36 + y) = 11y$
$180 + 5y = 11y$
$180 = 6y$
$30 = y$
Substitute 30 for y in $x = 36 + y$.
$x = 36 + 30 = 66$
The numbers are 66 and 30.

22. Let x = first number and y = second.
$x + y = 26$
$$\frac{2}{5}x + \frac{3}{8}y = 10$$
Solve first equation for x.
$x = 26 - y$
Substitute $26 - y$ for x in second equation.
$$\frac{2}{5}(26 - y) + \frac{3}{8}y = 10$$
$$40\left(\frac{52}{5} - \frac{2}{5}y + \frac{3}{8}y\right) = 40 \cdot 10$$
$416 - 16y + 15y = 400$
$416 - y = 400$
$y = 16$
Substitute 16 for y in $x = 26 - y$.
$x = 26 - 16 = 10$
The numbers are 10 and 16.

MIXED PRACTICE 16 p. 633

1. $$\begin{aligned} 6x - 15y &= 21 \quad \text{Multiplied by 3} \\ -6x + 4y &= 12 \quad \text{Multiplied by 2} \\ \hline -11y &= 33 \end{aligned}$$
$y = -3$
$6x - 15(-3) = 21$
$6x + 45 = 21$
$6x = -24$
$x = -4$
$(-4, -3)$ is the solution.

2. $$\begin{aligned} 6x - 9y &= 12 \quad \text{Multiplied by 3} \\ -6x + 10y &= -10 \quad \text{Multiplied by 2} \\ \hline y &= 2 \end{aligned}$$
$6x - 9(2) = 12$
$6x - 18 = 12$
$6x = 30$
$x = 5$
$(5, 2)$ is the solution.

3. $$\begin{aligned} 6x + 12y &= 5 \\ 20x - 12y &= -18 \quad \text{Multiplied by } -2 \\ \hline 26x &= -13 \end{aligned}$$
$$x = -\frac{1}{2}$$
$$6\left(-\frac{1}{2}\right) + 12y = 5$$
$12y = 8$
$$y = \frac{2}{3}$$
$\left(-\frac{1}{2}, \frac{2}{3}\right)$ is the solution.

4. $x - 3y = 7$
$3x + 2y = 10$
Solve first equation for x.
$x = 3y + 7$
Substitute $3y + 7$ for x in second equation.
$3(3y + 7) + 2y = 10$
$9y + 21 + 2y = 10$ Equation ①
$11y = -11$
$y = -1$
Substitute -1 for y in $x = 3y + 7$
$x = 3(-1) + 7 = -3 + 7 = 4$
The solution is $(4, -1)$.

5. $x + 2y = 15$
$5x - y = -2$
Solve first equation for x.
$x = 15 - 2y$
Substitute $15 - 2y$ for x in second equation.
$5(15 - 2y) - y = -2$
$75 - 10y - y = -2$
$-11y = -77$
$y = 7$
Substitute 7 for y in $x = 15 - 2y$.
$x = 15 - 2(7) = 15 - 14 = 1$
The solution is $(1, 7)$.

6. $$\begin{aligned} 12x + 21y &= -9 \quad \text{Multiplied by 3} \\ -12x + 8y &= 96 \quad \text{Multiplied by 4} \\ \hline 29y &= 87 \end{aligned}$$
$y = 3$
$12x + 21(3) = -9$
$12x + 63 = -9$
$12x = -72$
$x = -6$
$(-6, 3)$ is the solution.

7.

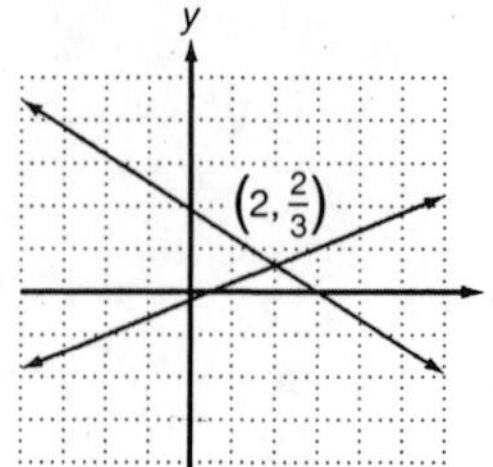

8.

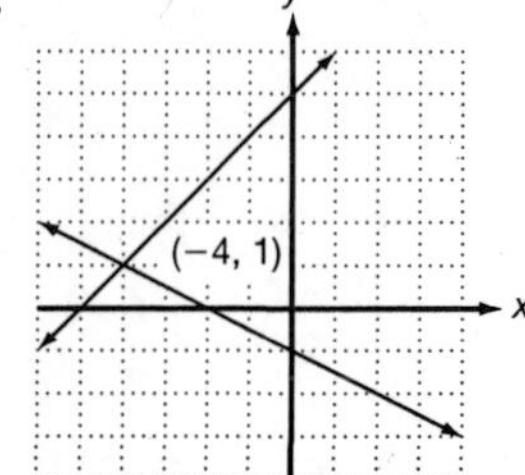

9. Let n = number of nickels, d = number of dimes.

$$n + d = 304$$
$$5n + 10d = 2240$$
$$n = 304 - d$$
$$5(304 - d) + 10d = 2240$$
$$1520 - 5d + 10d = 2240$$
$$5d = 720$$
$$d = 144$$
$$n + 144 = 304$$
$$n = 160$$

There are 160 nickels and 144 dimes.

10. Let x = tens digit and y = ones digit.

(1) $x + y = 11$

(2) $10y + x = 10x + y - 27$

$9y - 9x = -27$ Simplifying (2)

$y - x = -3$

$y + x = 11$

$2y = 8$ Adding

$y = 4$

Since $x + y = 11, x + 4 = 11, x = 7$.

The number is 74.

11. Let d = distance and r = rate of boat.

$$d = 2(r - 4)$$
$$d = 4(3.5)$$
$$4(3.5) = 2(r - 4)$$
$$14 = 2r - 8$$
$$22 = 2r$$
$$11 = r$$

The boat was traveling at 11 km/h.

12. Let a = adult tickets and s = student tickets.

$$a + s = 540$$
$$240a + 125s = 93{,}490$$
$$a = 540 - s$$
$$240(540 - s) + 125s = 93{,}490$$
$$129{,}600 - 240s + 125s = 93{,}490$$
$$-115s = -36{,}110$$
$$s = 314$$
$$a + 314 = 540$$
$$a = 226$$

226 adult tickets and 314 student tickets were sold.

13. Let x = first number and y = second number.

$x + y = 248$

$x - y = 64$

$2x = 312$

$x = 156$

Substitute 156 for x in the first equation.

$156 + y = 248$

$y = 92$

The numbers are 156 and 92.

14. $51t + 45t = 432$

$96t = 432$

$t = 4.5$ h

15. Let x = tens digit and y = ones digit.

$$10x + y = 4(x + y)$$
$$y = x + 4$$
$$10x + (x + 4) = 4(x + x + 4)$$
$$11x + 4 = 4x + 4x + 16$$
$$3x = 12$$
$$x = 4$$

Substitute 4 for x in $y = x + 4$.

$y = 4 + 4 = 8$

The number is 48.

16. Let d = distance and t = time.

$$d = 28t$$
$$d + 63 = 46t$$
$$28t + 63 = 46t$$
$$63 = 18t$$
$$3.5 = t$$

In 3.5 hours they will be 63 miles apart.

MIXED PRACTICE 17

1. $2x + 1 > 5$ or $x - 2 \le -1$

$2x > 4$ or $x \le 1$

$x > 2$ or $x \le 1$

2. $2x + 1 < 5$ and $x - 2 \ge -1$

$2x < 4$ and $x \ge 1$

$x < 2$

$1 \le x < 2$

3. $|3x - 7| = 11$

$3x - 7 = 11$ or $3x - 7 = -11$

$3x = 18$ or $3x = -4$

$x = 6$ or $x = -\frac{4}{3}$

4. $-|x - 3| = -5$

$|x - 3| = 5$

$x - 3 = 5$ or $x - 3 = -5$

$x = 8$ or $x = -2$

5. $-5 \le 2x + 3 < 21$

$2x + 3 \ge -5$ and $2x + 3 < 21$

$2x \ge -8$ and $2x < 18$

$x \ge -4$ and $x < 9$

$-4 \le x < 9$

6. $-x + 1 > 3$ or $2x - 5 > 3$

$-x > 2$ or $2x > 8$

$x < -2$ or $x > 4$

7. $2|5x - 3| = 26$

$|5x - 3| = 13$

$5x - 3 = 13$ or $5x - 3 = -13$

$5x = 16$ or $5x = -10$

$x = \frac{16}{5}$ or $x = -2$

8. $7 + |2x + 3| = 11$

$|2x + 3| = 4$

$2x + 3 = 4$ or $2x + 3 = -4$

$2x = 1$ or $2x = -7$

$x = \frac{1}{2}$ or $x = -\frac{7}{2}$

9. $x < -2$ or $x \ge 1$ **10.** $-1 \le x < 2$

11. $-4 \le x \le 3$ **12.** $x \le 1$ or $x > 3$

13. (a) $W = \{5, 10, 15, 20, 25, 30, 35\}$
(b) $W = \{x | x$ is a multiple of 5 and $0 < x < 38\}$

14. (a) $P = \{17, 19, 23\}$
(b) $P = \{x | x$ is prime and $15 < x < 25\}$

15. (a) $F = \{1, 2, 3, 4, 6, 12, 24\}$
(b) $F = \{x | x$ is an integer factor of 24 and $0 < x\}$

16. (a) $N = \{-5, -4, -3, -2, -1, 0, 1, 2, 3, 4, 5\}$
(b) $N = \{x | x$ is an integer and $|x| < 6\}$

17. $0 < w < 100$ **18.** $x < 58$ or $x > 97$ **19.** $40 \le x < 45$

20. $\{0, 2, 3, 5, 6, 7, 9\}$ **21.** $\{1, 3, 5\}$ **22.** $\{1, 2, 3, 5, 7, 9\}$

23. $\{3, 9\}$ **24.** $\{2, 3, 5\}$ **25.** $\{0, 1, 3, 5, 6, 7, 9\}$

26. $\{3, 5, 7\}$ **27.** $\{0, 1, 2, 3, 4, 5, 6, 9\}$

28. $x - 3 > -2$ and $x - 3 < 3$

$x > 1$ and $x < 6$

$1 < x < 6$

−6 −4 −2 0 2 4 6

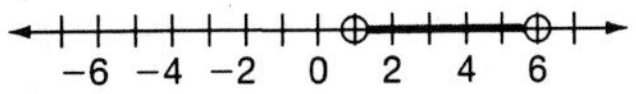

29. $-2 > x + 3$ or $x + 6 \ge 7$

$-5 > x$ or $x \ge 1$

−6 −4 −2 0 2 4 6

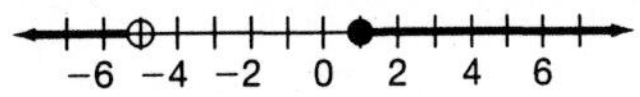

30. $-3x > 9$ or $2x - 5 > -3$
$x < -3$ or $2x > 2$
$x > 1$

−6 −4 −2 0 2 4 6

31. $2x + 3 > -7$ and $2x + 3 \leq 7$
$2x > -10$ and $2x \leq 4$
$x > -5$ and $x \leq 2$
$-5 < x \leq 2$

−6 −4 −2 0 2 4 6

MIXED PRACTICE 18

p. 635

1. $|y + 1| < 6$
$y + 1 < 6$ and $y + 1 > -6$
$y < 5$ and $y > -7$
$-7 < y < 5$

−10 −8 −6 −4 −2 0 2 4 6 8 10

2. $|3x| > 6$
$3x > 6$ or $3x < -6$
$x > 2$ or $x < -2$

−10 −8 −6 −4 −2 0 2 4 6 8 10

3. $|x - 4| > 2$
$x - 4 > 2$ or $x - 4 < -2$
$x > 6$ or $x < 2$

−10 −8 −6 −4 −2 0 2 4 6 8 10

4. $|y + 4| = 6$
$y + 4 = 6$ or $y + 4 = -6$
$y = 2$ or $y = -10$

5. $|2x + 1| = -5$
Absolute value is always ≥ 0, so no solution.

6. $|2x + 1| > 3$
$2x + 1 > 3$ or $2x + 1 < -3$
$2x > 2$ or $2x < -4$
$x > 1$ or $x < -2$
$\{x|x > 1$ or $x < -2\}$

7. $4|3y| > 20$
$|3y| > 5$
$3y > 5$ or $3y < -5$
$y > \frac{5}{3}$ or $y < -\frac{5}{3}$
$\left\{y \middle| y > \frac{5}{3} \text{ or } y < -\frac{5}{3}\right\}$

8. $2|3x| < 20$
$|3x| < 10$
$3x < 10$ and $3x > -10$
$x < \frac{10}{3}$ and $x > -\frac{10}{3}$
$\left\{x \middle| -\frac{10}{3} < x < \frac{10}{3}\right\}$

9. $|3y - 2| < 7$
$3y - 2 < 7$ and $3y - 2 > -7$
$3y < 9$ and $3y > -5$
$y < 3$ and $y > -\frac{5}{3}$
$\left\{y \middle| -\frac{5}{3} < y < 3\right\}$

10. $|3x + 2| < -3$
Absolute value is always ≥ 0, so no solution.

11. $2|-3x| = 24$
$|-3x| = 12$
$-3x = 12$ or $-3x = -12$
$x = -4$ or $x = 4$
$\{-4, 4\}$

12. $|2x - 7| = 21$
$2x - 7 = 21$ or $2x - 7 = -21$
$2x = 28$ or $2x = -14$
$x = 14$ or $x = -7$
$\{-7, 14\}$

13. $-2|x - 3| < -8$
$|x - 3| > 4$
$x - 3 > 4$ or $x - 3 < -4$
$x > 7$ or $x < -4$
$\{x|x > 7$ or $x < -1\}$

14. $|2a + 5| < 1$
$2a + 5 < 1$ and $2a + 5 > -1$
$2a < -4$ and $2a > -6$
$a < -2$ and $a > -3$
$\{a|-3 < a < -2\}$

15. $|3x + 1.5| = 5.7$
$3x + 1.5 = 5.7$ or $3x + 1.5 = -5.7$
$3x = 4.2$ or $3x = -7.2$
$x = 1.4$ or $x = -2.4$
$\{1.4, -2.4\}$

16.

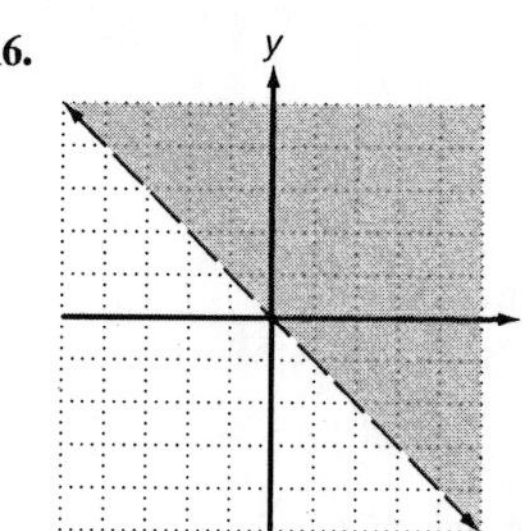

17.

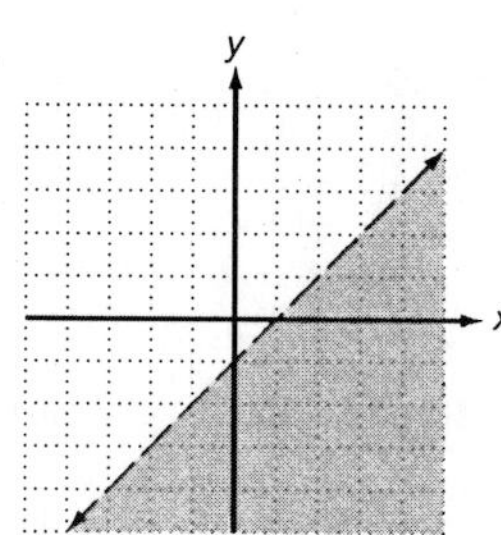

18.

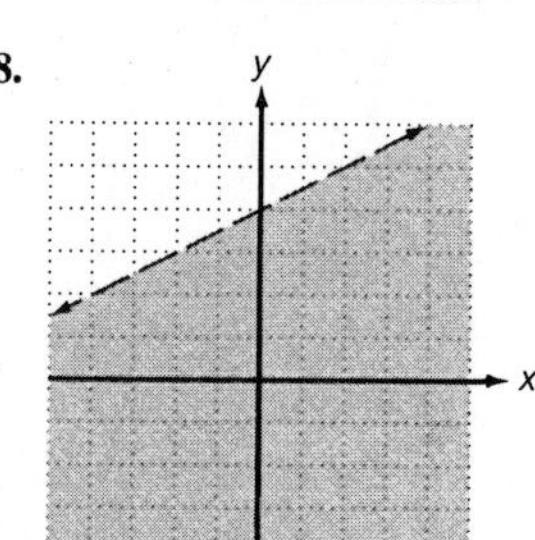

19. $2(1) - 3 > 5$
$2 - 3 > 5$
$-1 > 5$
No

20. $2(-2) + 3(3) \geq 5$
$-4 + 9 \geq 5$
$5 \geq 5$
Yes

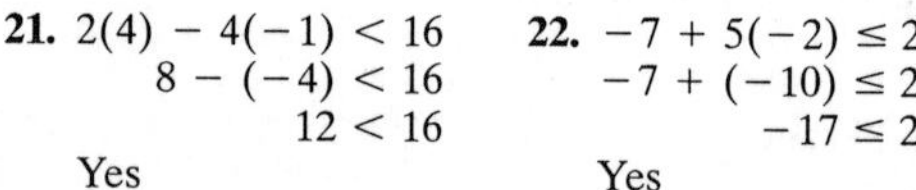

21. $2(4) - 4(-1) < 16$
$8 - (-4) < 16$
$12 < 16$
Yes

22. $-7 + 5(-2) \leq 2$
$-7 + (-10) \leq 2$
$-17 \leq 2$
Yes

23.

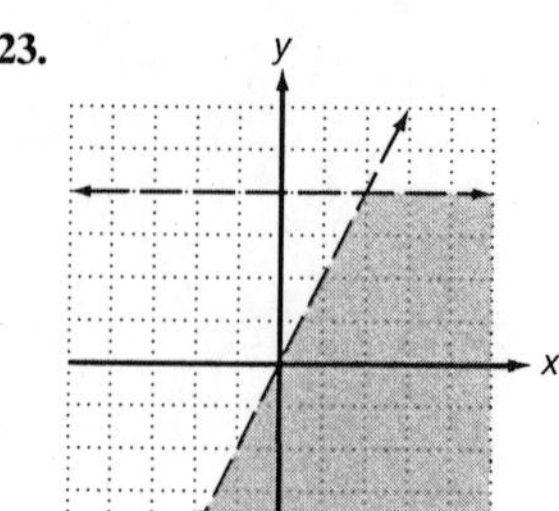

24.

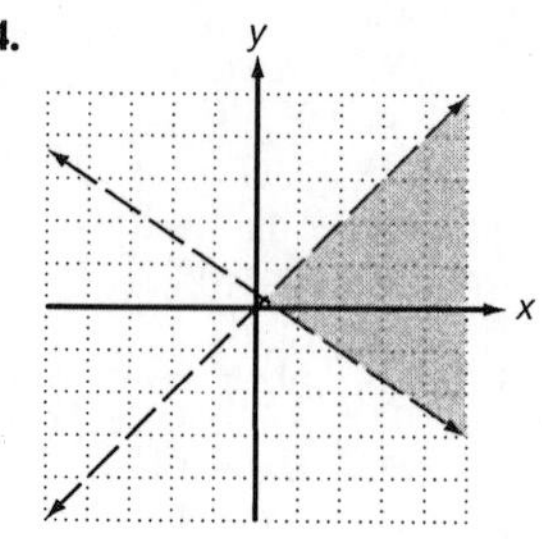

25.

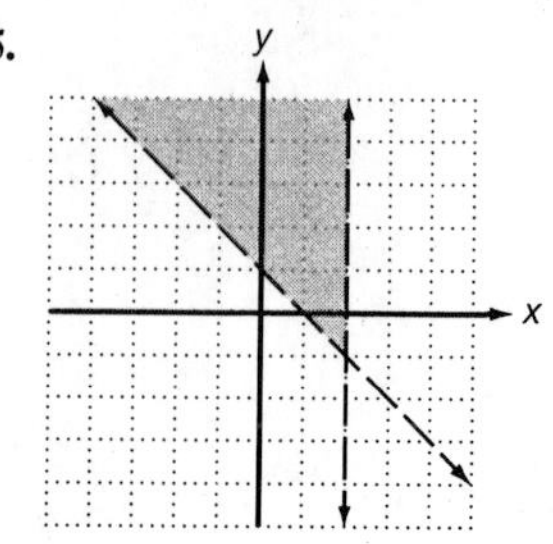

26. $y > -\frac{1}{2}x + 1$ **27.** $y < 3x + 3$ **28.** $y > x + 2$

29. $y \geq x - 1$ **30.** $y < 2$ **31.** $y < \frac{1}{2}x + 2$

$y > -x + 2$ $y > -x$ $y \leq -x - 2$

MIXED PRACTICE 19 p. 636

1. $\frac{x^2 - 2x - 3}{x^2 - 5x + 6} = \frac{(x - 3)(x + 1)}{(x - 3)(x - 2)} = \frac{x + 1}{x - 2}$

2. $\frac{25x^2 - 9}{5x + 3} = \frac{(5x + 3)(5x - 3)}{(5x + 3)1} = \frac{5x - 3}{1} = 5x - 3$

3. $\frac{5x^2 - 5}{10x^2 - 10} = \frac{1(5x^2 - 5)}{2(5x^2 - 5)} = \frac{1}{2}$

4. $\frac{2y^2 + 5y - 7}{2y + 7} = \frac{(2y + 7)(y - 1)}{(2y + 7)1} = \frac{y - 1}{1} = y - 1$

5. $\frac{16 - a}{a - 16} = \frac{-1(a - 16)}{a - 16} = -1$

6. $\frac{2x^2 - 6x}{2x^2 + 2x} = \frac{2x(x - 3)}{2(x + 1)} = \frac{x - 3}{x + 1}$

7. $\frac{2x + 9}{x + 7} + \frac{x + 12}{x + 7} = \frac{3x + 21}{x + 7} = \frac{3(x + 7)}{x + 7} = 3$

8. $\frac{7x + 9}{3x + 2} - \frac{7x + 6}{3x + 2} = \frac{3}{3x + 2}$

9. $\frac{3y + 1}{y - 3} - \frac{2y - 4}{y - 3} = \frac{y + 5}{y - 3}$

10. $\frac{3}{y} - \frac{y + 4}{y^2}$ LCM $= y^2$

$= \frac{y}{y} \cdot \frac{3}{y} - \frac{y + 4}{y^2} = \frac{3y}{y^2} - \frac{y + 4}{y^2} = \frac{2y - 4}{y^2} = \frac{2(y - 2)}{y^2}$

11. $\frac{3a}{a + 2} + \frac{12a}{a^2 - 4}$ LCM $= a^2 - 4$

$\frac{a - 2}{a - 2} \cdot \frac{3a}{a + 2} + \frac{12a}{a^2 - 4} = \frac{3a^2 - 6a}{a^2 - 4} + \frac{12a}{a^2 - 4}$

$= \frac{3a^2 + 6a}{a^2 - 4} = \frac{3a(a + 2)}{(a + 2)(a - 2)} = \frac{3a}{a - 2}$

12. $\frac{3m + 7}{4m} - \frac{4m + 11}{8m}$ LCM $= 2$

$= \frac{2}{2} \cdot \frac{3m + 7}{4m} - \frac{4m + 11}{8m} = \frac{6m + 14}{8m} - \frac{4m + 11}{8m} = \frac{2m + 3}{8m}$

13. $\frac{2 - x}{x^2 - 7x + 10} + \frac{x - 4}{x - 5}$ LCM $= x^2 - 7x + 10$

$= \frac{2 - x}{x^2 - 7x + 10} + \frac{x - 2}{x - 2} \cdot \frac{x - 4}{x - 5}$

$= \frac{2 - x}{x^2 - 7x + 10} + \frac{x^2 - 6x + 8}{x^2 - 7x + 10}$

$= \frac{x^2 - 7x + 10}{x^2 - 7x + 10} = 1$

14. $\frac{x}{x + 1} - \frac{1}{x - 1}$ LCM $= (x + 1)(x - 1)$

$= \frac{x - 1}{x - 1} \cdot \frac{x}{x + 1} - \frac{x + 1}{x + 1} \cdot \frac{1}{x - 1} = \frac{x^2 - x}{x^2 - 1} - \frac{x + 1}{x^2 - 1}$

$= \frac{x^2 - 2x - 1}{x^2 - 1}$

15. $\frac{1}{x} + \frac{x + 5}{x^2}$ LCM $= x^2$

$= \frac{x}{x} \cdot \frac{1}{x} + \frac{x + 5}{x^2} = \frac{x}{x^2} + \frac{x + 5}{x^2} = \frac{2x + 5}{x^2}$

16. $\frac{x^2}{x^2 - 1} - \frac{1}{x - 1}$ LCM $= x^2 - 1$

$= \frac{x^2}{x^2 - 1} - \frac{x - 1}{x - 1} \cdot \frac{1}{x + 1} = \frac{x^2}{x^2 - 1} - \frac{x - 1}{x^2 - 1} = \frac{x^2 - x + 1}{x^2 - 1}$

17. $\frac{x + 4}{2} + \frac{x + 4}{x}$ LCM $= 2x$

$= \frac{x}{x} \cdot \frac{x + 4}{2} + \frac{2}{2} \cdot \frac{x + 4}{x} = \frac{x^2 + 4x}{2x} + \frac{2x + 8}{2x}$

$= \frac{x^2 + 6x + 8}{2x} = \frac{(x + 4)(x + 2)}{2x}$

18. $\frac{a + 1}{a - 1} + \frac{a - 1}{a + 1}$ LCM $= (a - 1)(a + 1)$

$= \frac{a + 1}{a + 1} \cdot \frac{a + 1}{a - 1} + \frac{a - 1}{a - 1} \cdot \frac{a - 1}{a + 1}$

$= \frac{a^2 + 2a + 1}{a^2 - 1} + \frac{a^2 - 2a + 1}{a^2 - 1} = \frac{2a^2 + 2}{a^2 - 1} = \frac{2(a^2 + 1)}{a^2 - 1}$

19. $\frac{3}{2(x - 1)} \cdot \frac{4}{3(x - 1)} = \frac{12}{6(x - 1)^2} = \frac{2}{(x - 1)^2}$

20. $\frac{x^2 - 1}{x^2 - 4} \cdot \frac{x + 2}{x + 1} = \frac{(x + 1)(x - 1)(x + 2)}{(x + 2)(x - 2)(x + 1)} = \frac{x - 1}{x - 2}$

21. $\frac{m}{m + 1} \cdot \frac{m^2 - m - 2}{m^2 + m} = \frac{m(m - 2)(m + 1)}{(m + 1)(m + 1)m} = \frac{m - 2}{m + 1}$

22. $\frac{6x^2}{6x^2 + 9x + 3} \cdot \frac{6x + 3}{2x} = \frac{18x^2(2x + 1)}{6x(2x^2 + 3x + 1)}$

$= \frac{6x \cdot 3x(2x + 1)}{6x(2x + 1)(x + 1)} = \frac{3x}{x + 1}$

23. $\frac{mn + n^2}{m} \div \frac{m^2 - n^2}{mn^2} = \frac{n(m + n)}{m} \cdot \frac{mn^2}{(m + n)(m - n)}$

$= \frac{mn^3(m + n)}{m(m + n)(m - n)} = \frac{n^3}{m - n}$

24. $\frac{x^2 - x - 12}{x + 2} \div \frac{(x - 4)^2}{x + 2} = \frac{(x - 4)(x + 3)}{x + 2} \cdot \frac{x + 2}{(x - 4)^2}$

$= \frac{(x - 4)(x + 3)(x + 2)}{(x + 2)(x - 4)^2} = \frac{x + 3}{x - 4}$

25. $\frac{x^2 - 3x - 10}{x^2 + 2x - 15} \cdot \frac{x^2 + 8x + 15}{x^2 - 7x + 10}$

$= \frac{(x - 5)(x + 2)(x + 5)(x + 3)}{(x + 5)(x - 3)(x - 5)(x - 2)}$

$= \frac{(x + 2)(x + 3)}{(x - 2)(x - 3)}$

26. $\frac{x^2 - 4x}{x + 1} \div \frac{x^2 - 16}{x^2 - 1} = \frac{x(x - 4)}{x + 1} \cdot \frac{(x + 1)(x - 1)}{(x + 4)(x - 4)}$

$= \frac{x(x - 4)(x + 1)(x - 1)}{(x + 1)(x + 4)(x - 4)} = \frac{x(x - 1)}{x + 4}$

27. $\frac{x^2 - 9}{x + 5} \div \frac{x + 3}{x^2 + 2x - 15}$

$= \frac{(x + 3)(x - 3)}{x + 5} \cdot \frac{(x + 5)(x - 3)}{x + 3}$

$= \frac{(x - 3)^2(x + 3)(x + 5)}{(x + 5)(x + 3)} = (x - 3)^2$

28. $\frac{a^2 + 6a + 9}{a - 3} \div \frac{a^2 + 4a + 3}{a + 1}$

$= \frac{(a + 3)^2}{a - 3} \cdot \frac{a + 1}{(a + 3)(a + 1)}$

$= \frac{(a + 3)^2(a + 1)}{(a - 3)(a + 3)(a + 1)} = \frac{a + 3}{a - 3}$

29. $\frac{x^2 - 4}{x + 1} \div \frac{x + 2}{x - 2} = \frac{(x + 2)(x - 2)}{x + 1} \cdot \frac{x - 2}{x + 2}$

$= \frac{(x + 2)(x - 2)^2}{(x + 1)(x + 2)} = \frac{(x - 2)^2}{x + 1}$

30. $\frac{m - 1}{5} \div \frac{m^2 - 2m + 1}{m^2 + 2m - 3} = \frac{m - 1}{5} \cdot \frac{(m + 3)(m - 1)}{(m - 1)^2}$

$= \frac{(m - 1)^2(m + 3)}{5(m - 1)^2} = \frac{m + 3}{5}$

31. $\dfrac{2}{x^2 + 4x + 4} \cdot \dfrac{x + 2}{x - 2} = \dfrac{2(x + 2)}{(x + 2)^2(x - 2)} = \dfrac{2}{(x + 2)(x - 2)}$

32. $2x - 3 = 2x - 3$
$4x^2 - 9 = (2x - 3)(2x + 3)$
$\text{LCM} = (2x - 3)(2x + 3)$

33. $x^2 - 5x + 6 = (x - 3)(x - 2)$
$x^2 - 6x + 9 = (x - 3)^2$
$\text{LCM} = (x - 2)(x - 3)^2$

34. $x^2 - 16 = (x + 4)(x - 4)$
$2x + 8 = 2(x + 4)$
$\text{LCM} = 2(x + 4)(x - 4)$

35. $10 - 2a = -2(a - 5)$
$a^2 - 25 = (a - 5)(a + 5)$
$\text{LCM} = 2(a - 5)(a + 5)$

36. $24a^3b = 2^3 \cdot 3 \cdot a^3 \cdot b$
$18abc = 2 \cdot 3^2 \cdot a \cdot b \cdot c$
$\text{LCM} = 2^3 \cdot 3^2 \cdot a^3 \cdot b \cdot c = 72a^3bc$

37. $x^2 - 1 = (x + 1)(x - 1)$
$x^2 - 3x + 2 = (x - 2)(x - 1)$
$x^2 + x - 6 = (x + 3)(x - 2)$
$\text{LCM} = (x + 1)(x - 1)(x - 2)(x + 3)$

MIXED PRACTICE 20 p. 637

1. $\dfrac{x + 2}{x - 2} = x - 1 \qquad \text{LCM} = x - 2$

$(x - 2) \cdot \dfrac{x + 2}{x - 2} = (x - 2)(x - 1)$

$x + 2 = x^2 - 3x + 2$
$x^2 - 4x = 0$
$x(x - 4) = 0$
$x = 0 \quad \text{or} \quad x - 4 = 0$
$x = 0 \quad \text{or} \quad x = 4$

2. $\dfrac{x + 6}{x + 2} = \dfrac{x}{x - 1} \qquad \text{LCM} = (x + 2)(x - 1)$

$(x + 2)(x - 1) \cdot \dfrac{x + 6}{x + 2} = (x + 2)(x - 1) \cdot \dfrac{x}{x - 1}$

$(x - 1)(x + 6) = x(x + 2)$
$x^2 + 5x - 6 = x^2 + 2x$
$3x - 6 = 0$
$3x = 6$
$x = 2$

3. $\dfrac{4x - 5}{2x + 1} + \dfrac{x + 1}{x - 1} = 3 \qquad \text{LCM} = (2x + 1)(x - 1)$

$(2x + 1)(x - 1) \cdot \dfrac{4x - 5}{2x + 1} + (2x + 1)(x - 1) \cdot \dfrac{x + 1}{x - 1}$
$= 3(2x + 1)(x - 1)$
$(x - 1)(4x - 5) + (2x + 1)(x + 1) = 3(2x^2 - x - 1)$
$4x^2 - 9x + 5 + 2x^2 + 3x + 1 = 6x^2 - 3x - 3$
$6x^2 - 6x + 6 = 6x^2 - 3x - 3$
$-3x = -9$
$x = 3$

4. $2a - 1 = \dfrac{8a + 3}{a + 1} \qquad \text{LCM} = a + 1$

$(a + 1)(2a - 1) = (a + 1) \cdot \dfrac{8a + 3}{a + 1}$

$2a^2 + a - 1 = 8a + 3$
$2a^2 - 7a - 4 = 0$
$(2a + 1)(a - 4) = 0$
$2a + 1 = 0 \quad \text{or} \quad a - 4 = 0$
$2a = -1 \quad \text{or} \quad a = 4$
$a = -\dfrac{1}{2} \quad \text{or} \quad a = 4$

5. $0.28x + 0.48(250 - x) = 0.35(250)$
$0.28x + 120 - 0.48x = 87.5$
$-0.2x = -32.5$
$x = 162.5$
162.5 lb of mixture A and 87.5 lb of mixture B should be used.

6. $\dfrac{1}{x + 2} = \dfrac{3}{4} \cdot \dfrac{1}{x} \qquad \text{LCM} = 4x(x + 2)$

$4x(x + 2) \cdot \dfrac{1}{x + 2} = 4x(x + 2) \cdot \dfrac{3}{4x}$

$4x = 3(x + 2)$
$4x = 3x + 6$
$x = 6$
The number is 6.

7. $\dfrac{1}{8} + \dfrac{1}{12} = \dfrac{1}{t}$

$\dfrac{3}{24} + \dfrac{2}{24} = \dfrac{1}{t}$

$\dfrac{5}{24} = \dfrac{1}{t}$

$t = \dfrac{24}{5} \quad \text{or} \quad 4.8$

It would take them 4.8 hours.

8. $\dfrac{270}{r} = \dfrac{270}{r + 15} + 1.5 \qquad \text{LCM} = \text{r}(\text{r} + 15)$

$r(r + 15) \cdot \dfrac{270}{r} = r(r + 15) \cdot \dfrac{270}{r + 15} + r(r + 15) \cdot 1.5$

$270(r + 15) = 270r + 1.5r(r + 15)$
$270r + 4050 = 270r + 1.5r^2 + 22.5r$
$0 = 1.5r^2 + 22.5r - 4050$
$0 = r^2 + 15t - 2700$
$0 = (r + 60)(r - 45)$
$r + 60 = 0 \quad \text{or} \quad r - 45 = 0$
$r = -60 \quad \text{or} \quad r = 45$
Speed can't be negative, so the speed going was 45 mi/h.

9. $\dfrac{1}{x - 5} = 4 \cdot \dfrac{1}{2x}$

$2x(x - 5) \cdot \dfrac{1}{x - 5} = 2x(x - 5) \cdot \dfrac{4}{2x}$

$2x = 4(x - 5)$
$2x = 4x - 20$
$-2x = -20$
$x = 10$
The number is 10.

10. $\dfrac{3x^4 - 27x^3 + 3x^2}{3x^2} = \dfrac{3x^4}{3x^2} - \dfrac{27x^3}{3x^2} + \dfrac{3x^2}{3x^2} = x^2 - 9x + 1$

11.
$$\begin{array}{r} 4x^2 - 1 \\ 4x + 1\overline{)16x^3 + 4x^2 - 4x - 1} \\ \underline{16x^3 + 4x^2} \qquad\quad\;\; \\ -4x - 1 \\ \underline{-4x - 1} \end{array}$$

12.
$$\begin{array}{r} x + 7 - \dfrac{3}{x - 3} \\ x - 3\overline{)x^2 + 4x - 24} \qquad \\ \underline{x^2 - 3x} \qquad\qquad\quad \\ 7x - 24 \qquad \\ \underline{7x - 21} \qquad \\ -3 \qquad \end{array}$$

13.
$$\begin{array}{r} 5a - 4 \\ 2a + 3\overline{)10a^2 + 7a - 12} \\ \underline{10a^2 + 15a} \qquad \\ -8a - 12 \\ \underline{-8a - 12} \end{array}$$

14.
$$\begin{array}{r} 2x^2 + 5 \\ x^2 - 3\overline{)2x^4 - x^2 - 15} \\ \underline{2x^4 - 6x^2} \qquad\; \\ 5x^2 - 15 \\ \underline{5x^2 - 15} \end{array}$$

15.
$$\begin{array}{r} y^3 + y^2 - 3y - 3 \\ y - 1\overline{)y^4 \qquad - 4y^2 \qquad + 3} \\ \underline{y^4 - y^3} \qquad\qquad\qquad\qquad \\ y^3 - 4y^2 \qquad + 3 \\ \underline{y^3 - y^2} \qquad\qquad\quad \\ -3y^2 \qquad + 3 \\ \underline{-3y^2 + 3y} \qquad\; \\ -3y + 3 \\ \underline{-3y + 3} \end{array}$$

16. $\dfrac{\dfrac{x}{(3x-1)(x-y)}}{\dfrac{y}{(x-y)}} \cdot \dfrac{(3x-1)(x-y)}{(3x-1)(x-y)} = \dfrac{x}{y(3x-1)}$

17. $\dfrac{\dfrac{x(y-3)}{y}}{\dfrac{y-3}{x}} \cdot \dfrac{xy}{xy} = \dfrac{x^2(y-3)}{y(y-3)} = \dfrac{x^2}{y}$

18. $\dfrac{\dfrac{1}{m}+\dfrac{1}{n}}{\dfrac{1}{m}-\dfrac{1}{n}} \cdot \dfrac{mn}{mn} = \dfrac{n+m}{n-m}$

19. $\dfrac{1-\dfrac{1}{a^2}}{1-\dfrac{1}{a}} \cdot \dfrac{a^2}{a^2} = \dfrac{a^2-1}{a^2-a} = \dfrac{(a+1)(a-1)}{a(a-1)} = \dfrac{a+1}{a}$

20. $\dfrac{\dfrac{x^2}{x^2-y^2}}{\dfrac{x}{x+y}} \cdot \dfrac{x^2-y^2}{x^2-y^2} = \dfrac{x^2}{x(x-y)} = \dfrac{x}{x-y}$

21. $\dfrac{\dfrac{x}{2}-\dfrac{y}{3}}{\dfrac{2}{x}-\dfrac{3}{y}} \cdot \dfrac{6xy}{6xy} = \dfrac{3x^2y-2xy^2}{12y-18x} = \dfrac{xy(3x-2y)}{6(2y-3x)} = -\dfrac{xy}{6}$

MIXED PRACTICE 21 p. 638

1. $\sqrt{169} = 13$ 2. $-\sqrt{49} = -7$

3. $\sqrt{6^2+8^2} = \sqrt{36+64} = \sqrt{100} = 10$

4. $\sqrt{(6+8)^2} = \sqrt{14^2} = 14$

5. $\sqrt{m^2n^2} = mn$ 6. $\sqrt{25y^4} = 5y^2$

7. $\sqrt{(-2x)^2} = \sqrt{4x^2} = 2x$

8. $\sqrt{x^2-6x+9} = \sqrt{(x-3)^2} = x-3$

9. $\sqrt{9y^3} = 3y\sqrt{y}$ 10. $\sqrt{(x-2)^5} = (x-2)^2\sqrt{(x-2)}$

11. $2\sqrt{49m^3} = 14m\sqrt{m}$ 12. $\sqrt{75x^5y^2} = 5x^2y\sqrt{3x}$

13. $\sqrt{\dfrac{y^2}{100}} = \dfrac{y}{10}$ 14. $\sqrt{\dfrac{9m^4}{25n^6}} = \dfrac{3m^2}{5n^3}$

15. $\sqrt{\dfrac{36x^2}{49}} = \dfrac{6x}{7}$ 16. $\sqrt{\dfrac{x^2-8x+16}{x^2-2x+1}} = \sqrt{\dfrac{(x-4)^2}{(x-1)^2}} = \dfrac{x-4}{x-1}$

17. $5y \geq 0$
$y \geq 0$

18. $2x-1 \geq 0$
$2x \geq 1$
$x \geq \dfrac{1}{2}$

19. $2x-10 \geq 0$
$2x \geq 10$
$x \geq 5$

20. $2x^2 \geq 0$
$x^2 \geq 0$
Any value

21. $x^2+17 \geq 0$
$x^2 \geq -17$
Any value

22. $x+5 \geq 0$
$x \geq -5$

23. $\sqrt{25}\cdot\sqrt{32} = \sqrt{25\cdot 32}$
$= \sqrt{25\cdot 16\cdot 2}$
$= \sqrt{25}\cdot\sqrt{16}\cdot\sqrt{2}$
$= 20\sqrt{2}$

24. $\sqrt{14}\cdot\sqrt{2} = \sqrt{14\cdot 2}$
$= \sqrt{7\cdot 2\cdot 2}$
$= \sqrt{7}\cdot\sqrt{4}$
$= 2\sqrt{7}$

25. $\sqrt{5a}\cdot\sqrt{5ab} = \sqrt{5a\cdot 5ab}$
$= \sqrt{5a\cdot 5a}\cdot\sqrt{b}$
$= 5|a|\sqrt{b}$

26. $\sqrt{3}\cdot\sqrt{3}\cdot\sqrt{3} = \sqrt{3\cdot 3\cdot 3}$
$= \sqrt{3\cdot 3}\cdot\sqrt{3}$
$= 3\sqrt{3}$

27. $\sqrt{2x^2}\cdot\sqrt{2y} = \sqrt{2x^2\cdot 2y}$
$= \sqrt{2\cdot 2}\cdot\sqrt{x^2}\cdot\sqrt{y}$
$= 2|x|\sqrt{y}$

28. $\sqrt{8m}\cdot\sqrt{2m} = \sqrt{8m\cdot 2m}$
$= \sqrt{16}\cdot\sqrt{m^2}$
$= 4|m|$

29. $\sqrt{30b}\cdot\sqrt{2bc} = \sqrt{30b\cdot 2bc}$
$= \sqrt{4b^2}\cdot\sqrt{15c}$
$= 2|b|\sqrt{15c}$

30. $\sqrt{2}(\sqrt{2}-2) = \sqrt{2}\cdot\sqrt{2} - 2\sqrt{2}$
$= 2 - 2\sqrt{2}$

31. $\sqrt{15}\cdot\sqrt{45a^3} = \sqrt{15\cdot 45a^3}$
$= \sqrt{15\cdot 15\cdot 3a^3}$
$= \sqrt{15\cdot 15}\cdot\sqrt{a^2}\cdot\sqrt{3a}$
$= 15|a|\sqrt{3a}$

32. $\sqrt{12xy}\cdot\sqrt{18xyz} = \sqrt{12xy\cdot 18xyz}$
$= \sqrt{6\cdot 6\cdot 6\cdot x^2y^2z}$
$= \sqrt{6\cdot 6}\cdot\sqrt{x^2y^2}\cdot\sqrt{6z}$
$= 6|xy|\sqrt{6z}$

33. $\sqrt{10^2}\cdot\sqrt{x^{31}} = \sqrt{10^2\cdot x^{31}}$
$= \sqrt{10^2\cdot x^{30}\cdot x}$
$= 10|x^{15}|\sqrt{x}$

34. $\sqrt{8y^2}\cdot\sqrt{2y^3}\cdot\sqrt{12y^9} = \sqrt{8y^2\cdot 2y^3\cdot 12y^9}$
$= \sqrt{2^6\cdot 3\cdot y^{14}}$
$= 2^3|y^7|\sqrt{3} = 8|y^7|\sqrt{3}$

35. $\sqrt{512x^{315}} = \sqrt{256\cdot 2\cdot x^{314}\cdot x}$
$= 16x^{157}\sqrt{2x}$

36. $\sqrt{1500(x+1)^3} = \sqrt{100\cdot 15\cdot (x+1)^3}$
$= 10(x+1)\sqrt{15(x+1)}$

37. $\sqrt{25(x^4-1)^2} = 5(x^4-1)$

38. $\sqrt{9w^{32}} = 3w^{16}$

39. $\sqrt{18m^4n^5} = \sqrt{2\cdot 9m^4n^5}$
$= 3m^2n^2\sqrt{2n}$

40. $3a\sqrt{18a^3} = 3a\sqrt{2\cdot 9\cdot a^3}$
$= 3a\cdot 3a\sqrt{2a}$
$= (3a)^2\sqrt{2a}$ or $9a^2\sqrt{2a}$

41. $\sqrt{4x^2-40x+100} = \sqrt{4(x^2-10x+25)}$
$= \sqrt{4(x-5)^2}$
$= 2(x-5)$

42. $\sqrt{8x^2+16x+8} = \sqrt{8(x^2+2x+1)}$
$= \sqrt{2^3(x+1)^2}$
$= 2(x+1)\sqrt{2}$

43. $\sqrt{25x^2+50xy+25y^2} = \sqrt{25(x^2+2xy+y^2)}$
$= \sqrt{5^2(x+y)^2}$
$= 5(x+y)$

44. $\sqrt{\dfrac{100}{25}} = \dfrac{10}{5} = 2$

45. $\sqrt{\dfrac{50}{6}} = \sqrt{\dfrac{25}{3}\cdot\dfrac{2}{2}} = \sqrt{\dfrac{25}{3}} = \dfrac{5}{\sqrt{3}}\cdot\dfrac{\sqrt{3}}{\sqrt{3}} = \dfrac{5\sqrt{3}}{3}$

46. $\sqrt{\dfrac{y^7}{xy}} = \sqrt{\dfrac{y^6}{x}\cdot\dfrac{y}{y}} = \sqrt{\dfrac{y^6}{x}} = \dfrac{y^3}{\sqrt{x}}\cdot\dfrac{\sqrt{x}}{\sqrt{x}} = \dfrac{y^3\sqrt{x}}{x}$

47. $\sqrt{\dfrac{x^2y}{28}} = \dfrac{x\sqrt{y}}{2\sqrt{7}}\cdot\dfrac{\sqrt{7}}{\sqrt{7}} = \dfrac{x\sqrt{7y}}{14}$

48. $\sqrt{\dfrac{y^7}{x^3}} = \dfrac{y^3\sqrt{y}}{x\sqrt{x}}\cdot\dfrac{\sqrt{x}}{\sqrt{x}} = \dfrac{y^3\sqrt{xy}}{x^2}$

49. $\sqrt{\dfrac{48}{84}} = \sqrt{\dfrac{3\cdot 4\cdot 4}{3\cdot 4\cdot 7}} = \sqrt{\dfrac{4}{7}} = \dfrac{2}{\sqrt{7}}\cdot\dfrac{\sqrt{7}}{\sqrt{7}} = \dfrac{2\sqrt{7}}{7}$

50. $\sqrt{\dfrac{1}{256}} = \dfrac{1}{16}$

51. $\sqrt{\dfrac{75}{63}} = \sqrt{\dfrac{3\cdot 5\cdot 5}{3\cdot 3\cdot 7}} = \dfrac{5\sqrt{3}}{3\sqrt{7}}\cdot\dfrac{\sqrt{7}}{\sqrt{7}} = \dfrac{5\sqrt{21}}{21}$

52. $\dfrac{\sqrt{36x^3}}{\sqrt{6x}} = \sqrt{\dfrac{36x^3}{6x}} = \sqrt{\dfrac{6x \cdot 6x^2}{6x \cdot 1}} = \sqrt{6x^2} = |x|\sqrt{6}$

53. $\dfrac{\sqrt{48m^5}}{\sqrt{12m^2}} = \sqrt{\dfrac{48m^5}{12m^2}} = \sqrt{\dfrac{12m^2 \cdot 4m^3}{12m^2 \cdot 1}} = \sqrt{4m^3} = 2|m|\sqrt{m}$

54. $\dfrac{\sqrt{72}}{\sqrt{200}} = \sqrt{\dfrac{72}{200}} = \sqrt{\dfrac{36 \cdot 2}{700 \cdot 2}} = \sqrt{\dfrac{36}{100}} = \dfrac{6}{10} = \dfrac{3}{5}$

55. $\dfrac{\sqrt{7}}{\sqrt{252}} = \sqrt{\dfrac{7}{252}} = \sqrt{\dfrac{7 \cdot 1}{7 \cdot 36}} = \sqrt{\dfrac{1}{36}} = \dfrac{1}{6}$

56. $\dfrac{\sqrt{50x^3}}{\sqrt{2x}} = \sqrt{\dfrac{50x^3}{2x}} = \sqrt{\dfrac{2x \cdot 25x^2}{2x \cdot 1}} = \sqrt{25x^2} = 5|x|$

57. $\dfrac{\sqrt{7y^5}}{\sqrt{21y}} = \sqrt{\dfrac{7y^5}{21y}} = \sqrt{\dfrac{7y \cdot y^4}{7y \cdot 3}} = \sqrt{\dfrac{y^4}{3}} = \dfrac{y^2}{\sqrt{3}} \cdot \dfrac{\sqrt{3}}{\sqrt{3}} = \dfrac{y^2\sqrt{3}}{3}$

58. $\dfrac{\sqrt{m^2n}}{\sqrt{n^2m}} = \sqrt{\dfrac{m^2n}{n^2m}} = \sqrt{\dfrac{mn \cdot m}{mn \cdot n}} = \dfrac{\sqrt{m}}{\sqrt{n}} \cdot \dfrac{\sqrt{n}}{\sqrt{n}} = \dfrac{\sqrt{mn}}{|n|}$

59. $\dfrac{\sqrt{m^2n^2}}{\sqrt{25}} = \sqrt{\dfrac{m^2n^2}{25}} = \dfrac{|mn|}{5}$

60. $\dfrac{\sqrt{a-b}}{\sqrt{a+b}} \cdot \dfrac{\sqrt{a+b}}{\sqrt{a+b}} = \dfrac{\sqrt{a^2-b^2}}{\sqrt{a+b}}$

MIXED PRACTICE 22 p. 639

1. $\sqrt{25x} - 3\sqrt{x} = 5\sqrt{x} - 3\sqrt{x} = (5-3)\sqrt{x} = 2\sqrt{x}$

2. $\sqrt{54} - \sqrt{20} = \sqrt{9 \cdot 6} - \sqrt{4 \cdot 5} = 3\sqrt{6} - 2\sqrt{5}$

3. $\sqrt{18x+9} + \sqrt{2x+1} = \sqrt{9(2x+1)} + \sqrt{2x+1}$
$= 3\sqrt{2x+1} + \sqrt{2x+1}$
$= (3+1)\sqrt{2x+1} = 4\sqrt{2x+1}$

4. $3\sqrt{18} + 5\sqrt{12} - 3\sqrt{2} = 3\sqrt{9 \cdot 2} + 5\sqrt{4 \cdot 3} - 3\sqrt{2}$
$= 9\sqrt{2} + 10\sqrt{3} - 3\sqrt{2}$
$= (9-3)\sqrt{2} + 10\sqrt{3}$
$= 6\sqrt{2} + 10\sqrt{3}$

5. $2\sqrt{108} - 6\sqrt{3} + \sqrt{75} = 2\sqrt{36 \cdot 3} - 6\sqrt{3} + \sqrt{25 \cdot 3}$
$= 12\sqrt{3} - 6\sqrt{3} + 5\sqrt{3}$
$= (12 - 6 + 5)\sqrt{3} = 11\sqrt{3}$

6. $2\sqrt{147} + \sqrt{12} - \sqrt{432} = 2\sqrt{3 \cdot 49} - \sqrt{3 \cdot 4} - \sqrt{3 \cdot 144}$
$= 14\sqrt{3} + 2\sqrt{3} - 12\sqrt{3}$
$= (14 + 2 - 12)\sqrt{3} = 4\sqrt{3}$

7. $\sqrt{18x^5y} + \sqrt{32xy^3} - \sqrt{128xy}$
$= \sqrt{2 \cdot 9x^5y} + \sqrt{2 \cdot 16xy^3} - \sqrt{2 \cdot 64xy}$
$= 3x^2\sqrt{2xy} + 4y\sqrt{2xy} - 8\sqrt{2xy}$
$= (3x^2 + 4y - 8)\sqrt{2xy}$

8. $\sqrt{7x^4} - \sqrt{28x^2y^2} + \sqrt{7y^4}$
$= x^2\sqrt{7} - 2xy\sqrt{7} + y^2\sqrt{7}$
$= (x^2 - 2xy + y^2)\sqrt{7} = (x-y)^2\sqrt{7}$

9. $\sqrt{\dfrac{3}{8}} + \sqrt{\dfrac{2}{3}} + \sqrt{\dfrac{8}{12}} = \dfrac{\sqrt{3} \cdot \sqrt{8}}{8} + \dfrac{\sqrt{2} \cdot \sqrt{3}}{3} + \dfrac{\sqrt{2} \cdot \sqrt{3}}{3}$
$= \dfrac{\sqrt{24}}{8} + \dfrac{\sqrt{6}}{3} + \dfrac{\sqrt{6}}{3}$
$= \dfrac{2\sqrt{6}}{8} + \dfrac{\sqrt{6}}{3} + \dfrac{\sqrt{6}}{3}$
$= \left(\dfrac{1}{4} + \dfrac{2}{3}\right)\sqrt{6}$
$= \left(\dfrac{3}{12} + \dfrac{8}{12}\right)\sqrt{6} = \dfrac{11}{12}\sqrt{6}$

10. $\sqrt{\dfrac{1}{12}} - \sqrt{\dfrac{1}{8}} + \sqrt{\dfrac{3}{4}} = \dfrac{\sqrt{1} \cdot \sqrt{12}}{12} - \dfrac{\sqrt{1} \cdot \sqrt{8}}{8} + \dfrac{\sqrt{3} \cdot \sqrt{4}}{4}$
$= \dfrac{\sqrt{12}}{12} - \dfrac{\sqrt{8}}{8} + \dfrac{\sqrt{12}}{4}$
$= \dfrac{2\sqrt{3}}{12} - \dfrac{2\sqrt{2}}{8} + \dfrac{2\sqrt{3}}{4}$
$= \dfrac{\sqrt{3}}{6} - \dfrac{\sqrt{2}}{4} + \dfrac{\sqrt{3}}{2}$
$= \dfrac{2\sqrt{3}}{12} - \dfrac{3\sqrt{2}}{12} + \dfrac{6\sqrt{3}}{12}$
$= \dfrac{8\sqrt{3} - 3\sqrt{2}}{12}$

11. $\dfrac{5\sqrt{7}}{7\sqrt{5}} \cdot \dfrac{\sqrt{5}}{\sqrt{5}} = \dfrac{5\sqrt{35}}{35} = \dfrac{\sqrt{35}}{7}$

12. $\dfrac{3\sqrt{8}}{2\sqrt{2}} \cdot \dfrac{\sqrt{2}}{\sqrt{2}} = \dfrac{3\sqrt{16}}{4} = \dfrac{12}{4} = 3$

13. $\dfrac{14}{\sqrt{7}} \cdot \dfrac{\sqrt{7}}{\sqrt{7}} = \dfrac{14\sqrt{7}}{7} = 2\sqrt{7}$

14. $\dfrac{24\sqrt{3}}{18\sqrt{2}} \cdot \dfrac{\sqrt{2}}{\sqrt{2}} = \dfrac{24\sqrt{6}}{36} = \dfrac{2\sqrt{6}}{3}$

15. $\dfrac{10}{\sqrt{20}} \cdot \dfrac{\sqrt{5}}{\sqrt{5}} = \dfrac{10\sqrt{5}}{10} = \sqrt{5}$

16. $\dfrac{3\sqrt{21}}{5\sqrt{15}} \cdot \dfrac{\sqrt{15}}{\sqrt{15}} = \dfrac{3\sqrt{315}}{75} = \dfrac{3\sqrt{9 \cdot 35}}{75} = \dfrac{9\sqrt{35}}{75} = \dfrac{3\sqrt{35}}{25}$

17. $\dfrac{6\sqrt{27}}{4\sqrt{3}} \cdot \dfrac{\sqrt{3}}{\sqrt{3}} = \dfrac{6\sqrt{81}}{12} = \dfrac{54}{12} = \dfrac{9}{2}$

18. $\dfrac{5\sqrt{338}}{8\sqrt{2}} \cdot \dfrac{\sqrt{2}}{\sqrt{2}} = \dfrac{5\sqrt{676}}{16} = \dfrac{5 \cdot 26}{16} = \dfrac{130}{16} = \dfrac{65}{8}$

19. $\dfrac{2\sqrt{\frac{3}{5}}}{3\sqrt{\frac{1}{20}}} \cdot \dfrac{\sqrt{\frac{1}{20}}}{\sqrt{\frac{1}{20}}} = \dfrac{2\sqrt{\frac{3}{100}}}{\frac{3}{20}} \cdot \dfrac{\frac{2\sqrt{3}}{10}}{\frac{3}{20}} = \dfrac{4\sqrt{3}}{3}$

20. $\dfrac{\sqrt{\frac{3}{5}}}{\sqrt{\frac{5}{8}}} \cdot \dfrac{\sqrt{\frac{8}{5}}}{\sqrt{\frac{8}{5}}} = \dfrac{\frac{\sqrt{24}}{5}}{1} = \dfrac{\sqrt{24}}{5} = \dfrac{2\sqrt{6}}{5}$

21. $\dfrac{\sqrt{\frac{x}{y}}}{\sqrt{\frac{y}{x}}} \cdot \dfrac{\sqrt{\frac{x}{y}}}{\sqrt{\frac{x}{y}}} = \dfrac{\frac{x}{y}}{1} = \dfrac{x}{y}$

22. $\dfrac{\frac{3\sqrt{15}}{2}}{\frac{2\sqrt{5}}{3}} = \dfrac{3\sqrt{15}}{2} \cdot \dfrac{3}{2\sqrt{5}} = \dfrac{9\sqrt{15}}{4\sqrt{5}} \cdot \dfrac{\sqrt{5}}{\sqrt{5}} = \dfrac{9\sqrt{75}}{20} = \dfrac{45\sqrt{3}}{20} = \dfrac{9\sqrt{3}}{4}$

23. $12^2 + b^2 = 20^2$
$144 + b^2 = 400$
$b^2 = 256$
$b = \sqrt{256}$
$b = 16$

24. $8^2 + 15^2 = c^2$
$64 + 225 = c^2$
$289 = c^2$
$\sqrt{289} = c$
$17 = c$

25. $a^2 + 12^2 = 13^2$
$a^2 + 144 = 169$
$a^2 = 25$
$a = 5$

26. $a^2 + 4^2 = 5^2$
$a^2 + 16 = 25$
$a^2 = 9$
$a = 3$

27. $6^2 + b^2 = 10^2$
$36 + b^2 = 100$
$b^2 = 64$
$b = 8$

28. $16^2 + 30^2 = c^2$
$256 + 900 = c^2$
$1156 = c^2$
$34 = c$

29. $7mn\sqrt{32m^3n^2} = 7mn\sqrt{2 \cdot 16m^3n^2}$
$= 7mn \cdot 4mn\sqrt{2m}$
$= 28m^2n^2\sqrt{2m}$

30. $-5\sqrt{24} = -5\sqrt{4 \cdot 6} = -5 \cdot 2\sqrt{6} = -10\sqrt{6}$

31. $2x^2\sqrt{75xy} = 2x^2\sqrt{25 \cdot 3xy} = 2x^2 \cdot 5\sqrt{3xy} = 10x^2\sqrt{3xy}$

32. $\sqrt{27x}\cdot\sqrt{8x} = \sqrt{27x\cdot 8x}$
$= \sqrt{216x^2}$
$= \sqrt{36\cdot 6x^2} = 6x\sqrt{6}$

33. $\sqrt{10}\sqrt{3a}\sqrt{5a^3} = \sqrt{10\cdot 3a\cdot 5a^3}$
$= \sqrt{150a^4}$
$= \sqrt{25\cdot 6a^4} = 5a^2\sqrt{6}$

34. $\sqrt{x^{35}}\sqrt{10^{15}}\sqrt{10^4x^{21}} = \sqrt{x^{35}\cdot 10^{15}\cdot 10^4x^{21}}$
$= \sqrt{x^{56}\cdot 10^{19}}$
$= 10^9x^{28}\sqrt{10}$

35. $\dfrac{\sqrt{18x^3}}{\sqrt{24x}} = \sqrt{\dfrac{18x^3}{24x}} = \sqrt{\dfrac{3x^2}{4}\cdot\dfrac{4}{4}} = \dfrac{\sqrt{12x^2}}{4} = \dfrac{2x\sqrt{3}}{4} = \dfrac{x\sqrt{3}}{2}$

36. $\dfrac{\sqrt{27x^3y}}{\sqrt{48x}} = \sqrt{\dfrac{27x^3y}{48x}} = \sqrt{\dfrac{3x\cdot 9x^2y}{3x\cdot 16}} = \sqrt{\dfrac{9x^2y}{16}} = \dfrac{3x\sqrt{y}}{4}$

37. $\dfrac{\sqrt{65xy}}{\sqrt{5xy}} = \sqrt{\dfrac{65xy}{5xy}} = \sqrt{\dfrac{5xy\cdot 13}{5xy}} = \sqrt{13}$

38. $3\sqrt{2x-1} = 9$
$\sqrt{2x-1} = 3$
$(\sqrt{2x-1})^2 = 3^2$
$2x - 1 = 9$
$2x = 10$
$x = 5$

39. $2\sqrt{3y-2} = \sqrt{10y+4}$
$(2\sqrt{3y-2})^2 = (\sqrt{10y+4})^2$
$4(3y-2) = 10y + 4$
$12y - 8 = 10y + 4$
$2y = 12$
$y = 6$

40. $\sqrt{2x+20} = \sqrt{x+8}$
$(\sqrt{2x+20})^2 = (\sqrt{x+8})^2$
$2x + 20 = x + 8$
$x = -12$
No value

41. $5\sqrt{3x+7} = 2\sqrt{32x+4}$
$(5\sqrt{3x+7})^2 = (2\sqrt{32x+4})^2$
$25(3x+7) = 4(32x+4)$
$75x + 175 = 128x + 16$
$159 = 53x$
$3 = x$

42. $30^2 + 16^2 = c^2$
$900 + 256 = c^2$
$1156 = c^2$
$34 = c$
The wire must be 34 ft long.

43. $2\sqrt{x} = \frac{1}{5}x$
$\sqrt{x} = \frac{1}{10}x$
$(\sqrt{x})^2 = \left(\frac{1}{10}x\right)^2$
$x = \frac{1}{100}x^2$
$\frac{1}{100}x^2 - x = 0$
$x\left(\frac{1}{100}x - 1\right) = 0$
$x = 0$ or $\frac{1}{100}x - 1 = 0$
$\frac{1}{100}x = 1$
$x = 100$
The number is 0 or 100.

44. $9\cdot(-\sqrt{x}) = -72$
$-\sqrt{x} = -8$
$\sqrt{x} = 8$
$(\sqrt{x})^2 = 8^2$
$x = 64$
The number is 64.

MIXED PRACTICE 23

p. 640

1. Yes 2. No 3. Yes

4. $m(-4) = |-4| - 3(-4) = 4 - (-12) = 16$
$m(-2) = |-2| - 3(-2) = 2 - (-6) = 8$
$m(0) = |0| - 3(0) = 0 - 0 = 0$
$m(2) = |2| - 3(2) = 2 - 6 = -4$
$m(4) = |4| - 3(4) = 4 - 12 = -8$

5. $W(-3) = 3(-3) - 2 = -9 - 2 = -11$
$W(0) = 3(0) - 2 = 0 - 2 = -2$
$W(-1) = 3(-1) - 2 = -3 - 2 = -5$
$W(2) = 3(2) - 2 = 6 - 2 = 4$
$W(3) = 3(3) - 2 = 9 - 2 = 7$

6. $h(-5) = (-5)^2 - 4 = 25 - 4 = 21$
$h(3) = (3)^2 - 4 = 9 - 4 = 5$
$h(1) = (1)^2 - 4 = 1 - 4 = -3$
$h(-1) = (-1)^2 - 4 = 1 - 4 = -3$
$h(0) = (0)^2 - 4 = 0 - 4 = -4$

7. $f(-4) = (-4)^3 = -64$
$f(5) = (5)^3 = 125$
$f(1) = (1)^3 = 1$
$f(-1) = (-1)^3 = -1$
$f(2) = (2)^3 = 8$

8. $g(-3) = |-3| - (-3) = 3 - (-3) = 6$
$g(10) = |10| - 10 = 10 - 10 = 0$
$g(-2) = |-2| - (-2) = 2 - (-2) = 4$
$g(0) = |0| - (0) = 0 - 0 = 0$
$g(4) = |4| - 4 = 4 - 4 = 0$

9.
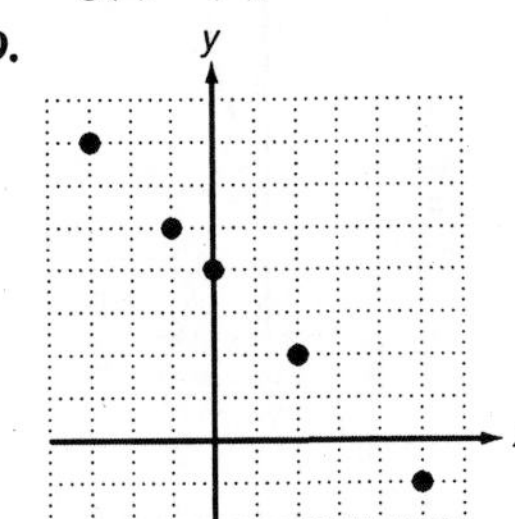

10.
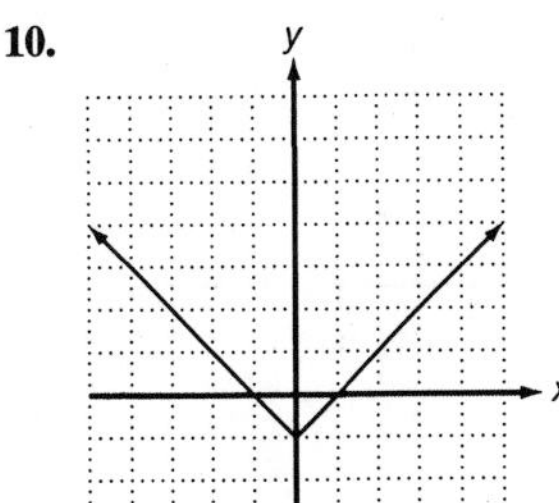

11.
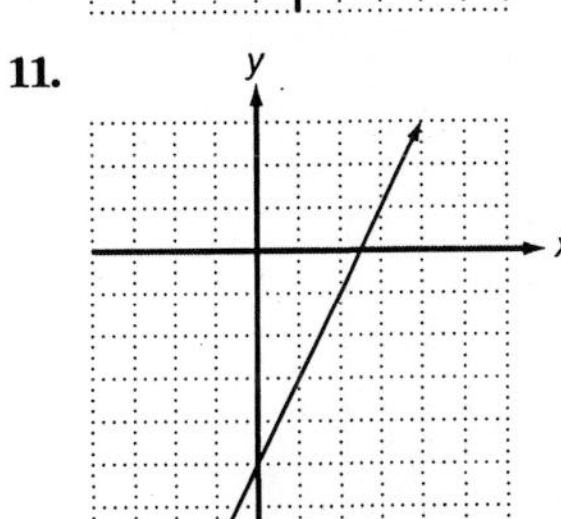

12.
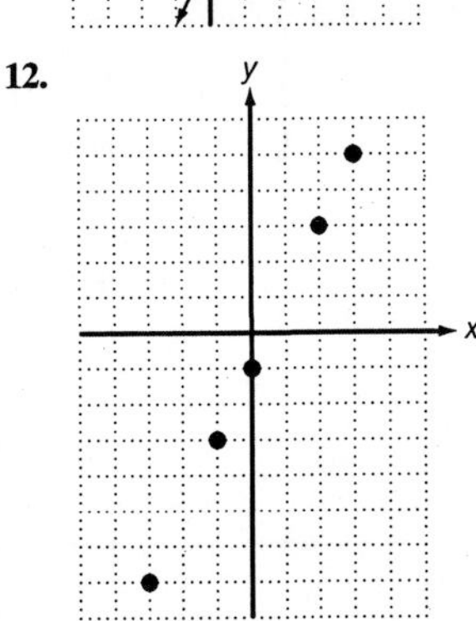

13. $f(x) = 4.15x + 3.00$
$f(14) = 4.15(14) + 3.00$
$= 58.10 + 3.00$
$= 61.10$
14 yards of flannel costs \$61.10.

14. $2285 = 180(12) + r$
$2285 = 2160 + r$
$125 = r$
The registration fee is \$125.
$f(x) = 180x + 125$
$f(14) = 180(14) + 125$
$= 2520 + 125$
$= 2645$
She will have to pay \$2645.

15. $f(c, l) = 40c + 5.50l$
$f(3, 16) = 40(3) + 5.50(16)$
$= 120 + 88$
$= 208$
The banner cost \$208.
$125 > 40(2) + 5.50(l)$
$125 > 80 + 5.50l$
$45 > 5.50l$
$8.\overline{18} > l$
You can have 8 letters.

16. $y = x^2 + x$

Vertex: $x = -\frac{b}{2a} = -\frac{1}{2}$

$y = \left(-\frac{1}{2}\right)^2 - \frac{1}{2}$

$y = \frac{1}{4} - \frac{1}{2} = -\frac{1}{4}$

$\left(-\frac{1}{2}, -\frac{1}{4}\right)$

Axis of symmetry: $x = -\frac{1}{2}$

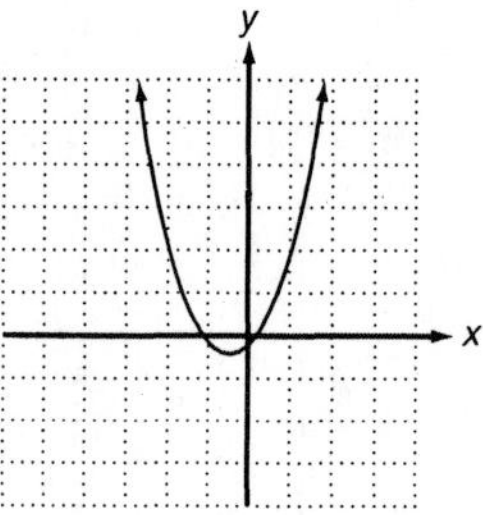

17. $y = x^2 - 3x + 2$

Vertex: $x = -\frac{b}{2a} = \frac{3}{2}$

$y = \left(\frac{3}{2}\right)^2 - 3\left(\frac{3}{2}\right) + 2$

$y = \frac{9}{4} - \frac{9}{2} + 2$

$y = \frac{9 - 18 + 8}{4} = -\frac{1}{4}$

$\left(\frac{3}{2}, -\frac{1}{4}\right)$

Axis of symmetry: $x = \frac{3}{2}$

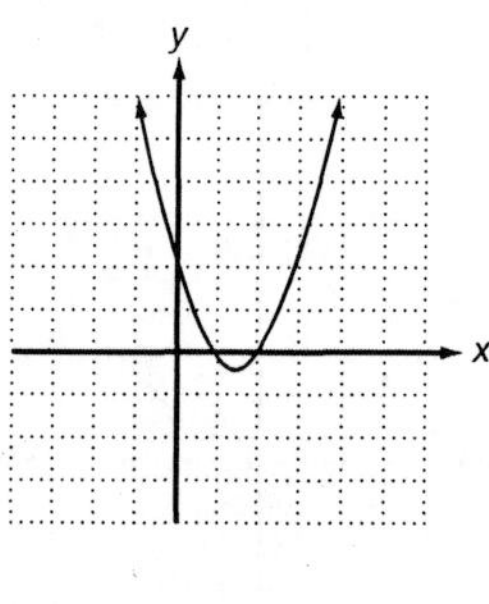

18. $y = -x^2 + 4$

Vertex: $x = -\frac{b}{2a} = 0$

$y = 0^2 + 4 = 4$
$(0, 4)$
Axis of symmetry: $x = 0$

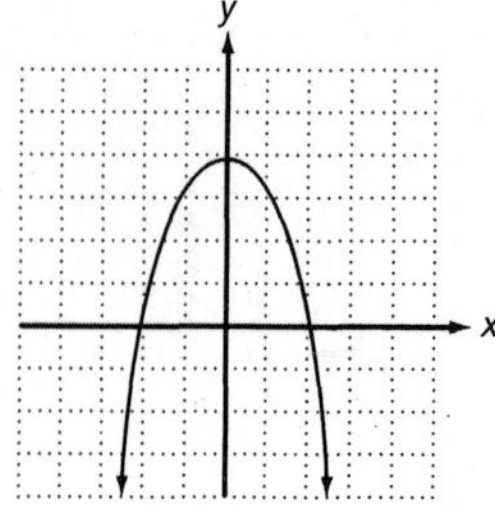

MIXED PRACTICE 24

p. 641

1. $y = kx$
$150 = k(0.75)$
$\frac{150}{0.75} = k$
$200 = k$
The formula is
$y = 200x$

2. $y = kx$
$128 = k(16)$
$\frac{128}{16} = k$
$8 = k$
The formula is
$y = 8x$

3. $y = kx$
$12 = k(30)$
$\frac{12}{30} = k$
$0.4 = k$
The formula is
$y = 0.4x$

4. $y = kx$
$0.36 = k(45)$
$\frac{0.36}{45} = k$
$0.008 = k$
The formula is
$y = 0.008x$

5. $y = \frac{k}{x}$
$26 = \frac{k}{18}$
$26(18) = k$
$468 = k$
The formula is
$y = \frac{468}{x}$

6. $y = \frac{k}{x}$
$0.2 = \frac{k}{15}$
$0.2(15) = k$
$3 = k$
The formula is
$y = \frac{3}{x}$

7. $y = \frac{k}{x}$
$1 = \frac{k}{100}$
$100 = k$
The formula is
$y = \frac{100}{x}$

8. $y = \frac{k}{x}$
$32 = \frac{k}{150}$
$32(150) = k$
$4800 = k$
The formula is
$y = \frac{4800}{x}$

9. $x = kyz$
$67.5 = k(6)(9)$
$67.5 = k(54)$
$\frac{67.5}{54} = k$
$1.25 = k$
The formula is
$x = 1.25yz$
Substituting:
$x = 1.25(4)(10)$
$x = 50$

10. $w = \frac{ky}{z}$
$12 = \frac{k(8)}{5}$
$60 = k(8)$
$\frac{60}{8} = k$
$7.5 = k$
The formula is
$w = \frac{7.5y}{z}$
Substituting:
$w = \frac{7.5(9)}{15}$
$w = 4.5$

11. $a = kbcd$
$24 = k(3)(2)(8)$
$24 = k(48)$
$\frac{24}{48} = k$
$0.5 = k$
The formula is
$a = 0.5bcd$
Substituting:
$a = 0.5(10)(1)(5)$
$a = 25$

12. $r = \frac{ks}{t}$
$2.7 = \frac{k(18)}{16}$
$43.2 = k(18)$
$\frac{43.2}{18} = k$
$2.4 = k$
The formula is
$r = \frac{2.4s}{t}$
Substituting:
$r = \frac{2.4(10)}{4}$
$r = 6$

13. If the amount of interest earned is increased, the balance in a standard savings account is increased. Therefore, these vary directly.

14. If the number of people working on a job is increased, the time needed to do a job is decreased. Therefore, these vary inversely.

15. If the size of the room is increased, the amount of paint needed is increased. Therefore, these vary directly.

16. If the weight of an object is increased, the distance a string is stretched is increased. Therefore, these vary directly.

17. If the number of people sharing a pizza is increased, the size of each share is decreased. Therefore, these vary inversely.

18. Let a = amount Tyler earns.
h = number of hours he works
$a = kh$
$101.25 = k(15)$
$\frac{101.25}{15} = k$
$6.75 = k$
The formula is
$a = 6.75h$
Substituting,
$a = 6.75(40)$
$a = 270$
Tyler earns \$270.

19. Let t = time to set up chairs.
p = number of people required
$t = \frac{k}{p}$
$5 = \frac{k}{3}$
$15 = k$
The formula is
$t = \frac{15}{p}$
Substituting,
$t = \frac{15}{20}$
$t = \frac{3}{4}$
It will take $\frac{3}{4}$ hour or 45 min.

MIXED PRACTICE 25

p. 642

1. $a^2 + 18a \quad (9^2) = 81$
$a^2 + 18a + 81 = (a + 9)^2$

2. $x^2 - 7x \quad \left(-\frac{7}{2}\right)^2 = \frac{49}{4}$
$x^2 - 7x + \frac{49}{4} = \left(x - \frac{7}{2}\right)^2$

3. $x^2 - 20x \quad (-10)^2 = 100$
$x^2 - 20x + 100 = (x - 10)^2$

4. $y^2 + 100y \quad (50)^2 = 2500$
$y^2 - 100y + 2500 = (y + 50)^2$

5. $x^2 - 12x \quad (-6)^2 = 36$
$x^2 - 12x + 36 = (x - 6)^2$

6. $m^2 - 6m \quad (-3)^2 = 9$
$m^2 - 6m + 9 = (m - 3)^2$

7. $3x^2 + 0x - 15 = 0$
$a = 3, b = 0, c = -15$

8. $x^2 - 6x + 4 = 0$
$a = 1, b = -6, c = 4$

9. $5y^2 + 3y - 91 = 0$
$a = 5, b = 3, c = -91$

10. $-t^2 + 8t - 9 = 0$ or $t^2 - 8t + 9 = 0$
$a = -1, b = 8, c = -9$ or $a = 1, b = -8, c = 9$

11. $x^2 - 11x + 9 = 0$
$a = 1, b = -11, c = 9$

12. $x^2 - 10x + 35 = 0$
$a = 1, b = -10, c = 35$

13. $b^2 - 4ac = (12)^2 - 4(1)(32) = 144 - 128 = 16$
Two real solutions

14. $b^2 - 4ac = (-10)^2 - 4(1)(25) = 0$
One real solution

15. $b^2 - 4ac = (-2)^2 - 4(1)(5) = -16$
No real solutions

16. $b^2 - 4ac = (-11)^2 - 4(1)(0) = 121$
Two real solutions

17. $3x^2 - 9x = 0$
$x(3x - 9) = 0$
$x = 0$ or $3x - 9 = 0$
$3x = 9$
$x = 0$ or $x = 3$

18. $2x^2 - 10x = 0$
$2x(x - 5) = 0$
$2x = 0$ or $x - 5 = 0$
$x = 0$ or $x = 5$

19. $4y^2 + 4y = 0$
$4y(y + 1) = 0$
$4y = 0$ or $y + 1 = 0$
$y = 0$ or $y = -1$

20. $5x^2 = 20$
$x^2 = 4$
$x = \pm\sqrt{4}$
$x = \pm 2$
$x = 2$ or $x = -2$

21. $9y^2 - 64 = 0$
$(3y - 8)(3y + 8) = 0$
$3y - 8 = 0$ or $3y + 8 = 0$
$3y = 8$ or $3y = -8$
$y = \frac{8}{3}$ or $y = -\frac{8}{3}$

22. $3x^2 - 243 = 0$
$3(x^2 - 81) = 0$
$3(x + 9)(x - 9) = 0$
$x + 9 = 0$ or $x - 9 = 0$
$x = -9$ or $x = 9$

23. $(x - 5)^2 = 121$
$x - 5 = \pm 11$
$x = 5 \pm 11$
$x = 5 + 11$ or $x = 5 - 11$
$x = 16$ or $x = -6$

24. $(y + 3)^2 = 7$
$y + 3 = \pm\sqrt{7}$
$y = -3 \pm \sqrt{7}$
$y = -3 + \sqrt{7}$ or $y = -3 - \sqrt{7}$

25. $(x + 4)^2 = 25$
$x + 4 = \pm\sqrt{25}$
$x + 4 = \pm 5$
$x + 4 = 5$ or $x + 4 = -5$
$x = 1$ or $x = -9$

26. $x(x - 2) = 15$
$x^2 - 2x = 15$
$x^2 - 2x - 15 = 0$
$(x - 5)(x + 3) = 0$
$x - 5 = 0$ or $x + 3 = 0$
$x = 5$ or $x = -3$

27. $9y^2 - 14y = 10y - 16$
$9y^2 - 24y + 16 = 0$
$(3y - 4)^2 = 0$
$3y - 4 = 0$
$3y = 4$
$y = \frac{4}{3}$

28. $x^2 + 3x - 10 = 30$
$x^2 + 3x - 40 = 0$
$(x + 8)(x - 5) = 0$
$x + 8 = 0$ or $x - 5 = 0$
$x = -8$ or $x = 5$

29. $(y - 1)^2 - 81 = 0$
$(y - 1)^2 = 81$
$y - 1 = \pm\sqrt{81}$
$y - 1 = \pm 9$
$y - 1 = 9$ or $y - 1 = -9$
$y = 10$ or $y = -8$

30. $m^2 + 6m - 6 = 21$
$m^2 + 6m - 27 = 0$
$(m + 9)(m - 3) = 0$
$m + 9 = 0$ or $m - 3 = 0$
$m = -9$ or $m = 3$

31. $x(2x + 1) = 28$
$2x^2 + x = 28$
$2x^2 + x - 28 = 28$
$(2x - 7)(x + 4) = 0$
$2x - 7 = 0$ or $x + 4 = 0$
$2x = 7$ or $x = -4$
$x = \frac{7}{2}$ or $x = -4$

32. $x^2 - 6x - 16 = 0$
$x^2 - 6x = 16$
$x^2 - 6x + 9 = 16 + 9$
$(x - 3)^2 = 25$
$x - 3 = \pm\sqrt{25}$
$x - 3 = \pm 5$
$x - 3 = 5$ or $x - 3 = -5$
$x = 8$ or $x = -2$

33. $y^2 - 4y = 3$
$y^2 - 4y + 4 = 3 + 4$
$(y - 2)^2 = 7$
$y - 2 = \pm\sqrt{7}$
$y = 2 \pm \sqrt{7}$
$y = 2 + \sqrt{7}$ or $y = 2 - \sqrt{7}$

34. $x^2 + 3x - 180 = 0$
$x^2 + 3x = 180$
$x^2 + 3x + \frac{9}{4} = 180 + \frac{9}{4}$
$\left(x + \frac{3}{2}\right)^2 = \frac{729}{4}$
$x + \frac{3}{2} = \pm\sqrt{\frac{729}{4}}$
$x + \frac{3}{2} = \pm\frac{27}{2}$
$x + \frac{3}{2} = \frac{27}{2}$ or $x + \frac{3}{2} = -\frac{27}{2}$
$x = \frac{24}{2}$ or $x = -\frac{30}{2}$
$x = 12$ or $x = -15$

35. $x^2 - 6x + 8 = 0$
$x^2 - 6x = -8$
$x^2 - 6x + 9 = -8 + 9$
$(x - 3)^2 = 1$
$x - 3 = \pm 1$
$x - 3 = 1$ or $x - 3 = -1$
$x = 4$ or $x = 2$

36. $a^2 - 7a + 12 = 0$
$a^2 - 7a = -12$
$a^2 - 7a + \frac{49}{4} = -12 + \frac{49}{4}$
$\left(a - \frac{7}{2}\right)^2 = \frac{1}{4}$
$a - \frac{7}{2} = \pm\sqrt{\frac{1}{4}}$
$a - \frac{7}{2} = \pm\frac{1}{2}$
$a - \frac{7}{2} = \frac{1}{2}$ or $a - \frac{7}{2} = -\frac{1}{2}$
$a = \frac{7}{2} + \frac{1}{2}$ or $a = \frac{7}{2} - \frac{1}{2}$
$a = \frac{8}{2}$ or $a = \frac{6}{2}$
$a = 4$ or $a = 3$

37. $x^2 - 15x - 15 = 1$
$x^2 - 15x = 16$
$x^2 - 15x + \frac{225}{4} = 16 + \frac{225}{4}$
$\left(x - \frac{15}{2}\right)^2 = \frac{289}{4}$
$x - \frac{15}{2} = \pm\sqrt{\frac{289}{4}}$
$x - \frac{15}{2} = \pm\frac{17}{2}$
$x - \frac{15}{2} = \frac{17}{2}$ or $x - \frac{15}{2} = -\frac{17}{2}$
$x = \frac{32}{2}$ or $x = -\frac{2}{2}$
$x = 16$ or $x = -1$

38. $x^2 - 5x + 4 = 0$
$x = \frac{5 \pm \sqrt{5^2 - 4(1)(4)}}{2(1)}$
$x = \frac{5 \pm \sqrt{25 - 16}}{2} = \frac{5 \pm \sqrt{9}}{2} = \frac{5 \pm 3}{2}$
$x = \frac{8}{2}$ or $x = \frac{2}{2}$
$x = 4$ or $x = 1$

39. $6t^2 - 5t - 6 = 0$
$t = \frac{5 \pm \sqrt{5^2 - 4(6)(-6)}}{2(6)} = \frac{5 \pm \sqrt{25 + 144}}{12}$
$= \frac{5 \pm \sqrt{169}}{12} = \frac{5 \pm 13}{12}$
$t = \frac{18}{12}$ or $t = -\frac{8}{12}$
$t = \frac{3}{2}$ or $t = -\frac{2}{3}$

40. $8x^2 = 60$
$8x^2 - 0x - 60 = 0$
$x = \frac{0 \pm \sqrt{0^2 - 4(8)(-60)}}{2(8)} = \frac{0 \pm \sqrt{0 + 1920}}{16}$
$= \frac{\pm\sqrt{1920}}{16} = \frac{\pm 8\sqrt{30}}{16} = \pm\frac{\sqrt{30}}{2}$

41. $2x^2 - x - 15 = 0$
$x = \frac{1 \pm \sqrt{(-1)^2 - 4(2)(-15)}}{2(2)}$
$= \frac{1 \pm \sqrt{1 + 120}}{4} = \frac{1 \pm \sqrt{121}}{4} = \frac{1 \pm 11}{4}$
$x = \frac{12}{4}$ or $x = -\frac{10}{4}$
$x = 3$ or $x = -\frac{5}{2}$

42. $m^2 + 5m - 24 = 0$
$m = \frac{-5 \pm \sqrt{(5)^2 - 4(1)(-24)}}{2(1)}$
$= \frac{-5 \pm \sqrt{25 + 96}}{2} = \frac{-5 \pm \sqrt{121}}{2}$
$= \frac{-5 \pm 11}{2}$
$m = \frac{6}{2}$ or $m = -\frac{16}{2}$
$m = 3$ or $m = -8$

43. $x^2 - 4x - 77 = 0$

$$x = \frac{4 \pm \sqrt{(-4)^2 - 4(1)(-77)}}{2(1)}$$
$$= \frac{4 \pm \sqrt{16 + 308}}{2} = \frac{4 \pm \sqrt{324}}{2} = \frac{4 \pm \sqrt{18}}{2}$$
$$x = \frac{22}{2} \text{ or } x = -\frac{14}{2}$$
$$x = 11 \text{ or } x = -7$$

44.
$$2x(x - 2) = 3(4 - x)$$
$$2x^2 - 4x = 12 - 3x$$
$$2x^2 - x - 12 = 0$$
$$x = \frac{1 \pm \sqrt{(1)^2 - 4(2)(-12)}}{2(2)}$$
$$= \frac{1 \pm \sqrt{1 + 96}}{4} = \frac{1 \pm \sqrt{97}}{4}$$

45.
$$(3x + 4)(5x - 1) = 0$$
$$15x^2 + 20x - 3x - 4 = 0$$
$$15x^2 + 17x - 4 = 0$$
$$x = \frac{-17 \pm \sqrt{(17)^2 - 4(15)(-4)}}{2(15)}$$
$$= \frac{-17 \pm \sqrt{289 + 240}}{30}$$
$$= \frac{-17 \pm \sqrt{529}}{30} = \frac{-17 \pm 23}{30}$$
$$x = \frac{6}{30} \text{ or } x = -\frac{40}{30}$$
$$x = \frac{1}{5} \text{ or } x = -\frac{4}{3}$$

46. $x^2 + bx + 81$
$$\left(\frac{b}{2}\right)^2 = 81$$
$$\frac{b}{2} = \pm 9$$
$$b = \pm 18$$
$\pm 18x$

47. $x^2 + bx + 30$
$$\left(\frac{b}{2}\right)^2 = 30$$
$$\frac{b}{2} = \pm\sqrt{30}$$
$$b = \pm 2\sqrt{30}$$
$\pm 2x\sqrt{30}$

48. $x^2 + bx + 24$
$$\left(\frac{b}{2}\right)^2 = 24$$
$$\frac{b}{2} = \pm 2\sqrt{6}$$
$$b = \pm 4\sqrt{6}$$
$\pm 4x\sqrt{6}$

49.
$$21x^2 = x$$
$$21x^2 - x = 0$$
$$x(21x - 1) = 0$$
$$x = 0 \text{ or } 21x - 1 = 0$$
$$21x = 1$$
$$x = \frac{1}{21}$$

50.
$$4x^2 + 12x + 5 = 0$$
$$(2x + 1)(2x + 5) = 0$$
$$2x + 1 = 0 \text{ or } 2x + 5 = 0$$
$$2x = -1 \text{ or } 2x = -5$$
$$x = -\frac{1}{2} \text{ or } x = -\frac{5}{2}$$

51.
$$8x^2 = 14x + 15$$
$$8x^2 - 14x - 15 = 0$$
$$(4x + 3)(2x - 5) = 0$$
$$4x + 3 = 0 \text{ or } 2x - 5 = 0$$
$$4x = -3 \text{ or } 2x = 5$$
$$x = -\frac{3}{4} \text{ or } x = \frac{5}{2}$$

52.
$$m^2 - 4m + 3 = 0$$
$$(m - 3)(m - 1) = 0$$
$$m - 3 = 0 \text{ or } m - 1 = 0$$
$$m = 3 \text{ or } m = 1$$

53.
$$x^2 - 9 = 3x$$
$$x^2 - 3x - 9 = 0$$
$$x = \frac{3 \pm \sqrt{(-3)^2 - 4(1)(-9)}}{2(1)}$$
$$x = \frac{3 \pm \sqrt{9 + 36}}{2}$$
$$x = \frac{3 \pm \sqrt{45}}{2} = \frac{3 \pm 3\sqrt{15}}{2}$$

54.
$$x^2 + 6x = 27$$
$$x^2 + 6x - 27 = 0$$
$$(x + 9)(x - 3) = 0$$
$$x + 9 = 0 \text{ or } x - 3 = 0$$
$$x = -9 \text{ or } x = 3$$

MIXED PRACTICE 26 p. 643

1.
$$\frac{9}{x - 3} - \frac{x - 4}{x - 3} = \frac{1}{4}$$
$$4(x - 3) \cdot \frac{9}{x - 3} - 4(x - 3) \cdot \frac{x - 4}{x - 3} = 4(x - 3) \cdot \frac{1}{4}$$
$$36 - 4(x - 4) = x - 3$$
$$36 - 4x + 16 = x - 3$$
$$52 - 4x = x - 3$$
$$55 = 5x$$
$$11 = x$$

2.
$$\frac{1}{x - 1} + \frac{2}{x} = 0$$
$$x(x - 1)\frac{1}{x - 1} + x(x - 1)\frac{2}{x} = 0$$
$$x + 2(x - 1) = 0$$
$$x + 2x - 2 = 0$$
$$3x - 2 = 0$$
$$3x = 2$$
$$x = \frac{2}{3}$$

3.
$$\frac{y^2}{6} = \frac{y}{3} + \frac{1}{2}$$
$$6\left(\frac{y^2}{6}\right) = 6\left(\frac{y}{3}\right) + 6\left(\frac{1}{2}\right)$$
$$y^2 = 2y + 3$$
$$y^2 - 2y - 3 = 0$$
$$(y - 3)(y + 1) = 0$$
$$y - 3 = 0 \text{ or } y + 1 = 0$$
$$y = 3 \text{ or } y = -1$$

4.
$$\frac{m}{m - 3} + \frac{6}{m + 3} = 1$$
$$(m^2 - 9)\left(\frac{m}{m - 3}\right) + (m^2 - 9)\left(\frac{6}{m + 3}\right) = (m^2 - 9)(1)$$
$$m(m + 3) + 6(m - 3) = m^2 - 9$$
$$m^2 + 3m + 6m - 18 = m^2 - 9$$
$$m^2 + 9m - 18 = m^2 - 9$$
$$9m = 9$$
$$m = 1$$

5.
$$x - 3 = \frac{1}{x - 3}$$
$$x - 3(x - 3) = x - 3\left(\frac{1}{x - 3}\right)$$
$$x^2 - 6x + 9 = 1$$
$$x^2 - 6x + 8 = 0$$
$$(x - 4)(x - 2) = 0$$
$$x - 4 = 0 \text{ or } x - 2 = 0$$
$$x = 4 \text{ or } x = 2$$

6.
$$x - 6 = \frac{x}{x-6}$$
$$(x-6)(x-6) = (x-6)\left(\frac{x}{x-6}\right)$$
$$x^2 - 12x + 36 = x$$
$$x^2 - 13x + 36 = 0$$
$$(x-9)(x-4) = 0$$
$$x - 9 = 0 \quad \text{or} \quad x - 4 = 0$$
$$x = 9 \quad \text{or} \quad x = 4$$

7.
$$x + \frac{x}{x+1} = \frac{4x+3}{x+1}$$
$$(x+1)x + (x+1)\frac{x}{x+1} = (x+1)\frac{4x+3}{x+1}$$
$$x^2 + x + x = 4x + 3$$
$$x^2 + 2x = 4x + 3$$
$$x^2 - 2x - 3 = 0$$
$$(x-3)(x+1) = 0$$
$$x - 3 = 0 \quad \text{or} \quad x + 1 = 0$$
$$x = 3 \quad \text{or} \quad x = -1$$
Only $x = 3$ checks.

8.
$$\frac{1}{x+5} + \frac{5}{x^2-25} = 0$$
$$(x^2-25)\left(\frac{1}{x+5}\right) + (x^2-25)\left(\frac{5}{x^2-25}\right) = (x^2-25)(0)$$
$$x - 5 + 5 = 0$$
$$x = 0$$

9.
$$\sqrt{3x-5} = 4$$
$$(\sqrt{3x-5})^2 = 4^2$$
$$3x - 5 = 16$$
$$3x = 21$$
$$x = 7$$

10.
$$\sqrt{x+5} = \sqrt{2x-3}$$
$$(\sqrt{x+5})^2 = (\sqrt{2x-3})^2$$
$$x + 5 = 2x - 3$$
$$8 = x$$

11.
$$\sqrt{x-3} = 6 - x$$
$$(\sqrt{x-3})^2 = (6-x)^2$$
$$x - 3 = 36 - 12x + x^2$$
$$0 = x^2 - 13x + 39$$
$$x = \frac{13 \pm \sqrt{13^2 - 4(1)(39)}}{2(1)}$$
$$x = \frac{13 \pm \sqrt{169 - 156}}{2}$$
$$x = \frac{13 \pm \sqrt{13}}{2}$$
Only $\frac{13 - \sqrt{13}}{2}$ checks.

12.
$$\sqrt{y-5} = y - 7$$
$$(\sqrt{y-5})^2 = (y-7)^2$$
$$y - 5 = y^2 - 14y + 49$$
$$0 = y^2 - 15y + 54$$
$$0 = (y-9)(y-6)$$
$$y - 9 = 0 \quad \text{or} \quad y - 6 = 0$$
$$y = 9 \quad \text{or} \quad y = 6$$
Only $y = 9$ checks.

13.
$$\sqrt{x} + \sqrt{7} = \sqrt{x+7}$$
$$(\sqrt{x} + \sqrt{7})^2 = (\sqrt{x+7})^2$$
$$x + 2\sqrt{7x} + 7 = x + 7$$
$$2\sqrt{7x} = 0$$
$$x = 0$$

14.
$$m + \sqrt{2m-6} = 3$$
$$\sqrt{2m-6} = 3 - m$$
$$(\sqrt{2m-6})^2 = (3-m)^2$$
$$2m - 6 = 9 - 6m + m^2$$
$$0 = 15 - 8m + m^2$$
$$0 = (5-m)(3-m)$$
$$5 - m = 0 \quad \text{or} \quad 3 - m = 0$$
$$5 = m \quad \text{or} \quad 3 = m$$
Only $m = 3$ checks.

15.
$$2x^2 - 5x + 3 = 0$$
$$(2x-3)(x-1) = 0$$
$$2x - 3 = 0 \quad \text{or} \quad x - 1 = 0$$
$$2x = 3 \quad \text{or} \quad x = 1$$
$$x = \frac{3}{2}$$

16.
$$(x+2)(x-1) = 10$$
$$x^2 + x - 2 = 10$$
$$x^2 + x - 12 = 0$$
$$(x+4)(x-3) = 0$$
$$x + 4 = 0 \quad \text{or} \quad x - 3 = 0$$
$$x = -4 \quad \text{or} \quad x = 3$$

17.
$$6x^2 - x = 1$$
$$6x^2 - x - 1 = 0$$
$$(3x+1)(2x-1) = 0$$
$$3x + 1 = 0 \quad \text{or} \quad 2x - 1 = 0$$
$$3x = -1 \quad \text{or} \quad 2x = 1$$
$$x = -\frac{1}{3} \quad \text{or} \quad x = \frac{1}{2}$$

18.
$$3t^2 + 5t = 28$$
$$3t^2 + 5t - 28 = 0$$
$$(3t-7)(t+4) = 0$$
$$3t - 7 = 0 \quad \text{or} \quad t + 4 = 0$$
$$3t = 7 \quad \text{or} \quad t = -4$$
$$t = \frac{7}{3}$$

19.
$$(3y-10)^2 = 0$$
$$3y - 10 = 0$$
$$3y = 10$$
$$y = \frac{10}{3}$$

20.
$$10x - 19 = x^2$$
$$0 = x^2 - 10x + 19$$
$$x = \frac{10 \pm \sqrt{100 - 4(19)}}{2}$$
$$= 5 \pm \frac{\sqrt{100-76}}{2}$$
$$= 5 \pm \frac{\sqrt{24}}{2}$$
$$= 5 \pm \frac{2\sqrt{6}}{2}$$
$$= 5 \pm \sqrt{6}$$

21.
$$561.80 = 500(1+r)^2$$
$$\frac{561.80}{500} = (1+r)^2$$
$$\pm\sqrt{\frac{561.80}{500}} = 1 + r$$
$$-1 \pm \sqrt{1.1236} = r$$
$$-1 \pm 1.06 = r$$
$$r = 0.06 \quad \text{or} \quad r = -2.06$$
Interest rate is positive, so the interest rate is 6%.

22.
$$(30-2x)(24-2x) = 520$$
$$720 - 108x + 4x^2 = 520$$
$$200 - 108x + 4x^2 = 0$$
$$50 - 27x + x^2 = 0$$
$$(25-x)(2-x) = 0$$
$$x = 25 \quad \text{or} \quad x = 2$$
Width must be less than frame dimensions, so width is 2 cm.

23.

$$\begin{aligned} x^2 + (x-7)^2 &= 13^2 \\ x^2 + x^2 - 14x + 49 &= 169 \\ 2x^2 - 14x - 120 &= 0 \\ 2(x^2 - 7x - 60) &= 0 \\ x^2 - 7x - 60 &= 0 \\ (x-12)(x+5) &= 0 \\ x - 12 = 0 \quad &\text{or} \quad x + 5 = 0 \\ x = 12 \quad &\text{or} \quad x = -5 \end{aligned}$$

Length is positive, so the legs are 12 m and $12 - 7 = 5$ m.

24.

$$\begin{aligned} w(w+15) &= 1000 \\ w^2 + 15w &= 1000 \\ w^2 + 15w - 1000 &= 0 \\ (w+40)(w-25) &= 0 \\ w + 40 = 0 \quad &\text{or} \quad w - 25 = 0 \\ w = -40 \quad &\text{or} \quad w = 25 \end{aligned}$$

Width is positive, so width is 25 ft.
The length is $25 + 15 = 40$ ft.

25.

$$\begin{aligned} \frac{20}{r+5} + \frac{20}{r-5} &= 3 \\ (r^2-25)\left(\frac{20}{r+5}\right) + (r^2-25)\left(\frac{20}{r-5}\right) &= (r^2-25)(3) \\ 20(r-5) + 20(r+5) &= 3r^2 - 75 \\ 20r - 100 + 20r + 100 &= 3r^2 - 75 \\ 3r^2 - 40r - 75 &= 0 \\ (3r+5)(r-15) &= 0 \\ 3r + 5 = 0 \quad &\text{or} \quad r - 15 = 0 \\ 3r = 5 \quad &\text{or} \quad r = 15 \\ r = -\frac{5}{3} & \end{aligned}$$

Speed is positive, so the speed of the boat is 15 km/h.

26. Together, they do the job in 2 hours. Alone, Marla can do $\frac{2}{3}$ of the job and Gene can do $\frac{2}{t}$ of the job in 2 hours.

$$\begin{aligned} \frac{2}{3} + \frac{2}{t} &= 1 \\ 3t\left(\frac{2}{3}\right) + 3t\left(\frac{2}{t}\right) &= 3t(1) \\ 2t + 6 &= 3t \\ 6 &= t \end{aligned}$$

It would take Gene 6 hours to type the report.

27. $a^2 + b^2 = c^2$

$$\begin{aligned} s^2 + s^2 &= (s+5)^2 \\ 2s^2 &= s^2 + 10s + 25 \\ 0 &= -s^2 + 10s + 25 \\ s &= \frac{-10 \pm \sqrt{100 + 100}}{-2} \\ s &= 5 \pm \frac{\sqrt{200}}{-2} \\ s &= 5 \pm \frac{10\sqrt{2}}{-2} \\ s &= 5 \pm -5\sqrt{2} \end{aligned}$$

Length is positive, so the side of the square is $5 + 5\sqrt{2}$ cm.